P9-CLB-985

ERNST FLOREY, Ph.D. Professor of Zoology
University of Washington
Seattle, Washington

AN INTRODUCTION TO *General and Comparative Animal Physiology*

W. B. SAUNDERS COMPANY / *Philadelphia London, 1966*

W. B. Saunders Company: West Washington Square
Philadelphia, Pa. 19105

12 Dyott Street
London W. C. 1

An Introduction to General and Comparative Animal Physiology

Preface

The fields of general physiology and comparative physiology have been active for many decades. In recent years the awareness of their importance has increased. This has been stimulated largely by the contribution comparative physiology has made to the understanding of fundamental physiological processes, and by the astounding advances in biophysics (the vanguard of general physiology). Emphasis has shifted considerably away from mammalian function. Through this shift in perspective, mammalian physiology (admittedly already leaning heavily on amphibian physiology) has come to be regarded as the physiology of a specialized group of animals, and the importance of other animal groups, regardless of their position on the tree of evolution, is now generally recognized.

The upsurge in the number of research publications in general and comparative physiology has not been accompanied by noticeable activity of textbook writers. The textbooks that have appeared since the inception of general physiology and comparative physiology during the middle of the nineteenth century can be listed on a single printed page. Many of these are classics. The importance of Claude Bernard's *Leçons sur la Physiologie Générale* need not be emphasized, and it is unlikely that the elegance of Bayliss' *General Physiology* will ever be surpassed. Books of the challenge like Verworn's *Allgemeine Physiologie* or Jaques Loeb's *General Physiology* may not be in store for a long time, nor is it likely that the sheer intellectual weight of Tschermak's *Allgemeine Physiologie* will be approached by a new text on the same subject. Von Buddenbrock's gigantic effort, *Vergleichende Physiologie*, and the two editions of the *Comparative Animal Physiology* by Prosser and Brown are major landmarks. Yet all these books are designed for the advanced student. This is also true for the recent textbooks on general physiology by Scheer and by Davson.

The need for an introductory text has been apparent for many years. Ever since I began my career as a teacher of general physiology and comparative physiology, I have been aware of this, and with what I now regard as the optimism of the inexperienced, I started to write a new text.

The task of adequately covering the wide range of topics with which both general and comparative physiology are concerned was formidable, particularly so since there was no model on which to base the organization of these large fields. From the beginning, it was my aim to combine general and comparative physiology, since these fields are inseparable. True, the orientation of a comparative physiologist differs from that of the general physiologist: the comparative physiologist looks for the range of variety of physiological mechanisms, whereas the general physiologist tries to discover the fundamental, general physiological mechanisms that underlie all this variety. Nonetheless, the generalities arise out of a knowledge of the variety, and the variety can be recognized only in terms of generalities.

Pütter's *Vergleichende Physiologie*, which appeared in 1911, was the last text in comparative physiology to include both plant and animal topics. General physiology up to Davson's latest edition in 1965 has, however, always considered both plants and animals. My text departs from this plan, and I am fully aware that this departure is a serious injustice to the unity of biological function throughout the animal and plant kingdoms. I felt, however, that animal organisms have sufficient functions peculiar to their kind to warrant a separate treatment. The decision to essentially eliminate references to plant physiology was facilitated by the obvious necessity to restrict the size and contents of the book.

This text is intended to prepare the student for more advanced texts and literature in both general and comparative physiology by introducing and discussing, at least on an elementary level, the important terms, concepts, and theories. The material is selected in such a way as to permit equal treatment of mammalian and nonmammalian physiology.

An introduction to physiology must not only describe what has been achieved, but must orient the student toward the future development of this science. We live at a critical time: the boundaries between the various disciplines of biology are falling and the aims of basic research within medical schools are now identical with those pursued within the administrative domains of zoology and its applied disciplines. Thus, the basis from which medical and nonmedical students progress toward advanced training in physiology is the same. It is my aim to present the general field of physiology from the comparative point of view and to give the student a sense of direction for future endeavors in this field. Also, those who do not intend to continue to work in one or the other field of physiology can gain an insight into the physiological approach to biology, and others may simply want to discover what physiology is all about.

Actually, this text consists of two books in one: interspersed among the chapters that treat the various topics of physiology are chapters and sections that, together, form an introductory text to physiological dynamics and kinetics. Their respective subject matters are placed ahead of the physiological topics for whose treatment they form an indispensable background. Much of this background material may be superfluous for many readers, particularly those who have experience in general chemistry, biochemistry, and physical chemistry. I find that my own students, many of whom had taken courses in all these fields, cannot always relate what they have learned in such courses to physiological situations and problems.

The introductory material also covers aspects of general zoology and biochemistry. The physiology text proper consists of Chapters 5, 9 through 13, 15, and 17 through 27. No attempt has been made to cover growth and reproduction, and from endocrinology only those aspects have been selected that are of immediate significance for acute body or tissue functions. General and comparative endocrinology are adequately covered in several excellent texts (C. D. Turner, *General Endocrinology*, Saunders, Philadelphia; A. Gorbman and H. A. Bern, *A Textbook of Comparative Endocrinology*, Wiley, New York; P. M. Jenkin, *Animal Hormones*, Pergamon Press, Oxford; and others). Sensory physiology is covered only in outline form. Its subject matter alone would fill a separate text, and is a topic for a separate academic course. An adequate textbook on this subject has yet to be written.

The chapters vary in depth. Some chapters contain only general remarks and should not be taken as a complete coverage of the subject; this is particularly true for Chapters 1, 2, 3, and 7. Some topics are treated, in separate chapters, on several levels—particularly neurophysiology and muscle physiology, Chapters 17 through 27. Intentionally there are many repetitions. It is hoped that they make it possible to select any number and combination of chapters as text for a variety of courses. I also included cross references to details covered in other chapters.

To facilitate the understanding of complex structures, phenomena, and concepts, I have included in this text a large number of illustrations. I have tried to provide legends that are instructive and have endeavored in many cases to use illustrations as devices to introduce additional subject matter. When possible, I have taken figures from important research papers or texts, but often I found it necessary to design illustrations myself, particularly when conceptual diagrams were needed.

At the end of each chapter is a list of references that support the statements in the text. Statements that are general knowledge or that concern topics that are only summarized are usually supported only by references to general, more advanced texts. Some fields of physiology rest on such a vast number of research publications that it is impossible to give even the majority of titles of relevant research papers. The extent of citation of original literature is thus roughly inversely proportional to the degree to which the presentation in a given chapter approaches the actual dimensions (in spread and in depth) of the subject matter covered. The treatment of the physiological literature therefore ranges from references to elementary textbooks to full reviews of the relevant research papers, like that given in Chapter 15 (Color Change and the Physiology of Chromatophores).

In accordance with the philosophy expressed in the Introduction, I have left out all aspects of cell function that are the proper domain of cell physiology, that is, all cell processes that are concerned with self-regulation, interactions between nucleus and cytoplasm, cell growth, and cell division. All this can be found in the excellent introductory text by A. C. Giese (*Cell Physiology*, Saunders, Philadelphia) and is the subject matter of separate courses in cell physiology.

As much as possible, I have emphasized a quantitative approach, particularly conspicuous perhaps in the chapters on osmoregulation and ionic regulation, circulation (hemodynamics), and nutrition.

This book is not intended to be a reference work or a collection of reviews. The reader may be disappointed if he cannot find a paper listed that he feels is relevant to a particular topic. If he happens to be the person who teaches the course to which the text is assigned, he is encouraged to make use of his knowledge and to let the students participate in it. If he is a student, he may congratulate himself and recognize his frustration as a sign of his coming of age as a scientist.

I have not hesitated to include among the references, papers and books written in languages other than English. Science is international.

Although the book is primarily written for undergraduate courses in general physiology, introductory physiology, or comparative physiology, it is hoped that it will also be of interest to biochemists, biophysicists, or mammalian physiologists, and perhaps even to psychologists and morphological zoologists who wish to acquaint themselves with the scope and perspectives of a general comparative physiology.

I apologize for the inadequacies of this book and implore my readers not to be patient but to communicate to me their suggestions for improvements.

Many colleagues and friends have given their time to read and criticize parts of the manuscript. I am particularly grateful to Drs. Mary Griffith, Paul Illg, A. W. Martin, and J. W. Woodbury of the University of Washington at Seattle, Dr. Paul Gross of the Massachusetts Institute of Technology, Dr. F. Crescitelli of the University of California at Los Angeles, Dr. Graham Hoyle and Dr. Melvin Cohen of the University of Oregon, Dr. K. Johannsen of the University of Oslo, Dr. Donald Kennedy of Stanford University, and Dr. W. T. W. Potts of the University of Birmingham. As much as I was able to, I followed their advice—even so, they may not be entirely satisfied.

The original illustrations were drawn by Mrs. Phyllis Wood. I am most grateful to her for her clever interpretations and meticulous execution of my sketches.

Mrs. Grace Y. Chapman has given much of her time providing invaluable help with the bibliography.

Special thanks are due the publishers, W. B. Saunders Company, for generous help, moral support, and understanding patience.

Seattle

Ernst Florey

Contents

INTRODUCTION

SOME DEFINITIONS

The historical development of physiology has led to the establishment of a number of fields; some of these have achieved a high degree of independence. The separation into fields is not representative of the nature of physiology as such. It is simply the consequence of the peculiarities of academic administration and instruction. The fields of physiology, which are represented by departments, institutes, courses, and textbooks, can be identified by the following major titles: general physiology, comparative physiology, cell physiology, vertebrate physiology (human physiology, mammalian physiology, etc.), invertebrate physiology, insect physiology, plant physiology, etc., biophysics, and biochemistry.

These titles correspond to the realities of teaching matter and the personal interests of their representative scientists. In this sense they are real and, in fact, distinct. On the following pages, an attempt is made to characterize these distinct kinds of physiology and its related sciences and to define them.

Fields that are associated with a specific group of animals (mammalian physiology, insect physiology, etc.) fall into Jordan's category of "special physiologies." These are concerned with cell and organ functions and with their interactions *as determined by the particular arrangements of the parts of a special group of organisms.* The general conclusions at which these special physiologies arrive cannot be applied directly to other animal groups. For example, when a mammalian physiologist concludes that "noradrenaline is a neurohormone released by the endings of sympathetic nerve fibers," this does not refer to other, nonmammalian organisms. In the first place, other types of organisms may not even have a sympathetic nervous system, and if they do, their neurohormone may be a substance other than noradrenaline.

Comparative physiology is different: its aim is to elucidate the functional systems of as many types of organisms as is practicable. For instance, starting with the concept of *neurohormones*, one attempts to discover *what* animals release *which* neurohormones at what type of nerve endings. *Comparative physiology seeks to investigate, describe, and systematize the variety of basic mechanisms throughout the animal and plant kingdoms.* In doing so, inevitably new facets of such mechanisms are discovered, which adds to our understanding of them. The scope of comparative physiology is not restricted to the organ level of function. It encompasses all levels of organization through the cellular, to the molecular and atomic, and perhaps even subatomic level of organismic structure and function.

Thus, the distinction between general and comparative physiology is a subtle one indeed. *General physiology seeks to establish the general principles of functional mechanisms that underlie the life processes of all organisms.* These general principles can be recognized only in the variety of their representations. The method of comparative physiology is *deductive*, that of general physiology *inductive*; but, like comparative physiology, general physiology encompasses all levels of organization through the cellular, to the molecular, atomic, and even subatomic level of organismic structure and function.

Both forms of physiology, of course, are interdependent and inseparable: general principles cannot be recognized unless the variety of their representations is known. The mechanism of synaptic transmission, for instance, was not a topic of general physiology until synaptic transmission was found to occur in all animal forms that had been studied; the same is true for the phenomenon of electrical spread of excitation through muscle tissues. How general a phenomenon or mechanism is can be seen only after a wide variety of organisms has been searched for it. Of course, the mechanism must first be recognized in one species, or, perhaps, in a group of related species. Thus it appears that the approach to general physiology begins with the physiology of a particular groups of organisms and then goes through the stage of comparative physiology.

The path of the topic of synaptic transmission exemplifies this: the term "synapse" was invented by the famous British neurophysiologist Sherrington at the end of the last century. It described first the peculiar form of junction between nerve cells within the spinal cord of mammals. The transfer of excitation from one nerve cell to another was termed "synaptic transmission." Similar junctions, or synapses, and their physiological correlate, synaptic transmission, were found to occur outside the spinal cord as well as in sympathetic ganglia. Soon it was recognized that the junctions between motor neurons and muscle fibers behaved like synapses and almost immediately synapses were found in many other groups of animals. In fact, many of the most prominent studies on synaptic transmission were carried out on certain invertebrate organisms (Mollusca, Crustacea, Insecta). From all these studies emerged general statements of a common mechanism of synaptic transmission—thus the phenomenon became a topic of general physiology.

From such considerations it becomes obvious why cell physiology was the first kind of physiology to be identified with general physiology: since the recognition of the cell theory, the universality of cell structure and function was established, and any cellular activity could thus be taken as a hint of the mode of operation of cellular organisms. Thus, it was argued, if cells are the basic units of living organisms, cell physiology must be the basic (general) physiology that can explain all organismic life processes.

A study of the history of physiology, particularly of the development of general physiology, as evident from the topics covered in general physiology texts, clearly shows that cell physiology, in itself, is insufficient to explain the progress of general physiology. Cell physiology as such could never have uncovered the general mechanism of synaptic transmission, for instance; nor is it, as a system of knowledge, in a position to cope with such topics of general physiological significance as hemodynamics or gas transport by extracellular fluid.

Cell physiology encompasses phenomena that are involved in cell growth and maintenance, in the self-regulation and division of cells (mitosis, meiosis), in interactions between nucleus and cytoplasm, and in the general behavior of protoplasm. The favorite objects of research of cell physiologists are egg cells, particularly those of echinoids (sea urchins), rhizopods (ameba), and plant cells. *The cell physiologist's interest is directed toward the functioning of cells as cells.* The cell, in fact, is the organism in which the cell physiologist is interested. Hence, he prefers cells that are not part of a hierarchy, that is, of a multicellular organism.

General physiology encompasses those cell functions and intercellular functional interactions that are of immediate significance for the understanding of the whole (multicellular) organism. Thus, the general physiologist is interested in the plasma membrane of nerve cells because it is the seat of ion exchange phenomena responsible for the conduction of nerve impulses. And he is interested in the behavior of contractile proteins within muscle cells, because he hopes to gain an insight into muscle contraction. He is interested in active transport in kidney tubules, because he wants to know how (among other things) this affects the ion balance of body fluids.

The general physiologist may be interested in the cell as a unit of function, but his main concern is not bound by the cell concept and encompasses the extracellular matter of organisms as well.

A sharp division between cell physiology and general physiology cannot be made, however. It can be argued that much of cell physiology is a part of general physiology, but in actual fact there are two recognized fields, and a look at the courses at various universities will convince the doubtful of this fact. The separation that does exist, and that has been defined in the preceding paragraphs, is dictated by the need to keep two fields of one science manageable.

Of course, an added reason for the separation is the training and experience of the scientists themselves who represent these fields. Cell physiologists are likely to have direct experience only with cell material that is particularly amenable to research on "the nature of living cells" (to use the title of a recent cell physiology text by Chambers and Chambers). Thus few cell physiologists would hesitate to identify themselves with cell physiology. It is quite different with general physiology: many of the scientists who, one way or another, represent general physiology, would rather identify themselves with special branches of physiology, such as neurophysiology, muscle physiology, or biophysics—in other words, with a small segment of physiology. The chief reason for this is that mastery of any of these fields and subfields requires such enormous preparation and training that there is little time and energy left for an intensive study of another area of physiology.

In this sense, any of these fields is on an equal footing with cell physiology—just as cell physiologists are interested in cells as cells (not as constituents of muscle or nervous systems), so are neurophysiologists interested in nerve cells and their interaction as nerve cells, and the muscle physiologists in muscle as muscle (not as a mass of cells). But inasmuch as they are concerned with the establishment of general principles of fundamental mechanisms of organismic life, they are general physiologists.

The distinction between cell physiology and general physiology is similar in character to the distinction between neurophysiology and general physiology or between muscle physiology and general physiology. The main distinction, in each case, is that general physiology is concerned with the general principles of organismic life, and views each mechanism with respect to its significance within organisms, whereas the other branches of physiology are interested in the functional aspects of the constituents of organisms as such.

General physiology thus appears (like comparative physiology) to be a supreme science which has its roots in specialized areas, of which cell physiology is one. General and comparative physiology are two aspects of physiology *per se*; all other kinds of physiology are their subdivisions or constituents: they are both inductive (comparative) and deductive (general).

WHAT PHYSIOLOGISTS DO

Experiments

The physiologist is interested in function, that is, in the time-space pattern, of life processes—or mechanisms—characteristic of living organisms. The time element is restricted to fractions of a second, seconds, minutes, or hours—only seldom to days. Systematic knowledge is derived from the interpretation of facts in the form of hypotheses and theories. Facts are obtained by experimentation. The sum of related facts is called *data*, the plural of *datum* (single fact).

Experiments are conducted in order to elucidate simple correlations between two variables: one is usually an environmental condition, the other a property of the organism or of one of its parts. For example, one may intentionally vary the temperature and observe (by suitable measurements) the heart rate, oxygen consumption, or rate of sweat production of an organism, or one may change the strength of an applied current and study the effect on the membrane potential of a nerve cell. Sometimes correlations are established by measuring a particular parameter or performance of a cell, organ, or even the whole organism, and then repeating the measurements with other, similar cells, organs, and organisms in order to correlate the results with one or the other parameter of the individual cells, organs, or organisms that show variation: thus the oxygen consumption of many specimens of a given species could be measured and correlated with their weights, or the conduction velocity of different nerve fibers could be measured and correlated with their diameters.

As a consequence of the peculiar mode of experimentation, the physiologist expresses his data in graphs, using Cartesian coordinates where the x axis gives the parameter that has been varied during the experiment, or that which differs in the specimens studied, while the y axis represents the measured physiological quantity, such as the amount of oxygen consumed or the conduction velocity.

Certain experiments employ a third variable, time—and more often than not time is a "hidden variable," that is, a component of the individual data. Consider, for instance, the well-known experiment in which the gastrocnemius muscle of a frog is made to twitch by electrical stimulation. Each muscle twitch has a space-time pattern consisting of contraction and relaxation. Each phase, by itself, can be recorded on a coordinate system by a kymograph drum and a writing lever. The rotation of the drum provides the x axis (the time axis), and the movement of the lever that records the twitch provides the y axis. The total area under each recorded event represents one twitch. If this quantity is then plotted on the y axis of a graph against the stimulus strength (entered on the x axis), a two-dimensional graph is obtained that contains time as a hidden element, because time is an intrinsic part of the recorded twitch data.

One of the first things the student of physiology has to learn is how to read and interpret graphs. This requires the development of abstract thinking, so that the shape of a curve represented within certain coordinates will not be confused with shapes known from everyday life. This is particularly obvious, of course, when one of the coordinates is time: a space-time shape is something entirely different from a shape in space!

This part of the physiological method is not different from the method employed by physicists and chemists.

The experiments themselves fall into several categories: *In vivo* experiments are performed on living matter—cells, organs, etc.—that is within the organism. *In vitro* experiments involve measuring structures excised and isolated from the organism.

In *acute experiments* the immediate effects of certain experimental procedures are observed. The majority of physiological experiments are of this type. They do not require precautions that ensure that the living structure under study remains viable for any extended period (more than, at most, a few hours). In *chronic experiments* an organism or certain of its parts are observed over extended periods of time (days, weeks, months, or even years). Examples are studies on nerve degeneration, on regeneration, and endocrinologic experiments that involve removal or implantation of hormone-secreting endocrine structures.

The instruments the physiologist uses range from pins and tweezers to the most advanced electronic devices, and from mortar and pestle to the most refined instruments of the chemists, such as flame spectrophotometers and gas chromatographs. The techniques the physiologist uses are limited only by the state of technology at the time of his experiments; in fact, many a physiologist has devised instruments that outperformed those designed by engineers and physicists of his time. There is no instrument that is uniquely physiological: whatever equipment the physiologist needs can be found in the laboratories of chemists, physicists, and engineers, although more often than not, it has to be adapted to the specific purpose.

A good physiologist must be a good technician, and the more technical skills he possesses the better will be his experiments. But even the most clever technician will not be a good physiologist unless he has the imagination and the gift of intuition that permit him to see possible correlations and connections between often widely differing phenomena, and the ability to recognize in the most elementary facts and in the most familiar life processes, the challenge for a new interpretation. It should be a consolation to those who work in laboratories of limited budgets and equipment that the most fundamental discoveries in physiology have been made with the aid of instrumentation that can be assembled by a good technician with materials available to the smallest purse. However, such discoveries can be fully utilized only when they reach the most modern and best equipped laboratories.

Training of students of physiology in advanced techniques is highly advisable, but it would be foolish to let the student bypass the stage in which he had to perform simple experiments with simple tools. These are the exercises that least detract from the true significance of the experiment. It is much easier to master a complicated machine (be it a multichannel oscillograph or an automatic amino acid analyzer) than to learn how to design a good experiment and to conceive of a new and significant hypothesis.

Publications

The physiologist who engages in research must publish the results of his experiments as soon as his interpretation of the data can contribute significantly to physiological knowledge; this, after all, is the reason why he carries out experiments. He may even publish earlier if his data can significantly aid the research of others. With his publications, the scientist repays his debt to society and government for moral and financial support and intellectual independence.

No publication, however, can convey the impact of a scientist's findings as well as personal communication where there is opportunity for direct, frank, and informative discussion. Therefore, physiologists, like other scientists, meet in larger and smaller groups on many occasions, and travel to other laboratories in order to learn new techniques and approaches, or simply in order to talk a problem over with a competent colleague.

As a rule, publication takes the form of a research paper, simply referred to as a *paper*. Such papers appear in special journals whose editors are competent scientists in the field in which the journal specializes. To be selected for membership on the editorial board of a scientific journal is a great honor and burden. Editors must uphold high scientific standards. They usually engage specialists (called *referees*) to evaluate the manuscripts submitted to them. The referees customarily remain unknown to the authors (much to their chagrin in case the manuscript is returned with unfavorable comments).

Manuscripts must be short and precise. Some decades ago, authors were allowed to write without much restriction; many engaged in lengthy polemics. At that time the scientist-author was paid for articles (per page). Today there is no remuneration for publication. But papers have become shorter because of an acute lack of space. The number of scientific papers published each year has about doubled every 10 years since the turn of the century.

A physiologist who would attempt to read all published articles that contain topics of physiological interest would spend day and night reading and would still be behind. In this respect it is fortunate that not all the research journals are available to him unless he resides at the Marine Laboratories of Woods Hole, Massachusetts, or Naples, Italy, which have the most complete scientific libraries in the world. However, special abstracting journals give the titles and a short summary (called an *abstract*) of practically all research papers.

The most important of these publications are: *Biological Abstracts*, *Berichte über die gesamte Biologie*, *Berichte über die gesamte Physiologie und experimentelle Pharmakologie*, and *Chemical Abstracts*.

Scientific fields are also surveyed by *reviews*, articles written by experts, which synthesize the results and hypotheses published in recent papers. Many review publications are of immediate interest to physiologists. The most important of these are: *Annual Review of Physiology*, *Annual Review of Pharmacology*, *Physiological Reviews*, *Biological Reviews*, *Ergebnisse der Physiologie*, *Ergebnisse der Biologie*, and *Fortschritte der Zoologie*.

Good reviews synthesize the current state of knowledge, and in addition give extensive lists of relevant publications (all quoted within the review article).

Reviews appear not only in the regular periodicals of which several were mentioned here, but in the published proceedings of special meetings, called *symposia* (see below), in which specialists summarize the knowledge of a particular field of physiology, from their own point of view. Symposium publications are numerous and not always easy to obtain. In order to facilitate the finding of relevant reviews, there are now *reviews of reviews*, such as those published in the *Annual Review of Pharmacology*.

The following journals are of particular interest to physiologists: American Journal of Physiology (United States), Archives internationales de physiologie (Belgium, international), Archiv für die gesamte Physiologie (Germany), Acta physiologica Scandinavica (Sweden), Acta physiologica Academiae Scientiarum Hungaricae (Hungary), Biological Bulletin (United States), Comparative Biochemistry and Physiology (United Kingdom), Journal of Cellular and Comparative Physiology (United States), Japanese Journal of Physiology (Japan), Journal of Experimental Biology (United Kingdom), Journal of Physiology (United Kingdom), Journal of Neurophysiology (United States), Journal of General Physiology (United States), Physiological Zoology (United States), Zeitschrift für vergleichende Physiologie (Germany). There are numerous others, published in several countries.

In addition to such journals containing regular research papers, many countries have one periodical containing scientific articles of more general interest, and so-called *short communications*. These are brief articles (usually limited to 2000 words), that describe new findings within current investigations.

This form of publication has the advantage of a short interval between submission of the manuscript and the appearance of the printed article. The journals appear weekly, and in certain cases biweekly. The best known of these are: Nature (United Kingdom), Naturwissenschaften (Germany), Science (United States), and Scientia (Switzerland).

Papers are rarely published by only one author. Usually there are two or even more authors, for it has become customary for scientists, and physiologists in particular, to collaborate on research projects. The practice of distinguishing between senior and junior authors is rapidly becoming outmoded. Formerly the name of the senior author (head of the laboratory, leader of the team, etc.) preceded that of the collaborator(s). If several authors contribute to a paper, their names are sometimes listed in the order of the relative importance of their individual efforts. It is not always easy, or fair, to judge this. Therefore authors' names commonly appear in alphabetical order, as is standard practice in some journals, for example the Journal of Physiology.

In recent years it has become common practice for scientists (physiologists not excepted) to ask authors for a reprint of their article. This is done on a pre-printed postcard, usually available at departmental offices. Authors are usually provided with 100 to several hundred reprints at cost. They are prepared to be asked for copies by interested colleagues, and they comply with such requests until the supply is exhausted. The gentlemanly practice of thanking the generous author by pre-printed postcard, assures the sender that his gift has been received, and he is spared the worry that a colleague might think him rude if by some malfunction of the mails, the reprint had not arrived.

For a student, not yet an accomplished scientist, it is more polite to request reprints by letter and to identify himself as a student. A good scientist more likely than not will accommodate the interested student in preference to an unknown colleague.

Societies and Meetings

Physiologists have their own professional organizations and societies. Most physiologists are members of at least one such society. The local, regional, and national organizations serve a vital function: not only do they publicly voice the accomplishments and needs of physiologists, but they also help to ensure highest scientific standards and ethics, and provide a forum for scientific meetings, designed for the exchange of information and for the discussion of old and new hypotheses and theories. Only outstanding scientists are elected into high offices within these societies and membership depends on the scientific accomplishments of the applicants.

Most countries where physiology is well developed have a national organization entitled the physiological society (or an equivalent name). These national organizations are affiliated with the International Union of Physiological Sciences (I.U.P.S.). The I.U.P.S., among other activities, organizes every three years an International Congress of Physiology, held each time in a different country. This congress is attended by accomplished physiologists of all nations.

The national societies hold a meeting at least once every year. These meetings are attended primarily by physiologists of the particular country, but guests from other nations are always welcome. Regional organizations likewise have general meetings, attended by their own membership. These meetings are held annually, sometimes monthly, and smaller societies even biweekly or weekly.

All these meetings—international, national, and regional—have a similar character: their most important aspect is the presentation, by individual physiologists, of short lectures (usually of not more than 10 minutes' duration) on their particular research. These lectures, called *papers*, are followed by a general discussion in which anyone in the audience may participate. Usually only five minutes or less is allowed for discussion. At national meetings in the United States (American Physiological Society, Federated Societies of Experimental Biology, American Association for the Advancement of Science) several hundred papers are given in several parallel sessions. The same, on an even grander scale, is true for international congresses. A participant in a congress or large meeting, therefore, must work out a precise schedule which, more often than not, involves moving from one lecture hall to another.

The significance of these regular meetings, even when they are taken for granted, cannot be overestimated. They give scientists the opportunity to get personally acquainted with each other, and to debate critical questions informally between sessions. They give science its human quality and keep it alive by letting others share the joys of discovery, by giving the feeling of personal challenge, and by exposing weak arguments to forthright critique.

Within regional, national, and international meetings there are usually one or more sessions called *symposia*. A symposium is a meeting in which only invited speakers and discussants participate. Open symposia admit a general audience; closed symposia are restricted to invited participants. Their purpose is not to present the immediate results of research, but to review and debate more far-reaching implications of research data. A selected group of competent specialists discusses new viewpoints, hypotheses, and emergent theories. The discussions and debates follow lengthy, formal lectures by the individual participants. Often the arguments are controversial, the ensuing debate lively.

Many symposia are held outside the regular meetings and congresses. A good number of them are international, even though the invited participants are few. Symposia are the proving grounds of new scientific concepts. They are expensive undertakings; therefore, the proceedings are usually recorded and published in the form of *symposium publications* or *symposium volumes*. Many published symposia contain edited discussions as well as the formal papers. To student and research workers alike (both, after all, are students in the truest sense), the printed discussions are sometimes more illuminating and educational than the debated papers themselves. The papers are always written with conviction, but the discussion shows that one need not necessarily be convinced. Both attack and defense may expose a fool or a master; and therein lies the intellectual pleasure that is the heart of science.

Table 1. The Phyla of the Animal Kingdom with some Important Classes, Subclasses, and Orders, and the Approximate Numbers of Species Contained Therein

Phylum	*Class*	*Subclass*	*Order*
Protozoa (20,000)			
	Flagellata		
	Sarcodina		
		Rhizopoda	
		Actinopoda	
	Sporozoa		
	Ciliata		
	Suctoria		
Porifera (5000)			
Mesozoa (50)			
Monoblastozoa			
Coelenterata (8900)			
	Hydrozoa		
	Scyphozoa (jellyfishes)		
	Anthozoa (sea anemones, corals)		
Ctenophora (80)			
Platyhelminthes (flatworms) (6000)			
	Turbellaria (planarians) (1600)		
	Trematoda (flukes) (2400)		
	Cestoda (tapeworms) (1500)		
Nemertinea (ribbon worms) (750)			
Acanthocephala (spiny-headed worms) (260)			
Rotifera (rotifers) (1500)			
Gastrotricha (150)			
Kinorhyncha (100)			
Priapuloidea (3)			
Nematoda (threadworms, roundworms) (5000)			
Gordiacea (horse-hair worms) (225)			
Calyssozoa (Endoprocta) (60)			
Bryozoa (Ectoprocta) (moss animals) (4000)			
Phoronida (18)			
Brachiopoda (lamp shells) (280)			
Mollusca (molluscs) (112,000)			
	Monoplacophora		
	Amphineura (chitons) (1150)		
	Gastropoda (snails, slugs) (85,000)		
		Prosobranchia (55,000)	
			Archaeogastropoda (limpets, ear shells)
		Opisthobranchia (10,000)	
			Pleurocoela (sea hares, *Aplysia*)
			Pteropoda
			Acoela (nudibranchs)
		Pulmonata (land snails, slugs) (20,000)	
	Bivalvia (Pelecypoda, Lamellibranchia) (bivalves, oysters, clams, mussels) (25,000)		
	Scaphopoda (tooth shells) (300)		
	Cephalopoda (2600)		
		Tetrabranchia	
			Nautiloidea (pearly nautilus)
		Dibranchia	
			Decapoda (squids, cuttlefish)
			Octopoda (octopuses, argonauts)
Sipunculoidea (250)			
Echiuroidea (70)			
Myzostomida			

Table 1. The Phyla of the Animal Kingdom with some Important Classes, Subclasses, and Orders, and the Approximate Numbers of Species Contained Therein (Continued)

Phylum	*Class*	*Subclass*	*Order*
Annelida (7000)			
	Chaetopoda		
		Polychaeta (4000)	
		Oligochaeta (earthworms, etc.) (2400)	
	Hirudinea (leeches) (300)		
Tardigrada (bear animalcules) (180)			
Pentastomida (60)			
Onychophora (70)			
Arthropoda (850,000)			
	Merostomata		
		Xiphosura	
			Xiphosurida (horseshoe crabs) (5)
	Arachnida (30,000)		
		Latigastra	
			Scorpionida (scorpions) (600)
		Caulogastra	
			Araneae (spiders) (20,000)
	Crustacea (20,000)		
		Branchiopoda	
			Anostraca (brine shrimps) (145)
			Cladocera (water fleas)
		Ostracoda (1500)	
		Copepoda (1800)	
		Cirripedia (barnacles) (760)	
		Malacostraca (14,000)	
			Isopoda (pill bugs, sow bugs) (1300)
			Amphipoda (scuds) (2700)
			Decapoda (crabs, crayfish, lobsters, shrimps, prawns) (8300)
			Stomatopoda (mantis shrimps) (170)
	Diplopoda (millipedes) (7200)		
	Chilopoda (centipedes) (2800)		
	Insecta (750,000)		
Chaetognatha (arrowworms) (50)			
Pogonophora (beard worms) (47)			
Echinodermata (5970)			
	Crinoidea (feather stars, sea lilies) (620)		
	Asteroidea (starfishes) (1500)		
	Ophiuroidea (brittle stars) (1900)		
	Echinoidea (sea urchins, etc.) (860)		
	Holothurioidea (sea cucumbers) (1100)		
Pterobranchia (20)			
Enteropneusta (acorn worms) (60)			
Planctosphaeroidea (1)			
Tunicata (1600)			
	Ascidiacea (sea squirts)		
Cephalochordata			
	Leptocardia		
		Amphioxi (*Amphioxus*, lancelets)	
Vertebrata (38,000)			

After Blackwelder, R. E.: Classification of the Animal Kingdom. Southern Illinois University Press, Carbondale, 1963; and Kaestner, A.: Lehrbuch der speziellen Zoologie. G. Fischer Verlag, Stuttgart.

SOME DIMENSIONS OF THE PHYSIOLOGIST'S WORLD

General and comparative physiology are both concerned with animal organisms, regardless of their position within the framework of systematic nomenclature. Animal physiology encompasses the entire animal kingdom and presupposes knowledge of morphology and systematics.

Table 1 lists the more important animal phyla, classes, subclasses, and orders according to recent nomenclatures.

Physiological data and measurements are always given in terms of the metric system, also known as the "centimeter-gram-second" system. The following is a summary of the most common dimensions of length, weight, time, and energy as used in this text:

Weight	*Length*	*Volume*
1 kg = 1000 g	1 m = 100 cm = 1000 mm	1 l = 1000 ml
1 g = 1000 μg or 1000 γ	1 cm = 10 mm	1 ml = 1000 μl or 1000 λ
	1 mm = 1000 μm or 1000 μ	
	1 μ = 1000 mμ or 10,000 Å	
	1 Å = 0.1 mμ = 10^{-8} cm	

Å, angström unit; *cm*, centimeter; *g*, gram; *kg*, kilogram; *l*, liter; λ, lambda; *m*, meter; *ml*, milliliter; *mm*, millimeter; *mμ*, millimicron; *μ*, micron; *μg*, microgram; *μl*, microliter; *μm*, micrometer; γ, gamma.

Energy = Force × Distance

unit of Force: 1 dyne. Definition: accelerates mass of 1 g at the rate of 1 cm/sec/sec, or 1 cm/sec^2

unit of Distance: 1 cm

unit of Energy: 1 erg. Definition: force of 1 dyne over distance of 1 cm

10^7 ergs = 1 joule = volt-coulomb; (1 coulomb = $\frac{1}{96,494}$ of the electrical charge carried by 1 gram equivalent of ion)

Power = time rate of doing Work = Work/Time

unit of Power: 1 watt. Definition: 1 joule/sec

1 watt = 1 volt-ampere

Energy = Power × Time

unit of Energy: 1 watt-second

Energy = Work = Mass × Distance lifted

unit of Mass: 1 gm; unit of Distance lifted: 1 cm

unit of Energy: 1 calorie = 42,685 gram-cm = 4.186 joules

1 joule = 0.239 calorie = 10,197 gram-cm = 1 watt-second

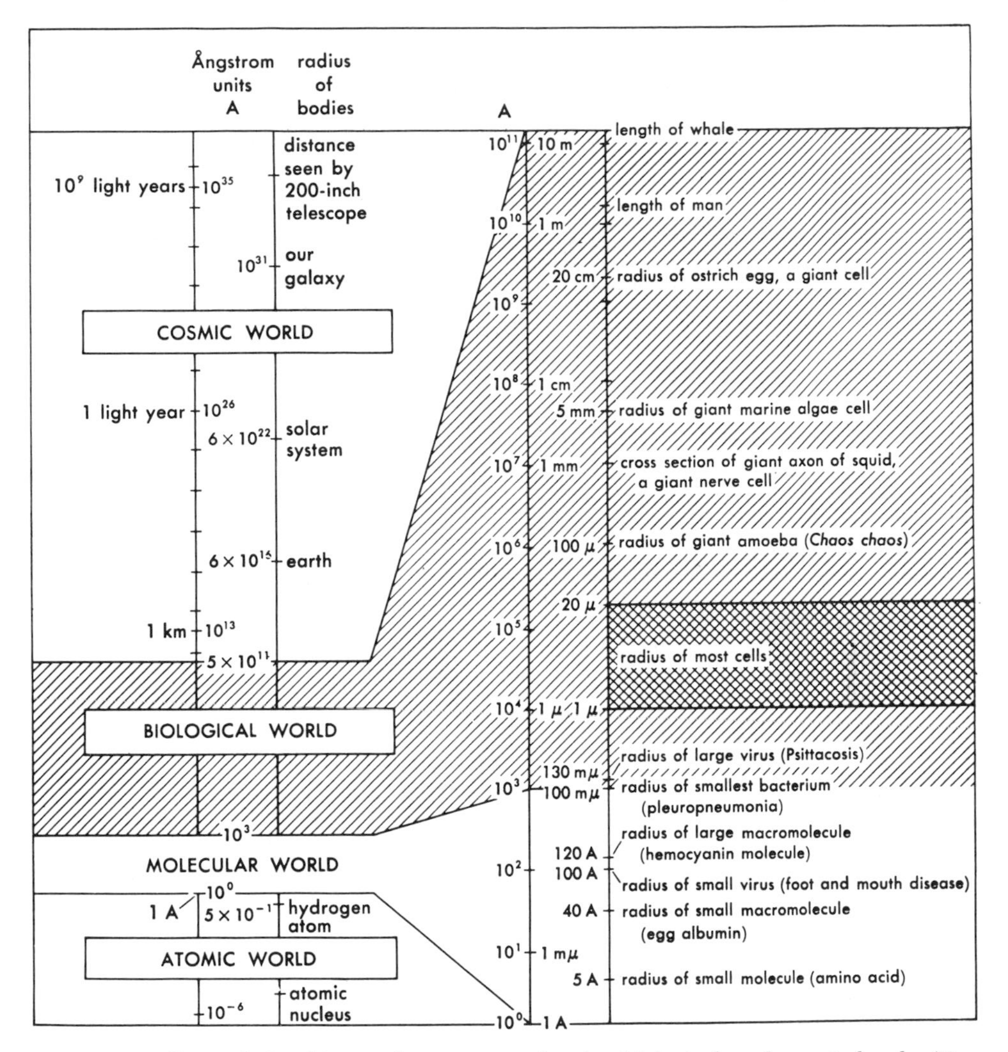

Figure 1. Size relationships at the atomic, molecular, biological, and cosmic levels. (From Loewy, A. G., and P. Siekevitz: Cell Structure and Function. Holt, Rinehart and Winston, New York, 1963.)

Some dimensions of the physical world are shown in Figure 1. There are, of course, many more physical constants with which the physiologist operates. Many of these appear elsewhere in the text. However, consult a good physics text whenever in doubt about a physical term or constant. The universe of the physiologist is by no means simpler than that of the physicist.

REFERENCES

Aristoteles' collected works. (1831–1870) Bekker, I., and A. Brandis, eds. G. Reimerum, Berlin.

Bayliss, L. E. (1964) Principles of General Physiology, Vols. I and II. Longmans, Green and Co., London.

Bayliss, W. M. (1924) Principles of General Physiology, 4th Ed. Longmans, Green and Co., London.

Bernard, C. (1872) Physiologie Générale. Hatchette et Cie., Paris.

Bernard, C. (1878–1879) Leçons sur les Phénomènes de la Vie Communs aux Animaux et aux Végétaux. 2 vols., J. B. Baillière et Fils, Paris.
Bernard, C. (1885) Leçons sur les Phénomènes de la Vie. J. B. Baillière et Fils, Paris.
von Bethe, A. T. (1952) Allgemeine Physiologie. J. Springer, Berlin.
von Buddenbrock, W. (1928, 1937) Grundriss der vergleichenden Physiologie. 2 vols. G. Borntraeger, Berlin.
von Buddenbrock, W. (1950–1961) Vergleichende Physiologie. 6 vols. Birkhäuser Verlag, Stuttgart.
Davson, H. (1964) A Textbook of General Physiology, 3rd Ed. Little, Brown and Co., Boston.
von Fürth, O. (1903) Vergleichende Chemische Physiologie der Niederen Tiere. G. Fischer Verlag, Jena.
Heilbrunn, L. V. (1952) An Outline of General Physiology, 3rd Ed. W. B. Saunders Co., Philadelphia.
Höber, R. (1945) Physical Chemistry of Cells and Tissues. The Blakiston Co., Philadelphia.
Hogben, L. T. (1926) Comparative Physiology. The Macmillan Co., New York.
Jordan, H. J. (1913) Vergleichende Physiologie Wirbelloser Tiere. G. Fischer Verlag, Jena.
Jordan, H. J. (1929) Allgemeine Vergleichende Physiologie der Tiere. Walter De Gruyter & Co., Berlin.
Loeb, J. (1905) Studies in General Physiology. 2 vols. University of Chicago Press, Chicago.
Milne-Edwards, H. (1857–1881) Leçons sur la Physiologie et l'Anatomie Comparée de l'Homme et des Animaux. 14 vols. V. Masson, Paris.
Mitchell, P. H. (1956) A Textbook of General Physiology, 5th Ed. McGraw-Hill Book Co., New York.
Müller, J. (1839–1842) Elements of Physiology, 2nd Ed. 2 vols. (Translated by W. Baly.) Taylor & Walton, London.
Pantelouris, E. M. (1957) A Handbook of Animal Physiology. Baillière, Tindall & Cox, London.
Prosser, C. L., and F. A. Brown, Jr., eds. (1961) Comparative Animal Physiology, 2nd Ed. W. B. Saunders Co., Philadelphia.
Pütter, A. (1911) Vergleichende Physiologie. G. Fischer Verlag, Jena.
Rogers, C. G. (1938) Textbook of Comparative Physiology, 2nd Ed., McGraw-Hill Book Co., New York.
Scheer, B. T. (1953) General Physiology. John Wiley & Sons, New York; Chapman & Hall, London.
Scheer, B. T. (1948) Comparative Physiology. John Wiley & Sons, New York; Chapman & Hall, London.
Stempell, W., and A. Koch (1923) Elemente der Tierphysiologie. G. Fischer Verlag, Jena.
von Tschermak, A. (1924) Allgemeine Physiologie. J. Springer, Berlin.
Verworn, M. (1922) Allgemeine Physiologie, 7th Ed. G. Fischer Verlag, Jena.
Winterstein, H. (1910–1925) Handbuch der vergleichenden Physiologie. 8 vols. G. Fischer Verlag, Jena.

1 THE ORIGIN OF LIFE

It seems appropriate to set the stage for the discussion of living systems, or organisms, by presenting some current ideas and concepts about their origin. It is sometimes said that it is futile for a scientist to speak about life as if it were something quite different from "ordinary" matter, since modern science does not acknowledge such a difference. And indeed we physiologists have to admit that there is no evidence that matter that composes an organism behaves in any way that is out of the ordinary by the standards of our physical and chemical concepts and theories. We have inherited the term "life" from ancient pre-scientific concepts, according to which there is a strict duality of animate and inanimate matter, and we are still influenced by Aristotelian philosophy, and thus the terms "substance" (composed of *matter* and *essence*) and "soul," the latter being by definition an immaterial being.

Today, in the age of the "exact sciences," no method can verify or even approach the concept of a nonmaterial formative (let alone perceptive) soul, and we find it satisfactory to reduce living organisms to measurable quantities having physical and chemical properties. Still, use of the term "life" is justifiable if we agree that it represents the *properties* of a "mixture" of substances that we call "protoplasm," rather than an *extramaterial force* that transforms matter into living protoplasm. We could even go further and define "life" as the collective properties of cells, since protoplasm always appears in the form of cells. After all, as we understand it, everything that is commonly called "living" consists of cells and can be explained (within the framework of physicochemical analysis) by the properties of such cells and their interaction. In fact, living "things" have so many features in common that the terms "living" and "life" assume a definite meaning.

Modern theories concerning the universe center around two hypotheses: according to the one the universe had no beginning. Two processes balance each other: continuous creation and destruction of matter (Hoyle, 1955). According to the other hypothesis, the universe was created five to ten billion years ago, the creation resulting in a gigantic explosion of primeval matter (Alpher and Herman, 1950). Both hypotheses have in common the assumption of an evolution of a primordial matter which leads, or lead, to the formation of elements. There is little doubt that the elements are still evolving and transforming. This can be observed in the changes in proportion of the isotopes of any element.

The origin of our solar system in usually considered to be about five billion years ago, and one assumes that here, as in other solar systems and galaxies, the formation of elements was followed by what Calvin (1956) calls "chemical evolution," the formation of molecules and their subsequent interaction. When the planet earth was formed, about four billion years ago, this process was well under way.

The question is now: How were the first organic compounds formed and what eventually produced the basis of all living substance, the proteins? As suggested by Haldane (1929), and proved by experiments of many scientists (Calvin, 1956), the constituents of proteins (the amino acids) can be formed by the action of ultraviolet rays on aqueous solutions of ammonia, nitric acid, nitrates, formic acid, or formaldehyde (Fig. 1–1). Another process that is likely to have resulted in large organic molecules as they are now found in living matter was proposed by A. I. Oparin (1938); it is the production of acetylene from metallic carbide (Fig. 1–1) that came in contact with water at the time of the first rain (the earth's surface and lower atmosphere had to cool to below 100° C before water vapor could condense). Under suitable conditions acetylene could have polymerized into organic colloids. Such a polymerization product of acetylene, called cuprene, is thought to be responsible for the red color of the surface of the planet Jupiter (Urey, 1952).

An interesting solution to the problem of the genesis of the chemical substrate of life is offered by studies of Garrison et al. (1954), which show that radioactivity, such as that of cosmic rays or radioactive material of the earth's crust, induces the formation of such compounds as formic, oxalic, and succinic acids (one-, two-, and four-carbon compounds, respectively) from carbon dioxide and water (Fig. 1–1). Furthermore, it has been shown that the high energies of lightning can produce amino acid type compounds from methane, hydrogen, ammonia, and water (Miller, 1953). The latter compounds (Fig. 1–1) were present in large amounts in the early atmosphere of the earth. In fact, photochemical studies reveal that the decomposition products of methane, for instance, react photochemically to form acetylene and its polymerization products, and that great quantities of such "atmospheric" organic compounds must have dissolved in the oceans of the primitive earth (Noyes and Leighton, 1941; Rollefson and Burton, 1939; Urey, 1952).

Before considering further the chemical conditions of the primitive surface and atmosphere of the earth, we may ask how these more complex organic amino acids and polymers could have undergone all those changes and transformations that constitute the "evolution" of living substance. One of the secrets lies undoubtedly in the fact that a large number of chemicals can act as *catalysts* of one or the other chemical reaction. *Catalysts are compounds* (sometimes even elements) *that by their presence determine direction and speed of certain*

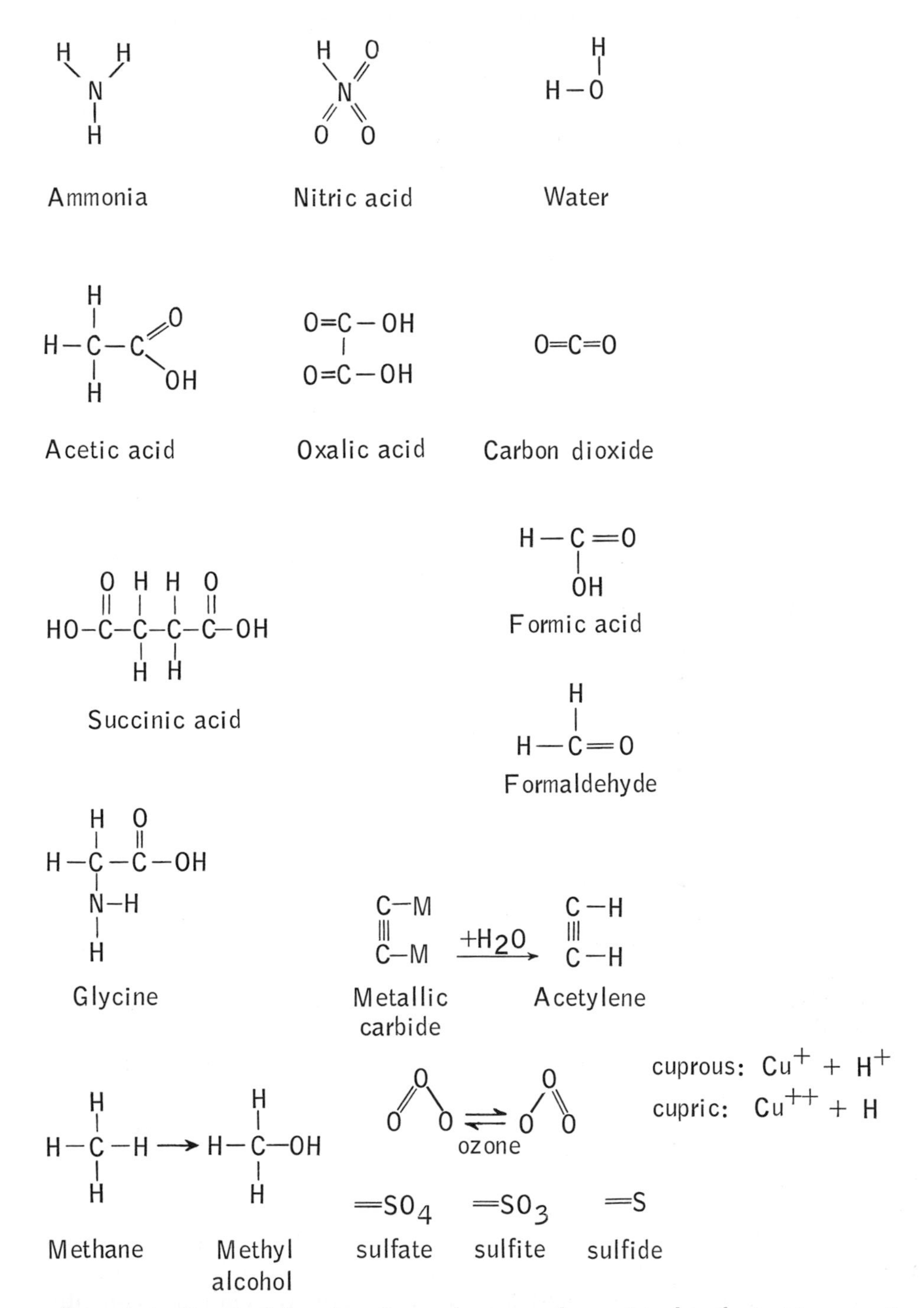

Figure 1–1. Structural formulas of several compounds mentioned in the text in connection with the chemical evolution of living systems. The symbol *M* in the formula for metallic carbide stands for "metal."

chemical reactions or reaction sequences without appearing among the reaction products of the reaction (Bodenstein, 1903; Stieglitz, 1908; Mittasch, 1935). Except for cases in which a catalyst slows down or inhibits a reaction, a catalyst induces a specific chemical reaction and lets it proceed at great speed and without "effort." The mode of operation of catalysts is little understood, but experience shows that they lower the *activation-energy* requirement of chemical reactions (see Chap. 6). Catalysts need be present only in minute quantities.

As far as we know, there is no rule as to which compounds can be catalysts. We may indeed assume that any element or compound is a potential catalyst; it catalyzes a reaction when the "right" reactants come in contact with it. Cuprous ion, for instance, is a catalyst when in contact with cupric ion and hydrogen: in its presence these two substances react to give hydrogen ion and cuprous ion (Fig. 1–1). As Calvin (1956) points out, the random occurrence of a cuprous ion in a solution of cupric ions and molecular hydrogen is sufficient to convert all the cupric ions into cuprous ions. Cuprous ion thus multiplies itself. It is the simplest example of an *autocatalyst*, a catalyst that catalyzes its own formation. Organic compounds are just as much catalysts as inorganic ones, and many function as autocatalysts.

If the starting materials or reacting compounds of two similar catalysts are the same compounds, we have here, even on this elementary scale, a *struggle for existence*: the more efficient catalyst will outrun the other and will thereby increase its changes of converting even more of the reactants, should they ever become available, into its own likeness. There are indications that organic catalysts increase their efficiency with growing complexity, and if they happen to be autocatalysts or if a series of such catalysts could induce the formation of complex and efficient catalysts, *natural selection* of the most efficient chemical system would result. Today autocatalysis of the most complex structures of living matter, the chromosomes, is an established fact, and we can look upon organisms as incredibly complex systems of interacting catalysts, the sum of whose actions approaches a steady state. The reaction products of one reaction are the starting material for another, and one system of catalysts produces still other compounds with catalytic properties that can induce reactions that benefit the whole.

Catalysis and autocatalysis are not the only phenomena that can be held responsible for the evolution of life. *Polymerization* was mentioned already; there is a general tendency for a spontaneous ordering of molecules into regular or periodic patterns. Proteins may show a periodic repetition of amino acid sequences (Fig. 1–2), and even such "advanced" structures as the chromosome substance (deoxyribonucleic acids) exhibit a repetitive pattern (Fig. 1–3). That we can speak of "the" chromosome substance and that we do not have to specify the organism to which this substance belongs indicates that the biochemical constitution of all organisms is remarkably similar and that all organisms (except, perhaps, bacteria) originate from the same original "model." Not only is the cellular organization of plants and animals similar, but the chemical constitution is so astonishingly alike in all these living forms that we find similar compounds in similar structures. For example, the chemical-metabolic machinery of a brain cell of a cockroach could almost be exchanged for that of a muscle cell of a crocodile.

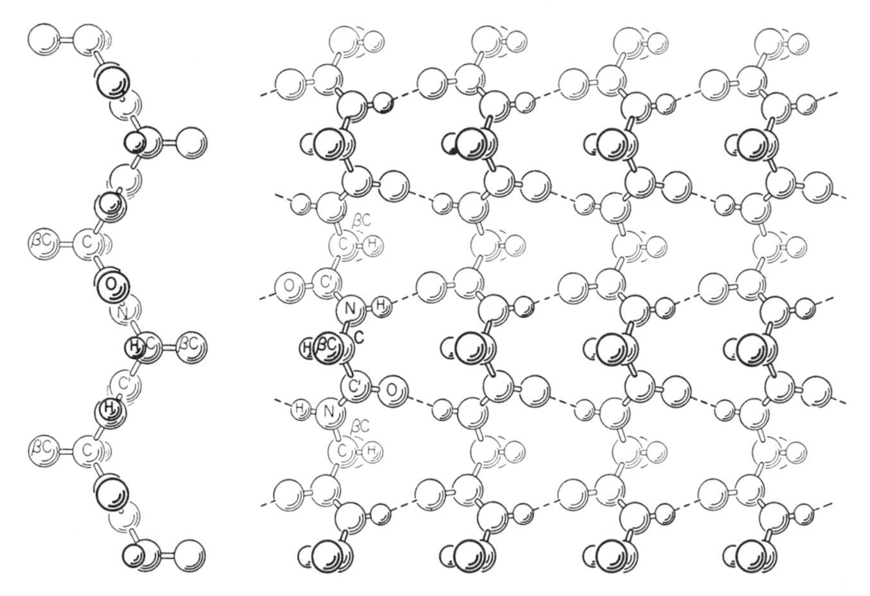

Figure 1–2. Diagrammatic representation of protein structures. **Left**, a segment of a single strand of a protein molecule. **Right**, a so-called parallel-chain pleated sheet in which many strands are held together by hydrogen bonds (stippled), which are approximately at right angles to the chain direction. This structure is typical for β-keratin, a scleroprotein found in vertebrate skin, hair, horns, and feathers. (From Pauling, L.: The Nature of the Chemical Bond, 3rd Ed. Cornell University Press, Ithaca, 1960.)

In addition, it is believed that all organisms not only have *formally* been derived from one original living form, but have *actually* differentiated from this one type of mother organism. Thus, the origin of organized life was probably a singular occurrence in the earth's history, due to a unique combination of conditions that permitted the emergence of a self-maintaining, autocatalytic chemical system.

At this point we return to a discussion of the conditions that prevailed on our planet when these earliest living forms appeared. The oldest remains of organisms are believed to be about 500 million years old. Since these remains indicate a high level of organization, the first organisms must have lived much earlier. On the basis of various calculations and assumptions, Urey (1952) adds another two billion years to account for the evolution from the first photosynthesis to the first organism.

As already mentioned, organic compounds of the complexities exhibited by amino acids can be formed in aqueous solution or in gaseous mixtures under the influence of powerful ultraviolet radiations, radioactivity, and lightning if such simple compounds as carbon monoxide, carbon dioxide, ammonia, methane, or carbide are present together with water. Furthermore, it has been shown that complex structures of specific catalytic activity, such as porphyrins, are formed from simplest nitrogen and carbon compounds. (For a more recent discussion of these findings, see Oparin, 1961.)

The question now is: What were the chemical and physical conditions of the earth's surface and atmosphere prior to 500 million or perhaps even prior

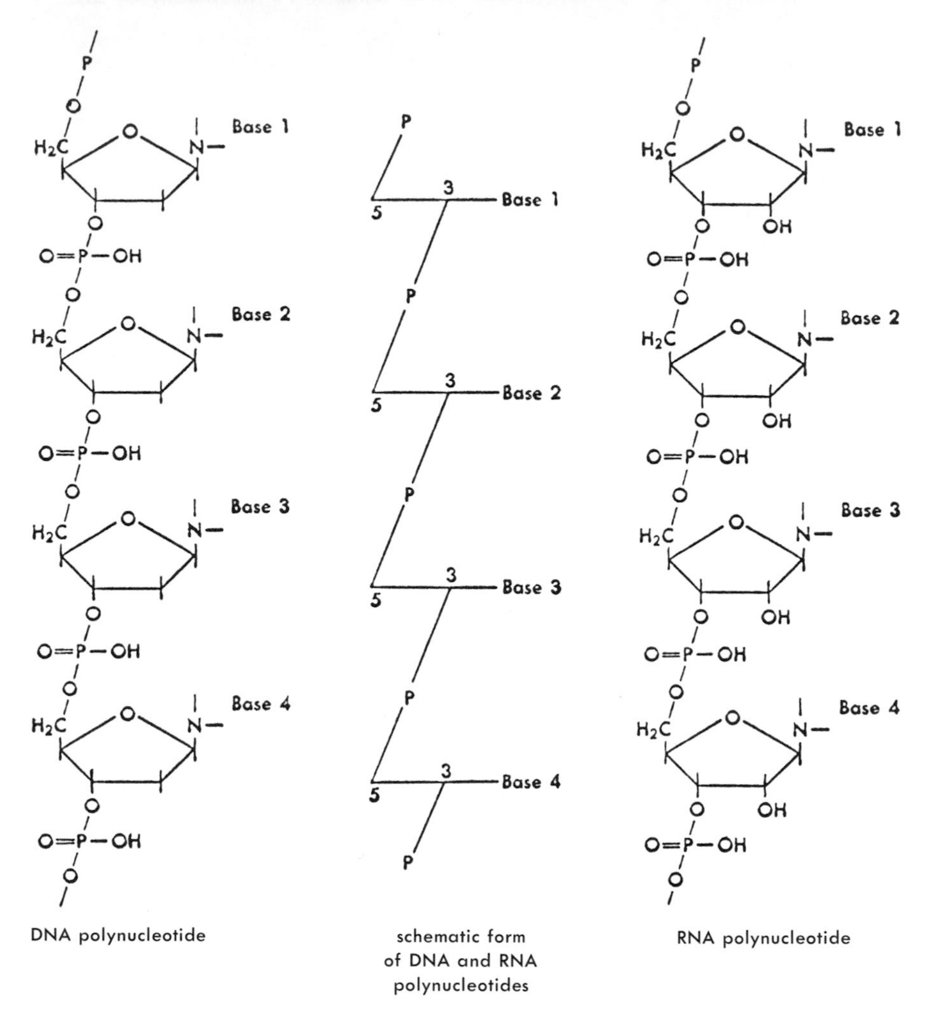

Figure 1–3. The structure of deoxyribonucleic acid (*DNA*) and ribonucleic acid (*RNA*) polynucleotides, exhibiting a repetitive pattern. (From Loewy, A. G., and P. Siekevitz: Cell Structure and Function. Holt, Rinehart and Winston, New York, 1963.)

to 1000 million years ago? All evidence indicates that little, if any, free, gaseous oxygen was present in the atmosphere. In fact, the term "hydrosphere" is often used to describe the earth's gas mantle of those days. This hydrosphere contained large quantities of ammonia and methane. On the whole it was a *reducing atmosphere* and it was only after the Laurentian Revolution in the early Cambrian Period (see Fig. 1–4) (about 800 million years ago) that the atmosphere became oxidative (Lane, 1917).

This change of condition, as we understand it today, was brought about by photosynthesizing living systems, that is, by plants. The oxygen of today's air is in a state of dynamic equilibrium: it is constantly being used up by oxidation and it is continuously renewed by the activity of green plants all over our globe. The total quantity of living substance on this earth has been calculated to be

ERA	PERIOD		EPOCH	BEGINNING OF INTERVAL (MILLION YEARS)	
CENOZOIC	QUATERNARY		Pleistocene	1	Man
	TERTIARY		Pliocene	13	Mammals
			Miocene	25	
			Oligocene	36	
			Eocene UPPER	45	
			Eocene MIDDLE	52	
			Eocene LOWER	58	
			Paleocene	63	
MESOZOIC	CRETACEOUS	UPPER	Maestrichtian	72	First mammals, modern birds, and fishes
			Campanian	84	
			Santonian	90	
			Coniacian		
			Turonian		
			Cenomanian	110	
		LOWER	Albian	120	
			Aptian		
			Neocomian	135	
	JURASSIC	UPPER			Giant reptiles, birdlike reptiles
		MIDDLE	Bathonian	166	
			Bajocian		
		LOWER		181	
	TRIASSIC	UPPER		200	Mammal-like reptiles
		MIDDLE			
		LOWER		(230)	
PALEOZOIC	PERMIAN	UPPER			Reptiles, etc.
		MIDDLE		260	
		LOWER		280	
	CARBONIFEROUS: PENNSYLVANIAN				First reptiles, insects, amphibia
	CARBONIFEROUS: MISSISSIPPIAN		Visean	320	Amphibia
			Tournaisian	345	
	DEVONIAN	UPPER		(365)	Insects, amphibia, (first land animals)
		MIDDLE		390	
		LOWER		405	
	SILURIAN			(425)	Fishes
	ORDOVICIAN	UPPER	Trenton	445	Echinoids, molluscs, sea scorpions (Arthropoda)
		MIDDLE			
		LOWER		500	Echinodermata
	CAMBRIAN	UPPER		530	(Asterozoa) Cephalopoda, (!) Arthropoda, Brachiopoda, etc.
		MIDDLE			
		LOWER			
?	?	?	?	?	?

Scale (million years): 0, 50, 100, 150, 200, 250, 300, 350, 400, 450, 500, 550, 600

Figure 1–4. Absolute time scale of geological history of the earth, as defined by isotopic age determination on rocks of known stratigraphic age, according to Kulp. To this table have been added the names of animal groups that first appear or are conspicuous in particular periods. (From Kulp, J. L.: Geologic time scale. Science *133*:1105–1112, 1961.)

1.5×10^{15} (1 million and 500 thousand billion) tons and the quantity of oxygen produced annually by this mass is about equal to the actual oxygen content of the atmosphere (Oparin, 1957; Urey, 1952). *The appearance of an oxidative atmosphere thus signals the advent of life.*

The earth's crust became greatly transformed by living organisms. Metal sulfides became transformed into sulfates (Szabo et al., 1950) about 700 to 800 million years ago (Fig. 1–1), and we have to assume that phosphorus, which today is largely present in the form of phosphates, was available as phosphites and hypophosphites before the dawn of organismic life. The significance of the abundance of incompletely oxidized phosphorus for the early evolution of living systems was pointed out by Gulick (1955). Phosphorus is *the* element involved in practically all the important energy "transactions" within organisms and in energy transfers responsible for the building up and maintenance of what we might term "organismic order." Such phenomena as plant photosynthesis and muscle contraction would be impossible without phosphorus.

Phosphorus is extremely insoluble in water. In sea water 4 milligrams per metric ton of water is a saturated solution. Phosphates are practically all insoluble. Today's organisms are well adapted to these extremely low levels of phosphorus in their environment. They have well developed mechanisms for concentrating and accumulating this element within their bodies. Sea urchin eggs, for instance, develop within 1 hour after fertilization, an active transport mechanism that carries phosphate into the cells against a concentration gradient of perhaps 1:1,000,000 (Litchfield and Whiteley, 1959).

If during the time of the hydrosphere only incomplete oxidations occurred, the waters of the oceans could have contained sufficient phosphorus to support the first steps toward life, the formation of phosphorus-containing catalysts: phosphites and hypophosphites are fairly soluble compounds!

The reducing atmosphere must have had another consequence, favorable for the evolution of life: lack of O_2 in the atmosphere also means lack of ozone (O_3). Today ozone is the main shield against the powerful irradiation of our planet by the ultraviolet rays of the sun. Before the appearance of quantities of oxygen and ozone in the atmosphere, ultraviolet radiation must have been intense and must have favored the formation of amino acids and other complex organic compounds (in the way suggested by Haldane, 1929).

In addition, the high energy radiation must have permitted photosynthesis in early plants possessing catalysts and catalytic systems much less complicated than those of today's plants (Gulick, 1955). It is tempting to speculate that by producing oxygen the early plants not only reduced their primary source of energy (sunlight) but with it "stimulated" their own evolution as more and more complex catalytic systems became essential for successful survival under the conditions of reduced intensity of ultraviolet light. Heterotrophic organisms (animals) would thus have found more and more complex chemical structures in their "food," and it is conceivable that the "forced evolution" of plants accelerated the evolution of animal organisms.

We have passed on from a consideration of the origin of life to the more complex question of the evolution of living organisms, which is not the subject of this chapter. Let us then return to a discussion of the conditions that favored the origin of living systems. One more question must be answered: How abundant were such compounds as methane and ammonia, and consequently how abundant were the organic compounds resulting from the action of ultraviolet light, radioactivity, and lightning on such simple carbon and nitrogen compounds? According to Urey's (1952) summary of recent data and calculations, the primitive oceans contained only about 10 per cent of the water found in today's oceans. These primitive oceans must have had an extremely high content of carbon compounds. According to Urey's estimates they represented a 10 per cent solution of organic compounds (based on the assumption that about half the surface carbon was soluble).

Under present conditions the existence of such a concentrated "soup" of organic material is unthinkable. Microorganisms would multiply in it with incredible speed and all organic matter would be either incorporated into living substance or subjected to fermentation and putrefaction, and would be broken down into its elementary constituents—CO_2, water, ammonia, and so forth. When these primitive "organic" oceans existed, however, there were no microorganisms or other forms of life. But under the influence of the intense ultraviolet rays, high temperature, raging thunder storms and lightning, and the powerful radioactivity, the chances for the formation of self-perpetuating catalysts must have been favorable indeed.

For detailed information on the "origin of life," refer to Blum (1955), Oparin (1961), and Oparin et al. (1959).

REFERENCES

Alpher, R. A., and R. C. Herman (1950) Theory of the origin and relative abundance and distribution of the elements. Rev. Mod. Phys. 22:153–212.

Blum, H. F. (1955) Time's Arrow and Evolution, 2nd Ed. Princeton University Press, Princeton, N.J.

Bodenstein, M. (1903) Discussion remarks on a paper by G. Bodlander: Technische Bedeutung der Katalyse. Z. Elektrochem. 9:732–736.

Bondi, H., and T. Gold (1948) The steady-state theory of the expanding universe. Monthly notices, Roy. Astron. Soc. *108*:252–270.

Calvin, M. (1956) Chemical evolution and the origin of life. Amer. Scient. *44*:248–263.

Garrison, W. M., D. C. Morrison, J. G. Hamilton, A. A. Benson, and M. Calvin (1954) Reduction of carbon dioxide in aqueous solutions by ionizing radiation. Science *114*:528–529.

Gulick, A. (1955) Phosphorus as a factor in the origin of life. Amer. Scient. *43*:479–489.

Haldane, J. B. S. (1929) The origin of life. Rationalist Annual; published in 1933 as Science and Human Life. Harper & Brothers, New York.

Hoyle, F. (1948) A new model for the expanding universe. Monthly notices, Roy. Astron. Soc. *108*:372–382.

Hoyle, F. (1955) Frontiers of Astronomy. Heinemann, London.

Lane, A. C. (1917) Lawson's correlation of the pre-Cambrian era. Amer. J. Sci. *43*:42–48.

Litchfield, J. B., and A. H. Whiteley (1959) Studies on the mechanism of phosphate accumulation by sea urchin embryos. Biol. Bull. *117*:133–149.

Miller, S. L. (1953) Production of amino-acids under possible primitive earth conditions. Science *117*:528–529.

Mittasch, A. (1935) Ueber Katalytische Verursachung im biologischen Geschehen. J. Springer, Berlin.

Noyes, W. A., and A. Leighton (1941) The Photochemistry of Gases. Reinhold Publishing Corp., New York.

Oparin, A. I. (1938) The Origin of Life. The Macmillan Co., New York.

Oparin, A. I. (1953) The Origin of Life. Dover Publications, New York.

Oparin, A. I. (1961) Life: Its Nature, Origin, and Development. Academic Press, New York.

Oparin, A. I., and V. Fesenkov (1957) The Universe. Foreign Languages Publishing House, Moscow.
Oparin, A. I., and A. G. Pasynskii, A. E. Braunshtein, and T. E. Pavlovskaya, eds. (1959) Proceedings of the first international symposium on The Origin of Life on the Earth. (F. Clark and R. L. Synge, eds. of English-French-German Edition.) Pergamon Press, New York.
Rollefson, G. K., and M. Burton (1939) Photochemistry. Prentice-Hall, New York.
Stieglitz, H. (1908) Studies in catalysis. I. The catalysis of esters and of imidoesters by acids. Amer. Chem. J. *39*:28–63.
Szabo, A., A. Tudge, J. MacNamara, and H. G. Thode (1950) The distribution of S^{34} in nature and the sulfur cycle. Science *111*:464–465.
Urey, H. G. (1952) The Planets. Yale University Press, New Haven.

2 THE STRUCTURAL ORGANIZATION OF CELLS

Cells are the functional and structural units of living animals. We recognize a large number of cell types and generally expect to find certain types associated with particular functional systems or organs of any animal we care to investigate. Thus, we can make certain general statements about the properties of nerve cells or of muscle cells and we can expect that these statements apply to most, if not all, species of multicellular animals.

Even among each category of cells, however, the overall dimensions and configuration vary greatly. Yet all cells are basically structurally alike, and the variations we observe are adaptations to specific "needs." A summary diagram of the common structural features of animal cells is shown in Figure 2–1.

General physiologists and comparative physiologists are particularly interested in cell structures that are of immediate significance for the performance of organ systems and for the normal functioning of the whole animal organism. While cell physiology is concerned with the life history of cells, their growth, mitotic behavior, and self-regulation and self-determination, general physiology as well as comparative physiology take cells for granted and are chiefly concerned with cell structures and interactions that directly affect the life of the whole organism. Many of the structural modifications can be understood only in the context of the part a cell has to play within the organization of the whole animal: consider, for example, the cells of the nephridium shown in Figure 2–2. Together they form a tube that permits the outward passage of excretory fluid. The specific structural adaptations are obviously dictated by the requirements of the animal as a whole.

Although we must recognize that the nucleus controls and regulates most cellular activities, we will, in this text, not be concerned with its function. The structures of primary interest are the surface membrane of cells and certain

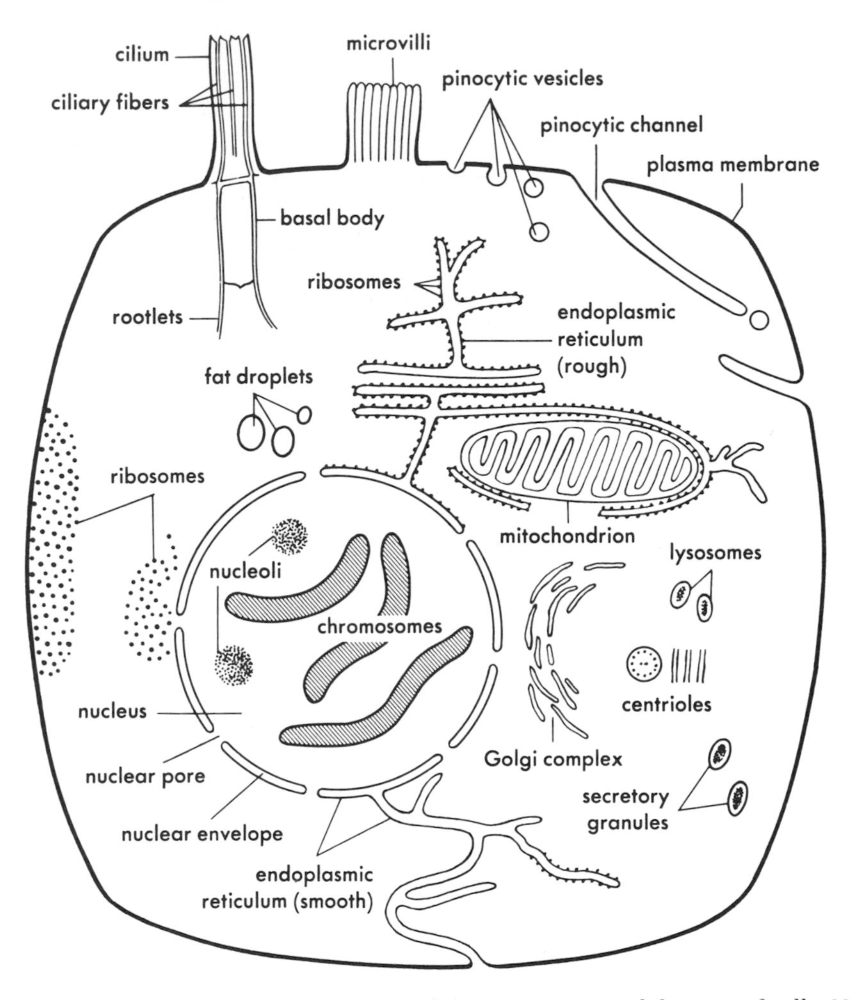

Figure 2–1. Diagrammatic representation of the major structural features of cells. Note the continuity and discontinuity of the membrane-enclosed spaces. (From Loewy, A. G., and P. Siekevitz: Cell Structure and Function. Holt, Rinehart and Winston, New York, 1963.)

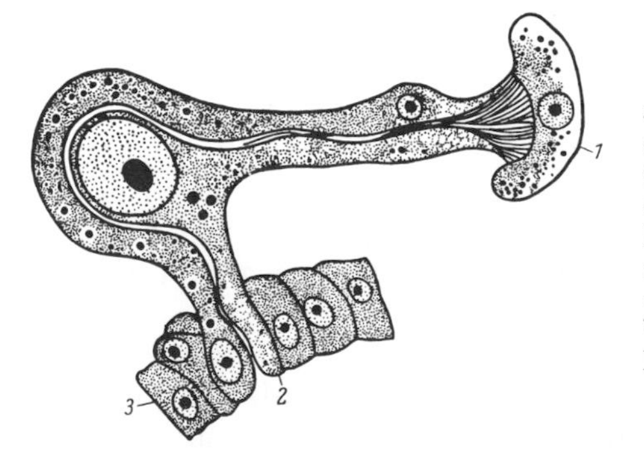

Figure 2–2. Nephridium of the embryo of a fresh-water snail, *Limnea*. The structural features of the cells that compose it can be understood only in relation to the organism as a whole. *1*, terminal cell extending a ciliary flame into intercellular lumen; *2*, outer opening; *3*, ectoderm. (After Meisenheimer, from Beklemischew, W. N.: Grundlagen der vergleichenden Anatomie der Wirbellosen, Vol. II. VEB Deutscher Verlag der Wissenschaften, Berlin, 1960.)

cell organelles, such as myofilaments of muscle cells or secretory vacuoles of glandular cells.

The total cell substance is known as *protoplasm*. This general term encompasses the substance of the nucleus, *nucleoplasm*, and that contained between the nucleus and cell membrane, the *cytoplasm*. The structure and function of nucleoplasm are the particular object of study of the cell physiologist and are not discussed in this text.

A number of terms apply to various aspects of the cytoplasm. "Ectoplasm" refers to the more solid, outer regions of cytoplasm, known also as the cell *cortex*. "Endoplasm" refers to the more liquid, inner regions. These two types of protoplasm are not strictly different and there is no definite borderline between them. The *main mass* of cytoplasm is usually referred to as *ground cytoplasm*, but names such as fundamental cytoplasm, basic cytoplasm, cytoplasmic matrix, and hyaloplasm are not uncommon in the literature.

The electron microscope has revealed that the cytoplasm of most cells is traversed by membranous sheaths, which may form a complex system of layers, known as the *endoplasmic reticulum* (Figs. 2–1 and 2–3). This is particularly conspicuous in cells that are secreting enzymes or hormones. These membranes seem to be actively involved in the manufacture of the secretion product. Parts of these membranes appear to break off to form the membranous covering of vesicles containing secretory material. The endoplasmic reticulum is also

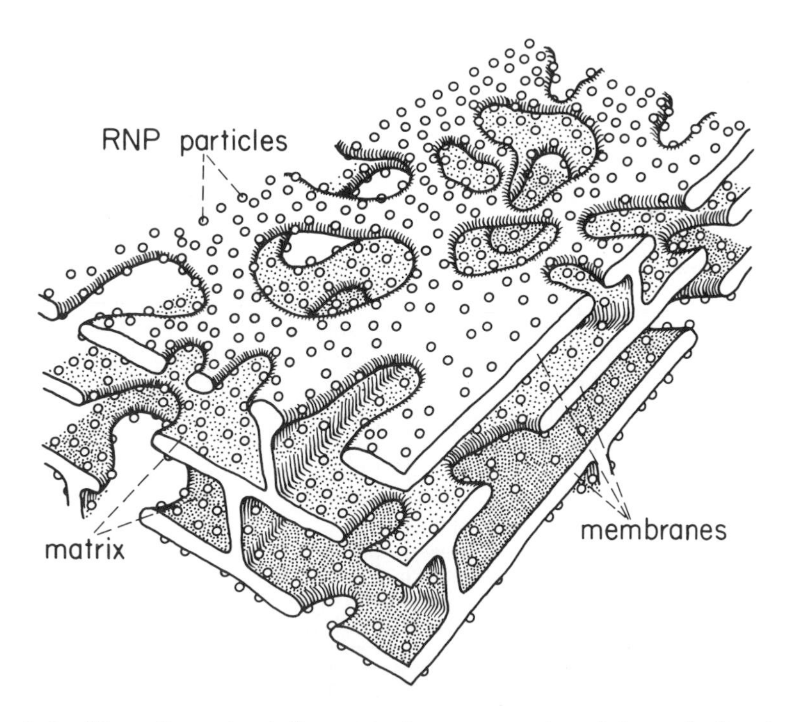

Figure 2–3. Three-dimensional diagrammatic representation of the endoplasmic reticulum and the attached ribosomes (*RNP particles*), which are supposed to be involved in protein synthesis. (After De Robertis, E. D. P., W. W. Nowinski, and F. A. Saez: Cell Biology, 4th Ed. W. B. Saunders Co., Philadelphia, 1965.)

engaged in protein synthesis; the *ribosomes*, the small granular bodies usually found associated with the endoplasmic reticulum, play a major role in protein synthesis.

Embedded in the cytoplasm are extremely small bodies, just within the limit of resolution of the light microscope. These bodies were first described by Altmann (1894), who considered them to be the elementary units of life and called them "bioblasts." Today the term "mitochondria" describes these granular or filamentous organoids of cells (Benda, 1897; see Benda, 1903). They may range in length from a few tenths of a micron to several microns. Sometimes the term mitochondrion is applied only to the granular fraction while the filaments and rods are called *chondrioconts*. In this text the term mitochondrion refers to both fractions. However, up to 1924 no less than 50 different names were applied to what we now simply call mitochondria (Cowdry, 1924), which indicates the great variety of mitochondrial forms encountered in different cells. Nevertheless, the number, location, and shape of mitochondria of each type of cell are similar.

The general shape and structure of mitochondria is illustrated in Figure 2–4. Each mitochondrion consists of a double membrane. The inner membrane

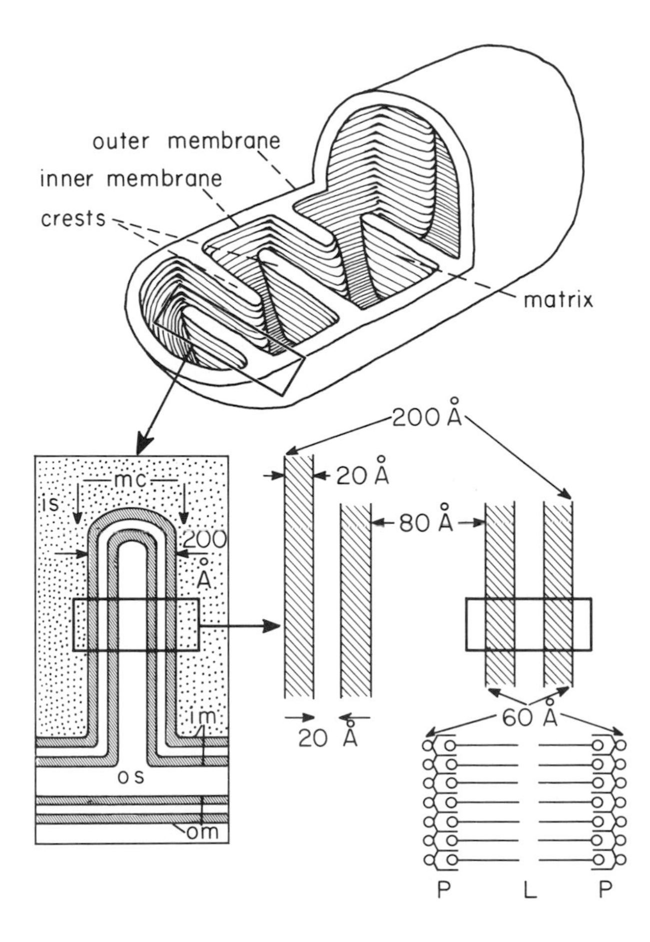

Figure 2–4. Diagrammatic representation of the ultrastructure of a mitochondrion. The areas marked by a rectangle are represented at higher magnification in the succeeding diagram of the sequence. Dimensions are given in Ångstrom units (Å). (After De Robertis, E. D. P., W. W. Nowinski, and F. A. Saez: Cell Biology, 4th Ed. W. B. Saunders Co., Philadelphia, 1965.)

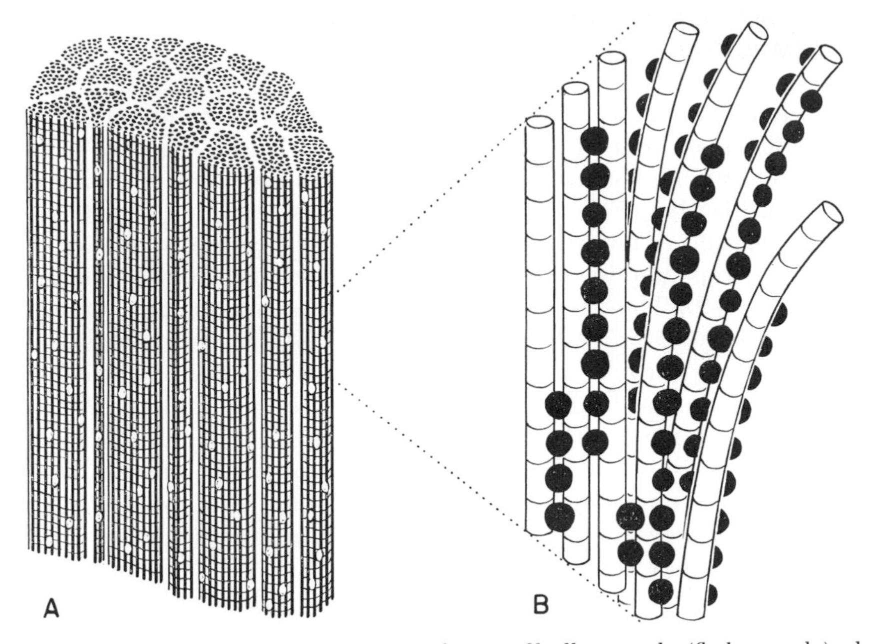

Figure 2–5. Diagram of the organization of insect fibrillar muscle (flight muscle), showing the relationship between the myofibrils and the sarcosomes (mitochondria) of myofibrils. **A** shows a small segment of a muscle mass containing 20 fibers. In **B** a part of a single fiber is much enlarged to show its subdivision into fibrils and sarcosomes. The paper from which this illustration is taken presented the first direct evidence for the identity of flight muscle sarcosomes with mitochondria. (Original figure by Dr. W. L. Nutting. From Watanabe, M. I., and C. M. Williams: Mitochondria in the flight muscles of insects. I. Chemical composition and enzymatic content. J. Gen. Physiol. *34*:675–689, 1951.)

forms partitions (cristae), which sometimes cut off one section of the mitochondrion from another and which greatly enlarge the internal surface area. It is assumed that the interior of mitochondrial bodies is filled with an aqueous medium. Mitochondria apparently can form from already existing membranous structures, such as the nuclear membrane, membranes of the endoplasmic reticulum, or even the cell membrane.

The proteins that compose the mitochondrial membrane appear to be enzymes. Mitochondria may, in fact, be considered the metabolic engines of oxidative metabolism: they contain all the enzymes that are necessary for the energy-liberating reactions known as the citric acid cycle, or Krebs cycle (see Chap. 7). Mitochondria consequently are found near the cellular sites of energy-demanding reactions. In muscle cells, for instance, they are structurally associated with the contractile myofibrils (Fig. 2–5), and in nerve cells they are found near the terminal endings, which are responsible for the transmission of nerve impulses (see Chap. 20, Fig. 20–2).

Cytoplasm often contains vacuoles of various sizes. These are usually spherical bodies, bounded by a membrane, containing nonplasmic substance, collectively referred to as *paraplasm*. The vacuoles may contain an aqueous medium, lipid polysaccharides, or certain cell products (hormones, enzymes) that are to be secreted to the outside. Usually, no structure is visible within the vacuoles when these are examined with the light microscope.

THE FUNCTIONAL ORGANIZATION OF PROTOPLASM (CYTOPLASM)

Protoplasm is not a compound but a complex of compounds. Its most characteristic constituents are protein molecules. These, together with lipids, carbohydrates, nucleic acids, inorganic ions, and water, form an intricate structural organization (Fig. 2–6). The proteins are by far the largest molecules. They are composed of long chains of amino acids. A certain sequence of amino acids is usually repeated in such chain molecules so that they assume a periodic structure (Fig. 1–2). The chains are organized into various complex structures, such as fiber strands, helices, and complex helices. The individual chains that compose a protein particle or molecule are bound together by various types of cross-linkages and cross-bridges, and hydrogen or covalent bonds. A number of such "links" are shown in Figure 2–7.

Protein molecules, like their constituent amino acids, possess many basic and acidic groups which may be ionized. Since protein is amphoteric (see Chap. 4), the molecules have a net positive charge in a medium in which the pH value is below that of their *isoelectric* point (see p. 60), and have a negative charge in a medium in which the pH is higher than the isoelectric point. Most cell proteins have an isoelectric point of about pH 5, which is slightly below the pH of the aqueous phase of the cytoplasm. Consequently, these proteins have a net negative charge. The ionized groups of a protein molecule attract

Figure 2–6. Conceptual diagram of the molecular and ionic structure of cytoplasm. ⊥⊥⊥⊥⊥, protein; •—, lipid; ≡, triglyceride molecules; o, water molecules; •, inorganic ions. The diagram shows the structure of a vacuole containing aqueous medium, an oil drop, and a droplet of lipid within the cytoplasm proper composed of a meshwork of protein molecules that contains within its framework water and other substances. (From Schmidt, W. J.: Der molekulare Bau der Zelle. Nova Acta Leopoldina 7:1–24, 1939.)

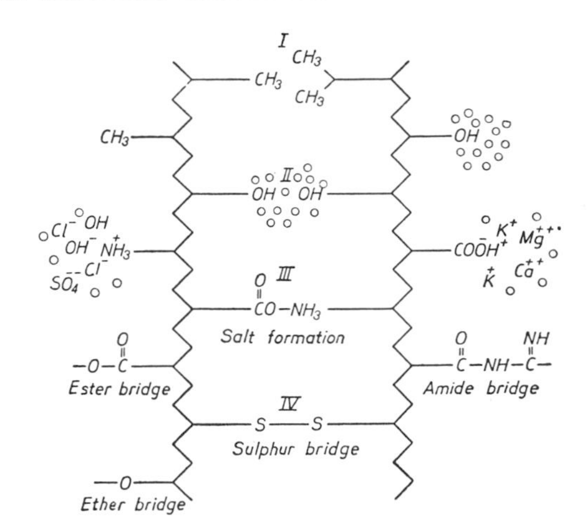

Figure 2–7. Schematic representation of the different junctions (bonds, bridges, etc.) between adjacent polypeptide (protein) chains. The open circles symbolize water molecules. (From Frey-Wyssling, A.: The Submicroscopic Morphology of Protoplasm and Its Derivatives. Elsevier Publishing Co., New York, 1953.)

water molecules and cause the water molecules to become oriented in such a way that their oppositely charged end points toward the charged group. The proteins within cytoplasm are thus *hydrated* and impart to the cell water an oriented structure. Proteins in this way form crystalloid structures which incorporate water in much the same way as water is bound as crystal water in certain inorganic salt crystals. The proteins within the cytoplasm form a complex organization comparable in structure to a three-dimensional network which holds water between its meshes (Fig. 2–6). This is known as *micellar structure*, and the individual units of the meshwork are called *micelles*.

Cytoplasm contains a considerable amount of hydrated inorganic ions, particularly K^+, Ca^{++}, Mg^{++}, Na^+, H^+, Cl^-, HCO_3^-, PO_3^-, OH^-, and O^{--}. These ions are attracted to the oppositely charged groups of protein molecules and are held within the micellar network where they are concentrated as they are absorbed into the protein structures. Depending on the properties of the micellar structure, certain ions are held more firmly than others. The diameter of the hydrated ions in relation to the diameter of the spaces between and within micelles and the nature of the available charged groups are important determining factors for the ion selectivity of the protein framework.

As a consequence of the absorption of inorganic ions by the protein skeleton of cytoplasm, the osmotic concentration rises. Therefore water enters and causes swelling. The swelling in turn may alter the micellar structure, thus leading to a change in the system's ion selectivity and charge pattern.

Not all the water within a cell is oriented or "bound," and the amount of water involved in the swelling and shrinking of certain areas of cytoplasm changes continuously. Indeed, observation of a living cell through the microscope usually reveals a striking movement of the protoplasm, usually a rapid *streaming*. We can assume that this streaming is caused, to a large degree, by progressive adsorption of ions, entry of water, swelling and dissolution of formerly rigid structures, and subsequent reorganization of the micellar structure. The liquid plasma is called *plasma sol*, whereas the more solid or rigid plasma is known as *plasma gel*. A change from one state to the other is called a "sol-gel transformation." Protoplasmic streaming is thought by some to be caused by a contraction of plasma gel that surrounds a portion of plasma sol. Gelation itself may be associated with reduction in water content, whereas liquefaction is accompanied by water uptake. Any shift in sol-gel condition must, therefore, result in plasma movement. Protoplasmic streaming creates *convection*, which facilitates transport of materials from one part of the cell to another.

MEMBRANES

The orientation of the cytoplasmic constituents is particularly obvious in the different membranes, in which the constituents assume a more rigid structure. The cytoplasmic body of a cell is bounded by a three-layered *plasma membrane*. The same type of membrane can be seen within the endoplasmic reticulum (electron microscope). The nuclear membrane and the mitochondrial membranes appear to have the same configuration. This three-layered structure is called the "unit membrane" (Fig. 2–8).

The plasma membrane is approximately 100 Å thick. Its middle layer (50 to 60 Å) is less dense than the other two. The membrane can be assumed to consist of two monomolecular layers of protein separated by a bimolecular layer of lipid. This structure has been deduced from birefringence studies using polarized light, and x-ray diffraction studies. Both techniques were originally developed for investigating crystal structures; explanations of these methods can be found in most textbooks on crystallography or physics. From crystallographic data, information about the composition of the three layers of the unit membrane has been obtained, while the dimension of the layers has been confirmed by electron microscopy. However, in regard to composition, we know only that the layers consist of *"protein"* and *"lipid."* The *kinds* of proteins and lipids that constitute different membranes of unit membrane structure may well differ.

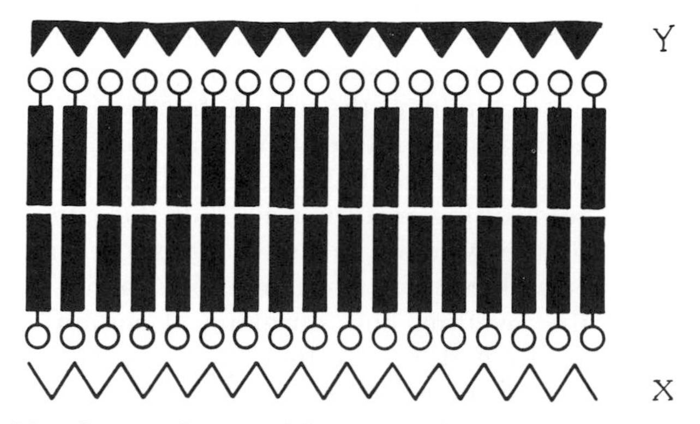

Figure 2–8. Highly schematic diagram of the unit membrane structure. This is assumed to be representative of all types of protoplasmatic membranes, including cell membranes, such as neurolemma, sarcolemma, and the membranes of Schwann cells which form, in specialized types of nerve tissue, myelin sheaths (see Figs. 17–24 and 17–26). The joined circles and bars represent lipid molecules, and the zigzag lines nonlipid monolayers, designated *X* and *Y*. (From Robertson, J. D.: New unit membrane organelle of Schwann cells. *In* Biophysics of Physiological and Pharmacological Actions. A. M. Shanes, Ed. Amer. Assn. Adv. Sci., Washington, D.C., 1961.)

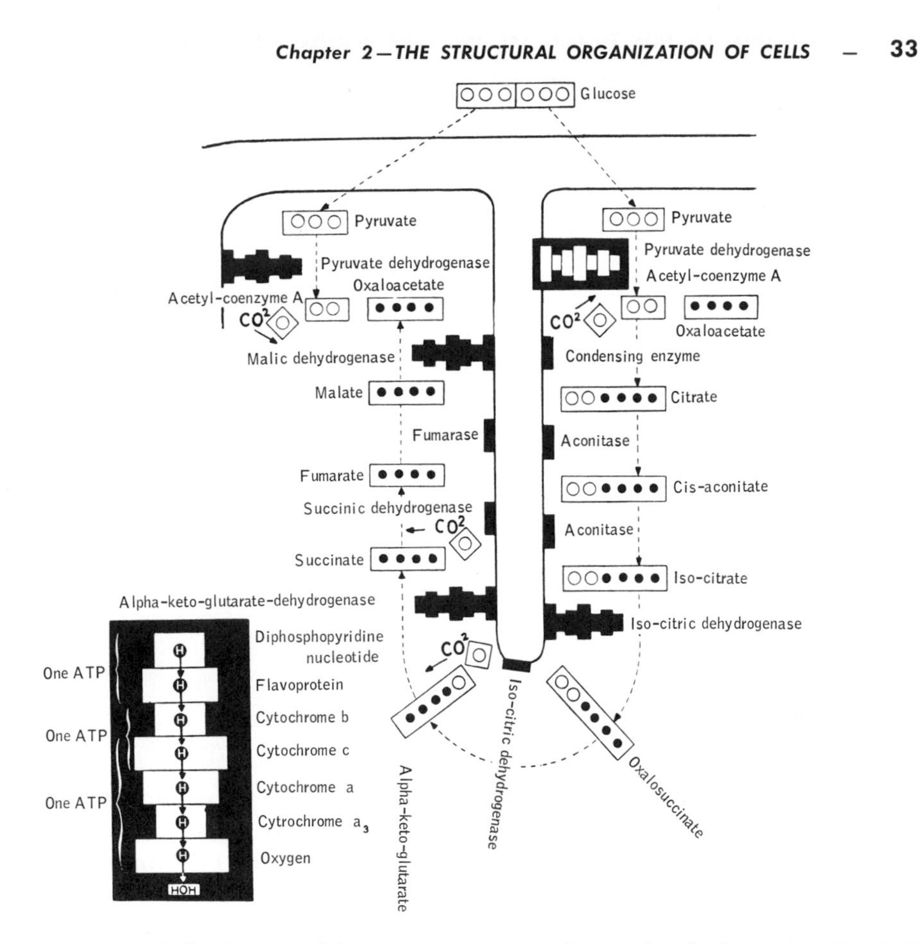

Figure 2–9. Symbolic diagram of the enzyme sequence of a mitochondrial crest (see Fig. 2–4). The piles of discs on top of dehydrogenase enzymes represent the electron transfer system, shown enlarged at the lower right. (Modified after The Cell, The Upjohn Co., 1958.)

As indicated, there is strong evidence that the proteins of mitochondrial membranes function as enzymes. Biochemists have isolated mitochondrial membranes from cells and identified the enzymes present. There is every indication that all the enzymes required for oxidative metabolism, in particular for the so-called citric acid cycle, are present together with the various cytochromes that are involved in the electron transport system, which is involved in the oxidation of hydrogen ions to water (see Chap. 7). Evidence has been provided that these enzyme molecules are arranged in an orderly sequence (see Fig. 2–9), which corresponds to the sequence required for the successive steps of oxidative metabolism.

The outer membrane of each mitochondrion may also contain enzyme molecules; some of these may function in the inward transport of metabolizable molecules.

Secretory vacuoles are usually surrounded by a typical unit membrane, as are the large food vacuoles of certain cells in the digestive tract.

From studies of living cells (phase microscope) and of fixed cells (electron microscope) it is known that the plasma membrane of some cells can invaginate

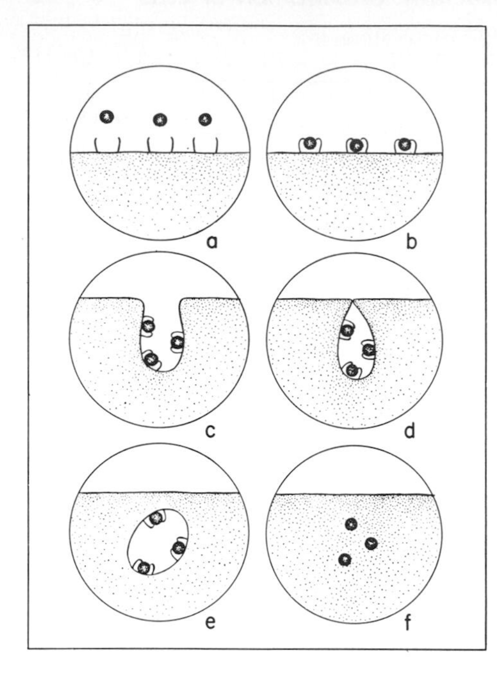

Figure 2–10. Conceptual diagram illustrating transport of extracellular components into a cell by invagination or vesiculation of the cell membrane (pinocytosis). According to this hypothesis, molecules, ions, or other particles attach to special binding sites on the cell membrane (**b**), whereupon the plasma membrane forms an invagination (**c**) that is pinched off (**d**) and enters the cytoplasm as a vacuole (**e**). The cell membrane surrounding the vacuole is then resorbed and the particles appear within the cytoplasm (**f**). (From Bennett, H. S.: The concepts of membrane flow and membrane vesiculation as mechanisms for active transport and ion pumping. J. Biophys. Biochem. Cytol. 2 Suppl.:99–103, 1956.)

and pinch off small vacuoles or vesicles, a process that allows extracellular matter to enter the cytoplasm of the cell (Fig. 2–10). This is known as *pinocytosis.* By the reverse process certain substances may be eliminated.

There is increasing evidence that the plasma membrane extends in places into the interior in the form of tubules. This is well illustrated in Figure 2–1 (see also Fig. 22–1). These tubules have great significance in muscle physiology (see Figs. 22–27 and 22–28).

According to the majority of physiological theories and hypotheses, cells are variously shaped bags filled with a homogeneous aqueous medium. The bags themselves are made up of "membrane." Many physiologists think of this external membrane of cells as endowed with complex properties: pores with or without fixed electrical charges on their walls, carrier molecules which actively transfer molecules or ions from the exterior environment of the cell into its interior, and specific "receptor substances" situated on the external surface of the membrane which react with specific substances such as hormones or with transmitter substances released from nerve cells and, by virtue of this reaction, give rise to a temporary alteration of membrane properties.

This simplified cell concept is adaptable to the physiology of osmoregulation and ionic regulation, most of neurophysiology and electrophysiology, and most of the physiology of respiration and circulatory systems. Only in the physiology of muscle and of glandular organs does intracellular organization become a major concern of the general or comparative physiologist.

The external membrane to which physiologists refer may well be the plasma membrane. It must be recognized, however, that the plasma membrane of most animal cells has an *extraneous coat.* This covering is a product of each cell and is composed of a polysaccharide, such as hyaluronic acid, chondroitin, chitin, or even cellulose, often conjugated with lipids, proteins, polyphenols, and so forth. The *cell membrane* to which the physiologist refers is likely to be composed of both the plasma membrane and the extraneous coat. On the other hand, the specific properties of cell membranes, such as selective permeability and remarkable electrical properties, are most likely those of the plasma membrane itself. The extraneous coat, even though morphologically prominent, probably does not contribute significantly to these properties because it is composed of large molecules, and in contrast to the tightly packed molecular structure of the plasma membrane, represents a relatively loose molecular network.

The extraneous coat provides mechanical resistance for the cell membrane, and serves as intercellular cement, uniting cells into tissues. It is not necessarily of uniform thickness all around each cell. The two-dimensional tissues of endothelial and epithelial cells produce on one side an especially thick "coat," the *basement membrane* (see also Figs. 17–7 and 17–8).

The cell membrane, and in particular the plasma membrane, is the boundary between the extra- and intracellular "environments." These media differ greatly in composition. This statement not only implies the obvious, namely, that the interior of a cell contains all the special structural components of the cell, but refers specifically to the relative concentrations of small molecules and ions in the aqueous phase of extra- and intracellular media. We can ascribe to the internal medium physicochemical properties that can be described in terms of properties of aqueous solutions. For instance, each species of ions has an osmotic concentration as well as a molar concentration.

In view of the complicated intracellular morphology, this is surprising. A number of investigators have discovered that the intracellular inorganic ions behave very much as if they were simply dissolved in water: they diffuse within a cell at about the same net velocity as in free solution in water. Studies of this type were carried out with radioactive potassium on giant squid axons and on frog muscle fibers (Hodgkin and Keynes, 1953; Caldwell and Keynes, 1960; Harris, 1954), and with radioactive sodium, also on squid axons (Hodgkin and Keynes, 1956). If this is true, the radical difference in composition of the intra- and extracellular media must be caused by the properties of the plasma membrane. The "membrane theory" of bioelectricity rests on this contention (see Chap. 16).

The experimental evidence in support of a free solution of inorganic ions in the interior of cells is, however, not unchallenged. A number of physiologists support the sorption theory, or *fixed-charge hypothesis*. Among the proponents of this are G. N. Ling (*The Physical Theory of the Living State*, 1962), and A. S. Troschin (*Das Problem der Zellpermeabilität*, 1958). They believe that the composition of the internal medium of cells is determined by the configuration, and the fixed charges, of the protein "scaffolding" of protoplasm. This is held responsible for selective *sorption* (electrostatic binding) of certain ions and is supposed to favor ions of dimensions that best fit the "liquid crystal" structure of protoplasm. According to this concept, ions are predominantly fixed, or bound, and cannot diffuse as if they were in free solution. The supporters of the sorption theory consider the experimental evidence mentioned above for free diffusion as insufficient: they argue that injected ions behave differently from those already in the cell. At present, one must hold against this view the fact that electrostatic binding does not imply binding of individual ions, but of "statistical" ions; that is, each ion is free to exchange with another ion of the same species. It must be assumed that injected radioactive ions exchange with nonradioactive ones. If now, even after such exchange, they move as in free solution, as indeed has been shown by Hodgkin, Keynes, Caldwell, and Harris, the difference in composition of the internal medium relative to that of the external environment must be ascribed to the plasma membrane.

Experiments of Baker, Hodgkin, and Shaw (1961) have come close to supplying direct experimental proof for this: when they extruded most of the protoplasm from large axons of giant nerve cells of squid, the remaining cell membrane (presumably with a layer of underlying cytoplasm) maintained the differences in ionic composition of fluids supplied to both sides (these fluids had the same compositions as normal extra- and intracellular media of the respective cells), and showed the normal ion exchange processes that accompany conducted action potentials (see Chap. 16).

Even though experimental evidence favors the membrane theory and justifies the hypothesis that the cell is a membranous bag filled with an aqueous medium, no physiologist can deny the complex structures of cytoplasm which have been elucidated through electron microscopy. Undoubtedly, future years will see a synthesis between the membrane theory and the sorption theory.

CELL COMPARTMENTS

The interior of a cell appears to be subdivided into a number of membrane-enclosed compartments of various dimensions. Each compartment contains a medium of special composition. The membranes separate the compartments, and we may assume that the membranes actively participate in the formation of the medium they contain. Just as the plasma membrane of each cell selectively transports molecules and ions into or out of the cell, so are the membranes of the mitochondria, vacuoles, nucleus, and so forth involved in transport, and they maintain a separation of two fluid compartments of different composition. Several kinds of activity can thus go on within the same cell: oxidations in one compartment, nonoxidative metabolism in another; protein synthesis in one area of cytoplasm, digestive degradation of protein in another; and glycogen storage in another region (see Fig. 23–1). However, remember that cells are not chambered and that the compartments are membrane-enclosed and embedded in a continuous phase of ground cytoplasm. A molecule or ion can diffuse to any part of the ground cytoplasm without traversing a membrane.

A physiologist must be thoroughly acquainted with cell structure. Unless he is aware of the discrepancy between the simplicity of his cell models and the complexities of cell morphology, his investigation of physiological processes will be impeded. Progress can come only from increasing ability to integrate all aspects of cell structure into the theories of organismic function.

REFERENCES

Altmann, R. (1894) Die Elementarorganismen und ihre Beziehung zu den lebenden Zellen. Veit & Co., Leipzig.

Baker, P. F., A. L. Hodgkin, and T. I. Shaw (1961) Replacement of the protoplasm of a giant nerve fibre with artificial solutions. Nature *190*:885–887.

Benda, C. (1903) Die Mitochondria. Ergebn. Anat. Entwicklungsgesch. *12*:743.

Bourne, G. H., ed. (1951) Cytology and Cell Physiology, 2nd Ed. Oxford University Press, London.

Brachet, J., and A. E. Mirsky (1959–1961). The Cell. 6 vols. Academic Press, New York.

Caldwell, P. C., and R. D. Keynes (1960) The permeability of the squid giant axon to radioactive potassium and chloride ions. J. Physiol. *154*:177–189.

Chambers, R., and E. L. Chambers (1961) Explorations into the Nature of the Living Cell. Harvard University Press, Cambridge.

Cowdry, E. V. (1924) General Cytology. University of Chicago Press, Chicago.

De Robertis, E. D. P., W. W. Nowinski, and F. A. Saez (1965) Cell Biology, 4th Ed. W. B. Saunders Co., Philadelphia.

Giese, A. C. (1962) Cell Physiology, 2nd Ed. W. B. Saunders Co., Philadelphia.

Haas, J. (1955) Physiologie der Zelle. G. Borntraeger, Berlin.

Harris, E. J. (1954) Ionophoresis along frog muscle. J. Physiol. *124*:248–253.

Hodgkin, A. L., and R. D. Keynes (1953) The mobility and diffusion coefficient of potassium in giant axons from *Sepia*. J. Physiol. *119*:513–528.

Hodgkin, A. L., and R. D. Keynes (1956) Experiments on the injection of substances into squid giant axons by means of a microsyringe. J. Physiol. *131*:592–616.

Ling, G. N. (1962) A Physical Theory of the Living State. Blaisdell Publishing Co., New York.

Picken, L. E. R. (1960) The Organization of Cells and Other Organisms. Clarendon Press, Oxford.

Robertson, J. D. (1959) The ultrastructure of cell membranes and their derivatives. Biochem. Soc. Symp. *16*:3–43.

Robertson, J. D. (1960) The molecular structure and contact relationships of cell membranes. Progr. Biophys. *10*:343–418.

Troschin, A. S. (1958) Das Problem der Zellpermeabilität (German translation from the Russian). VEB Deutscher Verlag der Wissenschaften, Berlin.

3 THE STRUCTURAL ORGANIZATION OF ANIMALS

In order to understand the principles of construction of animal bodies, one must know something about ontogenic development. It is not the purpose of this textbook to present in full detail the subjects of animal embryology and morphology. However, it is difficult for the physiologist, particularly if animal morphology has not been his major study, to extract from morphology textbooks the information that is so important to his understanding of the interrelation of body compartments and organ systems. Therefore, the unity of animal organization is summarized in the abstract diagrams of Figure 3–1, which present the major organizational features of representative species of several phyla (adult forms).

THE BODY COMPARTMENTS

Multicellular organisms usually arise from a fertilized ovum by multiple cell division. Their growth represents an increase in cell size as well as in cell number. Individuals of many species, once they reach sexual maturity, consist of billions of cells; others, such as the rotifers, consist of only several hundred. In spite of the vast diversity of animal forms, they have many structural properties in common: with the exception of the sponges, all of them form, during early embryological development, two cellular layers (called *germinal layers*)—the *ectoderm* and the *entoderm*. The ectoderm represents the outer body wall. The entoderm represents the digestive tube. Further embryological development is characterized by two processes: infolding of the ectoderm and outpouching of the entoderm. Special cells divide to form a conglomeration of cells which fills the space between the entoderm and ectoderm in the form of

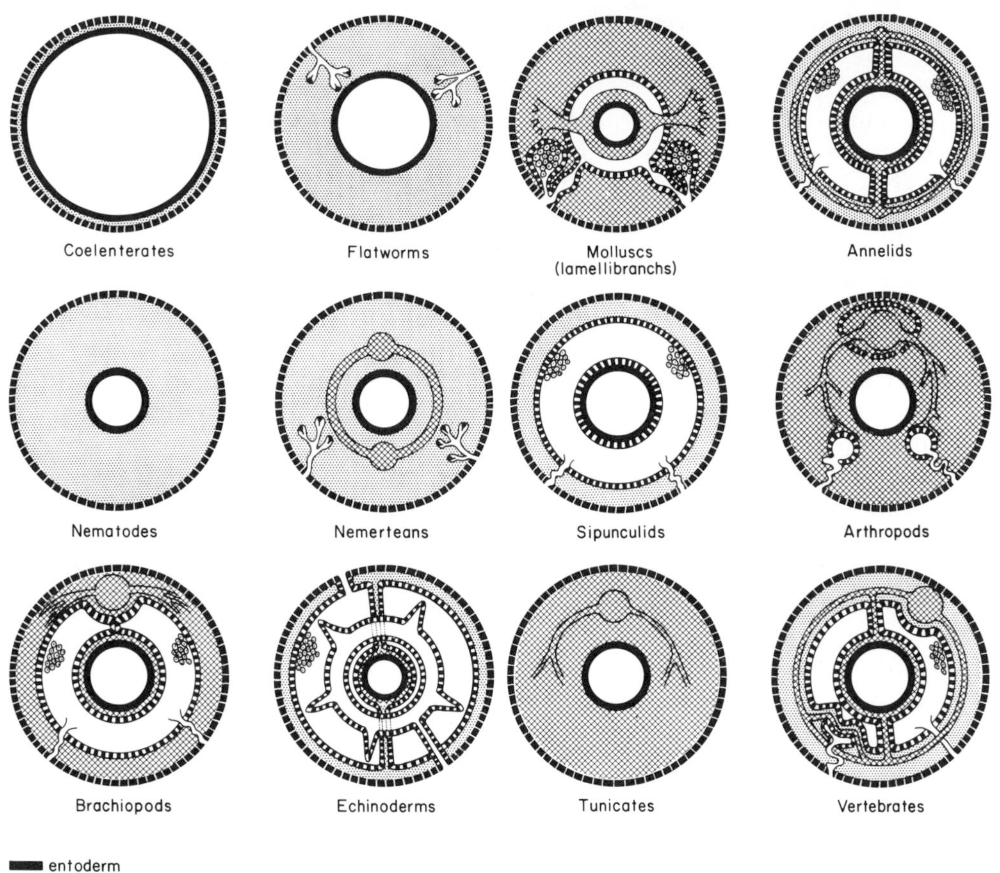

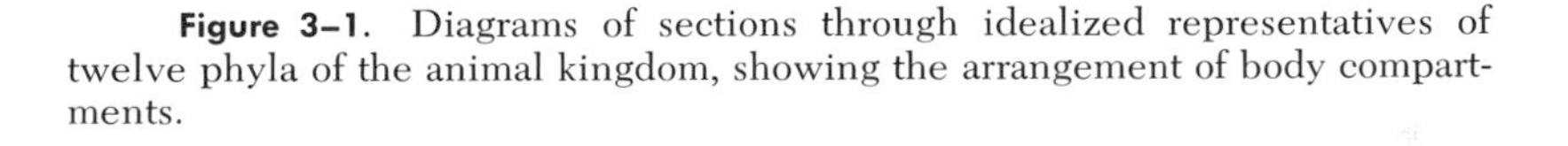
Figure 3–1. Diagrams of sections through idealized representatives of twelve phyla of the animal kingdom, showing the arrangement of body compartments.

mesenchyme. Wherever there is a space between entoderm and ectoderm, this is referred to as the *primary body cavity*, a *pseudocoel*, or a *schizocoel*. Infolding of the ectoderm gives rise to the neural tube, which differentiates into the nervous system. The outpouchings of the entoderm may transform the gut into a highly branched organ which reaches all regions of the body, as is the case in flatworms, or the outpouchings pinch off to form the third germinal layer, the *mesoderm.* Wherever this mesoderm forms a hollow structure this is called a *secondary body cavity*, or *coelom*. Certain cell groups of the mesenchyme or of the mesoderm proliferate to form the muscles (certain muscle cells also arise from ectoderm and entoderm). The mesodermal wall that forms the coelom does not persist in all animal phyla. In the Arthropoda, for instance, it largely disappears during development and in the adult persists only as a thin wall which forms a cavity around the heart (the pericardium), as small sacks which form the first segment of the nephridia, and as a membrane covering the gonads.

In the molluscs the coelom persists in the form of the pericardium, and another part of the coelom is filled with cells that represent the gonads, the gonadal coelom.

Vascular systems are formed from mesenchyme cells that organize themselves into a system of tubes. These often differentiate into layers and some of their cells become muscle cells. In the Nemertinea the vascular system consists of a closed system of tubes that is embedded in the mesenchyme. Similar closed vascular systems are found in many annelids and in the vertebrates. The fluid in this type of vascular system is properly referred to as *blood.* It never gets outside the blood vessels. Fluid is also present between the mesenchyme cells, and this fluid extends into the interstitial spaces between all other body cells. It is called *interstitial fluid, tissue fluid,* or simply *extracellular fluid.*

Nematoda have only a primary body cavity. There is no vascular system and no coelom; consequently, there is only one body fluid compartment, which is properly called *tissue fluid,* or *interstitial fluid.* Annelids have an additional body fluid compartment: the *coelomic fluid* which fills the coelomic cavities. Thus annelids that have a closed vascular system have three types of body fluid: blood, interstitial fluid, and coelomic fluid. In molluscs, arthropods, hemichordates, and tunicates, the vascular system is not closed: the vessels are continuous with the interstitial spaces, which in many parts of the body form lacunae, or large sinuses. In these four phyla, blood and interstitial fluid are usually considered to be identical: to do justice to this situation one speaks of *hemolymph* rather than blood. Many modern authors, however, prefer the term "blood."

Most recent experiments by Martin and coworkers (1958) indicate, however, that at least in cephalopods the sinus and lacunae are separated from interstitial spaces by a membrane. Cephalopod molluscs thus have both blood and interstitial fluid. In the arthropods the coelomic cavity of the pericardium is perforated and is, therefore, filled with hemolymph. Coelomic fluid proper is found only in the so-called coelomosacs of the nephridia and in the small interstitial spaces of the gonads. In molluscs, however, the pericardium is filled with coelomic fluid. In vertebrates the coelomic cavities surround the viscera, the gonads, and the initial parts of the nephrons. The body fluids of vertebrates are thus largely confined to three compartments: the closed vascular system (blood), the interstitial and extracellular spaces (lymph, or interstitial fluid), and the coelomic fluid. Since the internal organs are extremely compact, not much space is left for coelomic fluid.

The major compartments of body fluids (blood, coelomic fluid, and interstitial or tissue fluid) of any given group of animals show rather consistent relative volumes. Some representative data are assembled in Table 3–1; they include also the percentage of intracellular water and the total body water. It can readily be seen that the blood volume of animals with a closed vascular system (annelids, cephalopods, vertebrates) is 5 to 7.5 per cent of the body weight, whereas in animals with an open vascular system it ranges from 35 to 80 per cent. The coelomic fluid of representatives of three major phyla has a remarkably similar volume: 18 to 28 per cent of the total body water.

The coelom usually communicates with the outside environment through

Table 3–1. The Volumes of the Fluid Compartments of a Variety of Animals

	Total Body Water (% wet weight)	Blood Volume (% wet weight)	Blood Water (% body water)	Tissue Fluid (% body water)	Tissue Fluid (% wet weight)	Cell Water (% wet weight)	Cell Water (% cell weight)
ANNELIDA (1)							
Oligochaeta							
Glossoscolex giganteus	80.7	6.1	7.5	22.3	18.8	44.1	55.1
MOLLUSCA (2)							
Placophora							
Cryptochiton stelleri	85.1	43.8		*		41.3	76.6
Gastropoda							
Aplysia californianus	92.5	79.3		*		13.2	74.2
Archidoris sp.	92.4	65.5		*		26.9	82.9
Achatina fulica	86.4	40.3		*		46.1	77.1
Arion ater	86.3	36.6		*		49.7	79.0
Pelecypoda							
Mytilus californianus	88.9	50.8		*		38.1	79.7
Margaritana margaritifera	88.0	49.0		*		39.0	76.4
Cephalopoda							
Octopus hongkongensis	82.5	5.8			28.0	48.7	77.0

Table 3–1. The Volumes of the Fluid Compartments of a Variety of Animals (Continued)

	Total Body Water (% wet weight)	*Blood Volume (% wet weight)*	*Blood Water (% body water)*	*Tissue Fluid (% body water)*	*Tissue Fluid (% wet weight)*	*Cell Water (% wet weight)*	*Cell Water (% cell weight)*
ARTHROPODA (3)							
Crustacea							
Cambarus virilis		25.6 or 30.5% of body volume		*			
VERTEBRATA							
Pisces (4)							
Agnatha							
Petromyzon marinus	75.6	8.5			18.4	51.7	
		5.5 (plasma volume)					
Amphibia (5)							
Necturus maculosus	81.1	7.1					
		4.7 (plasma volume)			19.4	57.0	
Rana catesbeiana	79.0	5.3			18.0	57.3	
		3.7 (plasma volume)					

*No separate tissue fluid.

1. Martin, A. W.: unpublished data.
2. Martin, A. W., F. M. Harrison, M. J. Huston, and D. M. Stewart: The blood volumes of some representative molluscs. J. Exp. Biol. *35*:260–279, 1958.
3. Prosser, C. L., and S. J. F. Weinstein: Comparison of blood volume in animals with open and with closed circulatory systems. Physiol. Zool. *23*:113–124, 1950.
4. Thorson, T. B.: Partitioning of body water in sea lamprey. Science *130*:99–100, 1959.
5. Thorson, T. B.: The partitioning of body water in amphibia. Physiol. Zool. *37*:395–399, 1964.

the tubular structures known as nephridia or kidneys, and, in the case of the gonadal coelom, through the gonoducts. In coelomate animals the nephridia are generally open to the coelom, although sometimes provided with valves. In echinoderms the water-vascular system (one of the original four coelomic cavities) communicates directly with the outside. The tube leading to the outside in this case is not a nephridium but the *stone canal*. The other coelomic cavities fuse to varying degrees, forming what is known as a somatocoel. It contains the gonads and communicates with the outside through the gonoducts. In the vertebrates the coelomic cavity of the perivisceral space does not always communicate with the gonadal space and with the outside, and the coelom which communicates with the tubules of the metanephridia becomes separated from the perivisceral and gonadal coelom.

Nephridia are also present in animals that do not have a coelomic cavity. In such cases the nephridia have blind endings within the interstitial spaces of mesenchyme or parenchyme. Sometimes they are branched. Each end possesses a flame bulb, consisting of a mono- or multinucleate cell which extends a "flame" composed of cilia into the intercellular lumen of the organ (Fig. 2–2). Nephridia of this type are known as *protonephridia*.

Nephridia are absent in the following phyla: Hemichordata, Echinodermata, Nematoda, and Tunicata. In the Hemichordata pores connect the coelom to the outside; in echinoderms the stone canal and the gonoduct perform this function. As mentioned, the Nematoda have no coelom and this is likewise true for the Tunicata.

In addition to the three main body compartments, other compartments, found in certain animal groups, contain a fluid that is often distinctly different in composition from that found inside the vascular system, the coelomic cavities, or the interstitial spaces. Such special compartments are usually associated with the nervous system: In Onychophora the central nervous system is enclosed in a special sinus, as is true for echinoderms in which the central nerve ring and the radial nerves are contained in a perineural sinus, which obviously is filled with a fluid and which represents an environment distinctly separate from the coelomic fluid or from the interstitial fluid of the rest of the body. In insects, nerves and muscles are enclosed by dense connective tissue sheets containing a fluid fundamentally different from the hemolymph (see p. 427). In the vertebrates the central nervous system contains fluid-filled cavities—the ventricles and the spinal canal. The fluid, called cerebrospinal fluid, differs in certain regards from lymph fluid. In the Hemichordata the heart is supposed to be a closed organ, free of blood. The fluid between its cells thus would represent a separate fluid compartment.

SIGNIFICANCE OF EXTRACELLULAR MATTER

The physiologist must recognize that the animal organism, although the product of cellular organization, is not composed of cells only but of cells *and* extracellular matter. The body fluids that fill the passages and spaces between cells are a most important part of animal bodies. Body fluids can be assumed to be continuous within the body compartments (e.g., vascular system, coelom, hemocoel, lymph). Often the composition of these fluids is regulated by the cells with which the fluids are in contact; sometimes the fluids appear to be secreted by certain tissue cells and often the body cells contribute important organic constituents to the body fluids. The proteins found in hemolymph and blood are prominent examples.

Apart from the body fluids, the extracellular constituents of animal organisms are: the extraneous coats of cells, the ground substance, the collagen fibrils and membraneous sheets of connective tissue, and skeletal material.

The extraneous coat of tissue cells is produced by the living cell and covers the plasma membrane. This coat is not only protective but "cements" cells together so that they form tissues. An example is hyaluronic acid (a carbohydrate), which binds the endothelial cells of the vertebrate capillary blood vessels.

The ground substance is still a mysterious component of living systems. Its presence has not been demonstrated in many tissues but there is evidence that in many cases the extracellular spaces are not filled with the liquid of body fluids, but with a solid structureless mass of a chemical that appears to belong to the carbohydrates. The functional significance of this ground substance has not been established. It is possible that it is permeated with body fluid in a manner similar to that of a jelly which is imbibed with liquid.

Connective tissue fibrils, usually formed of collagen (a fibrous protein) are produced by connective tissue cells and form more or less dense networks surrounding cells and cell groups. Sometimes dense sheets are formed which constitute tough, impermeable membranes, such as those that surround the central nervous system of insects.

Skeletal material constitutes a large portion of extracellular matter, and is usually of inorganic composition but often consists of carbohydrate derivatives (chitin) or protein (keratin). All skeletal material is produced or deposited by living cells. The inorganic materials are largely water-insoluble salts of calcium (carbonate) and phosphorus, as in lamellibranch shells or vertebrate bones. These salts not only provide mechanical support but participate actively in the life of the organism because they are in continuous exchange with the body fluids.

Organic skeletal materials are usually found in the integument: chitin forms an important part of the exoskeleton of arthropods, and keratin is the chief solid of the integument of many vertebrate groups. It is possible that chitin serves as a source of energy-yielding carbohydrate, functioning as a reserve substance in a similar manner as glycogen. Keratin, however, is the result of "keratinization," in which this protein is manufactured within integumentary cells in excess, causing the cells to die. Keratin is, therefore, not a true part of the live organization of the animal and serves only as mechanical protection.

The metabolic role of the skeletal elements of sponges and echinoderms is difficult to assess. Where this material consists of keratin or glass, no physiological role is to be assumed, but where it consists of inorganic salts, particularly of calcium, it can be assumed to function as an ion exchanger.

Living systems could never function as they do if they were strictly cellular in composition. The question of whether or not the extracellular matter of organisms is alive is physiologically meaningless: materials are continuously exchanged between the intra- and extracellular constituents of living systems and the life of cells depends on, and in fact consists of, a controlled exchange within cells and across cell boundaries. Many, if not most, constituents of extracellular matter are the common property of both extra- and intracellular substances as they move in and out of cells.

EXCHANGE AND PROTECTION

In contrast to the multicellular plants, which tend to exhibit large surface areas as compared to their volume, animal bodies are usually compact and present little external surface. In this way the area to be defended against aggressors and adverse conditions of the external environment is minimized. The body surface must, however, serve also in certain exchanges between the inner and outer environment. For example, oxygen must diffuse inward and carbon dioxide must diffuse outward. Furthermore, the external body surface must provide the central nervous system with information about the external environment. For these reasons an enlarged surface area is advantageous. The conflicting needs for minimal and maximal surface area are met in the following ways: The body surface is divided into functionally separate regions. The respiratory exchange membranes are extremely large but folded or tubular, and thus occupy relatively little space, and in some forms (all terrestrial animals) extend into the interior of the body rather than form external appendages. The remainder of the body surface is kept to a minimal area but is equipped with sense organs and sensory innervation. This area is protected either by skeletal material in the cuticula, a hard shell, "armor" (tubes, burrows, and so forth), or by poison glands and protective pigmentation.

MEMBRANES

The principal features of the internal organization of animals are the enlargement of surfaces, the arrangement into cellular membranes, and the continuity of fluid-filled spaces. The life of all body cells depends on, and in fact consists of, the continuous exchange of matter between protoplasm (and paraplasm) of body cells and the internal and external environment of the organism.

Apart from active transport through the cell membranes (see p. 319), this exchange relies on convection and diffusion. Convection within the cells is provided by protoplasmic streaming and by the continuous rearrangement of the internal structure of protoplasm. Convection of extracellular body fluids is promoted by general body movement, by the action of special pulsatile organs (hearts), and by osmotic phenomena (see p. 113).

Substances of low molecular weight can diffuse through the aqueous phase of protoplasm nearly as rapidly as through water. Cell membranes, however, hinder diffusion. Therefore, it is essential that a substance traverse as few membranes as possible when progressing from an internal body cell to the outside or from the external environment to the protoplasm of internal body cells. In the most simple case, for instance that of a nematode, nutrients, once they have traversed the wall of the gut, can travel freely by convection and diffusion through the interstitial fluid to any cell of the body. Even in organisms as complex as vertebrates, not more than seven cell membranes need to be traversed before a substance starting from the lumen of the gut reaches the interior of a body cell. These membranes are: (1) the outer membrane of a cell lining an intestinal villus, (2) the inner membrane of the same intestinal cell, (3) the outer membrane of an endothelial cell of a blood capillary, (4) the inner membrane of the same endothelial cell, (5) the inner membrane of another endothelial cell of another capillary, (6) the outer membrane of the same endothelial cell, and (7) the membrane of the particular body cell. Since material may also be exchanged through the interstitial spaces between endothelial cells of capillaries, only three membranes need be traversed even if the substance were to travel in a giraffe from the small intestine to a cell in the tip of an ear. Material excreted through nephridia is merely taken up by the blood stream and filtered through the cell layer of the coelom. Once there, the material passes to the outside of the animal without encountering further membranes.

The cellular membranes through which nutrients and other substances are exchanged are usually only one cell layer thick. This is true for gill mem-

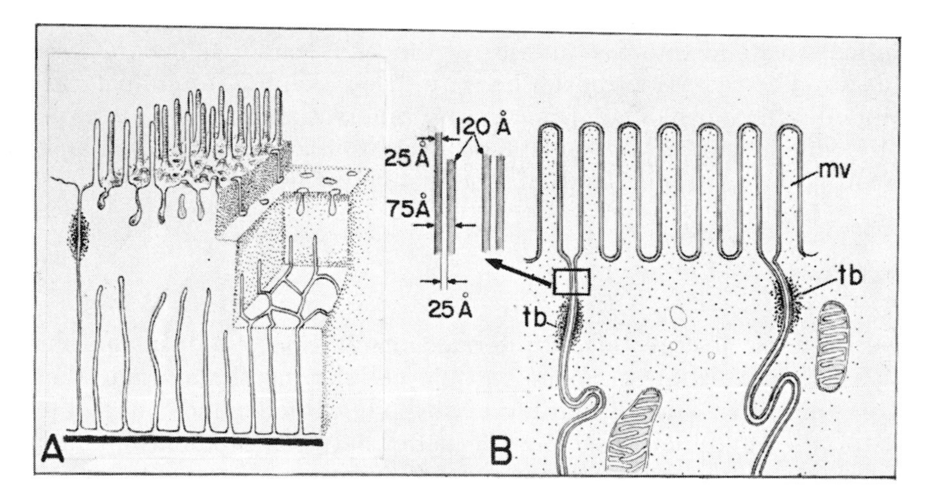

Figure 3–2. Two examples of surface increase by formation of *microvilli* (singular: microvillus). **A**, cell of proximal convoluted tubule of a nephron in a vertebrate kidney, showing extensive infolding of the plasma membrane on the outer (lower) surface, and numerous finger-like protrusions on the tubular surface. Note also the crypts between the protrusions or microvilli. **B**, section through the inner surface of an absorptive cell in a vertebrate intestine. The microvilli are 0.6 to 0.8 micron long. A single cell may have 3000 microvilli, and a square millimeter of intestinal surface may have no less than 200,000,000. This represents an enormous increase in cell surface. *mv*, microvillus; *tb*, terminal bars. (From De Robertis, E. D. P., W. W. Nowinski, and F. A. Saez: Cell Biology, 4th Ed. W. B. Saunders Co., Philadelphia, 1965.)

branes, the alveoli of lungs, the walls of blood capillaries, and the lining (*peritoneum*) of the coelom. Internal organs, such as muscles or digestive glands (liver), are provided with large "exchange" surfaces by an extremely rich vascular supply (particularly in organisms with a closed vascular system, such as vertebrates) or by assuming a highly branched or "capillary" structure: The digestive gland of the decapod Crustacea, for instance, consists of numerous fine, hollow tubes which float in the hemolymph, and the leg muscles are not compact structures but loose bundles of muscle fibers surrounded and bathed by the freely circulating hemolymph.

Cell membranes of cells engaged in active resorption of certain compounds and substances, for instance cells of intestinal epithelium or of "kidney" tubules, usually have greatly enlarged surface areas in the form of so-called *microvilli* (singular: microvillus). Examples are shown in Figure 3–2.

FREE CELLS

Not all body cells are stationary, being connected with others to form tissues and organs. Usually several cell types are free to move throughout the organism or to circulate within the fluid compartments of the body. Some of these are known as *interstitial cells*: these are undifferentiated cells which are usually located in epithelial structures and which migrate toward injured regions of the organism where they differentiate into tissue cells. Others are confined to the blood (e.g., red blood cells of vertebrates), others to the coelom (coelomocytes of holothuria), and still others can wander in and out of the vascular system (e.g., amebocytes of vertebrates). Some of these free cells contain pigments that serve in the transport of respiratory gases (oxygen and carbon dioxide), others take up waste material and deposit it in certain parts of the body, and still others carry nutrients from the digestive organs to tissue cells. Not all these functions are carried out by free cells in all types of animals, and in some animal forms such cells have not been found. The free body cells are dealt with in greater detail in later chapters. They are mentioned here simply to complete the generalized discussion of cellular animal organization.

SUMMARY

The organization of multicellular animals involves mainly body cells, extracellular structural elements, and body fluids. The extracellular structures provide mechanical stability and protection and in addition serve as storage and exchange agents for certain compounds, in particular for calcium and phosphate and the anions of their salts. The body cells (with the exception of the freely moving single cells) are arranged into tissues and organs in such a way as to provide large surfaces, either by forming cellular membranes or by permitting rich vascularization. The body fluids fill large continuous spaces and thereby permit diffusion over great distances, aided by convection.

REFERENCES

Barnes, R. D. (1963) Invertebrate Zoology. W. B. Saunders Co., Philadelphia.

Beklemischew, W. N. (1960) Grundlagen der vergleichenden Anatomie der Wirbellosen (German translation from the Russian) 2 vols. VEB Deutscher Verlag der Wissenschaften, Berlin.

Bronn, H. G. (1880–) Klassen und Ordnungen des Tierreichs. Numerous volumes, not completed. Akademische Verlagsgesellschaft, Leipzig.

Grassé, P. (1948–) Traité de Zoologie. 17 volumes, not completed. Masson, Paris.

Hyman, L. H. (1940–1959) The Invertebrates. 5 vols. McGraw-Hill Book Co., New York.

Kaestner, A. (1954–1963) Lehrbuch der speziellen Zoologie. G. Fischer Verlag, Stuttgart.

Kükenthal, W. (T. Krumbach, ed.) (1923–) Handbuch der Zoologie. Many volumes, not complete. W. De Gruyter & Co., Berlin.

Martin, A. W., F. M. Harrison, M. J. Huston, and D. M. Stewart (1958) The blood volumes of some representative molluscs. J. Exp. Biol. 35:260–279.

4 ELECTROLYTIC DISSOCIATION, DIFFUSION, AND OSMOSIS

ATOMS AND IONS

Matter, as we understand it today, is not "substance" in the Aristotelian sense; its expansion does not represent a continuously filled space but rather space occupied by a certain number of "elementary particles" separated by "fields of force." The concept of the atomic structure of matter, held until the turn of the century, has been replaced by the concept of the divisible atom and of the quantal nature of energy.

We believe that matter is composed of atoms, each with a diameter of the order of 10^{-8} cm (1 Ångström, or 1 Å), containing a nucleus of about 10^{-12} cm that has a mass density of 1.5×10^{17} gm/cm^3 and concentrates a net positive charge. The nucleus is surrounded by several concentric "shells" of electrons. Both the nuclear positive charge and the electronic negative charge are multiples of elementary units of charge which, whether positive or negative, are equivalent to 1.6×10^{-19} ampere seconds.

The lightest atom is that of hydrogen, consisting of one proton and one electron. Its properties are of fundamental importance for physiological phenomena. Each of the more than 100 different elements of matter has a different number of protons in the atomic nuclei. Almost all elements have isotopes, that is, they are represented by atoms with more than one type of nucleus: while the number of protons is always the same, the number of neutrons (the uncharged elementary particles with a mass of 1, equal to that of the protons) can vary. In chemistry and physics, as well as in physiology, elements are indicated simply by one or two letters, the *atomic symbol* (for instance, H, O, Cl,

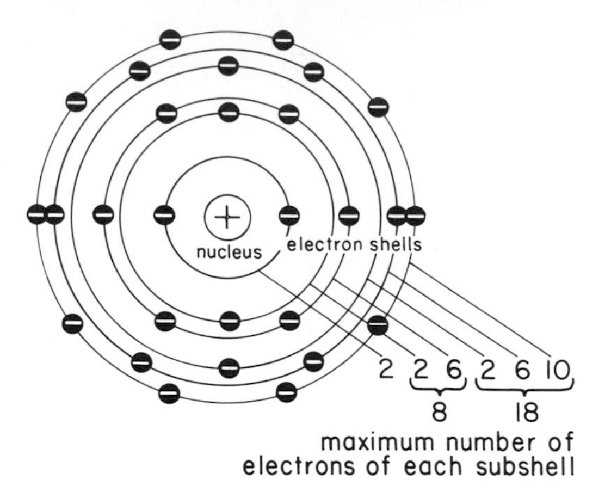

Figure 4–1. Symbolic representation of the structure of an atom with its positively charged nucleus and the shells of negatively charged electrons. Three shells are shown with a total of 2, 8, and 18 electrons, respectively. The latter two shells are composed of subshells. In relation to the size of the nucleus, the distance of the electrons is greatly reduced, but their size is exaggerated.

Mg). Isotopes are represented by the atomic symbol and the weight of the nucleus (for instance, ^{22}Na, ^{40}K, ^{14}C – in words: sodium twenty-two, potassium forty, carbon fourteen).

Many isotopes are radioactive; that is, their nuclei emit gamma rays (photons, light), alpha rays (protons, hydrogen ions), or beta rays (electrons). Radioactive isotopes are referred to as *radioisotopes*. An atom that emits alpha or beta particles changes from one element to another, since the emission alters the electrical charge of the nucleus.

Living organisms are weakly radioactive because of their potassium content: 0.012 per cent of their total potassium is an isotope (^{40}K), which is radioactive and emits beta and gamma rays. This radioisotope gradually transforms itself into ^{40}Ca and ^{40}Ar with a half-life of 1.2×10^9 years. The effects of this intrinsic radioactivity have not yet been assessed. It might be mentioned that the rate of radioactive decay does not change when an element is incorporated in diverse molecules. The radioactivity of potassium isolated from animal tissues is the same as that of potassium from inorganic sources.

The concentric electron "shells" can be maximally occupied by 2, 2, 6, 2, 6, 10, and so forth electrons, as shown in Figure 4–1. There is a tendency for each electron shell to acquire a full complement of electrons and for the whole atom to be surrounded by "saturated" electron shells. Atoms thus may gain or lose electrons to satisfy this tendency. Atoms that acquire electrons become negatively charged since the additional negative charges (electrons) are not balanced by an addition of positive charges. On the same grounds, atoms that lose electrons assume a positive charge since they do not lose protons to balance the loss of electrons. Such charged atoms are termed *ions*. Positively charged ions are called *cations*; negatively charged ions are called *anions*. Since the chemical properties of an element are largely determined by the number and arrangement of the electrons, gain or loss of electrons changes not only the net electric charge but also the chemical properties of the atoms involved. Thus, the atoms that become electrically charged become chemically inert: a solution containing the ions of the elements sodium and chlorine is known to form a suitable environment for living tissues and cells. The same

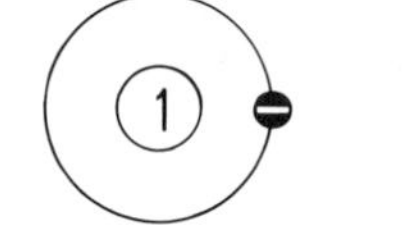

Figure 4–2. Symbolic representation of the relationship between a hydrogen atom and a hydrogen ion. The positively charged ion is more commonly considered.

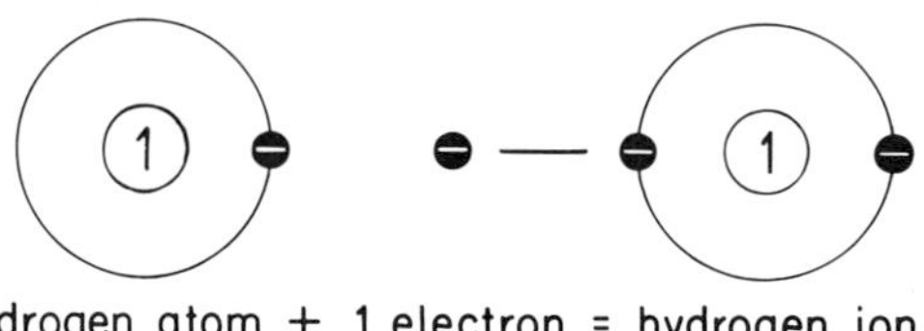

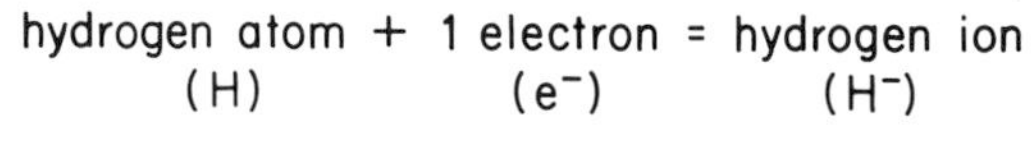

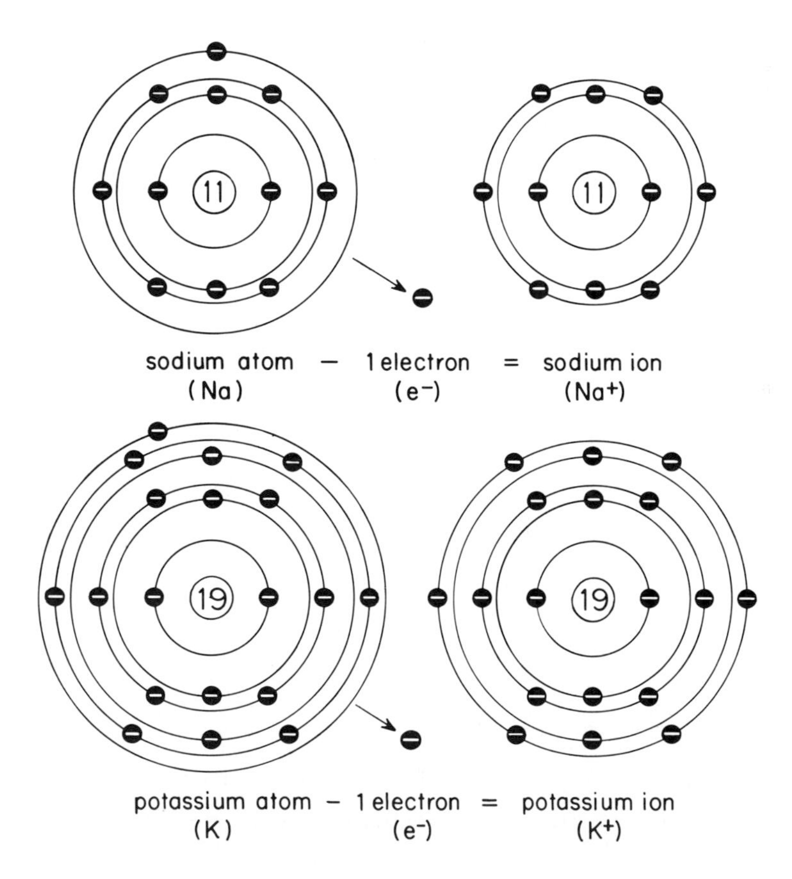

Figure 4–3. Symbolic representation of the structure of two common atoms and their ions: sodium and potassium. The number inside the nucleus is that of the protons.

concentrations of nonionized sodium and chlorine, however, would have lethal effects and would undergo violent chemical reactions. Figures 4–2, 4–3, and 4–4 illustrate the ionization of some physiologically important elements.

WATER AND ELECTROLYTIC DISSOCIATION

Corpora non agunt nisi soluta (substances cannot react unless they are dissolved) reflects the ancient experience that chemical reactions do not take place unless the reactants are in solution. The universal solvent of living systems is water. Each water molecule is composed of one atom of oxygen and two of hydrogen. From experimental evidence, it has been concluded that the water molecule has two hydrogen atoms situated at two corners of a tetrahedron, the center of which is occupied by the oxygen atom (Fig. 4–5). The angle of the bonds is 105°, rather than 109° 29″ as in a perfect tetrahedron. The oxygen atom accepts the "surplus" electron from each hydrogen atom in such a way that these two electrons travel in the outer electron orbit of the oxygen atom which had "lacked" two electrons (see Fig. 4–4). The electrons derived from the two hydrogen atoms of a water molecule orbit around the much larger oxygen nucleus most or all of the time. Consequently the water molecule is polarized:

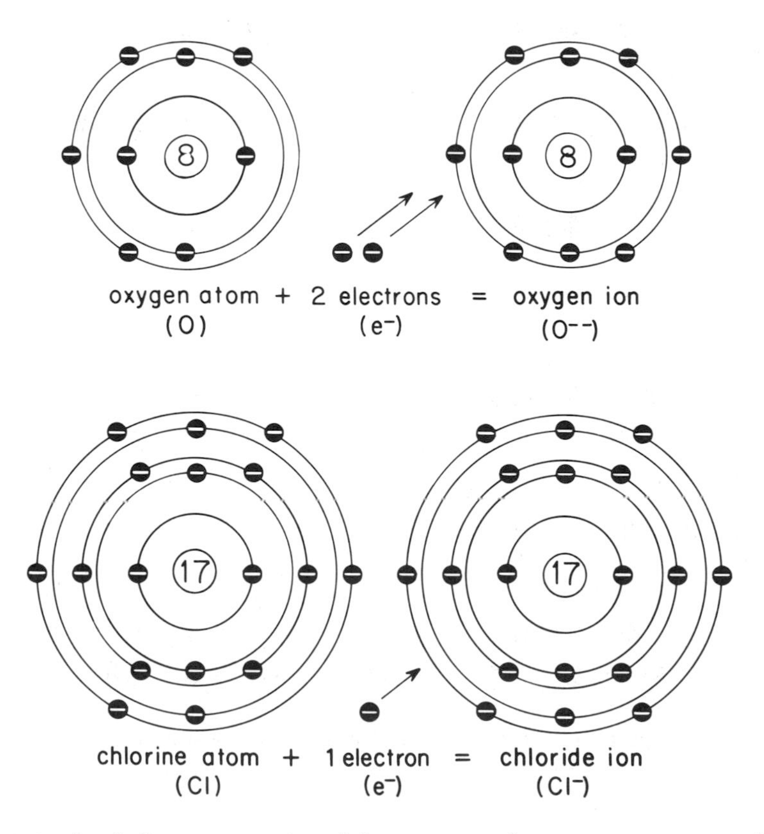

Figure 4–4. Symbolic representation of the structure of two common atoms and their ions: oxygen and chlorine (chloride). The number inside the nucleus is that of the protons.

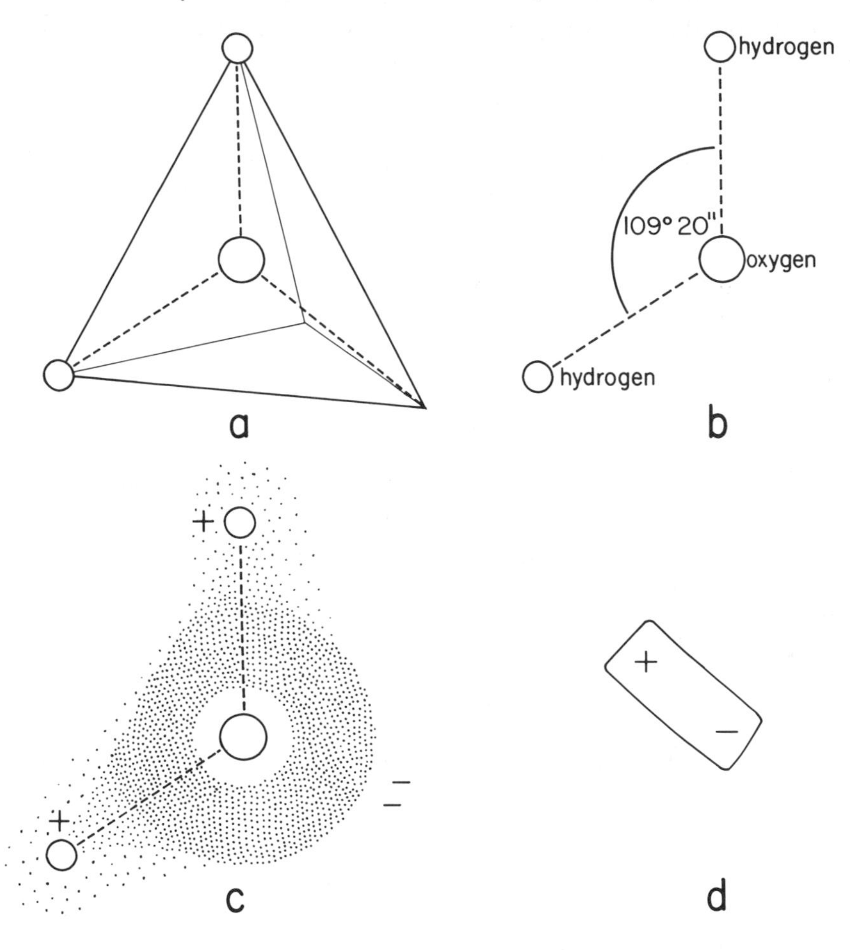

Figure 4–5. Four representations of the water molecule. a, the tetrahedron; two corners are occupied by hydrogen atoms, the center by the oxygen atom. **b**, the bond angle is 109° 20″. **c** symbolizes the "electron cloud" of the molecule, indicating the probability of electron positions by the density of stipple. **d** represents the abstraction of the water dipole as used in illustrating hydration of ions. (see Fig. 4–7).

one part of the molecule is positively charged, the other is negatively charged. Water molecules thus form *dipoles*. There is a certain probability that the electron of one or both hydrogen atoms will be completely removed.

The hydrogen ions (which in fact are protons) tend to separate from the molecule so that the water molecule dissociates into two components of opposite charge: a negatively charged hydroxyl ion (OH^-) and a positive hydrogen ion, or proton (H^+). Since the probability of this occurrence is rather small, only a small number of water molecules dissociate at any one time. Thus, 1 metric ton (1000 kilograms, or 1000 liters) of water at 22° C yields only 0.1 mg of hydrogen ions and 1.7 mg of hydroxyl ions. Only one out of 555,555,555 water molecules dissociates into ions.

The dissociation of water molecules into ions is reversible. Thus, we can write:

$$H_2O \rightleftharpoons H^+ + OH^- \quad (1)$$

The velocity of the forward reaction (that is, the number of dissociations per unit time) is a function of the concentration of undissociated water molecules:

$$v_1 = k_1 \cdot [H_2O] \quad (2)$$

where v_1 is the velocity of the forward reaction and k_1 is a constant.

The velocity of the reverse reaction (that is, the number of "associations" between H^+ and OH^- ions per unit time) is a function of the concentrations of hydrogen and hydroxyl ions, or:

$$v_2 = k_2 \cdot [H^+] \cdot [OH^-] \quad (3)$$

where v_2 is the velocity of the reverse reaction, and k_2 is a constant.

Now, equilibrium is reached when v_1 equals v_2 or when

$$k_1 [H_2O] = k_2 [H^+] \cdot [OH^-] \quad (4)$$

We can rewrite the equation to read:

$$\frac{[H^+] \cdot [OH^-]}{[H_2O]} = \frac{k_1}{k_2} \quad (5)$$

Since the quotient of two constants is always a constant, we can also say that

$$\frac{[H^+] \cdot [HO^-]}{[H_2O]} = K \quad (6)$$

K, the dissociation constant of water, is 1.8×10^{-16} mole/liter.

The equation can be rewritten to read:

$$[H^+] \cdot [OH^-] = K \cdot [H_2O] \quad (7)$$

The value of H_2O is known, since we know the weight of 1 liter of water (1000 gm) and we know its molecular weight (18). The molarity of water is thus 1000/18, or 55.5. Therefore, the ionic product of water is $(1.8 \times 10^{-16}) \times 55.5$, or 10^{-14}. This value is a constant, usually referred to as K_w.

$$[H^+] \cdot [OH^-] = K_w \quad (8)$$

This value is true only at 22° C, and varies considerably with the temperature (see Table 4–1).

The special significance of the constant K_w is the consequence that addition of hydrogen ions or of hydroxyl ions to water reduces the number of dissociated water molecules per unit volume. If 10 times more hydrogen ions are added than are present in neutral water, the hydroxyl ion concentration becomes reduced to one-tenth according to the equation $[H^+] \cdot [OH^-] = K_w$. This reduction occurs only if nine-tenths the original hydroxyl ions combine or reassociate with an equal number of hydrogen ions to form water molecules. A similar reduction of the number of dissociated water molecules takes place when hydroxyl ions are added to water.

Table 4–1.

Temperature (°C)	K_w	$[H^+]$
16	0.63×10^{-14}	0.79×10^{-7}
18	0.74	0.86
20	0.86	0.93
22	1.01	1.00
24	1.19	1.09
26	1.38	1.17
28	1.62	1.27
30	1.89	1.37
32	2.19	1.48
34	2.51	1.59
36	2.92	1.71
38	3.35	1.83
40	3.80	1.95

From Michaelis, L.: Die Wasserstoffionen-Konzentration, 2nd. Ed. J. Springer, Berlin, 1922.

Hydrogen ions are usually derived from acids, hydroxyl ions from bases. The relative concentrations of hydrogen and hydroxyl ions in a watery (aqueous) solution, is a measure of the *acidity* or *alkalinity* of the solution. Since the concentrations of hydrogen and hydroxyl ions are inversely proportional, the concentration of either ion can be taken as an index for the "reaction" (degree of acidity or alkalinity) of an aqueous solution. The reaction of a solution is usually described in terms of the hydrogen ion concentration. To simplify the expression of the hydrogen ion concentration, Sørensen (1909) introduced the term p_H (p_h in the German literature and pH in the American literature).

Table 4–2.

$[OH^-]$	$-\log_{10}[H^+]$ (pH)	$[H^+]$	*Conc.* [HCl]	*Conc.* [NaOH]
10^{-14}	0	1 N	1 N	0.0 N
10^{-13}	1	0.1 N	0.1 N	0.0 N
10^{-12}	2	0.01 N	0.01 N	0.0 N
10^{-11}	3	0.001 N	0.001 N	0.0 N
10^{-10}	4	0.0001 N	0.0001 N	0.0 N
10^{-9}	5	0.00001 N	0.00001 N	0.0 N
10^{-8}	6	0.000001 N	0.000001 N	0.0 N
10^{-7}	7	0.0 N	0.0 N	0.0 N
10^{-6}	8	0.0 N	0.0 N	0.000001 N
10^{-5}	9	0.0 N	0.0 N	0.00001 N
10^{-4}	10	0.0 N	0.0 N	0.0001 N
10^{-3}	11	0.0 N	0.0 N	0.001 N
10^{-2}	12	0.0 N	0.0 N	0.01 N
10^{-1}	13	0.0 N	0.0 N	0.1 N
1^{-1}	14	0.0 N	0.0 N	1.0 N

Table 4–3.

pH	$[H^+]$
n.00	$1.00 \cdot 10^{-n}$
n.10	$0.794 \cdot 10^{-n}$
n.20	$0.631 \cdot 10^{-n}$
n.30	$0.502 \cdot 10^{-n}$
n.40	$0.398 \cdot 10^{-n}$
n.50	$0.316 \cdot 10^{-n}$
n.60	$0.251 \cdot 10^{-n}$
n.70	$0.200 \cdot 10^{-n}$
n.80	$0.159 \cdot 10^{-n}$
n.90	$0.126 \cdot 10^{-n}$

This term signifies the negative logarithm to the base of 10 of the hydrogen ion concentration. Neutral water at 22° C has a pH of 7.0 since it has a hydrogen ion concentration of $10^{-7.0}$ mole/liter. The pH value of a solution can vary from 1 to 14. Values below pH 7 indicate acidity; values above pH 7 indicate alkalinity, as indicated in Table 4–2.

The actual hydrogen ion concentrations can be calculated from pH values according to Table 4–3.

At temperatures other than 22° C, the pH values above 7 differ considerably from those given in Table 4–3, owing to the temperature dependence of the dissociation of water.

ELECTROLYTES, ACIDS, AND BASES

The term electrolyte is applied to compounds that, when dissolved in water, dissociate into two or more ions of opposite charges. All inorganic salts that are of physiological significance dissociate completely in aqueous solution. Sodium chloride, for instance, dissociates into sodium (Na^+) and chloride (Cl^-) ions. Water-soluble organic salts are also highly dissociable. Compounds that are completely or highly dissociated in water are called *strong electrolytes*. Substances that dissociate to a lesser degree are called *weak electrolytes*. To the latter belong a number of organic and inorganic acids (carbonic acid, H_2CO_3; phosphoric acid, H_3PO_4; acetic acid, CH_3COOH; lactic acid, $CH_3CHOH \cdot COOH$), organic and inorganic bases (ammonia, NH_3; bicarbonate, HCO_3). Dissociation constants of weak electrolytes correspond to the following formulae:

$$\frac{[H^+]\,[A^-]}{[HA]} = k \qquad (9)$$

where A^- is the acid anion and k the dissociation constant of the acid. HA is the undissociated acid.

$$\frac{[B^+]\,[OH^-]}{[BOH]} = k \qquad (10)$$

where B^+ is the base cation and k the dissociation constant of the base, BOH is the undissociated base.

The hydrogen ion concentration of a weakly dissociating acid is given by the formula

$$[H^+] = \sqrt{k \cdot [A]} \qquad (11)$$

where k is the dissociation constant of the acid and A is the total concentration of dissociated and undissociated acid.

The hydroxyl ion concentration of a weakly dissociated base is given by

$$[OH^-] = \sqrt{k \cdot [B]} \qquad (12)$$

where k is the dissociation constant of the base and B is the concentration of dissociated and undissociated base. Since $[OH^-] = \frac{K_W}{[H^+]}$, the hydrogen ion concentration of a weakly dissociating base in water is:

$$[H^+] = \frac{K_W}{\sqrt{k \cdot [B]}} \qquad (13)$$

Many salts of physiological importance are the products of a weak acid and a strong base or of a strong acid and a weak base. For example, sodium acetate ($NaCOCH_3$) is a product of a weak acid and strong base, and ammonium chloride (NH_4Cl) is a product of a strong acid and a weak base. Salts are formed according to the equation:

$$\text{acid} + \text{base} = \text{salt} + H_2O \qquad (14)$$

Salt formation is reversible, according to our understanding of chemical equilibria. If both acid and base are strong electrolytes, that is, if they dissociate completely in water, they do not affect the pH of the solution. If, however, one of the two is a weak electrolyte, the pH changes in accordance with the dissociation constant of the weak electrolyte and the concentration of the salt in the aqueous solution (see Table 4–4).

According to Table 4–4, solutions of NH_4Cl (K = approximately 10^{-5}) have the following pH values: 4.5 (1 molar); 5 (0.1 molar); 5.5 (0.01 molar); 6.5 (0.001 molar). Solutions of $NaCH_3CO$ (K = approximately 10^{-5}) have the following pH values: 9.5 (1 molar); 9 (0.1 molar); 8.5 (0.01 molar); 7.5 (0.001 molar).

Solutions of weak acids and their salts (strongly dissociated) are also common in physiological systems. Examples are carbonic acid (H_2CO_3) and sodium bicarbonate ($NaHCO_3$). The $[H^+]$ of such a solution follows the equation

$$[H^+] = K \cdot \frac{[\text{acid}]}{[\text{salt}]} \qquad (15)$$

***Table 4–4.* pH Values of Solutions of the Salt of a Weak Base and a Strong Acid, or pOH Values of Solutions of the Salt of a Strong Base and a Weak Acid**

K	1 N	0.1 N	0.01 N	0.001 N
∞	7	7	7	7
10^{-2}	6	6.5	6.9	7.0
10^{-4}	5	5.5	6	7.0
10^{-6}	4	4.5	5	6.0
10^{-8}	3	3.5	4	4.5
10^{-10}	2	2.5	3	3.6
10^{-12}	1.02	1.6	2.2	3.0

K is the dissociation constant of the weaker component. From Michaelis, L.: Die Wasserstoffionen-Konzentration, 2nd Ed. J. Springer, Berlin.

where K is the dissociation constant of the acid. If more of the common anion (for instance, HCO_3^-) is added by increasing the concentration of the strongly dissociating salt, the hydrogen ion concentration is reduced.

If the concentration of the weak acid and of its salt are equal, $[H^+]$ will be equal to K, and the pH will equal the negative logarithm of K, that is, pK. Equation 15 can thus be rewritten:

$$pK = pH - \log \frac{[\text{salt}]}{[\text{acid}]} \tag{16}$$

or

$$pH = pK + \log \frac{[\text{salt}]}{[\text{acid}]} \tag{17}$$

Equation 17, known as the *Henderson-Hasselbalch equation,* is extensively used to decribe the behavior of buffer solutions (see below). If $[H^+]$ is replaced by $[OH^-]$, the equation can be adapted to the equivalent situation of a weak base and its salt:

$$[OH^-] = K \cdot \frac{[\text{salt}]}{[\text{base}]}$$

or

$$pOH^- = pK + \log \frac{[\text{salt}]}{[\text{base}]} \tag{18}$$

Solutions containing similar concentrations of weak acids and their salts, of of weak bases and their salts, are called *buffer solutions.* They resist changes in $[H^+]$ when other acids or bases are added to their mixture. The pH of such a buffer solution is determined by the *ratio* of [weak acid]/[salt] or of [weak base]/[salt]. The closer to unity, the more effectively the mixture resists pH changes. The capacity to resist changes in pH is called the *buffer capacity.* The buffer capacity also depends, naturally, on the total concentration of the "buffer mixture": the more buffer, the stronger the buffer capacity of the solution.

Body fluids contain one or more buffers, usually bicarbonate ($NaHCO_3$ and H_2CO_3), and phosphate buffers.

The following formulation explains the action of the bicarbonate buffer system:

HCl	+	$NaHCO_3$	=	NaCl	+	H_2CO_3
strongly ionized acid		strongly ionized (alkaline)		strongly ionized neutral		weakly ionized acid

AMPHOLYTES

Compounds that give off hydrogen ions (protons) or that bind hydroxyl ions are acids, whereas compounds that give off hydroxyl ions or bind hydrogen ions (protons) are bases. Many of the physiologically most important compounds, particularly the amino acids and proteins, are ampholytes; that is, they behave as acids as well as bases. This is due to the fact that they possess basic radicals or groups that can bind protons (amino, guanidine, and imidazole groups) and acid groups that can dissociate protons (carboxyl, sulfhydryl, and phenolic groups).

For example, a simple amino acid, alanine, has one amino group and one carboxyl group:

$$
\begin{array}{c}
\text{H} \\
| \\
\text{CH}_3 - \text{C} - \text{COOH} \\
| \\
\text{NH}_2
\end{array}
$$

In aqueous solution, this compound is doubly ionized so that most of its molecules assume the following form:

$$
\begin{array}{c}
\text{H} \\
| \\
\text{CH}_3 - \text{C} - \text{COO}^- \\
| \\
\text{NH}_3^+
\end{array}
$$

The basic, positively charged amino group has a rather low dissociation constant of $10^{-9.6}$ whereas the acid carboxyl group has a rather high dissociation constant of $10^{-2.4}$. In the absence of other compounds, the $[H^+]$ of an aqueous solution of alanine will be:

$$10^{-\left(\frac{9.6 - 2.4}{2}\right)} = 10^{-6}$$

and the pH of the solution will be 6.0.* At this pH value, the degrees of ioniza-

*If more than two different ionizable groups are present, these have to be considered also. In many cases, however, approximate values can be obtained by simply considering only the two most extreme dissociation constants. Note that the formula given is for the theoretical case of an infinitely high concentration. With diminishing concentrations, the pH value of the solution approaches 7.0, since the dissociation constant of water is greater the higher the proportion of water. Consequently, the pH of an aqueous solution of an ampholyte is always between the isoelectric point and pH 7.0. A theoretical treatment of this question was first given by Sørensen (1912). The situation becomes further complicated if salts are present in the solution. For a detailed discussion of these problems, see Edsall and Wyman (1958).

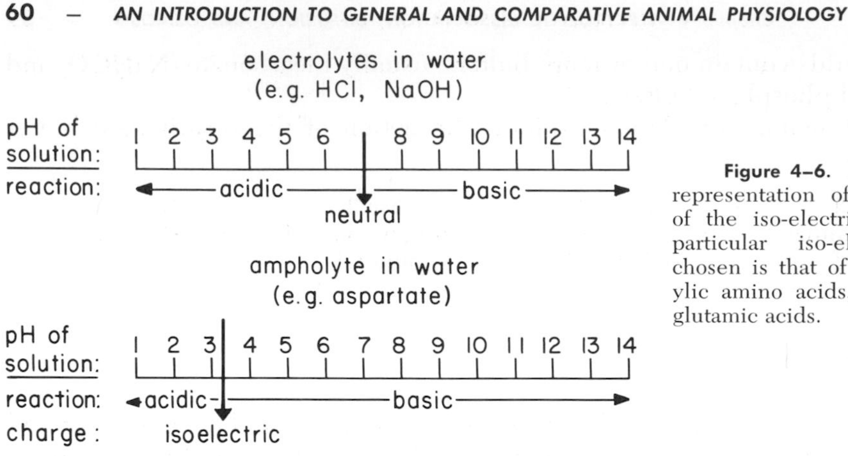

Figure 4–6. Diagrammatic representation of the concept of the iso-electric point. The particular iso-electric point chosen is that of the dicarboxylic amino acids, aspartic and glutamic acids.

tion of both the amino and the hydroxyl groups of the dissolved alanine molecules are the same. The numbers of negative and positive charges on the alanine molecules are equal under these circumstances. The molecules in this condition are termed *iso-ionic** or *iso-electric*,* and the pH at which this situation is given is called the *iso-ionic* or *iso-electric point*. The diagrams of Figure 4–6 illustrate this.

The amino and carboxyl groups are not the only sites of charges on amino acid molecules, particularly in proteins in which the carboxyl and amino groups of the amino acids are utilized in joining these building blocks together by peptide linkages.

$$NH_2 - R - COOH + NH_2 - R - COOH + NH_2 - R - COOH + NH_2 - R - COOH, \text{ etc.}$$

$$\begin{array}{cccc} +H_2O & +H_2O & +H_2O & +H_2O \end{array}$$
$$= NH_2 - R - CO - NH - R - CO - NH - R - CO - NH - R - CO - NH - R, \text{ etc.}$$

R symbolizes the variable residue of amino acid structure.

Guanidine, amidazole, phenolic, and sulfhydryl groups contribute significantly to the ionic dissociation of these molecules. Obviously, the interactions of the various ionic groups with their different dissociation constants complicate the simple picture which we have discussed considerably. However, the fact remains that proteins are double ions.† Referring to the possession of both acid and basic ionized groups, one speaks of the *amphoteric* nature of a compound. The compound itself is called an *ampholyte*.

*The term "iso-ionic" was introduced by Sørensen et al. in 1927. The term "iso-electric" was coined by Hardy in 1899 in reference to the reversal of charges on colloids (inorganic), and was later applied to proteins (Hardy, 1905). A definition of the iso-electric point based on the mathematical relationships of the degrees of dissociation of the acid and basic groups was introduced by Michaelis and Davidsohn in 1910.

†G. Bredig (1899), who is responsible for the term "ampholyte," called ions that possess opposite charges *Zwitterionen* (Zwitter ions).

In summary, ampholytes are electrically neutral when the hydrogen ion concentration of the environment is equal to or near their isoelectric point. They are positively charged and behave like bases in media that are acid with regard to the isoelectric point, and they are negatively charged and behave as acids in media that are alkaline with regard to the iso-electric point. The situation can be represented by the following formulae:

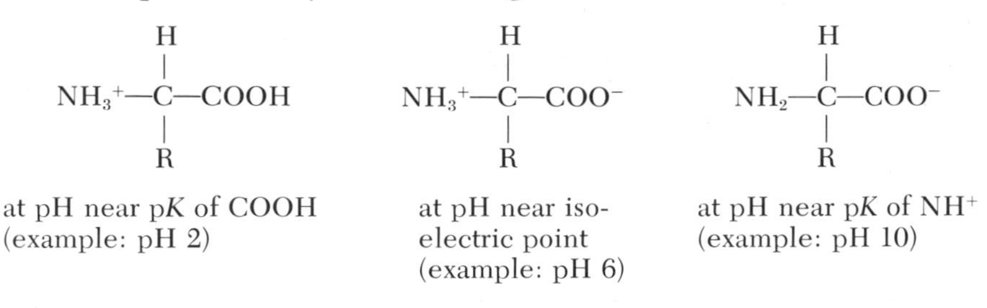

at pH near pK of COOH (example: pH 2) — at pH near iso-electric point (example: pH 6) — at pH near pK of NH^+ (example: pH 10)

Often a molecule, particularly a large protein molecule, has more than two ionized (or ionizable) groups. In the presence of base a protein molecule acts like many molecules of acid and in the presence of acid a protein can replace many molecules of base. Proteins, therefore, effectively neutralize acids and bases, and they play a most important role in maintaining a constant pH value within living systems.

The hydrogen ion concentration of the extracellular fluids is generally near or above pH 7, whereas that of the interior of most cells is slightly below pH 7. The iso-electric point of the majority of cellular proteins and free amino acids is below these pH values. Consequently, the cellular proteins and amino acids are predominantly acidic and negatively charged. This fact is largely responsible for a rather peculiar distribution of intra- and extracellular inorganic ions, and for the relatively large electrical potential gradients across cell membranes, which reach the order of 100,000 volts/cm (see p. 387 and Chap. 16).

HYDRATION OF IONS

Water molecules are electrically polarized. If water contains ions, these cause a characteristic orientation of the water dipoles: cations attract the negative ends of the water molecules while anions attract the positive ends of the water molecules. Ions in aqueous solution are thus surrounded by clusters of orientated water particles (Fig. 4–7). The molecules of a liquid are rather independent in their motions and are subject to considerable random motion. This inherent motion competes with the attraction offered by ions that tend to hold the dipoles in a fixed position. Since the electric field surrounding an electric charge diminishes with the square of the distance, the number of water molecules that are held by ions is limited. Ions are, therefore, surrounded by a water mantle of fairly definite dimensions.

Ions that carry a shell of oriented water molecules are called *hydrated ions*, and the water that is bound by electrostatic attraction is referred to as *water of hydration*, or *bound water*.

The water mantle makes ions considerably larger (see Table 4–5). The

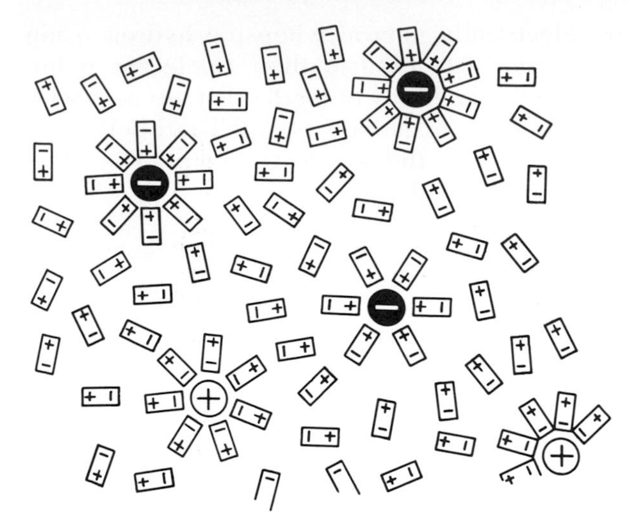

Figure 4–7. Symbolic representation of the hydration of ions. Cations as well as anions orient the water dipoles in their immediate vicinity to form a "water mantle."

diameter of the hydrated ion is determined both by the size of the ion and the distribution of its charges. The ions of elements are either positively or negatively charged atoms. The excess positive charges of the cations reside in the atomic nuclei (protons). These are surrounded by electron shells of considerable diameter. The heavier the nucleus, the larger is the diameter of the electron shell. The shell is a barrier to negative charges attracted by the extra charge of the ionic nuclei. Consequently, the orienting effect on surrounding water molecules decreases with increasing atomic weight (diameter) of the cation. The physiologically important monovalent cations K^+ and Na^+ have diameters of 2.66 and 1.9 Å, respectively, but in its hydrated form, the sodium ion is larger than the potassium ion (Fig. 4–8). For anions the situation is

Table 4–5. **Radius of Nonhydrated and Hydrated Inorganic Ions of Physiological Importance**

Ion	*Nonhydrated*	*Hydrated*	*Molecules of Water Carried*
K^+	1.33	3.8	3.8
Na^+	0.98	5.6	8.0
Ca^{++}	1.06	9.6	17.6
Mg^{++}	0.78	10.8	22.2
H^+	1.20		
Cl^-	1.80		

Note: The diameter of the ions is twice their radius.
Data from Conway, E. J.: Some aspects of ion transport through membranes. Symp. Soc. Exp. Biol. *8*: Active Transport and Secretion, pp. 297–324, 1954. (cations); and Pauling, L.: The Nature of the Chemical Bond. Cornell University Press, Ithaca, N. Y., 1960. (anions and H^+).

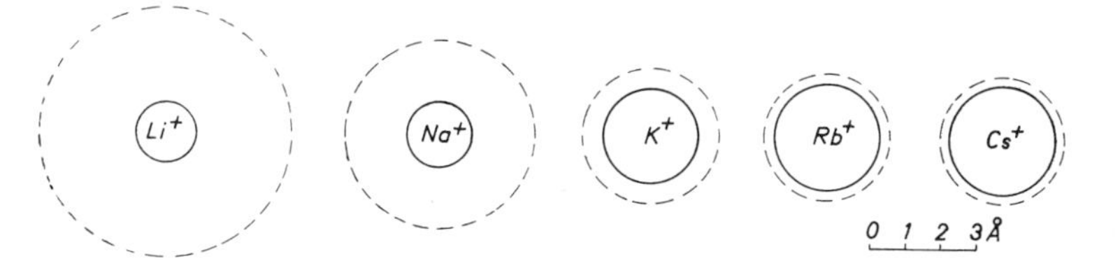

Figure 4–8. The sizes of various cations (Hofmeister series): with increasing diameter of the ion (solid circle) the diameter of the hydration layer (dotted circle) increases so that the smallest ion (lithium) becomes the largest. For ions to penetrate living membranes, the diameter of the hydrated form is of decisive importance; thus K^+ ions may penetrate pores that Na^+ cannot. (From Frey-Wyssling, A.: The Submicroscopic Morphology of Protoplasm and Its Derivatives. Elsevier Publishing Co., New York, 1953.)

different: the excess charges are located in the periphery of the ion, the electron shell. Therefore, the orienting action increases with increasing size of the ion.

For a more advanced treatment of the complex topic of the hydration (solvation) of ions, see Bockris (1949) and Chapter 3 of Kortüm and Bockris (1951).

Since the diameter of a hydrated ion represents a statistical value only, it does not differ from that of the hydrated ion by multiples of the diameter of the water molecule. At present the diameter of hydrated ions cannot be measured accurately. Determinations are based on either crystallographic data (Fig. 4–9) or mobility measurements. Whereas the distance of ions and the spacing of water molecules within a crystal can be determined fairly accurately, such data do not necessarily reflect the dimensions of the same ions and water

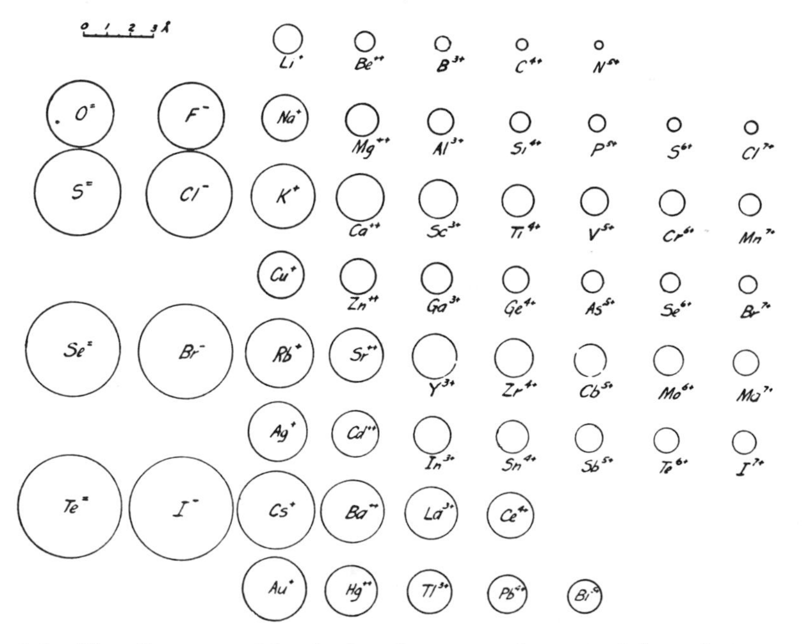

Figure 4–9. The diameters of (nonhydrated) ions, as determined from their crystal radii. (From Pauling, L.: The Nature of the Chemical Bond. Cornell University Press, Ithaca, 1960.)

molecules in free solution. Mobility measurements would be accurate if mobility is determined only by the temperature and viscosity of the solvent and by the diameter of the moving particles. However, a moving ion may well be slowed down by the fact that it loses energy in orienting the surrounding water molecules. The figures to which various physiologists subscribe differ widely. Those given for hydrated sodium ions, for example, range from 3.4 to 15.8 Å.

The beginner must be warned to distinguish carefully between figures referring to the radius of an ion and those referring to the ion diameter. The diameter is twice the radius. Unfortunately, some texts have quoted authors' figures for ionic radius and listed them as ionic diameter. The reliability of a table of values can be checked readily if one remembers that the unhydrated ionic radius of K^+ ions is 1.33 Å and that of Na^+ ions 0.98 Å. (The diameters of unhydrated ions are well established.)

The physiological actions of ions are largely determined by their hydrated condition, and the effective diameter of such ions in aqueous medium is that of the hydrated form.

Larger ions can also become hydrated, and this is particularly significant in the case of proteins. Proteins behave as *colloids*; that is, they exist in the form of a dispersion of relatively large particles (10^{-5} to 10^{-7} cm in diameter) in an aqueous medium. Protein molecules are ionized, and are, therefore, surrounded by oriented water molecules. The water mantle of colloids increases the stability of the solution by preventing the large molecules from coming in contact with each other and from forming larger units by chemical cross-linkages and electrostatic attraction.

Introducing inorganic salts (which ionize) into colloidal solutions greatly alters the behavior of the system. The ions of the salts compete for the available water and, if this is limited, take water away from the protein. In addition, the ions of the salts associate with the ionized groups of the proteins and in part "discharge" them. The characteristics of a colloidal solution are determined mainly by the type of ion introduced and in particular the degree of hydration of these ions. The characteristics are also determined by the relative concentrations of colloid and introduced ions, and the pH of the whole system which, as discussed before, determines the extent of ionization of the amphoteric proteins. The characteristics referred to are (1) the size and special arrangement of the colloidal particles, (2) the configuration of the molecules that constitute the colloid, and (3) physical and chemical interactions of the colloidal particles.

Inorganic ions can be placed in a sequence according to their increasing activity when introduced into colloidal systems. Sequences for anions and cations were first established by Franz Hofmeister in 1891 and are therefore termed *Hofmeister series*. The anion series is:

$$HPO_4^- > SO_4^{--} > Cl^- > Br^- > J^- > NO_3^- > SCN^-$$

The cation series is:

$$Mg^{++} > Ca^{++} > Sr^{++} > Ba^{++} > Li^+ > Na^+ > K^+ > Rb^+ > Cs^+$$

In each series, the ion that alters colloidal systems most effectively is on the right; the least effective is on the left. Note, however, that several exceptions to these series are known and that many more ions, including organic ones, can be fitted into the sequences.

DIFFUSION

Atoms and molecules move continuously. They are thought of as moving in one direction until they are repelled by another atom of a molecule: then they are deflected and change direction. The behavior of a number of atoms or molecules can be compared to that of a swarm of mosquitoes: although the shape of the whole group may not change appreciably, each individual changes position continuously. In such a system, there is no "net movement"; that is, the overall distributions of individual particles (or mosquitoes) remains the same. With regard to the movements of each particle, we use the term "random movement" to indicate that there is no preferred or predominant direction of movement. The amount or velocity of the individual motions is determined by the temperature. In fact, the temperature of a system is defined as the kinetic energy of its particles. The higher the temperature, the more rapidly the particles move and the more frequently they collide.

In solids the movement of the constituent molecules and atoms (or ions) is restricted, whereas in liquids there is more freedom of movement, and in gases the molecules and atoms are practically independent.

In physiology, we deal frequently with liquids. Even seemingly solid structures, such as "membranes," often must be considered as structures that can dissolve other compounds. But often we regard them simply as physical barriers whose internal composition is of little functional interest.

Liquids are practically always solutions. The major component of a solution is referred to as the *solvent*, and the substances that are dissolved in it are called the *solute*. Apart from the consideration of cell membranes, physiology is almost exclusively concerned with *aqueous solutions*, in which the solvent is water.

A crystal of sodium chloride placed into a volume of water dissolves to form a solution of sodium chloride. Ions of sodium and of chloride break loose from the crystal and move independently throughout the water. In the beginning of the process, the greatest number of sodium and chloride ions is in the vicinity of the dissolving crystal. But as the dissolving is completed, the random movement of all particles within the medium leads to an even distribution of all the different particles—the water molecules, sodium ions, and chloride ions. Until this is achieved, there is a net movement of sodium and chloride ions into the more distant areas of the medium where the amount of sodium and chloride is still low. This movement from higher to lower concentration of solute is called *diffusion*. Diffusion stops when the distribution throughout the medium is even. Then there is no more *net movement* of any component of the solution and the system is considered to be in *equilibrium* or a *steady state*.

Diffusion is expressed quantitatively in *Fick's law* (formulated by the German physiologist Adolf Fick in 1855):

$$\frac{dm}{dt} = - D \cdot S \cdot \frac{dc}{dx} \quad (19)$$

Expressed in words, the mass (m) of solute diffused per unit time (t) is equal to a constant (*the diffusion constant* D) times the cross-sectional area S through which diffusion takes place, multiplied by the concentration gradient dc/dx, where c is concentration and x the unit length perpendicular to the plane of S. The expression dm/dt stands for what is commonly called the *net flux*. The expression dc/dx represents the *concentration gradient*. If the concentration increases with increasing distance, the concentration gradient is negative. The direction of the net flux is opposite to the direction of the concentration gradient; in other words, the net flux is in the direction of the lower concentration. m is usually given in moles or millimoles, S in cm^2, c in moles/liter or millimoles/ml, x in cm.

It is most convenient to visualize diffusion as occurring in a cuboid compartment and in such a way that the total net movement is unidirectional, say from left to right, as illustrated in Figure 4–10.

The general formula, as stated in Equation 19, can be simplified, if certain standard conditions are assumed, such as that net flux is defined as the number of moles diffusing per second through an area of 1 cm^2. If this net flux is given the symbol F, we can write:

$$F = - D \frac{dc}{dx} \quad (20)$$

The concentration gradient can be given as $\frac{c_1 - c_2}{9}$, where c_1 and c_2 are the concentration of solute in moles/liter or mM/ml at the infinitesimally small volumes of the cross-sectional areas 1 and 2 which are parallel to each other and separated by the distance x (see Fig. 4–10). The equation for net flux then becomes:

$$F = - D \cdot \frac{(c_1 - c_2)}{x} \quad (21)$$

and the equation for the diffusion constant D can be written:

$$D = \frac{-F}{\frac{(c_1 - c_2)}{x}} \quad (22)$$

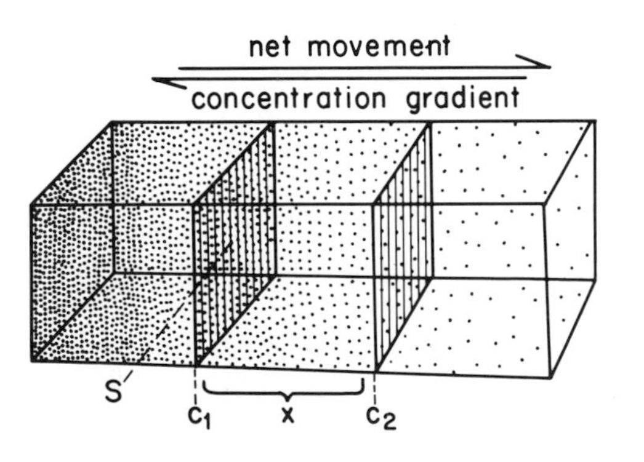

Figure 4–10. Symbolic representation of diffusion and of the terms employed in its mathematical formulation. Note that the direction of net movement (net flux) is opposite that of the concentration gradient.

F stands for moles/cm²/sec and the concentration gradient is expressed in moles/cm³/cm. Thus, if we write the formula for the diffusion constant in dimensions, this becomes:

$$D = \frac{\text{moles}}{\text{cm}^2 \cdot \text{sec} \cdot \dfrac{\text{moles}}{\text{cm}^3/\text{cm}}} = \frac{\text{moles}}{\text{cm}^2 \cdot \text{sec} \cdot \dfrac{\text{moles}}{\text{cm}^4}} = \text{cm}^2/\text{sec} \qquad (23)$$

The diffusion constant D can be defined as the mass of material (in moles) diffusing across a unit area in unit time under a concentration gradient of one.

The diffusion constant is given for each solute. It depends on the properties of both solute and solvent. The diffusion constant of a given solute in a given solvent increases with increasing temperature. Examples of diffusion constants are given in Table 4–6.

Table 4–6. Diffusion Constants of Various Substances in Free Solution and in the Extracellular Fluid of Various Tissues, All at 20° C

		D cm²/min
K^+	free solution	9.9×10^{-4}
	rat muscle	$4.1 - 10.9 \times 10^{-5}$
	frog muscle	7.0×10^{-4}
	rat brain	$3.2 - 7.2 \times 10^{-5}$
	rat nerve	$0.8 - 5.0 \times 10^{-5}$
	rat liver	$3.4 - 4.0 \times 10^{-5}$
Na^+	free solution	7.2×10^{-4}
	rat muscle	$1.1 - 3.2 \times 10^{-4}$
	frog muscle	$1.5 - 3.4 \times 10^{-4}$
	rat brain	$5.6 - 14.0 \times 10^{-4}$
	rat nerve	$0.7 - 1.2 \times 10^{-4}$
	cat nerve	9.0×10^{-4}
	frog nerve	1.1×10^{-6}
	rat liver	$8.3 - 12.7 \times 10^{-4}$
sucrose	free solution	3.1×10^{-4}
	rat muscle	3.4×10^{-4}
	rat brain	2.1×10^{-4}
	rat nerve	4.3×10^{-5}
inulin	free solution	1.0×10^{-4}
	rat muscle	1.2×10^{-4}
	rat brain	1.9×10^{-4}
	rat nerve	1.5×10^{-5}

Data from McLennan, H.: The diffusion of potassium, sodium, sucrose and inulin in the extracellular spaces of mammalian tissues. Biochim. biophys. Acta 24:1–8, 1957.

PERMEABILITY

Diffusion is an extremely slow process. However, it becomes significant in areas that are large compared to the distance through which net flux occurs. Diffusion across membranes is of utmost physiological importance. This occurs not only in cell membranes, but also in cellular membranes (membranes composed of cells). Diffusion across membranes is sometimes referred to as *passive transport* or *passive net flux*, to distinguish it from *active transport*, in which molecules or ions are transported across membranes by specific carrier mechanisms (known as pumps).

Membranes can be considered as layers of solvent, even if their physical properties are much more complex than those of a liquid. Granted the validity of this assumption, the net flux through a membrane is proportional to the diffusion constant in the membrane. The diffusion constants of membranes in living systems are always considerably lower than those measured in water. For all practical purposes, diffusion in the fluid compartments bordering the membrane can be neglected. Net flux through a membrane of thickness d can then be described by the equation:

$$F = -D \cdot \frac{(c_1 - c_2)}{d} = -\frac{D}{d} \cdot (c_1 - c_2) \tag{24}$$

D/d expresses the *permeability* of a membrane to a given substance, and is represented by *P*, which is called the *permeability constant*. It has the dimension of cm/sec. A graphic representation of net flux through a membrane is given in Figure 4–11.

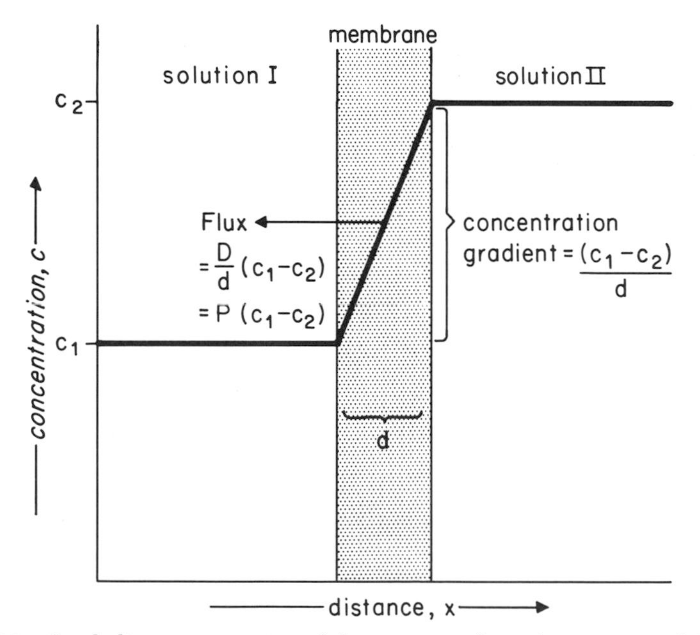

Figure 4–11. Symbolic representation of the concept of membrane permeability and of the terms employed in its mathematical formulation.

The permeability constant of K^+ ions in the cell membranes of amphibian skeletal muscle is about 10^{-6} cm/sec; that of Na^+ ions about 2×10^{-8} cm/sec. If the muscle fiber membrane were composed only of water, the permeability constant of K^+ ions would be no less than about 10 cm/sec. (Data from Woodbury, 1965.)

Diffusion constants and permeability constants depend critically on the temperature. Other conditions being equal, the constants D and P increase with increasing temperature. However, the relationships are complex, particularly because the temperature effects depend on the size of the diffusing molecules or ions. A formula that describes the temperature dependence of the diffusion constant D is the following:

$$D = \frac{R \cdot T}{N} \cdot \frac{1}{6\pi\eta r} \tag{25}$$

where N is Avogadro's number (6.023×10^{23}), R the gas constant (see p. 81), T the absolute temperature in °K, π the value 3.14, η the viscosity of the liquid, and r the radius of each diffusing molecule or ion. If T is known, the diameter (or radius) of the diffusing particles (molecules, ions) can be calculated. For a derivation and further discussion of the relationship, refer to the more advanced textbooks listed at the end of this chapter.

Permeability is not only expressed in terms of the permeability constant, but also directly as "permeability." Again, the dimension is cm/sec, but this is derived from the term $cm^3/cm^2/sec$, meaning cm^3 of liquid transferred per cm^2 of surface area of membrane per second per atmosphere pressure difference. This usage of "permeability" is almost exclusively employed to describe the permeability of living membranes to water. The dimensions are commonly adapted to the order of magnitude actually encountered, so that permeability to water is usually expressed in $\mu^3/\mu^2/sec$, or $\mu^3/\mu^2/hr$, or even as μ/day.

OSMOSIS

Practically no biological membrane is permeable to all solutes. The membranes are *selectively permeable* to certain solutes and *impermeable* to others. Ideal membranes that are permeable only to water (solvent) and impermeable to all solutes are called *semipermeable.* Although this term is useful for theoretical arguments, no biological, living membranes are strictly semipermeable. Many membranes, notably cell membranes, do, however, behave like semipermeable membranes if observed over a short time, because they are *relatively* much more permeable to water than to solutes (salts).

For the following discussion, the situations normally found in living systems are simplified by considering only water, to which membranes are permeable, and those solutes to which the same membranes are impermeable or almost impermeable. We are thus treating biological membranes as semipermeable membranes.

If a semipermeable membrane separates two volumes, or compartments, of water, one of which contains dissolved solute to which the membrane is impermeable, the concentration of solute on the one side of the membrane is higher than that on the other side. The concentration of water on the side of the membrane that does not contain indiffusible solute is higher than that on the other side. Differences in concentration lead to diffusion or net flux in the direction of the lower concentration. A net flux of water through a semipermeable membrane is called *osmosis*. We can define osmosis as net movement of water across a semipermeable membrane in the direction of the higher concentration of nonpermeating solute (or in the direction of the lower concentration of water).

If the two fluid compartments were contained within a cylinder and separated by a semipermeable membrane in the form of a sliding piston, and if

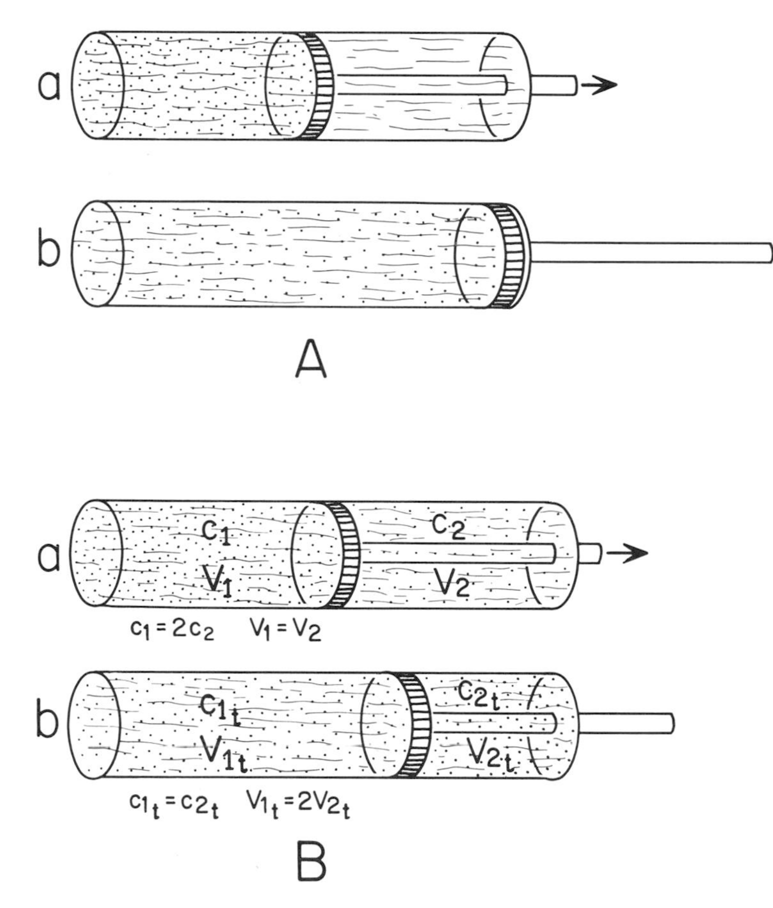

Figure 4–12. A, osmosis in a two-compartment system in which a semipermeable membrane (piston) separates an aqueous solution of nonpermeating solute from pure water. Osmosis ends as soon as there is no pure water left as the piston is displaced all the way to the right. **B**, osmosis in a two-compartment system in which a semipermeable membrane (piston) separates two solutions of nonpermeating solute. Initially the volumes of both compartments are equal but the concentration in compartment 1 (c_1) is twice that of compartment 2 (c_2). Osmosis ends as soon as c_2 becomes equal to c_1. At the same time the volume of compartment 1 (V_1) becomes equal to twice the volume of compartment 2 (V_2). The subscripts *t* indicate the concentrations (c) and volumes (V) when equilibrium is reached.

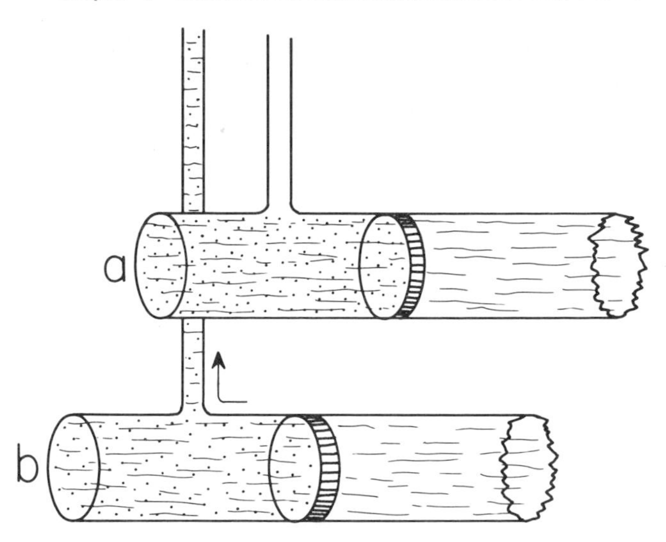

Figure 4–13. Osmosis in a two-compartment system in which a fixed semipermeable membrane separates pure water from a solution of a nonpermeating solute. The compartment containing the solute is provided with a vertical expansion tube. Water enters the solute-containing compartment until the hydrostatic pressure prevents further equalization of concentrations. When this happens the hydrostatic pressure is exactly equal to the osmotic pressure of the solution (provided the necessary corrections are made for the dilution).

only one compartment contained indiffusible solute, all the water would diffuse from the solute-free compartment into the solute-containing one, as indicated in Figure 4–12A. If both compartments contained solute, but each had a different concentration, the water would diffuse until the concentrations of solute (and of water) were equal on both sides of the membrane. If the volumes of both compartments were initially equal, they would then be inversely proportional to the original solute concentrations (or proportional to the initial concentrations of water) when equilibrium is reached (Fig. 4–12B). If the piston (the membrane) is fixed, the movement of water is prevented, provided the cylinder is closed at both ends, since water is practically incompressible and any entry of water would raise the pressure high enough to prevent any further passage of water. If the solute-containing compartment is provided with an outlet in the form of a vertical tube, osmosis can proceed and the solution can expand into the tube (Fig. 4–13). Provided the compartment containing pure water is large enough, water moves into the solute compartment until the hydrostatic pressure on the column of fluid in the vertical tube becomes so high that it prevents further entry of water. The rise of fluid in the tube indicates that considerable pressure has developed. This pressure is called *osmotic pressure* and can be measured by the height (multiplied by the specific gravity) of the fluid within the vertical tube when equilibrium is attained. Osmotic pressure can thus be expressed in terms of hydrostatic pressure, that is, in terms of the height of a column of water, or in terms of atmospheres of pressure, or in terms of the height of a column of mercury.

Osmotic pressure develops only if a semipermeable membrane separates

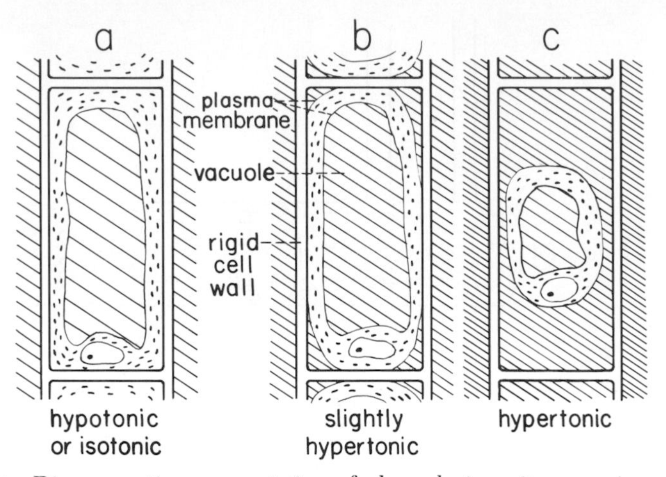

Figure 4–14. Diagrammatic representation of plasmolysis as it occurs in a root cell of *Zea mays* (corn plant). The density of cross-hatching is proportional to the osmotic concentration of the various fluid compartments involved. As water leaves the cell body (and the cell sap vacuole), the cell body (protoplast) withdraws from the rigid cell wall. (After Pfeffer, W.: Pflanzenphysiologie. Wilhelm Engelmann, Leipzig, 1897.)

two volumes of solvent (water) that contain different concentrations of non-permeating solute. The developing pressure is proportional to the difference in concentration and is maximal when the concentration of solute in one of the two compartments is zero.

We can consider the interior of animal cells as an aqueous solution of inorganic salts and of a number of organic compounds. Furthermore, we can, at least for the present purpose, consider the cell membranes as semipermeable. These membranes are somewhat elastic but not infinitely strong. An animal cell placed in pure water swells, and the developing osmotic pressure is great enough to disrupt the membrane and cause the cell to burst. On the other hand, if the cell is placed in an aqueous solution containing a higher concentration of solute than that inside the cell, osmosis in the direction of the outside results and the cell shrinks.

Plant cells, which have a solid cell wall (cellulose), show under such circumstances the phenomenon of *plasmolysis*: the mass of the cytoplasm, the protoplast, shrinks and withdraws from the cell wall (Fig. 4–14).

As is explained later, the developing osmotic pressure is solely a function of the number of nonpermeating particles per unit volume, regardless of their chemical composition. It is also without consequence if one side contains one kind of solute and the other side another.

To distinguish the concentration of any chemical from the concentration of osmotically active particles,* we use the term *osmotic concentration* to define the total number of nonpermeating particles per unit volume. The difference of osmotic concentrations on both sides of a semipermeable mem-

*For an explanation of this term see page 73.

brane is referred to as the *osmotic gradient*. Differences in concentration of any one chemical between the two compartments separated by a membrane are called *concentration gradients*. If the one compartment contains 10 moles of KCl and the other, 10 moles of NaCl per liter, and if both are separated by a semipermeable membrane, there would be large concentration gradients with regard to KCl and to NaCl, but there would be no osmotic gradient and no osmotic pressure would develop.

Solutions of equal osmotic concentration are called *isosmotic*. A solution that has a lower osmotic concentration than another solution is called *hypo-osmotic* (or *hyposmotic*), whereas the solution with the higher osmotic concentration is called *hyperosmotic*.

The condition of a solution of given osmotic concentration in relation to another solution is referred to as its osmoticity. Thus one can say: "whether a compartment osmotically gains or loses water depends on its osmoticity" and the condition of having a higher osmotic concentration may be defined as hyperosmoticity, and so forth.

The osmotic concentration of electrolyte solutions is always higher than that of equimolar solutions of nonelectrolytes due to the dissociation into ions. The osmotic pressure (or osmotic concentration) corresponds to the total number of solute particles, undissociated molecules as well as ions, but the relationship is complicated because, particularly at higher concentrations, ions interact by electrostatic attraction. The osmotic effects are therefore somewhat lesser than would be precicted on the basis of number of particles. The term osmotic concentration for this reason implies not more than that a given solution behaves as if it had a certain concentration of solute. To avoid this usage of a term that implies only a fictional concentration, the term *osmotic activity* has been introduced; it has the same general meaning as "osmotic concentration." Both terms have the dimension of moles/liter and can be defined as the molar concentration of an ideal nonelectrolyte solution having the same osmotic effects. For simple electrolyte solutions of known molar concentration, the ratio of osmotic concentration to true molar concentration is called the *osmotic activity coefficient*, and is usually assigned the symbol a. Thus, osmotic activity can be defined as $[C] \cdot a$, if C is the molar concentration of an electrolyte. It has become customary to refer to the term $[C] \cdot a$ as the *osmolarity* of the electrolyte solution.

As stated, the osmotic concentration, or osmotic activity, of any solution—electrolyte, nonelectrolyte, or mixed—can be equated with that of a solution of known molarity of an ideal nonelectrolyte. It has become customary to refer to this concentration as the *osmolarity* of a solution. By analogy, one uses the terms *osmole* or *milliosmole*, and *osmolar* and *milliosmolar*. An osmole is the amount of solute that, if dissolved in 1 liter of water, exerts the same osmotic pressure (or gives the same osmotic concentration) as 1 mole of an ideal nonelectrolyte dissolved in the same volume. One liter of a solution containing 1 osmole is said to be 1 osmolar. One thousandth of 1 osmole is equal to 1 milliosmole, and a 1 milliosmolar solution is equal to a 0.001 osmolar solution. Again it must be stressed that osmolarity does not refer to an actual concentration but describes the condition of a solution which behaves "as if" it had a certain concentration of solute particles. The term "osmotically active particles" or "concentration of osmotically active particles" refers to the quantity of nondissociated molecules plus the quantity of the ions of dissociated molecules. The relation between the number of osmotically active particles per unit volume of solution and the osmotic activity (or osmotic concentration) can be illustrated by the following example:

If a certain volume of solution contains 100 molecules of sucrose and 100 molecules of NaCl, the number of osmotically active particles will be: 100 particles (molecules) of sucrose plus 100 particles (ions) of Na^+ and 100 particles (ions) of Cl^-. Thus the total number of osmotically active particles of the solution is 300. But because of ionic interaction, the osmotic activity (or osmotic concentration) of the solution is not 300 particles but, perhaps, 284 particles in the given volume of solution. If the volume is such that the presence of 100 molecules would constitute a 1 molar solution, this particular solution would be 2 molar, and its osmotic activity 2.84 osmolar. The activity coefficient of the sucrose is zero; that of the NaCl, in this case, is 1.84 (or 184/100).

As stated, osmosis can be defined as net movement of water across a semipermeable membrane in the direction of the higher concentration of nonpermeating solute, or (what amounts to the same thing) in the direction of the lower concentration of water. If osmosis is allowed to proceed, it leads to the development of an actual hydrostatic pressure, the *osmotic pressure* (π, pronounced pi). Assuming that the open, outside compartment contains pure water, the osmotic pressure of a closed compartment containing nonpermeating solute can be defined as the pressure that is just sufficient to prevent osmotic influx of water. In this sense, an osmotic pressure can be assigned to any aqueous solution. This osmotic pressure is directly proportional to the osmotic activity of the solution. Its quantity, like that of other types of pressure, is conveniently expressed in terms of atmospheres or millimeters of mercury, 1 atm being equal to 760 mm Hg.

The osmotic pressure of a solution can be calculated by analogy with the gas laws. This was first recognized by the Dutch physicist van't Hoff after a botanist at the same University of Amsterdam, Hugo De Vries, had told him of his experiments with plasmolysis. These experiments were based on the earlier findings of the German plant physiologist Wilhelm Pfeffer, who had constructed the first accurate osmometers (see Fig. 4–16). Van't Hoff was particularly interested in Pfeffer's curious finding that the osmotic pressure of a given solution increased with each degree Centigrade by 1/273 the value measured at 0° C, and that the osmotic pressure of 1 molar nonelectrolyte solution was almost exactly 22.4 atm when measured at 0° C. As the following recapitulation of the behavior of gases shows, these figures suggest that the gas laws can be the basis for calculating osmotic pressure: One gram-molecule of mole of an ideal gas maintained at 0° C and 1 atm pressure occupies 22.4 liters of space. If this were compressed to 1 liter, its pressure would rise to 22.4 atm, since, according to the general gas laws, the product of gas pressure and gas volume are constant (provided the temperature remains the same). The state of an ideal gas is described by the equation

$$P \cdot V = n \cdot R \cdot T \qquad (26)$$

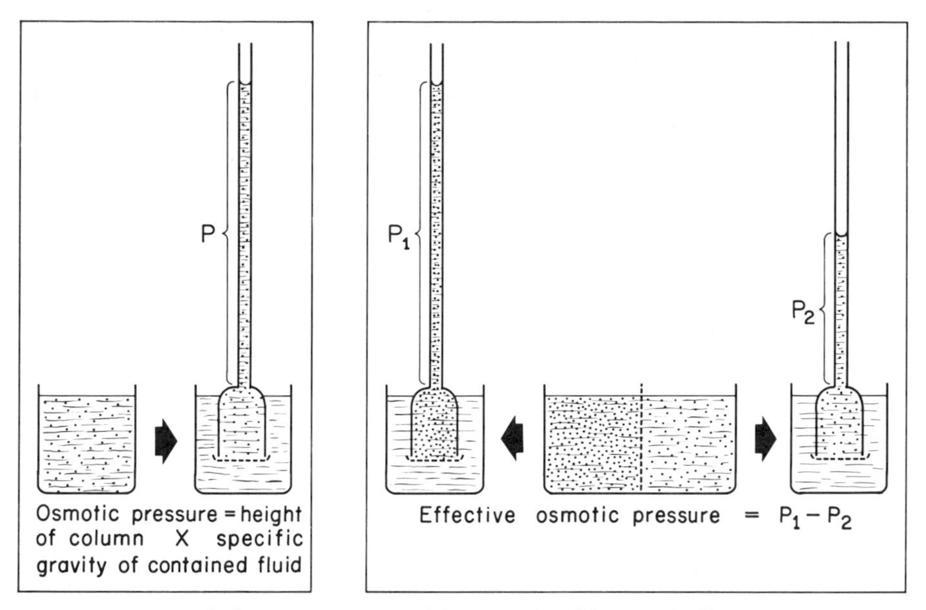

Figure 4–15. Symbolic representation of the meaning of the term "effective osmotic pressure." In an accurate experiment the volume of the vertical stem of the osmometers would have to be negligible in order to avoid significant dilution.

where P is the pressure in atmospheres, V the volume in liters, R the volume occupied by 1 mole of gas at 1° K, T the absolute temperature in °K, and n the number of moles of gas. The pressure can thus be given by the equation

$$P = \frac{n \cdot R \cdot T}{V} \qquad \text{or} \qquad P = R \cdot T \cdot \frac{n}{V} \tag{27}$$

R was found to be 0.082 liter at 1 atm pressure; thus at 0° C the volume of 1 mole of an ideal gas must be 0.082 · 273 = 22.4 liters, and with each degree this volume must increase by 1/273 · 22.4. Conversely, the pressure of 1 mole of an ideal gas must increase by 1/273 that measured at 0° C for each °C rise if the volume is maintained constant. Thus the pressure of a gas of constant volume can be calculated according to the equation:

$$P_t = P_0 \cdot \left(1 + \frac{1}{273}\,t\right) = P_0 \cdot (1 + 0.00367 \cdot t) \text{ atm} \tag{28}$$

where P_t is the pressure in atmospheres at the temperature t, P_0 is the pressure at 0° C, and t is the temperature in °C.

According to van't Hoff's new theory, these gas equations can be directly applied to solutions: the osmotic pressure of a solution is equal to the pressure of a gas which, at the given temperature, contains a number of molecules equal to that of the solute molecules in the same volume. In this form the theory applies only to nonelectrolytes. The modification which permits its applicability to nonelectrolyte solutions was introduced by the Swedish physicist Arrhenius, who was prompted by the discovery of the abnormal osmotic behavior of electrolyte solutions to formulate his revolutionary theory of electrolytic dissociation. This theory states that electrolytes dissociate into ions as soon as they dissolve in water. (Previously it was assumed that dissociation occurs only under the influence of strong electric current in electrolysis, hence the descriptive name "electrolytic dissociation.")

Van't Hoff had already introduced a coefficient i (van't Hoff's factor) to define the ratio between the actually observed osmotic pressure and that calculated according to the gas laws. Subsequently, Arrhenius' theory explained this factor rationally: van't Hoff's coefficient i can be calculated according to

$$i = \frac{m + k \cdot n}{m + n} \quad (29)$$

where m is the number of undissociated molecules, n is the number of dissociated molecules, and k is the number of ions into which every dissociating molecule splits.

Obviously, if all molecules are dissociated, i must be equal to k, so that if we are dealing with molecules of NaCl (for example), i should be equal to 2. This is indeed approximately true, but—as was mentioned in different words—at finite concentrations, particularly higher than 0.01 molar, i is always smaller than k, not because the electrolyte is not completely dissociated, but because the ions interact in such a way that the concentration appears to be lower than it actually is. The coefficient i was identified by Arrhenius with the degree of dissociation to which he assigned the symbol α (pronounced alpha), which, with a slight change in meaning, has become the modern activity coefficient a (see p. 73).

The van't Hoff-Arrhenius theory of osmotic pressure states that the equation $P = R \cdot T \cdot \frac{n}{V}$ derived from the behavior of gases adequately describes the osmotic pressure of a solution if P is the osmotic pressure (in atm), R the gas constant, T the absolute temperature, and n/V the concentration of solute in moles/liter multiplied by α (or in a more modern version, multiplied by a). It has become customary to assign the symbol π (pronounced pi) to the osmotic pressure so that the equation for osmotic pressure is written

$$\pi = R \cdot T \cdot (C \cdot a) \text{ atm} \quad (30)$$

where C stands for moles/liter.

Equation 30 is valid only when one assumes that the solution is brought in contact with pure water through a semipermeable membrane. If not pure water, but a solution of different concentration is present in the other compartment, the equation becomes

$$\pi = R \cdot T \cdot [(C_1 \cdot a) - (C_2 \cdot a)] \text{ atm} \quad (31)$$

where C_1 and C_2 are the molar concentrations of the solutions in compartments I and II (see Figs. 4–12 and 4–15) and the respective a represents the osmotic activity coefficients applicable to each solution. In the case of complex solutions involving several electrolytes and nonelectrolytes, Equations 30 and 31 become impractical, and it is better to replace the term $(C \cdot a)$ by the simple expression C, which then means solute concentration in osmoles/liter. The general equations for osmotic pressure then become

$$\pi = R \cdot T \cdot C \quad \text{and} \quad \pi = R \cdot T \cdot (C_1 - C_2) \quad (32)\ (33)$$

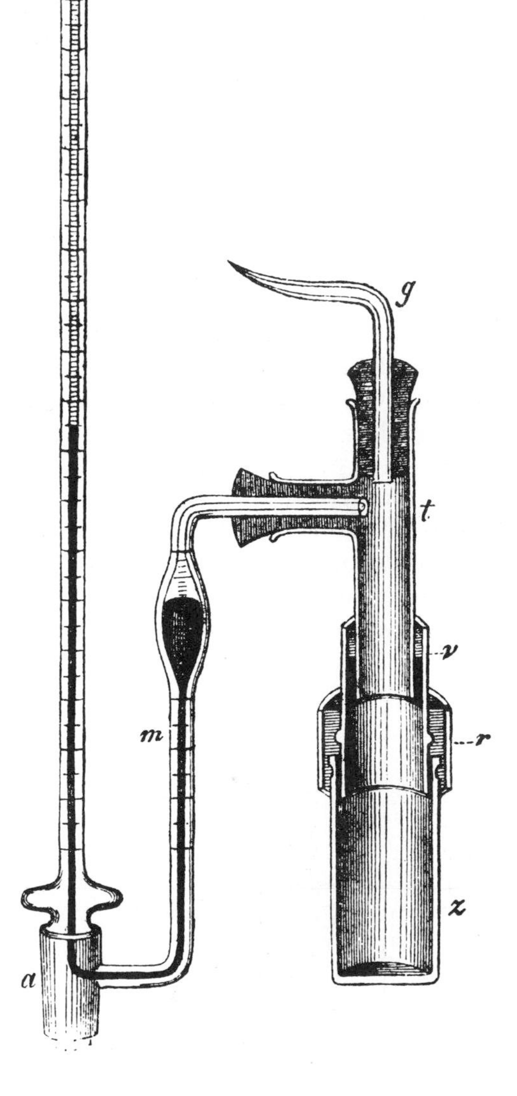

Figure 4–16. The original osmometer used by Wilhelm Pfeffer in his classic determinations of osmotic pressure. Such an osmometer was strong enough to withstand pressure differences of several atmospheres. For the actual experiment the whole apparatus was submerged in water of constant temperature. The manometer (*m*) was filled with mercury. The clay cell (*z*) with its internal precipitation membrane was filled with the solution whose osmotic pressure was to be determined. It was attached to the glass pieces *v* and *t* by means of a sealing ring, *r*. *a*, stopcock; *g*, glass tube that has been sealed as soon as air-free filling was achieved. "The manufacturing of suitable cells succeeds with great certainty if the indicated precautions are supplemented with exercise." (From Pfeffer, W.: Osmotische Untersuchungen. W. Engelmann, Leipzig, 1877.)

Several properties of a solution depend on the osmotic activity rather than the molar concentration of the solute. Thus the vapor pressure, boiling point, as well as freezing and melting points of a solution differ from those of the pure solvent by amounts that are proportional to the osmotic concentration or osmotic activity.

Without going into historical details, it can be stated that a 1 molar (or osmolar) aqueous solution has a freezing point of −1.86° C; thus the presence of 1 mole (or osmole) of solute lowers the freezing point of the solvent water by −1.86° C. This lowering of the freezing point of water is usually referred to as ΔF (pronounced delta eff), or simply as Δ. The freezing point can be measured readily, in fact this is much easier than the direct measurement of osmotic pressures or of osmotic concentrations. Thus the freezing point of a solution is often given as a measure of, or instead of, the osmotic pressure (or osmotic concentration). Like the osmotic pressure, the freezing point depends on the osmotic activity of the solution; thus the freezing point is often given as a measure of, or instead of, the osmotic pressure (or osmotic concentration). The relation between the two magnitudes is given by the equation

$$\frac{\Delta x}{1.86} = \frac{\pi}{22.4} \text{ atm, or } \pi = \frac{\Delta x}{1.86} \cdot 22.4 \text{ atm} \qquad (34)$$

where Δx is the measured freezing point (in °C) of the unknown solution and π the osmotic pressure of the solution expressed in atm.

The freezing point is measured with a kryoscope (Fig. 4–17). It is accurate to 0.001° C, so that differences in osmotic "pressure" of 0.012 atm (or 9.2 mm Hg) can be detected. In case of simple electrolyte solutions of known molarity, the freezing point depression can be used to determine with close approximation the osmotic activity coefficient, here called the *kryoscopic coefficient* (G). It can be defined as the ratio between measured freezing point and that calculated according to Equation 34 from the molarity of the solution. It can also be defined as that factor by which the freezing point calculated from the molarity has to be multiplied in order to give the actually measured freezing point.

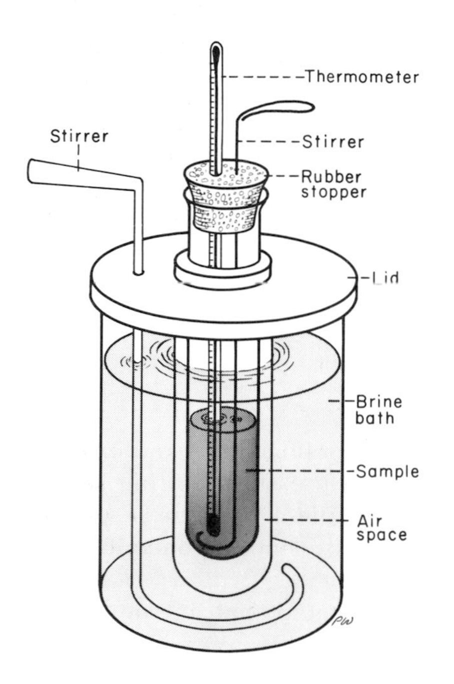

Figure 4–17. Apparatus used for the determination of the freezing point of solutions.

Table 4–7. The Kryoscopic Coefficient (G) at Various Molal Concentrations of Several Salts

	0.02	0.04	0.05	0.1	0.2	0.4	0.5	0.7
NaCl	1.921	1.900	–	1.872	1.843	1.819	–	1.808
KCl	1.919	–	1.885	1.857	1.827	–	1.784	–
$MgCl_2$	2.708	–	2.677	2.658	2.679	–	2.896	–
$CaCl_2$	2.673 (at 0.025 m)		2.630	2.601	2.573	–	2.680	–

From a more complete table in Heilbrunn, L. V.: An Outline of General Physiology, 3rd Ed. W. B. Saunders Co., Philadelphia, 1952.

The kryoscopic coefficients of several concentrations of a few electrolytes are given in Table 4–7.

The term "osmotic pressure" when applied to solutions has been much criticized on the basis that it is misleading and perhaps even indicative of a misconception of osmosis; after all, a solution by itself does not develop this osmotic pressure, and even if it is placed inside an osmometer, the very osmotic pressure that develops effectively prevents osmosis from continuing beyond the first entry of water that sets up the pressure (ideal osmometers permit only minimal expansion of the inner fluid volume). But even though they do not usually exhibit such pressures, solutions certainly behave in many respects as if they were under pressure: the freezing point of water that contains solute is almost exactly identical with the freezing point of water under a pressure equal to that calculated as the osmotic pressure of the solution. The boiling point of a solution likewise is identical to that of water under a pressure that is equal to that calculated as the osmotic pressure of the solution. And when a semipermeable membrane separates two solutions of different osmotic pressures, the resulting osmotic net flux of water is almost exactly the same as that resulting from a difference of hydrostatic pressures in the two compartments that is numerically equal to the difference in osmotic pressures. In this sense the term osmotic pressure has a real meaning and practical significance.

To some physiologists the terms isotonic, hypotonic, and hypertonic are synonymous with iso-osmotic, hyposmotic, and hyperosmotic. This is not correct. In contrast to osmolarity, *tonicity* is not amenable to exact physiochemical description. The latter term is properly employed when the osmotic relations between cells, tissues, or organisms on the one hand, and their aqueous environment on the other, are discussed. An aqueous solution is *isotonic* with the internal medium of an organism or a cell if the latter neither shrinks nor swells. If the cell (or organism) loses water to the medium owing to osmosis, the external medium is *hypotonic*. If the cell (or organism) swells owing to osmotic influx of water, the external medium is *hypertonic*.

As explained in later chapters, the aqueous media separated by cell or cellular membranes are in complex equilibrium where osmotic gradients balance electrochemical gradients. Therefore, an external medium can be isotonic even if it is not isosmotic with the internal medium of the cell or of the organism. In fact, this situation is the rule rather than the exception.

Osmotic Permeability to Water

The osmotic behavior of the living system depends not only on the permeability of the membranes to solute molecules and ions, but also on the permeability of the membranes to water. In fact, the latter property is of greatest significance for any understanding of osmoregulation, as will be discussed in Chapter 5. Obviously, the lower the permeability to water, the less energy must be expended per unit time to counteract the osmotic influx, or efflux, of water. Students of osmotic behavior of cells and organisms are, therefore, much concerned with the measurement of "water permeability."

The permeability to water is expressed as the volume of water (usually given in μ^3) that crosses a unit of area of a given membrane (usually given in μ^2) per unit time (usually 1 minute) under a pressure difference of 1 atm. Pressure difference means a difference in osmotic pressure (osmotic concentration).

The units of μ^3/μ^2/min/atm can be reduced to μ/min/atm, which is commonly referred to as *osmotic permeability coefficient*. This is not to be confused with the permeability constant P, as discussed on page 68. An alternative term is *unit of osmotic water permeability*.

The osmotic permeability coefficient can be measured in various ways—all involve placing the membrane-enclosed compartment (cell, organism) into a hypo- or hypertonic medium and measuring the rate of water entry or water loss. This can be done by weighing, observing the diameter (in the case of spherical cells), or measuring optical density, diffraction, or refraction of light.

For a more detailed discussion of the problem, refer to the review article by Dick (1959).

Osmotic Work

Osmosis depends on the difference in the "energy contents" of the two fluid compartments that are in contact with the semipermeable membrane. Osmosis, in fact, represents a transfer of energy from one compartment to the other, and the total two-compartment system can be said *to do work*. This can be calculated in the manner one calculates the work done by an expanding gas: according to the general gas laws, the volume of 1 mole of an ideal gas, V, is equal to $R \cdot T/P$. If the gas is allowed to expand, the pressure P diminishes to $P - dP$, and the energy content diminishes by an amount proportional to $V \cdot dP$. The work W done by the gas, therefore, is equal to $(R \cdot T/P) \cdot dP$, or $R \cdot T\ (dP/P)$, or $R \cdot T \cdot \ln \frac{P_1}{P_2}$, where P_1 and P_2 are the respective pressures before and after the expansion. If we substitute osmotic concentration (C) for pressure (P), osmotic work can be expressed as

$$\text{Work} = R \cdot T \cdot \ln \frac{C_1}{C_2} \qquad (35)$$

where C_1 is the osmolar concentration before osmosis, and C_2 the osmolar concentration at the completion of osmosis. C_2 is equal to the osmolar concentration of the "other" compartment at the beginning of osmosis. Note that

Table 4–8. Equivalent Values of the Gas Constant R in Energy Units per Degree (° C) per Mole

Mechanical	*Electrical*	*Thermal*	*Volumetric*
$8.314 \cdot 10^7$ ergs	8.314 joules	1.9864 cal	0.082 l-atm

the equation describes the work done when the compartment of concentration C_1 contains 1 osmole of solute. If the solute content is larger or smaller, the right side of the equation must be multiplied by *n* (the number of osmoles present):

$$\text{Work} = \text{R} \cdot \text{T} \cdot n \cdot \ln \frac{C_1}{C_2} \tag{36}$$

Energy can be transformed from one kind into another. The gas constant R has the dimension of energy, thus it has several equivalent numerical values, depending on whether we consider its thermal, mechanical, or electrical aspect. The four values of the gas constant are listed in Table 4–8.

In computations of osmotic work (see Chap. 5), it is customary to use the thermal equivalent of R and to express work in calories:

$$\text{Work} = 1.986 \cdot \text{T} \cdot n \cdot \ln \frac{C_1}{C_2} \text{ cal} \tag{37}$$

It is often more convenient to use the logarithm to the base of 10 (log) instead of the natural logarithm (ln). It is simple to convert ln to log: multiply by 2.3 so that Equation 37 can be written

$$\text{Work} = 2.3 \cdot 1.986 \cdot \text{T} \cdot n \cdot \log \frac{C_1}{C_2} \text{ cal} \tag{38}$$

The term "osmotic work" is also used to refer to the transport of solute across a water-permeable membrane, particularly when this is *active transport* (see Chap. 27), that is, transport by forces other than those responsible for diffusion. If solute is carried from a compartment with low solute concentration to a compartment with high solute concentration, energy is transferred from the former to the latter compartment and its amount is equal to the osmotic work which the newly established system can do in addition to that which it could have done before the solute transport occurred. In this sense the term osmotic work can be applied to solute transport across membranes (see Chaps. 5 and 16). The equations described in the preceding sections apply; thus the work required to transport 1 osmole of a solute from a concentration C_1 to a concentration C_2 can be calculated according to

$$\text{Work} = \text{R} \cdot \text{T} \cdot n \frac{C_1}{C_2} \tag{39}$$

It is often of interest to compute the power requirement of osmotic work. Power is work/time. The power of osmotic work is thus given in terms of work/

hour or work/minute, and in cal/hr or cal/min. Obviously, the power of osmotic work depends on the osmotic permeability coefficient. This is explained further in Chapter 5.

Electro-osmosis

Membranes can be either homogeneous, in which case the water or solute transport involves temporary solution of the moving water and solute in the membrane, or they can be porous, in which case transport is likely to occur through the pores.

So far we have considered the semi- (or selectively) permeable membrane as a purely mechanical device. With most living membranes, however, the situation is complicated by the fact that they are electrically charged and that in addition an electric potential exists across these membranes.

Situations in which the membranes of osmotic systems are electrically neutral are not too common. Living membranes are almost always electrically charged. With regard to nonelectrolytes, it makes little difference whether or not the membrane separating them from a compartment with a different concentration is charged. The difference, however, is striking when ions are involved.

In general, one assumes that negatively charged homogeneous membranes prevent passage of anions but accelerate the passage of cations, whereas positively charged membranes prevent transport of cations but accelerate passage of anions. Such membranes produce a flow of water which opposes that predicted from a knowledge of osmotic concentrations separated by them. The following example illustrates this:

Let us assume that the membrane is initially negatively charged and that it separates a 0.1 M NaCl solution from a 0.01 M NaCl solution. The membrane permits Na^+ ions to move into the dilute NaCl solution, but the Cl^- ions which must remain behind prevent anything more than the initial crossing of Na^+ ions. Therefore, the membrane acquires a double charge: on the side of compartment I it remains negatively charged, on the side of compartment II it becomes positively charged. In effect, the membrane behaves like a negatively charged body in an electric field. If it could move freely, it should move in the direction of the positive charge through the aqueous medium. Since it cannot move, water passes through it in the opposite direction. This water movement is enhanced by the normal tendency to establish equal concentrations of solute on both sides of the membrane. Thus an osmotic pressure is generated which is much larger than that predictable from the difference in concentration of NaCl in the two compartments (Loeb, 1920).

In general, it is assumed that most living membranes have pores through which water and ions can move, and it must be concluded from many lines of evidence that these pores are charged. Again it is thought that negatively charged pores facilitate passage of cations but prevent passage of anions and vice versa. Whenever such membranes are differentially charged, current flows through the pores and the body (or over the surface) of the membrane. If, as is generally the case, the outer surface of cell membranes is positively charged,

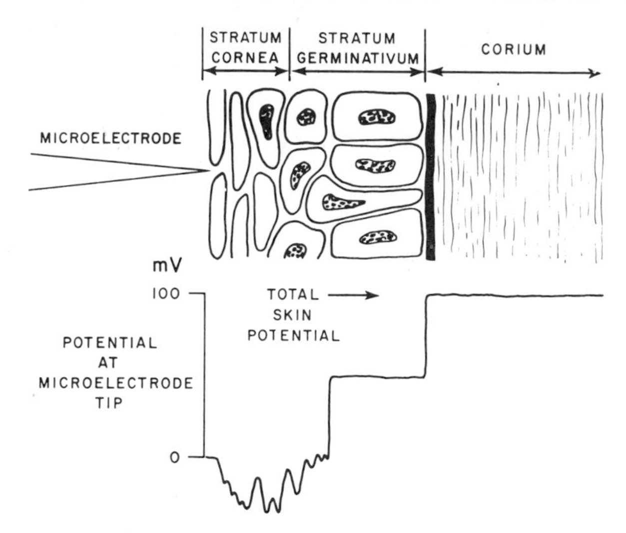

Figure 4–18. Diagrammatic representation of a histological cross section through the skin of a frog (*Rana pipiens*) and a microelectrode. The diagram also shows the potential recorded at the electrode tip as the microelectrode is slowly pushed through the skin. A positive potential of about 50 mV is recorded as the electrode penetrates one of the large epithelial cells of the *stratum germinativum.* The positivity suddenly increases as the electrode emerges at the other side of the cell. The potential remains constant from there on. The epithelial cells of the stratum germinativum must therefore be assumed to be responsible for the total "skin potential." An ionic model for this is shown in Figure 4–19. (From Hoshiko, T.: Electrogenesis in frog skin. *In* Biophysics of Physiological and Pharmacological Actions. A. M. Shanes, ed. Amer. Assn. Adv. Sci., Washington, D.C., 1961.)

and the inner surface negatively charged, and if the pores have positive charges, the membrane transports water into the cell. Such transport would occur even if the osmotic concentrations of the intra- and extracellular media are equal.

Cellular membranes, such as skin, are likewise electrically charged. A good part of the electric potential difference of the two sides of the skin of frogs, for instance, is due to an *active transport* of sodium ions into the animal (Figs. 4–18 and 4–19); at the same time water is transported outward. Active transport will be discussed in more detail in Chapter 27.

In summary, electro-osmosis consists in the movement of water across a charged membrane. This movement is independent of, and therefore increases or decreases, the water movement (osmosis) due to differences in osmotic concentrations.

The importance of electro-osmosis cannot be overemphasized, particularly since it is almost neglected and is usually never considered in the discussions of experiments on water and mineral balance, or on osmotic and ionic regulation. The theories of electro-osmosis have become very complex since the introduction of *irreversible thermodynamics* (De Groot, 1951). The classic theory, based on the equations for laminar flow in charged capillary tubes (Beutner, 1944; Schloegl, 1955), is not directly applicable to water flow through the narrow pores (pore channels) of cell membranes. The interested reader is referred to the paper of Dainty, Croghan, and Fensom (1963) for an introduction to the modern literature.

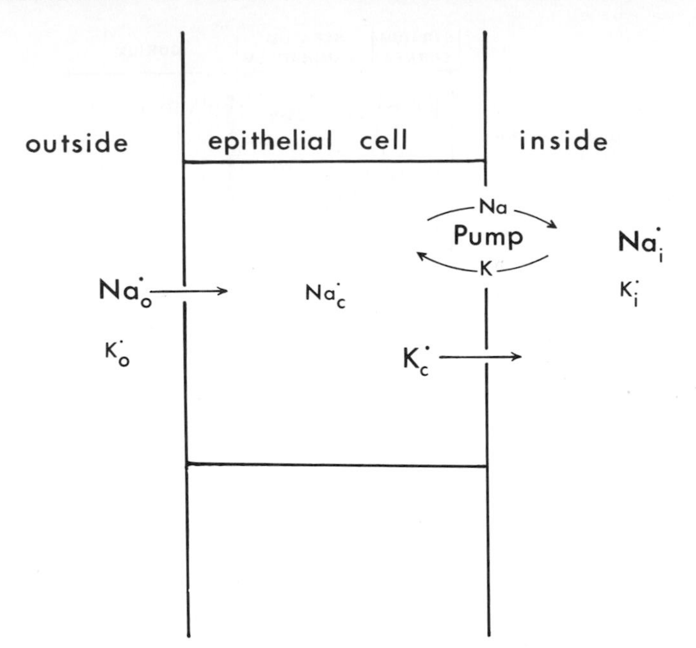

Figure 4–19. Frog skin model of Koefoed-Johnsen and Ussing. The diagram represents one of the basal epithelial cells of the stratum germinativum (see Figure 4–18). The cell membrane in contact with the outside medium (external to the animal) is presumed to be selectively permeable to Na^+, whereas the membrane in contact with the internal medium (body fluids) of the animal is selectively permeable to K^+. Large and small letters for Na and K symbolize large and small concentrations. An active transport mechanism (Na-K exchange pump) is assumed to be present in the membrane facing "inward"; Na^+ then is assumed to follow the concentration gradient into the epithelial cell and to be pumped into the interior of the animal by transport mechanism in the cell membrane facing the corium. The equations describing the Na^+ movement are given in Chapter 27 and p. 384. (After Hoshiko, T.: Electrogenesis in frog skin. *In* Biophysics of Physiological and Pharmacological Actions. A. M. Shanes, ed. Amer. Assn. Adv. Sci., Washington, D.C., 1961, pp. 31–47.)

The Gibbs-Donnan Equilibrium

We have seen that the presence of particles to which a membrane is impermeable causes movement (osmosis) of all those particles (solvent and solute) to which the membrane is permeable and that this movement continues until the osmotic concentrations are equal on both sides of the membrane. No reference was made to the composition of the solution in each compartment, and no particular attention was given to the fact that although the osmotic concentrations on both sides may be equal, the concentrations of the individual species of particles may not be. However, precisely this situation, namely, the presence, at equilibrium conditions, of unequal concentrations of ionic species on the two sides of biological membranes (e.g., cell membranes), gives rise to the often spectacular phenomena of bioelectricity, which are the bases of nerve impulses and the cause of muscular contraction.

The situation was first treated formally by the Irish physicochemist F. G.

Donnan in 1911, and the name Donnan appears in the terms "Donnan equilibrium," "Donnan ratio," and "Donnan potential," which appear frequently in the subsequent discussions.

The following arguments are based on the assumption that cells contain a homogeneous aqueous medium which is separated from an extracellular aqueous solution of inorganic ions by a selectively permeable membrane (the "cell membrane"), which is permeable only to certain ions and water. There are obvious faults in this assumption. The extracellular fluids are never protein-free, and the intracellular medium is not homogeneous, but has areas of different density, and it contains the cell nucleus, many inclusion bodies, and many membranous structures, such as those of the endoplasmic reticulum. Still, the assumption accounts for many of the fundamental electrical properties.

The pH of the intracellular aqueous medium usually is slightly below 7.0, but still higher than the average isoelectric point of the cell proteins (pH 5). The cell proteins consequently are negatively charged. Although the cell membrane is permeable to certain inorganic ions, it is not permeable to proteins. The presence of such nondiffusible negatively charged particles within cells gives rise to a peculiar distribution of the diffusible ions. This is best illustrated with a model:

Assume that the charged particles involved in the system under discussion are protein (P^-), sodium (Na^+), and chloride (Cl^-) ions only. Assume further that P^- is present only within the cell, whereas Na^+ and Cl^- are present within and without the cell, and that the cell membrane is impermeable to P^- but permeable to Na^+ and Cl^-.

As soon as the system is established, the diffusible ions Na^+ and Cl^- cross the membrane in both directions. These ions obviously tend to follow their concentration gradients: we can expect that if the Na^+ concentration is higher inside the cell than outside, Na^+ will show a net movement toward the outside. And we can expect Cl^- likewise to behave in this manner. A brief analysis reveals, however, that the situation is not this simple.

Oppositely charged ions attract each other; similarly charged ions repel each other. The tendency to establish equal concentrations of ionic species in the two media (the intra- and extracellular fluid) thus must compete with the tendency to establish electrical neutrality.

The intracellular fluid is electrically neutral if $[Na^+]_i = [P^-]_i + [Cl^-]_i$, whereas the extracellular fluid is electrically neutral if $[Na^+]_o = [Cl^-]_o$. It is immediately obvious that the intracellular concentration of Na^+ is greater than that of Cl^-, whereas the extracellular concentrations of Na^+ and Cl^- are equal.

In order for a diffusion equilibrium to be reached, the diffusible ions must finally be present in a stable distribution in such a way that there is no further net movement of ions across the semipermeable membrane. This is achieved when the energies of both compartments become equal. Once this is the case, equal amounts of work are required to transport a certain (small) amount of Na^+ across the membrane in one direction and an equal amount of Cl^- across the membrane in the opposite direction.

The work required to transport δn moles of Na^+ across the membrane from compartment i with a concentration $[Na^+]_i$ to compartment o with a concentration of $[Na^+]_o$ is equal to

$$\delta n \cdot R \cdot T \cdot \ln \frac{[Na^+]_i}{[Na^+]_o} \tag{40}$$

The work required to transport δn moles of Cl^- across the membrane from compartment o with a concentration of $[Cl^-]_o$ to compartment i with a concentration $[Cl^-]_i$ is given by the equation $\delta n \cdot R \cdot T \cdot \ln \frac{[Cl^-]_o}{[Cl^-]_i}$.

At equilibrium conditions

$$\delta n \cdot R \cdot T \cdot \ln \frac{[Na^+]_i}{[Na^+]_o} = \delta n \cdot R \cdot T \cdot \ln \frac{[Cl^-]_o}{[Cl^-]_i} \tag{41}$$

Dividing the equation by n · R · T and not taking logarithms, the equation becomes

$$[Na^+]_i \cdot [Cl^-]_i = [Na^+]_o \cdot [Cl^-]_o \tag{42}$$

Some persons refer to this equation as the *Donnan rule*.

Caution: The present discussion of the Donnan equilibrium is based on the assumption that all NaCl present in the system is completely dissociated into Na^+ and Cl^- ions. This conflicts with the apparent dissociation calculated from determinations of osmotic activities of the NaCl solutions. The contradiction is, however, not real: the kryoscopic, or activity, coefficient of the NaCl solutions is not lower than 2.0 because of incomplete dissociation of the NaCl but because the electrostatic attraction of the oppositely charged ions restricts their free movement. Even in more concentrated solutions, NaCl can be considered as completely dissociated. The experimental verification of the Donnan equilibrium confirms this.

Now, according to the so-called Donnan rule, $[Na^+]_i \times [Cl^-]_i = [Na^+]_o \times [Cl^-]_o$ under equilibrium conditions. Since $[Na^+]_o = [Cl^-]_o$, we can write:

$$[Na^+]_i \times [Cl^-]_i = [Na^+]_o^2 \tag{43}$$

and

$$[Na^+]_i = \frac{[Na^+]_o}{[Cl^-]_i} \times [Na^+]_o \tag{44}$$

or

$$[Cl^-]_i = \frac{[Na^+]_o}{[Na^-]_i} \times [Na^+]_o \tag{45}$$

and

$$[Cl^-]_i \times [Na^+]_i = [Cl^-]_o^2 \text{ or } [Cl^-]_i = \frac{[Cl^-]_o}{[Na^+]_i} \tag{46}$$

Because $[Cl^-]_i$ is lower than $[Na^+]_o$, it follows, according to Equation 44, that $[Na^+]_i$ must be greater than $[Na]_o$. Since $[Na]_i = [P^-] + [Cl^-]_i$, the total amount of solute in the cell ($[Na^+]_i + [P^-] + [Cl^-]_i$) can be expressed as $[Na^+]_i + [Na^+]_i$, or $2[Na^+]_i$.

The total amount of solute in the outside compartment is equal to $[Na^+]_o$ + $[Cl^-]_o$ or $[Na^+]_o$ + $[Na^+]_o$ (because $[Na^+]_o = [Cl^-]_o$). Since $[Na^+]_i$ is greater than $[Na^+]_o$, it follows that the total solute concentration at equilibrium conditions is greater inside the cell than outside. This is known as *Donnan equilibrium.*

The significance of the Donnan equilibrium lies, however, not only in the fact that it represents an osmotic imbalance but in the peculiar distribution of the diffusible charges. Thus, in spite of electric neutrality *within* each of the two fluid compartments, there results a difference in the concentration of *diffusible* positive charges in the two compartments and a difference of the concentration of *diffusible* negative charges. Differences in the concentration of electric charges represent a difference in electric potential and establish an *electromotive force* (EMF). Since the concentration differences of the oppositely charged species of ions have opposing gradients ($[Na^+]_i > [Na^+]_o$; $[Cl^-]_i < [Cl^-]_o$), the resulting potential differences are parallel.

The ratios of the inside and outside concentrations of the diffusible ions are called *Donnan ratios.* The electric potential that corresponds to each Donnan ratio is called a *Donnan potential.*

A system is in equilibrium if within the system there are no energy differences. In a Donnan equilibrium there *are* differences between the two compartments if only concentration energy, or if only electric energy, is considered. However, since the two differences go in opposite directions, they balance each other, and the total energies of each compartment are equal. Concentration difference and electric potential difference oppose each other in such a way that the concentration difference prevents equalization of potential.

In living cells the situation is, of course, much more complicated. Many more ions than just Na^+ and Cl^- are involved. Still, the principle established by the Donnan theory holds, and we will make good use of it in the discussion of membrane potentials in Chapter 16 (Bioelectricity).

REFERENCES

Arrhenius, S. (1887) Über die Dissociation der in Wasser geloesten Stoffe. Z. physik. Chem. *1*:631–648.

Bell, R. P. (1958) The hydration of ions in solution. Endeavour *17*:31–35.

Beutner, R. (1944) Bioelectricity. *In* Medical Physics. (O. Glasser, ed.) Year Book Publishers, Chicago.

Bockris, J. O'M. (1949) Ionic solvation. Quart. Rev. Chem. Soc. Lond. *3*:173–180.

Bredig, G. (1899) Über Amphotere Elektrolyte und innere Salze. Z. Elektrochem. *6*:33–36.

Dainty, J., P. C. Croghan, and D. S. Fensom (1963) Electro-osmosis, with some applications to plant physiology. Can. J. Botany *41*:953–966.

de Coppet, M. (1871–1872a) Recherches sur la temperature de congelation des dissolutions salines. I. Historique. Ann. Chim. Phys., ser. 4, *23*:366–405.

de Coppet, M. (1871–1872b) Recherches sur la temperature de congelation des dissolutions salines. VII. Constitution chimique de quelques dissolutions salines, d'après les expériences sur leur congelation et leur maximum de densité. Ann. Chim. Phys., ser. 4, *25*:502–553.

de Coppet, M. (1871–1872c) Recherches sur la temperature de congelation des dissolutions salines. VIII. Abaissement du point de congelation de dissolutions contenant un mélange de deux sels. Ann. Chim. Phys., ser. 4, *26*:98–121.

De Groot, S. R. (1951) Thermodynamics of irreversible processes. Nord Hollandsche, Amsterdam.

De Vries, H. (1884) Eine Methode zur Analyse der Turgorkraft. Jahrb. wiss. Bot. *14*:427–601.

Dick, D. A. T. (1959) Osmotic properties of living cells. Int. Rev. Cytol. *8*:388–448.

Donnan, F. G. (1911) Theorie der Membrangleichgewichte und Membranpotentiale bei Vorhandensein von nicht dialysierenden Elektrolyten. Ein Beitrag zur Physikalisch-Chemischen Physiologie. Z. Elektrochem. *17*:573–581.

Dutrochet, R. J. (1837) De l'Endosmose. Memoires pour servir à l'histoire anat. et physiol. des Végéteaux et des Animaux (Bruxelles) *1*:1–99.

Edsall, J. T., and J. Wyman (1958) Biophysical Chemistry, Vol. I. Thermodynamics, Electrostatics, and the Biological Significance of the Properties of Matter. Academic Press, New York.

Frank, P. (1957) Philosophy of Science. Prentice-Hall, Englewood Cliffs, N. J.

Glasstone, S. (1946) The Elements of Physical Chemistry. D. Van Nostrand Co., New York.

Hardy, W. B. (1905) Colloidal solutions. The globulins. J. Physiol. *33*:251–336.

Harris, E. J. (1960) Transport and Accumulation in Biological Systems. Academic Press, New York; Butterworths Scientific Publications, London.

Heisenberg, W. (1953) Nuclear Physics. Methuen & Co., London.

Hoeber, R., et al. (1945) Physical Chemistry of Cells and Tissues. McGraw-Hill Book Co. (Blakiston Div.), New York.

Kortüm, G., and J. O'M. Bockris (1951) Textbook of Electrochemistry. Elsevier Publishing Company, New York.

Kruyt, H. R., and J. T. G. Overbeek (1962) An Introduction to Physical Chemistry. Holt, Rinehart and Winston, New York.

Loeb, J. (1920) Electrification of water and osmotic pressure. J. Gen. Physiol. *2*:87–106.

Michaelis, L. (1922) Die Wasserstoffionen-Konzentration, 2nd Ed. J. Springer, Berlin.

Michaelis, L., and H. Davidsohn (1910) The theory of the isoelectric point. Biochem. Z. *30*:143–150.

Murphy, Q. R. (1957) Metabolic Aspects of Transport across Cell Membranes. University of Wisconsin Press, Madison.

Nageli, C., and K. Cramer (1855) Primordialschlauch und Diosmose (Endosmose und Exosmose) der Pflanzenzelle. Pflanzenphysiol. Unters. *1*:21.

Peierls, R. E. (1956) The Laws of Nature. Charles Scribner's Sons, New York.

Pfeffer, W. (1877 or 1921) Osmotische Untersuchungen. W. Engelmann, Leipzig.

Schloegl, R. (1955) Zur Theorie der anomalen Osmose. Z. phys. Chem. *3*:73–102.

Shanes, S. M., ed. (1955) Electrolytes in Biological Systems. The Ronald Press Co., New York.

Sørensen, S. P. L. (1909) Enzymstudien. II. Mitteilung. Über die Messung und die Bedeutung der Wasserstoffionenkonzentration bei enzymatischen Prozessen. Biochem. Z. *21*:131–304.

Sørensen, S. P. L. (1912) Über die Messung und die Bedeutung der Wasserstoffionenkonzentration bei biologischen Prozessen. Ergebn. Physiol. *12*:393–532.

Sørensen, S. P. L., K. Linderstrøm-Lang, and E. Lund (1927) The influence of salts upon the ionization of egg albumin. J. Gen. Physiol. *8*:543–600.

van't Hoff, J. H. (1886) Une propriété générale de la matériere diluée. Sv. Vet. Ak-s Handlinger *21*:43.

van't Hoff, J. H. (1887) Die Rolle des osmotischen Druckes in der Analogie zwischen Losungen und Gasen. Z. physik. Chem. *1*:481–508.

van't Hoff, J. H. (1894) Wie die Theorie der Lösungen entstand. Ber. dtsch. chem. Ges. *27*:6–19.

van't Hoff, J. H., and S. Arrhenius (1929) The foundations of the theory of dilute solutions. Alembic Club Reprints No. 19, Alembic Club, Edinburgh.

Woodbury, J. W. (1965) The cell membrane: ionic and potential gradients and active transport. *In* Medical Physiology and Biophysics. (T. C. Ruch and J. F. Fulton, eds.) 19th Ed. W. B. Saunders Co., Philadelphia, pp. 1–25.

5 OSMOREGULATION AND IONIC REGULATION

Osmotic pressure is remarkably powerful. If a cell or an animal whose internal osmotic concentration equals that of sea water is placed in fresh water, the osmotic concentration difference is about 1 osmole/liter. This difference (about 0.5 mole of NaCl/liter) causes a pressure of 22.4 atmospheres, which can raise a column of water to 224 meters (about 745 feet)! By comparison, a fully inflated automobile tire has an internal pressure of 2.5 to 3 atmospheres. True, the internal osmotic concentrations of most fresh water organisms are lower than that of sea water, but theoretically the gradients are large enough to give rise to osmotic pressures of from 0.75 (fresh-water mussel, *Anodonta*) to 14.1 atmospheres (wool-handed crab, *Eriocheir*).

A variety of mechanisms prevent the development of osmotic pressures and maintain an adequate internal osmotic concentration for the various life processes of cells and organisms; the functioning of these mechanisms is collectively referred to as *osmoregulation*.

Osmoregulation is not functionally separable from ionic regulation. Only for the sake of mental economy are inorganic ions referred to as "salts" in the following discussions.

Salts penetrate living membranes not as molecules but as ions. In fact, the anion and cation of a salt penetrate with different velocities, and frequently an organism contains more of the anion of a salt than of the cation, or vice versa. Even if the aqueous environment is isotonic with the internal body fluids of an animal, and if the latter are isotonic with the intracellular medium of the body cells, the body fluids usually have a different ionic composition (the relative proportions of the various ions) from the external medium, and differences in the ionic composition of intra- and extracellular fluids are even more striking. The mechanisms that maintain differences in ionic composition are the topic of *ionic regulation.*

OSMOTIC RELATIONS OF CELLS

The highly complex structure of the cell membrane separates the cellular protoplasm from the cell's environment. Cell membranes have many properties in common with semipermeable membranes (see p. 69), but their permeability characteristics are complicated by the following factors:

1. Fixed charges of membrane constituents tend to attract certain ions and to repel others. The presence of Ca^{++} ions within cell membranes is thought to increase permeability to inorganic anions (e.g., Cl^-) and to decrease permeability to cations (e.g., K^+). 2. The presence and size of pores give filter properties to these membranes so that molecules and (hydrated) ions smaller than the pore diameter are allowed to pass freely through the membrane while larger particles are prevented from entering through the pores. 3. Electric potentials across the cell membrane cause a characteristic distribution of ions and aids or hinders movement through the membrane. 4. Active transport mechanisms involving carrier molecules within the membrane permit selective transport of certain species of ions or molecules against osmotic or concentration gradients. 5. By pinocytosis, the active invagination of parts of the cell membrane, portions of the external medium are carried into the cell, and this permits exchange of matter that cannot be predicted from the permeability characteristics of the cell membrane.

In spite of all the complications, living cells appear to behave very much like osmometers; that is, they swell in media of lower osmotic concentration than that of their interior and shrink if in solutions of osmotic concentration higher than that of their interior. This, to a large extent, is due to the fact that the cell membranes are relatively more permeable to water than to any other compound or ion.

This swelling and shrinking has been studied extensively in red blood cells of vertebrates and eggs of marine animals. In both cases, the environment of the cells is normally isotonic, that is, the extracellular medium (blood plasma and sea water, respectively) has nearly the same osmotic concentration as the aqueous intracellular medium. The speed with which these cells swell or shrink in hypo- and hypertonic media has been taken as an indication of the permeability of the cell membranes to water. (This is further explained in Figure 5–1.)

If the degree of hyper- or hypotonicity of the extracellular medium is such that the cells do not become greatly changed in volume and assume abnormal shapes (example: crenated red blood cells, see Fig. 5–2) or rupture, the osmotic equilibrium leads to a change in volume that follows the equation $PV = constant$. This, in fact, is *Boyle's law* (see p. 92). P stands for pressure, meaning relative pressure, that is, the ratio of external to internal osmotic pressure. V, in this case, is not the total cell volume but the cell volume (V_c) minus the osmotically inert volume b (also called the *nonsolvent volume*). The *inert volume* is rep-

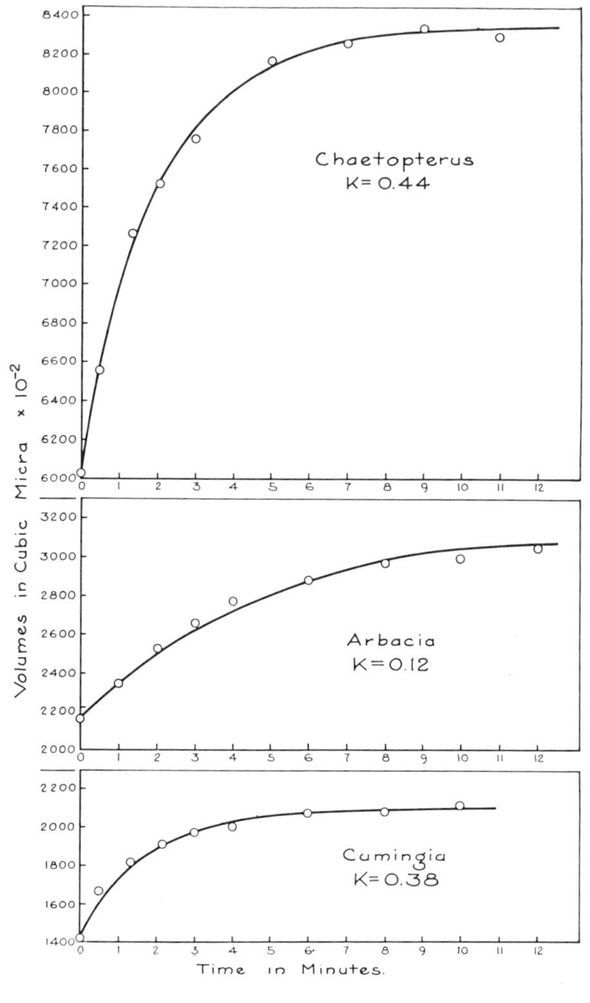

Figure 5–1. Curves of swelling of three kinds of cells (unfertilized eggs) transferred from normal (100 per cent) sea water to 60 per cent sea water. The "permeability" of the cell membrane to water (the rate of penetration, K) can be calculated from them, using the equation

$$K = \frac{dV}{dt}/S \cdot (P_1 - P_0),$$

where V is the cell volume (however, see p. 90), S is the surface area of the membrane, P_1 is the internal and P_0 the external osmotic pressure; t is time. The dimension of K is in $\mu^3/\text{min}/\mu^2/\text{atm}$. (From Lucke, B., H. K. Hartline, and R. A. Ricca: Comparative permeability to water and to certain solutes of the egg cells of three marine invertebrates, Arbacia, Cumingia and Chaetopterus. J. Cell. Comp. Physiol. *14*:237–252, 1939.)

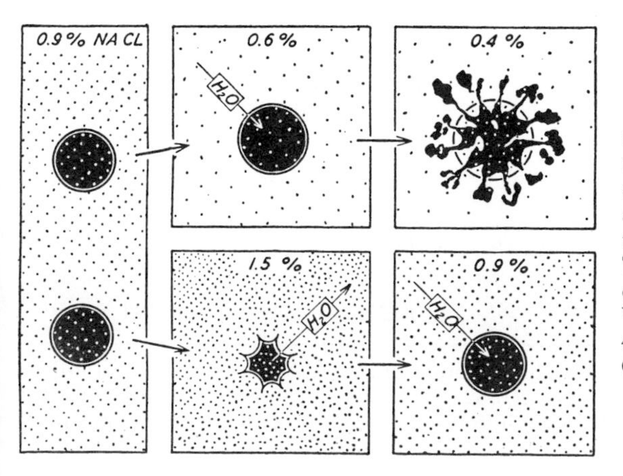

Figure 5–2. Schematic representation of the osmotic effects upon mammalian red blood cells, showing swelling and hemolysis when they are placed in a hypotonic medium, and shrinking when they are exposed to a hypertonic medium. The density of dots symbolizes the salt concentration. (From Carlson, A. J., and V. Johnson: The Machinery of the Body, 4th Ed. University of Chicago Press, Chicago, 1953.)

resented by the volume of the structural protein, lipid, and insoluble carbohydrate (glycogen) material of the cell. Lucke and McCutcheon, who reviewed the subject in 1932, gave figures that illustrate this point (Table 5–1). For *Arbacia* eggs the osmotically inert volume is 11 per cent, but for oyster eggs, Lucke and Ricca (1949) found an inert volume of 44 per cent. The osmotically inert volume does not correspond to any particular cell structure. Thus, the granular material in *Arbacia* eggs amounts to 55 per cent of the cell volume (Costello, 1939) but only 11 per cent of the volume is osmotically inert. It is likely that all the cell water participates in the solvent volume, and studies have shown that all the cell water, including the water bound to protein and ions, is available as solvent.

Cells contain a high concentration of protein. They are usually in a medium (blood plasma, hemolymph, aquatic environment of the organism) that contains much less, or no, protein. Thus, even if the osmotic concentrations of the external and internal media of a cell are equal, the intracellular colloid osmotic pressure is in excess. In addition, the cellular proteins are largely present as anions (see p. 85). These give rise to a Donnan equilibrium, which represents an osmotic imbalance so that the interior of the cell is somewhat hyperosmotic with regard to the outside medium. A cell, therefore, osmotically attracts water and develops an internal pressure or *turgor* which is balanced by the restraining force of the cell membrane. This actual osmotic pressure is responsible for the rigidity of the cells and provides a "hydrostatic skeleton."

By subjecting animal cells to media of different osmotic concentrations, one can determine the external osmotic concentration at which the cell establishes equilibrium. A medium with this osmotic concentration is *isotonic* with the cell. This type of physiological isotonicity is not identical with isosmoticity, as discussed on p. 73, because of the Donnan equilibrium and other complicating factors. However, it represents a stable condition. Remember these reservations when reading that a red blood cell is isotonic with a 0.9 per cent solution of NaCl.

By finding physiologically isotonic media, one can determine the *approximate* intracellular osmotic concentration, which is usually given in per cent

Table 5–1. Application of Boyle's Law to *Arbacia* Eggs

P	Volume Observed	PV_c	$P(V_c - b) = PV$
1.0	2.121	2.121	1.881
0.9	2.316	2.084	1.868
0.8	2.570	2.056	1.864
0.7	2.922	2.045	1.878
0.6	3.420	2.053	1.909
0.5	4.002	2.002	1.881

Modified data of Lucke and McCutcheon (1932), in Heilbrunn, L. V.: An Outline of General Physiology, 3rd Ed. W. B. Saunders Co., Philadelphia, 1952. The value b represents the osmotically inert volume and is taken to be 11 per cent of the initial volume. P stands for pressure, meaning the ratio of internal to external osmotic concentration.

NaCl, which means weight in grams of NaCl in 100 ml of solution, or in moles of NaCl/l.

The salt concentration of a medium that is isotonic with a certain type of cell is thus by no means identical with the intracellular concentration of inorganic ions. This is not only due to the Donnan distribution of ions on the two sides of the cell membrane, but also to the binding of certain ions by certain ionized groups of the protein molecules.

The presence of considerable amounts of organic compounds or organic ions of low molecular weight, which take the place of inorganic salts and ions, is responsible for considerable deviations.

In general, the body fluids of Metazoa are isotonic or nearly isotonic with the protoplasm of the body cells. The tonicity of the body cells, however, varies considerably with the state of metabolic activity. Slight variation of the internal hydrogen ion concentration can cause drastic changes in osmotic concentration, owing to changes in dissociation of proteins and organic salts, bases, and acids. Furthermore, the end products of metabolism, which consist of small molecules derived from large ones, increase the osmotic concentration.

In the discussion of gas transport in Chapter 9 (p. 176), we will see that vertebrate red blood cells swell under the influence of respiratory CO_2 and shrink as CO_2 is given off in the lungs. These volume changes take place within the circulation time of the blood, that is, within a few seconds. In spite of such osmotic changes, the body fluids are isotonic with a certain mean osmotic concentration of the cell substance.

The slight differences in osmotic pressure between different compartments of body fluids are discussed in the following chapter.

It is interesting to speculate about the peculiar situation of metazoan body cells that constitute the outer exchange membranes, particularly in organisms living in fresh water, which is hypotonic with regard to the interior of these cells. Such cells are in contact with a very hypotonic medium (fresh water) and an almost isotonic medium (blood). Consequently, these cells in their two-dimensional arrangement act as a membrane and water passes through them, following the osmotic gradient. The protective body wall of animals is usually built in such a way that the outer layer of cells is coated with a water-impermeable material.

If a unicellular organism lives in fresh water, its internal osmotic concentration draws water inward. In the absence of regulatory devices, the cell would soon swell and burst. Two mechanisms are resorted to: (1) formation of a highly impermeable cell wall and (2) excretion of the excess water. The second process is particularly conspicuous among fresh-water rhizopods and ciliates: water collects in one or more vacuoles that appear randomly (ameba) or in fixed places (paramecium). These vacuoles accumulate water and empty it through a pore. Such vacuoles may appear at regular intervals and in many cases appear to be definite organelles of the cell, as in most ciliates. Their mechanism is by no means understood. That water moves out of an area of high solute contraction contradicts every theory of osmosis. It is equally difficult to understand how the vacuole contracts as it discharges water to the outside. If we are dealing with a plasma membrane, its structure should consist of a molecular or bimolecular film, but it is difficult to see how such a film could contract. It is possible that while the vacuole enlarges, the membrane grows by rapidly incorporating more and more molecules, but such a membrane could hardly be assumed to contract. Observation of contractile vacuoles shows that their surface during contraction diminishes to at least 1/100 that of the filled vacuole.

The filling of these vacuoles with water is definitely related to the osmosis of water into the organisms, as shown by experiments in which the external osmotic concentration is raised. If this is done, the vacuolar output is diminished until it comes to a complete halt as the external medium becomes isotonic with the protoplasm (see Fig. 5–3). The German zoologist W. Stempell (1914) assumed that in the first step of vacuolar filling, osmotically active material is excreted into the vacuolar space and this material draws water into the vacuole osmotically. This hypothesis is still alive today; it meets with the difficulty that the vacuole would have to discharge fantastic quantities of material, since in its final stage of filling the vacuole would have to be assumed to be isotonic, if not slightly hypertonic to the rest of the cell. Since the various fresh-water ciliates discharge fluid volumes equal to their body volume in only a few

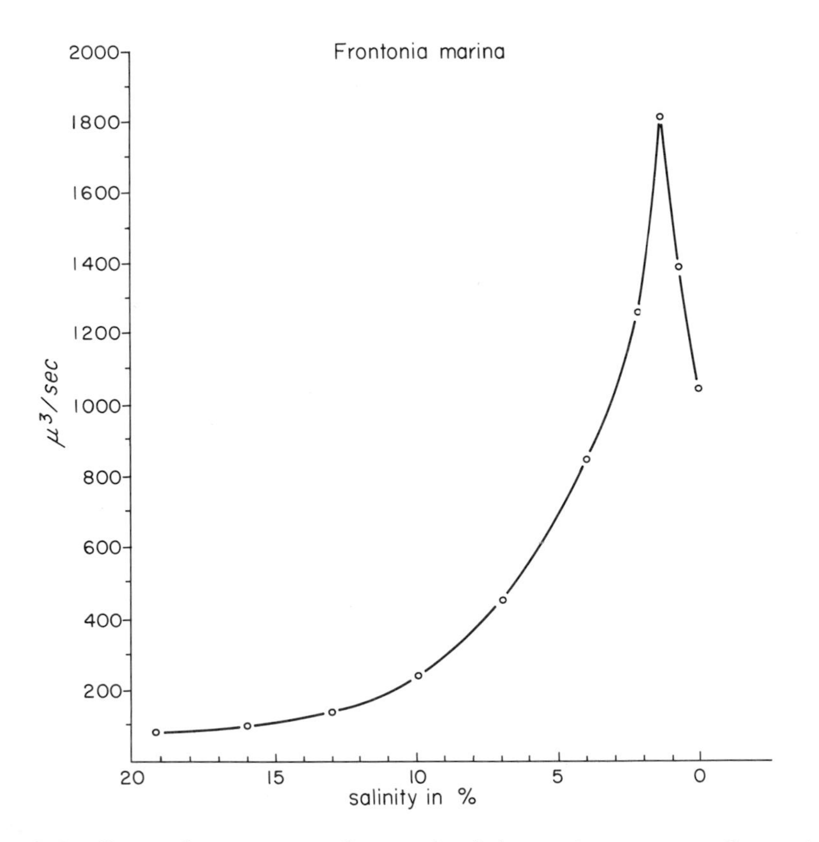

Figure 5–3. Output from a contractile vacuole of the marine protozoan *Frontonia marina* when the animal is placed into sea water of different salinities. (Based on data published by Müller, R.: Die osmoregulatorische Bedeutung der kontraktilen Vakuolen von *Amoeba proteus, Zoothamnium hiketes* und *Frontonia marina.* Arch. Protistenkunde 87:345–382, 1936.)

minutes to less than an hour, not only are considerable solids lost, but more solids must be taken up rapidly in order to make up for the great loss.

Not all the water that is excreted through the vacuoles is derived from osmosis. In ingesting food, Protozoa produce food vacuoles that always contain extracellular water. In addition, some water is produced during the normal course of metabolism. It is, therefore, not quite correct to calculate the permeability of the cell membrane to water only on the basis of the volume of water excreted per unit time, assuming that this quantity is equal to the rate of osmotic entry of water.

For an extensive discussion of this subject, see the reviews by J. A. Kitching (1938) and von Buddenbrock (1956). According to these authors, several genera of marine ciliates possess contractile vacuoles. However, these discharge more slowly than the vacuoles of the fresh-water forms. Most of the marine Protozoa have no contractile vacuoles.

The marine *Amoeba mira* eliminates water through the contractile vacuole if it lives in dilute sea water. Its water output is proportional to the extent of dilution. Water is eliminated only during ingestion of food. This indicates that the cell membrane of feeding animals is much more permeable to water than that of the nonfeeding ones. The relationship between vacuolar output and the osmotic concentration of the external medium is illustrated in Figure 5–2 (Kitching, 1938; Mast and Hopkins, 1941).

The body cells of fresh-water sponges possess contractile vacuoles (Jepps, 1947) and these probably are involved in removing water that enters the cell by osmosis.

Fresh-water coelenterates, like *Hydra,* can exist in their very hypotonic environment without obvious excretory mechanisms. Almost all their body cells are exposed to fresh water, and yet they maintain their normal size and function. S. J. Lilly (1955) showed that the cells of *Hydra viridis* are highly permeable to water. According to her calculations, the values range from 0.48 to 0.79 μ^3/μ^2/atm/min. In spite of this, the cells can maintain an internal osmotic concentration equivalent to that of 0.04 to 0.05 M sucrose, or 0.02 to 0.025 M NaCl. Why the intracellular medium does not become diluted by osmosis is unknown, but a mechanism for the excretion or exclusion of water must exist.

Cells in a hypotonic medium prevent the osmotic entry of water and the loss of salts to the outside by the following means: (1) the cell membranes are highly impermeable to the ions of inorganic salts and (2) the cells can actively transport these ions inward against concentration gradients; that is, they accumulate ions from a dilute solution. This has been clearly shown for *Pelmatohydra oligactis* (see Figs. 5–4 and 5–5).

The body cells of the higher Metazoa, even of those that live in hypo- or hypertonic media, are not faced with great osmotic problems, because (1) only a relatively small number of cells is exposed to the external environment and (2) they possess a well-regulated, internal medium, the body fluids, which is isotonic with the body cells. The body cells are in osmotic equilibrium with the body fluids which bathe them, and cells that come in direct contact with the animal's outside environment do so only with part of their surface, while the other part is bathed by isotonic body fluid.

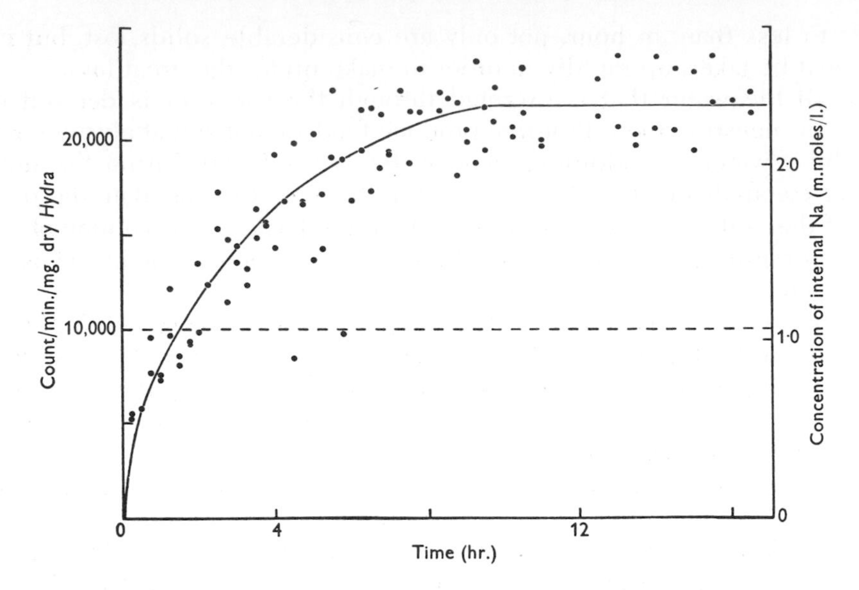

Figure 5–4. *Pelmatohydra oligactis* (Coelenterata). Uptake of ^{24}Na from a solution containing 1.068 m.moles/l NaCl. The broken line represents the concentration of ^{24}Na in the external solution expressed as m.moles/l Na. Other salts present in the solution are 4 mg/l KCl, 4 mg/l $CaCl_2$, 4 mg/l $NaHCO_3$, and 1 mg/l K_2HPO_4. The concentration of labeled Na in the animal reaches values considerably above that of the external solution. (From Lilly, S. J.: Osmoregulation and ionic regulation in Hydra. J. Exp. Biol. *32*:423–439, 1955.)

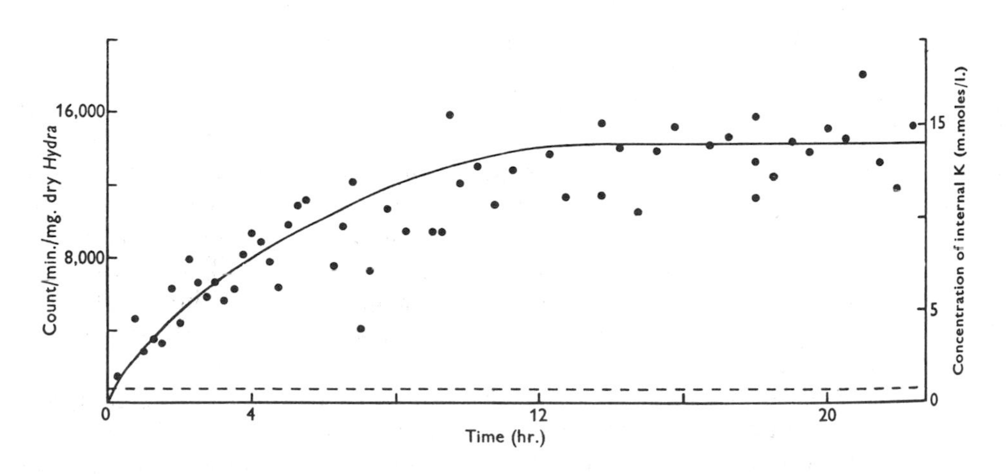

Figure 5–5. *Pelmatohydra oligactis* (Coelenterata). Uptake of ^{42}K from a solution containing 0.054 m.mole/l KCl. The broken line represents the concentration of ^{42}K in the external solution expressed as m.moles/l. Other salts present in the solution are 40 mg/l NaCl, 4 mg/l $NaHCO_3$, 4 mg/l $CaCl_2$, and 1 mg/l K_2HPO_4. The concentration of labeled K in the animal reaches several times that of the external solution. (From Lilly, S. J.: Osmoregulation and ionic regulation in Hydra. J. Exp. Biol. *32*:423–439, 1955.)

OSMOTIC RELATIONS OF MULTICELLULAR ANIMALS

The complex organization of the metazoan body is separated from the outside environment by a more or less complicated cellular and extracellular membrane. This membrane is continuous and completely encloses the organized mass of body cells and the body fluids. The enclosing membrane acts much like a semipermeable membrane, particularly if it acts as exchange membrane (see p. 45). Since the majority of animal forms are aquatic, they are subject to osmosis. On purely physical grounds there is a tendency toward osmotic equilibrium between body fluids and the external medium. In most types of marine animals, osmotic equilibrium does indeed exist: the internal aqueous medium (coelomic fluid, hemolymph, blood plasma) is isotonic with sea water. This was first established by the Italian biologist F. Bottazzi (1897) shortly after the significance of osmotic phenomena was recognized and they were explained quantitatively (see Chap. 4). It was also found that animals of the same species which live in sea water of different salinities show differences in the osmotic concentration of their blood which parallel the sea water concentrations. For a time, it was a "law" that the osmotic pressure of aquatic animals follows that of the external medium.

However, when reviewing the situation in 1908, Bottazzi found it to be much more complicated. Many exceptions had been found: particularly among marine fishes, the blood of teleosts is hypotonic (freezing point −0.65 to −0.7° C) to sea water (−1.85° C) whereas the elasmobranch fishes have a somewhat hypertonic blood (−1.85 to −1.9° C). It became evident that life in a hyper- or hypotonic medium presents osmotic problems, and that certain organisms must have special mechanisms for maintenance of osmotic imbalance particularly in the extreme situation of life in fresh water that has an extremely low salt content (freezing point −0.01° C). Although fresh-water animals have a lower internal osmotic concentration (−0.08 to −0.8° C) than marine animals, their internal osmotic concentration is much higher than that of their environment.

Such differences in osmotic concentration can be maintained only by special regulatory mechanisms that effectively counteract the osmotic influx, or loss, of water. This was first recognized by Rudolf Höber in 1902, who used the term "*Osmoregulation*" to describe the maintenance of an internal osmotic concentration that differs from that of the external medium. The mechanisms involved in such osmoregulation were not elucidated until about 1930 when a number of investigators experimented with various organisms by varying the outside osmotic concentration and studying the resultant changes in weight (water content!), internal salt concentration, urine production, and respiration. Experiments were also concerned with the movement of the different inorganic ions (the constituents of the salts) across the exchange membranes of animal bodies, and in the following decades it became more and more obvious that osmoregulation is related to active transport of different ionic species.

The subject matter was first treated concisely by the Danish physiologist August Krogh in his famous book Osmotic Regulation in Aquatic Animals (1939). Further progress is reported by Prosser and Brown (1961), von Buddenbrock (1956), Beadle (1957), Martin (1958), and Potts and Parry (1964). Osmoregulation and ionic regulation in insects has been reviewed by Edney (1957) and Shaw and Strobbart (1963).

General Terminology

In the following discussions aquatic environments of animal organisms are considered as media of various salt concentrations. The water of a river that flows out into the open sea has a whole range of salt concentrations. There we see all transitions from fresh water through all stages of brackish water to sea water proper. In the region around the mouth of a river, called an *estuary*, are found certain animal species that can live in an astonishing range of salt concentrations.

Animals that can withstand aquatic media that have a wide range of salt concentrations are called *euryhaline* species (Fig. 5–6b, d). This term includes *anadromous* species, which habitually migrate from regions of high salt content (the sea) to areas of low salt content (fresh water), and *catadromous* species, which migrate from fresh water to sea water. These two categories are composed almost exclusively of fishes. The most famous examples of these are the migratory species of eel and salmon. Among the invertebrates, the wool-handed crab (*Eriocheir*) exemplifies catadromous migration.

Some euryhaline forms can maintain a rather constant internal osmotic pressure in the face of changing outside osmotic pressure; in others, the body fluids follow more or less the outside osmotic pressure and they can withstand rather large changes of concentration of their body fluids.

Animals that survive only within a narrow range of salinities and that are bound to an environment of constant salt content are referred to as *stenohaline* (Fig. 5–6). Stenohaline animals usually do not have osmoregulatory mechanisms. They cannot maintain an internal environment that is independent of the osmotic concentration of the external environment, and cannot survive any change in external, and consequently in internal, osmotic concentration.

Aquatic animals whose internal osmotic concentration changes with that of the outside environment are called *poikilosmotic* (Fig. 5–6a, b). Stenohaline animals are usually poikilosmotic, and this property proves fatal whenever the salt concentration of the external sea water changes. Many euryhaline forms are more or less poikilosmotic, but their body cells can withstand the concentration changes of the body fluids.

Animals that maintain a more or less constant osmotic concentration of their body fluids despite a different or changed concentration of the external medium are called *homoiosmotic* (Fig. 5–6a, d, e). Many of the euryhaline species are more or less homoiosmotic, and so are many forms that always live in a medium (fresh water or sea water) of constant concentration that is hyper- or hypotonic to their body fluids.

The term "homoiosmotic" implies active osmoregulation. Remember, however, that it is unlikely that euryhaline, poikilosmotic animals can exist without osmoregulatory devices. We should rather draw the line between the two terms "poikilosmotic" and "homoiosmotic" by stating that the body cells

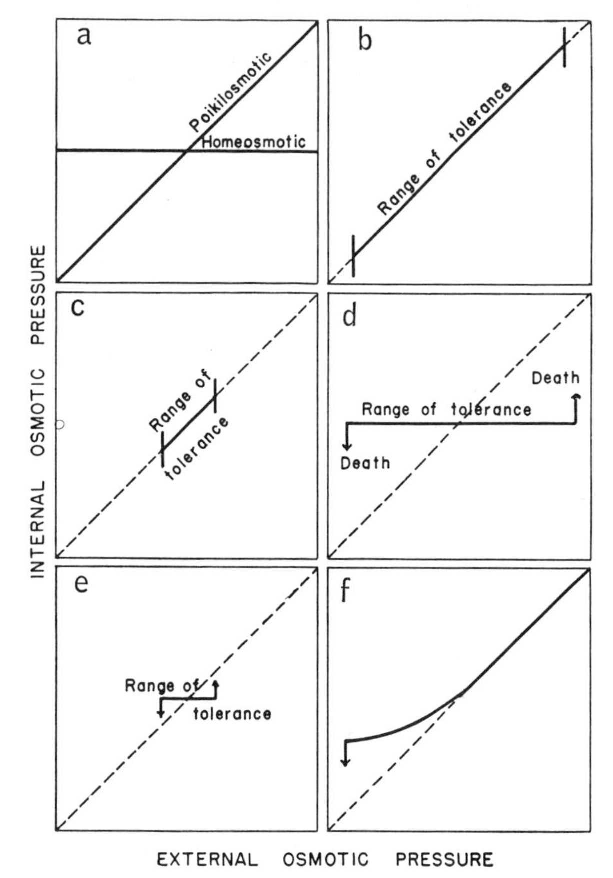

Figure 5-6. Diagrams to explain the terms "poikilosmotic," "homeosmotic," "stenohaline," and "euryhaline," relating external and internal osmotic pressures of aquatic animals. **a**, contrast between a completely homeosmotic and a completely poikilosmotic type of organism. **b**, euryhaline poikilosmotic type of organism. **c**, stenohaline homeosmotic type. **d**, euryhaline homeosmotic type. **e**, stenohaline homeosmotic type. **f**, hyperosmotic regulator. What would a diagram representing a hyperosmotic regulator look like? (Diagrams from Lifson, N., and M. B. Visscher: Osmosis in living systems. *In* Medical Physics. O. Glasser, ed. Year Book Publishers, Chicago, 1944, pp. 869–892.)

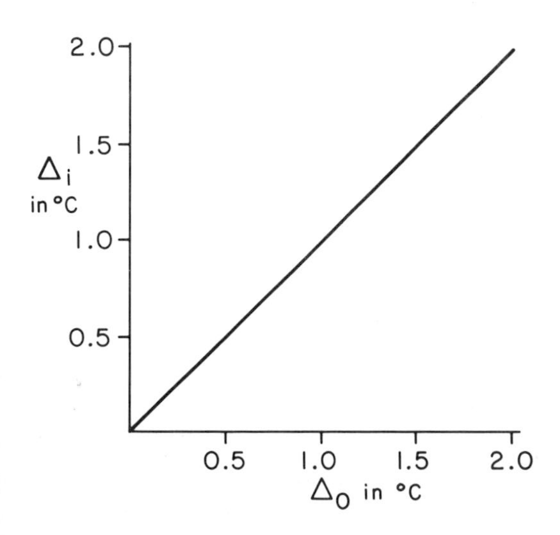

Figure 5-7. The relation between internal osmotic pressure (osmotic activity), Δ_i, and external osmotic pressure, Δ_o, both expressed in terms of lowering of the freezing point of the solvent water. This situation is true for ideal osmometers in complete osmotic equilibrium.

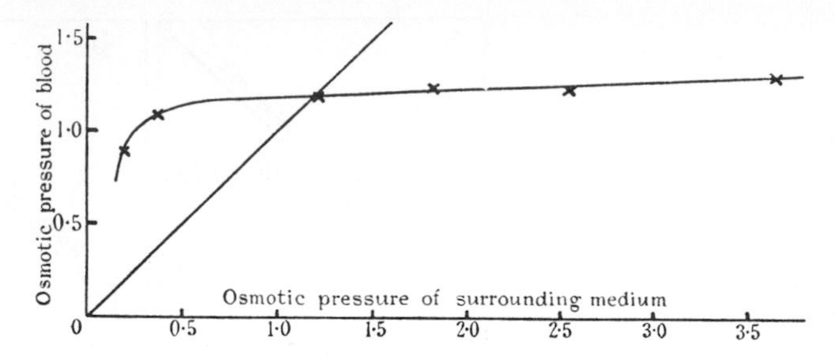

Figure 5–8. Exceptional ability of a marine teleost, *Conger vulgaris*, to osmoregulate. The osmotic pressure of blood is plotted as a function of the osmotic pressure of the external medium (artificially diluted sea water). The osmotic pressures are given in terms of concentration of NaCl in gm/100 ml. (From Margaria, R.: The osmotic changes in some marine animals. Proc. Roy. Soc. B *107*:606–624, 1931.)

of poikilosmotic animals can adjust or adapt to changes in the osmotic concentration of the body fluids, whereas in homoiosmotic organisms osmoregulation takes place at the level of the outer exchange membranes of the body.

No animal is perfectly homoiosmotic, although many are homoiosmotic within a certain range of salt concentrations. An ideal poikilosmotic animal is represented by a graph that relates external to internal osmotic concentration (expressed as lowering of the freezing point, or Δ) as shown in Figure 5–7. The resulting curve is a straight line with a slope of 45 degrees, which intercepts zero. An ideal homoiosmotic animal would give a curve as shown in Figure 5–6a, a horizontal line. Two animal species that conform most closely to this ideal behavior are the conger eel (*Conger vulgaris*) and the prawn (*Palaemonetes varians*). Curves representing the osmotic behavior of these two species are given in Figures 5–8 and 5–9.

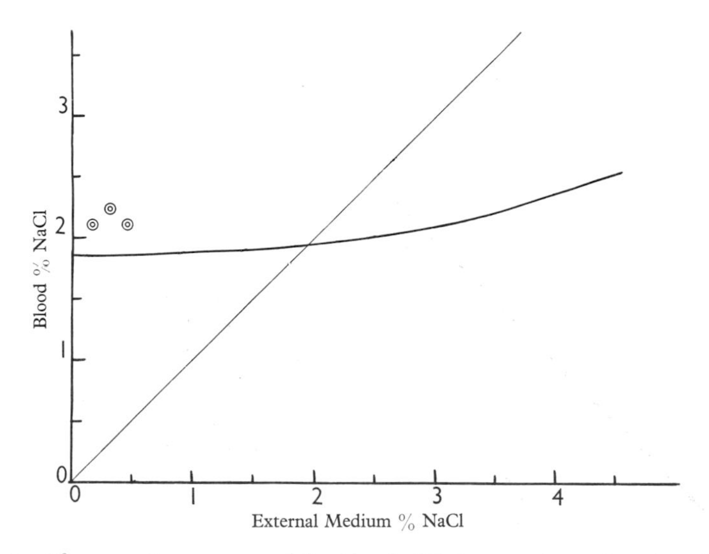

Figure 5–9. The osmotic pressure of the blood of *Palaemonetes varians* in relation to that of the external medium. The osmotic pressure is indicated in terms of per cent (weight per volume) of NaCl. The straight line indicates the isotonicity of the internal and external media. (From Panikkar, N. K.: Osmoregulation in some palaemonid prawns. J. Mar. Biol. Assn. U.K. 25:317–359, 1941.)

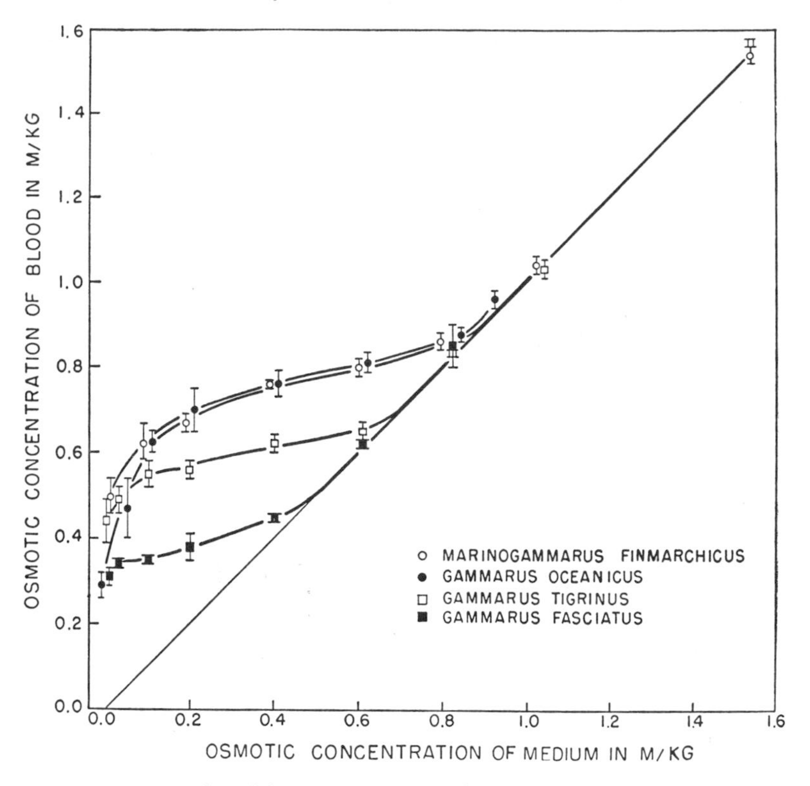

Figure 5–10. An example of hyperosmotic regulators: various species of gammarid crustaceans. *Gammarus tigrinus* lives in brackish water. *G. fasciatus* lives in fresh water. The other two species are marine. The graph plots the blood concentration (in moles of ideal solute per kilogram of water) against the concentration of the external medium. The vertical bars represent $\pm 2 \times$ the standard errors. (From Werntz, H. O.: Osmotic regulation in marine and freshwater gammarids [Amphipoda]. Biol. Bull. *124*:225–239, 1963.)

Some species regulate their internal osmotic concentration only as long as the external medium is hypotonic. As soon as this medium becomes isotonic and hypertonic, the internal osmotic concentration simply follows that of the external medium. Characteristic curves are given in Figure 5–10. The typical examples are the shore crab, *Carcinus maenas,* and various species of Gammaridae (amphipods).

In recent years, it has become customary to use the term "hypo-osmotic regulation" when an animal can maintain a hypotonic body fluid, and the term "hyperosmotic regulation" to describe the ability to main hypertonic body fluids. Animals that can do one or the other are correspondingly called *hypo-osmotic regulators* and *hyperosmotic regulators.*

Osmoregulation in a Hypotonic Environment

Animals living in fresh water and marine animals whose blood is hypertonic to sea water (elasmobranch fishes and several species of crabs) face the problem of osmotic entry of water and of loss of internal salt through outward diffusion of filtration. Without protective devices, these animals would either swell or lose so much salt that their internal fluids would not support the normal functioning of the body cells, unless these cells can adjust to different osmotic concentrations or body fluids. (For a discussion of the significance of inorganic salts, see the chapter on enzymes, carbon-dioxide transport, and on bioelectricity).

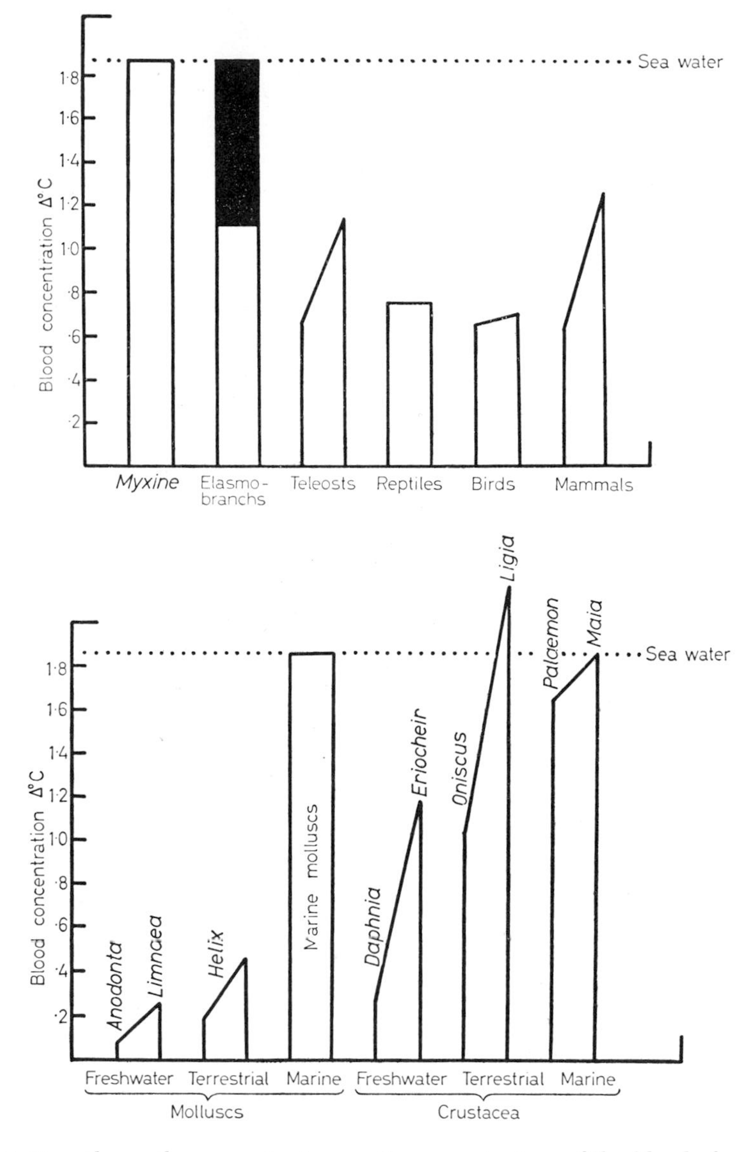

Figure 5–11. **Above**, the approximate osmotic concentrations of the blood of various marine vertebrates. Only the elasmobranchs and *Myxine* have blood nearly isosmotic with sea water. Note the considerable contribution of urea and trimethylammonium (indicated in black) to the total osmotic concentration of elasmobranch blood. **Below**, the osmotic concentrations of the blood of molluscs and crustaceans from various environments. (From Lockwood, A. P. M.: Animal Body Fluids and Their Regulation. Harvard University Press, Cambridge, Mass., 1964.)

The following are the most important devices and mechanisms employed in *hyperosmotic regulation* (maintenance of hyperosmotic body fluids):

1. A conspicuous adaptation to life in fresh water is the generally low internal salt content of the body fluids and body cells. Some fresh water molluscs, like the bivalve *Anodonta*, have the lowest known internal salt concentration. Their blood is isotonic with a 0.1 per cent NaCl solution. The salinities of body fluids of some marine and fresh-water animals are compared with the salinity of the external environment in Figure 5–11. Notice that although the osmotic gradient is reduced by the lowering of the salt concentration of body fluids from that of marine organisms to that found in fresh water, the difference in osmotic concentration is still large, even in animals like *Anodonta*. The lowering of internal salt concentration therefore reduces, but does not abolish, the osmotic problem.

2. Many fresh-water organisms have a highly impermeable body wall so that water can enter only slowly (see Nagel, 1934), but even so, it *does* enter and the low permeability helps only in so far as regulatory mechanisms can cope more readily with a slow rather than with a rapid entry of water. Some fresh-water forms have an absolutely impermeable body wall and their exchange membranes do not come in contact with water. Examples are the aquatic reptiles, birds and mammals, certain aquatic insect larvae, and the adult forms of aquatic insects.

3. The osmotic entry of water leads to the development of internal hydrostatic pressure. This is evident in the initial swelling of all marine animals that enter water of lower salinity. The increase in internal pressure, of course, is a persistent feature as long as the organism stays in the hypotonic environment.

The consequence of the high internal pressure is an increased filtration pressure, which leads to the production of larger volumes of urine. Fresh-water animals produce much more urine than marine animals. With the loss of urine a *volume regulation* is achieved and the internal pressure can thus remain within normal limits.

Urine is usually produced by filtration and, at least initially, represents an ultrafiltrate of blood or hemolymph. It, therefore, shows much the same composition as the body fluids, particularly with regard to the inorganic ions. Loss of urine thus means not only a loss of water, but also loss of salts. Homoiosmotic animals, therefore, have specific mechanisms that maintain a constant internal salt concentration.

4. One way to maintain the internal salt concentration is to prevent the loss of salt through excretion. This is achieved by active reabsorption of salts by the kidney tubules through which the urine flows on its way to the outside. Many fresh-water animals have well-developed tubules, in contrast to marine forms in which the tubules are usually shorter or even absent. This is particularly conspicuous if one compares related forms: Figure 5–12 shows the excretory organ of a marine species (*Gammarus pulex*) and that of a fresh-water species (*G. locusta*) of the same crustacean genus. Because the salts are reabsorbed by the kidney tubules (Fig. 5–13), the urine excreted is hyposmotic to the animal's body fluids. The excretion of a dilute urine is indeed a special

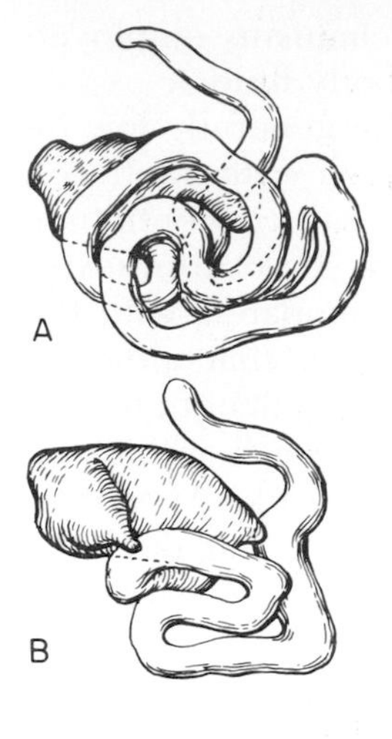

Figure 5–12. Renal organ (antennal gland) of **A**, a fresh-water amphipod, *Gammarus locusta*, and **B**, a marine amphipod, *G. pulex*. Note that the tubule of the fresh-water form is much longer than that of the marine form, which suggests the greater importance of the tubule because of the need for reabsorption of "salts." (After wax models by E. Schwabe, published by Schlieper, C.: Die Brackwassertiere und ihre Lebensbedingungen, vom physiologischen Standpunkt aus betrachtet. Verh. Internat. Verein. theor. angew. Limnologie 6:113–146, 1932.)

adaptation characteristically found in fresh-water animals and in certain euryhaline forms such as *Nereis diversicolor* (Jürgens, 1935). However, the fresh-water crabs *Eriocheir sinensis* and *Potamon* excrete an isotonic urine, and as far as is known no euryhaline Crustacea produce a urine that is hyposmotic to the hemolymph.

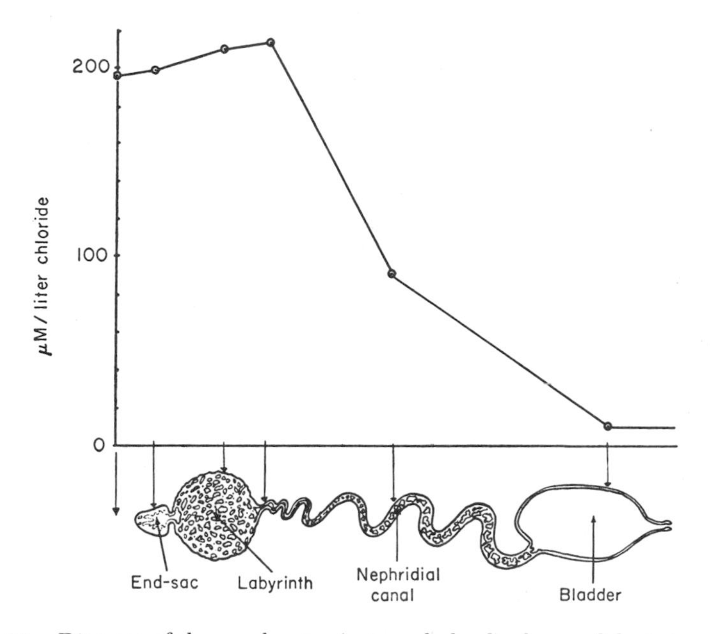

Figure 5–13. Diagram of the renal organ (antennal gland) of a crayfish, *Astacus*, after having been dissected and "unraveled." The graph shows the chloride concentration in the various segments of this organ. The chloride concentration serves as a rough index for the salt concentration. The salt concentration falls drastically toward the distal portion of the tubule (and bladder); this indicates reabsorption of "salts," probably by an active process. (From Parry, G.: Excretion. *In* The Physiology of Crustacea, Vol. I. T. H. Waterman, ed. Academic Press, New York, 1960.)

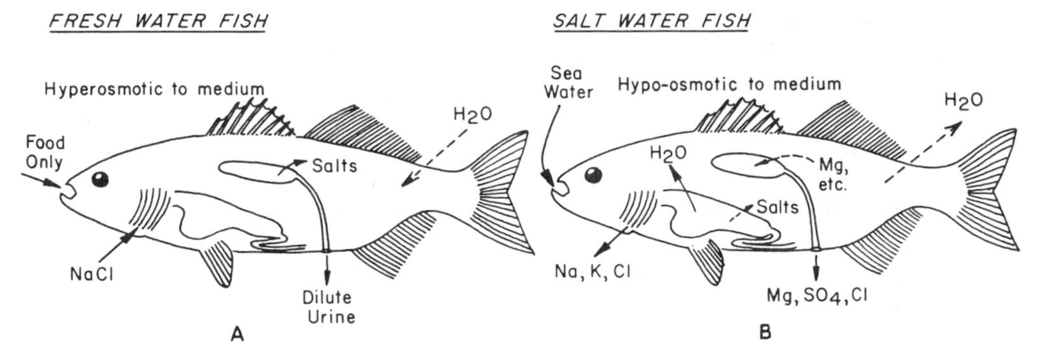

Figure 5–14. Schematic representation of the main paths of ion and water movement in osmoregulation of fresh-water (**A**) and marine (**B**) teleosts. Solid arrows: active transport; broken arrows: passive transport. (From Prosser, C. L., and F. A. Brown, Jr.: Comparative Animal Physiology, 2nd Ed. W. B. Saunders Co., Philadelphia, 1961.)

Fresh-water teleost fishes (Fig. 5–14) have nephridia that can reabsorb salt efficiently. Similar reabsorption takes place in the nephridia of fresh-water elasmobranch fishes.

The kidneys of fresh-water lamellibranch molluscs can reabsorb salts. This probably takes place in the organ of Bojanus which functions as a nephron (Fig. 5–15). Filtration takes place through the wall of the ventricle into the pericardium. The pericardial fluid is isotonic with the hemolymph. As it passes through the "nephron," salt is reabsorbed so that the osmotic concentration of the excreted urine is equivalent to 0.06 per cent NaCl (in contrast to the osmotic

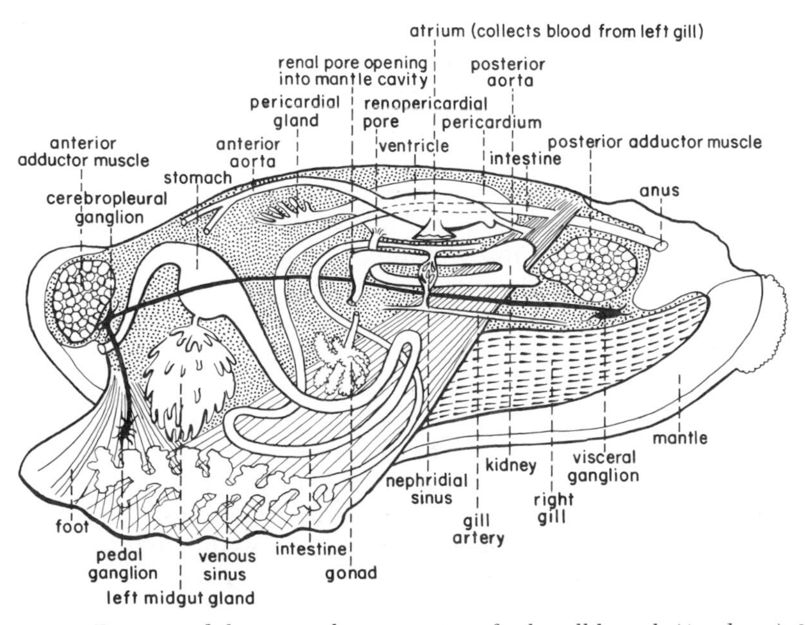

Figure 5–15. Diagram of the internal organization of a lamellibranch (*Anodonta*). Note the relation between the pericardium and the kidney (*organ of Bojanus*). (After Stempell, W.: Zoologie im Grundriss. G. Borntraeger, Berlin, 1926.)

concentration of pericardial fluid and hemolymph, which is equal to 0.1 per cent NaCl). Picken (1937) found that the filtration rate in *Anodonta* is so high that it excretes six times its own weight of urine per day. The reabsorption of 40 per cent of the filtered salts that pass through the nephrons, therefore, cannot be sufficient to maintain the internal salt concentration.

To a lesser extent, this is true for all fresh-water organisms: they all lose salts through their excretory organs (if not through other structures as well) in spite of more or less developed mechanisms of salt conservation which reside in the "kidneys."

5. To make up for such loss of salt into the hypotonic medium, euryhaline and fresh-water organisms actively absorb and accumulate salts from dilute solutions against the existing concentration gradients. In forms in which the body wall is relatively impermeable to salts and water, the gills actively take up salt. This has been shown for many fishes (Fig. 5–14), Amphibia, Crustacea, and aquatic insect larvae. In fishes and Crustacea, the salt uptake is a function of the gills. Gills of the fresh-water crabs *Potamon* and *Eriocheir* are particularly active (remember that these crabs excrete an isotonic urine, and consequently lose large amounts of salt): in these animals the salt uptake through the gills is about equal to the salt loss through body surface and through the urine (Krogh, 1938, Shaw, 1961). The mosquito larvae *Chironomus* and *Aedes* absorb salts through the anal papillae (Harnisch, 1934; Wigglesworth, 1933b and 1938).

6. The mechanisms discussed in Sections 2 to 5 are characteristic of homoiosmotic animals in hyposmotic environments. Some other animals are euryhaline but poikilosmotic: their internal osmotic concentration changes with the osmotic concentration of the external medium (sea water). This can happen in two ways:

a. The animal takes up water (or loses water) until the body fluids are isotonic or nearly isotonic with the external medium. In this case, the animals behave as osmometers and swell or shrink, depending on whether the outside is hypotonic or hypertonic. Characteristic examples are the sipunculids: the body wall behaves like a semipermeable membrane which is permeable to water but impermeable to salts (Adolph, 1936). This is illustrated in Figure 5–16. It is amazing that the obviously high internal pressure of swollen animals is not relieved by increased excretion of fluid through the metanephridia which appear to communicate with the voluminous coelomic cavity and the outside. A similar behavior is found with several marine molluscs (*Mytilus, Doris, Onchidium*).

b. Poikilosmotic animals adapt to hypotonic aqueous environments by excreting salt. This lowers the osmotic concentration of the body fluids sufficiently to make them isotonic with the outside medium and to prevent further entry of water. This excretion of salts is usually preceded by an initial phase of osmotic water uptake which is manifested by swelling and weight increase in the animal. Typical examples are the polychaete worm *Nereis diversicolor* and the marine snail *Aplysia* (Beadle, 1937, and Bethe, 1934). The reduction of volume due to secondary salt loss in hypotonic environments is called *volume regulation.*

7. An interesting regulatory mechanism is found in the turbellarian *Gunda ulvae*, a flatworm that lives on the Atlantic coast of England near the mouth

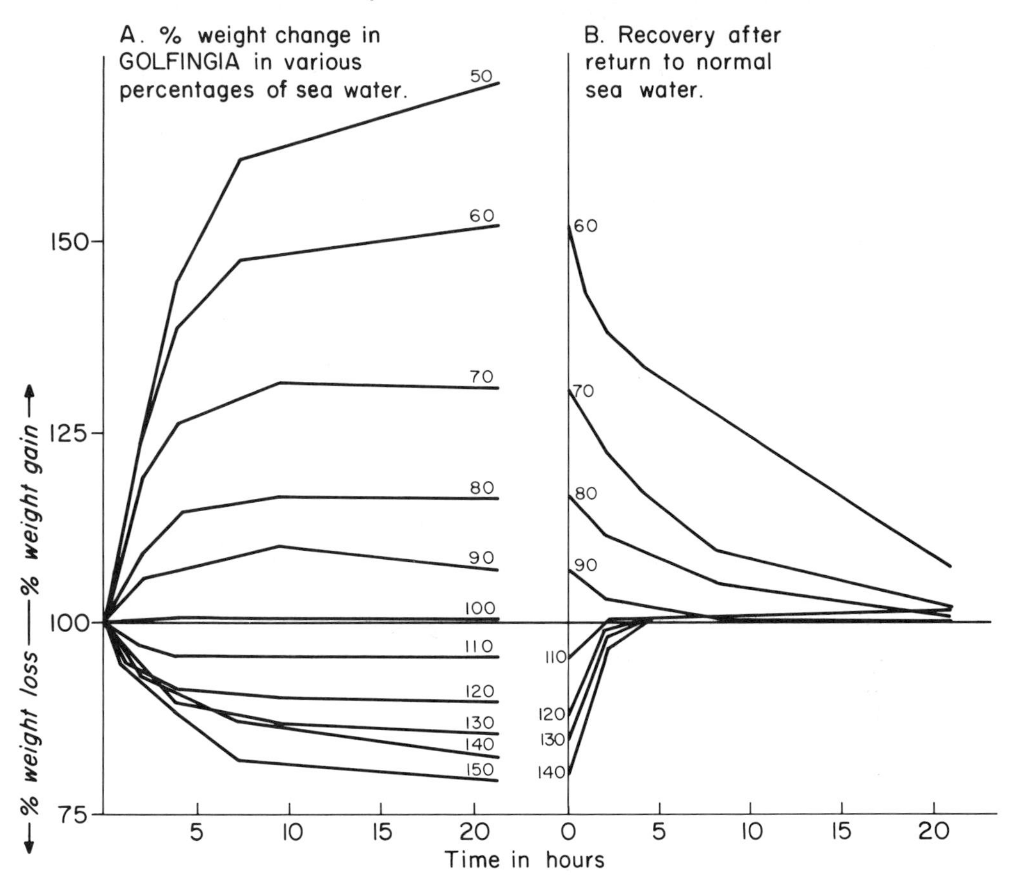

Figure 5–16. *Golfingia*, a sipunculid worm, is an example of an organism that behaves like an osmometer; that is, it swells in a hypotonic medium and shrinks in a hypertonic medium. Water uptake and water loss are indicated in terms of the weight change. (Data from a class experiment performed by H. Hetzel and J. Lauer.)

of rivers. Its habitat is flooded alternatively with sea water and hard fresh water. *Gunda* can live in undiluted sea water as well as in a mixture of 5 per cent sea water and 95 per cent fresh water. At low tide, when the salinity decreases rapidly, the worm swells considerably. The swelling of the tissues, however, is soon reduced. This is only in part due to excretion of salt; it is largely achieved by the formation of large water vacuoles within the cells of the intestine. These vacuoles are emptied toward the outside.

8. Salt conservation in hypotonic media is somewhat aided by the acquisition of salts contained in the food. All food material, whether animal or plant, contains by far more potassium than sodium ions, whereas the body fluids must maintain a large concentration of sodium ions and require only little potassium. A normal relationship between the internal concentrations of these two ions is achieved by selective absorption of sodium and excretion of excess potassium.

Eels in fresh water apparently depend entirely on salt uptake through their food, since their gills cannot absorb salts (Krogh, 1939). Only highly impermeable animals can depend on the salts in their foods.

9. The blood of the marine elasmobranch fishes (sharks, rays) is slightly hypertonic to sea water. They live, essentially, in a hypotonic medium. Much of the osmotic concentration of their blood is, however, not due to salts, but to a rather high concentration of urea (Staedeler and Frerichs, 1858) and trimethylamine (Smith, 1936). The hypertonicity is maintained by active reabsorption of urea in the kidney tubules and the excretion of a hyposmotic urine (Smith, 1936). Maintenance of the normal concentration of inorganic salts is no problem, since the external salt concentration is higher than the internal one.

10. The body wall of aquatic animals plays an important role in osmoregulation, owing to its mechanical resistance to extension. The osmotic influx of water can proceed only until the internal hydrostatic pressure is equal to the difference of osmotic pressure (see p. 75). The development of hydrostatic pressure within a compartment (we can consider the animal body as a fluid-filled compartment that is bounded by the body wall) depends on the resistance of its walls to a volume change. If the body wall is highly elastic, it offers little resistance to expansion of the internal volume and therefore hydrostatic pressure would increase slowly. On the other hand, a rigid and rather inelastic body wall would permit only slight increases in volume and the osmotic influx of water would give rise to considerable hydrostatic pressure. By allowing such pressures to develop, the inelastic, rigid body wall can effectively diminish the inward movement of water. The hard-shelled Crustacea are obvious examples. It is indeed found that in fresh-water Crustacea influx of water is much slower than in fresh-water molluscs that have a soft body wall. In euryhaline and fresh-water forms that have a muscular body wall, it can be expected that the muscles play an important role in osmoregulation inasmuch as they actively resist an increase in body volume.

Osmoregulation in a Hypertonic Environment

The following animal types are known to live in a hypertonic aquatic environment: (1) the marine teleost fishes, and the cyclostomes which live part of their life in the sea, (2) the marine crabs of the genera *Eriocheir*, *Pachygrapsus*, and *Leptograpsus*, (3) a number of palaemonid prawns, (4) the larvae of several species of dipteran insects, and (5) the brine shrimps, *Artemia*, which live in salt and alkali lakes.

All these organisms are in an environment that induces osmotic loss of water and an increase in internal salt concentration. If the external exchange membranes (e.g., the gills) were semipermeable, that is, impermeable to salts but permeable to water, the salt influx through the body surface would not present a problem. Actually, the influx of salts through the body surface is considerable. In addition, salts accumulate continuously through food uptake. Since pure water is not available to dilute the acquired salts, these animals must conserve water and actively excrete salts. The marine teleosts swallow sea water and actively excrete salts through the gills (Fig. 5–14). The kidneys of marine teleosts produce a urine that is hyposmotic to their blood, which means that their kidneys conserve salts, a function which seems to aggravate

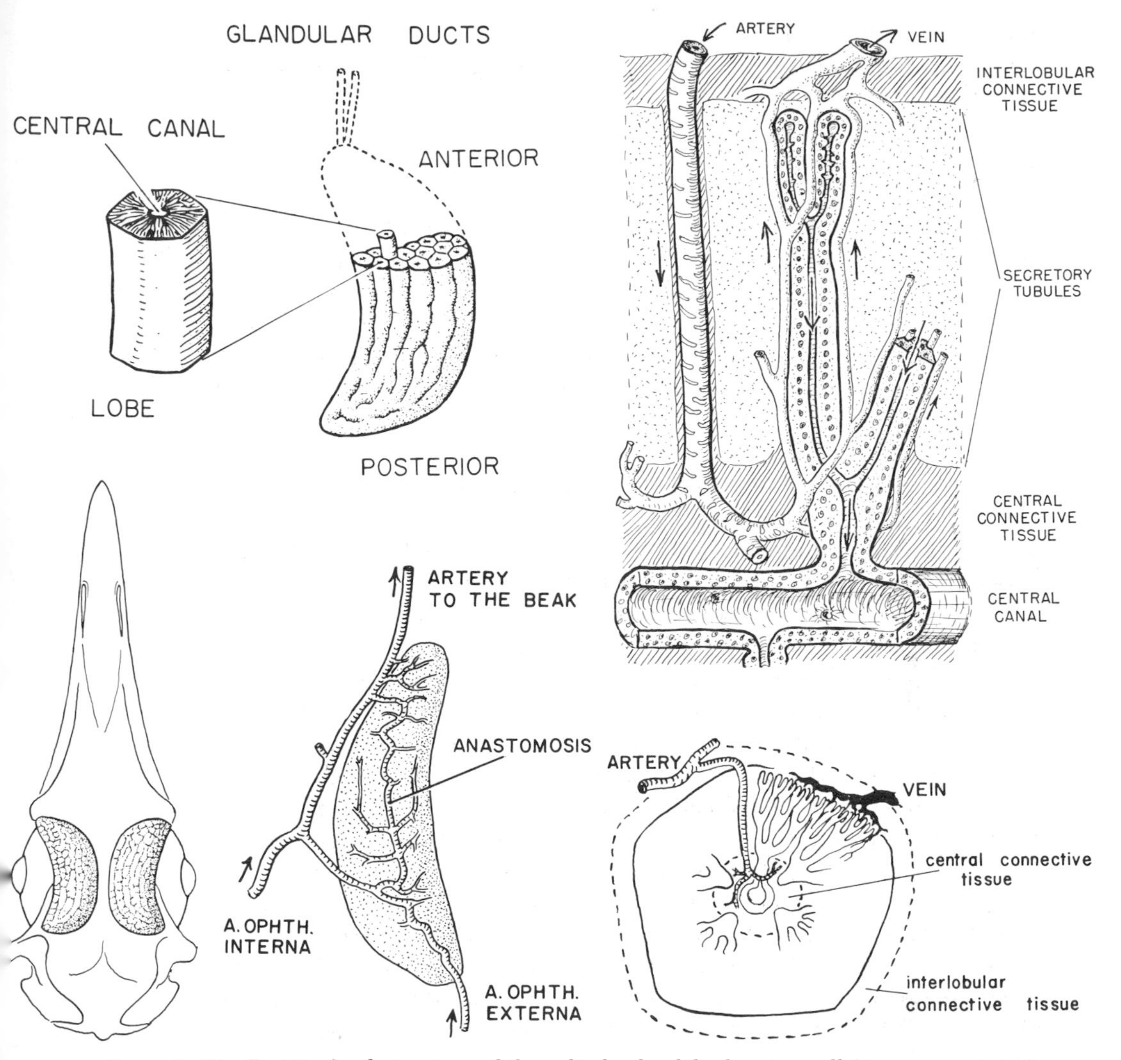

Figure 5–17. Position and structure of the salt glands of the herring gull (*Larus argentatus*). The two glands lie on top of the skull in the supraorbital grooves of the frontal bone. The ducts open into the anterior nasal cavity and secrete a highly concentrated solution of NaCl. (From Fänge, R., K. Schmidt-Nielsen, and H. Osaki: The salt gland of the herring gull. Biol. Bull. *115*, 162–171, 1959.)

the osmotic problem. Teleosts, which migrate from the sea into fresh water (the eel and the salmon), stop swallowing water a few hours after entering fresh water. The salmon go so far as to even stop feeding!

Almost nothing is known about osmoregulation in the migratory cyclostomes. (For relevant discussions see Black, 1957, and von Buddenbrock, 1956.)

The grapsoid crabs produce a urine that is hypertonic to their blood. It is possible that they absorb sea water through the digestive tract. They seem to achieve osmotic balance by (a) taking in hypertonic fluid and (b) losing salts more rapidly than water.

The brine shrimps can maintain considerable hypotonicity in their body fluids. Like the marine teleosts, they drink water (both orally and anally!) and excrete the surplus salts, largely through the first 10 pairs of branchiae (Croghan, 1958a, b, c, d).

Terrestrial Animals

The problems of water and salt balance in terrestrial organisms closely resemble those of marine animals. Both are surrounded by a medium that contains a lower concentration of water than the body fluids. Both obtain salts more or less readily through their food and both must, somehow, conserve water and excrete salts. The following considerations apply here:

1. Unless they inhabit a rather moist environment where the humidity of the surrounding atmosphere is high (*Peripatus*, Amphibia), terrestrial animals have a body wall that is rather impermeable to water. Since the respiratory surfaces are enclosed within body cavities, water vapor is conserved, which reduces evaporation across the respiratory membranes. The water vapor pressure in the earth's atmosphere is usually low (less than 1 mm Hg). In the lungs, however, the water vapor reaches a pressure of 40 mm Hg. Similarly high vapor pressures can be expected within the insect tracheal system.

2. In many warm blooded vertebrates certain areas of the skin contain sweat glands. These secrete water, which withdraws body heat during its evaporation from the body surface. This cooling device is under careful nervous control and often the areas of skin that can produce sweat are limited. In dogs, for instance, sweat can be produced only at the soles of the paws.

The loss of water through sweating does not increase the internal salt concentration, because the sweat glands secrete not only water, but also salt.

3. The kidneys of terrestrial animals can reabsorb most of the water that is filtered into the tubules. In mammals almost 99 per cent of the water filtered into the tubules is reabsorbed (see Chap. 13). Similarly, filtered water is absorbed in the excretory organs of insects (see Fig. 13–32). An example for the mechanism of salt excretion and water conservation was described by Ramsay (1955a) for the stick insect *Carausius morosus*. The hemolymph constitutes about 15 per cent of the insect's weight. The Malpighian tubules produce urine at a rate that would remove all the water from the hemolymph in less than a day. Actually, practically all the water of the urine produced is reabsorbed in the rectum and returns into the circulation. The filtration pressure appears to be low, and urine formation is based on osmosis. The distal portions of the tubules actively transport potassium ions into the lumen (sodium is transported to a much lesser degree). The accumulated salt osmotically draws water (and with it certain excretory products) into the lumen and thus starts the urine flow. As the urine passes through the gut, the water is reabsorbed and excreta and salt are eliminated in the form of dry fecal pellets.

The amphibian kidney simply stops urine production altogether (or reduces the flow to a minimum) when the animals stay on land (Rey, 1937, 1938). Urine production is also reduced temporarily in certain desert mammals such as the camel (see Schmidt-Nielsen et al., 1956) and the rabbit (Forster and Nyboer, 1955).

ENERGETICS OF OSMOREGULATION

As explained in Chapter 4 (p. 80), the work required to transport 1 mole of a solute from a concentration C_1 to a concentration C_2 can be calculated according to

$$W = RT \ln \frac{C_1}{C_2} \tag{1}$$

For any other amount transported, the formula must be modified to read

$$W = RT \cdot n \cdot \ln \frac{C_1}{C_2} \tag{2}$$

where n represents the number of moles transported (n may, of course, be smaller than 1).

This work (W) can be expressed in calories: all that is necessary is to use the value 1.986 for R (see Table 4–8):

$$W = RT \cdot n \cdot \ln \frac{C_1}{C_2} \text{ cal,} \qquad \text{or} \qquad 1.986 \cdot T \cdot n \cdot \ln \frac{C_1}{C_2} \text{ cal} \tag{3}$$

To assess the energy requirements of a physiological process, it is desirable to know not only the work required, but also the power required. Power is the time rate of doing work, that is, work per unit time, or W/t.

The following approach closely follows that presented by Potts (1954): For a fresh-water animal that produces isosmotic urine, such as the wool-handed crab *Eriocheir*, it can be assumed that the amount of "salt" entering by active transport through the gills must about equal the amount lost with the urine, and the power required for this active transport can be immediately calculated from the known solute losses: if U is the "salt" concentration of urine (moles/liter) and V the volume of urine voided per hour, then the amount UV is transported in 1 hour from the low concentration of the medium, M (given in moles/liter), to that of the blood or body fluids, B (also given in moles/liter). The power required for this is

$$W/hr = RT \cdot UV \cdot \ln \frac{B}{M} \text{ cal/hr} \tag{4}$$

It is somewhat more complicated to calculate the energy required to produce a hyposmotic urine. It is assumed that blood filters into the excretory passage (e.g., kidney, nephridium, pericardium, coelom) and that the solute concentration of the initial urine is equal to the solute concentration of the filtered body fluid (blood), with symbols: U = B. Subsequently the solute content of the urine is reduced by active reabsorption and U changes to $B - \delta B$ or $U - \delta U$. To avoid confusion as to the meaning of the symbol U, one can introduce the symbol x to denote the initial urine concentration (x moles/liter), and U the final urine concentration ($x - \delta x$ moles/liter). The work required to change x to U is

$$W = RT \cdot V \ln \frac{B}{x} \, \delta x \text{ cal} \tag{5}$$

Table 5–2.

	Potamobius (60 g)	*Anodonta* (60 g)	*Eriocheir* (60 g)
M (mole/l)	0.0060	0.006	0.006
B (mole/l)	0.420	0.042	0.320
U (mole/l)	0.124	0.0236	0.320
V (l/hr)	$9.5 \cdot 10^{-5}$	$5.0 \cdot 10^{-4}$	$1.04 \cdot 10^{-4}$
Metabolic energy liberated (cal/hr)	10.0	1.2	14
PA (l/hr)	$2.307 \cdot 10^{-4}$	$1.42 \cdot 10^{-2}$	$3.312 \cdot 10^{-4}$
W/hr (cal/hr)			
total	0.0367	0.0145	0.0757
excretory organ	0.0079	0.0014	
body surface	0.0288	0.0131	
% of total metabolic energy liberated	0.3	1.2	0.5

Data from Potts, W. T. W.: The energetics of osmotic regulation in brackish- and fresh-water animals. J. Exp. Biol. *31*:618–630, 1954.

Thus the work required to change the concentration of the urine from that of B to U is

$$W = -RT \cdot V \ln \frac{B}{x}\,\delta x = -RT \cdot V\left[U \cdot \ln \frac{B}{U} + U - B\right] = -RT \cdot VU\left[\frac{B-U}{U} - \ln \frac{B}{U}\right] \text{cal} \tag{6}$$

Animals living in an hypotonic environment (brackish or fresh water) lose some "salt" to the outside, even if they excrete a hyposmotic urine, because this urine is certainly not "salt"-free. To maintain osmotic balance they must thus take up salt (ions) from the outside medium in an amount equal to UV. The power required for this can be calculated according to Equation 4.

Assuming that salt is lost only by way of urine, the total (minimal) power required to maintain osmotic balance must then be

$$\begin{aligned} W/hr &= RT \cdot UV \cdot \ln \frac{B}{M} + RT \cdot VU\left[\frac{B-U}{U} - \ln \frac{B}{U}\right] \\ &= RT \cdot UV\left[\ln \frac{B}{M} + \frac{B-U}{U} - \ln \frac{B}{U}\right] \\ &= RT \cdot V\left[U \ln \frac{U}{M} + B - U\right] \text{cal/hr} \end{aligned} \tag{7}$$

If the volume of an animal living in a hypotonic environment remains constant, it can be assumed that the amount of water entering the body is equal to that leaving it by way of the produced urine. Since the amount (V) that enters per unit time is proportional to the permeability of the body wall, P (liters/cm^2/molar concentration difference/hr), and to the total area of water permeable body surface, A (given in numbers of cm^2), we find that

$$V = PA\ (B - M) \qquad (8)$$

Thus, the total osmotic work per hour can also be computed by the formula

$$W/hr = RT \cdot PA\ (B - M) \cdot \left[U \ln \frac{U}{M} + B - U\right] \text{cal/hr} \qquad (9)$$

From these equations one can calculate the following from measured values of M, B, U, and V: PA, total W/hr, W/hr in excretory organ, and W/hr at body surface required to maintain osmotic balance. If the oxygen consumption of the organism is known, one can also calculate the percentage of the total rate of production of metabolic energy that is tied up in osmoregulation. Table 5–2 gives data and resulting figures for three fresh-water invertebrates, the crayfish (*Potamobius*), the mussel (*Anodonta*), and the wool-handed crab (*Eriocheir*). In all these cases the calculated minimal power requirements appear small compared to the total available energy. However, the thermodynamic data indicate only the minimal work required. The formulae do not take into consideration the efficiency of the cellular transport mechanisms. If, for example, the efficiency is 20 per cent, the values for the minimum power requirements must be multiplied by 5.

It has indeed been shown (Schlieper, 1929) that there is a striking correlation between oxygen consumption and the gradient B/M so that oxygen consumption may rise 20 to 40 per cent with strong dilution of the external medium (brackish water). It is likely that a large fraction of this additional oxidative metabolism is directly involved in osmoregulation (support of osmotic work), indicating that the thermodynamic computation leads to a large *under*-estimate of the cost of osmoregulation to the animal.

Where the concentrations of the individual constituents of the external medium, the blood (or plasma), and the urine are known, the thermodynamic calculations can be more refined than the summary treatment just presented. In this case the concentration work for each individual constituent must be computed and the concentrations corrected for the osmotic activity of the different solutes or ions; the osmotic concentration being $a \cdot \frac{N}{V} RT$, where a is the osmotic activity coefficient (see p. 73, Chap. 4) and N is the number of moles per volume V. As an example the detailed computation of the thermodynamic osmotic work performed by the human kidneys is shown in Table 5–3.

Internal Osmotic Phenomena: The Starling Hypothesis

The separation of body compartments by membranes (the coelomic lining, the endothelium of the blood-vascular system) brings with it osmotic phenomena. Membranes are not equally permeable to all solutes, and the membranes mentioned are no exception. We know, however, too little about the

Table 5–3. Concentration Work of Kidneys in Producing 1 Liter of Typical 24-Hour Urine From Plasma

$$2.3\ RT = 2.3 \times 1.987 \times 310 = 1420\ cal$$

Constituent	*Plasma Concentration in Mole/kg Water* (C_1)	*Urine Concentration in Mole/kg Water* (C_2)	$Log \frac{C_2}{C_1}$	*N in Moles*	*W in cal* +	*W in cal* −
Na^+	0.155	0.155	0.00	0.152	0	. . .
K^+	0.00512	0.0384	0.87	0.0384	48	. . .
Ca^{++}	0.00224	0.00375	0.22	0.00375	1	. . .
Mg^{++}	0.00103	0.00247	0.38	0.00247	1	. . .
Cl^-	0.104	0.166	0.20	0.166	48	. . .
HPO_4^-	0.000807	0.00326	0.60	0.00326	3	. . .
$H_2PO_4^=$	0.000140	0.0125	1.95	0.0125	35	. . .
SO_4^-	0.000312	0.0187	1.78	0.0187	47	. . .
HCO_3^-	0.0266	0.00106	−1.39	0.00106	. . .	2
Creatinine	0.000089	0.00664	1.87	0.00664	18	. . .
Urea	0.00500	0.333	1.82	0.333	861	. . .
Uric acid	0.000238	0.00289	1.08	0.00289	5	. . .
NH_4^+	0.000554	0.0222	1.61	0.0222	50	. . .
Water	0.994(X_1)	0.986(X_2)	−0.0035	54.2	. . .	267
				Totals	+1117	−269
					−269	
				Net	848 cal	

Note: Instead of $RT \cdot N \cdot \ln \frac{B}{U}$ one can write $2.3\ RT \cdot N \cdot \log \frac{B}{U}$.

From Lifson, N., and M. B. Visscher: Osmosis in living systems. *In* Medical Physics. (O. Glasser, ed.) Year Book Publishers, Chicago, 1944. Data from Borsook and Windgarden, 1931.

Table 5–4. Composition of Human Blood Plasma and of Lymph Fluid

	Plasma	*Lymph*
Protein (%)	6.85	2.61
Sugar (mg/100 ml)	123	124
Nonprotein N (mg/100 ml)	27.2	27
Urea (mg/100 ml)	22	23.5
Amino acid N (mg/100 ml)	4.9	4.8
Calcium (mg/100 ml)	10.4	9.2
Chloride (mg/100 ml)	392	413

After Drinker, C. K., and J. M. Yoffey: Lymphatics, Lymph and Lymphoid Tissue. Harvard University Press, Cambridge, 1941.

specific permeability characteristics of most cellular or intercellular membranes to make many general statements. A notable exception is the relationship between the vascular fluid compartment (blood or blood plasma) and the extravascular compartment of tissue fluid (interstitial fluid) in mammals. Both can be sampled readily, the former by drawing blood from a large blood vessel, the latter by drawing lymph.

The compositions of blood plasma and lymph of a vertebrate organism are given in Table 5–4. Note that the main difference is in the protein concentrations. All other constituents are nearly equal in concentration. For all practical purposes, the tissue fluid can be considered as an *ultrafiltrate* of blood plasma. Ultrafiltration is a process by which colloidal matter is separated from the noncolloidal particles of a liquid by filtration through a filter of suitable pore diameter. The endothelium of blood capillaries represents such an ultrafilter. The chief passage of fluid appears to be not through the endothelial cells themselves but through the intercellular cementing substance (Chambers and Zweifach, 1947) which, in this case, represents an intercellular membrane. The colloid that is held back, of course, is the protein. The structure of vertebrate capillaries is explained in Figure 5–18.

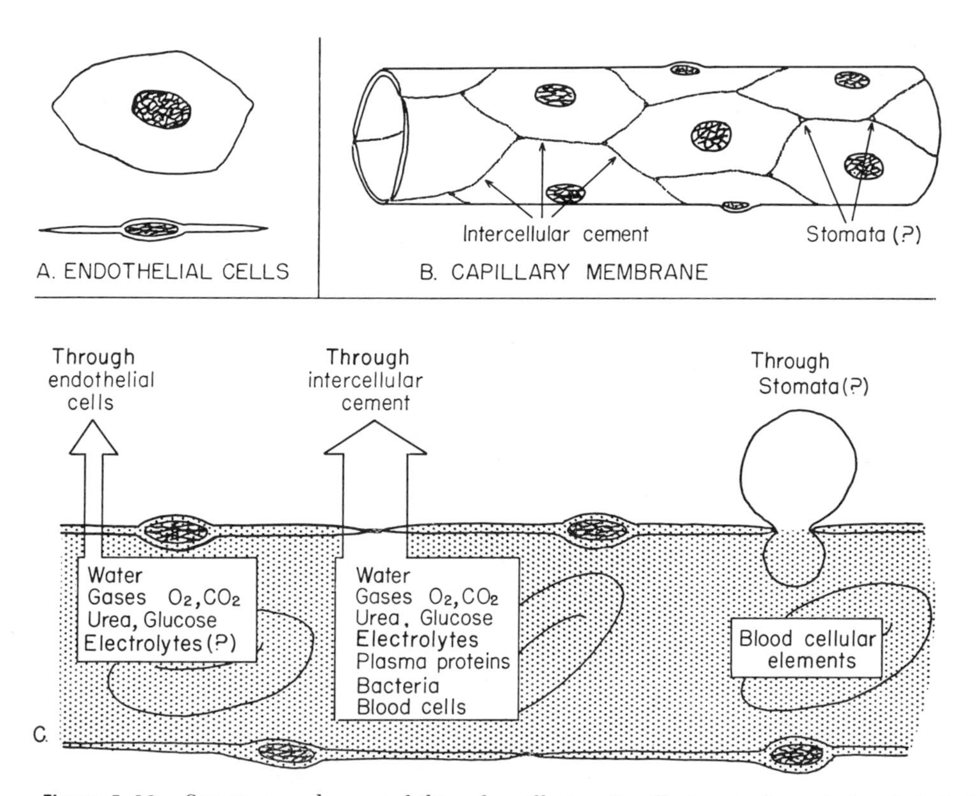

Figure 5–18. Structure and permeability of capillaries. Capillaries are formed of endothelial cells joined at their edges by "intercellular cement" (hyaluronic acid) to form tubes. Although water, gases, small organic molecules, and electrolytes may pass through endothelial cells, most of the capillary exchange takes place through the intercellular cement. Blood cells may pass through orifices between endothelial cells called *stomata* (singular: stoma). (From Rushmer, R. F.: Cardiovascular Dynamics, 2nd Ed. W. B. Saunders Co., Philadelphia, 1961.)

The protein, whose passage is prevented by the membrane, is a nonpermeating solute and as such causes an osmotic pressure—or, at least, osmosis. Keeping in mind the reservations attached to the term "osmotic pressure" (see pp. 71 and 79), we find that this osmotic pressure follows the equation (33) of Chapter 4:

$$\pi = RT\ (C_1 - C_2)$$

C_1 and C_2 represent the osmolal protein concentration in plasma and tissue fluid, respectively.

Although the weight of protein in both kinds of body fluids is high (2 to 6g/100 ml) the osmolar concentration of protein in each fluid compartment is rather low due to the large molecular weight of the protein: the large weight is represented by relatively few molecules. Thus the difference in osmotic pressure amounts to only 0.03 to 0.04 atmosphere of pressure.

Because this osmotic pressure is caused by colloid, it is called *colloid osmotic pressure*. Again, this term does not signify an actual pressure but the equivalent of a certain osmotic concentration (*colloid osmotic concentration*), or osmotic concentration difference. As Table 5–4 shows, the difference is in favor of the vascular compartment, which means that osmosis is likely to take place in the direction of blood plasma. The energy that drives water (and the contained permeating solutes) through the membrane that separates plasma and tissue fluid is equal to a pressure difference of 0.03 to 0.04 atmosphere. Thus, the so-called colloid osmotic pressure counteracts the effects of the hydrostatic pressure in the vascular system. Whereas the hydrostatic pressure tends to act as filtration pressure, forcing blood fluid (plasma) through the endothelial wall into the tissue spaces, the "colloid osmotic pressure" draws fluid in the opposite direction. This situation is depicted in the conceptual diagram of Figure 5–19.

Direct measurement of the hydrostatic pressures in capillaries, by the ingenious American physiologist E. M. Landis (1927, 1933, 1934), established that filtration outward through the capillary wall occurs only if the hydrostatic pressure within the capillary is greater than the colloid osmotic pressure. Now, numerous measurements carried out on Amphibia as well as on mammals have shown that the hydrostatic pressue in the venous ends of capillaries is generally lower than the colloid osmotic pressure, while in the arterial ends of the capillaries it is considerably higher. Thus, the venous ends of the capillaries, fluid moves from the tissue spaces into the capillaries, whereas it moves in the opposite direction at the arterial ends of the capillaries. The energy that drives fluid in either direction can be expressed in terms of pressure, that is, in atmospheres (atm) or in mm Hg. It is referred to as the *effective filtration pressure* and follows the general formula:

$$\text{Filtration pressure} = \text{hydrostatic (blood) pressure} - (\text{colloid osmotic pressure} + \text{tissue pressure})$$

For instance, if the hydrostatic pressure is 35 mm Hg, the colloid osmotic pressure 25 mm Hg, and the tissue pressure 4 mm Hg, the effective filtration pressure is $35 - (25 + 4) = 6$ mm Hg. On the other hand, if the hydrostatic pressure is 20 mm Hg, everything else being equal, the effective filtration pres-

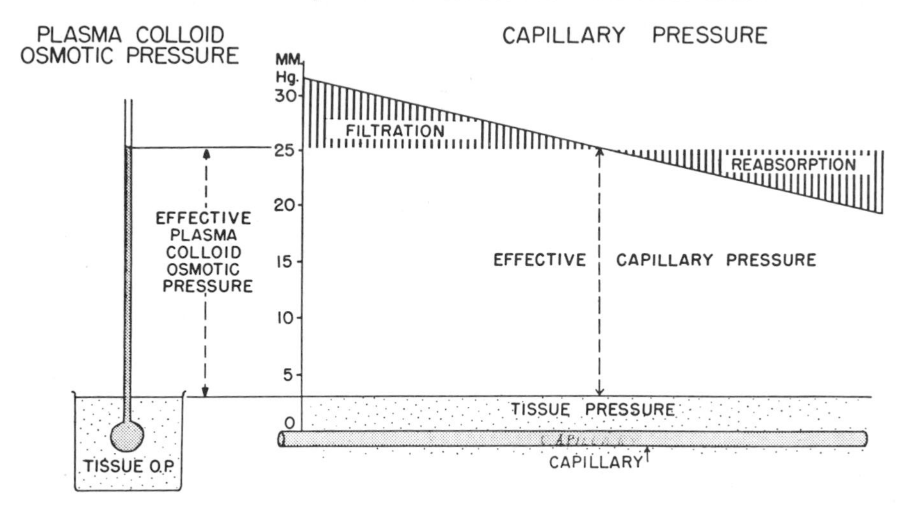

Figure 5-19. Factors determining fluid exchange in capillaries (Starling hypothesis). The term *TISSUE O.P.* means osmotic pressure of extracellular tissue fluid. *Effective capillary pressure* means hydrostatic pressure equal (but opposite in direction) to plasma colloid osmotic pressure. *Tissue pressure* means hydrostatic pressure of tissue fluid. Fluid filters out of the capillaries when the hydrostatic pressure in the capillaries is greater than the colloid osmotic pressure of plasma. Fluid is reabsorbed into the capillaries when the hydrostatic pressure is lower than the colloid osmotic pressure. (From Rushmer, R. F.: Cardiovascular Dynamics, 2nd Ed. W. B. Saunders Co., Philadelphia, 1961.)

sure is $20 - (25 + 4) = -9$ mm Hg; in other words, the filtration pressure is negative if the hydrostatic pressure in the capillaries is lower than the sum of colloid osmotic pressure and tissue pressure. This is known as the *Starling theory* or *hypothesis*. It was proposed in 1895 by E. H. Starling and, because of its convincing simplicity, has been honored in textbooks ever since.

There is not much doubt that the theory applies to any vascular system. However, the details of the mechanisms that govern capillary permeability and osmotic fluxes are far more complex. Not only do capillary pressure measurements (and capillary pressures) vary greatly, but the capillary wall is probably not acting as a *simple* filter through which all solutes pass with equal ease—but some solutes pass more readily than others. However, so little is known about the permeability constants of the various solutes of blood plasma in capillary membranes, that the Starling theory is unchallenged.

Tissue pressure also is variable. Although in most instances it can be considered low compared with the hydrostatic pressure and colloid osmotic pressure, it may rise to considerable value in the tissue spaces of muscles.

The Starling theory makes it easy to visualize a mechanism that allows an efficient transfer of materials in and out of the vascular system. There must be, in fact, a "transvascular circulation" consisting of a stream of fluid (ultrafiltrate) leaving the capillaries at their arterial ends, and another stream entering the capillaries at their venous ends. This is depicted in Figure 5-20. According to this theory, there must be a rather delicate balance between the respective hydrostatic pressures in arteries and veins on the one hand, and the colloid osmotic pressure on the other. An overall increase in hydrostatic pressure, for instance, would cause more fluid to leave the vascular compartment than

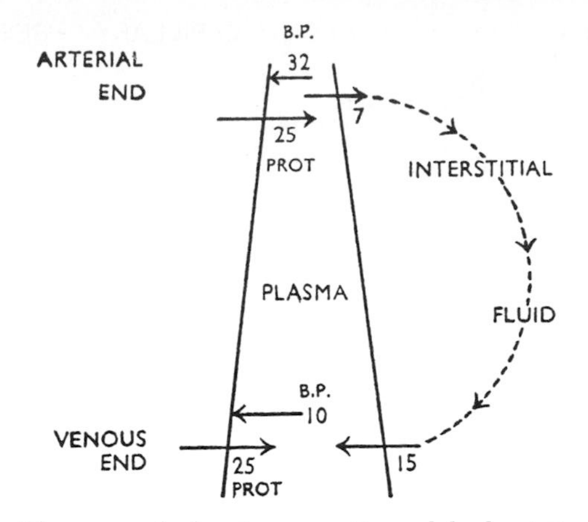

Figure 5–20. A capillary vessel showing osmotic and hydrostatic pressure with resultant flow of tissue fluid, as formulated in the Starling hypothesis. The values used are those of human capillaries. *B.P.*, blood pressure; *PROT*, colloid osmotic pressure (25 mm Hg). At the arterial end of the capillary the blood pressure is 7 mm Hg greater than the colloid osmotic pressure, whereas at the venous end the blood pressure is 15 mm Hg less than the colloid osmotic pressure. The difference (+ or –) between hydrostatic pressure and colloid osmotic pressure represents the effective filtration pressure that drives fluid out of and into the capillaries. The diagram does not take into account the colloid osmotic pressure of the interstitial (tissue) fluid; this, however, is considerably lower than that of the blood plasma, leaving enough effective colloid osmotic pressure to allow the system to function essentially as depicted in the diagram. (From Bell, G. H., J. N. Davidson, and H. Scarborough: Textbook of Physiology and Biochemistry, 4th Ed. Williams & Wilkins Co., Baltimore, 1959.

returns to it, causing tissues to swell. A diminished colloid osmotic pressure (as may be caused by a fall in blood protein during starvation) likewise leads to a loss of fluid to the tissue spaces, again causing tissue swelling. Such swelling that is caused by an increase in interstitial or tissue fluid is known as *edema.*

Low blood pressure or increased colloid osmotic pressure can cause dehydration of tissues, that is, a shift in body fluid from the interstitial spaces to the vascular compartment.

The Starling theory has been confirmed not only by the work of Landis but by that of Pappenheimer and Soto-Rivera (1948). Their data show that in cat limbs the rate of fluid movement amounts to about 7 ml/hr/mm Hg/kg of tissue; that is, for each millimeter Hg of effective filtration pressure 7 ml is filtered each hour per kilogram of tissue. Assuming perfect balance of hydrostatic and colloid osmotic pressures, we can assume that half of that volume moves out of and the other half into the vascular compartment. If, in each case, the effective (+ or –) filtration pressure is 10 mm Hg, this means that 70 ml of fluid is exchanged each hour, or 2.64 l/day.

This exchange, described by the Starling theory, is, of course, not the sole mechanism of exchange across vascular membranes. Diffusion is an additional, significant factor.

There is an interesting correlation between colloid osmotic pressure and blood pressure: the higher the typical blood pressure of an animal species, the higher the colloid osmotic pressure. This appears to hold true even in cases in

Table 5–5. **Relation of Colloid Osmotic Pressure and Blood Pressure**

Animal	*Colloid osmotic pressure* (mm Hg)	*Blood Pressure* (mm Hg)
Aplysia	0.02	1.8
Homarus	1.15	8.5
Octopus	3.24	40
"Amphibia"	4.2	50
Oryctogalus	20.2	99
Homo	29.1	120

Data from Florkin & Blum, Sur la teneur en protéines du sang et du liquide coelomique des invertébrés. Arch. Int. Physiol. 38:353–364, 1934.

which the circulatory system is open and blood communicates directly with the extracellular or tissue fluid (e.g., *Aplysia* and *Homarus*). Examples are given in Table 5–5.

IONIC REGULATION

Ionic Regulation of Cells

The relative and absolute concentrations of inorganic and organic ions within body cells, with rare exceptions, differ considerably from those of the body fluids, even though the total concentrations of all ions combined are rather similar in both fluid compartments. The topic of "ionic regulation" of cells is concerned with the mechanisms that permit the maintenance of a special intracellular ionic environment.

There are usually two major differences between intra- and extracellular media: (1) The intracellular medium contains more potassium and less sodium and chloride than the extracellular fluid, and (2) the intracellular fluid contains higher concentrations of *organic* ions, in particular of free amino acids, than the extracellular fluid.

Regulation of Inorganic Ion Concentration. The concentrations of intra- and extracellular sodium, potassium, calcium, magnesium, and chloride ions of some representative cell types are compared in Table 5–6. K^+ and Na^+ ions represent the major amount of intracellular cation. This amount must be equal to that of the intracellular anions. Thus, if the concentration of one of the two cations is high, the concentration of the other must be low. Any excess intracellular cations would create an excess of positive charge which would repel cations and effectively prevent their entry into the cell. However, the electrochemical equilibrium does not explain the proportion of K and Na in the cell. In fact, if this were the only determining factor, both ions should be present in equal concentration.

Table 5–6. Inorganic Ions in Circulating Body Fluids and in Tissue Cells of Various Species* (All data in mM/l or mM/kg H_2O)

Organism		*Na*	*K*	*Ca*	*Mg*	*Cl*
Sipunculoidea						
Phascolosoma	serum	378	38	10.5	—	430
	muscle	122	106	8.5	—	91
Mollusca						
Anodonta	serum	15.4	0.38	5.3	0.35	10.55
	muscle	5.18	10.5	5.39	2.46	10.6
Mytilus	blood	474	12.00	11.90	52.6	553
	muscle	79	152	7.3	34	94
Loligo	blood	456	22.2	10.6	55.4	578
	nerve	50	400	0.4	10	40
Arthropoda						
Carcinus	blood	531	12.26	13.32	19.5	557
	nerve	41	422	—	—	27
Nephrops	blood	541	7.81	11.95	9.28	552
	muscle	24.5	188	3.72	20.3	53.1
Vertebrata						
Myxine	blood	537	9.21	5.87	18.0	542
	muscle	137	113	2.2	10.8	121
Rana	serum	109	2.6	2.1	1.3	77.9
	muscle	15.5	12.6	3.3	16.7	1.2
Ratus	serum	150	6.4	3.4	1.6	119
	muscle	16	152	1.9	16.1	5.0
Felis	serum	161	4.6	—	—	128.7
	nerve	41	182			17.5

*Data collected from the literature, as documented by Prosser, C. L., and F. A. Brown, Jr.: Comparative Animal Physiology, 2nd Ed., W. B. Saunders Co., Philadelphia, 1961; and Potts, W. T. W., and G. Parry: Osmotic and Ionic Regulation in Animals, Pergamon Press, Oxford.

It is now well established that the maintenance of unequal concentrations of K and Na ions in cells requires the continuous expenditure of energy. Just how this energy is used is still debated. The majority of physiologists believe in the existence of a so-called *sodium pump*, a mechanism that transports any sodium ion that diffused into the cell back to the outside. Such a pump operates against the concentration gradient (see Chap. 4, p. 83) and against an electrochemical gradient (Chap. 16). This pump is assumed to be located in the cell membrane itself or just beneath it. Other physiologists believe that the energy needed to keep sodium ions out of the cell is employed to maintain the protoplasm in a state that favors the selective adsorption of potassium ion and tends to exclude sodium. For the latter hypothesis, the cell membrane is not the seat of an ion-regulating mechanism. Evidence for the latter concept is given in the books by Troschin (1958) and Ling (1962). At present, this evidence cannot surmount the evidence that favors the membrane theory of ionic regulation. Perhaps the most forceful argument in favor of a sodium pump that is localized within or just beneath the cell membrane is provided by the experiments of Baker, Hodgkin, and Shaw (1961): these authors squeezed out nearly all the protoplasm of a giant nerve fiber without damaging the cell membrane. Then they filled the empty membrane with artificial "intracellular fluids" of low Na content and found that the remaining membrane maintained the difference in sodium and potassium gradients.

Compounds that interfere with oxidative metabolism "inhibit" the sodium extrusion mechanism. This has been observed in a variety of cells. It is significant that injection of adenosine triphosphate can, to a certain extent, reactivate the pump even when metabolism remains impaired (Hodgkin and Keynes, 1955; Caldwell, 1960; Caldwell et al., 1960).

The extrusion of Na ions appears to be coupled with an inward transport of K ions. Where that is the case, one can speak of a sodium-potassium pump. Evidence for this is the failure or reduction of sodium extrusion when no potassium is present in the extracellular fluid.

In contrast to the active regulation of the proportion of internal cations (Na^+ and K^+), it appears that the inorganic anions Cl^- and HCO_3^- (chloride and bicarbonate) passively follow the electrochemical gradients established by active cation transport and that they are distributed across the membrane according to the principles discussed in Chapter 4 under "Donnan equilibrium." In other words, these ions are not themselves actively transported and any concentration differences between the intra- and extracellular media are a secondary effect.

For a more extensive discussion of active transport see Chapter 27.

Regulation of Organic Ion Concentration. There is a good deal of evidence that amino acids are actively transported into cells by specific carrier mechanisms (Van Slyke and Meyer, 1913; Krebs, Eggleston, and Hems, 1949; Piez and Eagle, 1958; Christensen and Riggs, 1952). Table 5–7 gives data of the free amino acids in some nerve tissues and muscles.

The concentrations of amino acids appear to be regulated; that is, they are found to be constant under a given set of circumstances, and one can expect to find the same concentrations of the different amino acids whenever one analyses healthy cells of the same kind. Under certain kinds of stress, the concentrations change.

Particularly in crustacean muscle cells it has been found that the concentration of certain amino acids varies in accordance with the outside osmotic concentration. Examples for this are given in Figure 5–21. It is interesting that only certain ones of the several kinds of amino acids present show a conspicuous change. It is almost certain that the change in concentration is not caused by a loss of the regulating amino acid to the outside (or vice versa, an uptake from

Table 5–7. Amino Acids in Body Fluids and Tissues (All Values in mM/l or mM/kg cell water)

Organism*	Tissue	Total Amino Acids	Arg	Ala	Asp	Cys	Glu	$GluNH_2$	Gly	His	Ileu	Leu	Lys	Meth	Prol	Ser	Taur	Threo	Val	Other Amino Acids	Reference
(T) Man	plasma	4	0.3	0.1	0.03		0.08	0.55	0.2				0.2		0.2		0.03		0.3		1
(T) Rat	plasma	4	0.4	0.02	0.04		0.11		0.3			0.15	0.35		0.3	0.59	0.4	0.25	0.19		2
	muscle	about 50	3.5	2.1	3.1		4.4		1.7						0.5	1.6	30.4				2
(T) *Schistocerca*	blood	about 100	4	0	0		5	11	33						4	35	0				3
(T) *Bombyx*, pupa	blood	about 83	6	2	0.3		4	16	12	10			5	7	6		?				4
(T) *Helix*	plasma	about 1	0.2	?	0.03		0.17	0.15	0.13						Trace	0.17	?				5
	brain	about 28	4.2	?	0.4	2.0	4.3	2.3	1.2				4.0		0		?				5
(F) *Astacus*	plasma	5	1.4	0.2	0.1		2.0		0.8		0.5				0.3		?		0.5		6
	muscle	186	14	66	1.4		6	?	24	6			9		23		?				6, 7
(F) *Anodonta*	muscle	18.4	1.4	3.0	4.7		2.9		2.6		0.7	0.4	0.9		0.1		?	0.4			8
(F) *Eriocheir*	muscle	239	50	17	6		35		89						30		?			less than 12	9, 10
(M) *Mytilus*	muscle	393	54.6	34.3	21.4		31		76						3.6		?			less than 4	8
(M) *Arenicola*	body wall	525	118	0.3	22		17		357						0		?			less than 10	7
(M) *Cancer*	blood	3	0.20	0.21	0.02		0.07		0.47				0.14		0.34	0.28		0.14			11
	muscle	510	56	65	2		9		330						18		?			less than 15	6

*(F), fresh-water animal; (M), marine animal; (T), terrestrial animal.

1. Camien, M. N., H. Sarlet, G. Duchâteau, and M. Florkin: J. Biol. Chem. *193*:881–885, 1951.
2. Duchâteau, G., and M. Florkin: J. Physiol. *48*:520, 1956.
3. Duchâteau, G., H. Sarlet, and M. Florkin: Arch. Int. Physiol. *60*:103–104, 1952.
4. Duchâteau, G., and M. Florkin: Arch. Int. Physiol. *62*:487, 1954.
5. Duchâteau-Bosson, G., C. Jeuniaux, and M. Florkin: Arch. Int. Physiol. *69*:30, 1961.
6. Florkin, M.: Proc. Int. Congr. Biochem. Vienna *12*:63–73, 1959.
7. Kerkut, G. A., and G. A. Cottrell: Comp. Biochem. Physiol. *5*:227–230, 1962.
8. Scharff, R., and I. G. Wool: Nature *202*:603, 1964.
9. Stevens, T. M., C. E. Howard, and R. W. Schlesinger: Comp. Biochem. Physiol. *3*:310, 1961.
10. Treherne, J. E.: J. Exp. Biol. *36*:533–545, 1959.
11. White, A., P. Handler, E. L. Smith, and D. Stetten: Principles of Biochemistry, 2nd Ed. McGraw-Hill Book Co., New York, 1959.

the outside), but is achieved within the confines of the cell. Conceivably, this is done by depolymerization or polymerization. The precise mechanisms by which changes in the external osmotic concentration effect a change in the internal amino acid pool are not known.

Ionic Regulation of Organisms

If we disregard the insects, the majority of animal species live in water, most of them in the sea. On the whole, the ionic composition of their body fluids is similar to that of sea water. In fact, the body fluids of many marine organisms contain inorganic ions in the same proportion in which they occur in sea water. Sea water contains far more sodium than any other cation. This is followed by magnesium, potassium, and calcium. Of the anions, chloride is the most prominent. It is followed by sulfate. The concentrations of all of these ions, expressed in millimoles per liter, are given in Table 5–8. The table also presents data concerning the inorganic ion concentrations in the body fluids of a variety of aquatic animals.

Close scrutiny of this table reveals that the ion concentrations of the body fluids of certain animals differ from those of sea water. In most cases, the chloride ion concentration is somewhat higher and the sulfate ion concentration is correspondingly lower than that of sea water. This is generally true for coelenterates, arthropods, molluscs, chordates, and, to a limited degree, annelids and sipunculids. Some exceptions are curious. The blood of *Mytilus gallprovincialis*, for instance, has a higher concentration of sulfate than does sea water.

Magnesium ions are present in lower concentration than in sea water in body fluids of many Crustacea and chordates. In several molluscan species belonging to lamellibranch, gastropod, and cephalopod groups, magnesium is actually concentrated (Bethe, 1929; Bethe and Berger, 1931; Robertson, 1949, 1953).

Potassium ions are more concentrated than in sea water in the body fluids of most molluscs. In the squid *Loligo* the concentration is more than twice that of sea water.

In annelids, the ion concentrations of the body fluids vary only slightly from those of sea water, even where some ionic regulation occurs. Echinoderms have little, if any, power to maintain ionic concentrations different from those of sea water.

As mentioned in the section on osmoregulation (pp. 101–108) part of the total osmotic concentration of the body fluids of elasmobranch fishes is made up of urea and trimethylamine. The inorganic ions (K^+, Na^+, Ca^{++}, Mg^{++}, Cl^-, SO_4^-, HCO_3^-) are therefore all maintained at a concentration that is considerably lower than in sea water.

The regulation of the specific ionic composition of body fluids depends on a number of mechanisms: 1. The permeability properties of the body wall, in particular, the exchange membranes. 2. The active inward and outward transport of ions in gills and nephridia (kidneys). 3. Passive transport due to electrical potentials that are maintained across the exchange membranes.

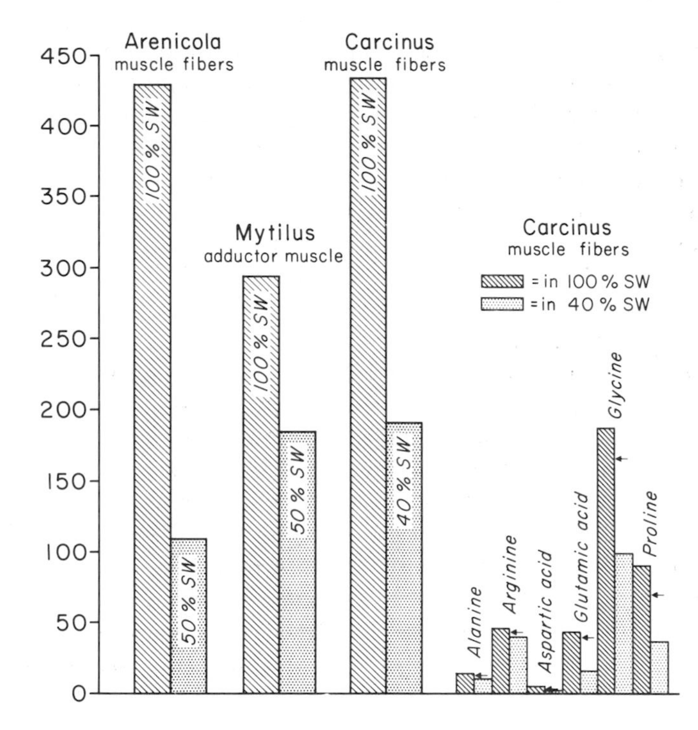

Figure 5–21. Variations in amino acid contents of muscle fibers in response to exposure to hypotonic extracellular medium. **Left**, changes in the total amino acid pool. **Right**, changes in concentration of the individual amino acids. The control animals were left in normal sea water (100 per cent SW) and the experimental animals were maintained in dilute sea water (50 per cent SW and 40 per cent SW) before the muscles were analyzed. The arrows point to the concentrations to be expected according to the change in water content of the cells. (Data from Cowey, C. B., and J. Shaw, quoted in Potts: W. T. W.: The inorganic and amino acid composition of some lamellibranch muscles. J. Exp. Biol. 35:749–764, 1958; and from Duchateau, G., M. Florkin, and C. Jeuniaux: Composante aminoacide des tissus chez les Crustaces. I. Arch. Int. Physiol. 67:489–500, 1959.)

Table 5–8. Concentrations of Common Ions (mM/kg water) in the Circulating Body Fluids of Some Marine Animals Compared with the Concentrations in Sea Water

Sea water	*Na* 478.3	*K* 10.13	*Ca* 10.48	*Mg* 54.5	*Cl* 558.4	*SO_4* 28.77
Aurelia	474	10.72	10.03	53.0	**580**	**15.77**
Aphrodita	476	10.50	10.45	54.6	557	26.50
Echinus	474	10.13	10.62	53.5	557	28.70
Mytilus	474	**12.00**	11.90	52.6	553	28.90
Loligo	**456**	**22.20**	10.60	55.4	578	**8.14**
Ligia	**566**	**13.30**	**34.90**	**20.2**	**629**	**4.03**
Maia	488	**12.37**	**13.56**	**44.1**	**554**	**14.50**
Carcinus	**531**	**12.26**	**13.32**	**19.5**	557	**16.46**
Nephrops	**541**	**7.81**	**11.95**	**9.28**	552	19.8
Myxine	**537**	9.12	**5.87**	**18.0**	542	**6.33**

Ion concentrations that differ by more than 10 per cent from those found in standard sea water are shown in boldface.

From Potts, W. T. W., and G. Parry: Osmotic and Ionic Regulation in Animals. Pergamon Press, Oxford, 1964.

The permeability to ions is usually proportional to the diameter of the ion in question: the larger the "hydrated" diameter, the lower the permeability. This, in part, explains the exclusion of magnesium and sulfate ions. Obviously, permeability alone is not sufficient to determine concentration differences across the body wall, but differential permeability can help in the maintenance (regulation) of the concentration differences. Active transport must be relied on as the chief mode of ionic regulation. This requires energy and relies on oxidative metabolism.

Active transport across cellular membranes presupposes an asymmetry of the cells that constitute the membrane: Transport across the membranes bordering the body fluids must be different from that across the "outer" membranes, even if in nothing else but the direction in which a given ion species is carried: For instance, for sodium ions to be carried outward, the "inner" membranes must carry sodium into the cell while the "outer" membranes carry it out.

A good example of the complexities of transcellular transport is shown in Figures 5–22 and 5–23, which illustrate some of the ion-transport mechanisms of the vertebrate kidney tubules.

For a more detailed, recent survey of ionic regulation, refer to Potts and Parry (1964): Osmotic and Ionic Regulation in Animals.

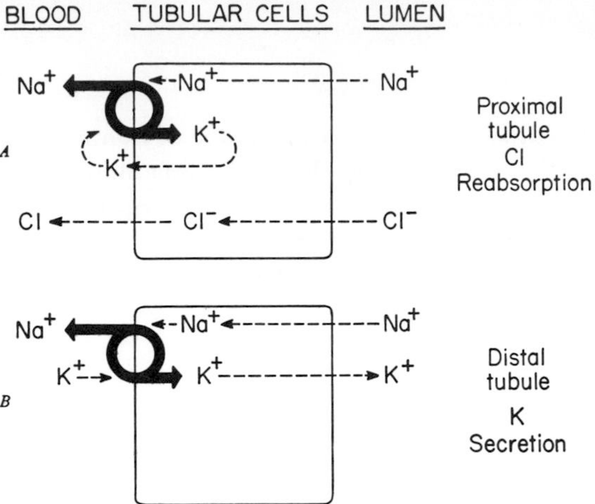

Figure 5–22. Proposed mechanism by which a coupled $Na^+ - K^+$ pump causes Na^+ reabsorption with associated anion (Cl^-) reabsorption in the cells of the proximal segment and Na^+ reabsorption and K^+ secretion in the distal segment of mammalian kidney tubules. Note that the pump is located only on one side of the cells. (From Koch, A.: The kidney. *In* Physiology and Biophysics, 19th Ed. Ruch, T. C., and H. D. Patton, eds. W. B. Saunders Co., Philadelphia, 1965.)

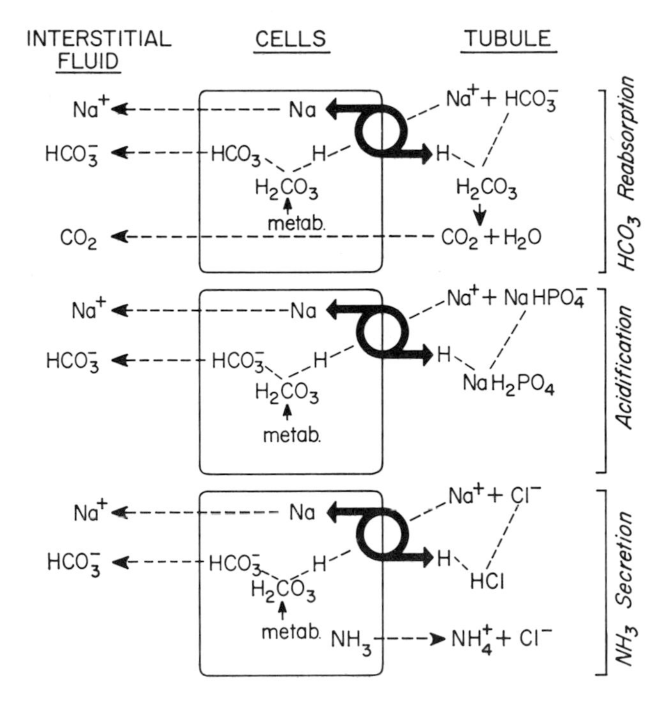

Figure 5–23. Three aspects of the ion-exchange mechanisms going on in the distal segment of the mammalian kidney tubules: bicarbonate reabsorption, acidification, and ammonia secretion. Note how hydrogen and ammonium ions are "trapped" in the tubules by being incorporated into molecules of bicarbonate, phosphate, and chloride. The broken lines indicate passive transport (following concentration gradients); the solid lines symbolize active transport involving exchange of H^+ for Na^+ and vice versa. (From Koch, A.: The kidney. *In* Physiology and Biophysics, 19th Ed. Ruch, T. C., and H. D. Patton, eds. W. B. Saunders Co., Philadelphia, 1965.)

REFERENCES

Adolph, E. F. (1936) Differential permeability to water and osmotic changes in the marine worm *Phascolosoma*. J. Cell. Comp. Physiol. 9:117–135.

Baker, P. F., A. L. Hodgkin, and T. I. Shaw (1961) Replacement of the protoplasm of a giant nerve fibre with artificial solutions. Nature *190*:885–887.

Beadle, L. C. (1937) Adaptation to changes of salinity in the polychaetes. Control of body volume and of body-fluid concentration in *Nereis diversicolor*. J. Exp. Biol. *14*:56–70.

Beadle, L. C. (1957) Comparative physiology: osmotic and ionic regulation in aquatic animals. Ann. Rev. Physiol. *19*:329–358.

Bethe, A. (1929) Ionendurchlässigkeit der Körperoberfläche von wirbellosen Tieren des Meeres als Ursache der Giftigkeit von Seewasser abnormer Zusammensetzung. Pflügers Arch. ges. Physiol. *234*:344–362.

Bethe, A. (1934) Die Salz- und Wasser-Permeabilität der Körperoberflächen versschiedener Seetiere in ihren gegenseitigen Verhältnis. Pflügers Arch. ges. Physiol. *234*:629–644.

Bethe, A., and E. Berger (1931) Variationen im Mineralbestand verschiedener Blutarten. Pflügers Arch. ges. Physiol. *227*:571–584.

Black, V. S. (1957) Excretion and osmoregulation. *In* The Physiology of Fishes, Vol. 1. (M. E. Brown, ed.) Academic Press, New York.

Borsook, H., and H. M. Windgarden (1931) The work of the kidney in the production of urine. Proc. Nat. Acad. Sci. *17*:3–12.

Bottazzi, F. (1897) La pression osmotique du sang des animaux marins. Arch. ital. de Biol. *28*:61–66.

Bottazzi, F. (1908) Osmotischer Druck und elektrische Leitefähigkeit der Flüssigkeiten der einzelligen, pflanzlichen und tiereschen Organismen. Ergebn. Physiol. *7*:161–402.

von Buddenbrock, W. (1956) Vergleichende Physiologie, Bd. III: Ernährung, Wasserhaushalt und Mineralhaushalt der Tiere. Birkhäuser Verlag, Basel.

Caldwell, P. C. (1960) Some aspects of the part played by phosphate compounds in the regulation of certain inorganic ions in cells. *In* Regulation of the Inorganic Energy Content of Cells. (G. E. W. Wolstenholme and C. M. O. O'Conner, eds.) J. & A. Churchill, London.

Caldwell, P. C., A. L. Hodgkin, R. D. Keynes, and T. I. Shaw (1960) The effects of injecting energy rich phosphate compounds on the active transport of ions into the giant axons of *Loligo*. J. Physiol. *152*:561–590.

Chambers, R., and B. W. Zweifach (1947) Intercellular cement and capillary permeability. Physiol. Rev. *27*:436–463.

Christensen, H. N., and T. R. Riggs (1952) Concentrative uptake of amino acids by the Ehrlich mouse ascites carcinoma cell. J. Biol. Chem. *194*:57–68.

Costello, D. P. (1939) The volumes occupied by the formed protoplasmic components in marine eggs. Physiol. Zool. *12*:13–21.

Croghan, P. C. (1958a) Ionic fluxes in Artemia salina L. J. Exp. Biol. *35*:425–436.

Croghan, P. C. (1958b) The osmotic and ionic regulation of Artemia salina L. J. Exp. Biol. *35*:219–233.

Croghan, P. C. (1958c) The mechanism of osmotic regulation in Artemia salina L.: The physiology of the branchiae. J. Exp. Biol. *35*:234–242.

Croghan, P. C. (1958d) The mechanism of osmotic regulation in Artemia salina L.: the physiology of the gut. J. Exp. Biol. *35*:243–249.

Duval, M. (1925) Recherches physio-chemiques et physiologiques sur le milieu intérieur des animaux aquatiques. Modifications sous l'influence du milieu extérieur. Ann. Inst. Oceanogr., Monaco, N. S. *2*:232–407.

Edney, E. B. (1957) Water Relations of Terrestrial Arthropods. Cambridge University Press, London.

Forster, R. P., and J. Nyboer (1955) Effect of induced apnea on cardiovascular renal functions in the rabbit. Amer. J. Physiol. *183*:149–154.

von Gelei, G. (1939) Neuere Beiträge zum Bau und zu der Funktion des Exkretionssystem vom Paramecium. Arch. Protistenkunde 92:384–400.

Harnisch, O. (1934) Osmoregulation und Osmoregulatorischer Mechanismus der Larve von *Chironomus thummi*. Z. vergl. Physiol. *21*:281–295.

Heilbrunn, L. V. (1952) Outline of General Physiology, 3rd Ed. W. B. Saunders Co., Philadelphia.

Höber, R. (1902) Physikalische Chemie der Zellen und Gewebe, 1st Ed.

Hodgkin, A. L., and R. D. Keynes (1955) Active transport of cations in giant axons from *Sepia* and *Loligo*. J. Physiol. *128*:28–60.

Jepps, M. W. (1947) Contribution to the study of the sponges. Proc. Roy. Soc. *134*:408–417.

Jürgens, O. (1935) Die Wechselbeziehungen von Blutkreislauf, Atmung, und Osmoregulation bei Polychäten. Zool. Jahrb., Allg. Zool. Physiol. Tiere 55:1–46.

Kitching, J. A. (1938) Contractile vacuoles. Biol. Rev. *13*:403–444.

Kitching, J. A. (1954) The physiology of contractile vacuoles. X. Effects of high hydrostatic pressure on the contractile vacuole of a suctorian. J. Exp. Biol. *31*:76–83.

Krebs, H. A., L. V. Eggleston, and R. Hems (1949) Distribution of glutamine and glutamic acid in animal tissues. Biochem. J. *44*:159–163.

Krogh, A. (1938) The active absorption of ions in some freshwater animals. Z. vergl. Physiol. *25*:335–350.

Krogh, A. (1939) Osmotic Regulation in Aquatic Animals. Cambridge University Press, London.

Landis, E. M. (1927) The relation between capillary pressure and the rate at which fluid passes through the walls of single capillaries. Amer. J. Physiol. *82*:217–238.

Landis, E. M. (1933) Poiseuille's law and the capillary circulation. Amer. J. Physiol. *103*:432–443.

Landis, E. M. (1934) Capillary pressure and capillary permeability. Physiol. Rev. *14*:404–481.

Lifson, N., and M. B. Visscher (1944) Osmosis in living systems. *In* Medical Physics, Vol. I, pp. 869–892. (O. Glasser, ed.) Year Book Publishers, Chicago.

Lilly, S. J. (1955) Osmoregulation and ionic regulation in *Hydra*. J. Exp. Biol. *32*:423–439.

Ling, G. N. (1962) A Physical Theory of the Living State. Blaisdell Publishing Co., New York.

Lucké, B., and M. McCutcheon (1932) The living cell as an osmotic system and its permeability to water. Physiol. Rev. *12*:68–139.

Lucké, B., and R. A. Ricca (1949) Osmotic properties of the egg cells of the oyster (Ostrea virginica). J. Gen. Physiol. *25*:215–227.

Martin, A. W. (1958) Comparative physiology (excretion). Ann. Rev. Physiol. *20*:225–242.

Mast, S. O., and D. L. Hopkins (1941) Regulation of the water content of *Amoeba mira* and adaptation to changes in the osmotic concentration of the surrounding medium. J. Cell. Comp. Physiol. *17*:31–48.

Müller, R. (1936) Die osmoregulatorische Bedeutung der kontraktilen Vakuolen von *Amoeba proteus, Zoothamnium hiketes* und *Frontonia marina*. Arch. Protistenkunde *87*:345–382.

Nagel, H. (1934) Die Aufgaben der Exkretionsorgane und der Kiemen bei der Osmoregulation von *Carcinus maenas*. Z. vergl. Physiol. *21*:468–491.

Panikkar, N. K. (1941) Osmoregulation in some palaemonid prawns. J. Mar. Biol. Assn. U. K. *25*:317–359.

Pappenheimer, J. R., and A. Soto-Rivera (1948) Effective osmotic pressure of the plasma proteins and other quantities associated with the capillary circulation in hind limbs of cats and dogs. Amer. J. Physiol. *152*:471–491.

Picken, L. E. R. (1937) The mechanism of urine formation in invertebrates. II. The excretory mechanism in certain molluscs. J. Exp. Biol. *14*:20–34.

Piez, K. A., and H. Eagle (1958) The free amino acid pool of cultured human cells. J. Biol. Chem. *231*:533–545.

Potts, W. T. W. (1954) The energetics of osmotic regulation in brackish- and freshwater animals. J. Exp. Biol. *31*:618–630.

Potts, W. T. W., and G. Parry (1964) Osmotic and Ionic Regulation in Animals. Pergamon Press, Oxford.

Prosser, C. L., and F. A. Brown, Jr. (1961) Comparative Animal Physiology, 2nd Ed. W. B. Saunders Co., Philadelphia. Chapters 2 and 3.

Ramsay, J. A. (1955a) The excretion of sodium, potassium and water by the malpighian tubules of the stick insect, *Dixippus morosus* (Orthoptera, Phasmidae). J. Exp. Biol. *32*:200–216.

Ramsay, J. A. (1955b) The excretory system of the stick insect. *Dixippus morosus* (Orthoptera, Phasmidae). J. Exp. Biol. *32*:183–199.

Rey, P. (1937) Recherches expérimentales sur l'économie de l'eau chez les batrachiens. I. Ann. Physiol. Physicochim. Biol. 13:1081-1144.

Rey, P. (1938) Recherches expérimentales sur l'économie de l'eau chez les batrachiens. II. Ann. Physiol. Physicochim. Biol. *14*:1–66.

Robertson, J. D. (1949) Ionic regulation in some marine invertebrates. J. Exp. Biol. *26*:182–200.

Robertson, J. D. (1953) Further studies on ionic regulation in marine invertebrates. J. Exp. Biol. *30*:277–296.

Schlieper, C. (1929) Über die Einwirkung niederer Salzkonzentrationen auf marine Organismen. Z. vergl. Physiol. *9*:478–514.

Schmidt-Nielsen, B., K. Schmidt-Nielsen, T. R. Houpt, and S. A. Jarnum (1956) Water balance of the camel. Amer. J. Physiol. *185*:185–194.

Shaw, J. (1961) Sodium balance in Eriocheir sinensis M.-Edw. J. Exp. Biol. *38*:154–162.

Shaw, J., and R. H. Strobbart (1963) Osmotic and ionic regulation in insects. Adv. Insect Physiol. *1*:315–399.

Smith, H. W. (1936) The retention and physiological role of urea in the Elasmobranchii. Biol. Rev. *11*:49–82.

Staedler, G., and F. T. Frerichs (1858) Über das Vorkommen von Harnstoff, Taurin und Scyllit in der Organen der Plagiostomen. J. prakt. Chemie *73*.

Starling. E. H. (1895) On the absorption of fluids from the connective tissue spaces. J. Physiol. *19*:312–326.

Steinbach, H. B. (1954) The regulation of sodium and potassium in muscle fibers. Symp. Soc. Exp. Biol. *8*:438–452.

Stempell, W. (1914) Über die Funktion der pulsierenden Vakuole und einen Apparat zur Demonstration derselben. Zool. Jahrb., Allg. Zool. Physiol. Tiere *34*:437–478.

Troschin, A. S. (1958) Das Problem der Zellpermeabilität (German translation from the Russian). VEB Deutscher Verlag der Wissenschaften, Berlin.

Van Slyke, D. D., and G. M. Meyer (1913) The fate of protein digestion products in the body. III. The absorption of amino acids from the blood by the tissues. J. Biol. Chem. *16*:197–212.

Wigglesworth, V. B. (1933a) The effect of salts on the anal gills of the mosquito larva. J. Exp. Biol. *10*:1–15.

Wigglesworth, V. B. (1933b) The function of the anal gills of the mosquito larva. J. Exp. Biol. *10*:16–26.

Wigglesworth, V. B. (1938) The regulation of osmotic pressure and chloride concentration in the haemolymph of mosquito larvae. J. Exp. Biol. *15*:235–247.

6 THE ENZYMES

The complex chemical reaction sequences that constitute the activity of living systems are the direct result of the action of a peculiar class of substances known as enzymes. Our present knowledge of enzymes and enzyme actions is the fruit of ingenious experiments, bold hypotheses, and painstaking work for which we are indebted to the great masters of chemistry and biochemistry.

In 1902 Wilhelm Ostwald defined a catalyst as "any substance that changes the velocity of a chemical reaction without appearing in the final end product of the reaction." This concept is the nucleus of our present ideas of the function of enzymes as "biocatalysts." It is indeed characteristic of enzymes that they are not used up in chemical reactions that they catalyze and that, therefore, only extremely small amounts of enzyme are necessary to process large amounts of reactants. Enzymes, thus, are the tools of living systems: like tools they can perform highly specialized actions, and like tools they are not part of the end product.

Before we can properly discuss the action of enzymes it is necessary to recapitulate a few principles of chemical reactions. In general, chemicals react according to the *law of mass action*. Let us assume that compounds A and B react with each other to form two new substances C and D. The newly formed compounds can also react with each other to re-form A and B, since chemical reactions are reversible. If A and B are allowed to react to form C and D, the latter two compounds, as soon as they are formed, begin to react also and lead to the production of A and B. In general, the production of C and D is speeded up if the amounts of A and B are increased, and the formation of A and B from C and D will be accelerated if C and D increase. The velocity of each reaction (measured in amount of end product formed per unit time) depends on the concentration of the respective reactants. Thus, the velocity v_1 of the formation of C and D can be expressed as $k_1 \cdot [A] \cdot [B]$, and the velocity of the reverse reaction, v_2, can be expressed as $k_2 \cdot [C] \cdot [D]$, k_1 and k_2 being constants. If we allow both reactions to continue they will reach an equilibrium which is characterized by the fact that both velocities are equal. This situation can be expressed by the following formula:

$$k_1 [A] \cdot [B] = k_2 [C] \cdot [D] \quad (1)$$

Now according to the second law of thermodynamics, complete reversibility is impossible; in every transaction involving energy, some energy is irreversibly lost as heat. Heat cannot be completely reconverted into other forms of energy. Energy is defined as the "ability to do work." The term "work" here represents a transfer function and means "energy in transit from one system to another." If a chemical reaction yields energy that is not incorporated into the reaction products, it is called an *exergonic reaction*; if the formation of products requires the "uptake" of energy from the environment of the reactants, one speaks of an *endergonic reaction* (Coryell, 1940).

Spontaneous reactions are always exergonic. In the chemical equations describing them the products of the exergonic reaction are customarily on the right. In symbols, the relationship is: $A + B \longrightarrow C + D +$ energy.

The "energy content" of the chemical system A + B can be represented by the symbol H_1, that of the system C + D as H_2. If the reaction $A + B \longrightarrow C + D$ is exergonic, the energy released is equal to $H_1 - H_2$. The difference in "energy level" of the two systems is usually called the *heat of reaction* and is expressed by the symbol ΔH (pronounced delta H). Since some of this energy is irreversibly lost as heat, it has been found useful to introduce another term to define the part of the "released" energy that can perform useful work (this includes also the amount of produced heat energy that *can* be transformed into other forms of energy). It is expressed as *change of free energy* with the symbol ΔF.

The heat that is irreversibly lost appears as random motion of atomic, ionic, or molecular particles in the environment of the reactants. The degree of "randomness" is expressed by the term *entropy*. Any system within the universe can gain or lose entropy, but the universe as a whole gains entropy with any energy transaction.

The entropy change of a system is given the symbol ΔS. It is related to ΔH and ΔF by the equation:

$$\Delta S = \frac{\Delta H - \Delta F}{T} \quad (2)$$

Even in exergonic reactions ΔH can be smaller than ΔF if, while the reaction is in progress, some energy is absorbed from the environment. An example is the oxidation of glucose: $C_6H_{12}O_6 + 6O_2 \rightarrow 6CO_2 + 6H_2O$. The ΔF of this reaction (at 25° C) is −688 Calories/mole. The ΔH is −673 Cal./mole. The minus sign indicates that the reaction is exergonic, which means that energy is given off. The free energy change (ΔF) is slightly larger than the total energy change of the reaction (ΔH) because a solid (glucose) and a gas (oxygen) react to produce a gas (carbon dioxide) and a liquid (water), thereby causing the reacting system to expand. The expansion represents work, but since the system is in thermal equilibrium with its environment, the expansion proceeds without heat loss. Normally expansion is always accompanied by cooling, but in this case heat is absorbed from the heat "reservoir" of the environment. This amount of "borrowed" heat energy shows up in the slightly increased value of ΔF.

The energy represented by ΔF is available for work and can drive the reaction in the opposite direction: energy + C + D $\longrightarrow$ A + B.

Now, according to the law of mass action, the velocity of the forward reaction (A + B $\longrightarrow$ C + D + energy) is equal to the velocity of the reverse reaction (energy + C + D $\longrightarrow$ A + B) at equilibrium conditions. The velocities cannot be calculated from the thermodynamic equations and therefore do not depend on the values ΔH or ΔF. Consequently, the fact that energy equal to ΔF is liberated in the forward reaction and is available to permit the reverse reaction does not mean that at equilibrium the concentrations of A and B are equal to those of C and D. In most cases the concentrations are quite different, but the velocities are equal.

A physical model clarifies this: A closed container, as shown in Figure 6–1, contains a small amount of water and is otherwise filled with air. In this system water can be expected to evaporate until the saturated vapor pressure of water is reached (see also Chap. 8). From then on equal numbers of water molecules leave and enter the body of water. In other words, when equilibrium is reached the velocity of the forward reaction (water $\longrightarrow$ vapor) is equal to that of the reverse reaction (vapor $\longrightarrow$ water). The velocity of each reaction is obviously related to the concentrations of water and of vapor, because initially, when less vapor is present in the air of the container, more vapor is produced per unit time than later. If vapor is injected into the container after equilibrium is reached, more vapor condenses than at equilibrium. Now, although these velocities are related to the concentrations, they depend strictly on the temperature of the system: the higher the temperature, the more vapor. But again, no matter how high the temperature, an equilibrium is reached in which the velocities of both reactions (vapor production from water and water production from vapor) are equal.

We can conclude that the relation of the velocities of forward and reverse reactions is a function of the concentrations involved, or, in other words, the relative velocities are a function of the concentrations, but the absolute value of the reaction velocities is determined by the temperature of the system. In order for a molecule to leave the body of water, it has to reach a certain energy level, a certain amount of kinetic energy. The heat energy of the system is a function of the temperature. The more heat, the more molecules of water become sufficiently activated to leave the body of liquid and become vapor. The pressure exerted by the resulting vapor is an expression of the energy liberated by the reaction. From here on the discussion of the model becomes somewhat complicated because it must be assumed that the gas pressure rises with increasing temperature (according to the gas laws); thus the pressure developing within the closed vessel is the composite of the temperature-dependent gas pressure and the pressure of the added amount of vapor. It is not difficult to see that the total pressure within the vessel rises much faster than the temperature.

To return to chemical reactions: although the velocities of these are a function of the respective concentrations of reactants and products, the absolute value of the velocities depends on the number of "activated" molecules.

Chemical reactions usually do not get started unless the reactants are activated. In other words, energy has to be added in order to start the reaction.

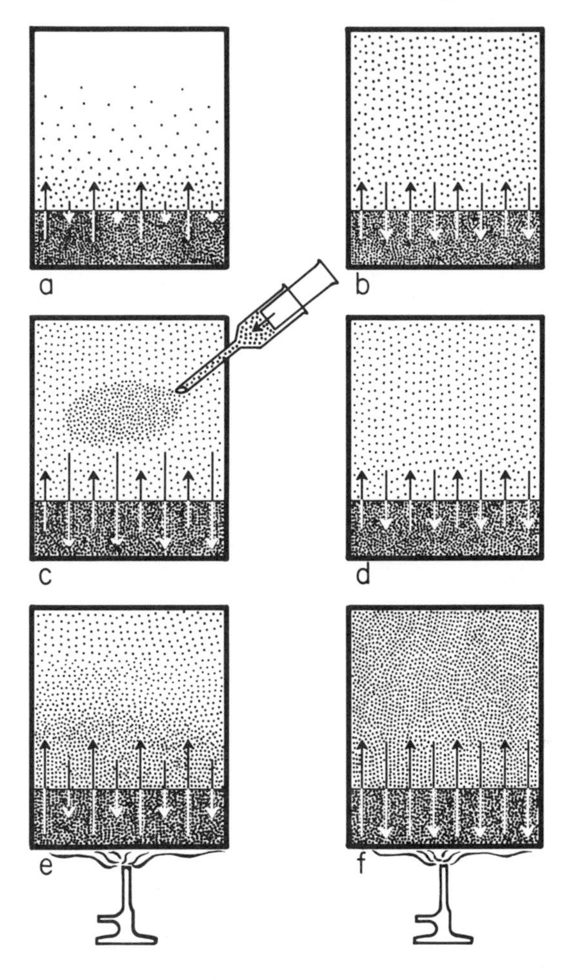

Figure 6–1. Kinetic model of the relation between vapor pressure and temperature to illustrate reaction kinetics as they also apply to enzyme-catalyzed chemical reactions. Arrows pointing upward represent the velocity of the reaction water → vapor; the arrows pointing downward represent the velocity of the reaction vapor → water. Note that whenever equilibrium is reached, both velocities are the same. For further explanation see text.

This energy is called *activation energy.* For example, when one volume of oxygen gas and two volumes of hydrogen gas are mixed together, nothing happens; a burning match, however, can bring the mixture to explosion. The heat energy from the match activates a part of the oxygen and hydrogen molecules, and, as they react, sufficient energy is liberated to activate all the others. Once started, the reaction is self-perpetuating and goes to completion.

The activation energy is, of course, not derived from the system of reactants but must be provided from the outside. It is interesting, and of greatest importance for living systems, that the required activation energy can vary with circumstances. Catalysts are agents that lower the requirement for activation energy of a system of reactants. The catalysts of living systems are the enzymes. Enzymes bring about the activation of the reactants with minimal energy expenditure. Their usefulness can be compared to that of a tool: it is easy to sink a screw into a block of wood if one has the use of a screw driver. But how difficult and time and energy consuming is it to perform the same action without this tool!

Remember that the *enzymes do not alter the energy yield of the reaction.* The values of ΔH or ΔF, which can be calculated from noncatalyzed reactions, apply also to enzyme-catalyzed reactions. The *enzymes change only the activation energy.* But this is of great consequence: the induced chemical reactions go on not only at temperatures that are compatible with living protoplasm, but also at a greatly accelerated rate. Like all catalysts, *enzymes increase the velocity of chemical reactions* by lowering the required activation energy. Enzymes do not interfere with the laws of thermodynamics; their significance lies in their ability to activate the reactants and to increase the velocity of the resulting reaction.

The substance that a particular enzyme activates is called its *substrate.* There is little doubt that the substrate is activated by direct contact with the enzyme. This union of enzyme (E) and substrate (S) is known as the *enzyme-substrate complex*, ES.

It appears that the structure of both substrate and enzyme is altered during the brief moment of union; among evidence for this is the change in the characteristic absorption spectrum of an enzyme (example: peroxidase) when the substrate (hydrogen peroxide) is added.

The union between enzyme and substrate is short, since the activated substrate undergoes a chemical reaction in which it is transformed. The transformed molecule is then exchanged for another molecule of substrate and so forth. Thus, in general, the velocity of the enzyme-catalyzed reaction does not depend on the concentrations of enzyme and substrate according to the law of mass action, so that a small amount of enzyme can cause the transformation of a great quantity of substrate. The number of substrate molecules transformed per minute under the influence of one enzyme molecule is the *turnover number* of the enzyme. In the case of the enzyme peroxidase, this is 2,680,000!

THE CHEMICAL AND FUNCTIONAL STRUCTURE OF ENZYMES

In 1926, Sumner succeeded as the first to isolate and crystallize an enzyme, urease. He found it to be a protein. Since then many enzymes have been purified and crystallized, and in every case they have been shown to be either proteins or conjugated proteins. Enzymes are thus large molecules of a highly complex internal structure, extremely sensitive to the conditions of their environment.

It appears that only small portions of the enzyme molecule unite with the substrate. These are called the *active sites* of the enzyme molecule. They possess a critical specific structure which enables the enzyme to act on a specific substrate. Enzymes are extremely sensitive to any agent that can alter the structure of proteins, for the amino acid chain of protein molecules is usually organized into more complex geometric structures, such as a helix or a double helix, and the active site may be composed of adjacent radicals or side groups

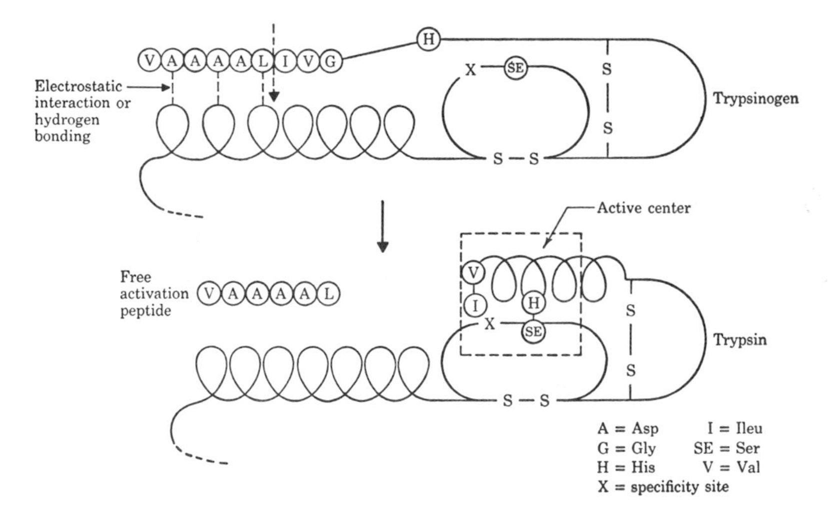

Figure 6–2. Schematic representation of the structural changes involved in the activation (by trypsin) of trypsinogen. The process involves splitting off of a polypeptide by rupturing the lysyl-isoleucine bond (dotted arrow). The newly formed N-terminal region of the enzyme's polypeptide chain assumes a helical configuration which brings certain amino acids into the proper spatial relationship so that they can function as an active site. Note the juxtaposition of histidine and serine, *X*, the site at which the substrate is bound to the enzyme during enzyme-substrate interaction. (From Neurath, H.: Protein structure and enzyme action. *In* Biophysical Science: A Study Program. J. L. Oncley, ed. John Wiley & Sons, New York, 1959.)

belonging to neighboring turns of the helix (see Fig. 6–2). Obviously, the active site is destroyed when the protein structure is altered so that the formerly adjacent parts of the molecule separate, as during denaturation.

The active sites by themselves, however, cannot carry out the enzymatic action. Fragments of the enzyme molecule that contain the active site are either completely or almost inactive. Therefore, the whole molecule provides the necessary "background" structure for the active sites. It is not known precisely how this works.

The active site of many enzymes is represented by a distinct molecule that is bound to the enzyme protein but can be separated from it by relatively mild chemical or physical treatments. Such an active molecule is referred to as a *prosthetic group* or as a *coenzyme*. The protein part of the enzyme to which the prosthetic group or coenzyme belongs, is called *apoenzyme* and the whole apoenzyme-coenzyme complex is referred to as *holoenzyme* (see Fig. 6–3).

Different enzymes may have identical prosthetic groups and coenzymes. The catalase and peroxidase enzymes, for example, have as a prosthetic group a porphyrin molecule of the structure of *heme* (see p. 339, Chap. 14), and the coenzyme of several different dehydrogenase enzymes (see Chap. 7) is diphosphopyridine nucleotide (DPN), while the coenzyme of a series of decarboxylase enzymes is pyridoxal phosphate (vitamin B_6). For some reason it is not customary to refer to the heme part of hemeproteins as coenzyme, and DPN and vitamin B_6 are never called prosthetic groups. In general, molecules referred to as coenzymes are not bound firmly to the apoenzyme. This can be seen when the enzyme solution is enclosed in a membranous bag (e.g., of

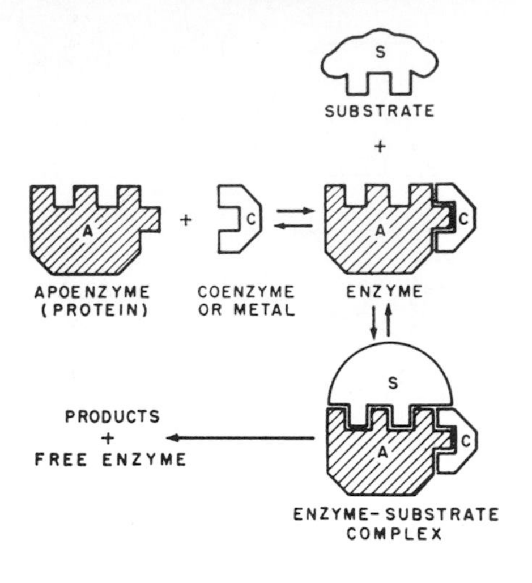

Figure 6–3. Schematic diagram to illustrate the pathway of enzyme-catalyzed reactions involving coenzyme and substrate. (From Sizer, I. W.: Chemical aspects of enzyme inhibition. Science *125*:54–59, 1957.)

cellophane) whose pores are large enough to let the small coenzyme pass but too small to let the apoenzyme through. In such a situation the coenzyme diffuses into the outer medium, leaving the inactive apoenzyme behind. The coenzyme may, in fact, be thought of as a substrate for the enzyme: during the enzyme-catalyzed reaction the coenzyme is indeed altered and reacts chemically with the molecule which is the substrate that gives the enzyme its name. Without this latter substrate there is no reaction, but without the coenzyme (the other substrate) there is no reaction either. Substrate and coenzyme can thus be considered to be the reactants A and B that were discussed on page 130. The following illustrates this:

The enzyme lactic dehydrogenase has DPN as a coenzyme. In order for the oxidation of lactic acid to proceed, the apoenzyme requires lactic acid *and* DPN. When the two unite with the apoenzyme, two hydrogen atoms are transferred from lactic acid to DPN, whereby lactic acid is transformed into pyruvic acid and DPN into $DPNH_2$. As illustrated in Figure 6–4, the situation is identical with that of the action of peroxidase: here the enzyme requires not only hydrogen peroxide as a substrate, but another molecule as well from which two hydrogen atoms can be transferred to the peroxide to form two molecules of water. Dehydrogenase and the peroxidase differ in that lactic dehydrogenase can act only on lactic acid and with DPN, and on no other compound, while peroxidase can catalyze the hydrogen transfer from several different substances (*hydrogen donators*) to hydrogen peroxide. In other words, dehydrogenase is specific for both "substrates," peroxidase only for one (the peroxide).

ENZYME ACTIVATION

Isolated and chemically pure enzymes are often rather inactive. Careful studies have revealed that they need to be "activated" before they become fully active catalysts. In many cases inorganic ions, such as K^+, Cl^-, Mg^{++}, or Ca^{++}, are required. The amylase in saliva, for instance, requires chloride ions

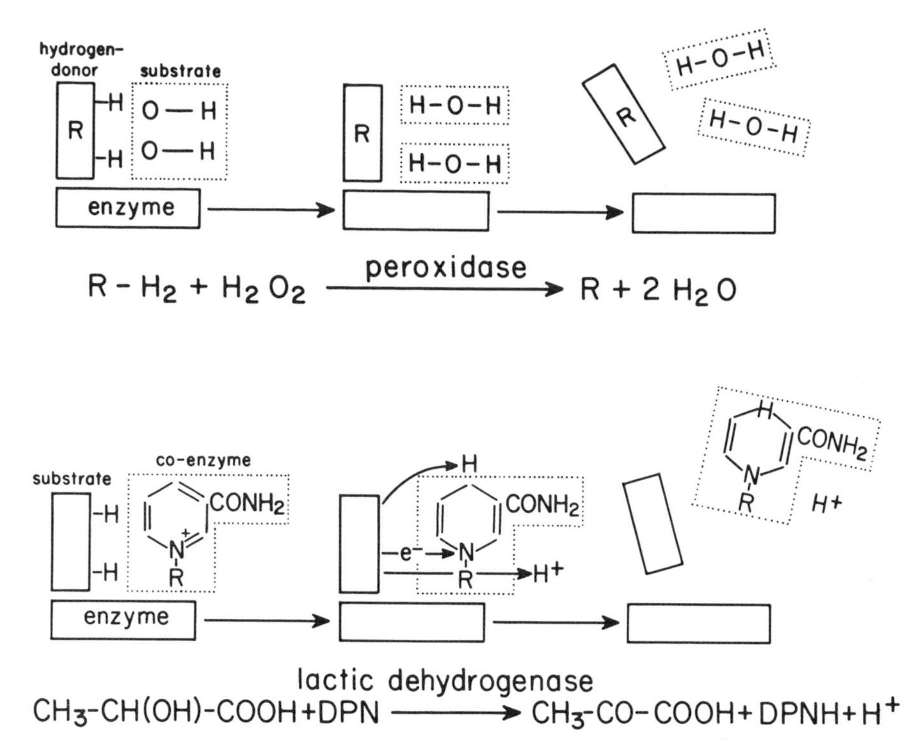

Figure 6–4. Diagrams illustrating the similarity of "substrate" and "coenzyme": both are required for an enzyme-catalyzed reaction involving dehydrogenation of a "hydrogen donator" and both are modified in the reaction.

in order to become fully active. Often certain trace elements, such as Mn, Mo, Zn, or Co, function as activators by attaching to "sensitive" spots on the enzyme molecule and altering its electronic structure. What is true for reactions going on in the test tubes of the biochemist is also true for reactions in living cells: inorganic ions and trace elements are an indispensable and vital part of the living systems and are integrated in their structure.

There are other reasons why an enzyme may be inactive: many of the highly reactive radicals of protein molecules are liable to independent chemical reactions or to formation of cross-linkages with other reactive groups belonging to a nearby part of another, or even of its own, enzyme molecule. Sulfhydryl groups are an example. They easily form cross-linkages, with other —SH groups (—S—S—). If an enzyme depends for its activity on fully reactive —SH groups, regeneration of these is a prerequisite for its action. Agents like the amino acids cysteine or glutathione, which reactivate sulfhydryl groups, are therefore effective enzyme activators.

It must be assumed that many of the protein molecules within living protoplasm are potential enzymes which can spring into action as soon as the right activators appear. In some instances the dormant enzyme is known. One speaks here of *proenzymes*. Best known perhaps is *trypsinogen*, the proenzyme of the digestive enzyme trypsin. This proenzyme is transformed into the active enzyme by another enzyme, enterokinase. The proenzyme in this case appears to consist of the enzyme proper and a polypeptide, which is attached to its active sites. The enzyme-polypeptide complex appears to be a permanent enzyme-substrate complex, and polypeptides are indeed the substrates proper of trypsin; only this one is a special kind of substrate that is not chemically "digested" by the trypsin molecule. Activation here consists of the removal of the "inhibiting" polypeptide, as shown in Figure 6–2.

Enzymes may be inhibited when associated with a particular molecule (see the following section). Some of these inhibitions can be reversed by light. The inhibition of cytochrome oxidase by carbon monoxide (CO), for instance, is removed by illumination. Light, in such a case, is an enzyme activator.

ENZYME SPECIFICITY AND ENZYME INHIBITION

The protein nature of enzymes permits an almost infinite variety of structures, and one may indeed expect an equal variety of enzyme actions. Even if the active sites, prosthetic groups, and coenzymes of several enzymes are identical, one must expect differences in their function. The three heme-containing enzymes catalase, peroxidase, and cytochrome oxidase have indeed three rather different actions: catalase induces the reaction $2H_2O_2 \longrightarrow 2H_2O + O_2$, peroxidase catalyzes the reaction $H_2O_2 + 2H \longrightarrow 2H_2O$, and cytochrome oxidase induces the reaction $\frac{1}{2}O_2 + 2$ electrons $+ 2H^+ \longrightarrow H_2O$. Although the iron atom within the prosthetic group (heme) is the key element in the three types of catalysis, the special features of each are due to the differences of the proteins that represent the apoenzyme of each enzyme.

Even if the catalyzed reactions are the same, the responsible enzymes are likely to differ in their protein structure if the enzymes are derived from different organisms, and even if derived from different cells within the same animal, or from the same cell at different times of its life span. The differences may not be expressed in the chemical formula of the catalyzed reaction, but they certainly would be evident in differences in the velocities of the reaction. The name catalase, therefore, stands for a whole class of molecules, as do the terms cytochrome oxidase, succinic dehydrogenase, and so forth. When the biochemist must generalize, that is, when he is not concerned with an enzyme obtained from a specific source, he speaks of catalas*es*, peroxidas*es*, dehydrogenas*es*, and so forth.

Enzymes have been recognized by the nature of the catalyzed reaction long before they have actually been identified, and many enzymes are known only through their actions. In several instances, two or three different enzymes which were originally recognized and defined by the reaction they induced, turned out to be identical. Polyphenol oxidase and tyrosinase are the same, as are cytochrome a_3 and cytochrome oxidase. Sometimes an enzyme that is highly specific for a particular reaction can catalyze another similar reaction, only the latter proceeds much more slowly than the former. Polyphenol oxidase, for instance, which rapidly oxidizes tyrosine, also acts as a monophenol oxidase, but in contrast to a true monophenol oxidase it oxidizes the monophenol substrate only slowly.

Thus, each individual enzyme can catalyze a range of reactions; that is, it exhibits a range of substrate specificities with an optimum specificity toward one particular substrate and reaction. Each chemical reaction in turn can be catalyzed by a range of enzymes, one of which shows optimal catalytic activity.

Even though an enzyme exhibits a range of substrate specificities, the substrates are always structurally related—in fact, this structural similarity makes it possible for one and the same enzyme to process the different substrates.

If several different enzymes catalyze the same chemical reaction, it can be assumed that they have certain key structures (active sites) in common. It has recently become evident that enzymes, identified by the reaction they catalyze, may consist of populations of somewhat different molecules that have in common the same configuration of their active site. By analogy with the terms isotope and isomere, the term *isozyme* has been coined to identify a group of identically acting but structurally different enzyme molecules. Just as a given element has isotopes and a given compound has isomeres, a given enzyme has isozymes.

Enzymes can combine with certain compounds that are structurally similar with a regular substrate compound of this enzyme, but that are not similar enough to become activated by the enzyme. Such a compound acts as an enzyme inhibitor because it ties up, at any given moment, a certain number of enzyme molecules. Since this inhibiting molecule competes with the substrate proper for the active sites of the enzyme, it is called a competitive inhibitor, and inhibition resulting from its interaction with the enzyme is known as *competitive inhibition*. The amount of inhibition here depends on: (1) the relative affinity of the enzyme for the substrate proper and for the inhibitory compound, and (2) the relative concentration of each. The first factor is a constant, but the second is subject to variation: the larger the proportion of substrate proper, the greater the chance that the enzyme combines with it rather than with the inhibitory compound. Competitive inhibition can thus be overcome by increasing the substrate concentration.

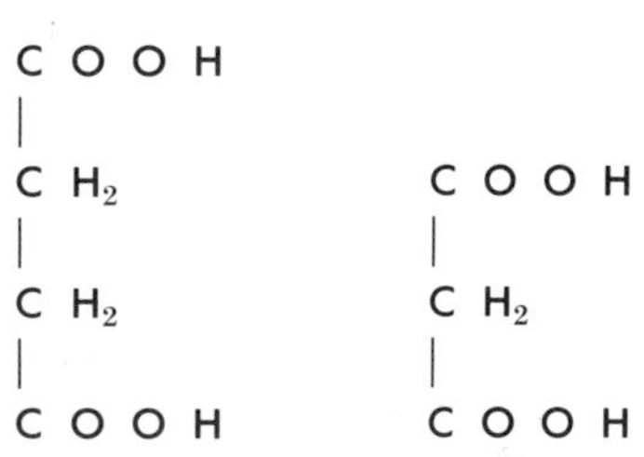

$$\begin{array}{c}COOH\\|\\CH_2\\|\\CH_2\\|\\COOH\end{array}\qquad\qquad\begin{array}{c}COOH\\|\\CH_2\\|\\COOH\end{array}$$

Succinic acid — Malonic acid

Figure 6-5. Structures of two compounds that can combine with succinic dehydrogenase. The enzyme can act only on succinic acid, catalyzing the transfer of a pair of hydrogen atoms to DPN. Malonic acid simply occupies the active site of the enzyme, thus preventing by *competitive inhibition* the dehydrogenation of succinic acid.

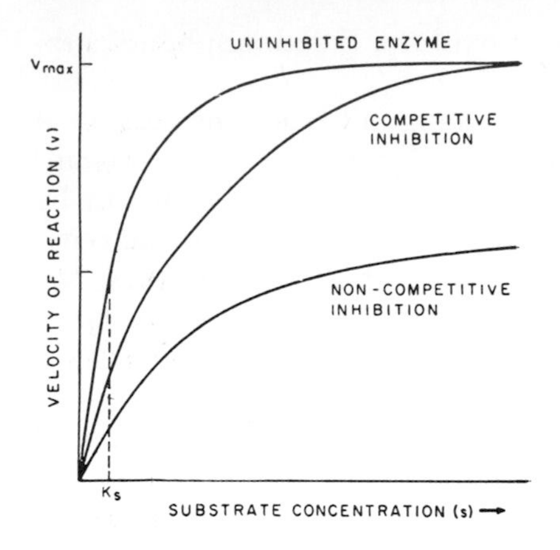

Figure 6–6. Generalized graph showing the rate of the catalyzed reaction as a function of the substrate concentration in the case of uninhibited enzyme, competitive inhibition, and noncompetitive inhibition. Velocity here means the amount of end product produced per unit time. V_{max}, maximal velocity; K_S, substrate concentration at which one-half the maximal velocity is reached when the enzyme is not inhibited. (From Sizer, I. W.: Chemical aspects of enzyme inhibition. Science *125*:54–59, 1957.)

The enzyme succinic dehydrogenase oxidizes succinic acid by transferring a pair of hydrogen atoms to diphosphopyridine nucleotide (DPN), which serves as a coenzyme. As shown in Figure 6–5, the chemical structure of malonic acid is similar to that of succinic acid. Because of this similarity, malonic acid can cause competitive inhibition of succinic dehydrogenase. This can be largely overcome by adding more succinic acid, or, of course, by reducing the concentration of malonate.

In contrast to competitive inhibition is the *noncompetitive inhibition* in which a chemical (*the enzyme inhibitor*) combines with a part of the enzyme molecule other than the active site. This kind of inhibition reduces or abolishes the ability of the enzyme to react with its normal substrate. This kind of inhibition cannot be overcome by increasing the substrate concentration.

The difference between noncompetitive and competitive inhibition is illustrated in Figure 6–6, in which substrate concentration is related to the velocity of the enzyme-catalyzed reaction.

For a discussion of the problems of enzyme specificity and enzyme inhibition, in particular to reaction kinetics, refer to Ernest Baldwin's Dynamic Aspects of Biochemistry (1960), and to the texts recommended for biochemistry courses.

The effects of temperature and of pH on enzyme activity are discussed in Chapter 11 in connection with a discussion of the digestive enzymes.

REFERENCES

Baldwin, E. (1960) Dynamic Aspects of Biochemistry, 3rd Ed. Cambridge University Press, London.

Cantarow, A., and B. Schepartz (1962) Biochemistry, 3rd Ed. W. B. Saunders Co., Philadelphia.

Coryell, C. D. (1940) The proposed terms "exergonic" and "endergonic" for thermodynamics. Science 92:380.

Edsall, J. T., and J. Wyman (1958) Biophysical Chemistry, Vol. I. Thermodynamics, Electrostatics, and the Biological Significance of the Properties of Matter. Academic Press, New York.

Fruton, J. S., and S. Simmonds (1958) General Biochemistry, 2nd Ed. John Wiley & Sons, New York.

Gaebler, O. H., ed. (1956) Enzymes: Units of Biological Structure and Function. Academic Press, New York.

Johnson, F. H., H. Eyring, and M. J. Polissar (1954) The Kinetic Basis of Molecular Biology. John Wiley & Sons, New York.
Karlson, P. (1962) Kurzes Lehrbuch der Biochemie, 3rd Ed. Georg Thieme Verlag, Stuttgart.
Krebs, H. A., and H. L. Kornberg (1957) A survey of the energy transformations in living matter. Ergebn. Physiol., Biol. Chem., exp. Pharmakol. *49*:212–298.
Laidler, K. J. (1954) Introduction to the Chemistry of Enzymes. McGraw-Hill Book Co., New York.
Laidler, K. J. (1958) The Chemical Kinetics of Enzyme Action. Oxford University Press, London.
Lehninger, A. L., C. L. Wadkins, C. Cooper, T. M. Devlin, and J. L. Gamble, Jr. (1958) Oxidative phosphorylation. Science *128*:450–456.
Pigman, W. (1957) The Carbohydrates. Chemistry, Biochemistry, Physiology. Academic Press, New York.
Sumner, J. B. (1926) The isolation and crystallization of the enzyme urease. J. Biol. Chem. *69*: 435–441.

7 OXIDATIVE METABOLISM

Living systems are characterized by the multitude of chemical and physical activities within them at all times. The maintenance of the highly complex order, the synthesis of complex chemicals, and the changes of structure involved in movement and growth demand a continuous supply of energy. This energy must be acquired from the outside and must then be released or utilized within the organism. Almost all the energy utilized in living organisms is chemical energy released by the breakdown of certain compounds. This breakdown, of course, involves the transformation of complex structures into simple structures. In order for this to occur, complex chemicals must be synthesized before being broken down. Most of the energy for this primary synthesis is provided by the powerful radiation of the sun (sunlight). The capture of the sun's energy in the formation of complex compounds is called *photosynthesis*. Organisms capable of this photosynthesis of organic compounds are called *autotrophic*. They are all plants.

Animals cannot carry out the primary steps of organic synthesis, and depend on plant food as a source of complex organic compounds. Organisms that feed on autotrophs are classified as *heterotrophs*.

It is one of the astonishing findings of modern biochemistry that the mobilization of chemical energy for all the complex processes within all the diverse forms of living organisms always follows a similar pattern whether the organism is a plant or any type of animal. It consists in the phosphorylation and breakdown of glucose or an analogous compound, with the formation of adenosine triphosphate (ATP) and subsequent release of chemical energy. If we find differences in this procedure, they are only modifications of one basic pattern. The key processes in the acquisition and internal release of energy are the following:

1. Water is split catalytically into hydrogen and oxygen atoms by photosynthesizing autotrophs, and the hydrogen is added to carbon compounds (e.g.,

CO_2) in the photosynthesis of carbohydrates. 2. Phosphate groups are added to carbohydrate. The phosphorylated carbohydrate breaks down into three-carbon compounds. The phospho-tricarbon compounds are phosphorylated further, and the phosphate groups are transferred to adenosine diphosphate (ADP) to form ATP. 3. Hydrogen is removed from the three-carbon compounds and subsequently the hydrogen is oxidized in a stepwise process and more ATP is formed. 4. Controlled hydrolysis of ATP follows, with release of energy.

Reaction 1 is carried out by autotrophs (plants), and requires the capture of the sun's energy. Reactions 2 to 4 take place in autotrophs as well as in heterotrophs. Reaction 2 is commonly called anaerobic glycolysis; oxygen is not required. Reaction 3 is aerobic; it requires oxygen, which acts as a hydrogen acceptor at the end of the stepwise oxidation of hydrogen which accomplishes a stepwise release of energy that is recaptured in the formation of ATP molecules. The release of energy from ATP molecules in reaction 4 is the final goal. ATP indeed seems to be the key compound of plant as well as animal cells, since it appears to be the only compound that directly supplies the energy needed for mechanical work, absorption processes, synthetic processes, the maintenance of certain electrical potentials, or the production of light (bioluminescence). Since the subject of photosynthesis is beyond the scope of this textbook, only the breakdown of carbohydrate and the formation of ATP are discussed here.

ANAEROBIC GLYCOLYSIS (Figs. 7–1 and 7–2)

The carbohydrate utilized in this reaction is almost universally glucose. Quantities of glucose are stored within certain animal cells in the form of glycogen. This compound essentially consists of a chain of glucose units, all linked together to form large molecules. Glycogen, often referred to as "animal starch," is rather insoluble in aqueous media and, owing to the size of its molecules, cannot leave the cells. Thus, it is an ideal storage form of glucose.

In order for glycolysis to take place, glucose units have to be split off the glycogen molecule by hydrolysis, or more commonly by phosphorylation. The latter process is known as *glycogenolysis* (Baldwin, 1952). It requires an enzyme, *phosphorylase*, which attaches a phosphate group to the terminal glucose unit of a glycogen molecule and splits off this phosphorylated glucose (glucose-1-phosphate). Another enzyme, *phosphoglucomutase*, rearranges the molecule so that the phosphate group comes to lie at the carbon-6 atom of the glucose molecule, thus forming glucose-6-phosphate.

If glucose itself is available, another enzyme is present, called *hexokinase*, which attaches a phosphate group derived from ATP directly to the carbon-6 position, giving rise to glucose-6-phosphate.

Now another transmutation takes place; the enzyme *phosphohexo-* (or phosphogluco-) *isomerase* rearranges the constituents of the molecule in such a way that this becomes fructofuranose-6-phosphate. At this point, the molecule reacts with ATP in the presence of an enzyme, *phosphohexokinase*: as the result, the terminal phosphate group of the reacting ATP molecule is trans-

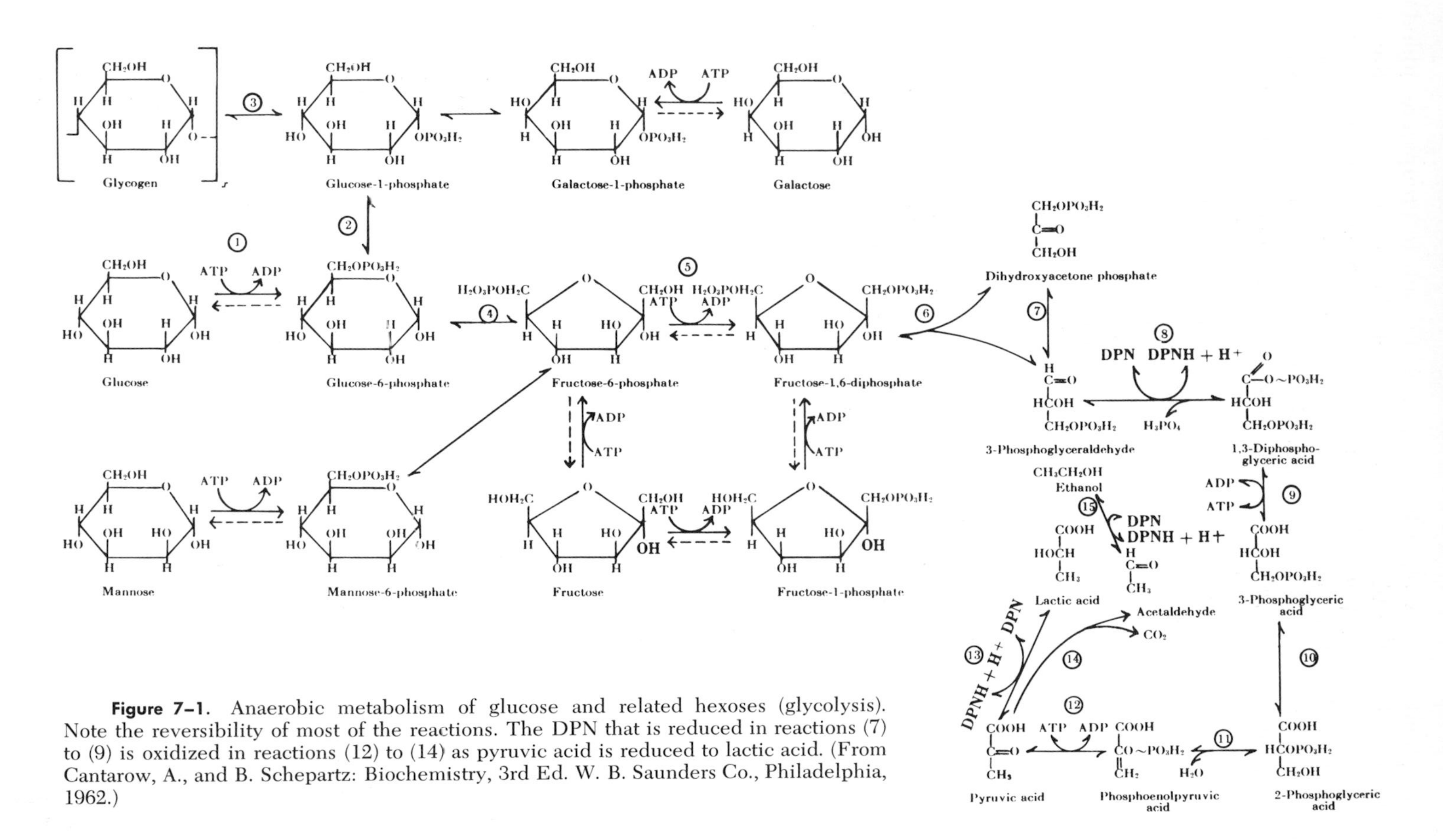

Figure 7–1. Anaerobic metabolism of glucose and related hexoses (glycolysis). Note the reversibility of most of the reactions. The DPN that is reduced in reactions (7) to (9) is oxidized in reactions (12) to (14) as pyruvic acid is reduced to lactic acid. (From Cantarow, A., and B. Schepartz: Biochemistry, 3rd Ed. W. B. Saunders Co., Philadelphia, 1962.)

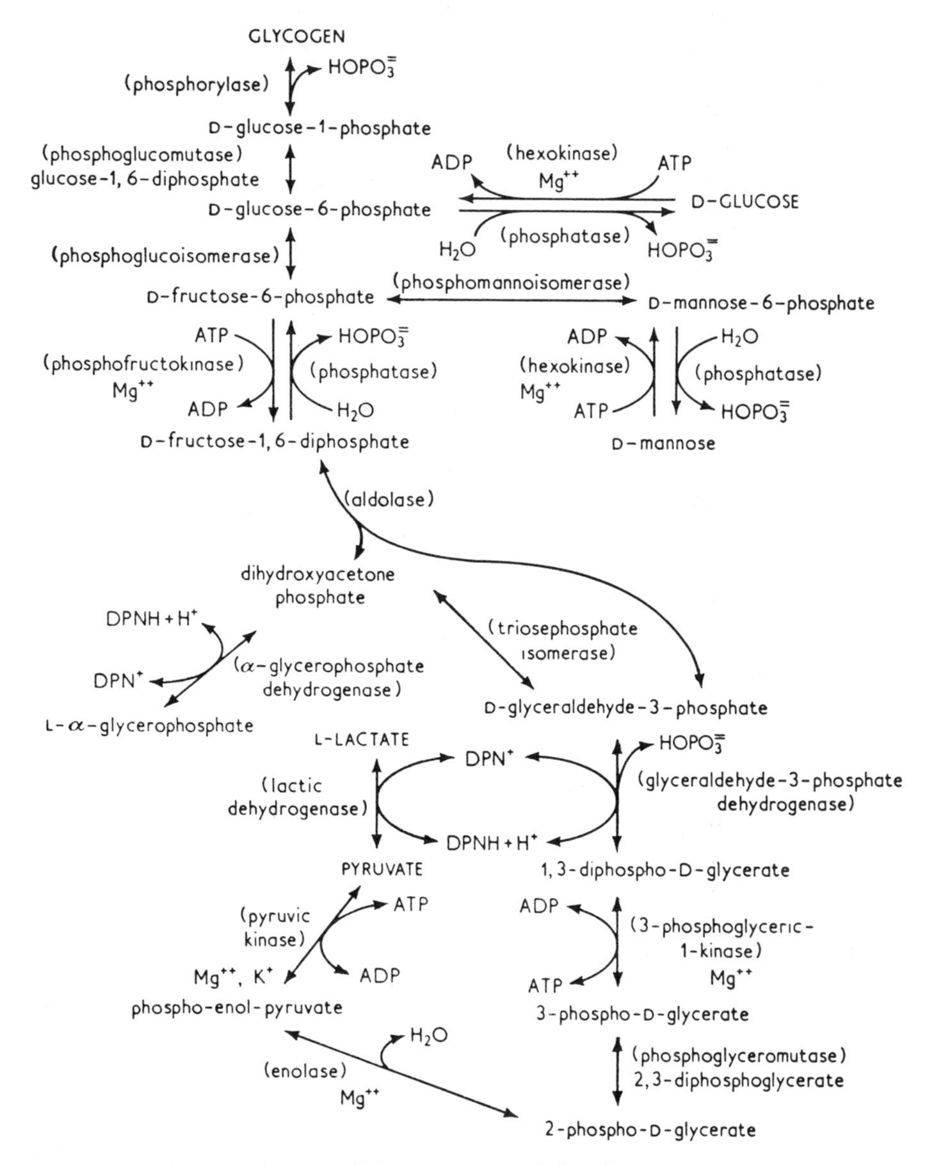

Figure 7–2. The complete metabolic sequence of glycolysis, its enzymes, coenzymes, and other cofactors. (From Gilmour, D.: The Biochemistry of Insects. Academic Press, New York, 1961.)

ferred to the fructofuranose-6-phosphate, thus forming ADP and fructofuranose-1,6-phosphate. The latter six-carbon compound (therefore called a hexose) is then split in two halves (two triose molecules), one molecule of 3-phosphoglyceraldehyde and one molecule of phosphodihydroxy-acetone, under the influence of the enzyme *aldolase*. The two trioses contain the same numbers of carbon, hydrogen, and oxygen atoms as well as one phosphate group; only the arrangement of the atoms differs. Thus, the two molecules are isomers. The enzyme *phosphotriose isomerase* effects the transformation of phospho-dihydroxy-acetone into phosphoglyceraldehyde; therefore, two molecules of phosphoglyceraldehyde result from one molecule of glucose. Each of the two 3-phosphoglyceraldehyde molecules then combines with another phosphate group (derived from inorganic phosphate), and right away two hydrogen atoms are removed from each molecule and transferred to a compound called diphosphopyridine nucleotide (DPN). DPN is considered to be the coenzyme of *phosphoglyceraldehyde dehydrogenase*, and is often referred to as coenzyme I (Co-I), or cozymase. This coenzyme is discussed later. At present remember that it acts as a hydrogen acceptor in the oxidation of 1,3-phosphoglyceraldehyde. The oxidized compound is 1,3-diphosphoglyceric acid.

What has been achieved by this complicated sequence of chemical reactions? First, four phosphate groups have been attached to the original glucose unit. Second, a total of four hydrogen atoms has been removed from the two "halves" of the phosphorylated glucose unit. But perhaps most significant is the result of the repeated rearrangement of the molecular configuration: the concentration of energy in the phosphate bonds, the so-called "high energy" phosphate bonds. In the course of the configuration changes, the energy holding together the phosphorylated carbohydrate molecules was shifted around—diminished in some places, increased in others—until a large quantity was stored in the linkage between the glyceric acid and one of the two phosphate groups of the molecules.

These phosphate groups can then be transferred to ADP molecules to form ATP. One of the secrets of life lies in the fact that phosphate groups are transferred together with their high bond energy. Of course, this requires again the action of an enzyme, *phosphokinase*. Two molecules of ATP and two molecules of 3-phosphoglyceric acid result. Again the molecular configuration changes, catalyzed by the enzyme *phosphoglyceromutase*, so that the remaining phosphate group shifts from the third to the second carbon atom. There are then two molecules of 2-phosphoglyceric acid. From each of these one molecule of water is removed by the enzyme *enolase*, leading to the production of phosphoenolpyruvic acid.

By now the remaining phosphate groups have acquired a large quantity of energy in their linkage with carrier molecules (enolpyruvic acid). They are transferred to ADP molecules together with their bond energy by the action of *pyruvic phosphokinase*. Thus two more ATP molecules are produced and two molecules of pyruvic acid appear. In the absence of oxygen this pyruvic acid is immediately reduced to lactic acid. The reduction consists in the transfer from DPN of the two hydrogen atoms previously removed from 1,3-diphosphoglyceraldehyde. The transferring enzyme this time is lactic dehydrogenase.

In summary, anaerobic glycolysis of one molecule of glucose utilizes two molecules of ATP and produces four new molecules of ATP. There is thus a net gain of two ATP molecules for each molecule of glucose glycolyzed, or a gain of two high energy bonds. The glucose molecule itself is transformed, or broken down, into two molecules of lactic acid.

AEROBIC GLYCOLYSIS, THE CITRIC ACID CYCLE (Fig. 7–3)

In the presence of oxygen, the pyruvic acid produced in the anaerobic phase of glycolysis is not reduced to lactic acid. The hydrogens transferred from 1,3-diphosphoglyceraldehyde to DPN do not return to the breakdown product of glycogen. They are in fact oxidized and end up in the form of water.

Before proceeding further in our discussion, we have to review the meaning of the term "oxidation." Three kinds of chemical events are called oxidation: combination with oxygen, removal of hydrogen, and removal of electrons (gain of a positive valency). When it is stated that aerobic glycolysis consists of the complete oxidation of glucose, this does not imply addition of oxygen atoms to the carbon atoms of the glucose molecule with subsequent production of CO_2. The "complete oxidation," in fact, consists of the repeated removal of hydrogen atoms. The energy derived from this process results from the oxidation of the removed hydrogen atoms to water.

As we understand it then, two separate chains of reactions are involved in aerobic metabolism: (1) hydrogen atoms are removed repeatedly and (2)

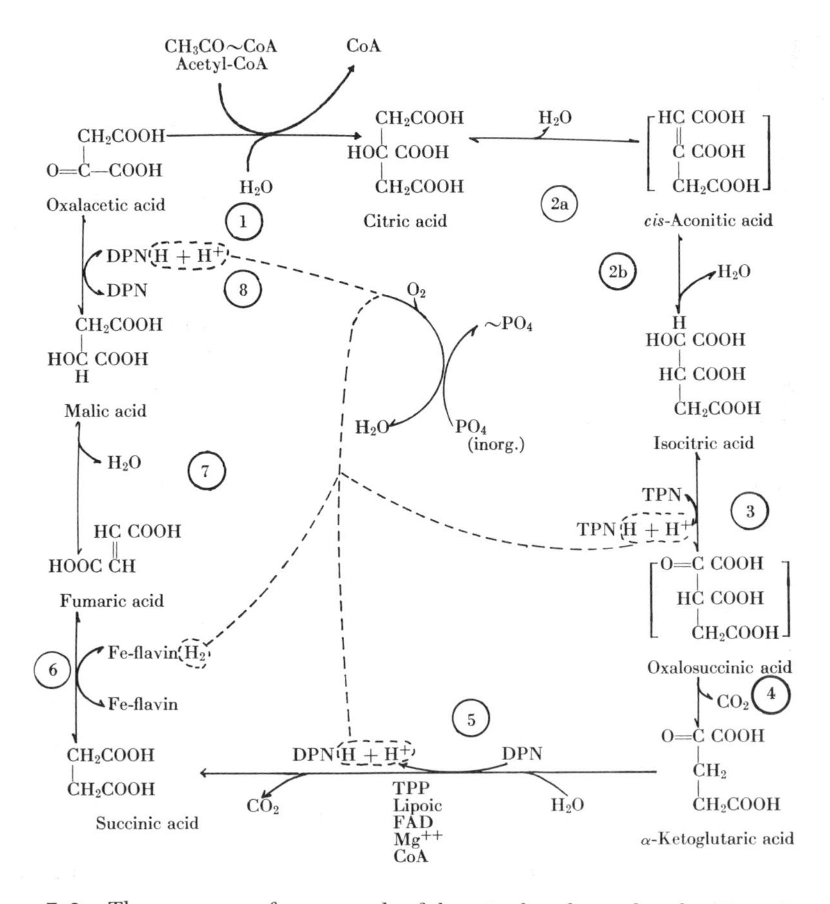

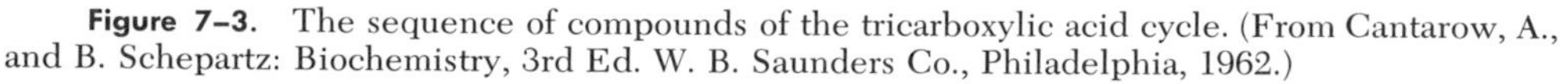

Figure 7–3. The sequence of compounds of the tricarboxylic acid cycle. (From Cantarow, A., and B. Schepartz: Biochemistry, 3rd Ed. W. B. Saunders Co., Philadelphia, 1962.)

these hydrogen atoms are oxidized in a stepwise process. These two procedures are governed by (1) the enzymes of the citric acid cycle and (2) the respiratory enzymes.

The function of the citric acid cycle enzymes is to (a) repeatedly attach water, (b) repeatedly remove hydrogen atoms, and (c) repeatedly remove CO_2 in the course of pyruvate metabolism.

The function of the respiratory enzymes is to (a) activate oxygen, (b) take over the hydrogen produced in glycolysis and activate it, and (c) release energy by inducing a series of electron transfers, thereby allowing the formation of high energy phosphate bonds (ATP).

During glycolysis the first "oxidation," that is, the first removal of one pair of hydrogen atoms, takes place during the transformation of phosphoglyceraldehyde into 1,3-phosphoglyceric acid, where a dehydrogenase enzyme transfers two hydrogen atoms to its coenzyme, diphosphopyridine nucleotide (DPN). As will be discussed, this transferred hydrogen is eventually oxidized to water. Under anaerobic conditions, hydrogen atoms are not oxidized, and the hydrogen atoms are accepted from DPN by the pyruvic acid that is being produced, to form lactic acid.

Under aerobic conditions pyruvic acid is metabolized in a process called the *citric acid cycle*. The name is derived from the fact that pyruvic acid together with oxalacetic acid form citric acid, a six-carbon compound. The condensation of pyruvic acid and oxalacetic acid to form citric acid proceeds with the production of 1 CO_2 and 1 H_2. The mechanism of this seems to be (1) the decarboxylation of pyruvic acid (production of CO_2) by the action of a decarboxylase and a co-decarboxylase, (2) the formation of "active acetate," a high energy bond between acetate and *coenzyme* A, and (3) the condensation of the active acetate and oxalacetic acid under the influence of a "condensing enzyme."

Citric acid is transformed into *cis*-aconitic acid, and this into isocitric acid, both reactions being catalyzed by the enzyme *aconitase*. *Isocitric dehydrogenase* transfers two hydrogen atoms to its coenzyme *triphosphopyridine nucleotide* (TPN), thus forming *oxalosuccinic acid* and reduced TPN. The enzyme *oxalosuccinic decarboxylase* liberates CO_2 from this acid, and in this way generates *α-ketoglutaric acid*. In the next step in the cycle 1 H_2O is added and H_2 is removed in the production of *succinic acid*, from which *succinic dehydrogenase* removes still another pair of hydrogen atoms; thus *fumaric acid* is produced. An enzyme, *fumarase*, adds one molecule of H_2O to this compound, forming *malic acid*. *Malic dehydrogenase* transfers two hydrogen atoms to DPN and produces oxalacetic acid. This end product of the "breakdown," or oxidation, of citric acid can react again with acetate derived from pyruvic acid, forming another molecule of citric acid. The pyruvic acid produced in (anaerobic) glycolysis thus enters a cyclic reaction. This was first suggested by Krebs and Johnson (1937). The citric acid cycle has been named the Krebs cycle, in honor of this great biochemist.

The complete series of transformations of glucose into six molecules of CO_2 and two molecules of oxalacetic acid yields a total of 12 pairs of hydrogen atoms, attached either to DPN or TPN.

As mentioned, the hydrogens will be oxidized and the end step of this is their union with oxygen. Involved in the oxidation of hydrogen (Fig. 7–4) are two classes of compounds: the flavoproteins (or yellow enzymes) and the hemochromogen proteins. The flavoproteins (FAD) transport the hydrogen pairs from the dehydrogenase coenzymes (DPN and TPN) to the first compound in the series of hemochromogen pigments, called cytochrome c. Cytochrome c oxidizes the hydrogen atoms by removing their electrons. Consequently, hydrogen atoms become hydrogen ions, and the key atom of cytochrome c, Fe^{+++}, becomes reduced to Fe^{++} as the iron picks up the electrons, thus diminishing its positive charge. Cytochrome c then reduces a similar molecule, cytochrome a, by transferring the acquired electrons, and cytochrome a transports the electrons to still another hemochromogen protein, called *cytochrome oxidase*. The latter compound then reacts with and reduces molecular oxygen by transferring the two electrons to one oxygen atom, transforming it into an oxygen ion (O^{--}). To say that dehydrogenase coenzyme reduces flavoprotein, flavoprotein reduces cytochrome oxidase, and cytochrome oxidase reduces oxygen is the same as saying that oxygen oxidizes cytochrome oxidase, cytochrome oxidase oxidizes cytochrome a, cytochrome a oxidizes cytochrome c, cytochrome c oxidizes a flavoprotein, and this flavoprotein oxidizes the dehydrogenase coenzyme. A substance that reduces another becomes oxidized, and a substance that oxidizes another becomes reduced.

In each step of the chain of oxidations energy is released and certain of the electron transfers yield sufficient energy for the formation of one high energy phosphate bond. It has been calculated that for each pair of electrons transported over the chain of dehydrogenase, flavoprotein, cytochromes, cytochrome oxidase, to oxygen, 3.5 high energy phosphate bonds (3.5 molecules of ATP) are produced. Since aerobic glycolysis produces 12 pairs of hydrogen atoms or 12 pairs of electrons, the metabolism of one molecule of glucose yields the equivalent of 42 high energy phosphate bonds, or 42 molecules of ATP in addition to the two molecules of ATP produced in the (anaerobic) dephosphorylation of phosphorylated triose. Since the energy contained in the terminal phosphate

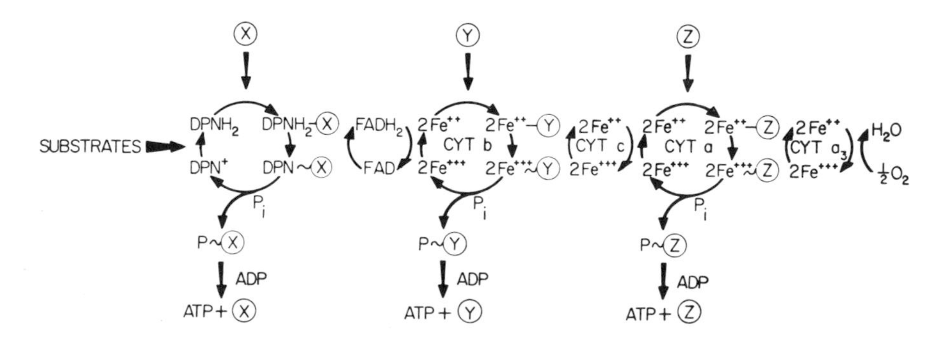

Figure 7–4. A possible mechanism of oxidative phosphorylation involving three substances labeled *X, Y,* and *Z,* which first form a high energy complex with the carriers DPN, cytochrome b, and cytochrome a, and then exchange the carriers for a phosphate group which in turn is given up to ADP, leading to the formation of ATP. (From Lehninger, A. L., C. L. Wadkins, C. Cooper, T. M. Devlin, and J. L. Gamble: Science *128*:450, 1958.)

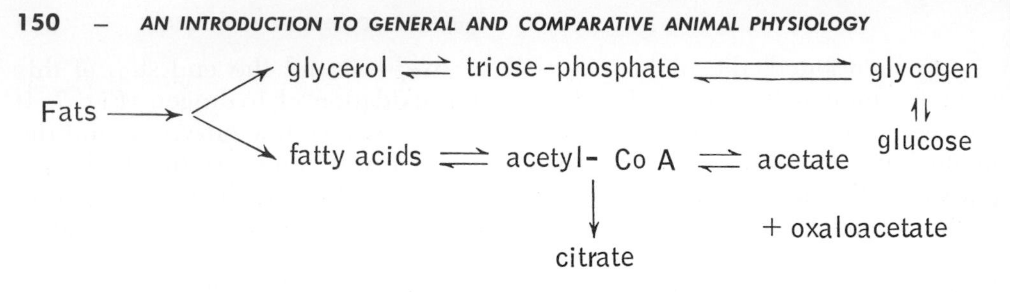

Figure 7–5. General pattern of the oxidative metabolism of fats. (From Baldwin, E.: Dynamic Aspects of Biochemistry. Cambridge University Press, Cambridge, 1960.)

bond of ATP is 7000 calories/mole, the aerobic glycolysis of 1 mole of glucose produces 529,000 calories of energy that can be used to initiate mechanical work, synthesis, electric current absorption, excretion, and so forth. This figure is obviously slightly high, because some energy is used up to maintain certain steps in the glycolytic process (e.g., the phosphorylation of glucose-6-phosphate). But energy gains up to about 400,000 calories/mole of glucose metabolized have been verified experimentally. As Baldwin (1952) points out, this energy yield surpasses that of the most efficient man-made machines, such as super-heated steam turbines.

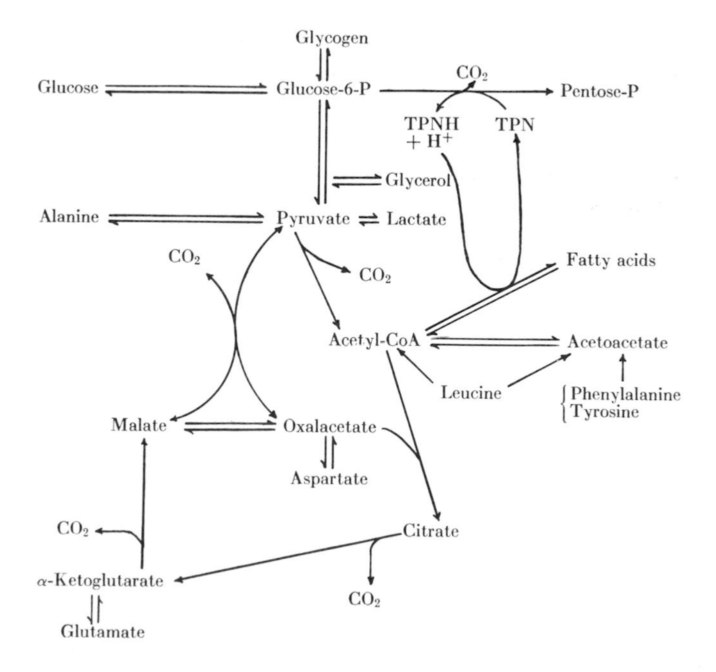

Figure 7–6. Metabolic interrelations of carbohydrates with fatty acids and amino acids. Citrate, α-ketoglutarate, and malate are part of the tricarboxylic acid cycle. Many additional interrelations are known. (From Cantarow, A., and B. Schepartz: Biochemistry, 3rd Ed. W. B. Saunders Co., Philadelphia, 1962.)

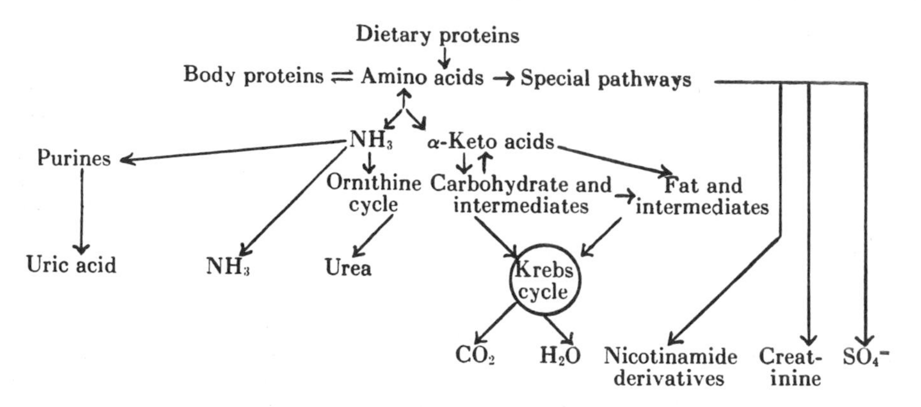

Figure 7–7. General pathways of protein and amino acid metabolism. (From Cantarow, A., and B. Schepartz: Biochemistry, 3rd Ed. W. B. Saunders Co., Philadelphia, 1962.)

The advantages of oxidative (aerobic) metabolism over anaerobic metabolism are obvious, if we compare the energy yields. The evolution of such a complicated biochemical system as that involved in glycolysis becomes thus understandable. Since the same, or nearly the same, chemical system is found in practically all animals and plants, its evolution may have preceded the differentiation and evolution of organisms into plants and animals, and it is likely that this efficient metabolic machine was the starting point of the establishment of life on this planet.

Carbohydrate metabolism in animal cells does not necessarily start with glucose. Other sugars serve as well, but they are first converted to hexoses, trioses, or phosphohexoses or phosphotrioses and, as such, they enter the pathways described under the headings "Anaerobic Glycolysis" and "Aerobic Glycolysis."

The *metabolism of fats* (Figs. 7–5 and 7–6) is intimately connected with that of carbohydrates: fats are split by hydrolysis into glycerol and fatty acids. Glycerol is converted directly into glucose; the fatty acids are broken down into two-carbon units (acetate) that combine with coenzyme A to form *active acetate* which, with oxalacetate, contributes to the formation of citric acid. Thus fats are "fed" into the pathways of glycolysis and the citric acid cycle.

Protein metabolism (Fig. 7–7) likewise leads to products (amino acids) that are transformed into glucose (glycogen) via pyruvic acid. Any of these forms in turn is then metabolized according to the patterns outlined for glycolysis and the citric acid cycle. The prerequisite for this is the deamination of the amino acids (of their corresponding amines): carbohydrates and their derivatives contain no nitrogen!

Energy-yielding oxidative metabolism of proteins and amino acids, therefore, leads to the production of surplus nitrogen in the form of amino groups or of ammonia derived from them. This nitrogen is not utilized by the animal organism but is excreted. This is discussed in more detail in Chapter 13.

Refer to the references at the end of this chapter for further outlines and discussions of metabolism.

REFERENCES

Baldwin, E. (1952) Dynamic Aspects of Biochemistry. Cambridge University Press, London.

Block, K. (1960) Comparative mechanisms for fatty acid oxidation. *In* Comparative Biochemistry, Vol. 1, pp. 75–106. (M. Florkin and H. S. Mason, eds.) Academic Press, New York.

Bueding, E., and E. Farber (1960) Comparative biochemistry of glycolysis. *In* Comparative Biochemistry, Vol. 1, pp. 411–440. (M. Florkin and H. S. Mason, eds.) Academic Press, New York.

Cantarow, A., and B. Schepartz (1962) Biochemistry, 3rd Ed. W. B. Saunders Co., Philadelphia.

Conn, E. E. (1960) Comparative biochemistry of electron transport and oxidative phosphorylation. *In* Comparative Biochemistry, Vol. 1, pp. 441–485. (M. Florkin and H. S. Mason, eds.) Academic Press, New York.

Dickens, F. (1951) Anaerobic glycolysis, respiration, and the Pasteur effect. *In* The Enzymes, Vol. 2. (J. B. Sumner and K. Myrbäck, eds.) Academic Press, New York.

Fruton, J. S., and S. Simmonds (1958) General Biochemistry, 2nd Ed. John Wiley & Sons, New York.

Green, D. E. (1959) Electron transport and oxidative phosphorylation. Advanc. Enzymol. *21*:73–129.

Greenberg, D. M. (1961) Carbon catabolism of amino acids. *In* Metabolic Pathways, Vol. 2, pp. 79–172. (D. M. Greenburg, ed.) Academic Press, New York.

Krebs, H. A. (1943) The intermediary stages in the biological oxidation of carbohydrate. Advanc. Enzymol. *44*:191–252.

Krebs, H. A. (1949) The tricarboxylic acid cycle. Harvey Lect. *44*:165–199.

Krebs, H. A. (1954) The tricarboxylic acid cycle. *In* Chemical Pathways of Metabolism, Vol. 1, pp. 109–171. (D. M. Greenberg, ed.) Academic Press, New York.

Krebs, H. A., and W. A. Johnson (1937) The role of citric acid in intermediary metabolism in animal tissues. Enzymologia *4*:148–156.

Krebs, H. A., and J. M. Lowenstein (1960) Comparative biochemistry of glycolysis. *In* Comparative Biochemistry, Vol. 2. (M. Florkin and H. S. Mason, eds.) Academic Press, New York.

Schoenheimer, R. (1946) The Dynamic State of Body Constituents. Harvard University Press, Cambridge.

Slater, E. C. (1958) The constitution of the respiratory chain in animal tissues. Advanc. Enzymol. *20*:147–199.

Stumpf, P. K., and G. A. Barber (1960) Comparative mechanisms for fatty acid oxidation. *In* Comparative Biochemistry, Vol. 1, pp. 75–106. (M. Florkin and H. S. Mason, eds.) Academic Press, New York.

8 SOLUBILITY OF GASES IN LIQUIDS

The fact that certain substances or compounds dissolve in a given solvent more readily than others holds true not only for solids but also for gases. Carbon dioxide (CO_2), for instance, is much more soluble in water than is oxygen or nitrogen. To our knowledge, however, no gas is completely miscible with any solvent—a solvent can take up only a certain amount of any given gas; gas in excess of this amount can be present only in the form of gas bubbles. The maximal amount of a gas that can dissolve in a liquid depends on: (1) the pressure of the gas, (2) the temperature of the solvent, and (3) the solute content of the solvent. The solubility of a gas increases with increasing pressure but decreases with increasing temperature and with increasing solute content.

The term "amount of gas" means either the "number of gas molecules" or "gas volume." Obviously, the same number of gas molecules occupy different volumes depending on the gas temperature: the higher the temperature, the fewer molecules are present in the same volume. The gas volume can, however, express the number of gas molecules if the temperature and pressure are stated also. Remember that 1 liter of an ideal gas at 0° C and 1 atm pressure contains 2.69×10^{22} molecules (Avogadro's rule). It is customary to express amounts of gases in terms of volumes at N.T.P. (normal temperature and pressure = 0° C and 1 atm or 760 mm Hg).

The maximal amount of gas at N.T.P. that can dissolve in a particular liquid at 0° C is called the *absorption coefficient* of the gas in the given solvent. The absorption coefficient is defined as the volume of gas at N.T.P. dissolved in a volume of solvent. Thus the absorption coefficient of CO_2 is 1.713; of O_2, 0.049; and of N_2, 0.024. In other words, 1 ml of water at 0° C dissolves 1.713 ml of CO_2, or 0.049 ml of O_2, or 0.024 ml of N_2 if these gases are at 1 atm pressure.

Absorption coefficients can also be given for solvents at temperatures other

Table 8–1. Absorption Coefficients

Temperature (°C)	CO_2	O_2	N_2
0	1.713	0.0489	0.0239
10	1.194	0.0380	0.0196
20	0.879	0.0310	0.0164
30	0.665	0.0261	0.0138
40	0.530	0.0231	0.0118

than 0° C. In these cases the amount of dissolved gas is given by the volume this dissolved gas would occupy at N.T.P.—in spite of the fact that the gas goes into solution at a temperature different from 0° C. Table 8–1 gives values of absorption coefficients of CO_2, O_2, and N_2 in water of different temperatures.

If the gas is present at a pressure of a fraction of an atmosphere, its solubility will be diminished by the same fraction. Thus only 0.00489 ml of O_2 (instead of 0.0489 ml) dissolves in 1 ml of water at 0° C if this oxygen has a pressure of 1/10 atm, or 76 mm Hg. Note that this is true regardless of whether other kinds of gas are present. Normal air, at sea level, contains about 21 per cent oxygen. Although this air has a pressure of 760 mm, the amount of oxygen that dissolves corresponds to a pressure of 159.6 (21 per cent of 760) mm Hg. In general, the gases constituting a gas mixture (atmosphere) dissolve not according to the total pressure of the mixture but according to their individual *partial pressure*. The term "partial pressure" is defined as the pressure that each gas of the gas mixture contributes to the total pressure of this mixture; it is proportional to the volume of each gas within the total volume of the gas mixture. The partial pressure of a gas is given in mm Hg. If the total pressure is equal to 1 atm, the partial pressure of a gas is given by the formula

$$p = \frac{x}{100} \cdot P \qquad (1)$$

where p is the partial pressure, x is the per cent volume of the particular gas within the total volume of the mixture, and P is the total pressure of the mixture. Air at 1 atm pressure containing 21 per cent oxygen (21 ml oxygen in 100 ml air), therefore, has a partial pressure of oxygen (pO_2) of:

$$pO_2 = \frac{21}{100} \cdot 760 = \frac{15{,}960}{100} = 159.60 \text{ mm Hg}$$

We can now calculate the solubility of any gas if we know the absorption coefficient *a*, the partial pressure *p*, and the pressure *P* of the total gas mixture. The general formula (when P = 1 atm) is

$$V = \frac{a \cdot p}{760} \text{ ml} \qquad (2)$$

V in this case is the volume in milliliters of the gas reduced to conditions of N.T.P. that dissolves in 1 ml of solvent. If we want to know what volume of a given gas dissolves in a given volume of liquid, the formula becomes

$$V = \frac{a \cdot v \cdot p}{760} \text{ ml} \tag{3}$$

where v is the volume of liquid in milliliters.

In computing the partial pressure of a gas mixture that is in contact with a liquid, one must consider the vapor pressure. This is true also for air in contact with water: The higher the temperature, the more water evaporates per unit time. The water vapor represents a gas that takes up volume within the air above the liquid water. Of course, it does not change the atmospheric pressure, but it changes the proportion of the gases present in the atmosphere. Increasing vapor pressure causes a decrease in the partial pressure of oxygen or of any other gas present in air. Table 8–2 gives values of vapor pressure of water at different temperatures.

If we want to calculate the pO_2 in an atmosphere in immediate contact with water of higher temperature, Formula 1 must be modified to correct for the vapor pressure, vp:

$$p = \frac{x}{100} \cdot (P - vp) \tag{4}$$

The volume of gas that dissolves in one or more volumes of water at a temperature higher than that at which vp = 0 is given by Formulas 2 and 3, provided p is calculated according to Formula 4.

The following example illustrates this: Lake Titicaca on the altiplano between Peru and Bolivia has an altitude of almost 14,000 feet. The barometric pressure is about 450 mm Hg. How much oxygen can dissolve in 1 liter of the lake water at 20° C?

$$pO_2 = \frac{21}{100} \cdot (450 - 17.5) = 90.825 \text{ mm Hg}$$

$$V = \frac{0.031 \cdot 1000 \cdot 90.8}{760} = 3.56 \text{ ml}$$

At sea level 1 liter of water at 20° C would dissolve 6.36 ml of oxygen (N.T.P.) because

$$pO_2 = \frac{21}{100} \cdot (760 - 17.5) = 156 \text{ mm Hg}$$

Thus

$$V = \frac{0.031 \cdot 1000 \cdot 156}{760} = 6.36 \text{ ml}$$

Table 8–2. Vapor Pressure of Water (in mm Hg) at Different Temperatures (in °C)

°C	mm Hg	°C	mm Hg
0°	4.58	40°	55.1
10°	9.21	60°	149.2
20°	17.5	80°	355.1
30°	31.7	100°	760.0

Table 8–3. Coefficients of Saturation of Atmospheric Gases in Water of Different Salinities (Concentrations of oxygen, nitrogen, and carbon dioxide [in ml/l] in equilibrium with one atmosphere (760 mm Hg) of designated gas.)

Salinity in gm NaCl/kg solution	*0° C*			*12° C*			*24° C*		
	O_2	N_2	CO_2	O_2	N_2	CO_2	O_2	N_2	CO_2
0	49.24	23.00	1715	36.75	17.80	1118	29.38	14.63	782
28.91	40.1	15.02	1489	30.6	11.56	980	24.8	9.36	695
36.11	38.0	14.21	1438	29.1	10.99	947	23.6	8.96	677

Data from Sverdrup, H. U., M. W. Johnson, and R. H. Fleming: The Oceans. Prentice-Hall, New York, 1942.

Instead of the absorption coefficient the equivalent *coefficient of saturation* may be given. It is defined as the number of milliliters (at NTP) of a given gas of 760 mm Hg pressure that dissolves in 1 liter of liquid at a given temperature.

As mentioned, the amount of gas that can dissolve in a solvent diminishes with increasing amount of solute. The absorption coefficient of a gas in water thus diminishes with increasing solute content. Sea water dissolves considerably less oxygen than does the almost salt-free fresh water of the same temperature. Table 8–3 gives the coefficient of saturation of water of different salt content.

When gas molecules are contained within a gas-filled space or atmosphere, we speak of the *pressure* or *partial pressure* of the gas. When gas molecules are present in a liquid-filled space, we speak of the *tension* of the gas in the liquid. If oxygen is dissolved in water, we speak of the *oxygen tension* of the water. Since at equilibrium the oxygen tension of water depends on the pO_2 in the atmosphere in contact with the water, the oxygen tension is related to the oxygen pressure. Therefore oxygen tension can be expressed in terms of the oxygen pressure. Water at 0° C in equilibrium with normal atmospheric air of 1 atm has an oxygen tension of 159.6 mm; at 20° C, 156 mm Hg.

If water having a certain gas tension is transferred to another container in such a way that it completely fills that container, leaving no gas space, it maintains its gas tension. As soon as it is exposed to an atmosphere of lower partial pressure of the particular gas, the dissolved gas leaves the solution until the amount left corresponds to the new partial pressure. This phenomenon is well known to anyone who has ever opened a bottle of soda water or beer: the carbon dioxide that had dissolved under high pressure leaves the solution when the latter becomes exposed to atmospheric air.

If two fluids of different oxygen tension are mixed, oxygen becomes distributed evenly throughout the combined fluid volume. If the fluid volumes are not mixed but come in contact with each other, oxygen (or any other dissolved gas) moves from the region of high tension to that of low tension until the tensions are equal.

The gas tension of a solution can be determined experimentally by transferring the solution into a container whose volume can be increased by moving a piston. The transfer must be achieved without bringing the solution in contact with a gas atmosphere, and the container must initially be filled completely. Then when the piston is moved a vacuum is created above the liquid, in other words, a space at zero pressure. The gas will almost quantitatively leave the solution. If the extracted gas is then separated from the liquid, its volume can be measured by: (1) analytical or chemical methods or (2) subjecting it to an external pressure of 1 atm and then measuring. The gas tension (partial pressure) is then given by the formula

$$pO_2 = \frac{v \cdot 760}{a} \text{ mm Hg} \qquad (5)$$

The latter method is useful only if it is known that only one gas was dissolved.

The term "gas tension" tells us only that the liquid in question has taken up an amount of gas that corresponds to a certain (partial) pressure. It does not indicate *how much* gas has been dissolved.

If a liquid contains as much gas as corresponds to the *theoretical* equilibrium between gas and liquid at a given temperature and pressure, the liquid is said to be *saturated* with the gas. From what has been said previously, it follows that solutions of different salt content or different temperatures may have the same gas tension, but different amounts of gas are dissolved in each case. All these solutions may be saturated, yet one contains more gas than the other. Therefore, the expression that water is saturated with oxygen does not tell us whether it contains sufficient oxygen to sustain the life of an animal.

For certain aspects of respiratory physiology a knowledge of the oxygen tensions is useful. But often it is desirable to have a more direct measure of the actual numbers of gas molecules per volume of liquid. This is given by the *gas density*, which is defined as the number of moles of gas per liter of liquid, or more commonly, the number of milligrams of gas per liter of liquid.

Gas tension and gas density refer always, and only, to dissolved gas and not to gas molecules chemically combined with other compounds. In fresh water, and to a much greater extent in sea water, a certain portion of CO_2 combines with metallic cations to form bicarbonate. Once chemically bound, this CO_2 does not contribute to the CO_2 tension (or density) of the water. Oxygen carried by blood pigments (hemoglobin, hemocyanin, and so forth) also does not represent dissolved oxygen; in other words, the oxygen carried by blood pigments does not diminish the capacity of the blood liquid to carry oxygen in physical solution.

Up to this point in the chapter, all the equations and calculations have been based on a knowledge of the respective absorption coefficients. There are situations, however, where this is not the case or where, in fact, the absorption coefficient must be calculated from experimental data. The following equations and relations are then applicable:

If the volume of gas is known that dissolves under certain experimental conditions (that is, at a given partial pressure of the gas and a given temperature) in a volume of liquid, the absorption coefficient (a) can be calculated according to

$$a = \frac{V' \cdot P' \cdot 273}{760 \cdot T} \quad \text{or} \quad a = \frac{V' \cdot P' \cdot 273}{760 \cdot (273 + t)} \qquad (6)$$

V′ is the dissolved volume of gas at the temperature at which the experiment is conducted, P′ is the pressure of the gas (or its partial pressure, if other gases are present) at which equilibration with the liquid occurred, T is the absolute temperature, and t is the temperature in degrees Centigrade. The same equation can be used to reduce any measured gas volume from that at a given temperature and pressure to that at N.T.P.:

$$V = \frac{V' \cdot P' \cdot 273}{760 \cdot T} \quad \text{or} \quad V = \frac{V' \cdot P' \cdot 273}{760 \cdot (273 + t)} \qquad (7)$$

All the symbols here are the same as in Equation 6. V is the gas volume corrected for standard temperature and pressure.

The activity coefficient a is related to the solubility coefficient s (the maximum gas volume of temperature T that dissolves in 1 volume of liquid of the same temperature): $a = s \cdot 273/T$, and $s = a \cdot T/273$.

As mentioned, the amount of dissolved gas can be given in terms either of gas volume (usually at N.T.P.) or of milligrams (mg) of gas per liter. The number of milligrams per liter is often referred to as the number of "parts per million" or ppm. One mg/l is equal to 1 ppm. In order to convert mg O_2/l to ml O_2/l, one simply divides the number of milligrams by 1.43.

REFERENCES

Carpenter, T. M. (1921) Tables, Factors and Formulas for Computing Respiratory Exchange and Biological Transformations of Energy. Carnegie Institute, Washington, No. 303.

Findlay, A. (1924) Physical Chemistry for Students of Medicine. Longmans, Green and Co., New York.

Glasstone, S., and D. Lewis (1960) Elements of Physical Chemistry, 2nd Ed. D. Van Nostrand Co., New York.

Markham, A. E., and K. A. Kobe (1941) The solubility of gases in liquids. Chem. Rev. 28:519–588.

Truesdale, G. A., A. L. Downing, and G. F. Loweden (1955) The solubility of oxygen in pure water and sea-water. J. Appl. Chem. 5:53–62.

9 RESPIRATION

Oxygen plays a key role in energy metabolism. The pattern of this metabolism is similar throughout the animal kingdom, and consists of sequential oxidations. Carbon-containing molecules are transformed to release carbon dioxide (CO_2) and pairs of hydrogen atoms. The hydrogen atoms become hydrogen ions and are oxidized to water as they combine with oxygen ions. The CO_2 is not utilized but leaves the cells and tissues by diffusion and, eventually, passes out of the organism.

Oxygen consumption and CO_2 production by living systems are more or less inseparable. Together they are called *respiration*.

Discussions of respiration are customarily divided into: (1) external respiration, (2) internal respiration, and (3) gas transport. External respiration is concerned with the intake of oxygen from the outside environment and with the release of CO_2. Of particular concern to the physiologist are the problems of gas transfer across the external boundaries (exchange membranes) of animal organisms, and the special morphological and functional adaptations that facilitate and regulate this transfer. Internal respiration involves the utilization of the acquired oxygen by the cells that constitute the organism. It is essentially a biochemical process.

Since not all cells of a multicellular organism are located at its surface, oxygen has to be transported to them, and the CO_2 they produce has to be carried to the body surface before it can leave the organism. The term "gas transport" is somewhat misleading, for it seems to imply that the respiratory gases are transported in the gaseous state. This is true only for tracheate animals (e.g., insects, Onychophora, Myriapoda) in which respiratory gases are carried to and from all body cells by a system of gas-filled tubes. In all other animals gases are carried by the body fluids, but only to a limited extent in physical solution: both oxygen and CO_2 are transported in the form of chemical compounds (CO_2) or chemical complexes (O_2).

Oxidative metabolism requires molecular oxygen. This is present in the atmosphere as well as in the water mantle of the earth. Organisms acquire oxygen directly from air and water. The primary event in the uptake of oxygen is simple inward diffusion through the body surface or through specialized regions of the body surface. CO_2, likewise, is lost by outward diffusion. As yet, no active transport mechanisms have been discovered that might be involved in the respiratory gas exchange across the respiratory exchange membranes. Theories of external respiration thus rest entirely on the concept of gas diffusion.

We have learned that diffusion is a "statistical" event and that net diffusion across membranes means a net transfer of a substance: more particles move in the one direction than in the other. The term "diffusion" in this chapter refers to net diffusion.

The respiratory gas exchange of most animal types is restricted to specialized areas of the body, "the respiratory surfaces" or respiratory membranes. These are mainly the cellular membranes of the gills (and gill-like structures) and lungs, but in a number of species, external respiration involves part of the gut, the body wall, or specialized internal structures, such as the water lungs of holothurians or the swim bladder of many species of fish. Leeches, for instance, have no respiratory structures and respire through the highly vascularized body wall. Amphibia respire to a considerable degree through their skin, particularly at high temperatures (see Figs. 9–1 and 9–2).

The amount of substance that diffuses across a given membrane is proportional to the surface area of the membrane and to the concentration gradient. Where specialized respiratory organs exist, they are always characterized by large surface areas. Maximum oxygen uptake is achieved by maintaining the highest possible concentration gradient across the respiratory membranes: the concentration of oxygen must remain high outside and low inside.

Oxygen diffuses extremely slowly. It has been calculated that in vertebrate connective tissue (which uses up practically no oxygen), oxygen diffuses at a rate of 0.0001 ml/cm^2/cm/atm. We may assume that this value corresponds closely to the rate of diffusion through most kinds of living substance. Assuming an average oxygen consumption of 0.1 ml O_2/gm tissue/hr, one can calculate that with an outside oxygen concentration equal to that of air or aerated water, diffusion alone would be sufficient only for the distance of 0.5 mm: diffusion is so slow that at the normal rate of oxygen consumption by living substance no oxygen would reach a greater depth. This means that only organisms of up to 1 mm diameter can get all their oxygen supply through mere diffusion of this gas. If an organism's diameter exceeds 1 mm, a special oxygen transport system is required. If an organism is spheroidal, its diameter cannot exceed 1 mm. However, the size of a flat animal is not limited by oxygen availability, as long as the animal is not more than about 1 mm thick. In fact, if the cells of an organism remain in layers not thicker than 1 mm, these layers can assume almost any configuration, as long as they all remain in contact with an oxygen-containing medium (air or water). Examples of this are most coelenterates and the flatworms.

The value of 1 mm is, of course, based on an oxygen consumption of 0.1 ml/gm/hr, and on the assumption that oxygen is brought to the interior by diffusion only. With lower oxygen consumption, the organism could "afford" a

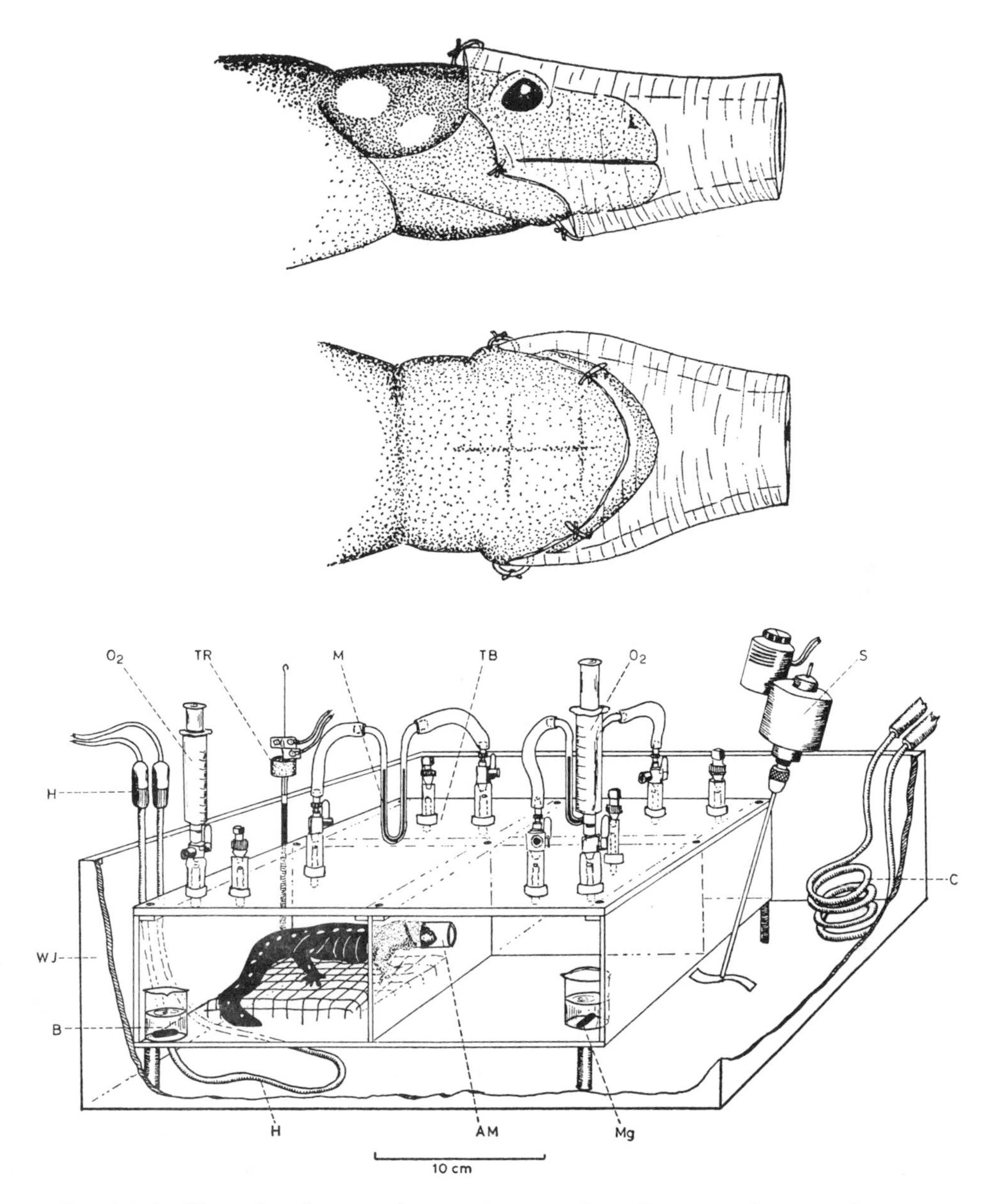

Figure 9–1. Example of a complex respirometer that allows simultaneous determination of pulmonary and cutaneous respiratory gas exchange of a salamander (*Ambystoma maculatum*). **Above**, plastic mask attached to the animal. *AM*, animal mask; *B*, barium hydroxide solution in beaker; *C*, cooling coil; *H*, heating coil; *M*, manometer; *Mg*, magnetic stirring bar; O_2, oxygen syringe; *TB*, thermobarometer chamber; *TR*, temperature regulator; *S*, stirrer; *WJ*, water jacket. (From Whitford, W. G., and V. H. Hutchison: Cutaneous and pulmonary gas exchange in the spotted salamander, Ambystoma maculatum. Biol. Bull. *124*:344–354, 1963.)

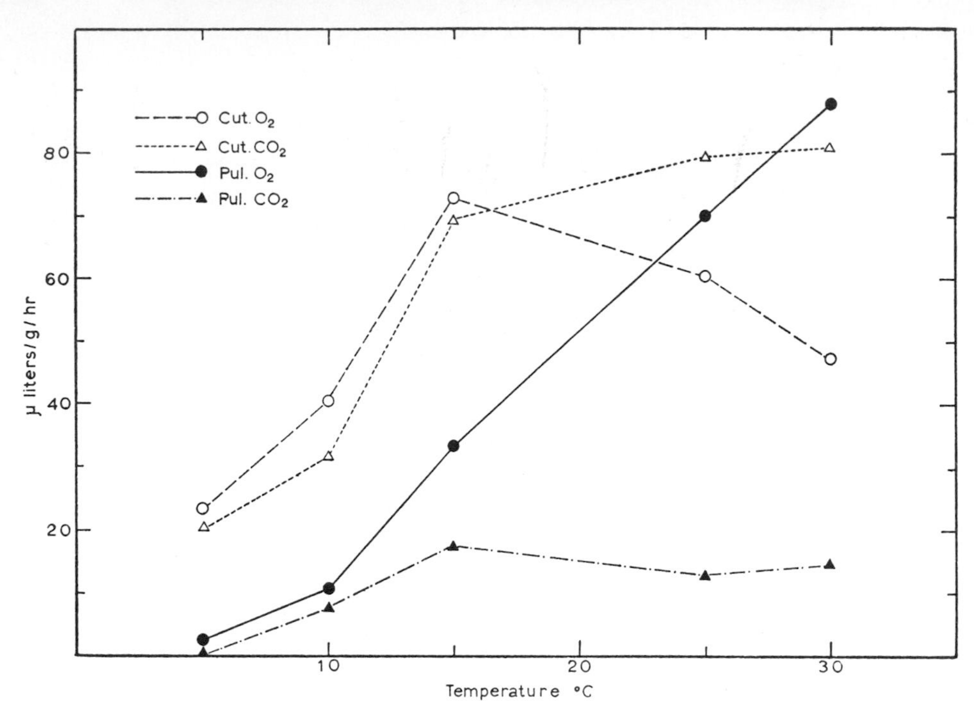

Figure 9–2. Mean cutaneous (*Cut.*) and pulmonary (*Pul.*) gas exchange at different temperatures, as measured in spotted salamanders (*Ambystoma*). Pulmonary oxygen consumption increases linearly and outruns cutaneous oxygen consumption. Note that the loss of CO_2 through the skin is at all temperatures much greater than that through the lungs. (From Whitford, W. G., and V. H. Hutchison: Cutaneous and pulmonary gas exchange in the spotted salamander, Ambystoma maculatum. Biol. Bull. *124*:344–354, 1963.)

larger diameter, but animals that consume less than 0.05 ml/gm/hr are rare. It is likely that protoplasmic streaming within the body cells greatly aids oxygen transport.

If an organism remained in one place and if the surrounding medium (air or water) remained completely stagnant, the concentration of oxygen in the immediate vicinity of the respiratory membranes would get depleted, or at any rate sufficiently diminished so that the organism could not get adequate quantities of oxygen.

In order to meet the demands, the respiratory surface of the organism must come in contact with new volumes of oxygen-containing medium. The animal has to replace the oxygen-deficient medium with fresh medium that contains a new amount of oxygen. This can be achieved in two ways: 1. The animal moves into new areas of the oxygen-containing medium or stays in a continually moving medium. As a fish swims through the water, oxygen-containing medium moves over its gills; the depleted medium is left behind. Fresh-water Turbellaria cling to rocks in rapidly streaming brooks. 2. The animal induces movement (convection) of the external medium. In terrestrial, air breathing animals, air is moved in and out of the respiratory cavities, the lungs, and tracheae by the rhythmic contraction of certain muscles (diaphragm and intercostal muscles in terrestrial vertebrates, abdominal and thoracic muscles in insects). In aquatic animals rhythmic movements of body parts associated with specialized respiratory structures induce water movement; in many cases, the respiratory structures (gills, ctenidia) are covered by a ciliated epithelium and the water is moved as a constant stream. In other aquatic animals, external convection is produced by body movements which, in some forms, consist of regular, undulating movements.

Induced convection of the external medium for the "purpose" of respiration is called *ventilation*. Where this is achieved with rhythmic movements, the number of pumping actions per unit time is called the *ventilation rate*. Where the pumps do not show an obvious rhythm, ventilation rate is expressed in terms of the volume of external medium moved over the respiratory surfaces per unit time. This is the case, for instance, with lamellibranch molluscs where the ciliated epithelium of the gills produces a steady stream of water that flows over the gill surfaces.

Famous examples of ventilating aquatic animals are the fresh-water oligochaetes of the genus *Tubifex*. They live in large colonies; each worm has its own tube built into the mud in shallow water. Only the rear end of each animal sticks out into the water if this contains sufficient oxygen. As soon as the flow of water (and with it that of the available oxygen) diminishes, a larger portion of the worm appears and begins to wiggle in such a way as to move a stream of water toward its tube (Alsterberg, 1922). The length of the portion of the worm's body that projects into the water and wiggles is inversely proportional to the oxygen content of the water.

Crabs and many other forms of decapod crustaceans stay for many hours in one place. Their gills are almost completely enclosed by the carapace. In order to prevent asphyxiation during quiescent periods, these animals continuously pump great quantities of water through their gill chambers with the aid of specialized legs, the scaphognathites, located at the base of the second maxillae.

Terrestrial vertebrates possessing lungs periodically fill and empty these "air bags" and thus replenish the oxygen content of their immediate respiratory environment.

The insects, possessing a tracheal system for gas transport, either rely entirely on gas diffusion throughout the tracheal tubes or accelerate the exchange by rhythmically compressing their abdomen with the aid of specialized musculature. During flight, the changes in shape and volume of the thorax brought about by the contractions of the massive flight muscles likewise aid in accelerating gas transport. Abdominal respiratory movements can be observed readily in wasps and bees.

Gases do not diffuse rapidly in narrow tubes, in spite of the fact that gas diffuses in air about 10,000 times faster than in water. Even with the aid of rhythmic, mechanical compression, the system of tracheal tubes is efficient only if these tubes do not exceed a certain maximum length. The tracheal system of insects thus imposes a limit to body size. The largest insects that ever lived were dragonflies with a wing span of about 2 feet, but their body, as that of modern Odonata, was cylindrical and did not exceed 5 cm in diameter, and thus was not larger than that of the biggest tropical insects (beetles) living today.

The largest insects are found in hot climates because diffusion is accelerated by an increase in temperature, so that even with longer tracheal tubes gas exchange is adequate.

All the mechanisms of external respiration mentioned so far can be classified as induced convection of the external oxygen-containing medium. By induced convection the external oxygen concentration remains high. Since oxygen uptake depends on a difference in concentration of oxygen in the external and the internal media bordering the respiratory membranes, it is equally important to keep the oxygen concentration of the internal medium of the respiratory organs at a low level. This again is achieved by convection: the body fluid that serves as transporting agent is circulated past the respiratory membrane in such a way as to carry away oxygen that had diffused inward, and to bring oxygen-poor fluid to the respiratory membranes. Thus equilibrium is never reached and oxygen continues to diffuse inward at a maximal rate. Similarly, carbon dioxide continues to diffuse outward.

If the body fluid that serves as a transport medium flows within blood vessels, the flow is effected by rhythmic contractions of blood vessels or hearts. In echinoderms, the fluid inside the water-vascular system (coelomic fluid) is continuously kept in motion by a ciliated epithelium. Since gas is exchanged through the tube feet and certain accessory respiratory papillae ("gills"), the movement or convection of the coelomic fluid inside them serves the same purpose as the movement of blood through the alveolar capillaries in the lungs of mammals (Buddington, 1942).

An amazing arrangement is found in aquatic insect larvae, the larvae of Ephemeroidea and of Odonata. In contrast to the terrestrial insects, whose tracheae open to the outside, these animals have a closed tracheal system. Here the gases diffuse through the thin-walled expansions of the body wall (abdominal tracheal gills of ephemerids) or of the inner wall of the hindgut (Odonata) into the tracheae. The outside water is convected by movement of the tracheal gills and a rhythmic expulsion of water from the hindgut with subsequent refilling. Internal convection is provided only by pressure changes caused by body movements.

In summary, external respiration consists of the inward diffusion of oxygen and the outward diffusion of carbon dioxide across certain exchange membranes of the body. Gas exchange is facilitated by the enlarged surface area of the exchange membrane and by the large concentration gradient that is maintained across the exchange membrane. The mechanisms employed in this involve induction of external as well as internal convection.

QUANTITATIVE ASPECTS OF EXTERNAL RESPIRATION

The intensity of external respiration can be measured. Since it largely consists of the inward diffusion of oxygen and the outward diffusion of CO_2, one can determine either the amount of oxygen consumed per unit time, or the amount of CO_2 given off, or both. The most common method is to measure the *oxygen consumption*, or *oxygen uptake*. This is usually expressed as volume

Table 9–1. **Oxygen Consumption of Various Species of Animals (in ml O_2/gm/hr)**

Protozoa		Arthropoda	
Paramecium	1	*Uca*	0.05
Amoeba	0.2	*Homarus*	0.5
Porifera		*Cambarus*	0.10
Suberites	0.24	*Calliphora*	1.7
Coelenterata		*Vanessa*	0.6
Anemonia	0.013	Echinodermata	
Aurelia	0.0034	*Holothuria*	0.01
Nematoda		*Strongylocentrotus*	0.004–0.027
Ascaris	0.50	*Asterias*	0.03
Rotylenchus	0.66	Tunicata	
Mollusca		*Salpa*	0.008
Anodonta	0.002	Vertebrata	
Mytilus	0.055	Goldfish	0.07
Limnea	0.011	Trout	0.22
Octopus	0.09	Rat	0.95
Annelida		Cat	0.44
Arenicola	0.031	Man	0.2
Chaetopterus	0.008		

Selected data from the literature as collected by Heilbrunn, L. V.: An outline of General Physiology, 3rd Ed. W. B. Saunders Co., Philadelphia, 1952; and Prosser, C. L., and F. A. Brown, Jr.: Comparative Animal Physiology, 2nd Ed. W. B. Saunders Co., Philadelphia, 1961.

(reduced to 0° C and 1 atm pressure), of O_2 taken up per gram of animal per minute or per hour. (See Table 9–1 for examples.) However, these figures alone are insufficient. One must state the condition of the animal (e.g., resting, running, starved, age, temperature), and the condition of the oxygen-containing outside medium (temperature, oxygen content, extent of convection, etc.).

Often it is possible to measure the volume of an oxygen-containing medium passing over the respiratory membranes per unit time (Fig. 9–3). Passage of the oxygen-containing medium toward the respiratory membranes is called *inspiration*; removal of the medium from these membranes is called *expiration*.

The difference in the oxygen content of the inspired and the expired media can be used as a measure of the oxygen consumption. If the inspired and expired volumes are known, one can also determine the *utilization* of oxygen, that is, the proportion of the oxygen of the inspired medium that is taken up by the organism. Oxygen consumption is an absolute measure; oxygen utilization a relative one. Oxygen consumption is expressed in ml/gm/min (hr); oxygen utilization is expressed in per cent.

The expression of oxygen consumption in ml/gm/min is by no means ideal. A milliliter, of course, is always a milliliter, but 1 gm of one animal is not necessarily identical with 1 gm of another animal. It is well known that the oxygen consumption per gram of animal decreases with increasing size of the animal. The meaning of this, however, is not understood.

In order to obtain comparable results, one usually measures the oxygen consumption of animals in a state of complete rest and when one can assume that no internal activity, such as digestion, is taking place. Such metabolism is termed *basal metabolism*, and the rate of oxidative metabolism, as judged by the measured rate of oxygen consumption, is called the *basal metabolic rate*.

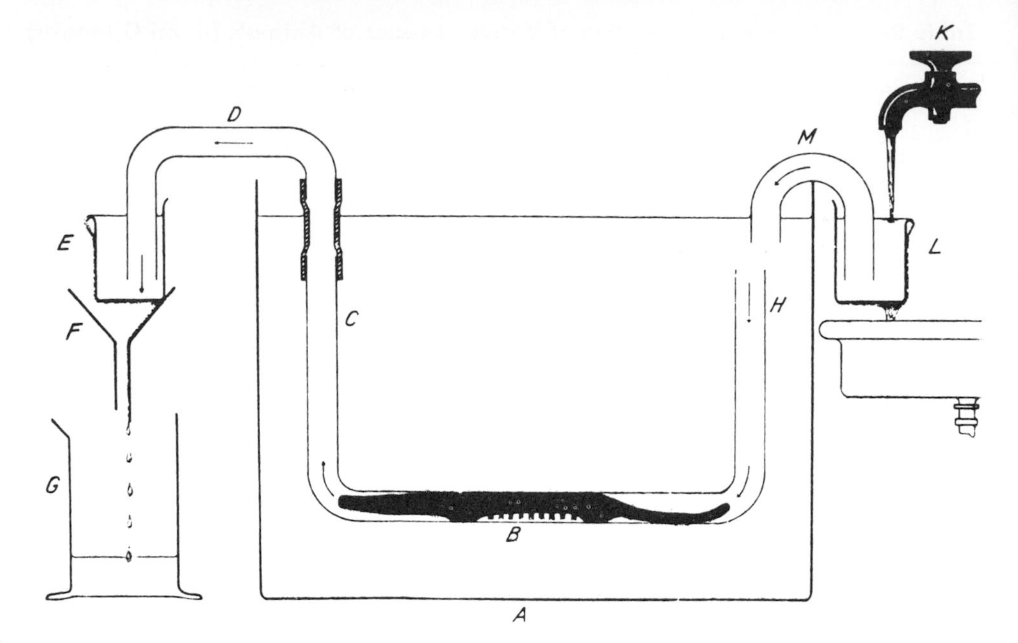

Figure 9–3. Determination of the ventilation volume in *Arenicola*. (From van Dam, L.: On the utilization of oxygen and regulation of breathing in some aquatic animals. Thesis, Groningen, 1938.)

In an attempt to compare oxygen consumptions of different species or of different animals of the same species, one determines the basal metabolic rates and actually compares the oxygen consumptions of such "basal" animals.

If the data obtained in studies of this kind are plotted on a graph, the abscissa of which represents the logarithm of the animal's weight and the ordinate of which represents the logarithm of the oxygen consumed per gram of animal per hour, a more or less straight line is usually obtained (see Fig. 9–4), which shows a characteristic slope and can be represented by the formula $M = k \cdot W^{0.7-0.8}$. M here stands for metabolism as expressed by the oxygen consumption per gram of animal per hour, and W stands for the total wet weight of the animal; k is a constant characteristic for the species.

Curves showing this typical slope were first obtained from studies on man and warm-blooded animals (mammals and birds). They were interpreted as indicating a relationship between surface area and respiration inasmuch as with linearly increasing length the surface of a body increases with the square of the length, whereas the weight increases with the cube of the length. Since heat loss would be greater with relatively greater surface, a small warm-blooded animal would have to produce more heat and have a higher metabolism than a larger one, and oxygen consumption would rise with the 2/3 power of the animal's weight. This point of view has been propounded by Voit (1901) and by Rubner (1883). But in 1911, Pütter showed that even in cold-blooded animals (fish, Crustacea), respiration increases with surface area rather than with weight. He argued that the rate of oxygen consumption is determined not by the degree of metabolism but by the size of the respiratory surfaces (gills, lungs, and so

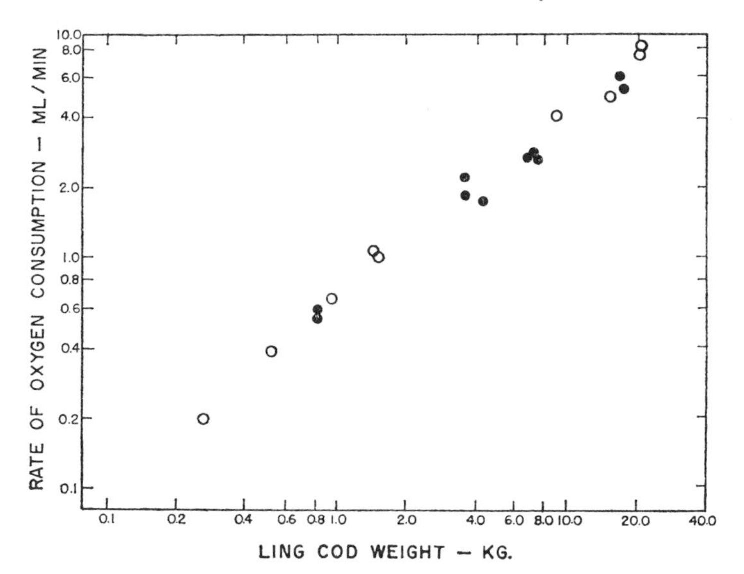

Figure 9–4. Rate of oxygen consumption in relation to body weight. Both scales are logarithmic. All points lie close to a straight line with a slope of 0.78. The animal chosen for the experiments was the ling cod (*Ophiodon elongatus*) from which specimens of an extremely wide range of weights can be obtained. Open circles: normal fish; closed circles: sedated fish. (From Pritchard, A. W., E. Florey, and A. W. Martin: Relationship between metabolic rate and body size in an elasmobranch [Squalus suckleyi] and in a teleost [Ophiodon elongatus]. J. Mar. Res. *17*:403–411, 1958.)

forth), and is proportional to the area involved in gas exchange. The "two-thirds rule" was later confirmed by Rubner (1924) in pike and tench. For most species, however, the "ideal" exponent of 0.66 (or 2/3) is somewhat too low, the value being in most cases between 0.7 and 0.8, as stated.

In summary, in a great variety of animal species the basal oxygen consumption is proportional to the 0.7 to 0.8 power of the body weight. The values obtained for related species often fall on the same curve. The relationship as represented by the formula $M = k \cdot W^{0.7-0.8}$ is a purely mathematical expression. No causal relationship between the values of M and W has been established.

Insects, having a tracheal system, do not follow the above-mentioned relationship. Their oxygen uptake is actually proportional to body weight, according to studies of Slovtzoff (1909). In lamellibranch molluscs, oxygen consumption is also directly proportional to weight (Schwartzkopff and Wesemeier, 1959).

Many textbooks present lists of animals and their oxygen consumption. The value of such lists is dubious, since usually the size or age of the animals and the amount of available oxygen are not indicated. Still, they do show the wide range of metabolic rates within the animal kingdom. Values may be as low as 0.009 ml O_2/gm/hr (*Pecten*), or as high as 100 ml O_2/gm/hr (*Vanessa*). As a point of reference, the oxygen consumption of a resting adult man is 0.16 to 0.33 ml/gm/hr in an environment at 20° C (Heilbrunn, 1953).

Oxygen consumption increases markedly with the activity of the animal. This is discussed on p. 171. Up to 100 times as much oxygen is taken up during activity as during rest. A striking example is the butterfly *Vanessa*, which, according to Zeuthen (in Krogh, 1941), at 20° C consumes 0.6 ml O_2/gm/hr while at rest, but 100 ml O_2/gm/hr when flying. In mammals and in man, the oxygen consumption rises to values 15 to 20 times higher than the basal metabolic rate (Bishop, 1950).

As pointed out in Chapter 7, in the metabolism of pyruvic acid (citric acid cycle), three molecules of CO_2 are produced for each molecule of pyruvic acid. Also, breakdown products of fats or proteins may enter the citric acid cycle whenever they are identical with one of the intermediates of the cycle. Acetic acid, α-ketoglutarate, and so forth can be derived from protein breakdown. They enter the cycle at the appropriate point (see Chap. 7). The later their entry, the fewer molecules of CO_2 are produced. This is in accordance with the observation that an animal expires less carbon dioxide if it metabolizes protein or fat (carnivorous animal, starving animal), than if it metabolizes carbohydrate (glucose), as is the case during muscular activity in almost all animals and as is typical for herbivorous (plant eating) organisms.

The ratio of the number of CO_2 molecules produced to the number of O_2 molecules taken up can be determined readily. Since equal numbers of molecules of any gas occupy equal volumes (provided temperature and pressure are the same), one simply determines the volume of O_2 consumed and the volume of CO_2 given off by an animal during a definite interval. The ratio of these volumes is equal to the ratio of the number of molecules of each gas. The ratio of the volume of CO_2 produced to the volume of O_2 consumed is called the *respiratory quotient* (R.Q.), which is formulated in this way:

$$\text{R.Q.} = \frac{\text{vol CO}_2\text{ given off}}{\text{vol O}_2\text{ consumed}}$$

The oxidative metabolism of one molecule of glucose leads to the production of two molecules of pyruvic acid and subsequently yields six (2×3) molecules of CO_2. During this process 12 pairs of hydrogen atoms are removed from the resulting compounds, and these use up 12 atoms (six molecules) of oxygen in the formation of water; thus for each molecule of oxygen consumed, one molecule of CO_2 is produced. Consequently, the R.Q. during pure carbohydrate (glucose) metabolism is 1.0.

With few exceptions, an R.Q. of 1.0 indicates pure carbohydrate metabolism. If fat is metabolized, less CO_2 is produced than O_2 consumed. The same is true for protein metabolism. The R.Q. during oxidative metabolism of fat is about 0.7, and during oxidative metabolism of protein, about 0.8.

Under certain circumstances, R.Q.'s are higher than 1.0, such as when carbohydrate is transformed into fat—for example, in pigs or geese fattened on a carbohydrate diet (Bleibtreu, 1894; Smedley, 1912; and Smedley and Lubrzinska, 1913). Bleibtreu found that the R.Q.'s of a goose fed on rye flour were 1.34, 1.19, and 1.22. The goose increased in weight from 2020 to 6570 gm within 42 days. The high R.Q.'s are due to the fact that carbohydrates contain a much higher proportion of oxygen than do fats, so that during the transformation, oxygen is actually "liberated" and made available for cellular oxidations. The animal thus requires less atmospheric oxygen.

In hibernating mammals the R.Q. values may be low (marmot, squirrel, hedgehog, hamster, and so forth). Values as low as 0.3 have been recorded

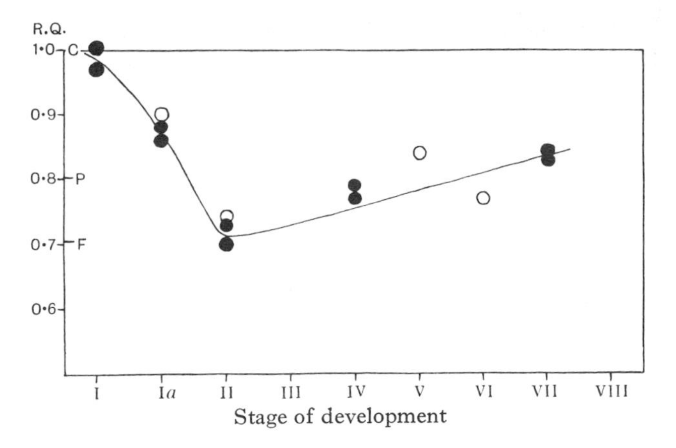

Figure 9–5. Example of a dramatic change of the respiratory quotient (*R.Q.*) during development. The diagram shows the respiratory quotients of embryos of a crab, *Carcinus*, at different stages of development. Closed circles: measured at 37° C.; open circles: measured at 15° C. *C*, *P*, and *F*, the theoretical respiratory quotients for combustion of carbohydrate, protein, and fat, respectively. (From Needham, J.: The energy sources in ontogenesis. VII. The respiratory quotient of developing crustacean embryos. J. Exp. Biol. *10*:79–87, 1933.)

(Nagai, 1909; Pembrey, 1903). These low R.Q. values are explained by the conversion of fat into carbohydrate, which is metabolized.

The R.Q. can give valuable hints as to the type of metabolic activity going on within an animal, and even reflect the animal's diet. During development, an animal's R.Q. can show characteristic changes, as for instance in crabs (Fig. 9–5).

The efficiency of the external respiratory apparatus is expressed by the utilization values (see Table 9–2). If these are high, most of the available oxygen is withdrawn from the inspired medium; if these are low, only a small proportion of the available oxygen is utilized. The data, of course, do not indicate the absolute quantities of oxygen removed. Most lamellibranchs, for instance, have a low utilization, but the quantities of water passed over their gills are large enough to allow sufficient oxygen uptake. On the whole, however, utilization is higher in aquatic animals than in terrestrial animals. Some approximate utilization values are as follows: man, 4 to 5 per cent; eel, 80 per cent; the worm *Arenicola*, 30 to 50 per cent; clams, 5 to 10 per cent (data from Irving, Scholander, and Grinnel, 1942; van Dam, 1938; Hazelhoff, 1938–1939). These utilization values apply to animals in a medium of normal, optimum oxygen content. If greater or lesser amounts of oxygen are present, utilization may be altered (see p. 171).

Oxygen utilization in air breathers differs from that of water breathers. Although the oxygen tensions may be identical in air and water (see Chap. 8), the contained volumes certainly are not. At a pO_2 of 159 mm Hg, air contains 210 ml O_2/liter, whereas water (0° C) contains only 12.5 ml/liter; in other words, the water contains about 1/17 the amount of O_2 present in air even though the oxygen tension is equal to the pO_2 in air. Water breathers therefore require a volume of oxygen-containing medium 17 times greater than that required by air breathers in order to extract the same amount of oxygen. Since the viscosities

Table 9–2. Oxygen Utilization (in %) of Various Animals*

Filter Feeders		*Nonfilter Feeders*			
Sponges		Annelida		Cephalopoda	
Sycon	39	*Eunice*	50	*Octopus*	63
Leucandra	11	*Aphrodite*	66	Echinodermata	
Leuconia	7	*Hermione*	55	*Astropecten*	49
Chondrosia	21	*Chaetopterus*	39	*Echinocardium*	54
Suberites	15	*Rhynchobolus*	44	*Holothuria*	55
Reniera	6	*Bonellia*	30	Pisces	
Hircinia	20	Crustacea		*Scyllium*	46
Aplysina	57	*Palinurus*	43	*Scorpaena*	53
Lamellibranchia		*Scyllarus*	43	*Trigla*	59
Cardium	8	*Dromia*	43	*Uranoscopus*	82
Solen	9	*Calappa*	76	*Hippocampus*	55
Pinna	5	*Maja*	29	*Siphonostoma*	65
Tunicata		*Anilocra*	45		
Ciona	7	Gastropoda			
Phallusia	6	*Haliotis*	56		
Ascidia	4	*Murex*	38		
		Tritonium	79		
		Doris	67		

*Average figures from extensive data given by Hazelhoff, E. H.: Über die Ausnützung des Sauerstoffs bei verschiedenen Wassertieren. Z. vergl. Physiol. *126*:306–327, 1938–1939.

of the two media differ greatly, aquatic respiration is far more demanding than terrestrial respiration.

REGULATION OF EXTERNAL RESPIRATION

Oxygen as well as CO_2 *diffuses* across the respiratory exchange membranes; they are not actively transported. Passive net transport depends on the concentration gradient, the membrane area, and the temperature. Thus, the oxygen uptake of an animal should increase with increasing external oxygen concentration and should decrease with decreasing external oxygen concentration.

Indeed many animal species show this relationship: their mode of respiration is termed *dependent respiration* (Fig. 9–6). In many animals the oxygen uptake (oxygen consumption) is proportional to the available oxygen. This is by no means a primitive condition, since it is exhibited even by such "advanced" animals as the lobster *Homarus vulgaris* (see Fig. 9–7).

An animal cannot take up more oxygen than it uses in its metabolism, but metabolism is limited by the amount of oxygen available to the cells. Dependent respiration, therefore, implies that the metabolic rate decreases and increases with any fall or rise of the external oxygen concentration, respectively. Oxidative metabolism can be assumed to have a maximum. Once this is reached, any further increase in external oxygen concentration cannot cause a further increase in oxygen consumption.

In many animal species oxygen uptake is regulated in such a way that oxygen utilization is increased when less oxygen is available than normally:

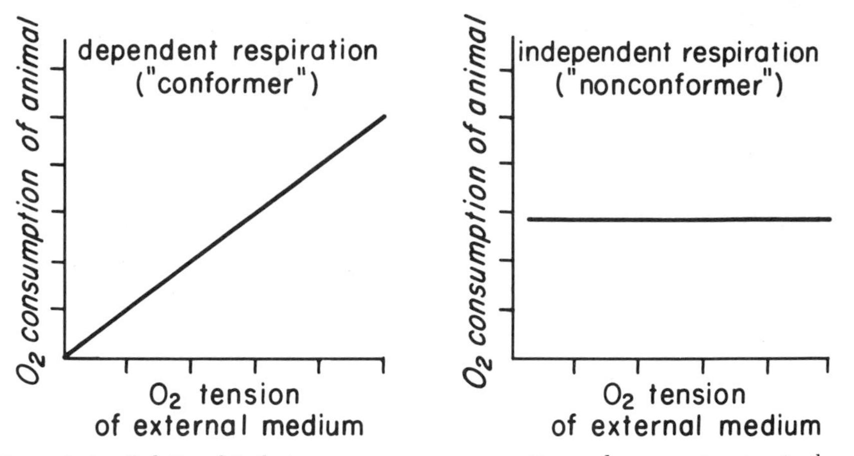

Figure 9–6. Relationship between oxygen consumption and oxygen tension in the external medium. Both parameters are given in arbitrary units. The two diagrams represent, in idealized form, the behavior of animals showing *dependent respiration* (left) and *independent respiration* (right). Actually, independent respiration is possible only above a minimal external oxygen tension.

their oxygen consumption is independent of the external oxygen concentration within a wide range. This is known as *independent respiration* (Figs. 9–6 and 9–8).

Oxygen consumption and oxygen uptake can be controlled in many ways:

1. The most elementary factor is the intensity of oxidative metabolism. If this metabolism is stimulated, internal oxygen utilization is increased, and con-

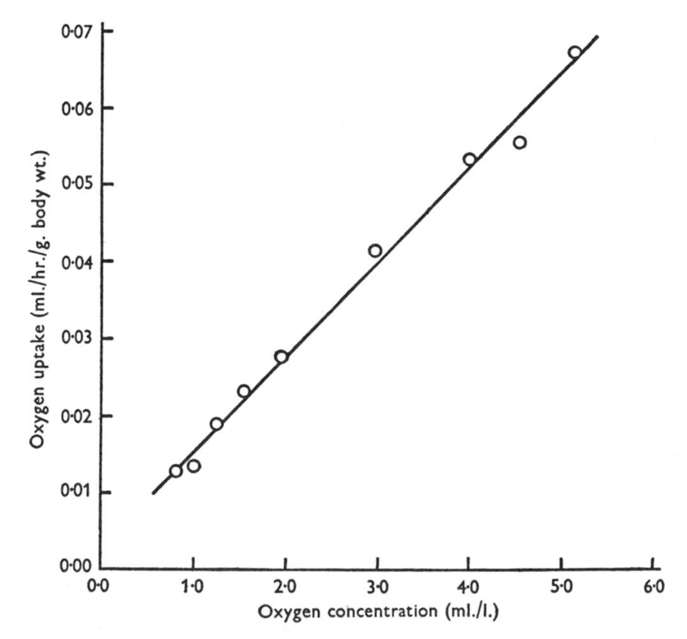

Figure 9–7. An example of oxygen consumption that is dependent on the external oxygen concentration (tension): dependent respiration of a "conformer," the lobster *Homarus vulgaris*. The experiment was conducted at 15° C. (From Thomas, H. J.: The oxygen uptake of the lobster [Homarus vulgaris]. J. Exp. Biol. *31*:228–251, 1954.)

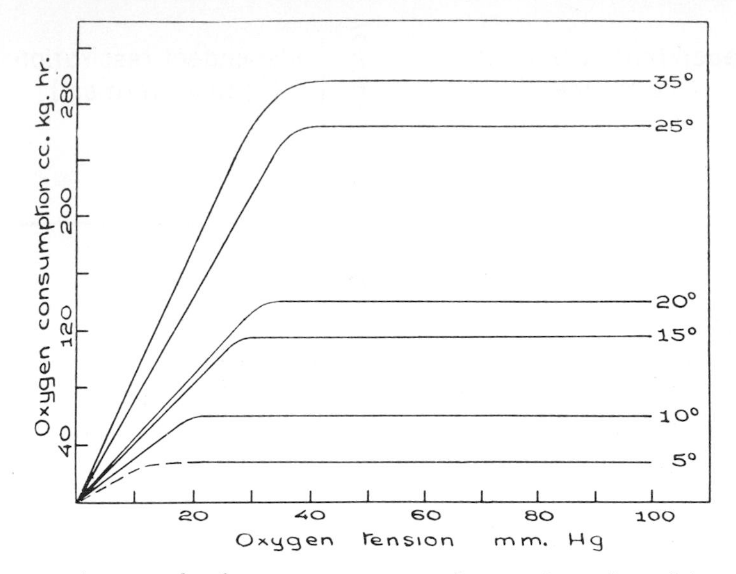

Figure 9–8. An example of oxygen consumption that is independent of the external oxygen concentration (tension) above a certain minimal value: independent respiration of a "nonconformer," the goldfish. The experiments were conducted at different temperatures, as indicated. (From Fry, F. E. J., and J. S. Hart: The relation of temperature to oxygen consumption in the goldfish. Biol. Bull. *94*:66–77, 1948.)

sequently the tissue oxygen tension is lowered. This, in turn, increases the oxygen concentration gradient between tissue fluid and blood, and thus more oxygen can diffuse to the tissue cells. As the oxygen concentration of the blood falls, the concentration gradient between the external (environment) and internal (blood) oxygen rises, and more oxygen diffuses inward through the respiratory membranes.

2. An increase in ventilation rate effectively increases oxygen uptake because the oxygen-depleted medium just outside the respiratory membranes is removed more rapidly and a higher outside concentration of oxygen favors more rapid inward diffusion across the respiratory membranes. If the oxygen tension of the external medium declines, the rate at which oxygen is consumed can be maintained by an increase in ventilation rate.

3. Just as effective as an increase in the external convection (ventilation rate) is an increase in the internal convection (velocity of blood circulation and volume of blood brought toward the respiratory membranes). This is brought about by an increased pumping rate of the heart and by a dilation of the blood vessels that supply the respiratory body surfaces (gills, lungs, body wall).

4. In addition to short-term regulation of oxygen consumption are mechanisms that provide for long-term regulation, that is, for adaptation to higher, or lower, oxygen tensions. These consist of (a) increase in size of respiratory exchange membranes and (b) increase in the amount and oxygen affinity of blood pigments (see under "Oxygen Transport").

One of the most intriguing questions facing the physiologist is: What actually turns on these regulating mechanisms? So far, we know of two conditions that stimulate oxygen uptake: low oxygen tension and high CO_2 tension. The effective agent can be determined by the following type of experiment:

If, when external CO_2 concentration is increased without significantly changing the available oxygen, there is an increase in oxygen consumption, ventilation rate, or oxygen utilization, it can be concluded that the increase in CO_2 concentration stimulated respiration. If there is no change, but respiratory activity increases following a lowering of the external oxygen tension, the latter situation acts as the stimulus.

Experiments of this kind have been performed with many animal species. In mammals, for instance, CO_2 stimulates the rate and amplitude of ventilation, probably by acting directly on the respiratory control centers in the brain (Gesell, 1939). Notable exceptions to this rule are diving mammals: for instance, the respiratory centers of beavers, seals, and porpoises are insensitive to CO_2. Increased CO_2 tension stimulates respiration in many invertebrates (molluscs, arthropods, and a few annelids), but several species of annelids (*Tubifex, Limnodrilus*) and Crustacea (*Balanus, Carcinus, Ligia*) are insensitive. Lack of oxygen is an effective stimulant in most animals.

Lack of oxygen may affect the organism indirectly: reduction of available oxygen usually leads to an accumulation of lactic acid (or an analogous organic acid). The resulting reduction in pH of body fluids increases the internal CO_2 tension (liberation of CO_2 from bicarbonate). Both the increased internal CO_2 and increased acidity of body fluids (increased H^+ concentration) may stimulate respiratory mechanisms. Particularly in invertebrates, much needs to be done to elucidate the precise mechanisms of respiratory control. Available data can be gleaned from literature surveys of Bishop (1950), Prosser (1961), Winterstein (1921), and Babak (1921). In particular, we need to know more about nervous control of respiration and about the sensory receptor structures that are sensitive to changes in either O_2 tension, CO_2 tension, or, perhaps, H^+ concentration.

The study of regulation of oxygen consumption is concerned not only with the agents that stimulate or depress respiration, but also with the specific mechanisms that regulate this. These mechanisms, as listed above, are: 1. Increase (or decrease) of oxidative metabolism within body cells. 2. Increase (or decrease) of internal convection (circulation of body fluids). 3. Increase of external convection. Much is known about the first, but is beyond the scope of this text. The interested reader should refer to such publications as the Annual Review of Biochemistry. The second mechanism, that is, increase of internal convection, involves the following: increased pumping rate of the heart, and dilation of blood vessels that supply the respiratory exchange membranes of gills, lungs, and epidermis. The third mechanism, increase in external convection, consists of an increase in ventilation rate. At least the last two mechanisms are controlled by the nervous system. The hearts of all animals that have been studied in this regard are under nervous control. This is usually a dual control: one set of nerves causes acceleration and enhancement of the heartbeat and the other leads to slowing and diminished contractions. The muscles that are responsible for respiratory movements, whether in an insect, crustacean, cephalopod, or mammal, are rhythmically activated by nerves arising from the central nervous system. Their activity pattern is determined by the "spontaneous" rhythmic activity of certain cells within the central nervous system which are collectively referred to as the *respiratory center*. The center itself is influenced by the activity of yet other nerve cells which, in turn, are affected by such conditions as high CO_2 tension, lack of O_2, or increased acidity.

The following terms denote the condition of respiratory activity: *eupnea*, normal ventilation; *hyperpnea*, increased ventilation rate; and *apnea*, cessation of respiratory movements or of ventilation. Apnea has been observed in many diverse animal species. It usually results from exposure to abnormally large external oxygen tensions or oxygen pressures. Examples are shown in Figures 9–9 and 9–10.

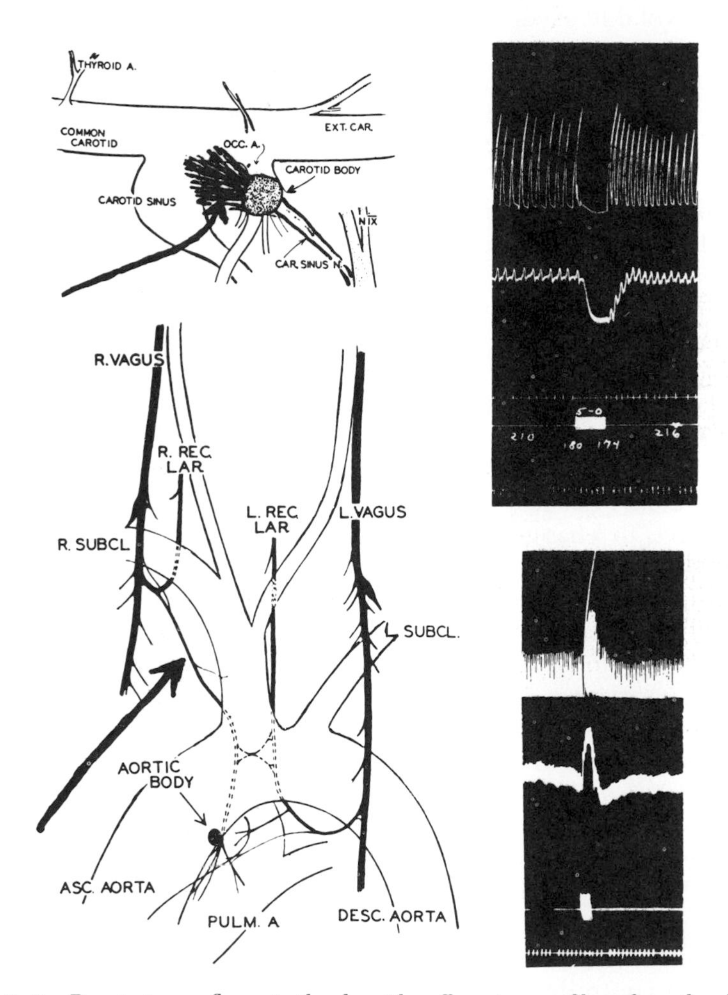

Figure 9–9. Respiratory reflexes in the dog. The afferent nerve fibers from the chemoreceptors located in the carotid and aortic bodies (see diagrams on the left) stimulate the respiratory centers in the brain and cause increase in frequency and amplitude of ventilation and an increase in heart rate and arterial blood pressure (records, lower right). Afferent nerve fibers from the pressoreceptors diffusely situated in the adventitial coats of the aortic arch and carotid sinuses cause depression of respiratory centers, slowing of the heart, and a fall in blood pressure (records, upper right). The two kymograph records shown indicate from top to bottom: respiratory movements, blood pressure, the volume of expired air (upper record only) indicated by the distance between vertical deflections, and the duration of electrical stimulation of the afferent nerve as indicated by a block of vertical deflections. (After Schmidt, 1940, from Lambertsen, C. L.: Neurogenic control of respiration. *In* Medical Physiology, 11th Ed. P. Bard, ed. The C. V. Mosby Co., St. Louis, 1961.)

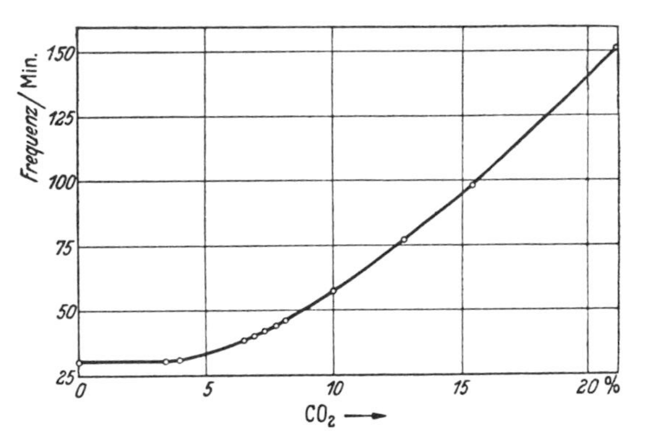

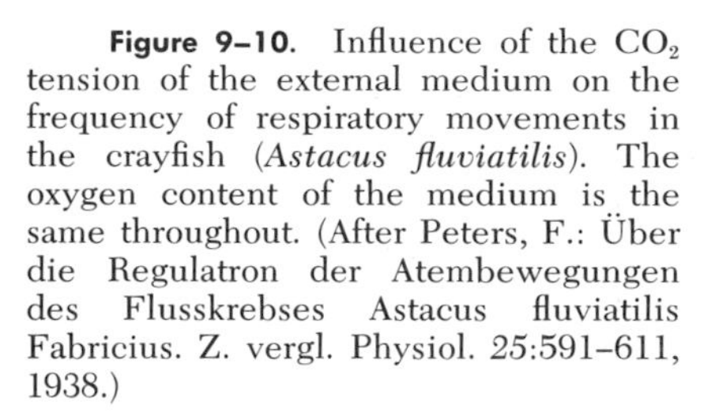
Figure 9–10. Influence of the CO_2 tension of the external medium on the frequency of respiratory movements in the crayfish (*Astacus fluviatilis*). The oxygen content of the medium is the same throughout. (After Peters, F.: Über die Regulatron der Atembewegungen des Flusskrebses Astacus fluviatilis Fabricius. Z. vergl. Physiol. 25:591–611, 1938.)

Unfortunately, little is known about the reflex control of respiratory functions. Only two groups of animals have been studied successfully in this regard: the vertebrates (predominantly mammals) and cephalopods. It is well established that the activity of the respiratory center of mammals is controlled by nerve fibers that innervate chemoreceptors (sensory cells sensitive to chemicals) situated in the so-called carotid bodies (Fig. 9–9) and the aortic body (Fig. 9–9). These are excited by low O_2 tension, low pH, and high CO_2 tension. This excitation in turn activates the cells of the respiratory center and these give rise to stronger and more frequent contractions of the muscles responsible for inspiration and expiration. In addition to this chemically induced reflex control of respiratory movements, are reflexes elicited by the mechanical excitation of stretch receptors located in the lungs: certain receptors are excited (stretched) during inflation of the lungs, and cause inhibition of those nerve cells in the central nervous system that are responsible for the contraction of "inspiratory" muscles. Other receptors are excited by the mechanical stimulation caused by the deflating of the lungs. These cause excitation of the same nerve cells that cause inspiration. Both reflexes are known as *Hering-Breuer reflexes* (Hering and Breuer, 1868). Further reflex control of respiratory movements is initiated by pressoreceptors located within the wall of the aortic arch and of the carotid sinus. These are excited by an increase in blood pressure. The sensory fibers, when activated, mediate an inhibition of the respiratory center, causing depression or cessation of respiratory movements.

In cephalopods, similar reflex controls of respiratory movements have been observed. Inspiratory movements (expansion of the mantle cavity) are initiated by the reflex action of receptor nerve cells that are excited by outside pressure acting on the gills. Expiratory movements (contraction of the mantle muscles) are reflexly elicited by the excitation of stretch receptors in the mantle which results from distension during inspiration. This has been described for the octopod *Eledone* by von Uexküll (1891), who also located the inspiratory and expiratory centers in the brain of this animal. Similar findings have been reported by Fredericq (1878, 1879) for *Octopus vulgaris* and by Polimanti (1912) for *Sepia officinalis*. There is no evidence that in cephalopods respiratory reflexes are induced by chemoreceptors.

GAS TRANSPORT

With the exception of tracheate animals, Protozoa, Porifera, and Coelenterata, gas is transported between respiratory exchange membranes and tissue cells by circulating body fluids. Blood, coelomic fluid, and tissue fluid (interstitial fluid) are all involved in gas transport, even though the most efficient vehicle is the circulating blood. The latter moves in vascular channels and is propelled by muscular pumps (hearts). Coelomic fluid is circulated either by ciliary action or alterations of the internal pressure of various parts of the body due to body movements. The same is true for circulation of tissue fluids, but here an additional mechanism of circulation is prominent—the convection produced by interaction between tissue pressure, blood pressure, and blood colloid osmotic pressure. The latter mechanism, the subject of the so-called Starling hypothesis, is discussed in Chapter 5.

Both CO_2 and oxygen are carried in solution, but in addition they are transported in chemical combination with certain components of the body fluids.

CO_2 *Transport*

CO_2 upon dissolving in water forms carbonic acid (H_2CO_3). This process is accelerated by the enzyme *carbonic anhydrase*, which has been detected in many species of animals. In the vertebrates, this enzyme is found predominantly in the red blood cells. Carbonic acid dissociates into hydrogen ion and bicarbonate ion (H^+ and HCO_3^-). The hydrogen ion is taken up by the protein molecules of the body fluids in exchange for metal ions (K^+, Na^+). Diffusion of CO_2 from respiring tissue cells into body fluids, therefore, leads to the formation of the bicarbonates of sodium and of potassium. Except in certain herbivorous insects (see p. 427), the body fluids invariably contain far more Na^+ than K^+, Ca^{++}, or Mg^{++}—usually more than 10 times as much. Thus the addition of CO_2 leads almost exclusively to the formation of Na^+ bicarbonate. In animals whose body fluids transport cells with a high K^+ content, the bicarbonate ions inside these cells associate with K^+ rather than with Na^+ ions.

When protein is insufficient to take up the hydrogen ions liberated during the dissociation of freshly formed carbonic acid, the body fluids become acid. Proteins carried in body fluids serve as important buffer agents which permit maintenance of a constant pH value. But even these body fluids that contain high concentrations of protein cannot stay buffered if they cannot rid themselves of CO_2; the continuous influx of CO_2 from the tissues eventually produces so much acid that the supply of exchangeable alkali metal ions becomes exhausted. The condition of body fluids turning acid because of exhaustion of the "*alkali reserve*" is known as *acidosis*.

CO_2 is lost in the following ways: 1. Carbonic anhydrase is present in the respiratory exchange membranes (gills) of polychaetes, cephalopods, lamellibranchs, and crustaceans. This enzyme catalyzes not only the reaction $CO_2 + H_2O \rightarrow H_2CO_3$, but also the reverse reaction $H_2CO_3 \rightarrow H_2O + CO_2$. The direction in which the reaction proceeds depends entirely on the relative concentrations of H_2CO_3 and CO_2. Where the concentration of CO_2 is high (e.g., near the tissue cells), H_2CO_3 is formed, which in turn gives rise to the bicarbonate compounds mentioned. Where the CO_2 tension is low (e.g., in the immediate vicinity of the respiratory exchange membranes), H_2CO_3 is split into H_2O and CO_2. The latter immediately follows the concentration gradient across the respiratory membrane and is lost to the outside environment which has a low CO_2 tension.

Loss of CO_2 means also loss of bicarbonate ion and leads to a reversal of the original exchange of alkali metal ions for hydrogen ions so that the circulating proteins take up the freed metal ions in exchange for the hydrogen ions that went into the formation of carbonic acid. The schema of events is shown in Figure 9–11. 2. Blood or coelomic fluids containing hemoglobin (either in cells or in colloidal solution) liberate hydrogen ions from the protein part of this blood pigment when this combines with oxygen: oxygenated hemoglobin becomes acidic (liberates hydrogen ions) when it combines with oxygen. This is known as the *Haldane effect* (after its discoverer, John Scott Haldane, the British physiologist whose book Respiration, 1922, is a landmark of biology). The liberation of hydrogen ion is followed by the formation of salts between the acid, oxygenated hemoglobin, and the alkali metal ions that had been part

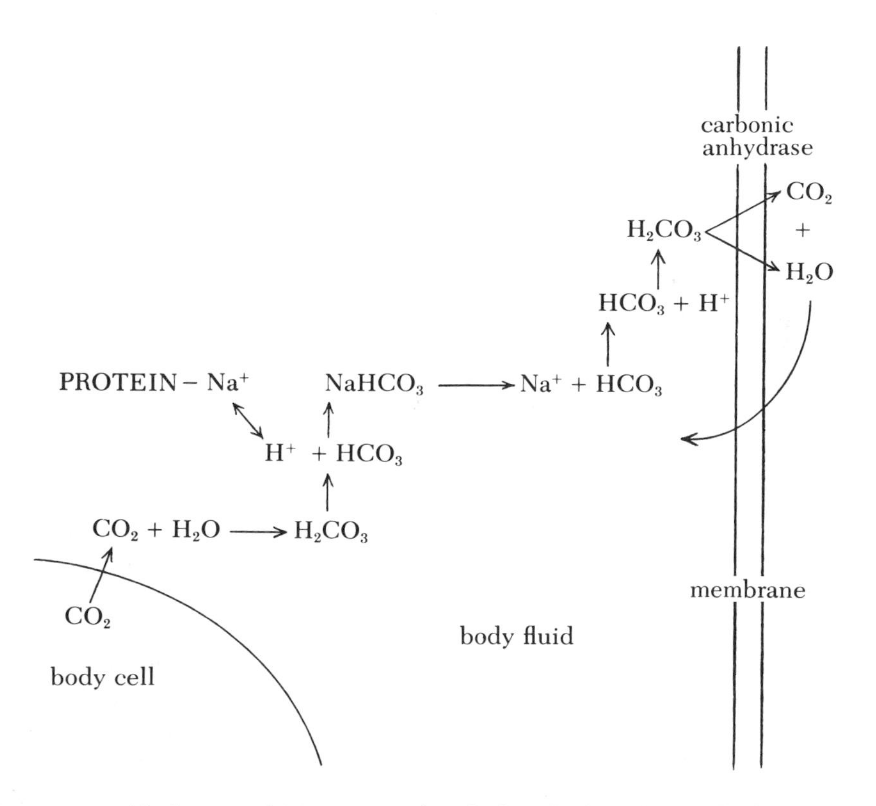

Figure 9–11. Mechanism of CO_2 transport from body cells through body fluids to the animal's external environment. The "membrane" indicated in the diagram represents the respiratory membrane (lung, gill, etc.).

of the bicarbonate. This leaves the bicarbonate ions free to combine with hydrogen to give rise to carbonic acid. This is split by carbonic anhydrase into water and CO_2. The CO_2 immediately diffuses out of the body across the respiratory membranes.

In addition to its transport in physical solution and in the form of carbonic acid–bicarbonate, CO_2 is carried in the form of *carbamino compounds*. Free amino groups of circulating proteins and amino acids can combine with CO_2 according to the following formula:

$$R - NH_2 + CO_2 = R - NH - COOH$$

This combination is unstable and depends on a relatively high CO_2 tension. Low CO_2 tension leads to dissociation of the compound and to liberation of CO_2. Carbamino compounds that have been formed at the site of high tissue CO_2 tension give up CO_2 when they reach the respiratory membranes where, owing to outward diffusion of CO_2, the tension of this gas is low.

Oxygen Transport

In many animals oxygen is carried by body fluids in simple physical solution. As far as is known, this is true for coelenterates, the flatworms, lamellibranch molluscs, and a number of fishes. Many animal groups, however, are characterized by having oxygen-carrying pigments in one or the other of their body fluids. These pigments are always of large molecular weight and contain metal ions (Fe^{+++} or Cu^{+}) which are instrumental in the binding of oxygen. These circulating respiratory pigments are not oxidized by oxygen, rather they are *oxygenated*, that is, they combine reversibly with molecular oxygen (O_2). The amount of oxygen bound by a given amount of pigment depends on the oxygen tension: if the tension is sufficiently high, all the available pigment combines with oxygen. Under such conditions the pigment is said to be *saturated* or *100 per cent saturated.* At low oxygen tensions, only part of the pigment molecules combine with oxygen. Pigment that is entirely free of oxygen is often referred to as *reduced* pigment; the term "reduced," however, is not employed with the usual meaning it carries in chemistry.

There is no entirely satisfactory name that can be applied to all the oxygen carrying pigments. The term "respiratory pigment" applies only partially, since it also includes the cellular and mitochondrial cytochromes. The term blood pigment is too restrictive, since it does not include the oxygen-carrying pigment of coelomic fluids. The name "oxygen-carrying pigment," as employed here is adequate but cumbersome. Fortunately it is used infrequently in this chapter.

The advantage of oxygen-carrying pigments is threefold: 1. They carry molecular oxygen, and in such a way as to load it at sites of relatively high oxygen tension and unload it at sites of low oxygen tension. 2. By removing oxygen from the solution (body fluid), these pigments make it possible for the body fluid to take up additional oxygen. 3. They can load oxygen at tensions below that corresponding to the partial pressure of oxygen in the atmosphere.

The total and maximal amount of oxygen that can be taken up by a unit volume of body fluid is called the *oxygen capacity*. This includes both the amount in physical solution and that held by the contained pigment. Table 9–3 lists oxygen capacities of a variety of body fluids. In many cases, more than 100 times as much oxygen is carried by the pigment as is dissolved in physical solution. The oxygen capacity alone, however, is not necessarily the significant feature of body fluids with oxygen-carrying pigment. In some cases such body fluids, after equilibration with atmospheric air, do not carry significantly more O_2 than can be carried in physical solution alone. Here the true significance of the pigment appears only at low oxygen tensions. Because the pigment can load oxygen at low tensions, the particular body fluid can, at such low tensions, carry more oxygen than it can carry in physical solution.

A classic example of this is the study by Redmond (1955): 100 ml of blood

Table 9–3. Oxygen Capacity of Blood of Various Animals after Equilibration with Air

Animal	*Blood Pigment*	*ml* O_2/100 *ml Blood*
Glycera siphonostoma	Hemoglobin	2.5 - 3.0
Spirographis	Chlorocruorin	9.8 - 10.6
Urechis	Hemoglobin	2.2 - 6.7
Nepthys		0.18 - 0.48
Arenicola	Hemoglobin	5.7 - 8.7
Sipunculus	Hemerythrin	1.6
Busycon canaliculatum	Hemocyanin	2.10 - 3.35
Planorbis corneus	Hemoglobin	1.2 - 2.8
Helix pomatia	Hemocyanin	1.15 - 1.57
Loligo pealei	Hemocyanin	3.8 - 4.5
Octopus vulgaris	Hemocyanin	3.1 - 5.0
Limulus polyphemus	Hemocyanin	0.74 - 2.14
Maja squinado	Hemocyanin	0.84 - 1.13
Callinectes sapidus	Hemocyanin	1.29
Carcinus maenas	Hemocyanin	1.14 - 1.16
Cancer irroratus	Hemocyanin	1.23 - 1.69
Cancer pagurus	Hemocyanin	1.6
Palinurus vulgaris	Hemocyanin	1.43 - 1.48
Homarus vulgaris	Hemocyanin	3.0 - 3.1
Astacus fluviatilis	Hemocyanin	2.4
Chironomus plumosus	Hemoglobin	6
Carp	Hemoglobin	12.5
Rana esculenta	Hemoglobin	9.8
Crocodilus acutus	Hemoglobin	8 - 10
Columba	Hemoglobin	20
Homo sapiens	Hemoglobin	20

Data from the literature, as collected by Dhéré, C.: Sur quelques pigments respiratoires des Invertébrés. Rev. Suisse Zool. 35:277–289, 1928; and Prosser, C. L., and F. A. Brown, Jr.: Comparative Animal Physiology. W. B. Saunders Co., Philadelphia, 1961.

of the rock lobster (*Panulirus interruptus*), the lobster (*Homarus americanus*), and the sheep crab (*Loxorhynchus grandis*) deliver to the tissues no more than 0.46, 0.26, and 0.24 ml of oxygen, respectively. This is about as much oxygen as the same volume of sea water would carry. The oxygen tension of blood coming from the gills, however, is not higher than 7 mm Hg (even though that of the external sea water is 100 mm Hg). At that low tension, the blood could carry only 0.03 ml of oxygen in physical solution. Thus, practically all the oxygen delivered to the tissues must be transported by the pigment. Indeed the blood pigment these animals carry can be about 50 per cent saturated with oxygen at an oxygen tension of only 7 mm. Near the tissues, the oxygen tension of blood drops to about 3 mm Hg. At that tension, the pigment can hold much less oxygen and less than 20 per cent remains saturated; most of the oxygen dissociates and is free to diffuse into the tissues.

This example (illustrated in Figure 9–12) is important. It teaches us, among other things, that the function of a respiratory pigment cannot be assessed until it is known what the oxygen tension of the body fluids (blood or coelomic fluid) is (a) near the respiratory membranes (arterial blood) and (b) near the tissues (venous blood), and how this relates to the ability of the particular pigment to become saturated at low oxygen tensions.

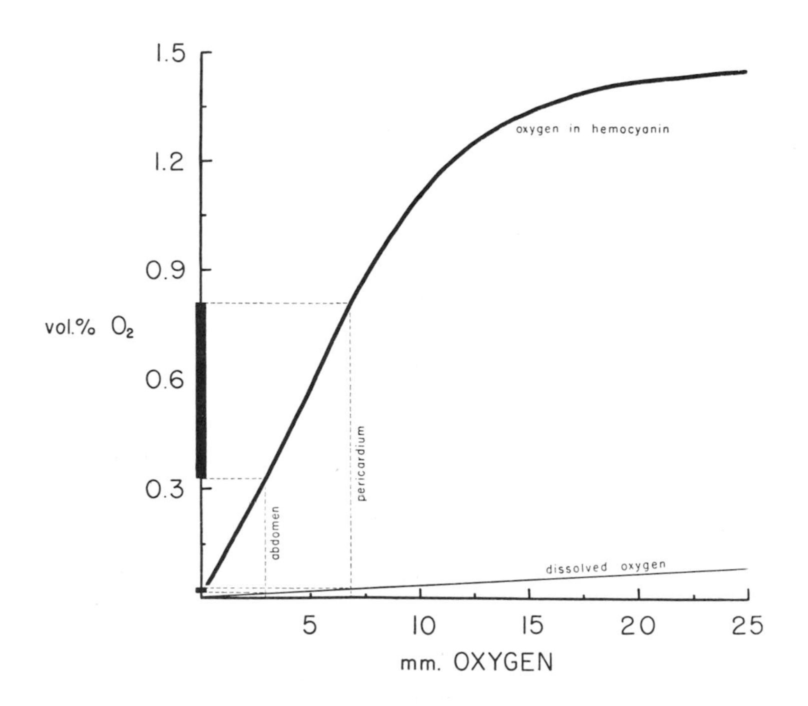

Figure 9–12. Summary of the respiratory function of hemocyanin in a decapod crustacean, *Panulirus interruptus*. Saturation is reached at a pO_2 of 25 mm Hg. But even with a normal oxygen tension of 150 mm Hg the freshly oxygenated blood coming from the gills shows a tension of only 7 mm, while the blood bathing the tissues has an oxygen tension of about 3 mm Hg. Thus hemocyanin can carry many times the amount of O_2 that is carried in physical solution at these low oxygen tensions. With drawn blood shaken in air (pO_2 about 150 mm Hg) the pigment would not offer much advantage over the ability of the blood-water to dissolve oxygen. (From Redmond, J. R.: The respiratory function of hemocyanin in Crustacea. J. Cell. Comp. Physiol. *46*:209–247, 1955.)

If per cent saturation is plotted against oxygen tension, a curve is obtained which is characteristic of the pigment under study. Curves of this type are called *oxygen dissociation curves.* Certain fixed values of these curves have been given special names: that tension at which 95 per cent of the pigment of a given body fluid is saturated with oxygen is called the *saturation tension* or *loading tension of the pigment.* That tension at which 50 per cent of the pigment is saturated has been called *unloading tension.* Mammalian blood is nearly fully saturated at the oxygen tension of arterial blood (about 100 mm Hg) and the blood reaching the lungs does indeed load oxygen at that tension; also the oxygen tension near the tissues (venous blood) is such that only 50 per cent of the pigment remains saturated so that the blood unloads a considerable quantity of oxygen. If the terms are applied, however, to the situation found in the decapod crustaceans previously mentioned, they would be physiologically meaningless: at the gills, where the blood would be loading oxygen, the tension permits only 50 per cent saturation. To call this "unloading tension" would be grossly misleading, because the pigment that had given up most of its oxygen to the tissues at a tension of about 3 mm Hg actually loads (and not unloads) oxygen when it reaches the gills. To avoid confusion, the terms "loading tension" and "unloading tension" should be replaced by the terms "*saturation tension*" and "*half-saturation tension,*" which are already widely used.

However, if the saturation tension and the half-saturation tension of a pigment are known, we cannot determine from this the tensions at which the pigment loads and unloads oxygen in the animal.

The half-saturation tension of a pigment is a measure of the affinity of the pigment for oxygen: a low half-saturation tension means high affinity, a high one a low affinity for oxygen.

An abstraction of an oxygen dissociation curve is shown in Figure 9–13 together with the appropriate terminology. In fact, the dissociation curves show several shapes, of which a hyperbolic and sigmoid curve are the extreme variants. Figure 9–14 demonstrates that even if two pigments have the same saturation tension, they may function quite differently if one exhibits the characteristics of a hyperbolic oxygen dissociation curve, while the other follows a sigmoid pattern. Assuming that the oxygen tensions near the respiratory exchange membranes are the same in both cases, and that the oxygen tensions in the body fluid near the tissues are likewise identical, we find that the pigment with the hyperbolic dissociation curve delivers much less oxygen to the tissues than that with the sigmoid curve.

Four types of oxygen-carrying pigments are known: hemoglobin, chlorocruorin, hemerythrin, and hemocyanin. Of these, *hemoglobin* has by far the widest distribution. It is the characteristic oxygen-carrying pigment of annelids (exception: sabellids and serpulids), echiuroids, phoronids, nemerteans, and, of course, vertebrates. In addition, it is found in a few Crustacea (*Artemia, Daphnia, Triops, Apus*) and insects (*Chironomus* larvae), molluscs (*Solen, Arca, Pectunculus, Planorbis*), some parasitic flatworms and nematodes, and a few Protozoa. Hemoglobin is found in blood or blood cells, in coelomic fluid or coelomocytes, in muscle cells (where it is usually referred to as *myoglobin*), and, occasionally, in nerve cells. It is a conjugate protein consisting of a globin

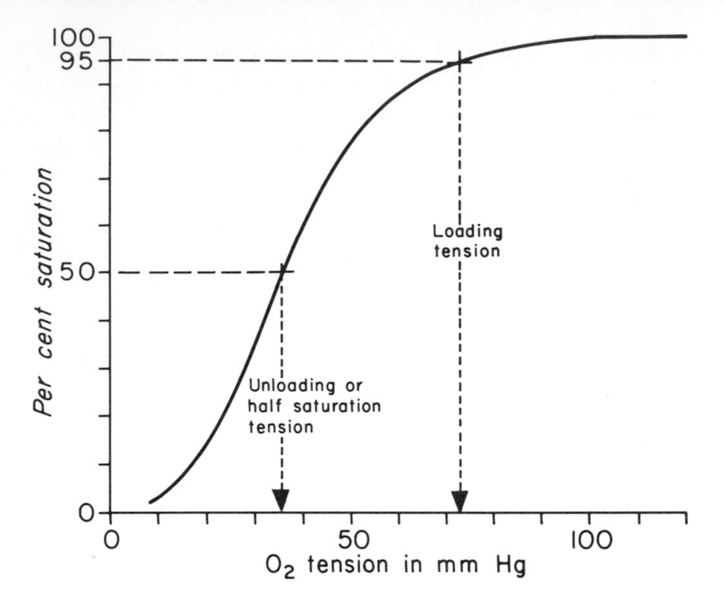

Figure 9–13. Conceptual diagram to explain the terminology applied to oxygen dissociation curves of oxygen-carrying pigments.

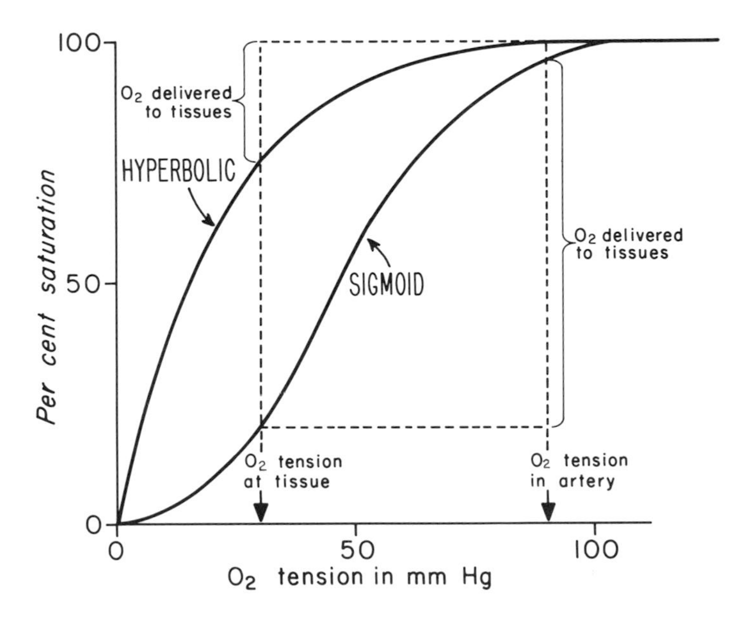

Figure 9–14. Conceptual diagram of a hyperbolic and a sigmoid oxygen dissociation curve of two hypothetical oxygen-carrying pigments. The diagram demonstrates the enormous difference in the amount of oxygen the two pigments "unload" at the tissues. In order to define the actual amount of oxygen delivered to the tissues, one must know the oxygen capacity of the pigmented body fluid and the amount of oxygen that reaches the tissues per unit time. If the scale of per cent saturation is replaced by one reading per cent oxygen capacity, the volume of oxygen delivered to the tissues can be read directly from the curve.

molecule associated with a molecule of *heme*, a tetrapyrrole ring with an iron (ferrous) atom (Fe^{++}) held in its center. Intracellular hemoglobin has a lower molecular weight than extracellular hemoglobin, which may reach weights up to several million (*Lumbricus*, *Arenicola*). Some hemoglobin molecules are actually complexes of several globin-heme molecules. Human hemoglobin with a molecular weight of 68,000 consists of four molecules of molecular weight 17,000. Each heme can combine with one molecule of oxygen (O_2). The knowledge concerning hemoglobin structure is extensive. It includes details of the amino acid sequence of the protein moiety, the binding sites of heme, and the interactions between hemoglobin molecules and their hemes as well as the biochemical "machinery" that puts the hemoglobin molecule together. Hemoglobin is bright red when oxygenated and dark red when free of oxygen.

The structure of *chlorocruorin* closely resembles that of hemoglobin. The basic difference lies in the exchange of one vinyl group for a formyl group in one of the four pyrrole rings that make up the heme molecule. The pigment is green in both the oxygenated and "reduced" form; the absorption spectra are similar to those of hemoglobin but shifted toward longer wavelengths. The molecular weight is large (about 3,000,000). The pigment occurs in two families of marine polychaetes, the Serpulidae and Sabellidae; in all cases it is present in colloidal solution in the blood. As with hemoglobin, one molecule of oxygen combines with each heme.

Hemerythrin is not a heme-protein, even though the name suggests that it is (Gr. *hem* = blood). It is found in three phyla: the Sipunculida, the Priapulida, and the Brachiopoda. The pigment is purple when oxygenated and colorless when "reduced." It is contained in the cells (coelomocytes) that circulate with the coelomic fluid. (*Note*: The coelomic nature of the body cavity of priapulids is still debated.) Hemerythrin is a protein with a molecular weight of the order of 100,000. It is associated with several iron atoms. Two to three iron atoms combine with one molecule of oxygen.

Hemocyanin is the characteristic blood pigment of gastropod and cephalopod molluscs, and of crustaceans, arachnids, and Xiphosura (*Limulus*). It is always present in colloidal solution, never enclosed in blood cells. Its molecular weight is greater than 1,000,000. Hemocyanin is the only blood protein in the cephalopods. Oxygenated pigment is blue; "reduced" pigment is colorless. The protein carries copper atoms that combine with oxygen (one molecule of oxygen per Cu atom). The reddish or pink color of "reduced" blood of certain Crustacea is due to the presence in the blood of a lipochrome, tetronerythrin, which is not an oxygen-carrying pigment (Halliburton, 1885).

The properties of these four types of pigment are summarized in Table 9–4.

Hemocyanin is not unique as a copper protein, although so far it is the only one to which an oxygen-carrying capacity has been ascribed. The enzyme polyphenol oxidase (tyrosinase) is found in body fluids of a variety of animals. It is blue when combined with a substrate (Kubowitz, 1938). Mammalian serum contains a blue protein, ceruloplasmin, of unknown function (Holmberg and Laurell, 1951), and Mann and Keilin (1938) found in vertebrate erythrocytes a copper-containing protein which they named hemocuprein; its function is unknown.

Table 9–4. Characteristics of Oxygen-Carrying Pigments of Body Fluids

Molecular Weight	*Color*		*Metal Ion*		*Number of O_2 Bound per Metal Ion*
	Reduced	*Oxygenated*	*Reduced*	*Oxygenated*	
Chlorocruorin 3,000,000	green	green	Fe^{+++}	Fe^{+++}	1
Hemerythrin about 100,000,000	colorless	purple	Fe^{+++}	Fe^{++}	1/2 – 1/3
Hemocyanin 1,000,000 – 7,000,000	colorless	blue	Cu^{++}	Cu^{+}	1
Hemoglobin 17,000 – 3,000,000	dark red	brick red	Fe^{+++}	Fe^{+++}	1

The presence of one type of oxygen-carrying pigment does not exclude another: in several species of serpulid worms, the blood contains both hemoglobin and chlorocruorin, whereas in other species only one or the other is found. In certain molluscs (the gastropods *Busycon* and *Ischnochiton*), the blood contains hemocyanin while the radular muscle contains myoglobin.

Oxygen dissociation curves of body fluids containing different pigments may look very much alike, but they may also show great differences, even when the body fluids contain the same type of pigment. These differences are due to differences in the general affinity of a given pigment for oxygen. Figure 9–15 compares dissociation curves of hemoglobin-containing bloods of various animal species. Figure 9–16 (also 18, 19, and 20) gives examples of dissociation curves of bloods containing hemocyanin, and Figure 9–17 shows dissociation curves for

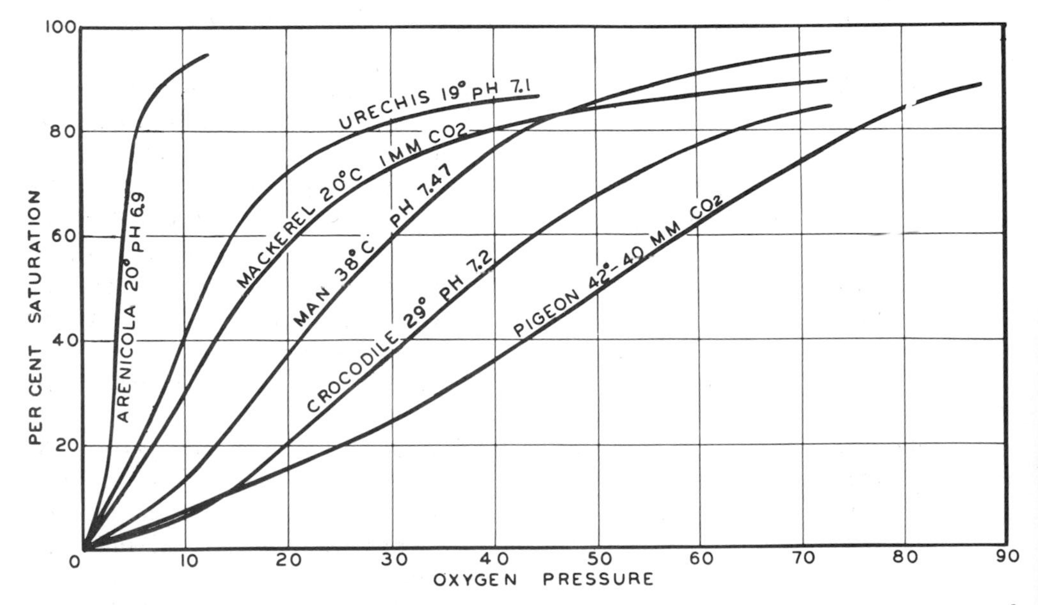

Figure 9–15. Oxygen dissociation curves of hemoglobin-containing blood of a variety of animals. (After Redfield, from Prosser, C. L., and F. A. Brown, Jr., eds.: Comparative Animal Physiology, 2nd Ed. W. B. Saunders Co., Philadelphia, 1961.)

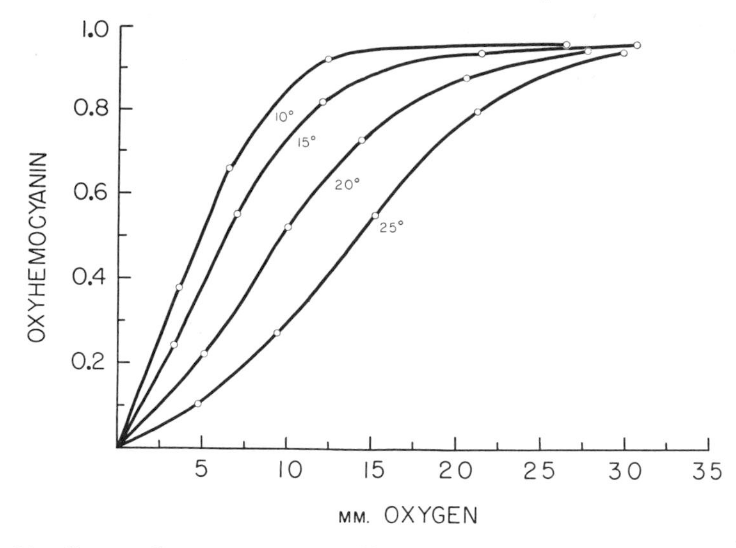

Figure 9–16. Oxygen dissociation curves of hemocyanin-containing blood of *Panulirus interruptus* (decapod Crustacea), determined at different temperatures. To appreciate the effect of temperature, read the relative amount of oxyhemocyanin at oxygen tension of 10 mm Hg, which is about that found in freshly oxygenated blood in the pericardium. (From Redmond, J. R.: The respiratory function of hemocyanin in Crustacea. J. Cell. Comp. Physiol. *46*:209–247, 1955.)

coelomic fluid containing intracellular hemerythrin. Some of the curves are given for different CO_2 tensions.

In 1904, Bohr and coworkers described the oxygen-liberating action of CO_2 on certain hemoglobins. Since then, similar effects have been reported for hemocyanin-, chlorocruorin-, and hemerythrin-containing body fluids. This oxygen displacing effect of CO_2 has been named the *Bohr effect*. Where this effect occurs the dissociation curves obtained at increasing CO_2 tensions appear further and further displaced to the right. The strongest Bohr effect has been observed with the blood of cephalopods, as shown in Figure 9–18.

The significance of the Bohr effect is obvious where the tissue CO_2 tension is considerably higher than the CO_2 tension near the respiratory membranes.

Several species do not exhibit the Bohr effect. This is true for sipunculids, certain annelids (*Urechis, Arenicola*) and certain fishes. In others, CO_2 enhances the uptake of oxygen by the pigment. Where this occurs one speaks of an *inverse* (or *negative*) *Bohr effect.* Examples of the latter are *Helix* and *Busycon* among the molluscs, and *Limulus* among the arthropods. The inverse Bohr effect has been interpreted as facilitating oxygen uptake in situations of high external CO_2 tension and low oxygen tension. All forms in which the Bohr effect is absent or reversed live in stagnant water or in mud. It can be assumed that in *Helix*, a terrestrial animal, internal CO_2 tensions are high during hibernation.

Even where the Bohr effect occurs, it may not be physiologically significant: in amphibia (frogs) and decapod Crustacea, the difference in CO_2 tension between arterial and venous blood is negligible, so that the dissociation curve applies throughout the circulatory system. However, additional oxygen can be

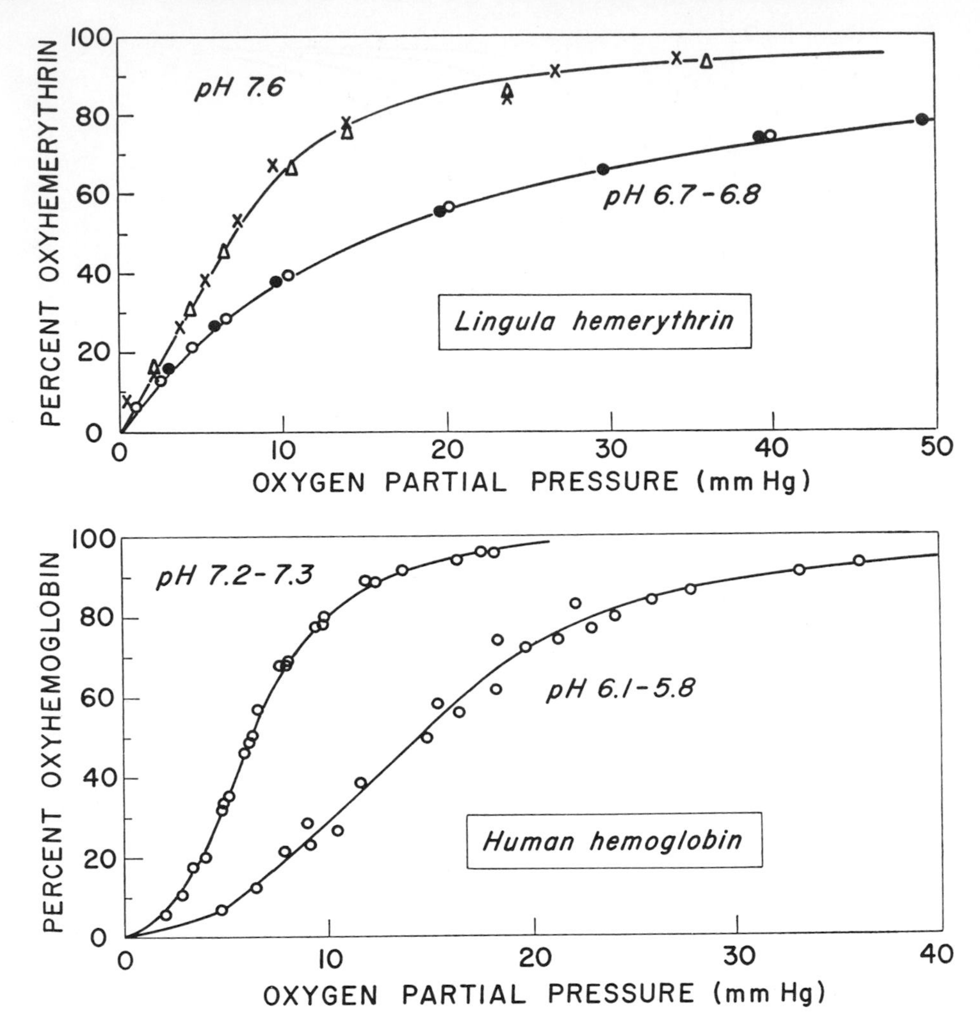

Figure 9–17. Oxygen dissociation curves showing the Bohr effect: solutions of hemerythrin (from the brachiopod *Lingula*) and of hemoglobin (from human blood) were used. Temperature, 22° to 24° C; potassium phosphate buffer, ionic strength approximately 0.2; hemerythrin concentrations, 2 to 3 per cent; hemoglobin concentrations, 7 to 15 per cent. Reversibility of Bohr effect of hemerythrin is demonstrated by bringing sample (o), originally at pH 6.77, to pH 7.63 (△) and back again to pH 6.74 (•); control experiment is a second sample whose oxygen equilibrium is determined at pH 7.65 (x). (From Manwell, C.: Oxygen equilibrium of brachiopod Lingula hemerythrin. Science *132*:550–551, 1960.)

liberated when extra large amounts of CO_2 are liberated during strenuous muscular exercise (such liberation would be due in part to respiratory production of CO_2, in part to increased acidity caused by formation of lactic acid).

Dissociation curves do not indicate the absolute amounts of oxygen that can be carried by a given volume of body fluid. They show only relative amounts (per cent saturation). In order to assess the true function of the pigment, one must know not only the dissociation curves at the CO_2 tensions prevalent near respiratory membranes and near the tissues, but also the oxygen capacity of the

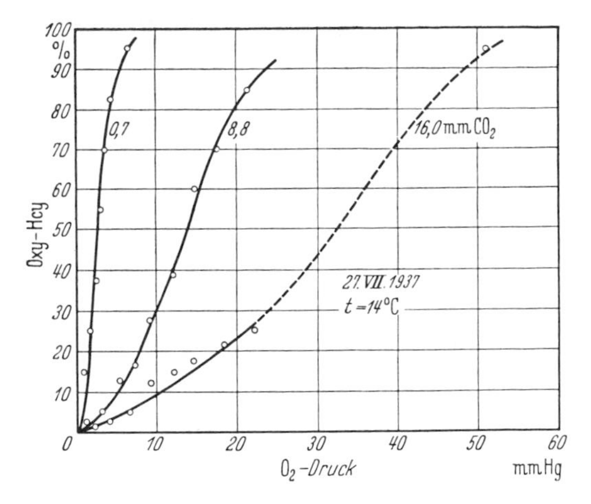

Figure 9–18. Oxygen dissociation curves of blood from *Octopus vulgaris*, measured at 14° C. Note the pronounced "Bohr effect." (From Wolvekamp, H. P.: Über den Sauerstofftransport durch Haemocyanin von Octopus vulgaris Lam. Z. vergl. Physiol. 25:540–547, 1938.)

circulating body fluid and the volume of this fluid that moves, per unit time, from respiratory organs to the tissues. When the actual *volume* of oxygen carried by a given body fluid is plotted against oxygen tension, one speaks of an *oxygen-equilibrium curve* (Fig. 9–19).

Oxygen-carrying pigments are sensitive to temperature changes. Invariably, their affinity for oxygen decreases when the temperature increases. This is expressed graphically in a shift of the dissociation curves to the right with higher temperatures. Perhaps the most pronounced temperature sensitivity is shown by cephalopod blood, as demonstrated in Figure 9–20.

The temperature sensitivity of oxygen-carrying pigments limits the temperature range within which an animal can survive. With the exception of warm-blooded vertebrates (birds and mammals), who can maintain a constant body temperature, the body temperature of all animals follows closely that of the environment. The temperature limits are given by the highest temperature at which the pigment can still load sufficient quantities of oxygen, and by the lowest temperature at which the pigment can give up enough oxygen to the tissues. If kept at 0° C, an octopus asphyxiates even though his blood is fully oxygenated. Artificial lowering of the body temperature of man (hypothermia) cannot be carried far for the same reason that at lower temperatures hemoglobin does not give up enough oxygen to the tissues.

The oxygen-carrying pigments of some invertebrate animals have such a low saturation tension that it is believed that they do not, under normal circumstances, unload the oxygen to the tissues at all. This would indeed be expected if the saturation tension is below the tissue oxygen tension. Under these circumstances, the pigment would serve as an oxygen store which would deliver oxygen at times of stress. It has been calculated that the total oxygen stored by the blood of *Urechis*, a marine polychaete, would be sufficient for 3 hours of aerobic life (Redfield and Florkin, 1931). *Arenicola* blood also has an extremely low loading tension (only 5 to 10 mm Hg), and it has been suggested that this, again, is characteristic of a storage function of the oxygen-carrying pigment.

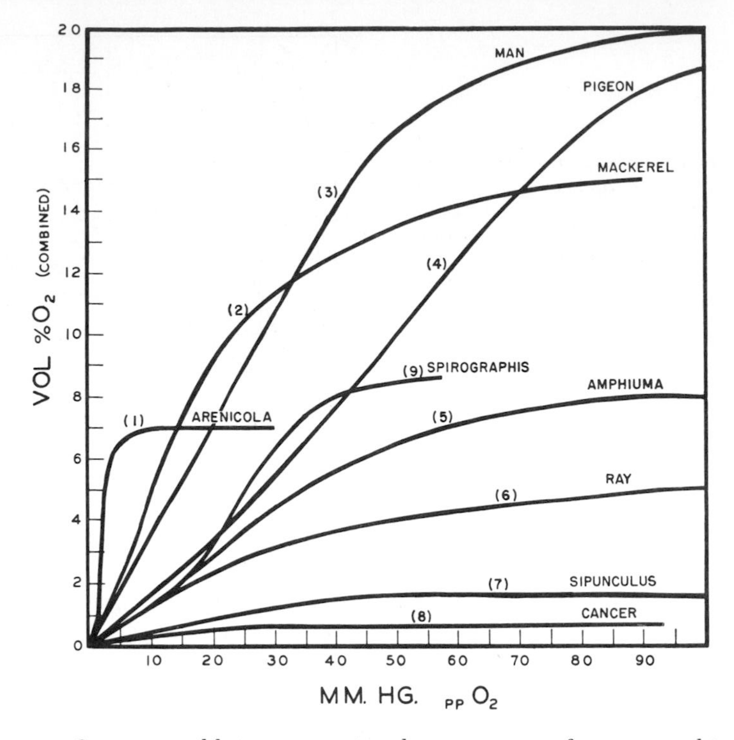

Figure 9–19. Oxygen equilibrium curves in volumes per cent of oxygen combined (ml O_2/100 ml blood or coelomic fluid) as a function of the partial pressure of oxygen (expressed in mm Hg). (*1*) *Arenicola*, at 20° C, pH 4.9; (*2*) mackerel, 20° C, 1 mm CO_2; (*3*) man, 38° C, pH 7.4; (*4*) pigeon, 42° C, 40 mm CO_2; (*5*) *Amphiuma*, 20° C, 43 mm CO_2; (*6*) ray, 10.4° C, pH 7.8; (*7*) *Sipunculus*, 19° C, pH 7.7; (*8*) *Cancer*, 23° C, 1 mm CO_2; (*9*) *Spirographis*, 20° C, pH 7.7. In contrast to dissociation curves that give per cent saturation regardless of the actual amount of oxygen combined, these curves indicate the "carrying capacity" of body fluids of different species. Compare the curve shown for *Cancer* with that for another crustacean, *Panulirus*, presented in Figure 9–19. (After Redfield, from Prosser, C. L., and F. A. Brown, Jr., eds.: Comparative Animal Physiology, 2nd Ed. W. B. Saunders Co., Philadelphia, 1961.)

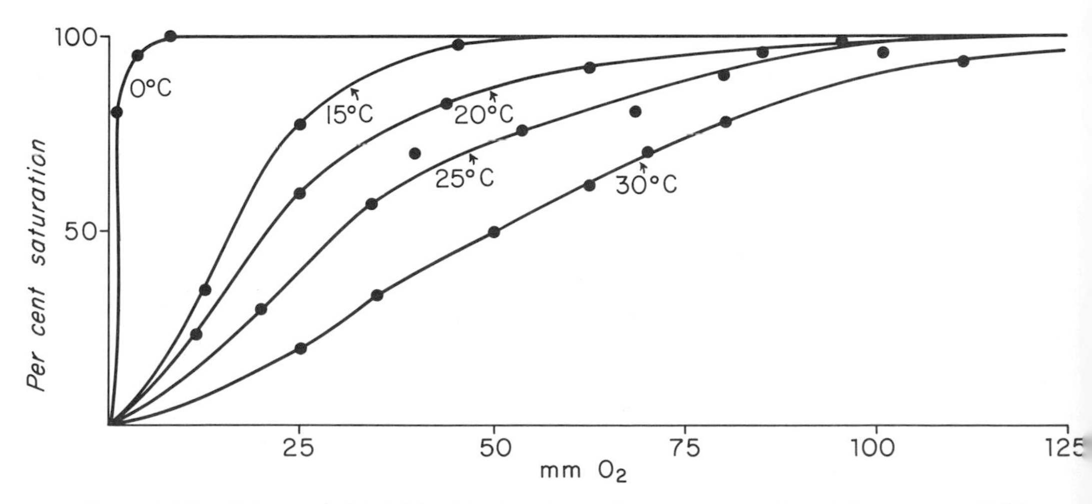

Figure 9–20. *Octopus dofleini*, blood temperature effect on oxygen dissociation curve, pH 7.2.

Both *Urechis* and *Arenicola* live in tubes in mud that may be exposed to low tide and have a low oxygen tension. Under these conditions, it is assumed that the oxygen tensions in the body fluids fall also, thus permitting the release of oxygen from the pigment.

The difficulty with such an interpretation is that we do not know the tissue oxygen tension and cannot explain why the oxygen liberated from the blood pigment is not lost to the external environment.

Gas Transport by Osmosis

Fresh-water animals are subject to osmotic influx of water. Judging from the rate at which water leaves the animal (urine, contractile vacuoles), we find that this osmotic flow of water is, in some cases, considerable. In some rotifers, the contractile "bladder" expels a volume equal to that of the whole animal during a 10 minute period. Rather large volumes of water (relative to the body volume) are also excreted by fresh-water Protozoa. *Anodonta*, the fresh-water mussel, also produces a copious urine flow, indicative of a large osmotic influx of water.

It is more than likely that water enters the organisms together with its dissolved gases. An animal that requires 0.1 ml O_2/gm/hr could derive about two-thirds the required oxygen from water entering by osmosis, provided the influx per hour is 10 times its body volume. At 20° C water dissolves 0.031 ml O_2/ml/atm; in contact with normal atmospheric air, it would contain 20 per cent of this, or 0.0062 ml/ml. If 10 ml of water flows through each milliliter of the organism per hour, 0.062 ml of oxygen would reach the tissues contained in each milliliter of the organism. In rotifers, 6 ml of water flows through the animal per milliliter of body volume per hour. If their oxygen consumption were about 0.1 ml/gm/hr and we assume a specific gravity of 1, the osmotic flow of water could provide 37 per cent of the total oxygen required.

The concept of gas transport by osmosis was first expressed by Hartog in 1896. But already in 1888, in his Lehrbuch der vergleichenden Anatomie, Lang discussed the idea that the water-vascular system (excretory system) of flatworms might serve as a respiratory organ engaged in gas transport from regions near the body surface to the deeper tissues. In fresh-water forms, it is conceivable that this system which must be responsible for the elimination of water that enters by osmosis, serves such a respiratory transport function by virtue of the osmotic flow.

Anaerobiosis

In the following habitats oxygen tension is extremely low or oxygen is absent altogether: (1) soil in swamps, (2) the interior of plants (the habitat of leaf-mining and woodboring insects), (3) the bottom of certain lakes, ponds, and parts of the oceans, and (4) the intestinal tract, particularly of warm-blooded animals. In addition, there are habitats where the oxygen tension may fall temporarily to low values. Soil, after a heavy rain, loses the oxygen contained in its pores rather rapidly, owing to biological oxidations and clogging of the pores with water, which prevents renewal of the contained gas (Merker, 1931).

Similarly, oxygen diminishes in mudflats at low tide, particularly in burrows and tubes in them, where water circulation is reduced or even absent.

Animals living in such environments are adapted to them and can live temporarily (facultative anaerobiosis) or permanently (obligatory anaerobiosis) in the absence of oxygen—or at extremely low oxygen pressures. Anaerobiosis means metabolism without oxygen. Glycolysis is an anaerobic form of metabolism and is the main form of energy metabolism during anaerobiosis. The chief problem associated with this form of metabolism is that of coping with the accumulating acid (lactic acid or its analogues). Animals that possess a calcium carbonate skeleton or shell (most molluscs, echinoderms, brachiopods, Crustacea, many sponges, and Protozoa) neutralize these accumulating acids by forming calcium salts or calcium bicarbonate.

Intertidal lamellibranch molluscs show conspicuous erosion of the inner surface of their shells after periods of anaerobiosis. It is possible, though nobody has attempted to prove this, that the skeletal elements of echinoderms and sponges serve in the neutralization of acids produced during anaerobiosis.

Anaerobiosis does not necessarily mean that the metabolism is entirely nonoxidative. Although oxygen is not available as a terminal hydrogen acceptor, other compounds may serve in this capacity. Unsaturated fatty acids or fats have this function. Wintering carps, for instance, which live in stagnant ponds under a layer of ice, consume no oxygen but carry on a limited amount of oxidative metabolism. They simply accumulate fat!

It is generally believed that muscle derives mechanical energy from anaerobic chemical reactions (glycolysis). Under severe exercise, vertebrate muscle accumulates lactic acid, because there is not enough oxygen to oxidize the lactic acid, even though the oxygen consumption is elevated. Organisms that are forced to rely predominantly on glycolysis and associated anaerobic metabolism owing to temporary insufficiency of the oxygen supply are said to have an *oxygen debt*. In vertebrates and many invertebrate species, such oxygen debts are repaid by prolonged elevated oxygen consumption when the oxygen supply more than satisfies the energy requirement of the animal. The extra oxygen consumed is utilized in the resynthesis of glycogen. An alternative to the repayment of an oxygen debt is the excretion or neutralization of the produced acid.

Antoine Laurent Lavoisier was the first to demonstrate that animals utilize oxygen and produce CO_2. On May 3, 1777, Lavoisier announced before the Académie des Sciences in Paris that one sixth of the air in a closed container in which an animal was asphyxiated consisted of a gas that can be absorbed by soda lime, gaseous carbonic acid, and that while the animal had still been respiring, the same air had lost a similar volume of a life-sustaining gas, which he called *oxygène*. With Pierre Simon de Laplace, he measured respiratory quotients.

Lavoisier assumed that most of the oxygen was used in oxidation of carbon within the lungs, while a small part oxidized hydrogen to water. The oxidation was thought to provide "animal heat"—the energy that makes life possible. Blood was considered as a transporting vehicle for the heat produced in the lungs.

It is amazing indeed that until the end of the eighteenth century, man did not know the significance of his breathing.

REFERENCES

Alsterberg, G. (1922) Die Respiratorischen Mechanismen der Tubificiden. Eine experimentelle-physiologische Untersuchungen auf oekologische Grundlage. Lunds Univ. Arsskr. N.F. 18, Avd. *2*:1–175.

Babak, E. (1921) Die Mechanik und Innervation der Atmung. *In* Handbuch der vergleichenden Physiologie, Vol. 1, pp. 265–1027. (H. Winterstein, ed.) G. Fischer Verlag, Jena.

Bleibtreu, M. (1894) Fettmast und respiratorischer Quotient. Pflügers Arch. ges. Physiol. *56*:464–466.

Botjes, J. O. (1948) Die Atmungsregulierung bei *Corixa geoffloyi* Leach. Z. vergl. Physiol. *17*: 557–564.

von Brand, T. (1946) Anaerobiosis in Invertebrates. Biodynamica, Normandy 21, Missouri.

Buddington, R. A. (1942) The ciliary transport-system of *Asterias forbesi*. Biol. Bull. *83*:438–450.

Burke, J. D. (1953) Oxygen capacity in mammals. Physiol. Zool. *26*:259–266.

van Dam, L. (1938) On the utilization of oxygen and regulation of breathing in some aquatic animals. Thesis, Groningen.

Dotterweich, H., and E. Elssner (1935) Die Mobilisierung des Schalenkalkes für die Reaktionsregulation der Muscheln (*Anodonta cygnea*). Biol. Zbl. *55*:138–163.

Dugal, L. P. (1939) The use of calcareous shell to buffer the product of anaerobic glycolysis in *Venus mercenaria*. J. Cell. Comp. Physiol. *113*:235–251.

Eliassen, E. (1954) The physiology of the vascular system of invertebrates. 1. A monograph on the pigments. Univ. Bergen. Årb. med. R. Nr. 11.

Fox, H. M. (1945) The oxygen affinities of certain invertebrate haemoglobins. J. Exp. Biol. *21*:161–164.

Fox, H. M. (1949) On chlorocruorin and haemoglobin. Proc. Roy Soc. Lond., B *136*:378–388.

Fox, H. M. (1951) Oxygen affinities of respiratory blood pigments in *Serpula*. Nature *168*:112.

Fox, H. M., and E. J. Baldes (1935) The vapor pressures of the blood of arthropods from swift and still waters. J. Exp. Biol. *12*:174–178.

Fredericq, L. (1878) Recherches sur la physiologie du poulpe commun (*Octopus vulgaris*). Arch. Zool. Exp. et Gen. *7*:534–583.

Fredericq, L. (1879) Sur l'innervation respiratoire chez le poulpe. C. R. Acad. Sci. *88*:346–347.

Gesell, R. (1939) Respiration and its adjustments. Ann. Rev. Physiol. *1*:185–216.

Haldane, J. S. (1922) Respiration. Yale University Press, New Haven.

Haldane, J. S., and J. G. Priestley (1935) Respiration. Oxford University Press, London.

Halliburton, W. D. (1885) On the blood of decapod Crustacea. J. Physiol. *6*:300–335.

Hartog, M. (1896) Rotifera. Gastrotricha and Kinorhyncha. The Cambridge Natural History, Vol. 2, pp. 197–238. (S. F. Harmer and A. E. Shipley, eds.)

Hazelhoff, E. H. (1927) Die Regulierung der Atmung bei Insekten und Spinnen. Z. vergl. Physiol. *5*:179–190.

Hazelhoff, E. H. (1938–1939) Über die Ausnützung des Sauerstoffs bei verschiedenen Wasertieren. Z. vergl. Physiol. *26*:306–327.

Hering, E., and J. Breuer (1868) Die Selbststeuerung der Atmung durch den Nervus Vagus. Sitzber. Akad. Wiss. Wien, math.-nat. Kl. *57*:672–677; *58*:909–937

Holmberg, C. G., and C. B. Laurell (1951a) Investigations in serum copper III. Coeruloplasm as an enzyme. Acta chem. Scand. *5*:476–480.

Holmberg, C. G. and C. B. Laurell (1951b) Investigations in serum copper. IV. Effect of different anions on the enzymatic activity of coeruloplasmin Acta chem. Scand. *5*:921–930.

Irving, L. (1939) Respiration in diving mammals. Physiol. Rev. *19*:112–133.

Irving, L., P. F. Scholander, and S. W. Grinnell (1941) The respiration of the porpoise, or *Pursiops truncatus*. J. Cell. Comp. Physiol. *17*:145–168.

Irving, L., P. F. Scholander, and S. W. Grinnell (1942) Experimental studies of the respiration of sloths. J. Cell. Comp. Physiol. *20*:189–210.

Krogh, A. (1941) The Comparative Physiology of Respiratory Mechanisms. University of Pennsylvania Press, Philadelphia.

Kubowitz, F. (1938) Spaltung und Resynthese der Polyphenoloxydase und des Haemocyanins. Biochem. Zeitschr. *299*:32–57.

Kuehnelt, W. (1954) Wege zu einer Analyse der oekologischen Valenz. Verh. dtsch. Zool. Ges. in Tuebingen, pp. 292–299.

Lavoisier, A. L. (1784) Memoire sur la chaleur. Hist. Acad. Roy. Sci., pp. 355–408.

Mann, T., and D. Keilin (1938) Haemocuprein and helatocuprin, copper-protein compounds of blood and liver in mammals. Proc. Roy. Soc. B, *126*:303–315.

Merker, E. (1926) Die Empfindlichkeit feuchthäutiger Tiere im Lichte. II. Warum kommen Regenwürmer in Wasserlachen um und warum verlassen sie bei Regen ihre Wohnröhen? Zool. Jahrb., Allg. Zool. Physiol. Tiere *42*:487–555.

Merker, E. (1931) Treibt Atemnot oder Wassersnot den Regenwurm aus der Erde? Zool. Jahrb, Allg. Zool. Physiol. Tiere *48*:667–696.

Nagai, H. (1909) Der Stoffwechsel des Winterschläfers. Z. allg. Physiol. 9:243–367.

Nicol, J. A. C. (1960) The Biology of Marine Animals. Chap. 4: Respiration. Interscience Publishers, New York.

Pembrey, M. S. (1903) Further observations upon the respiratory exchange and temperature of hibernating mammals. J. Physiol. *29*:195–212.

Polimanti, O. (1912) Beitraege zur Physiologie von *Sepia officinalis* L. II. Die Atmung. Arch. (Anat. u.) Physiol., p. 52.

Pritchard, A., E. Florey, and A. W. Martin (1958) Relationship between metabolic rate and body size in an elasmobranch (*Squalus suckleyi*) and in a teleost (*Ophiodon elongatus*). J. Mar. Res. *17*:403–411.

Prosser, C. L. (1961) Oxygen: respiration and metabolism. *In* Comparative Animal Physiology, 2nd Ed., pp. 153–197. (C. L. Prosser and F. A. Brown, Jr., eds.) W. B. Saunders Co., Philadelphia.

Pütter, A. (1911) Vergleichende Physiologie. G. Fischer Verlag, Jena.

Raud, J. T. (1954) Vertebrates without erythrocytes and blood pigment. Nature *173*:848–850.

Redfield, A. C. (1933) The evolution of the respiratory function of blood. Quart. Rev. Biol. 8:31–57.

Redfield, A. C., and M. Florkin (1931) The respiratory function of the blood of *Urechis caupo*. Biol. Bull. *61*:185–210.

Redmond, J. R. (1955) The respiratory function of hemocyanin in Crustacea. J. Cell. Comp. Physiol. *46*:209–247.

Rubner, M. (1883) Über den Einfluss der Körpergrösse auf Stoff- und Kraftwechsel. Z. Biol. *19*: 534–562.

Rubner, M. (1924) The life of cold-blooded animals. I. The fishes. Biochem. Z. *148*:222–267.

Slovtzoff, B. (1909) Über den Gasstoffwechsel der Insecten und dessen Beziehung zur Temperatur der Luft. Biochem. Z. *19*:497–503.

Smedley, I. (1912) The biochemical synthesis of fatty acids from carbohydrate. Proc. Physiol. Soc., *in* J. Physiol. *45*:XXV–XXVII.

Smedley, I., and E. Lubrzinska (1913) The biochemical synthesis of the fatty acids. Biochem. J. 7:364–374.

Thomas, H. J. (1954) The oxygen uptake of the lobster (*Homarus vulgaris*). J. Exp. Biol. *31*:228–251.

von Uexküll, J. (1891) Physiologische Untersuchungen an *Eledone moschata*. Z. Biol. *28*:550–566.

von Uexküll, J. (1895) Physiologische Untersuchungen an *Eledone moschata*. IV. Zur Analyse der Functionen des Zentralsnervensystems. Z. Biol. *31*:584–609.

Voit, E. (1901) Über die Grösse des Energiebedarfes der Tiere im Hungerzustande. Z. Biol. *41*:113–154.

Waterman, T. H., and D. F. Travis (1953) Respiratory reflexes and the flabellum of *Limulus*. J. Cell. Comp. Physiol. *41*:261–290.

Winterstein, H. (1921) Die physikalisch-chemischen Erscheinungen der Atmung. *In* Handbuch der vergleichenden Physiologie, pp. 1–264. Vol. 1. (H. Winterstein, ed.) G. Fischer Verlag, Jena.

Zeuthen, E. (1941) Quoted in Krogh, A.: The Comparative Physiology of Respiratory Mechanisms. University of Pennsylvania Press, Philadelphia, p. 129.

Zeuthen, E. (1953) Oxygen uptake as related to body size in organisms. Quart. Rev. Biol. *28*:1–12.

10 THE CIRCULATORY SYSTEM

The body fluids in the various body compartments (see Chap. 3) are in motion: their constituents move within the compartments (circulation) and across the boundaries of compartments (diffusion, osmosis, filtration, active transport).

This chapter is concerned chiefly with the mechanical aspects of the circulation of body fluids. The physiological functions of body fluids in respiration, nutrition, excretion, and endocrine regulation are discussed in other chapters.

THE TYPES OF BODY FLUIDS

Although one usually distinguishes only three types of body fluids—interstitial fluid or tissue fluid, blood (or hemolymph), and coelomic fluid—there may be others. As pointed out in Chapter 3 (p. 43), the nervous system of many animals is contained within special fluid compartments (see Figs. 17–5 and 17–6). Similarly, there is reason to believe that in some groups of animals, certain organs, such as muscle, have an extracellular fluid that is kept separate from the general interstitial fluid or hemolymph. This situation is typical of insects.

Because each fluid compartment is continuous, the contained fluid is free to circulate through this space. Circulation is restricted only by the frictional resistance due to the confining cells and by the internal friction (viscosity, etc.) which the fluid itself develops. The three major causes of circulation are: (1) concentration gradients and osmotic gradients, (2) density differences due to temperature gradients within each compartment, and (3) mechanical forces. The latter are the most effective agents that dominate the pattern of fluid circulation. If the arrangement of a body compartment is such that mechanical forces can and do create an organized and regular pattern of fluid movement, we speak of a circulatory system. Such an arrangement consists of well-defined vascular channels, some of which are contractile. The body compartment that constitutes the circulatory system is usually called the *blood-vascular system*. The body fluid that fills it is known as *blood*.

With the exception of the echinoderms, in which the coelom (water-vascular system) forms tubes and channels suitable for regular circulation, the coelom is rarely employed as a circulatory system. In the majority of species (including those of the large phyla of arthropods and molluscs), the circulatory system contains blood and consists of specialized blood vessels and blood sinus. (*Note*: The singular of "sinus" is also "sinus.") The total complex of vessels and sinus is called the *blood-vascular system*.

In arthropods and molluscs, the body cavity (the hemocoel) is derived from both primary and secondary body cavities. In recognition of this, and because the circulating body fluid was thought to occupy all of its space and communicate freely with the interstitial (tissue) fluid, the blood of molluscs and arthropods has been termed *hemolymph*. This term is unnecessary, however, and can be replaced by the term *blood*.

Vertebrates and many annelids are examples of organisms that have a clear-cut separation of three, if not four, body compartments, each with its own fluid.

1. The blood-vascular system contains blood and causes it to circulate in a *regular pattern of unidirectional flow*.

2. The coelomic spaces contain coelomic fluid. In vertebrates, such spaces are the pericardial coelom, the genitovisceral coelom, and the interior of the nephridial capsules. In annelids, the coelom forms the major body cavity. The coelomic fluid can be assumed to be in a diffusion equilibrium with blood, complicated by fluxes due to pressure differences (both hydrostatic and osmotic). Coelomic fluid shows no regular flow pattern (exception: capsular fluid in vertebrate nephridia which is dominated by filtration pressure of constant direction). Circulation in most coelomic compartments is irregular and can be described as random mixing. In annelids, this is largely caused by movements of the muscular body wall. The same is true for the visceral coelom of vertebrates. The inner surface of the pericardial space contracts and expands, owing to the rhythmic action of the heart.

3. The interstitial spaces between the tissue cells communicate as extracellular space. The fluid contained in it, the interstitial fluid or tissue fluid, is in diffusion equilibrium with blood, coelom, and intracellular "fluid," complicated by pressure differences (both hydrostatic and osmotic), by electrical potential differences, and by active transport phenomena. The narrow passages with their relatively large surface areas offer high frictional resistance and the flow rate is low. No true circulation occurs, but random mixing and convection are prominent.

In vertebrates, the tissue fluid diffuses and is filtered into blind-ending lymph vessels which join to form lymph channels that eventually open at one place or another into the regular blood-vascular system. It is widely assumed that the composition of lymph fluid is identical with interstitial or tissue fluid. This assumption is, however, justified only to the extent to which blood plasma can be assumed to be identical with tissue fluid. In other words, if we know of complex dynamic equilibria across the wall of blood vessels between plasma and tissue fluid, the same considerations apply to the relation between tissue fluid and lymph. For this reason, *tissue fluid should not be called lymph*, as is done so often.

4. In the vertebrates, the cerebrospinal fluid constitutes a fourth type of body fluid (see Chap. 17).

MODES OF PROPULSION

The coelomic fluid in the water-vascular system of echinoderms is propelled by the cilia of the coelomic epithelium. Blood, on the other hand (even in echinoderms), is always propelled by the pumping action of specialized portions of the blood-vascular system. These specialized vessels, known as *hearts*, are hollow muscles that contract rhythmically. They are multicellular. The contractions of all their muscle cells are coordinated in such a way as to achieve unidirectional net flow of blood: excitation spreads from a so-called *pacemaker region* to the other muscular elements of the organ so that they contract in sequence (see Figs. 10–1 and 10–2). Each contraction sequence is called a *pulsation*.

Each contraction is followed by relaxation or expansion. In long, tubular hearts (insects, Xiphosura, Stomatopoda, many annelids, and tunicates), the initial part of the heart may be expanding while the further portions are contracting. In the more compact hearts (lamellibranchs, gastropods, decapod crustaceans, vertebrates), the wave of contraction passes so quickly from one end of the heart to the other that the *whole* heart seems to contract and then to relax. Such near synchronous contractions are known as *systole*, near synchronous relaxation (or expansion) as *diastole*.

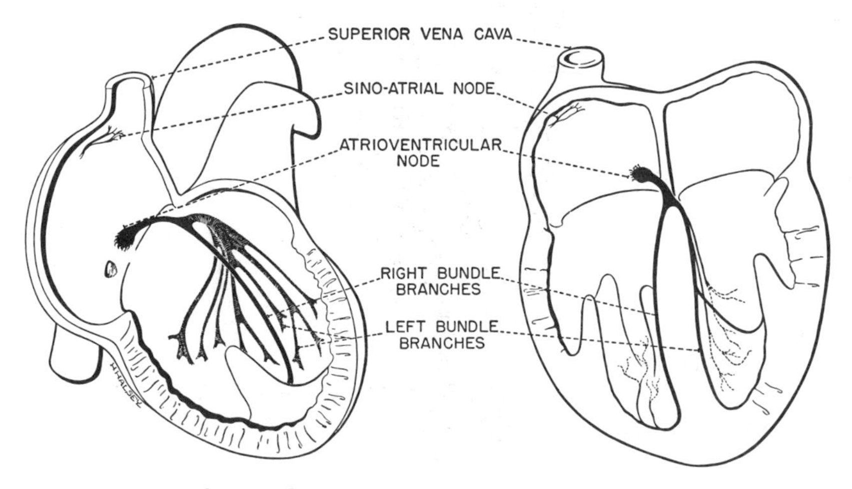

Figure 10–1. Pacemakers and conduction system of the mammalian heart. The sino-atrial node is the normal pacemaker. Excitation of the atria activates the atrioventricular node from which excitation is conducted along the bundles of Purkinje fibers to the ventricles. (From Rushmer, R. F.: Cardiovascular Dynamics, 2nd Ed. W. B. Saunders Co., Philadelphia, 1961.)

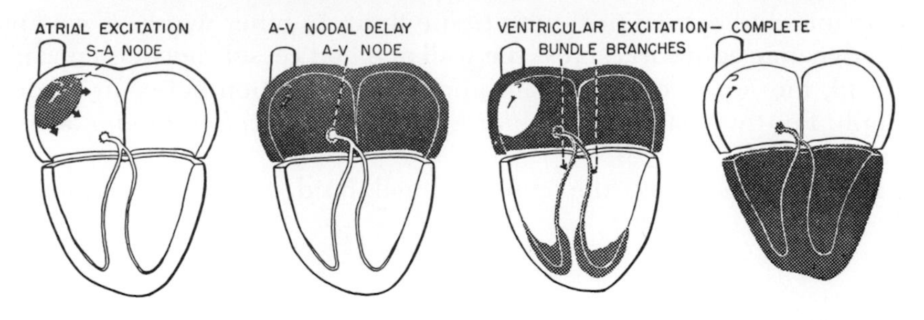

Figure 10–2. Sequence of excitation in the mammalian heart. Active regions are indicated in black. The excitatory impulse is generated in the sino-atrial (*S-A*) node from which it spreads throughout the atria. After a slight delay the atrioventricular (*A-V*) node is activated and sends impulses along the Purkinje system to the apex of the ventricles from which the excitation spreads over the entire ventricular musculature. (From Rushmer, R. F.: Cardiovascular Dynamics, 2nd Ed. W. B. Saunders Co., Philadelphia, 1961.)

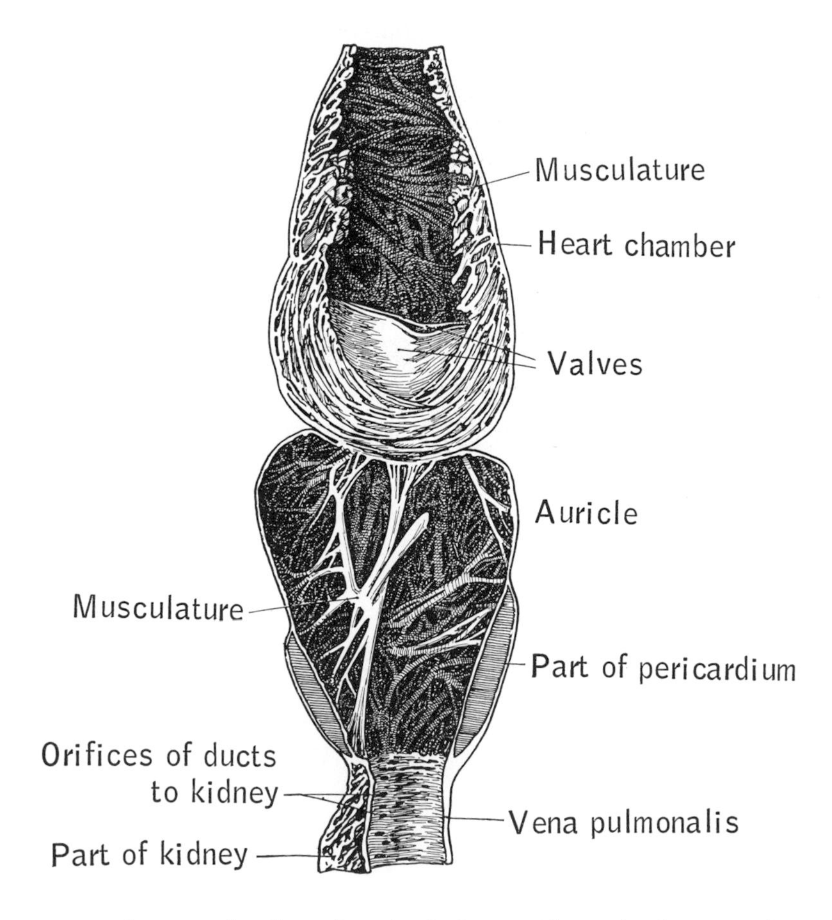

Figure 10–3. An example of a rather simple heart with a valve between the auricle and ventricle is the heart of the snail *Helix pomatia*, shown in longitudinal section parallel to the orientation of the valves. (From Jordan, H. J.: Allgemeine vergleichende Physiologie der Tiere. Walter De Gruyter & Co., Berlin, 1929.)

Most circulatory systems have valves that open if fluid pressure is greater on one side than on the other and close if the pressure difference reverses. Valves are particularly important where the contraction is propagated rapidly. This is always the case in the more compact hearts, such as those of molluscs (exception: Amphineura) and of vertebrates. Examples of such internal valves are shown in Figures 10–3 and 10–4.

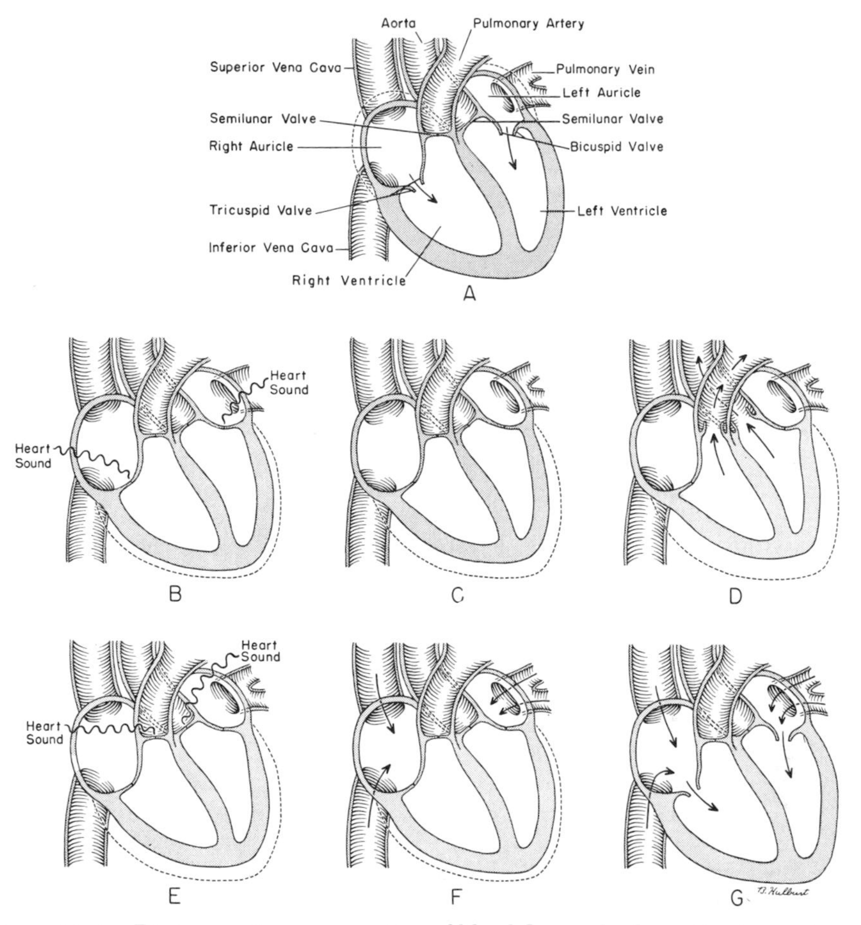

Figure 10–4. Diagrammatic representation of blood flow and valve action in one heart cycle. Human heart. Arrows indicate the direction of the flow of blood; dotted lines indicate the change in size as contraction occurs. **A**, atrial systole; atria contract, blood is pushed through the open tricuspid and bicuspid valves into the ventricles. The semilunar valves are closed. **B**, beginning of ventricular systole; ventricles begin to contract, pressure within ventricles increases and closes the tricuspid and bicuspid valves, causing the first heart sound. **C**, period of rising pressure. Until the pressure within the ventricles equals that in the arteries, the semilunar valves remain closed, and no blood flows in or out of the ventricles. **D**, the semilunar valves open when the pressure within the ventricles exceeds that in the arteries, and blood spurts into the aorta and pulmonary artery. **E**, beginning of ventricular diastole. When the pressure in the relaxing ventricles drops below that in the arteries, the semilunar valves snap shut, causing the second heart sound. **F**, period of falling pressure; ventricles continue to relax, and the pressure within them decreases. The tricuspid and bicuspid valves remain closed because the pressure in the ventricles is still higher than the pressure in the atria. Blood flows from the veins into the relaxed atria. **G**, the tricuspid and bicuspid valves open when the pressure in the ventricles falls below that in the atria, and blood flows into the ventricles. (From Villee, C. A.: Biology, 4th Ed. W. B. Saunders Co., Philadelphia, 1962.)

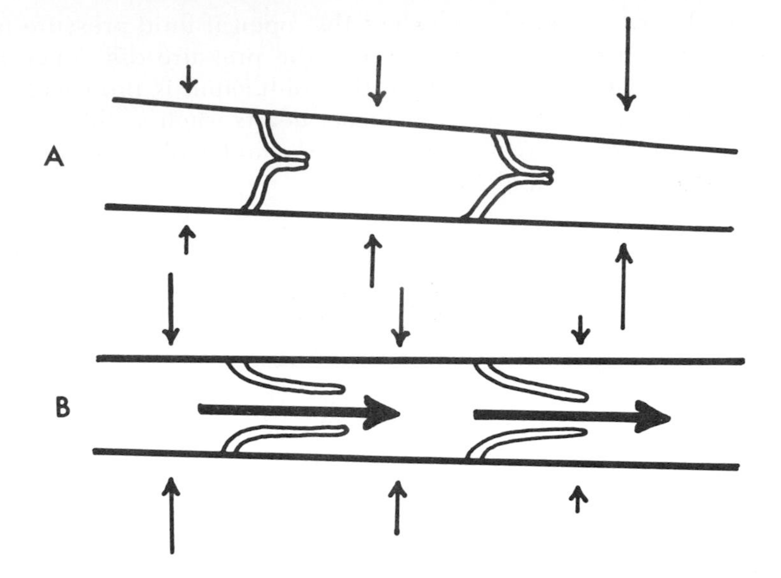

Figure 10–5. Conceptual diagram to explain how valves in a blood vessel accomplish unidirectional flow with alternating external pressure gradients.

Hearts (pulsating blood vessels) are not the only mechanisms engaged in blood circulation. Body movements and any muscular activity cause propulsion of blood. They achieve such fluid movement by creating new areas of pressure which act on blood vessels, and by reducing the internal pressure in other parts of the body. If the vessels on which such shifting pressures act are provided with valves, body movements and muscle contractions lead to unidirectional blood flow. This is explained in the diagram of Figure 10–5.

HEMODYNAMICS

The branch of biophysics concerned with the experimental and mathematical treatment of the physical behavior of blood as a fluid within vessels is known as hemodynamics. It is not concerned with filtration or with aspects of exchange of gases, nutrients, and so forth across the walls of blood vessels. So far, hemodynamics has been restricted almost exclusively to the study of vertebrates – particularly mammals and man. Research on invertebrates has only begun. Most notable in this regard are the pioneering studies of Johansen and Martin (1962) on the *Octopus*.

Although the vertebrate circulatory system is rather unusual compared to all the other known circulatory systems in that it consists of a single heart and (with negligible exceptions) has no sinus, it serves as an important starting point for any general physiology of circulatory systems and for hemodynamics, largely because of its relative simplicity. The following brief exposition of hemodynamics therefore follows the approach of the mammalian physiologists.

Hemodynamics considers the following factors:

Force. The force with which the heart expels blood into the aorta and arteries (in ergs/ml or in dynes/cm^2), and the pressure drop per unit length (cm) of vessel (in dynes/cm^2). The force with which the heart ejects blood into the blood vessels results in (a) kinetic energy of the moving mass of blood, (b) pressure acting on the wall of the blood vessels (lateral pressure), and (c) heat.

One of the most difficult physiological terms to comprehend is *blood pressure*. While the blood is in motion, a large part of its energy is kinetic. This energy can be recorded as pressure (blood pressure) only when the blood flow is obstructed. In physiological experiments, mercury is employed to obstruct the blood flow. By a suitable arrangement (manometer), the developing pressure is allowed to lift a column of mercury. The height of this column is an index of pressure, which is then expressed in millimeters of mercury. The measured pressure is an *end pressure*. This is not to be confused with the lateral pressure, which is considered later.

The kinetic energy of blood emerging from the pumping heart is gradually transformed into heat, owing to the friction within the moving blood column (viscosity) and the frictional resistance offered by the blood vessels. This loss of kinetic energy can be measured as a decrease in pressure, that is, as a pressure drop.

The pressure drop along a given length of blood vessel, that is, the pressure that can be measured at point A minus the pressure that can be measured at point B, represents the *effective*, or *driving pressure* (Fig. 10–6). The force acting on the column of blood at point A is, therefore, not equal to the pressure measured at point A but is equal to the difference between the pressures measured at points A and B.

The factors that affect the pressure drop in fluids flowing through tubes are formulated in *Poiseuille's law*, as explained in Figure 10–7.

Viscosity. The viscosity of the blood is defined as the resistance to shearing

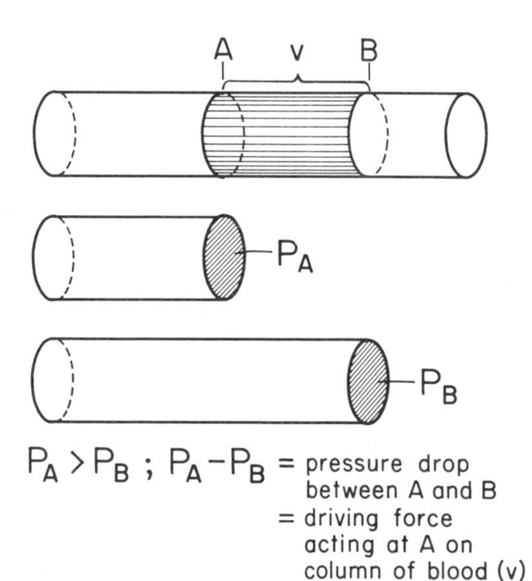

Figure 10–6. Conceptual diagram to explain the term "effective driving pressure." The tubes represent blood vessels. *P*, pressure.

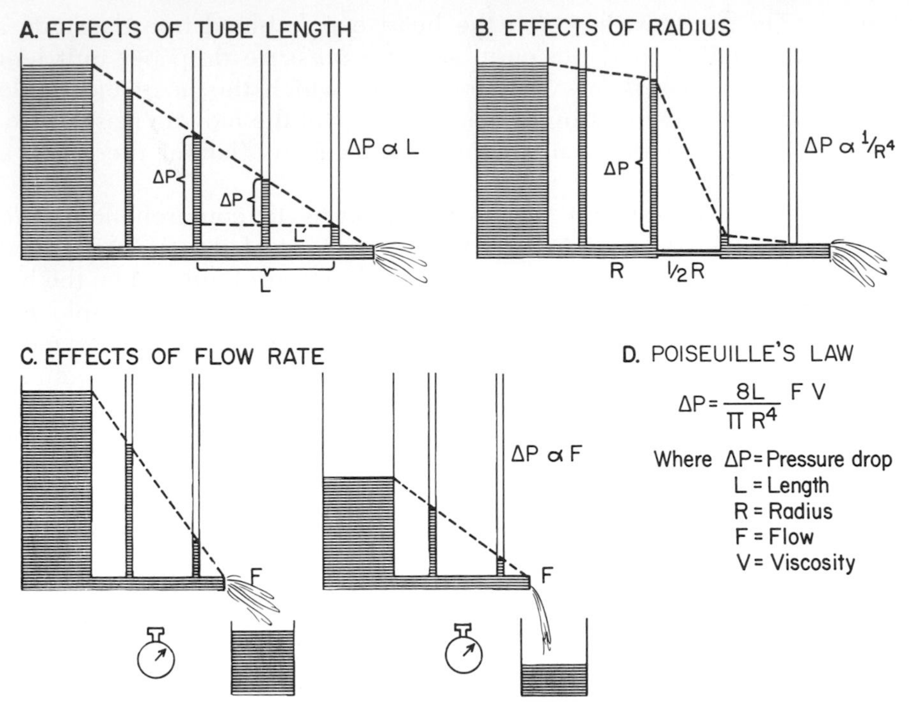

Figure 10–7. Factors influencing the pressure drop in fluids flowing through tubes (Poiseuille's law). **A**, the drop in pressure (ΔP) during laminar flow of a homogeneous fluid through a rigid tube of constant caliber is directly proportional to the length of the tube. **B**, under the same conditions, the pressure drop is also inversely proportional to the reciprocal of the radius to the fourth power ($1/R^4$) and directly proportional to the volume flow (F) through the tube and to the viscosity (V) of the fluid. The relationships between these factors are included in the formula, which is an expression of Poiseuille's law. (From Rushmer, R. F.: Cardiovascular Dynamics, 2nd Ed. W. B. Saunders Co., Philadelphia, 1961.)

forces. We may call it "internal friction." It is usually treated as a phenomenon of the *laminar flow* of blood within tubular vessels: the fluid is considered as a series of concentric layers, or laminae, which slide past each other (shearing motion) when exposed to a pressure gradient along the long axis of the vessel. Viscosity, then, is the tangential force (expressed in dynes/cm^2) on the interface between any two such (assumed) layers under the impact of a velocity gradient (cm/sec/cm).

Viscosity is usually given in terms of the *viscosity coefficient*, that is, the factor by which the viscosity of water must be multiplied in order to equal the viscosity of a particular fluid. Human blood, for instance, has a viscosity coefficient of 1.8, which means that it is 1.8 times as viscous as water. The unit of *absolute viscosity* is the *poise* (named after Poiseuille). The absolute viscosity of water at 20.2° C is 0.01 poise, or 1 centipoise. The symbol for absolute viscosity is η (the Greek letter eta), and represents dynes/cm^2 at a velocity gradient of 1 cm/sec/cm.

The Velocity of Blood Flow Through the Vessels. If observed at the cross-sectional area of a given vessel, the flow is not homogeneous but laminar: the outermost lamina (layer) adheres to the wall of the vessel and is essentially immobile. The next layer moves somewhat faster, the next one faster still, and the core of the laminar fluid column moves fastest. The whole pattern is shown in the diagram of Figure 10–8. The velocity profile is a parabola, described by the following equation:

$$V_r = V_{max} \cdot \left(1 - \frac{r^2}{R^2}\right) \quad (1)$$

where V_r is the velocity of flow at any radius r, and V_{max} is the maximal flow at the radius R of the vessel. According to this formula, the velocity at $r = R$ (that is, within the outermost lamina of blood) is zero.

The maximal velocity is related to the pressure drop per cm (P) and to the viscosity (η) by the equation:

$$V_{max} = \frac{P \cdot R^2}{4\eta} \quad (2)$$

Total Blood Flow. The total blood flow through a particular length of blood vessel (in ml/sec) follows the famous *Poiseuille-Hagen equation*:

$$F = (P_A - P_B) \cdot \left(\frac{\pi}{8}\right) \cdot \left(\frac{1}{\eta}\right) \cdot \left(\frac{R^4}{l}\right) \quad (3)$$

where F is the total flow, $P_A - P_B$ the pressure difference (in dynes/cm^2) between points A and B, η the viscosity in poises, and R the diameter and l the length (in cm) of the vessel between A and B.

The formula shows that the flow is proportional to the pressure drop and

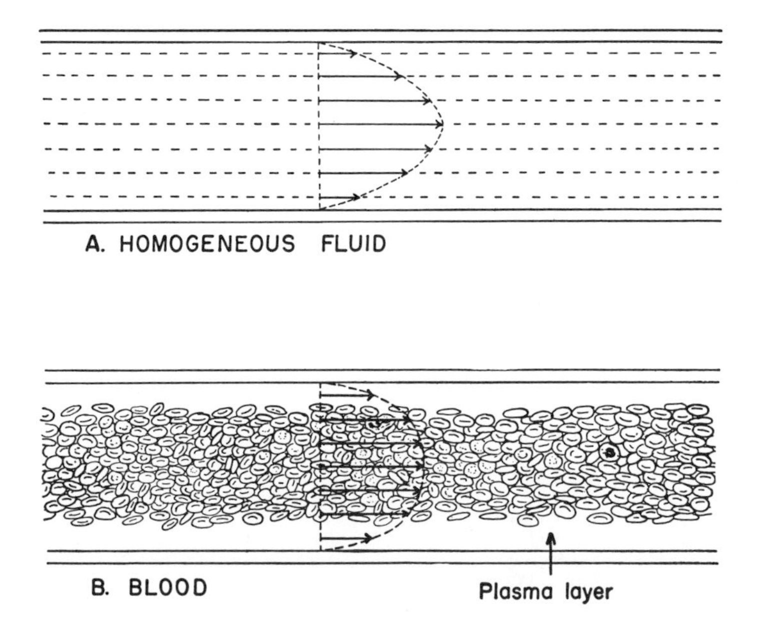

Figure 10–8. Laminar flow in tubes. **A**, the arrows show the velocity profile. **B**, the blood cells concentrate in the layers of high flow velocity. (From Rushmer, R. F.: Cardiovascular Dynamics, 2nd Ed. W. B. Saunders Co., Philadelphia, 1961.)

inversely proportional to the absolute viscosity of the fluid: at a given pressure, the flow through a given vessel is faster the lower the viscosity, or slower, the higher the viscosity. Most significant is the term (R^4/l) of the equation. It means that at a given length of vessel the flow rate (ml/sec) is proportional to the fourth power of the diameter.

From these startling facts one can see that mathematics is indispensable in physiology. In this particular case, we learn that a reduction of the diameter of a blood vessel by 1/16 reduces the blood flow to 1/2. If a blood vessel constricts (under the influence of hormones or nerves) to 1/2 its original diameter, the blood flow is thereby reduced to 1/16. This is shown in Figure 10–9.

The considerations concerning the relation of diameter (cross-sectional area) and flow velocity apply also to the circulatory system as a whole, as explained in Figure 10–10.

Lateral Pressure. The force that drives blood into and through a blood vessel acts not only in the direction of the long axis of the vessel but also transversely to the walls of the vessel. A definite relation exists between the achieved velocity of blood flow and the amount of pressure exerted laterally on the walls of the vessel. According to *Bernouilli's principle*, the lateral pressure is higher the lower the velocity (see Fig. 10–11), or, vice versa, the higher the velocity, the lower the lateral pressure. Theoretically, the velocity could reach such a high value that the lateral pressure would be less than 1 atm. Under these cir-

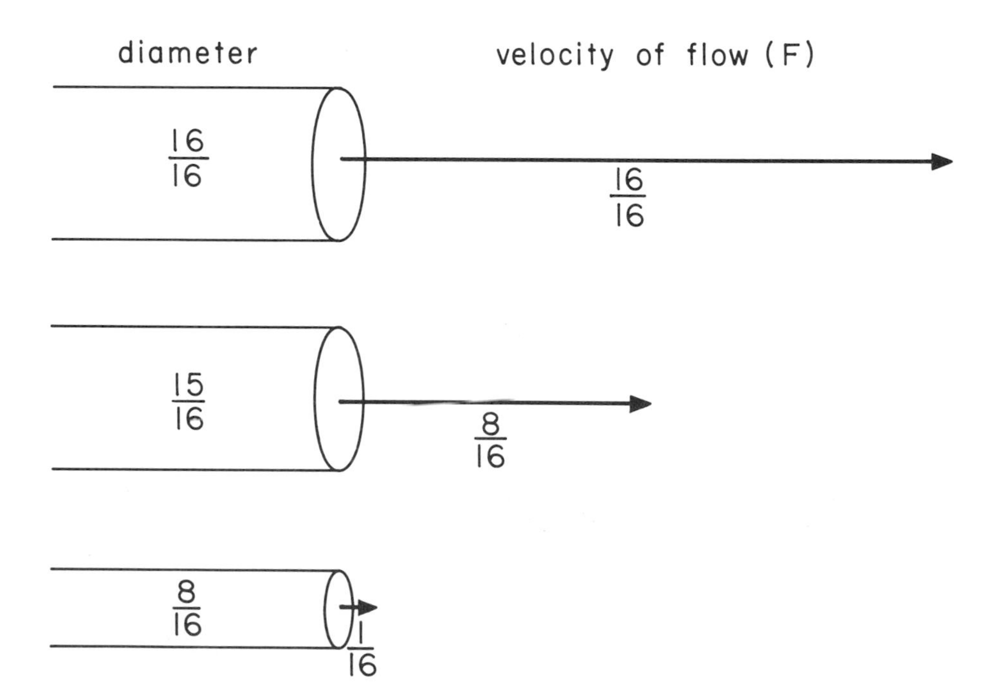

Figure 10–9. Conceptual diagram to explain the relation between change in diameter of a blood vessel and the resulting change in flow velocity: a reduction in diameter of 1/16 reduces the velocity to 1/2, a constriction to 1/2 the original diameter slows the flow to 1/16 the original velocity.

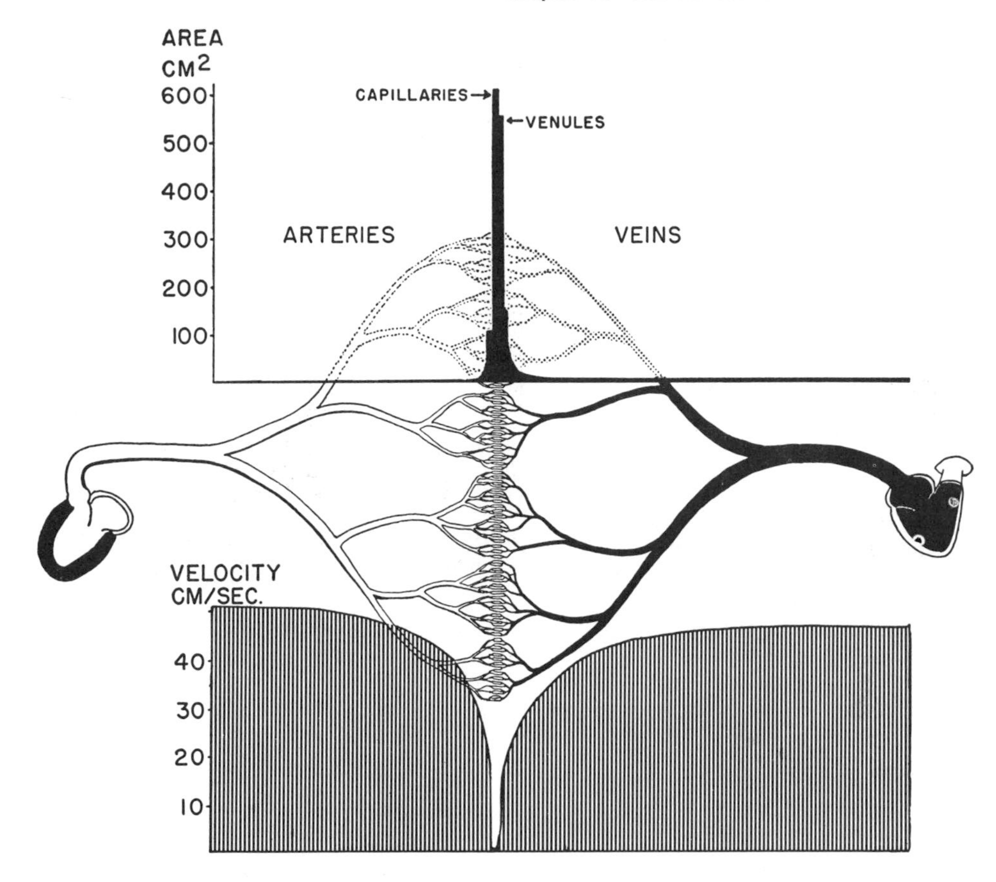

Figure 10–10. The relation between cross-sectional area and the velocity of flow in the circulatory system of a 13 kg dog. Note the tremendous area in the arterioles, capillaries, and venules. The velocity of blood flow is inversely proportional to the cross-sectional area, so that blood flows through the capillaries at about 1/100 the speed with which it flows through the large arteries and veins. (From Rushmer, R. F.: Cardiovascular Dynamics, 2nd Ed. W. B. Saunders Co., Philadelphia, 1961.)

cumstances, the blood vessel would collapse, at least momentarily: as soon as the passage is closed, the velocity would fall to zero and the increased lateral pressure would re-open the vessel.

Elasticity of the Blood Vessels. According to the *law of Laplace*, the pressure, P (dynes/cm^2), in a cylindrical elastic vessel is equal to the tension, T, of the wall (in dynes/cm, or gm/cm) divided by the radius, R (in cm), of the vessel.

$$P = \frac{T}{R} \tag{4}$$

If the pressure inside the vessel and the diameter of the vessel are determined, the tension of the vascular wall can be calculated simply. That of the human aorta is about 200 gm/cm; that of the human skin capillaries about 15 mg/cm.

The relation expressed by Laplace's law is an index of the amount (and performance) of elastic tissue (elastin and, to a certain extent, collagen) in the

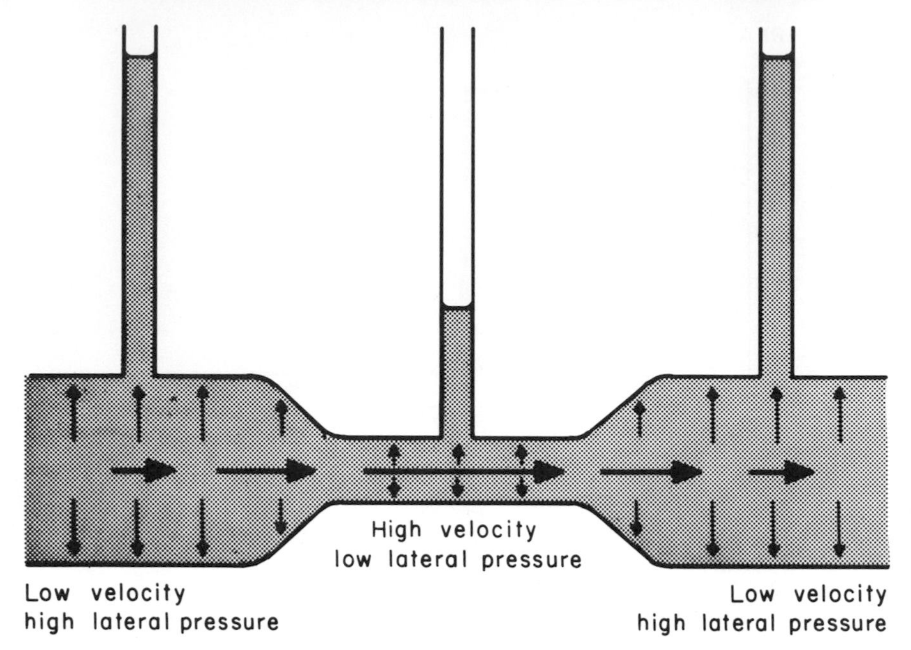

Figure 10–11. Diagrammatic representation of Bernoulli's principle: in steady flow through a tube a definite volume of fluid passes each cross-sectional area of the tube per unit time; the velocity is inversely proportional to the diameter of the tube, the lateral pressure is proportional.

wall of blood vessels. The relation also allows other predictions: if the tension of the vascular wall is high, a rather large rise in pressure is required to increase the diameter of the vessel, whereas in a vessel whose walls offer little resistance to extension, a slight rise in pressure greatly increases the diameter. If a larger volume of blood enters an artery, the pressure rises markedly, whereas the diameter changes only moderately. The same volume entering an easily distensible vein increases the pressure in the vein only slightly.

When the heart ejects blood into the aorta and large arteries, these thick-walled but elastic vessels are momentarily distended, owing to the pressure exerted by the heart. When the heart muscle relaxes during diastole, the heart valves close and prevent a backflow of blood into the ventricle. The tension of the distended arterial walls then exerts a pressure on the blood contained in the arteries and aids in expelling it into the arterioles and capillaries (Fig. 10–12). In this way, the time during which blood pressure is generated is greatly prolonged: without the additional action of the arteries, the propulsive force would be available only during active contraction of the heart muscle. The elastic arteries prolong the pulsation. Thus the blood volume ejected by the heart flows more evenly. The arteries are said to act as a "Windkessel," a device that evens out pressure fluctuations.

Flow Resistance. In rigid tubes, the flow (ml/sec) is proportional to the driving pressure. In distensible, elastic tubes, the flow is not directly proportional to the pressure, and the pattern of flow in relation to pressure becomes most complicated if there is an *active tension* (contraction) of the muscle fibers in the wall of a blood vessel. Since this active tension does not result from the distension by pressure (elastic tubes develop passive tension in response to internal pressure), it upsets the otherwise existing equilibrium between wall tension and internal pressure and leads to a closing of the vessel by constriction. The resistance to blood flow may then become infinite. Minute changes in active tension of the muscular walls of blood vessels can have enormous effects on the flow resistance.

If no elastic tissue is present so that the vessel cannot be distended significantly beyond its normal (resting) diameter, even a slight contraction of muscles in the wall of the vessel can lead to complete closure. The process is as follows:

As contraction begins, the lumen of the vessel constricts slightly, and this causes an increase in flow rate. The increase in flow rate is accompanied by a reduction of lateral pressure. The load on the muscle fibers is thereby diminished and they shorten further (this need not be accompanied by an increase in muscle tension), thus constricting the vessel even more. Flow rate increases, and the lateral pressure diminishes further. In no time at all, the vessel collapses as the lateral pressure diminishes to a value below that of the pressure

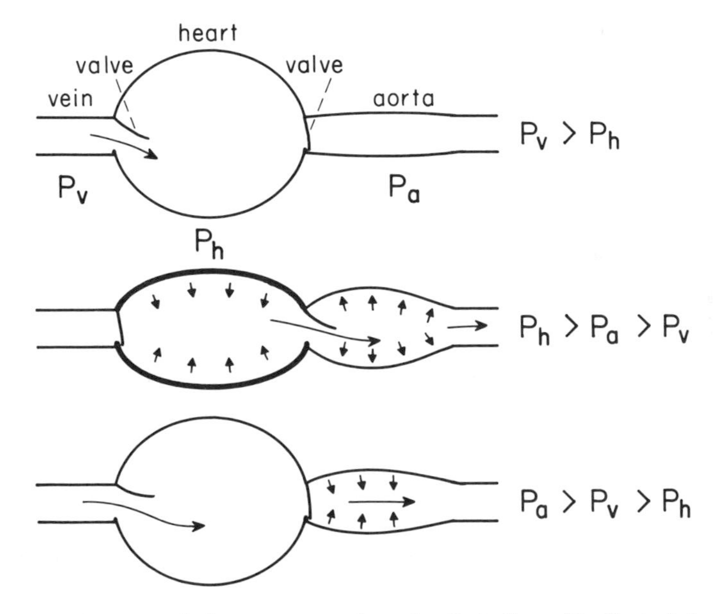

Figure 10–12. Conceptual diagram to explain the "windkessel" effect of the elastic aorta. P, pressure; the subscripts v, h and a stand for vein, heart (ventricle), and aorta, respectively. When the venous blood pressure is higher than the pressure inside the heart, blood flows into the heart and distends it. When the heart muscle contracts, the blood pressure in the heart becomes high, closes the valve toward the vein, and opens the valve toward the aorta. The lateral blood pressure distends the elastic wall of the aorta. When the heart contraction is over, the blood pressure inside the heart falls again and the valve toward the aorta closes. The energy stored in the distended elastic wall of the aorta now acts on the blood volume inside the aorta, and as the walls constrict again, they drive a further volume of blood out into the arteries so that the flow continues for some time after the heart itself has stopped expelling blood.

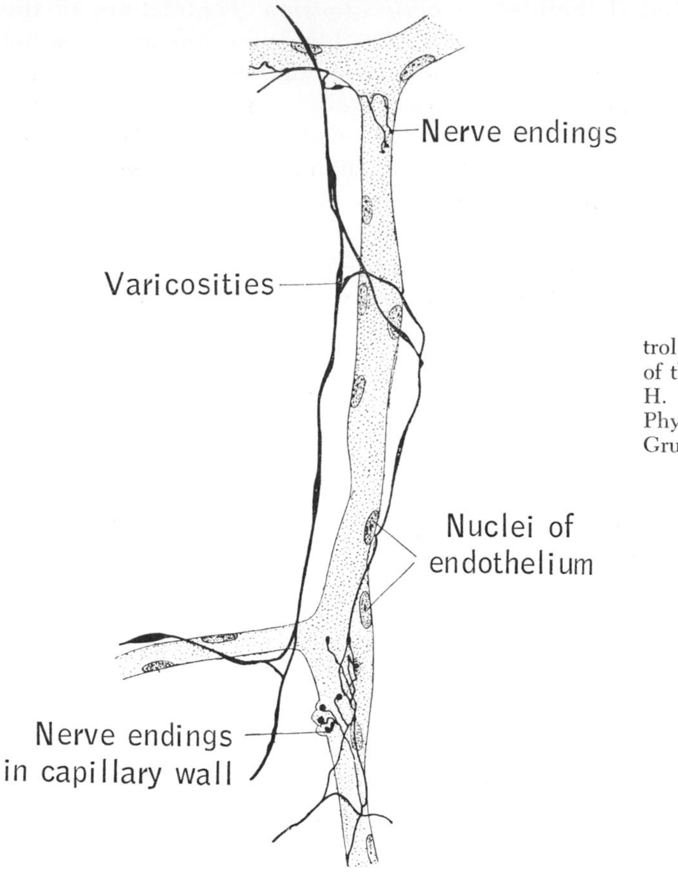

Figure 10–13. Nervous control of blood vessels: capillaries of the human brain. (From Jordan, H. J.: Allgemeine vergleichende Physiologie der Tiere. Walter De Gruyter & Co., Berlin, 1929.)

of the tissues surrounding the vessel. With no further resistance to contraction, the muscle fibers shorten maximally and can keep the vessel closed as long as their contraction is maintained by the action of nerve impulses arriving over the so-called vasomotor nerves (Fig. 10–13) or by the action of hormones (adrenaline and others).

Resistance to blood flow is measured in resistance units, R. The unit is defined as that resistance which requires a pressure of 1 mm Hg to move 1 ml of blood through a given vessel. Or, in other words, a vessel has unit resistance if the blood pressure at two points separated by a length corresponding to 1 ml differs by 1 mm Hg (Fig. 10–14). In order to determine the resistance of a given blood vessel, or even of a given part of a circulatory system, we need to know the amount of blood that moves through the vessel(s) per second, and the difference in blood pressure at the beginning and at the end of the vessel(s) examined. The following formula applies:

$$\frac{(P_1 - P_2)}{V} = \text{R units} \tag{5}$$

For example, if the volume of blood flowing through a blood vessel is 20 ml/sec

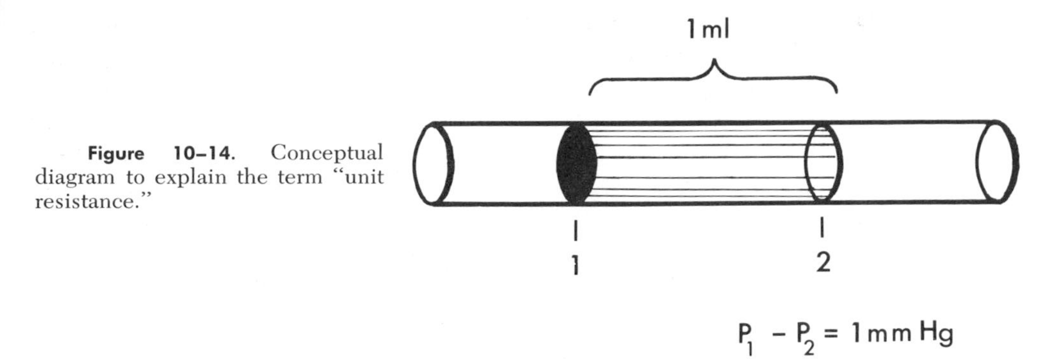

Figure 10–14. Conceptual diagram to explain the term "unit resistance."

and the blood pressure measured at the beginning (P_1) of the vessel is 40 mm Hg and that at the end (P_2) is 30 mm Hg, the resistance is equal to $\frac{(40-30)}{20} = \frac{10}{20} =$ 0.5 R unit.

It must be understood, of course, that the pressure diminishes *because* of the resistance—the resistance is not caused by a pressure drop.

Since vertebrates have only one heart, which is, in fact, the only pulsatile vessel, it is relatively simple to measure the flow resistance of the entire vascular system—often called *peripheral resistance* (an inappropriate term). For this purpose, the following, readily available data are required: arterial blood pressure (ideally, of course, this should be measured at the aorta, but this is not practicable), venous blood pressure (ideally that of the vena cava; this is not measured but simply assumed to be zero), and the volume of blood ejected per second by the heart (the volume ejected per minute divided by 60). For example, a 70 kg man has a mean arterial blood pressure of 92 mm Hg and his heart pumps 5.5 liters of blood per minute, or 91.6 ml/sec. The total flow resistance is $92 - 0/91.6 = 1.04$ R units.

The greatest pressure drop occurs in the blood vessels of smallest diameter—the arterioles, venules, and capillaries. In mammals the pressure drop along the capillaries (from arterioles to venules) may approach 100 mm Hg.

Cardiac Output: Stroke Volume and Minute Volume. In investigating the dynamics of a circulatory system, one must know the amount of fluid that moves through it in a given interval. If, as in the vertebrates, the heart is the only pulsating organ, this amount is that ejected by the heart during the interval under consideration. The volume of blood ejected per systole is called the *stroke volume*. The amount ejected per minute is known as the *minute volume*. The minute volume is equal to the stroke volume multiplied by the number of systoles (heartbeats) per minute.

Cardiac output cannot always be measured directly, particularly in small animals. Where large efferent blood vessels are accessible, the experimenter can, however, attach flowmeters. This technique requires surgical procedures and may alter the performance of the circulatory system.

Indirect determinations have been successful. Two of them are:

1. The *direct Fick method*, based on the so-called *Fick principle*, makes

use of the fact that blood is employed in respiratory gas exchange. The Fick principle is based on the assumption that all blood ejected by the heart passes through the respiratory organ (pulmonary circuit). According to the Fick principle, the number of liters of blood ejected per minute is equal to the number of milliliters of oxygen used by the organism per minute divided by the difference (in ml) of the oxygen contents of arteries and veins. The formula for cardiac output (C.O.) is:

$$\text{C.O. (in l/min)} = \frac{\text{ml } O_2 \text{ consumed per min}}{(\text{ml } O_2/\text{l of arterial blood} - \text{ml } O_2/\text{l of venous blood})} \quad (6)$$

For example, if the blood taken from the femoral artery contains 200 ml O_2/l and that obtained by catheter from the right ventricle (venous blood) contains 150 ml O_2/l, and if the subject consumes 250 ml O_2/min (as measured with a

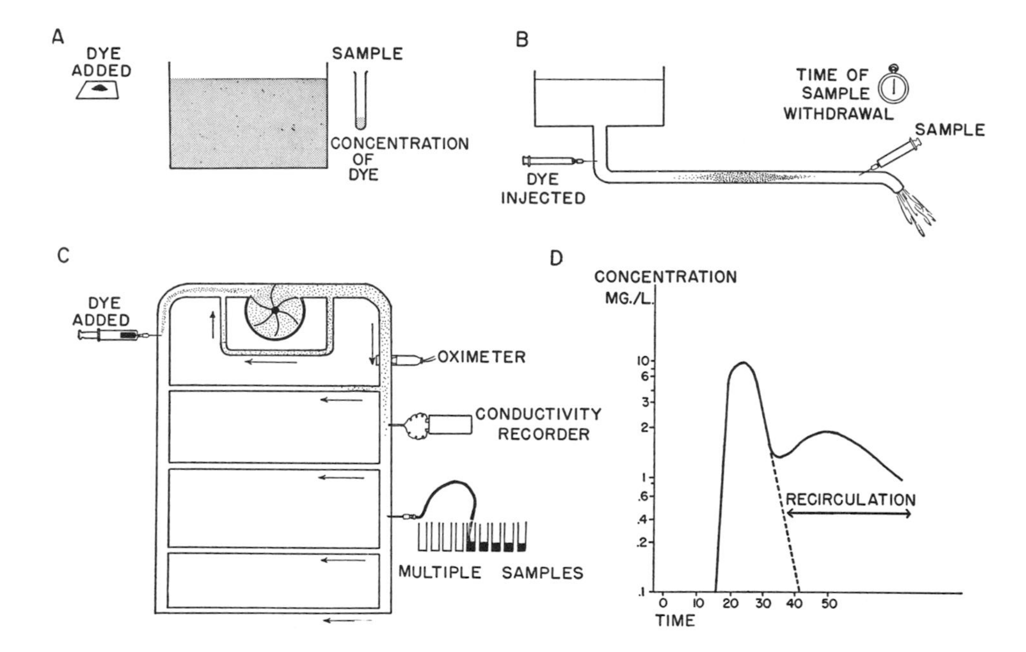

Figure 10–15. Diagrammatic explanation of the dye dilution method of determining the blood volume.

A, the volume of stationary fluid in a reservoir can be determined by completely mixing a known amount of dye and analyzing a sample for the concentration of the dye.

B, the volume flow through a simple tube can be estimated by injecting a known quantity of dye, withdrawing a sample at constant rate during the passage of the dye-containing fluid, and determining the mean concentration of the sample.

C, a hydraulic model simulating the circulatory system illustrates the fact that an indicator substance may pass through short circuits and begin to recirculate before the mass of dye has passed the sampling point. Therefore it is necessary to devise means by which the amount of recirculating dye can be separated from the amount of dye sampled during its initial passage to arrive at a reliable mean concentration.

D, if the concentration of the dye passing a sampling point is plotted on semi-log paper, the descending limb after the peak can be extended to the baseline as a straight line. The area under the initial curve can be used to derive the mean concentration of the dye during its first circulation.

(From Rushmer, R. F.: Cardiovascular Dynamics, 2nd Ed. W. B. Saunders Co., Philadelphia, 1961.)

respirometer), the cardiac output (minute volume) is equal to 250/(200–150) = 250/50 = 5 liter/min.

2. The *dye dilution method* involves injecting a known amount of dye* into a vein and measuring the dye concentration in samples of arterial blood taken at frequent intervals. Radioactive compounds, or radioactively tagged blood cells, are often used instead of dyes. As shown in Figure 10–15, the dye concentration in arterial blood rises, then falls and rises again. The second rise indicates that blood is circulating past the sampling point for the second time. If the concentrations measured are plotted on a logarithmic scale against a linear time scale, the falling phase of the curve can be extrapolated to zero concentration. This gives the time-concentration curve for the first circulation. From this, dilution of the amount originally injected can be read off for any given number of seconds after injection. If 12 mg is injected at time zero, and a concentration of 4 mg/l is read off at 30 sec, the 12 mg had been diluted by 3 liters of blood (4:1 liter = 12: x liter, $x = \frac{12}{4}$ liters. The blood flow (minute volume), therefore, is 3 liters/30 sec, or 6 liters/min.

COMPARATIVE PHYSIOLOGY OF CIRCULATORY SYSTEMS

Patterns of Blood Flow

Copious detail is available concerning the morphological features of circulatory systems of almost all the known animal groups. To gain an insight into the enormous variety and complexity of the various circulatory systems, consult advanced texts on animal morphology. The major texts in the field of morphological biology (with references to physiology) are those of Hyman (The Invertebrates, 1940–1959), Grasse, ed. (Traité de Zoologie, 1948–), Kükenthal and Krumbach, ed. (Handbuch der Zoologie, 1923–), and Bronn, ed. (Klassen und Ordnungen des Tierreiches, 1880–). See Martin and Johansen (1965) for a comprehensive review of Adaptations of the Circulation in Invertebrate Animals.

Vertebrate morphology is by no means typical of all animal groups. However, a large variety of diverse systems fit into major patterns.

Nemerteans and Annelids. Characteristically, these animals have a closed circulatory system, consisting of a major, dorsal vessel which is joined to lateral vessels (nemerteans), or to a ventral vessel and to lateral vessels (annelids) by commissural vessels. Most of the vessels that connect the dorsal vessel with the other major longitudinal vessels branch out to form a system of capillaries which unite again to form larger vessels that complete the connection, as shown in Figure 10–16. The dorsal vessel is a tube with a muscular wall that contracts rhythmically in peristaltic waves which pump blood forward. Some of the commissural vessels also act as pumps. In some annelids, the dorsal vessel

*(Large molecules are used, because they stay within the vascular system and do not pass through the endothelium.)

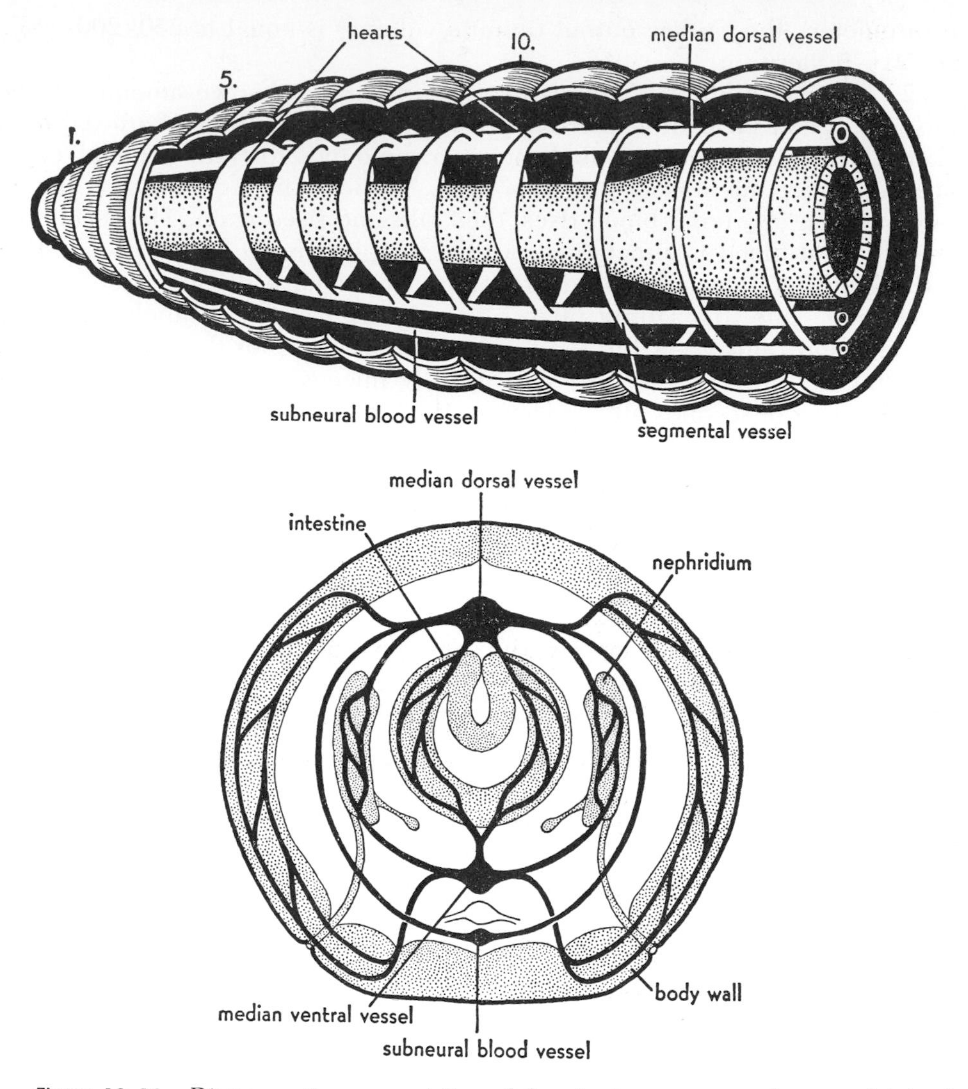

Figure 10–16. Diagrammatic representation of the circulatory system of an annelid (earthworm). **Top**, anterior end of an earthworm, showing the principal blood vessels. Five pairs of hearts surround the esophagus and pump blood from the dorsal to the ventral blood vessel in which it flows backward (except in the first six segments where it moves forward in the ventral vessel). The dorsal blood vessel is pulsatile and pumps blood forward. The hearts generate a rather high blood pressure not far below that of the human body. **Bottom**, cross section through an earthworm, showing the main segmental blood vessels and the capillary beds of gut, nephridia, and body wall. (From Buchsbaum, R.: Animals Without Backbone, 2nd Ed. University of Chicago Press, Chicago, 1948.)

shows, in the anterior part of the animal, a chamber-like enlargement which is referred to as a heart. This is found particularly in sedentary polychaetes. The gut is supplied by capillary networks or by blood lacunae or by both.

Capillary networks also supply the nephridia and the gonads, and special vessels carry blood to the central nervous system. Oligochaeta and Hirudinea often have a rich capillary supply of the body wall; in marine annelids (Polychaeta) such superficial capillary networks are usually prominent in the appendixes serving in respiration (the parapodia of *Nereis*, the gills of *Arenicola*, and the tentacular crown of serpulids and sabellids).

Although in several annelid species the circulatory system is reduced or rudimentary, the classic pattern is a closed system of tubes. The same is true for the nemerteans.

Molluscs. In the Mollusca, the circulatory system is characterized by a chambered heart (one or more *atria* and one *ventricle*), which pumps blood into arteries that branch out into capillary networks, blood sinuses, and lacunae (Fig. 10–17). (The term "sinus" denotes large blood spaces; the term "lacuna" signifies a small blood space.) In the cephalopods, the endothelium is continuous throughout the blood-vascular system. In all other molluscan groups, as far as is known, the endothelial lining does not extend throughout the sinus and lacunae so that blood communicates with the tissue fluid and directly bathes the tissue cells. In the latter forms, the blood volume is about 50 per cent of the total body volume, whereas in cephalopods, this amounts to about 15 per cent of the body volume. Regardless, however, of whether the circulatory system is "open" or "closed," blood flow is orderly, and more or less unidirectional.

Return of blood from the capillaries or blood spaces to the heart is accomplished by a system of veins which join to form a major vessel (vena cava; plural: venae cavae) which open into the atrium (plural: atria). Molluscan veins are characteristically contractile and actively pump blood back to the heart. In cephalopods, one can observe regular pulsations of the major veins. The venous blood pressure is consequently higher than the pressure in the blood sinus. Cephalopods have, in addition, two so-called *gill hearts*, muscular enlargements of the veins that carry blood to the gills (Fig. 10–18). These provide the pres-

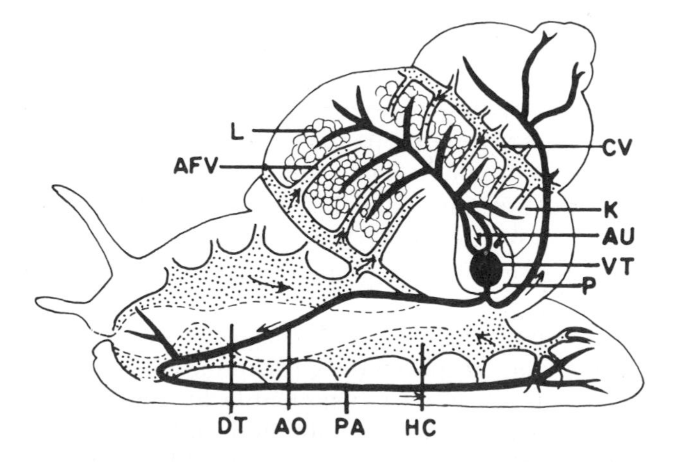

Figure 10–17. Schema of circulatory system of a pulmonate. Major vessels are shown in black; the hemocoel and branchial afferents are dotted. AFV, afferent branchial vein; AO, aorta; AU, auricle; CV, connecting vein; DT, digestive tract; HC, hemocoel; K, kidney; L, lung; P, pericardium; PA, pedal artery; VT, ventricle. (From Martin, A. W., and K. Johansen: Adaptations of the circulation in invertebrate animals. *In* Handbook of Physiology, Sect. 2, Vol. III, pp. 2545–2581. W. F. Hamilton and P. Dow, eds. The Williams & Wilkins Co., Baltimore, 1965.)

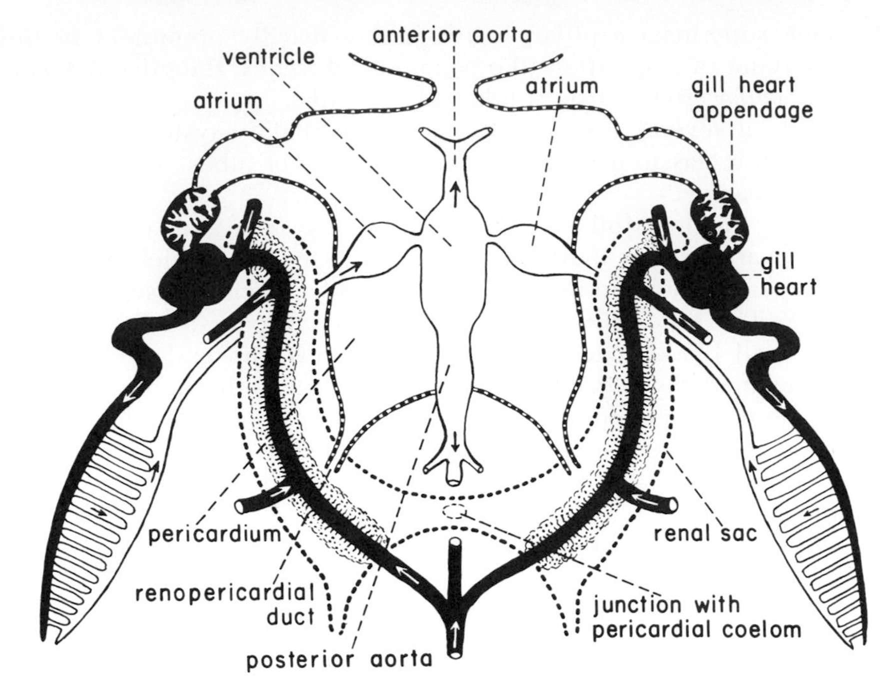

Figure 10–18. Major features of the cephalopod circulatory system (*Sepia*). Note the relationship between the pericardium and the renal sac. (After Stempell, W.: Zoologie im Grundriss. Borntraeger, Berlin, 1926.)

sure to overcome the frictional resistance of the narrow passage through the rather extensive gills.

Arthropods. Arthropods, like most molluscs, have an open circulatory system in which the blood is carried from a major heart (a single chamber) through arteries and capillaries into blood spaces that are not lined by endothelium but communicate with the tissue spaces so that the blood bathes the tissue cells directly (Figs. 10–19 and 10–20). The return of blood to the heart, however, is quite different from the pattern found in the Mollusca. Blood flows either through veins or through communicating spaces and channels into a major blood sinus that surrounds the heart (pericardium). It enters the heart through openings set into the heart wall (known as *ostia*; singular: ostium). The ostia are complicated valves that open when the heart muscle relaxes and close when it contracts.

In contrast to the molluscs, in which the heart lies free in the pericardial sinus, the arthropod heart is provided with numerous suspensory ligaments. These ligaments are elastic and are responsible for the filling of the heart: as the heart muscle relaxes after each contraction, the ligaments pull the heart walls apart and create the suction necessary for filling. In the molluscs, the heart is filled by the pressure difference between veins and atria, and between atria and ventricle.

Whereas in the crustaceans the blood vessels do not pulsate or contract, insects and arachnids have many pulsating blood vessels. These "accessory

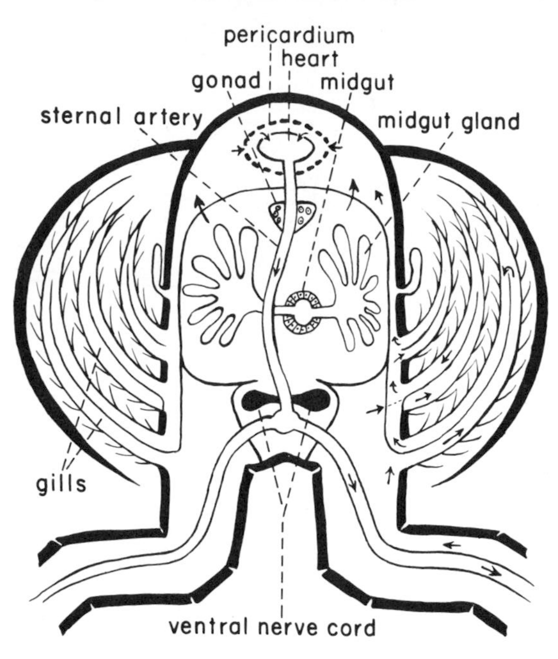

Figure 10–19. Some features of the circulatory system of a decapod crustacean, the crayfish (*Astacus*), as shown in a cross section through the cephalothorax. This is an example of an open circulatory system, characterized by the absence of veins. (After Stempell, W.: Zoologie im Grundriss. Borntraeger, Berlin, 1926.)

hearts" aid in supplying blood to the limbs and wings, and to the nervous system.

Tunicates. Tunicates have a unique circulatory system (Fig. 10–21). Its main feature is a tubular heart that consists of a single layer of muscle cells. At each end a major blood vessel gives rise to branches which, in turn, divide into capillaries and deliver blood into tissue spaces. The circulatory system is thus considered to be "open." What makes the tunicate heart—and the whole cardiovascular system—so interesting is the periodic reversal of blood flow:

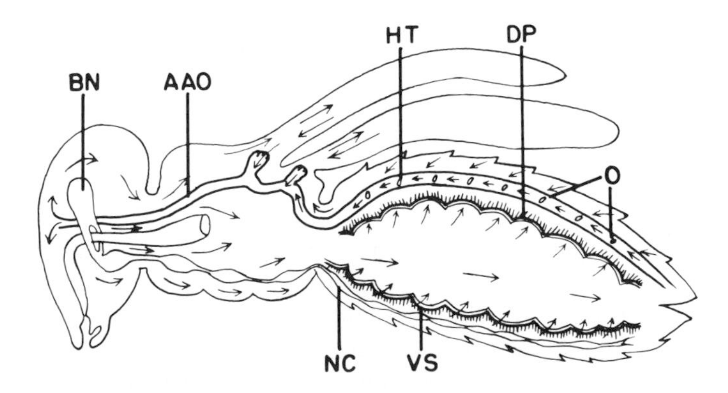

Figure 10–20. Generalized insect circulatory system. AAO, anterior aorta; BN, brain; DP, pericardium; HT, heart; NC, nerve cord; O, ostia; VS, ventral septum. (From Martin, A. W., and K. Johansen: Adaptations of the circulation in invertebrate animals. *In* Handbook of Physiology, Sec. 2, Vol. III, pp. 2545–2581. W. F. Hamilton and P. Dow, eds. The Williams & Wilkins Co., Baltimore, 1965.)

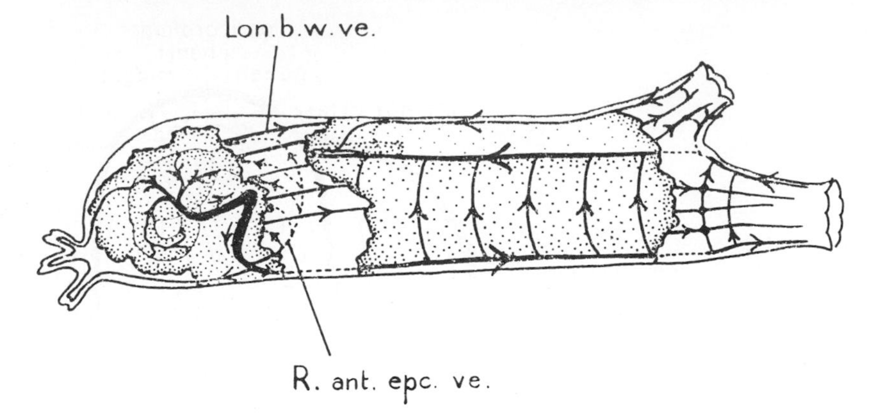

Figure 10–21. *Ciona intestinalis.* General course of the circulation during the abvisceral phase of the heartbeat. Large parts of the body wall have been omitted in the branchial and visceral regions. The arrows on vessels indicate the direction of blood flow. During advisceral beats the opposite directions would obtain. *R. ant. epc. ve.*, right anterior epicardiac vessel; *Lon. b. w. ve.*, longitudinal body wall vessel. Even though this looks like a typical closed circulatory system, it may well be an open one because it has not been established that the capillaries are lined by an endothelium; they may well be nothing more than channels between tissue cells. (From Millar, R. H.: Ciona. L.M.B.C. Memoirs, Vol. 35. University Press of Liverpool, 1953.)

for a certain period, the heart pumps blood in one direction, and then, for a similar period, reverses the direction of pulsations and pumps blood in the opposite direction. Thus, the main blood vessels serve alternately as arteries and as veins.

The stimulus for the reversal of the direction of the heart pulsations is the increase in pressure in the part of the vascular system that serves as an arterial system. The peripheral resistance, apparently, is so high that the blood pressure generated by the heart is insufficient to drive all the cardiac output through it and completely return it to the heart. Recent experiments of Kriebel (1963) have shown that an increase of 0.1 mm Hg in the average arterial blood pressure is sufficient to reverse the heartbeat. It can easily be imagined that such a slight pressure change (lateral pressure) is due to "congestion" of the arteries.

Vertebrates. The typical vertebrate circulatory system is closed, and the only pump is a chambered heart. Although the major blood vessels have a muscular wall that is controlled by hormones (adrenaline, histamine) and nerve fibers, they do not pump but merely regulate blood flow and blood pressure by changing their internal diameter. As a rule, the heart acts as a pressure pump; that is, it fills because the pressure in the veins is higher than that of the heart chamber (sinus venosus, atrium) that accepts it. In elasmobranch fishes, however, the pericardium is stiffened by cartilage so that a negative pressure is generated around the heart when it contracts and expels blood through the arteries. This negative pressure facilitates the relaxation of the heart muscle and the expansion of the heart chambers, and this, in turn, produces negative pressure within the heart itself so that such elasmobranch hearts act like suction pumps. Their method of filling is thus similar to that found in arthropod hearts, in which negative pressure is created by the elastic, suspensory ligaments.

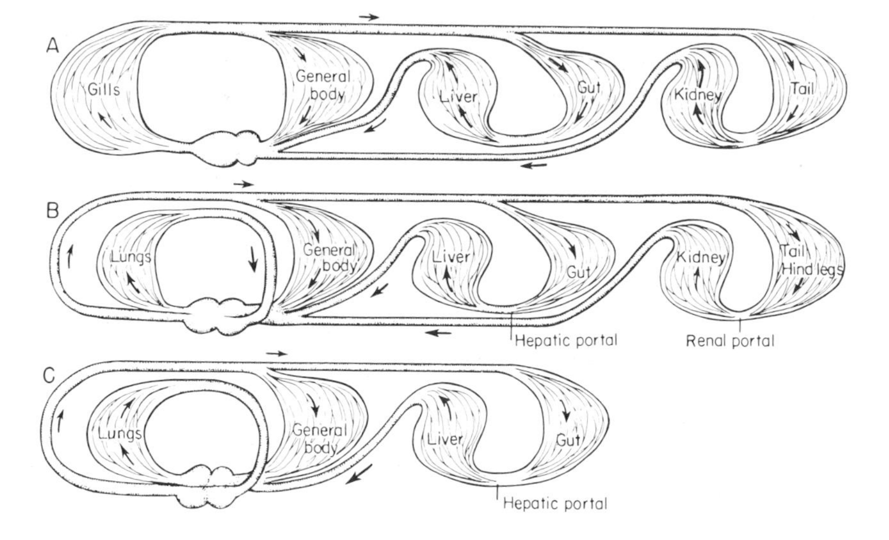

Figure 10–22. Three patterns of closed circulatory system, as found in vertebrates: **A**, a typical fish. **B**, a terrestrial amphibian or a reptile (with elimination of gill circulation and introduction of pulmonary circuit). **C**, a mammal or bird (elimination of renal portal system). (From Romer, A. S.: The Vertebrate Body, 3rd Ed. W. B. Saunders Co., Philadelphia, 1962.)

Even the vertebrate circulatory system is not entirely "closed." In several places the blood flows into larger sinus and lacunae, and even the endothelial lining may be absent so that blood bathes the cells of certain tissues. In mammals, this occurs in the spleen and placenta; in lower vertebrates blood lacunae are found in additional regions. Blood sinus are most prominent in the most primitive vertebrates, the cyclostomes. Large blood spaces along the path of circulating blood cause an abrupt fall in blood pressure wherever they occur. Blood is returned to the heart by accessory hearts and specialized pumps.

Nervous Control of Cardiovascular Systems

Of the types of circulatory systems discussed so far, only those of tunicates appear to lack nervous control. Although the cyclostome heart itself appears to be without innervation, the accessory hearts are, at least in part, under nervous control. Nervous control of cardiovascular systems (1) affects the diameter of blood vessels by altering the tonus* of their musculature and (2) alters the frequency and amplitude of the contractions of the heart and accessory hearts.

In pulsating blood vessels, accessory hearts, and main hearts, the nervous control may be direct or indirect. If control is *direct*, the pulsations are initiated by the action of nerve cells, and the rhythm of the contractions is dominated by the rhythm of the periodic activity of the nerve cells. The nerve cells are usually situated in a compact structure, known as a *heart ganglion*, or cardiac ganglion.

---

*The term refers to a state of contraction that is maintained by repetitive activation through nerve impulses.

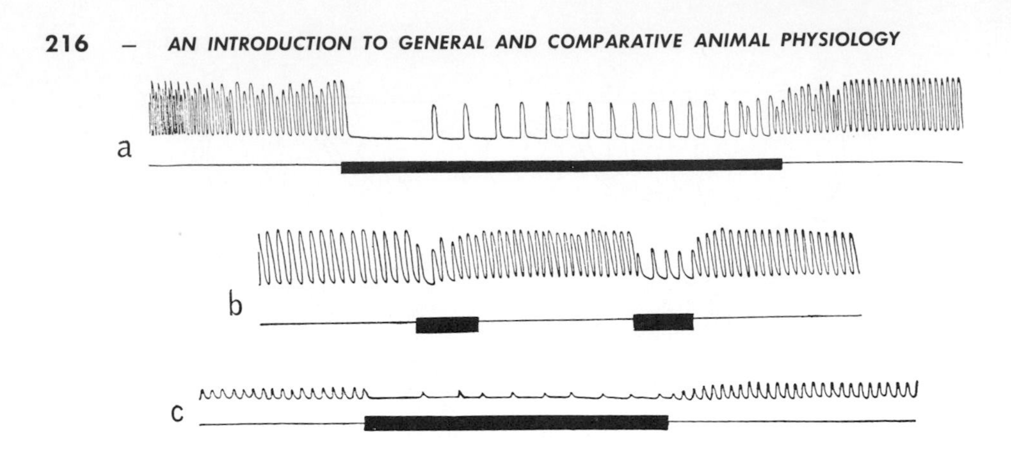

Figure 10–23. Action of inhibitory nerves on the heartbeat of *Limulus polyphemus*. **a**, record from the anterior end of the heart on stimulation of the brain, the hemal nerves being intact. Incomplete inhibition (weak interrupted current). **b**, reflex inhibition of the heart by stimulating the ambulacral nerves with a weak interrupted current. **c**, record from the sixth segment of the heart; inhibition by stimulation of the inhibitory nerves in the pericardium. (From Carlson, A. J.: The nature of cardiac inhibition with special reference to the heart of Limulus. Amer. J. Physiol. *13*:217–240, 1905.)

The ganglion in turn is controlled by nerves emerging from the central nervous system. This latter control consists of a regulation of the frequency and duration (or intensity) of the activity periods of the heart ganglion.

Pulsating organs in which the pulsations are initiated by nerve impulses are referred to as *neurogenic* organs. The best known examples are the hearts of decapod crustaceans, Xiphosura (*Limulus*), and scorpions (see Figs. 10–23, 10–24, 10–25, and 10–26). Ganglion cells have also been found in the hearts of many molluscan species and annelids, but it is uncertain what role these play.

Other pulsating organs are *controlled indirectly* by nerves emerging from the central nervous system that can change the frequency and amplitude of the pulsations. Indirect control, as a rule, does not initiate pulsations. Pulsations of such indirectly controlled organs arise from so-called *pacemaker activity*

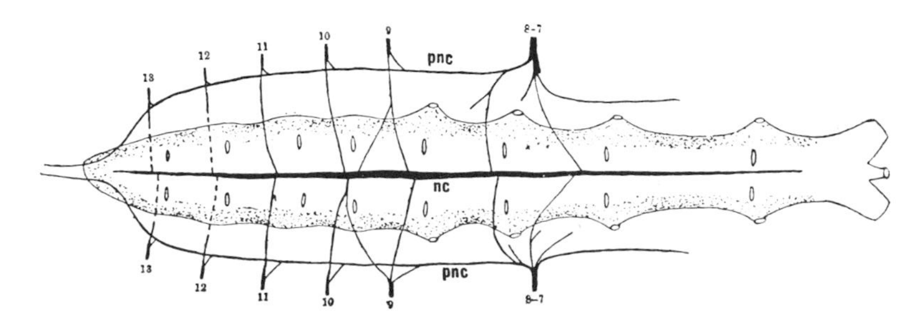

Figure 10–24. Heart of *Limulus*, dorsal view. *nc*, dorsomedian nerve cord. *pnc*, pericardial nerves; *7–8*, cardiac branch from the last two hemal nerves from the brain; *9–13*, cardiac branches from the hemal nerves of the abdominal ganglia. *7–8*, contain inhibitory fibers; *9–11*, augmentor fibers. (From Carlson, A. J.: The nature of cardiac inhibition with special reference to the heart of Limulus. Amer. J. Physiol. *13*:217–240, 1905.)

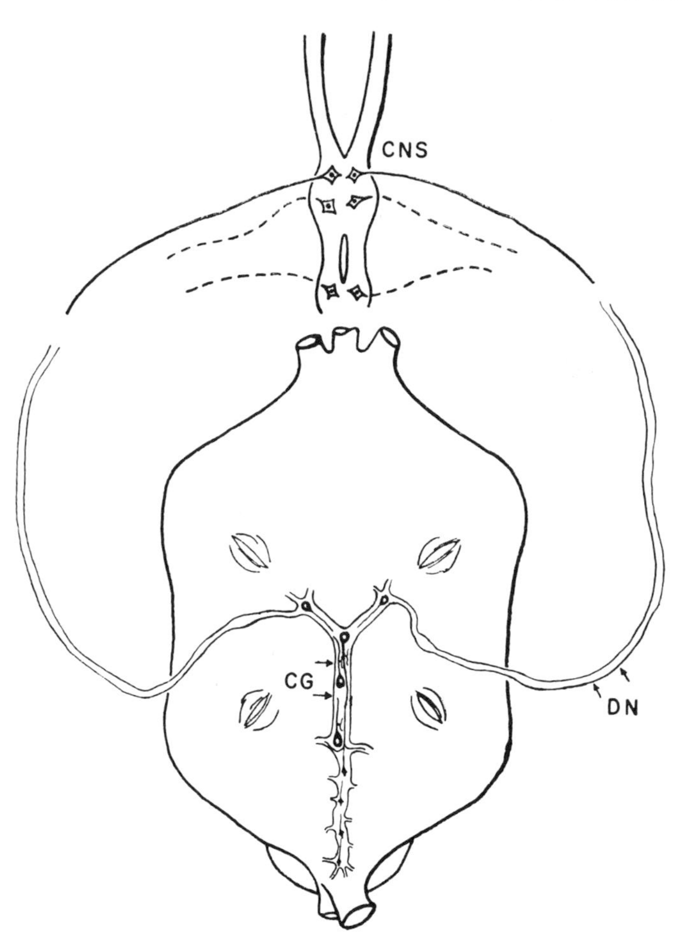

Figure 10–25. Diagram of the lobster heart (*Homarus americanus*) with its heart ganglion (*CG*) and the regulatory nerve supply. The cardiac ganglion contains nine nerve cells: four small ones, called pacemaker cells, and five large ones, called follower cells. They are the motor nerve cells that cause the heart muscle to contract. All nine cells generate coordinated bursts of nerve impulses which cause a brief tetanic contraction of the heart muscle. Two accelerator nerve fibers and one inhibitory nerve fiber leave on each side of the central nervous system (*CNS*) and join the dorsal nerve (*DN*) that enters the heart. Their connections with the ganglion cells are shown in Figure 10–26. (From Maynard, D. M.: Cardiac inhibition in decapod Crustacea. *In* Nervous Inhibition. E. Florey, ed. Pergamon Press, Oxford, 1961.)

within the organs themselves. As they are understood today, pacemakers are modified muscle cells, usually situated within limited areas of the pulsating organs. These cells undergo periodic "self-excitation" and can pass on this excitation (impulse to contract) to the other muscle cells of the organ.

Pulsating organs with "muscular" pacemakers are called *myogenic* organs. Typical examples are vertebrate and tunicate hearts. The hearts of lamellibranch and gastropod molluscs are generally considered to be myogenic, but the unresolved function of the nerve cells which have been observed in the heart wall (myocardium, notably that of the atria) makes this uncertain. The hearts of insects are most likely myogenic.

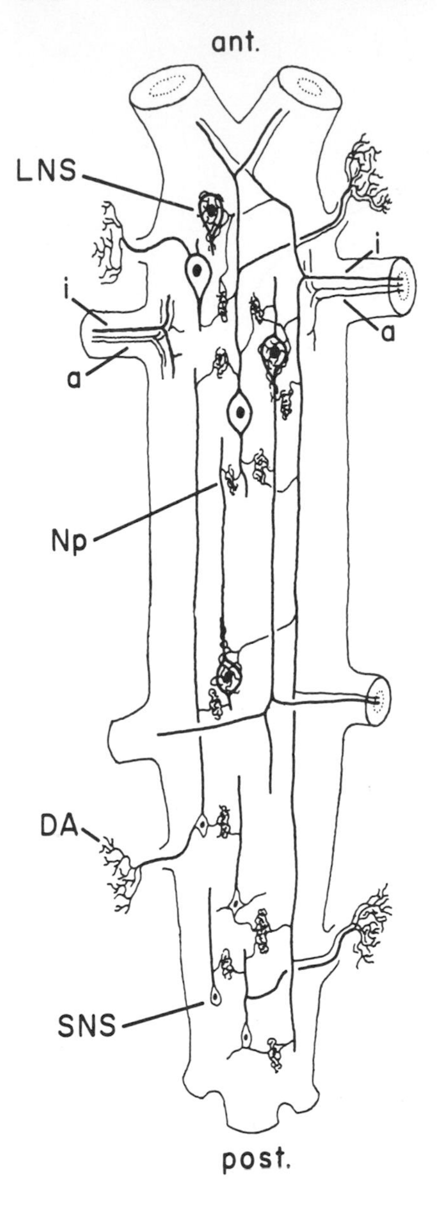

Figure 10–26. Diagram of cardiac ganglion of the lobster (*Panulirus*). Whereas the corresponding ganglion of *Homarus* is Y-shaped (Fig. 10–25), this one is unbranched, 1 to 2 cm long. The width is exaggerated in this diagram to facilitate the presentation of the interconnections. Even so, only a fraction of the cell processes are shown. The regulatory nerve fibers are as in Figure 10–25. *LNS*, large neuron soma: two large cells send axons anteriorly, three send axons posteriorly, all have dendritic arborizations (*DA*), pericellular inhibitor networks, and collaterals to neuropiles (*Np*). *SNS*, small neuron soma: all small cell axons go anteriorly; pericellular inhibitor networks are absent, but dendritic arborizations and neuropiles are universal. The inhibitor fiber, *i*, and two accelerator fibers, *a*, enter on each side through the dorsal nerve. The inhibitor fiber branches terminate on: DA, LNS, and Np. Branches also go out into the cardiac muscle and may have terminations in the muscle itself. (From Maynard, D. M.: Cardiac inhibition in decapod Crustacea. *In* Nervous Inhibition. E. Florey, ed. Pergamon Press, Oxford, 1961.)

Figure 10–27 illustrates the two major types of nervous control. Two nerves are shown to emerge from the central nervous system: one causes acceleration and augmentation, the other, a slowing and weakening of the pulsations. In neurogenic organs, the heart ganglion (and its activity) is affected; in myogenic organs, both pacemaker and normal muscle cells are affected. Although this pattern of *double innervation* is typical, it is by no means universal. In several cases, only the inhibitory nerve is present (elasmobranch fishes, cladoceran Crustacea); in others, only the accelerator nerve has been found (certain lamellibranchs). Literally nothing is known about the nervous regulation of the heartbeat in the so-called minor phyla.

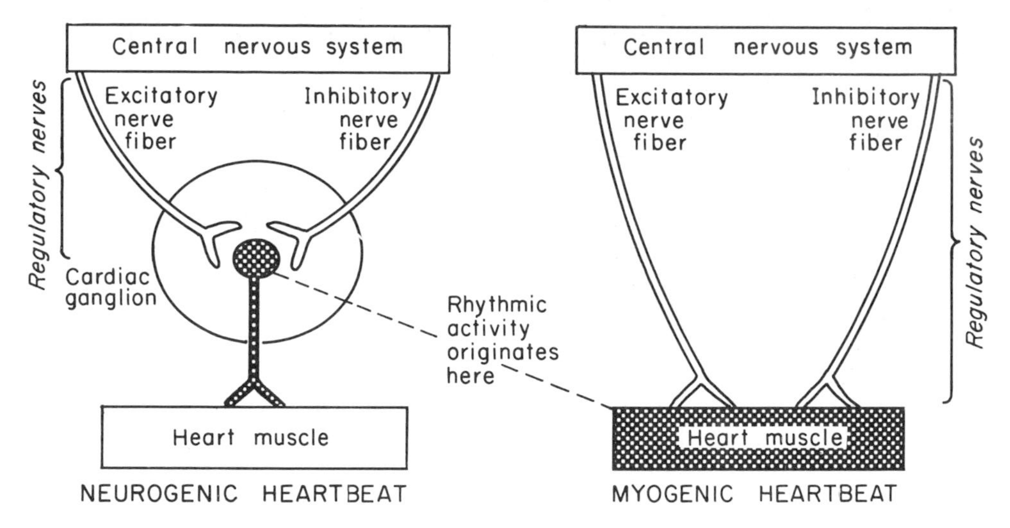

Figure 10–27. Conceptual diagram to explain the difference between a neurogenic and a myogenic heart and its regulatory nerve supply.

The classic papers on the nervous regulation of the heartbeat of numerous species of several invertebrate phyla were presented by Carlson in the American Journal of Physiology from 1904 to 1908. A few of his morphological and physiological observations are reproduced in Figures 10–28 and 10–29. More recent literature is reviewed by Krijgsman (1952 to 1956). Cardiac physiology of the Crustacea has been treated comprehensively by Maynard (1960) in The Physiology of Crustacea edited by Waterman.

The role of the central nervous system in the control of neurogenic as well as myogenic hearts remains to be studied. It is only in regard to mammals that we have considerable knowledge of reflex control of the heart rate. Even less is known about effects of the nerves that supply blood vessels and accessory hearts—in most cases, we do not know whether such innervation even exists. Knowledge of vascular reflexes of mammals, however, is extensive.

The two types of reflexes in mammals are: *intrinsic reflexes*, originating in excitation of mechanoreceptors or chemoreceptors located within the walls of certain parts of the cardiovascular system, and *extrinsic reflexes*, originating in the excitation of receptors located outside the circulatory system. Both types of reflexes affect the frequency and amplitude of the heartbeat as well as the muscle tone (state of active tension) of blood vessels. Since the reflexes are eminently complex, refer to comprehensive reviews, such as those of Heymans and Neil (1958) and Bard (1961) for an adequate description. These reflexes are of paramount importance in regulating blood flow according to a variety of situations, such as increased or decreased oxygen supply, increased acidity (or CO_2 tension) of blood, abnormal blood pressure, or muscular exercise.

The study of the reflex control of cardiovascular systems of animals (other than mammals) is a vast and challenging field in which many a physiologist could earn his laurels.

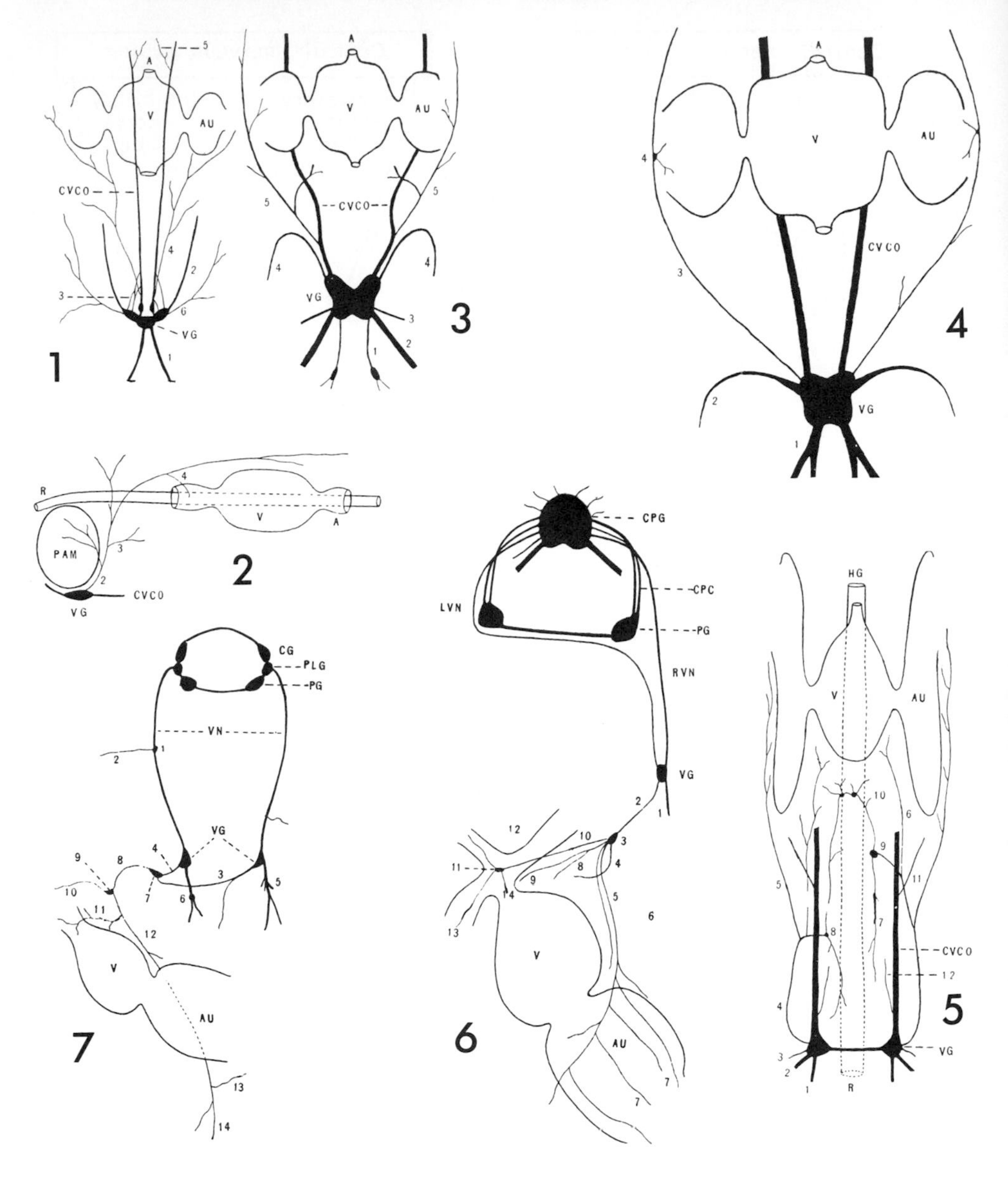

Figure 10–28. Diagrammatic representation of heart innervation of a number of molluscs.

1, *Mya arenaria*, ventral view. *1*, nerve to mantle and siphon; *2*, branchial nerve; *3*, nerve plexus on ventral surface of kidney; *4*, nerves to kidney and heart; *5*, nerves from cerebrovisceral commissure to reproductive organs; *6*, nerves to kidney.

2, *Mya arenaria*, lateral view. *1*, nerve to mantle and siphon; *2*, nerve to posterior adductor muscle, dorsal body wall, and pericardium; *3*, branch to kidney; *4*, branch to posterior aorta and hindgut.

3, *Tapes staminea*, ventral view. *1*, posterior mantle nerves; *2*, siphonal nerves; *3*, nerves to posterior adductor muscle; *4*, nerve to osphradium and gill; *5*, renocardiac nerves.

4, *Platydon cancellatus*, ventral view. *1*, nerves to siphon and mantle; *2*, nerves to osphradium and gill; *3*, nerves to renal organ and heart; *4*, ganglia at base of auricles.

5, *Mytilus californianus*, dorsal view. *1*, posterior mantle nerve; *2*, branchial nerve; *3*, nerve to posterior adductor muscle; *4*, nerves to dorsal body wall and pericardium; *5*, nerves to base of

Legend continued on opposite page

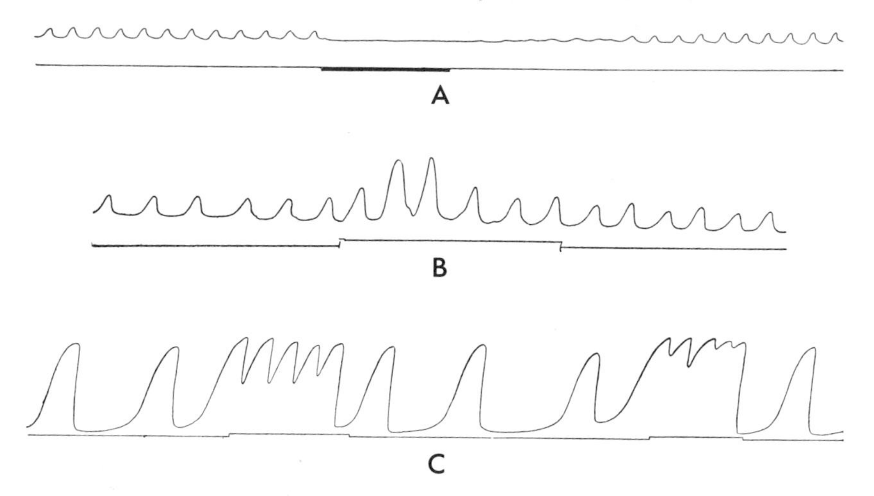

Figure 10–29. Examples of mechanical records of heartbeats from a variety of molluscs, showing the effects of stimulation of the cardioregulator nerves. **A**, tracing from the ventricle of the clam, *Tapes*, showing inhibition resulting from electrical stimulation (heavy line of lower trace) of the visceral ganglion. **B**, tracing from the ventricle of a limpet, *Lucapina*, showing augmentation upon stimulation of the pleurovisceral nerves. **C**, tracing from the ventricle of *Aplysia* showing augmentation upon stimulation of the pleurovisceral commissures. (From Carlson, A. J.: Comparative physiology of the invertebrate heart. II. The function of the cardiac nerves in molluscs. Amer. J. Physiol. *13*:396–426, 1905.)

Figure 10–28. *Continued.*
auricle; 6, nerves to body wall and pericardium; 7, nerves passing posteriorly in dorsal body wall; 8, 9, 10, ganglia on nerves 4; 11, nerves from cerebrovisceral commissure to kidneys; 12, nerves from cerebrovisceral commissures to adductor muscles of foot and byssus.

6, *Pleurobranchia californica*, dorsal view. *1*, nerve to osphradium and gill; *2*, nerve to viscera; *3*, accessory visceral ganglion; *4*, genital nerve; *5*, nerve to pericardium and auricle; *6* and *8*, branches to pericardium; *7*, nerves in walls of auricle; *9*, branch to pericardium and aortic sinus; *10*, branch to aortic sinus; *11*, ganglion on aortic sinus; *12*, branch to lateral artery; *13*, branch to posterior artery; *14*, branch to aortic sinus, probably entering the ventricle.

7, *Bulla globosa*, dorsal view. *1*, ganglia on left visceral nerve; *2*, nerve to dorsum of neck; *3*, commissure between the right and the accessory visceral ganglia; *4*, commissure between the left and the accessory visceral ganglia; *5*, nerve to osphradium, gill, and roof of gill chamber; *6*, nerve to inferior pallium and dorsum; *7*, accessory visceral ganglion; *8*, nerve to viscera; *9*, ganglion on visceral nerve; *10*, genital nerve; *11*, branch to aortic sinus and aorta; *12*, nerve to pericardium, kidney, and auricle; *13*, branch to auricle; *14*, branch to kidney.

A, anterior artery; *AU*, auricle; *CG*, cerebral ganglion; *CPC*, cerebropedal commissure; *CPG*, cerebropleural ganglion; *CVCO*, cerebrovisceral commissure; *HG*, hindgut; *LVN*, left visceral nerve; *PAM*, posterior adductor muscle; *PG*, pedal ganglion; *PLG*, pleural ganglion; *R*, rectum; *RVN*, right visceral nerve; *V*, ventricle; *VG*, visceral ganglion; *VN*, visceral nerve.

Hormonal Control of Cardiovascular Systems

In most animals, heartbeat or *vasomotor tone* (amount of active tension of the muscular wall of blood vessels) may well be controlled by hormones. Our knowledge, however, is restricted. Where such hormones have been identified (vertebrates, molluscs, arthropods), they invariably accelerate the heartbeat, and have an orthodiphenol structure (vertebrates, insects, and annelids) (Cameron, 1953; Kopenec, 1949; Prosser and Zimmerman, 1943). However, even though the hormone (adrenaline or a close relative) is found in the respective organisms, its role in the regulation of the cardiovascular system has not been established—except in mammals.

Adrenaline, noradrenaline, and 5-hydroxytryptamine (an indole alkylamine) cause marked acceleration of the heartbeat in molluscan and decapod crustacean species (e.g., Welsh, 1957). However, whether these substances *normally* act as hormones is unknown. A compound that acts like 5-hydroxytryptamine, but is not identical with it (though possibly related to it), has been extracted from the so-called *pericardial organs* of decapod Crustacea. These organs, which consist of a mass of neurosecretory nerve endings, are assumed to release a hormone into the blood stream that might be involved in the regulation of the heartbeat (Alexandrowicz and Carlisle, 1953). In the molluscs, particularly lammellibranchs, there is suggestive evidence that 5-hydroxytryptamine is released by the cardio-accelerator nerves. In that case, it acts not as a hormone, but as a transmitter substance (see Chap. 20).

The other compound that is involved in the control of vascular tone and heartbeat is *acetylcholine*. This compound is released as a transmitter substance from parasympathetic nerve fibers of vertebrates, and from cardio-inhibitory fibers of many lamellibranch molluscs. Although it has pronounced excitatory effects on the hearts of decapod crustaceans and of annelids (Welsh, 1942; Prosser and Zimmerman, 1943), its role as a transmitter substance of cardio-accelerator nerves is, at best, uncertain. In "lower" Crustacea, acetylcholine has no effect on the heart or causes inhibition (*Daphnia*). Inhibition by acetylcholine has also been observed in scorpions.

Properties and Functions of Blood

The circulatory system is often called the *distributing system*. This descriptive name is indicative of our notion about the chief function of blood: to distribute and transport substances, such as respiratory gases, nutrients, and excretory products as well as hormones.

Blood contains cells, inorganic ions, organic ions and molecules, and proteins. These constituents are maintained in rather constant concentrations. In most animals, the relative concentrations of inorganic ions are similar to those found in sea water, except that sulfate and magnesium ions are often present in lower concentration than in sea water. The inorganic composition of blood is similar to that of the other body fluid compartments of the same animal. A conspicuous exception is the herbivorous insects, many species of which have almost no sodium in their blood, but carry exceptionally large quantities of potassium and magnesium.

The inorganic compositions of a variety of bloods are given in Table 5–7. From recent studies on moths, it is evident that the extracellular fluid of the nervous system of these animals contains a proportion of sodium and potassium that corresponds to that customarily found in the body fluids of other animals. This fluid is separated from blood by a thick sheath of connective tissue and by a layer of glia cells. If blood is allowed to enter the nervous system (after the sheath has been cut or removed), the nerve cells cease to function (Hoyle, 1953; Thornton, 1964).

Blood contains proteins in colloidal solution in concentrations up to 10 per cent (weight per volume). The concentrations are fairly constant in each animal species. This protein provides the colloid osmotic pressure that is so important for the mechanism of fluid exchange between blood and tissue fluid where the two are separated by an endothelium (see the discussion of the Starling hypothesis in Chap. 5).

Only one kind of protein is found in the blood of cephalopods: *hemocyanin*. In most other animal groups, more than one protein is present. These proteins and conjugated proteins have several functions: They (1) serve in gas transport, (2) act as buffers (maintain constant blood pH), (3) bind (and therefore hold in reserve) inorganic cations (see alkali reserve, p. 176), (4) bind and transport hormones, (5) give rise to colloid osmotic pressure, (6) are the basis of blood coagulation, and (7) act as antibodies in immune reactions (the latter phenomenon occurs in vertebrates only).

Proteins, or conjugated proteins, serving in gas transport (O_2 and CO_2) are colored. Only four different kinds are known: *hemoglobin* (red), *hemerythrin* (purple), *chlorocruorin* (green), and *hemocyanin* (blue). Their chemistry and function as well as their distribution in the animal kingdom are discussed in Chapters 9 and 14. Whereas hemocyanin and chlorocruorin are found only in colloidal solution, hemerythrin is found only in blood cells, and hemoglobin may occur in colloidal solution (annelids, certain insect larvae, cladocerans, and gastropods), or in blood cells (vertebrates, nemerteans). These gas-carrying pigments are known as respiratory pigments, or oxygen-carrying pigments.

Cells that contain hemoglobin are known as *erythrocytes*. Their main function appears to be gas transport. The same is true for the cells that carry hemerythrin. Wherever such pigment-containing cells occur, the pigment is confined to them while the surrounding blood fluid (*plasma*) is colorless. In these cases, the pigment-containing cells are most numerous and may comprise up to 50 per cent of the total blood volume. The relative volume of blood cells is known as the *hematocrit*.

The other types of blood cells (nonpigmented) are variously known as hemocytes, lymphocytes, amebocytes, phagocytes, or leukocytes. Their functions range from the transport of nutrients and enzymes (the latter has been described only in holothurians) to the elimination of excretory products and cell fragments. In the vertebrates, such blood cells are involved in immune responses. One of the important functions of arthropod blood cells is initiation of blood clotting. This is also true for blood cells of other invertebrate groups. Blood does not clot in the molluscs and annelids.

For detailed discussions of blood clotting and blood cell functions, refer to the comprehensive review of Grégoire (1962).

REFERENCES

Alexandrowicz, J. S. (1932) The innervation of the heart of Crustacea. I. Decapoda. Quart. J. Micr. Sci. *75*:181–249.
Alexandrowicz, J. S. (1934) The innervation of the heart of Crustacea. II. Stomatopoda. Quart. J. Micr. Sci. *76*:511–548.
Alexandrowicz, J. S. (1952) Innervation of the heart of *Ligia oceanica*. J. Mar. Biol. Assn. U. K. *31*:85–96.
Alexandrowicz, J. S. (1953) Nervous organs in the pericardial cavity of the decapod Crustacea. J. Mar. Biol. Assn. U. K. *31*:563–580.
Alexandrowicz, J. S. (1954) Innervation of an amphipod heart. J. Mar. Biol. Assn. U. K. *33*:709–719.
Alexandrowicz, J. S., and D. B. Carlisle (1953) Some experiments on the function of the pericardial organs in Crustacea. J. Mar. Biol. Assn. U. K. *32*:175–192.
Bard, P. (1961a) Medical physiology, 11th Ed. Part I, Circulation, pp. 15–297. The C. V. Mosby Co., St. Louis.
Bard, P. (1961b) Regulation of the systemic circulation. *In* Medical Physiology, 11th Ed. pp. 191–221. (P. Bard, ed.) The C. V. Mosby Co., St. Louis.
Baumann, J. H. (1921) Das Gefässystem von *Astacus fluviatilis (Potamobius astacus* L.). Z. wiss. Zool. *118*:246–312.
Beklemischew, W. N. (1960) Grundlagen der vergleichenden Anatomie der Wirbellosen. 2 vols. (German Translation from the Russian.) VEB Deutscher Verlag der Wissenschaften, Berlin.
Bottazzi, F. (1925) Das Blut (haemolymphe) der wirbellosen Tiere. A. Coelenterata; B. Echinodermata; C. Vermes (Wuermer). *In* Handbuch der vergleichenden Physiologie, Vol. 1, pp. 461–592. (H. Winterstein, ed.) G. Fischer Verlag, Jena.
Bronn, H. G., ed. (1880–) Klassen und Ordnungen des Tierreichs. Numerous volumes, not completed. Akademische Verlagsgesellschaft, Leipzig.
von Bruecke, E. T. (1925) Die Bewegung der Körpersäfte. *In* Handbuch der vergleichenden Physiologie, Vol. 1, part 1, pp. 827–1110. (H. Winterstein, ed.). G. Fischer Verlag, Jena.
Burger, J. W., and Smythe, C. M. (1953) The general form of circulation in the lobster, *Homarus*. J. Cell. Comp. Physiol. *42*:369–383.
Burton, A. C. (1960) Hemodynamics and the physics of the circulation. *In* Medical Physiology and Biophysics, Chap. 4, pp. 643–666. (T. C. Ruch and J. F. Fulton, eds.) W. B. Saunders Co., Philadelphia.
Burton, A. C. (1962) Physical principles of circulatory phenomena: the physical equilibria of the heart and blood vessels. *In* Handbook of Physiology, Sec. 2, Vol. I, pp. 85–105. (W. F. Hamilton and P. Dow, eds.) The Williams & Wilkins Co., Baltimore.
Cameron, M. L. (1953) Secretion of an orthodiphenol in the corpus cardiacum of the insect. Nature *172*:349–350.
Dubuisson, M. (1928a) Recherches sur la circulation du sang chez les crustacés. 1. Amphipodes. Circulation chez les gammariens; synchronisme des mouvements respiratoires et des pulsations cardiaques. Arch. Zool. Exp. et Gen. *67*:93–104.
Dubuisson, M. (1928b) Recherches sur la circulation du sang chez les crustacés. 2. Pressions sanguines chez les décapodes brachyoures. Arch. Biol. (Liège) *38*:9–21.
Grassé, P., ed (1948–) Traitée de Zoologie. 17 volumes, not completed. Masson et Cie, Paris.
Green, H. D. (1944) Circulation: physical principles. *In* Medical Physics, Vol. 1, pp. 208–232. (O. Glasser, ed.) Year Book Publishers, Chicago.
Grégoire, C. (1962) Blood coagulation. *In* Comparative Biochemistry, Vol. 4, pp. 435–482. (M. Florkin and H. S. Mason, eds.) Academic Press, New York.
Hamilton, W. F. (1953) The physiology of the cardiac output. Circulation *8*:527–543.
Hamilton, W. F. (1962) Measurement of cardiac output. *In* Handbook of Physiology, Sec. 2, Vol. I, pp. 551–583. (W. F. Hamilton and P. Dow, eds.) The Williams & Wilkins Co., Baltimore.
Hardung, V. (1962) Propagation of pulse waves in visco-elastic tubings. *In* Handbook of Physiology, Sec. 2, Vol. I, pp. 107–135. (W. F. Hamilton and P. Dow, eds.) The Williams & Wilkins Co., Baltimore.
Heymans, C., and E. Neil (1958) Reflexogenic Areas of the Cardio-vascular system. Little, Brown and Co., Boston.
Hoyle, G. (1953) Potassium ions and insect nerve muscle. J. Exp. Biol. *30*:121–135.
Hyman, L. H. (1940–1959) The Invertebrates. 5 vols. McGraw-Hill Book Co., New York.
Johansen, K., and A. W. Martin (1962) Circulation in the cephalopod, *Octopus dofleini*. Comp. Biochem. Physiol. *5*:161–176.
Kaestner, A. (1954–1963) Lehrbuch der speciellen Zoologie. G. Fischer Verlag, Stuttgart.
Kopenec, A. (1949) Farbwechsel der Larve von *Corethra plumicornis*. Z. vergl. Physiol. *31*:490–505.

Kriebel, M. E. (1963) Effect of blood pressure on the isolated tunicate heart. Biol. Bull. *125*:358.
Krijgsman, B. J. (1952) Contractile and pacemaker mechanisms of the heart of arthropods. Biol. Rev. *27*:320–346.
Krijgsman, B. J. (1952) Contractile and pacemaker mechanisms of the heart of arthropods. Biol. Rev. *27*:320–346.
Krijgsman, B. J. (1956) Contractile and pacemaker mechanism of the heart of tunicates. Biol. Rev. *31*:288–312.
Krijgsman, B. J., and G. A. Divaris (1955) Contractile and pacemaker mechanisms of the heart of molluscs. Biol. Rev. *30*:1–39.
Kükenthal, W. (T. Krumbach, ed.) (1923–) Handbuch der Zoologie. Many volumes, not complete. W. De Gruyter & Co., Berlin.
Lawson, H. C. (1962) The volume of blood—a critical examination of methods for its measurement. *In* Handbook of Physiology, Sec. 2, Vol. I, pp. 23–49. (W. F. Hamilton and P. Dow, eds.) The Williams & Wilkins Co., Baltimore.
Martin, A. W., and K. Johansen (1965) Adaptations of the circulation in invertebrate animals. *In* Handbook of Physiology, Sec. 2, Vol. III, pp. 2545–2581. (W. F. Hamilton and P. Dow, eds.) The Williams & Wilkins Co., Baltimore.
Maynard, D. M. (1953) Activity in a crustacean ganglion. I. Cardio-inhibition and acceleration in *Panulirus argus*. Biol. Bull. *104*:156–170.
Maynard, D. M. (1960) Circulation and heart function. *In* The *Physiology of Crustacea*, Vol. 1, pp. 161–258. (T. H. Waterman, ed.) Academic Press, New York.
Nicol, J. A. C. (1960) The Biology of Marine Animals. Chap. 3: Body fluids and circulation, pp. 84–134. Interscience Publishers, New York.
Patterson, S. W., H. Piper, and E. H. Starling (1914) The regulation of the heart beat. J. Physiol. *48*:465–513.
Prosser, C. L. (1940) Acetylcholine and nervous inhibition in the heart of *Venus mercenaria*. Biol. Bull. *78*:92–102.
Prosser, C. L. (1942) An analysis of the action of acetylcholine on hearts, particularly in arthropods. Biol. Bull. *83*:145–164.
Prosser, C. L. (1961) Circulation of body fluids. *In* Comparative Animal Physiology, 2nd Ed., pp. 386–416. (C. L. Prosser and F. A. Brown, Jr., eds.) W. B. Saunders Co., Philadelphia.
Prosser, C. L., and G. L. Zimmerman (1943) The effects of drugs on the hearts of Arenicola and *Lumbricus*. Physiol. Zool. *16*:77–83.
Quagliariello, G. (1925) Das Blut der wirbellosen Tiere. D. Mollusken. *In* Handbuch der vergleichenden Physiologie, Vol. 1, part 1, pp. 597–668. (H. Winterstein, ed.) G. Fischer Verlag, Jena.
Rangnekar, P. V. (1954) A comparative study of the blood volume in the crustaceans *Scylla serrata*, *Panulirus polyphagus* and *Paratelpheusa guerini*. J. Anim. Morphol. Physiol. *1*:62–64.
Rushmer, R. F. (1961) Cardiovascular Dynamics, 2nd Ed. W. B. Saunders Co., Philadelphia.
Rushmer, R. F. (1962) Effects of nerve stimulation and hormones on the heart; the role of the heart in general circulatory regulation. *In* Handbook of Physiology, Sec. 2, Vol. I, pp. 533–549. (W. F. Hamilton and P. Dow, eds.) The Williams & Wilkins Co., Baltimore.
Schulz, F. N. (1925) Das Blut der wirbellosen Tiere. E, Crustaceen; F, Tracheaten; G, Tunicaten (Manteltiere). *In* Handbuch der vergleichenden Physiologie, Vol. 1, Part 1, pp. 669–826. (H. Winterstein, ed.) G. Fischer Verlag, Jena.
Schwartzkopff, J. (1953) Die Kreislaufzeit einiger Crustaceen. Naturwissenschaften *40*:585–586.
von Skramlik, E. (1938) Ueber den Kreislauf bei den niedersten Chordaten. Ergebn. Biol. *15*: 166–308.
von Skramlik, E. (1941) Ueber den Kreislauf bei den Weichtieren. Ergebn. Biol. *18*:88–286.
Smith, R. I. (1947) The action of electrical stimulation and of certain drugs on cardiac nerves of the crab, *Cancer irroratus*. Biol. Bull. *93*:72–88.
Spencer, M. P., and F. C. Greiss (1962) Dynamics of ventricular ejection. Circ. Res. *10*:274–279.
Tait, J., and Gunn, J. D. (1918) The blood of *Astacus fluviatilis*: A study in crustacean blood, with special reference to coagulation and phagocytosis. Quart. J. Exp. Physiol. *17*:35–80.
Thornton, J. W. (1964) The relationship of the low sodium, herbivorous diet of sphingidae to the ionic composition of their haemolymph and the activity and histology of their nervous system. Thesis, University of Washington, Seattle.
Welsh, J. H. (1939) Chemical mediation in crustaceans. II. The action of acetylcholine and adrenalin on the isolated heart of *Panulirus argus*. Physiol. Zool. *12*:231–237.
Welsh, J. H. (1942) Chemical mediation in crustaceans. IV. The action of acetylcholine on isolated hearts of *Homarus* and *Carcinides*. J. Cell. Comp. Physiol. *19*:271–279.

Welsh, J. H. (1957) Serotonin as a possible neurohumoral agent: evidence obtained in lower animals. Ann. N.Y. Acad. Sci. *66*:618–630.

Wiersma, C. A. G., and E. Novitski (1942) The mechanism of the nervous regulation of the crayfish heart. J. Exp. Biol. *19*:255–265.

Zierler, K. L. (1962) Circulation times and the theory of indicator-dilution methods for determining blood flow and volume. *In* Handbook of Physiology, Sec. 2, Vol. I, pp. 585–616. (W. F. Hamilton and P. Dow, eds.) The Williams & Wilkins Co., Baltimore.

11 THE DIGESTIVE SYSTEM

Animals are *heterotrophic*, that is, they depend on organic nutrients as an energy source. An important function of the digestive system is to make organic matter available to the body cells. This is done by (1) mechanical disruption and breakdown of organic matter entering the digestive system, (2) extra- and intracellular enzymatic breakdown of large, complex molecules into small diffusable compounds, and (3) transfer of these diffusible compounds through the membranes of the digestive tract into the body fluids. These are the three stages of *digestion*.

The digestive systems of the higher Metazoa are morphologically similar, consisting of a *gastrointestinal tract*, essentially a tube that traverses the animal from mouth to anus (exception: flatworms) and its associated *digestive glands*. The digestive tract is usually compartmentalized; its chief components are the *esophagus*, *stomach*, and *intestine*. The stomach is often chambered and the intestine may consist of several functionally different segments. The digestive glands are represented by diffuse glandular cells within the wall of the gastrointestinal tract and by compact, separate glands that communicate with the lumen of the gastrointestinal tract. Digestive glands that have a duct opening into the esophagus (or pharynx) near the mouth are called *salivary glands*. Their secretions contain lubricants (mucus), digestive enzymes, and toxins—often only one of these. The other digestive glands or gland cells produce digestive enzymes, mucus, emulsifying agents, and, in certain cases, acid. Usually each is specialized for the production of only one of these; often there is a sequence of differentially specialized glands or gland cells

In many types of digestive system, the epithelial cells of the digestive tract function as phagocytes, even though they do not necessarily migrate to other parts of the body. *Phagocytosis* is the process by which cells engulf particulate matter. The digestion of particulate matter that is digestible food is called *intracellular digestion*. This takes place in fluid-filled *food vacuoles* into which enzymes are secreted. Digestion in the lumen of the digestive system is called *extracellular digestion*. In this case, the molecules resulting from the digestion of complex compounds are passively (diffusion) and actively transported by the epithelial cells (or migrating phagocytes?) from the lumen of the digestive system to the body fluid compartment.

Among the Protozoa, digestion is usually an intracellular process, and many Protozoa (Rhizopoda, some ciliates and flagellates) function as phagocytes. In Porifera (sponges) the free-moving amebocytes (archaeocytes) digest the food particles collected by the flagellate *choanocytes* present in the internal canal system of the organism (Kilian, 1952). Nothing is known about the mechanism by which nutrients are transferred from the amebocytes to the other, nondigesting body cells.

In the coelenterates the entoderm contains glandular cells that secrete protein-digesting enzymes. This has been described for *Metridium* (Bodansky, 1924) and *Hydra* (Beutler, 1926), and is likely to occur also in corals and other coelenterates feeding on animals (Yonge and Nicholls, 1930). Many cells of the coelenterate entoderm are capable of intracellular digestion. In addition, there are wandering phagocytes.

Often we do not know to what extent the digestive enzymes present in the digestive system of higher Metazoa (vertebrates excepted) act intracellularly. However, a vast literature describes the digestive enzymes that can be detected in *extracts* of various portions of the digestive system of numerous species. Of course, we can assume that enzymes produced in distinct digestive glands (hepatopancreas, "liver," midgut glands, and so forth) are actually secreted into the lumen of the digestive gland, and into the lumen of the digestive tract.

The secretions of digestive glands form a *digestive juice*. The juice of salivary glands is known as *saliva*. Analysis of the juice is often difficult because it is usually mixed with food and is often secreted only when food is present in the digestive tract. In only a few species (mammals, reptiles, and cephalopods) has it been possible to elicit secretion of digestive juices (saliva in the case of cephalopods) by electrically stimulating the nerve supply of the digestive glands. In general, however, the nature and function of digestive enzymes are studied by (1) introducing substrates into the digestive tract and observing their fate and (2) extracting portions of the digestive tract or digestive glands and observing the effect of these extracts on various substrates under various conditions of pH and temperature.

All known digestive enzymes belong to the general group of *hydrolases*. The reactions that they catalyze follow the general schema (in which R represents part of a molecule):

$$R - R + H_2O \rightarrow R - OH + H - R$$

These reactions do not liberate significant amounts of energy. In this regard, they differ strikingly from the intracellular reactions that are known collectively as *metabolism* and, more specifically, as *energy metabolism*.

DIGESTIVE ENZYMES

Like other enzymes, the digestive enzymes consist of protein. Owing to their complex protein structure, it is at present impossible, or at least impracticable, to compare one enzyme obtained from one organism with another enzyme obtained from a different species. In fact, enzymes usually are classified not by structure, but by the chemical reactions that they catalyze. Although two enzyme preparations may catalyze the same chemical reaction, they may show a different temperature optimum; one catalyzes the reaction at a faster rate than the other. Even the proper names given to enzymes, such as *pepsin* or *trypsin*, are not specific: the pepsin obtained from the stomach of a salmon, for instance, differs in its reaction kinetics from that of the stomach of a shark.

General Classification

The digestive enzymes are divided into the following classes and categories:

PROTEASES

Proteinases or *Endopeptidases* (break down proteins to polypeptides)
- *Pepsinases* (pH optimum 1.5 to 2.5).
- *Cathepsins* (pH optimum 4 to 6).
- *Tryptases* (*trypsin, chymotrypsin*) (pH optimum in the alkaline range).

Peptidases or *Exopeptidases* (break down polypeptides to peptides and amino acids).
- *Polypeptidases*
- *Tripeptidases*
- *Dipeptidases*

CARBOHYDRASES

Polyases or *Polysaccharidases* (break down high molecular weight carbohydrates, such as starches, glycogen, and cellulose to oligosaccharides, disaccharides, and monosaccharides).
- *Amylases* (split starch into α-maltose molecules).
- *Cellulases* (usually associated with β-glucosidases) break down cellulose to simple sugars.
- *Chitinases* (break down chitin to simple sugars); these enzymes are derived from the flora of the digestive tract and are not produced by animals themselves.

Oligases or *Oligosaccharidases* (break down trisaccharides and disaccharides to simple sugars)
- *α-Glucosidases* (substrate: maltose, saccharose, melecitose, α-glucoside)
- *β-Glucosidases* (cellobiose, gentiobiose, β-glucoside)
- *α-Galactosidases* (melibiose, raffinose, α-galactoside)
- *β-Galactosidases* (lactose, β-galactoside)
- *β-Fructosidases* (saccharose, raffinose, gentianose).

ESTERASES (hydrolyze esters)

Lipases (hydrolyze the long chain esters formed by glycerol with long chain fatty acids)

Esterases proper (hydrolyze short chain, common esters)

These three classes of digestive enzymes occur in all animals, as far as we know. They correspond to the three classes of organic compounds that represent the chief source of nutrition: proteins, carbohydrates, and fats. Although the type of food as well as nutritional requirement varies greatly among different species, the basic types of organic material used as food are the same. Variations affect only the predominance of one class of nutrients over another.

The following is a brief survey of the biochemical and biological aspects of digestive enzyme function in relation to the kind of food utilized.

Proteinases and Peptidases. The proteinases are often referred to as *endopeptidases* because they act on peptide bonds that are situated more centrally along the length of the amino acid chain that constitutes the protein molecules. The peptidases have been given the name *exopeptidases*, because they can act only on peptide bonds that connect the *terminal* amino acids to the main amino acid chain. The general formula of protease action is:

$$R - CO - NH - R + H_2O \xrightarrow[\text{protease}]{} R - COOH + NH_2{-}R$$

Cathepsin and trypsin activities, as well as peptidases, have been detected in various Protozoa (Holter and Lovtrup, 1949; Krijgsman, 1936; Schlottke, 1936; Sawano, 1938). Proteases of the trypsin type occur intracellularly as well as extracellularly in the digestive system of coelenterates (Beutler, 1927; Krijgsman and Talbot, 1953; Smith, 1936; Yonge and Nicholls, 1930). Similar enzymes (trypsins and cathepsins as well as peptidases) are likely to occur in all the higher Metazoa, with the exception of the parasitic Cestoda, which utilize nutrients already digested by the host.

The pepsin enzymes (*pepsinases*) are not known outside of the vertebrates. However, the knowledge of digestive enzymes in animals other than mammals is amazingly limited, considering the ease with which digestive enzymes can be identified. They are identified simply by establishing the kind of protein or peptide they attack and by determining the pH optimum. In some cases, the findings have been misleading: pepsin activity has been described by several authors in several coelenterates; the measured pH of the enterogastric space, however, is always in the alkaline range. Therefore, the pH optima of enzyme preparations may not reflect the biological conditions, and unless the pH optimum of an enzyme is compared with the actual pH of the extra- or intracellular digestive fluids, the usefulness of the data on pH optima is questionable. Only those enzyme-catalyzed reactions can be considered biologically significant that have a pH optimum equal to, or at least near to, the pH of the digestive fluids.

In contrast to the rather universal distribution of trypsin and cathepsin enzymes, the pepsins appear to be restricted to the vertebrates. Acid digestive juices, likewise, occur almost exclusively among vertebrate animals. Among invertebrates, the "stomach" of *Nais* (Oligochaeta) contains an acid fluid.

Carbohydrases. *Starches* are the predominant carbohydrate utilized from plant food; *glycogen* is the chief carbohydrate obtainable from animals. Both are polysaccharides. Starch consists of two kinds of molecules: *amylose*, an unbranched chain molecule composed of hundreds of glucose units, and *amylopectin*, a branched giant molecule, also composed of hundreds, if not thousands, of glucose units. Partial structures of both are shown in Figure 11–1. The structure of glycogen resembles that of amylopectin.

The amylose molecules are arranged in a helix, as shown in Figure 11–2. This explains the well-known "iodine reaction" of starch: the iodine atoms are incorporated, one each, into each turn of the helix. Their electronic structure is thereby influenced to alter their optical behavior and to give starch a blue color. This is not a chemical but a physical reaction.

The enzymes that hydrolyze starch and glycogen are known as *amylases*. They break these polysaccharides down to *maltose* (disaccharide) and, to a limited degree, to glucose. The amylase of mammalian saliva is sometimes called *ptyalin*. All known amylases of animal origin have pH optima between 5.5 and 7.2. An example is shown in Figure 11–3.

Plants contain enormous quantities of another polysaccharide, *cellulose* (Fig. 11–1). Like starch and glycogen, this consists of branched chains of glucose units, but whereas the former are composed of α-glucose units, cellulose is made up of β-glucose molecules. In spite of the abundance of this potential foodstuff, extraordinarily few animals can utilize cellulose directly. The majority depend on enzymes, *cellulases*, produced by *symbiontic bacteria* or *Protozoa*. The extracellular cellulase found in the lumen of the intestine of the snail *Helix* is produced by bacteria (Florkin and Lozet, 1949). A similar situation is found in termites and many beetle larvae (Mansour and Mansour-Bek, 1934). A modification of the schema is found in those cases (beetle larvae) in which the microflora does not produce extracellular cellulase but digests cellulose intracellularly. In this case, the bacteria (or Protozoa) are digested by the animal after they have digested the cellulose from the intestinal lumen (Rössler, 1955; Lasker and Giese, 1956). Many of the herbivorous mammals (ruminants) contain cellulase-producing microorganisms and Protozoa in special compartments of their digestive tract.

The wood-boring pelecypod *Teredo* (shipworm) produces a cellulase in its digestive glands, as does the *silverfish*, *Ctenolepisma*, a primitive arthropod (Greenfield and Lane, 1953; Lasker and Giese, 1956). Excellent documentation for cellulose digestion by a cellulase produced in the digestive tract has been given for the wood-boring isopod, *Limnoria lignorum* (Ray and Julian, 1952). These animals contain no symbionts in their digestive tract.

Cellulase activity occurs in the *crystalline style* (see below) of lamellibranch molluscs. Although the enzyme may well be produced by the cells of the digestive glands, it cannot be concluded, with certainty, that the enzymes are derived from symbiontic spirochaetes (Newell, 1953; Dean, 1958; Stone and Morton, 1958). Cellulases hydrolyze cellulose to cellobiose (Fig. 11–1). A chitin-digesting enzyme, *chitinase*, has been detected in the intestinal tracts of earth-

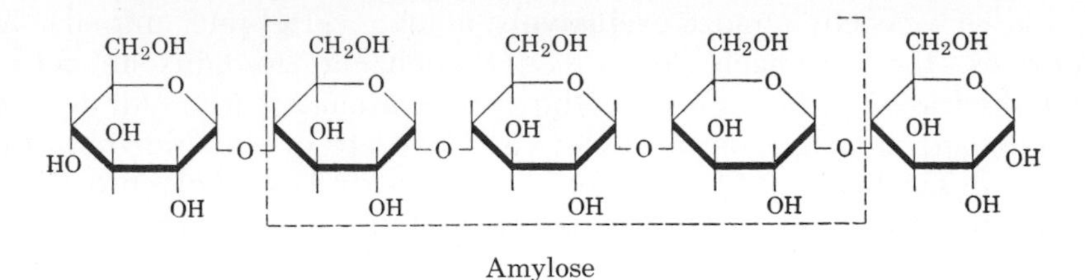

Amylose

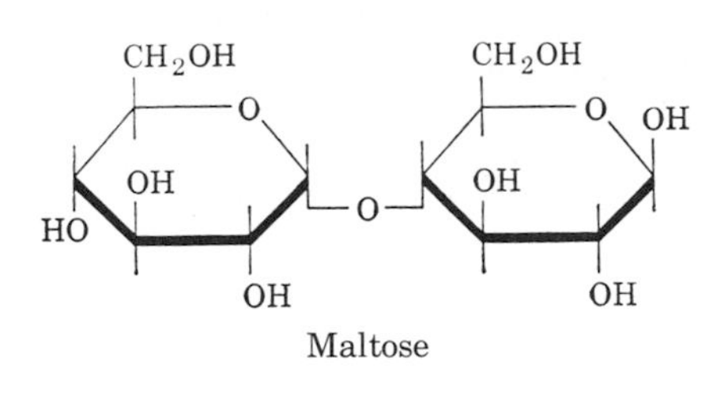

Maltose

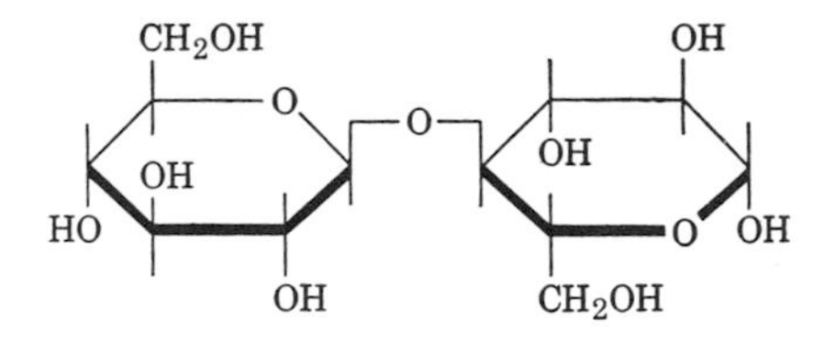

Cellobiose

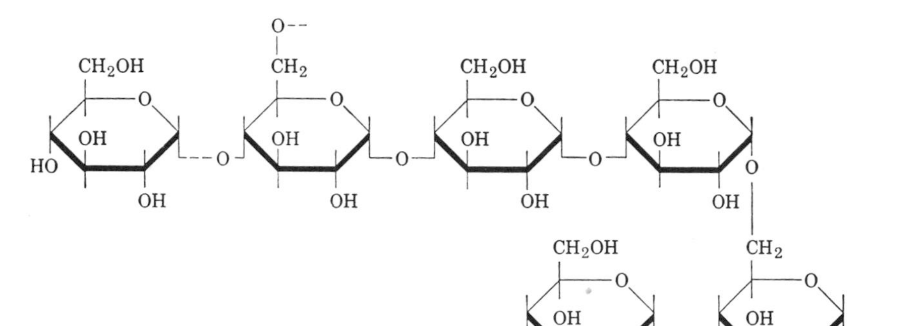

Amylopectin

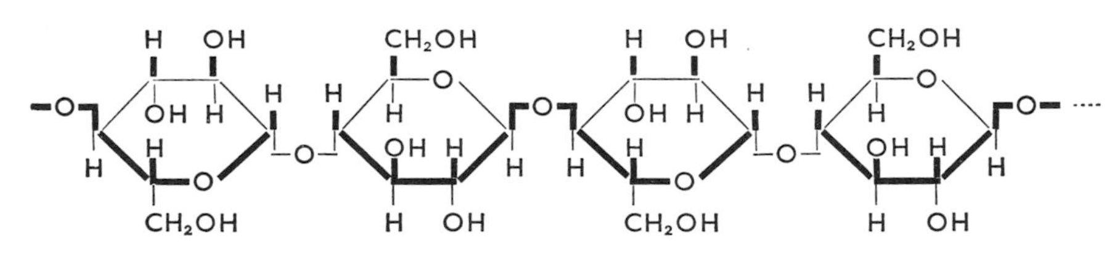

Cellulose

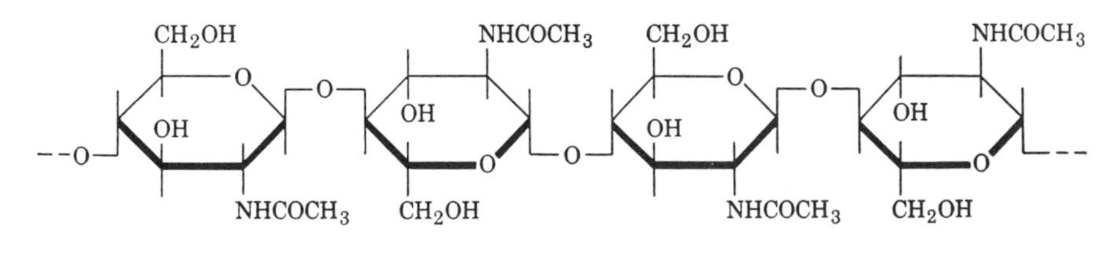

Chitine

Figure 11–1. Structure of important polysaccharides and their elementary units. (From Fruton, J. S., and S. Simmonds: General Biochemistry, 2nd Ed. John Wiley & Sons, New York, 1958; and Harrow, B., and A. Mazur: Textbook of Biochemistry, 8th Ed. W. B. Saunders Co., Philadelphia, 1962.)

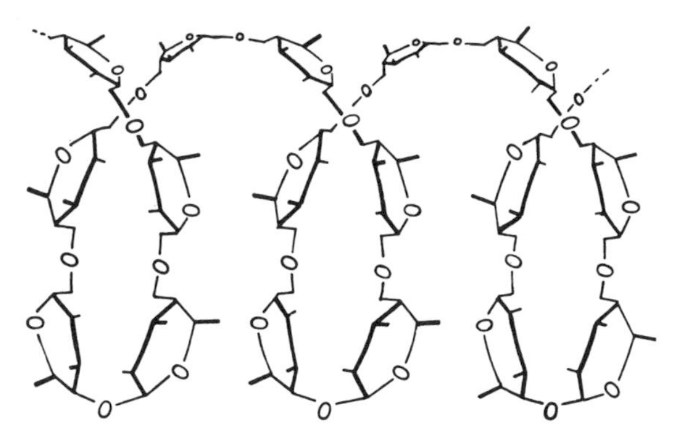

Figure 11–2. Diagrammatic representation of the structure of amylose, showing the helical arrangement of the chain molecule. (From Karlson, P.: Biochemie. Georg Thieme Verlag, Stuttgart, 1962.)

worms (*Lumbricus*), several snails (*Helix, Agriolimax, Limax, Arion*), and in soil amebae (*Hartmannella, Schizopyrenus*). In contrast to the amebae, the earthworm and the snails derive their chitinase from intestinal bacteria (Tracey, 1951, 1955; Jeuniaux, 1950, 1954).

The *oligosaccharidases* may be grouped into five classes of enzymes (Weidenhagen, 1940), as indicated on page 229. The class names do not refer to single, identifiable enzymes, but represent a convenient schema into which oligosaccharides of a large variety of organisms can be fitted. However, recent findings on sugar-digesting enzymes of insects point out that certain oligosaccharidases do not fit into this schema (see Gottschalk, 1950; Evans, 1958).

Esterases and Lipases. The difference between esterases proper and lipases is not always clear-cut, and both types of enzyme may attack the same substrate. In fact, many investigators have employed small molecule esters, such as methyl-butyrate, tributyrin, or triacetin, to detect lipase activity (see Ammon and Jaarma, 1950; Sumner and Myrbäck, 1950). Olive oil is commonly used to test for the presence of lipase.

The pH optima of digestive esterases and lipases can be from pH 5 to 8.

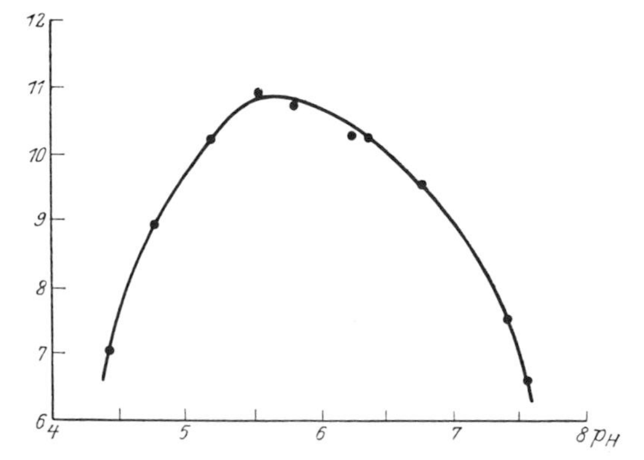

Figure 11–3. Relation of enzyme activity and pH: amylase obtained from stomach juice of the crayfish (*Astacus*) was incubated for 45 minutes with a starch solution adjusted with buffers to different pH values. The enzyme activity is given on the ordinate in relative units. (From Wiersma, C. A. G., and R. van der Veen: Die Kohlehydratverdauung bei Astacus fluviatilis. Z. vergl. Physiol. 7:268–278, 1928.)

GENERAL BIOLOGICAL AND BIOCHEMICAL ASPECTS OF DIGESTIVE ENZYMES

Occurrence

In general, the digestive enzymes are adapted to the food available to the organism, but this is by no means always true. For example, cellulases are found in many animals that live on cellulose-containing food, but many other animals acquire the same food but cannot digest cellulose because they possess no cellulase. Caterpillars that are exclusively herbivorous cannot use cellulose, although this polysaccharide is abundant in their food. The same is true for many vertebrates.

Since all animals are heterotrophic, and therefore depend on plant food (whether obtained directly by ingesting plants or indirectly by ingesting herbivorous animals), the rarity of cellulose-digesting enzymes of animal origin is astonishing. Amylases and proteases, on the other hand, are ubiquitous, as are lipases and esterases.

Cofactors, Proenzymes, Activation

Many digestive enzymes require coenzymes and cofactors, such as inorganic ions. These requirements are not always known. Human salivary amylase requires chloride ions; this is probably true for all amylases. Cathepsins B and C of mammals are activated by cysteine, H_2S, and HCN (hydroxyl group activators). These activators are not necessary for the action on all substrates (Tallan and Buchs, 1947; Tallan, Jones, and Fruton, 1952). Similar requirements for sulfhydryl group activators have been reported for invertebrate cathepsins. Vertebrate lipases are activated by leucyl-glycyl-glycine and by bile salts.

Vertebrate pepsin and trypsin are secreted in an inactive form, called *pepsinogen* and *trypsinogen*, respectively. These are transformed into the active enzymes by the action of special enzymes: pepsin activates pepsinogen, and trypsinogen can be activated by enterokinase and also by trypsin. Where the active enzyme catalyzes the transformation of the inactive to the active enzyme, one speaks of *autocatalysis*.

pH Optimum

Like other enzymes, the digestive enzymes have a definite pH optimum (see Figs. 11–3 and 11–4). But, as mentioned, the pH optimum of an isolated digestive enzyme does not indicate the pH of the digestive juice in which it normally occurs. Under natural conditions, the enzyme may, in fact, act in an environment in which it cannot function maximally. Digestion can usually proceed normally, however, because the food material stays in contact with the enzyme-containing juice for a sufficient time.

The pH optimum of enzymes that act on several different substrates is not constant but varies, depending on the kind of substrate used. To mention two examples: the pH of the intestinal contents of carnivorous vertebrates may be 6 to 6.5, whereas the pH optimum of the secreted lipases is about pH 8

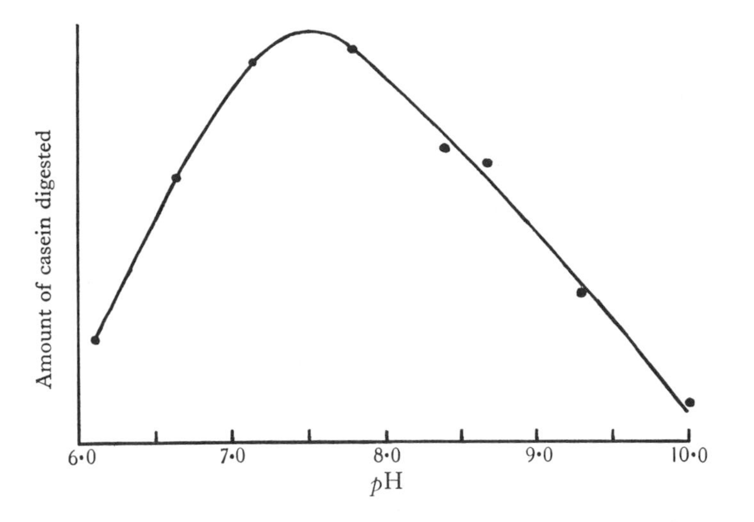

Figure 11–4. The pH optimum of salivary protease acting on casein. The enzyme is from salivary glands of *Peripatopsis* spp. (Onychophora). (From Heatley, N. G.: The digestive enzymes of the Onychophora [Peripatopsis spp.]. J. Exp. Biol. 33:329–343, 1936.)

(Vonk and Wolvekamp, 1929). The pH optimum of pepsin is 1.8, 2.3, and 2.5, respectively, when casein, gelatine, or hemoglobin are substrates (Northrop, 1922).

The pH of the actual secretions of digestive glands is not necessarily the pH that prevails during digestion: even in the acid-secreting stomach of vertebrates, the low pH prevails only near the wall of the stomach, while the inside of the digesting food mass can retain a pH value much more close to neutrality for a long time. The pH inside the digestive tract may also be altered by the products of digestion. Some intestinal bacteria produce acids.

In spite of these obvious complications, there is a close correspondence between pH optima of the active digestive enzymes and the pH of the contents of the digestive tract in which they occur. The case mentioned above, of a discrepancy of 2 pH units, is extreme.

Unpurified enzyme extracts obtained from digestive glands often show not only one, but two or even three pH optima. In the older literature, these were often considered to be true pH optima of the same enzyme. In most cases, however, it was later shown that a mixture of enzymes was present, each with its own pH optimum (Vonk, 1937; Buchs, 1954). In some cases, it is likely, however, that an enzyme has more than one active site, and that each active site has a characteristic pH optimum.

Temperature Optimum

Temperature greatly affects enzyme-catalyzed reactions. Although chemical reactions are generally speeded up by an increase in temperature, the relationship, in the case of enzyme actions, is not a simple one because the labile protein structure of the enzyme is heat sensitive and even a moderate rise in temperature may partially or completely inactivate the enzyme. The *true*

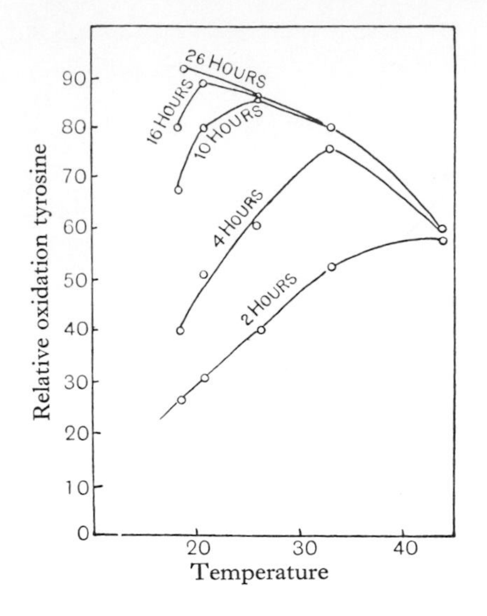

Figure 11–5. Shift in the temperature optimum of an enzyme when the incubation period is altered. The example used to illustrate this shows the behavior of crustacean *tyrosinase*. This enzyme is released from disintegrating blood cells and oxidizes tyrosine which circulates free in the blood stream. (From Pinhey, K. G.: Tyrosinase in crustacean blood. J. Exp. Biol. 7:19–37, 1930.)

temperature optimum of a digestive enzyme may lie in a temperature range in which the enzyme is rapidly inactivated. Therefore, the true temperature optimum can be detected only if the incubation period is kept as short as possible. Longer incubation periods result in a different (lower) optimum temperature, which represents the *effective temperature optimum* characteristic of the particular length of incubation. With increasing duration of these times, a series of effective temperature optima can be found. This is illustrated in Figures 11–5 and 11–6 (Pinhey, 1930; Berrill, 1929).

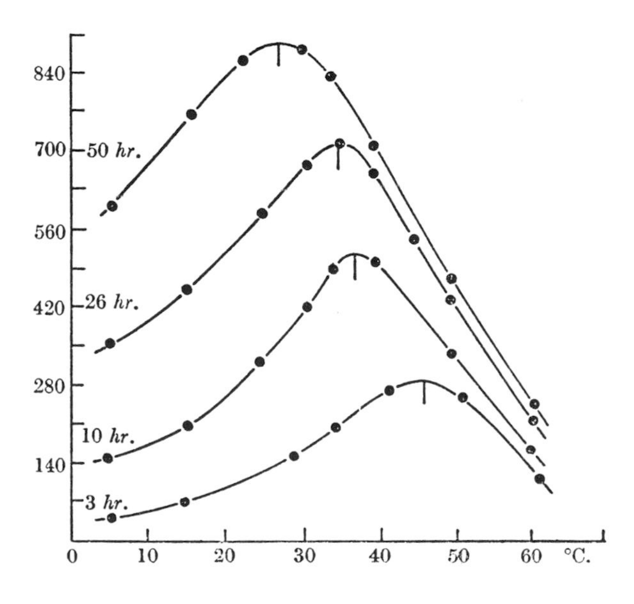

Figure 11–6. Influence of temperature on the digestive proteinase of the tunicate *Tethyum*. Note that the temperature optimum of the enzyme action is higher the shorter the incubation period: at longer incubation periods enough enzyme is inactivated (denatured) by the higher temperatures to significantly depress the total enzyme activity and to shift the apparent temperature optimum toward lower temperature. Ordinate: milligrams of amino nitrogen per liter. (After Berrill, N. J.: Digestion in ascidians and the influence on temperature. Brit. J. Exp. Biol. 6:275–292, 1929, from Baldwin, E.: Dynamic Aspects of Biochemistry, 3rd Ed. Cambridge University Press, 1960.)

Within the animal, the incubation period is represented by the interval during which the food mass stays within the part of the digestive tract that contains the particular digestive enzyme. This interval is controlled by the musculature (or ciliary action) of the digestive tract, which is responsible for the propulsion of the food mass. *The significant (effective) temperature optimum of a digestive enzyme is that temperature at which the substrate is digested at the fastest rate during the natural incubation period.* In general, the optimum temperature is near the environmental and body temperature of the animal. Given the same enzyme, the adaptation to lower body (and environmental) temperatures must consist in a prolongation of the incubation period (that is, the time the food mass remains in the digestive tract).

For more detailed discussions and reviews of the available literature, refer to Barrington, 1962; von Buddenbrock, 1956; Prosser and Brown, Jr., 1961; Yonge, 1937; Vonk, 1937; and Woodman, 1930.

THE DIGESTIVE TRACT

Morphological Aspects

Although the morphology of the digestive tract of the various groups is the subject matter of comparative anatomy, it is worth recalling certain features significant to physiology.

The interior of the digestive tract (lumen) is essentially an extension of the external environmental medium into or through the animal. Matter within the digestive tract is not within the organism proper. There is, therefore, no fundamental difference between the more common *internal digestion*, which takes place within the digestive tract, and *external digestion* (*Octopus*, scorpions, starfish), which takes place in the immediate environment of the organism. In both cases, digestive enzymes are secreted to the "outside" environment where digestion occurs.

In the *Porifera*, the digestive tract is represented by the often complex system of canals. The patterns of their general structure are shown in Figure 11–7. Water and food particles enter through pores in the body wall and leave through a chimney-like *osculum* (asconoid and syconoid types) or through several oscula (leuconoid types). Water (and food) is moved by the incessant beating of the many flagella of the *choanocytes* that line the chambers of the organism. This stream is continuous and always unidirectional.

The propulsion of food-containing medium through the digestive tract by the action of ciliated epithelia is employed by many animal types. In the coelenterates, this is a general feature, particularly obvious in the often complex, branched gastrovascular system of Hydromedusae (Fig. 11–8). It is also common in the Platyhelminthes (flatworms), Rhynchocoela (nemerteans), Rotifera, Echinodermata, Chaetognatha, Hemichordata, Phoronide, Ectoprocta, Brachiopoda, Sipunculida, Annelida, and Mollusca (Figs. 11–9, 11–10, 11–11, 11–12), but is absent in the digestive system of Trematoda, Kinorhyncha, Nematoda, and Arthropoda, and is present only to a limited extent (esophagus) in the Vertebrata. Although the propulsion of the contents of the digestive tract is

(Text continued on page 241.)

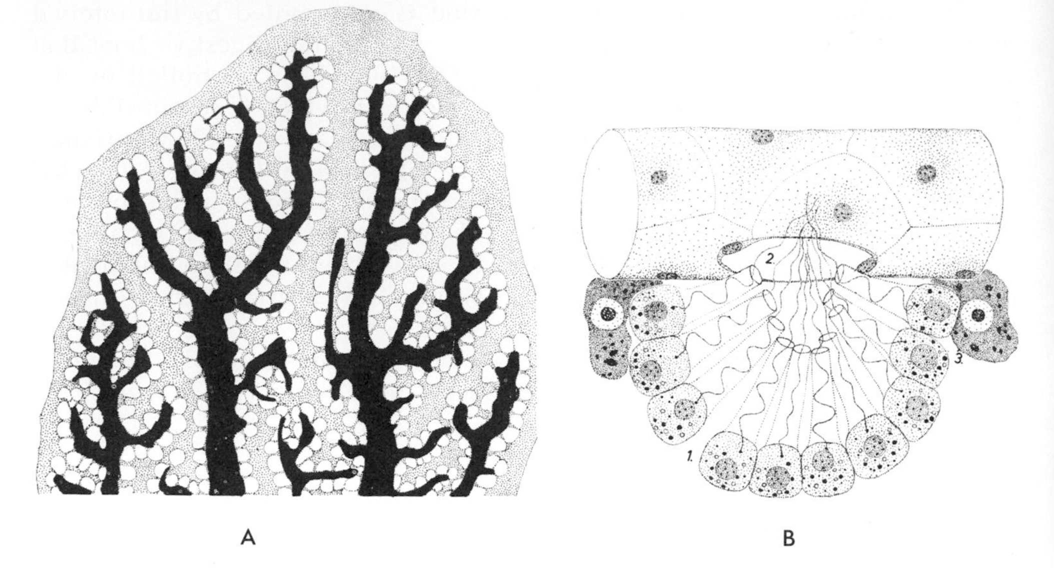

Figure 11–7. A, inhalant (stipple) and exhalant (black) canals with ciliary chambers (white) of a fresh-water sponge, *Ephydatia fluviatilis*. **B**, an enlarged segment of an exhalant canal with ciliary chamber. The flagella of the collared choanocytes (*1*) sweep food particles toward the cell body. The particles are then picked up by wandering archeocytes (*3*) and distributed (in digested form?) to the other body cells. (From Kilian, E. F.: Wasserströmung und Nahrungsaufnahme beim Süsswasserschwamm *Ephydatia fluviatilis*. Z. vergl. Physiol. *34*:407–447, 1952.)

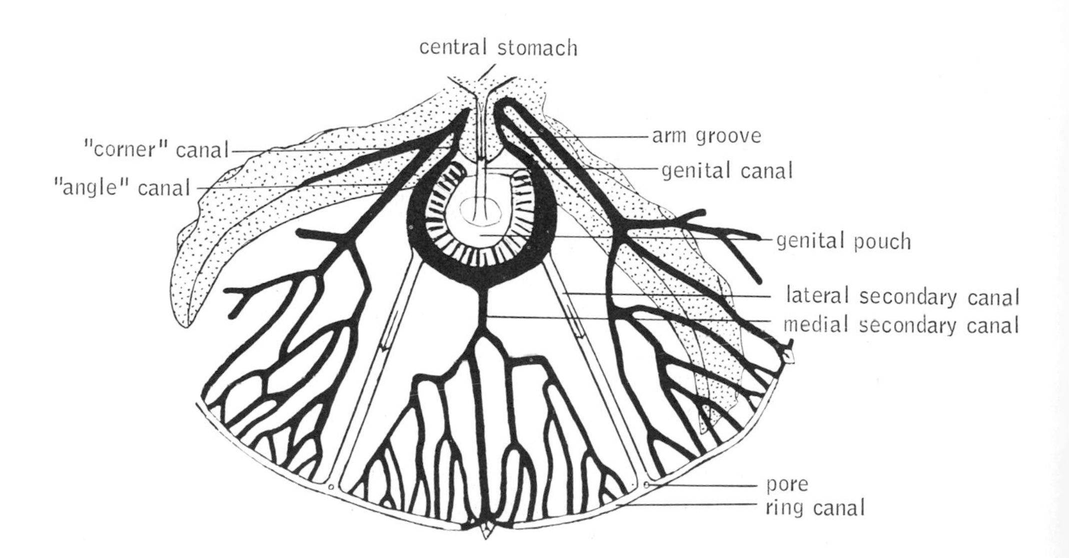

Figure 11–8. Ciliary water currents in the gastrovascular system of a hydromedusa: *Aurelia aurita*. From the central stomach the water flows via the genital canal into the genital pouch, where it is swept into the lateral secondary canals and through them reaches the peripheral ring canal. From there it returns by way of the medial and lateral secondary canals toward the arms that surround the mouth. The cilia of the arm groove return the water and contained particles back to the outside medium. A small amount of water leaves through the eight pores of the ring canal. (From von Widmark, E. M. P.: Über die Gastrovascularströmungen bei Aurelia aurita L. und Cyanea capillata Eschz. Zool. Anz. *38*:378–382, 1911.)

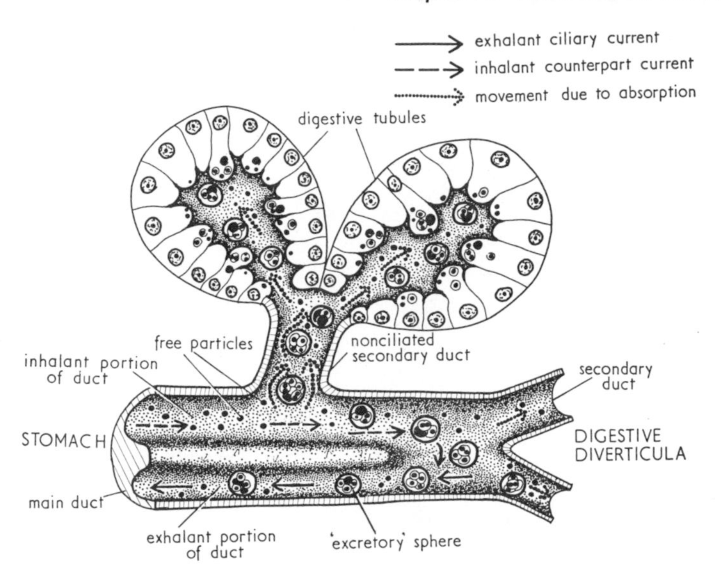

Figure 11–9. The probable circulation of fluid and particles within the digestive diverticula of the Anisomyaria and Eulamellibranchia shown diagrammatically. (See also Figure 11–10.) (From Owen, G.: Observations on the stomach and digestive diverticula of the Lamellibranchia. I. The Anisomyaria and Eulamellibranchia. Quart. J. Micr. Sci. *46*:517–538, 1955.)

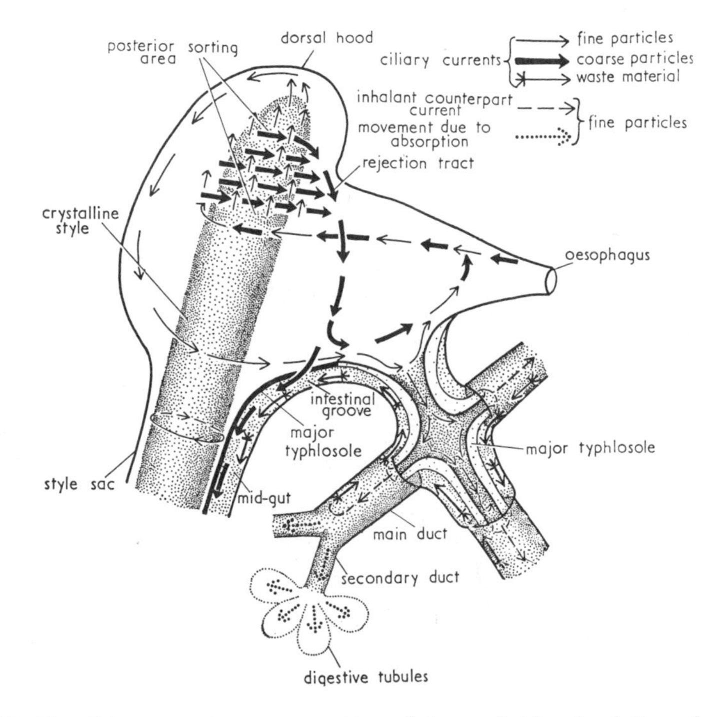

Figure 11–10. Diagrammatic representation of the probable circulation of material within the stomach and digestive diverticula of most Eulamellibranchia. Cilia are not shown. (See, however, Figures 11–11 and 11–12.) (From Owen, G.: Observations on the stomach and digestive diverticula of the Lamellibranchia. I. The Anisomyaria and Eulamellibranchia. Quart. J. Micr. Sci. *96*: 517–538, 1955.)

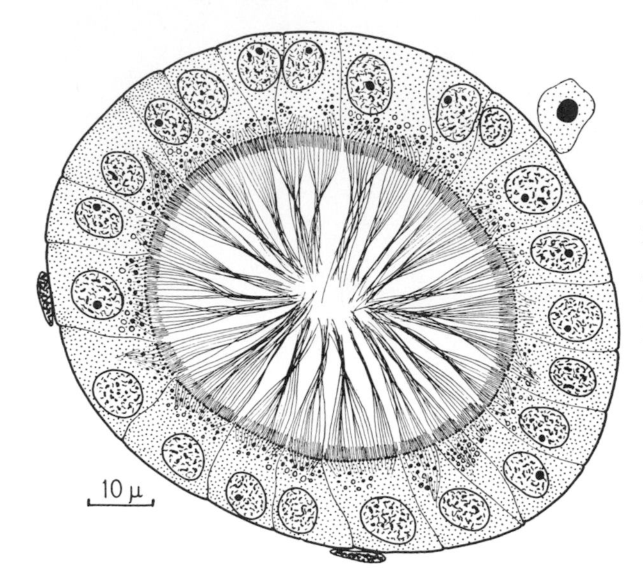

Figure 11-11. Transverse section through a secondary duct of the digestive diverticula of the lamellibranch *Nucula sulcata*. Note the long cilia. (See Fig. 11-10.) (From Owen, G.: Observations on the stomach and digestive diverticula of the Lamellibranchia. II. The Nuculidae. Quart. J. Micr. Sci. 97:541-568, 1956.)

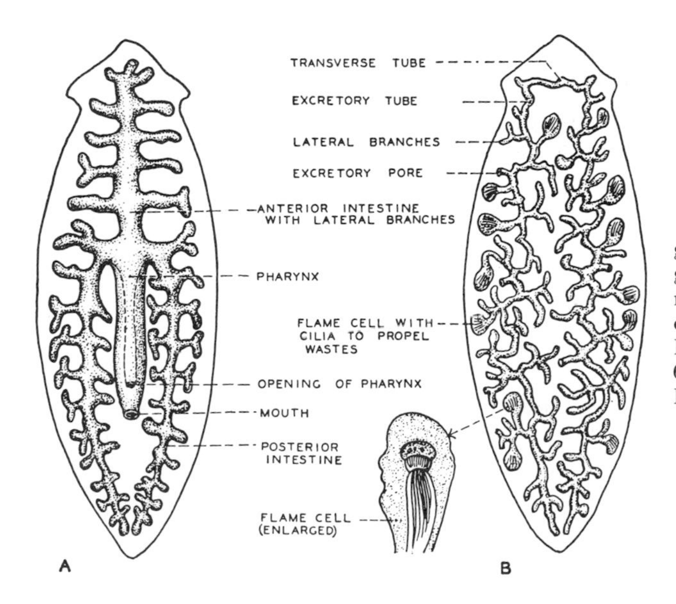

Figure 11-12. Schematic diagram of the highly branched digestive tract and the elaborate network of the nephridial system of a flatworm, *Dugesia*. (From Beaver, W. C.: General Biology, 6th Ed. The C. V. Mosby Co., St. Louis, 1962.)

usually aided by the musculature associated with it, the cilia are almost exclusively responsible for this in the serpulid and sabellid polychaetes and in the flatworms.

Where musculature is involved, this always consists of two layers of muscle fibers: longitudinal and circular. The two are co-ordinated by a complex nerve plexus which is usually under the control of the central nervous system The longitudinal and circular muscle fibers produce a characteristic pattern of alternate contractions and relaxations, known as *peristalsis*. This consists of propagated waves of contraction and relaxation. Movement of the food mass toward the stomach or mouth is termed *antiperistalsis*; in the special case where the mass is actually returned to the esophagus or mouth cavity, one speaks of *regurgitation*. The latter process is familiar from the behavior of the ruminant mammals, but it also occurs in certain invertebrates (scorpions), where the sole source of digestive enzymes is the salivary glands.

Whereas the digestive tract of coelenterates is entirely composed of entodermal epithelium, that of the higher metazoan phyla involves all three germinal layers: invagination of the ectoderm forms a *mouth* or *oral cavity* and a *pharynx* (collective term: *stomodaeum*). In several forms, even the stomach is of ectodermal origin (Arthropoda). The epithelium of the intestine may be entirely entodermal or, as in higher phyla (above the platyhelminthes), it may be met by that of another invagination of the ectoderm, the *proctodaeum*, which forms the anus and, as in the decapod Crustacea, the hindgut. The mesoderm attaches to the ecto- and entodermal epithelia of the digestive tract and forms layers of connective tissue and muscle (exception: platyhelminthes, which have a schizocoel; their intestine proper consists solely of entodermal epithelium —the pharynx, however, is composed mainly of muscles of ectodermal origin).

The digestive tract often shows a characteristic enlargement of the surface area: in flatworms, the intestine is branched (Fig. 11–12), whereas in the higher Metazoa, it is tubular but often elongated and coiled (Fig. 11–13). However, this enlargement of the internal surface area of the digestive tract is not universal: in molluscs and arthropods, the digestive tract is rather short, for digestion and resorption take place in the lumen of widely branched midgut glands (hepatopancreas). A more common occurrence is the enlargement of the pharynx, stomach, or intestines by blind-ending appendages called *diverticula* (singular: diverticulum) or *caeca* (singular: caecum). Examples are shown in Figures 11–14, 11–15 and 11–16. A specialization found in vertebrate intestines is the *villi* (singular: villus), tiny, finger-like protrusions of intestinal epithelium which greatly enlarge the surface area (Fig. 11–17). In general, the digestive tract of herbivorous animals is conspicuously longer than that of carnivorous animals (exception: arthropods and molluscs with widely branched digestive midgut glands). In the vegetarian sea urchins, the intestine is long; in the usually carnivorous starfishes, it is short. The digestive tract of echinoids (sea urchins) is constructed curiously: a *siphon* forms a tube that connects the lumen of the esophagus (pharynx) with the lumen of the intestine. Some forms have even two siphons (see Fig. 11–18). These siphon water back from the intestine into the esophagus, thereby concentrating the food mass.

(Text continued on page 245.)

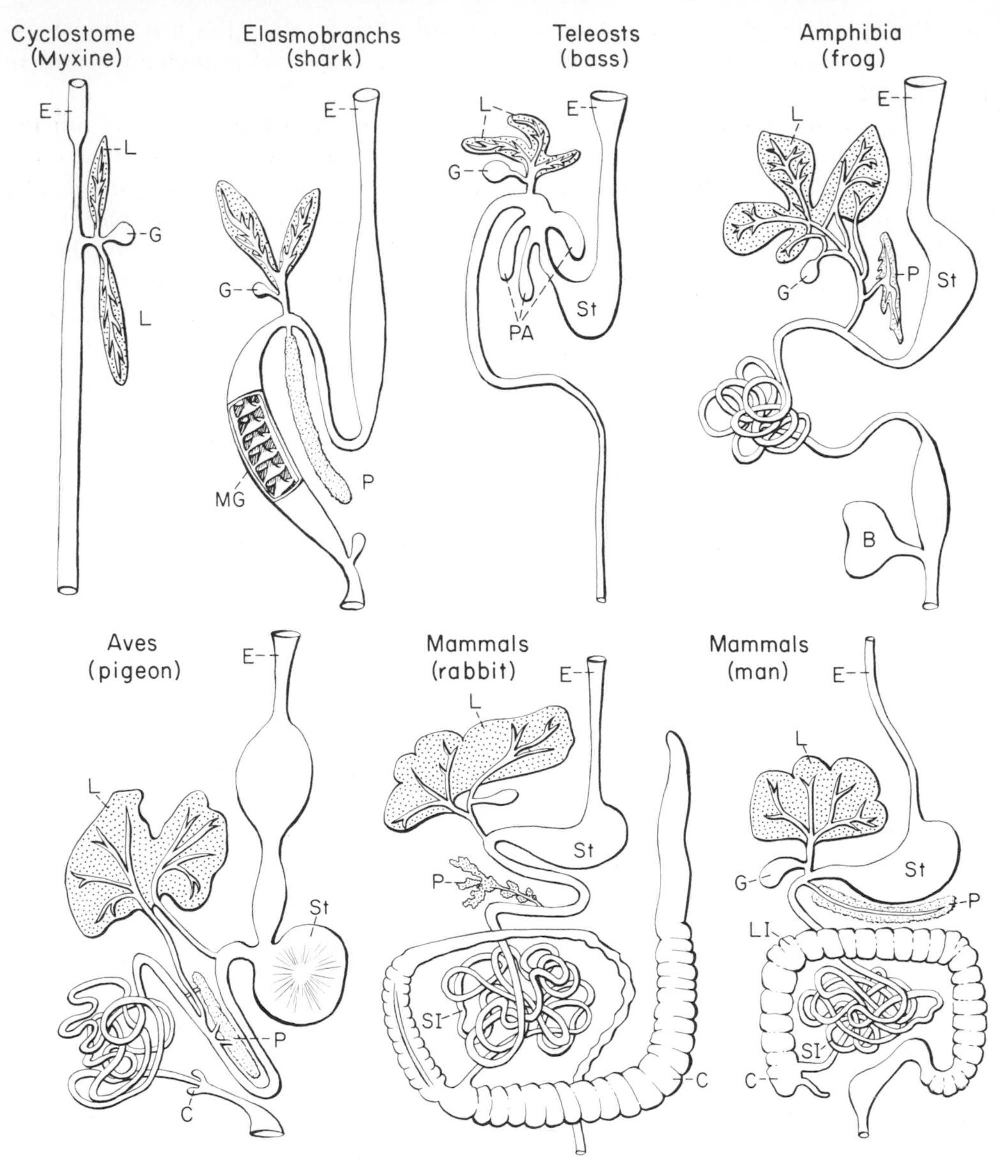

Figure 11-13. The digestive tracts of vertebrate animals. *B*, bladder; *C*, cloaca; *E*, esophagus; *G*, gallbladder; *L*, liver; *LI*, large intestine; *MG*, spiral gut; *P*, pancreas; *PA*, pyloric appendices; *SI*, small intestine; *St*, stomach. (After Stempell, W.: Zoologie im Grundriss. G. Borntraeger, Berlin, 1926.)

Figure 11-15. Types of digestive diverticula present in the Lamellibranchia, shown diagrammatically. **A**, hypothetical primitive condition and also many larval lamellibranchs. **B**, septibranchs, some eulamellibranchs, and the wide diverticula of the Nuculanidae. **C**, Anisomyaria and most Eulamellibranchia. **D**, Nuculidae. Double-headed arrows represent movement resulting from muscular activity; single-headed arrows represent ciliary currents. (From Owen, G.: Observations on the stomach and digestive diverticula of the Lamellibranchia. II. The Nuculidae. Quart. J. Micr. Sci. 97:541–568, 1956.)

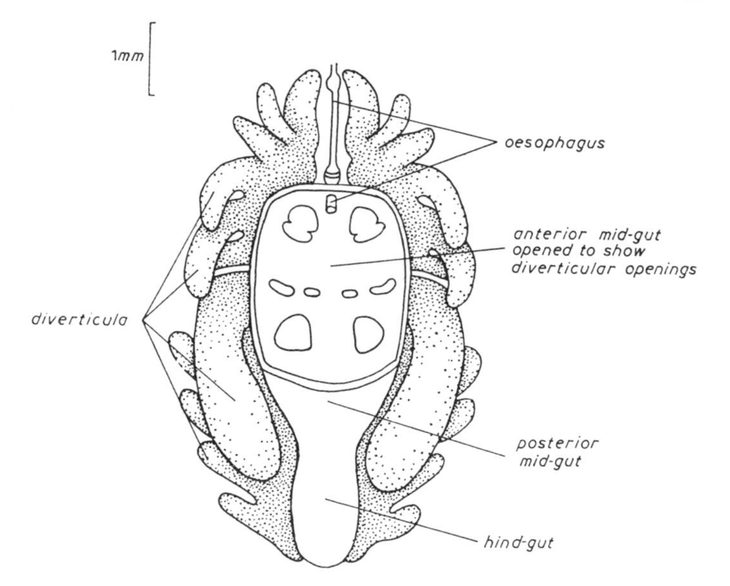

Figure 11–14. General morphology of the gut of a harvest spider (Opiliones), *Mitopus morio*. Ventral view. Note the many diverticula. (From Phillipson, J.: Histological changes in the gut of Mitopus morio [Phalangiidae] during protein digestion. Quart. J. Micr. Sci. *102*:217–226, 1961.)

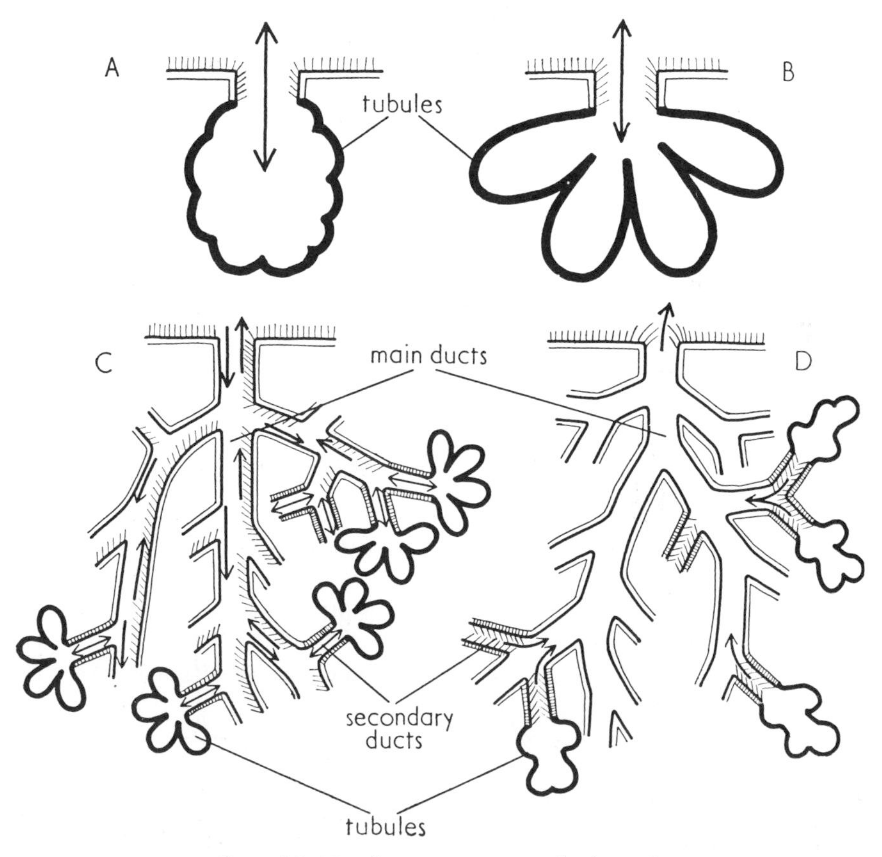

Figure 11–15. *See opposite page for legend.*

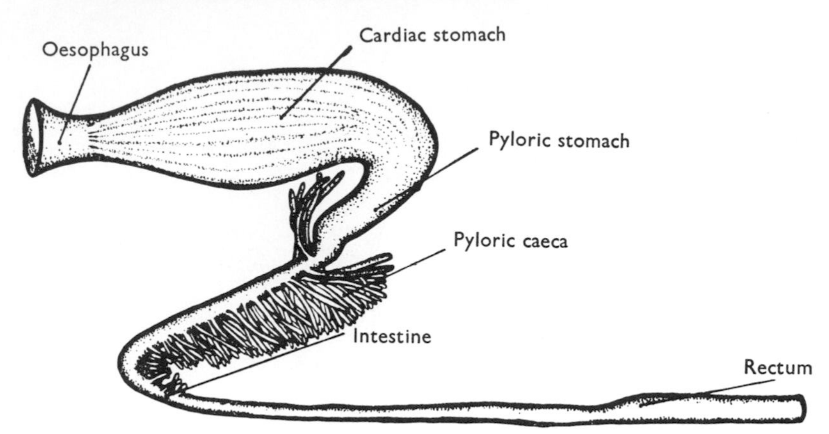

Figure 11–16. Diagram of the gross anatomy of the gut of the brown trout *Salmo trutta*. Note the extensive caeca. (From Burnstock, G.: Reversible inactivation of nervous activity in a fish gut. J. Physiol. *141*:35–45, 1958.)

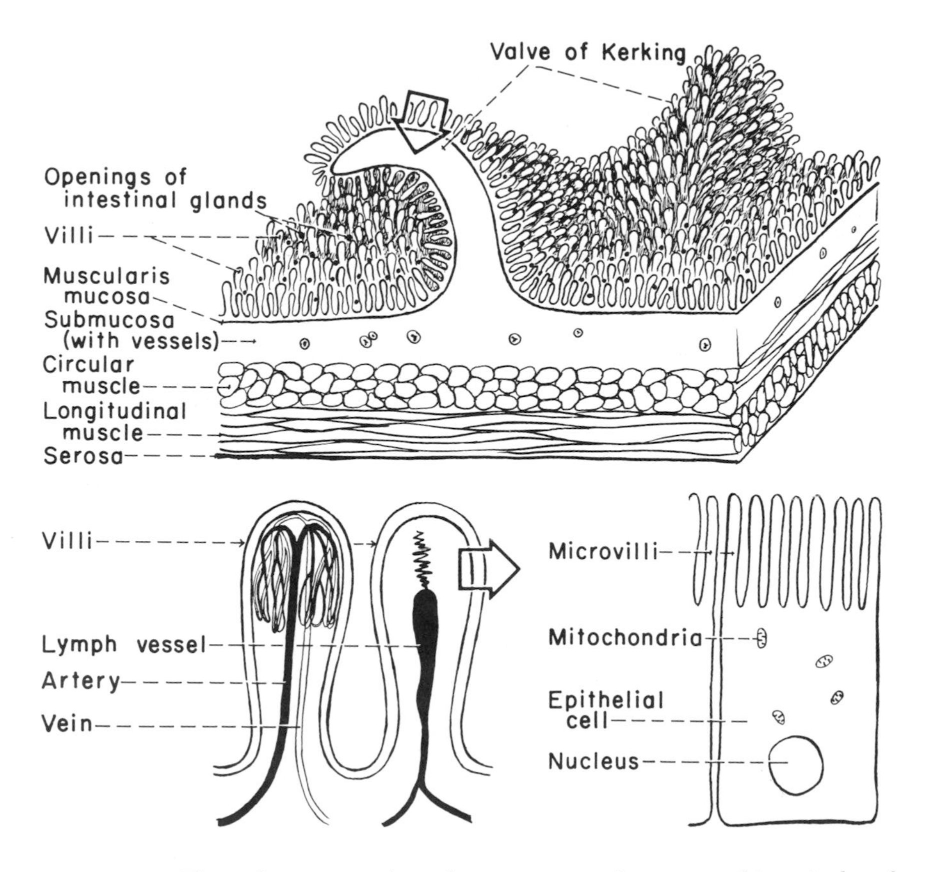

Figure 11–17. Three diagrams to show the enormous enlargement of intestinal surface by villi and microvilli. The villi within the arrow of the top diagram are represented on the lower left and a cell from the epithelium of such a villus is shown on the lower right. The three-dimensional representation is of a piece of mammalian small intestine.

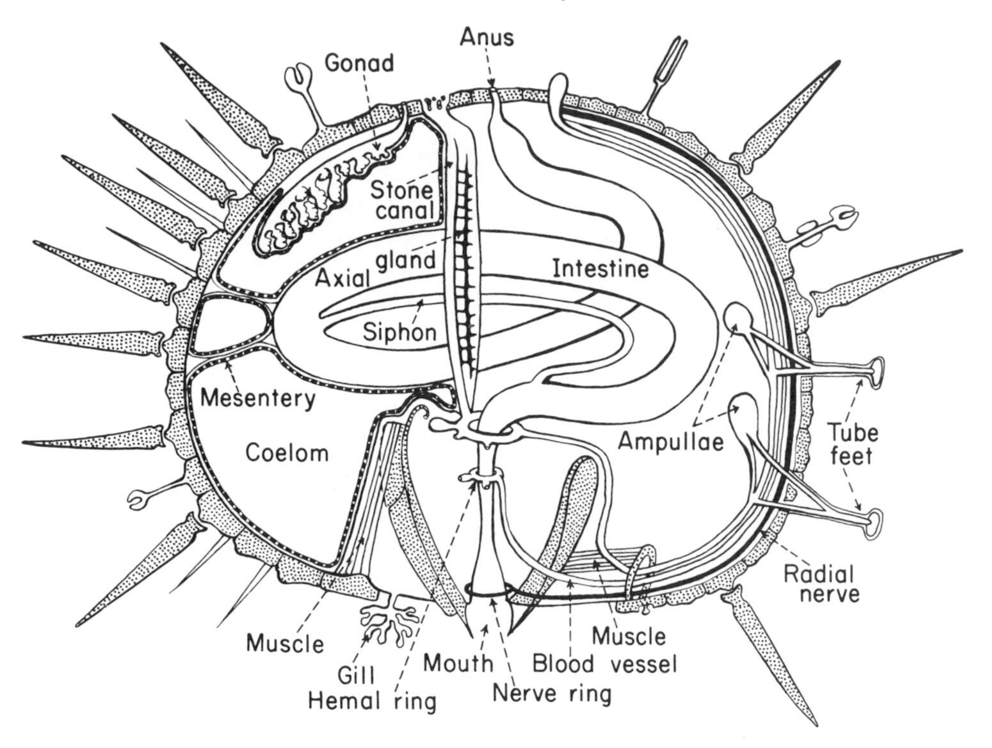

Figure 11–18. Diagrammatic representation of the anatomy of an echinoid. (After Stempell, W.: Zoologie im Grundriss. G. Borntraeger, Berlin, 1926.)

Functional Aspects of the Digestive Tract

Passive and Active Transport: Resorption. The epithelium of the digestive tract is an important exchange membrane (see Chap. 2). Portions of the digestive tract—usually the intestine, and to a certain extent the stomach (where it occurs)—serve in the passive and active transport of nutrients (the end products of digestion). Passive transport occurs by diffusion through the epithelial cells, active transport by phagocytosis and specialized carrier mechanisms as discussed in Chapter 27. *The total of passive plus active transfer of nutrients from the lumen of the digestive tract to the body fluids is termed resorption.*

Most of the nutrients simply diffuse through the resorbing epithelium. The diffusion rate depends on: (1) the concentration gradient across the epithelium, (2) the size of the diffusing molecules, and (3) the lipid-solubility of the diffusing molecules. The smaller and the more lipid-soluble, the easier a molecule penetrates the pores or the lipid layer of the cell membranes.

Large concentration gradients are maintained by the circulation of body fluids (blood, hemolymph, interstitial fluid). With the exception of the lower phyla, which lack true circulatory systems, the digestive tract is always supplied with blood vessels. Even in animal types with a rather rudimentary or reduced vascular system, the digestive tract is supplied with a special circulatory system. As an example, we may recall the situation in echinoderms, as depicted in Figure 11–19. It is the obvious function of the vascular supply to carry the

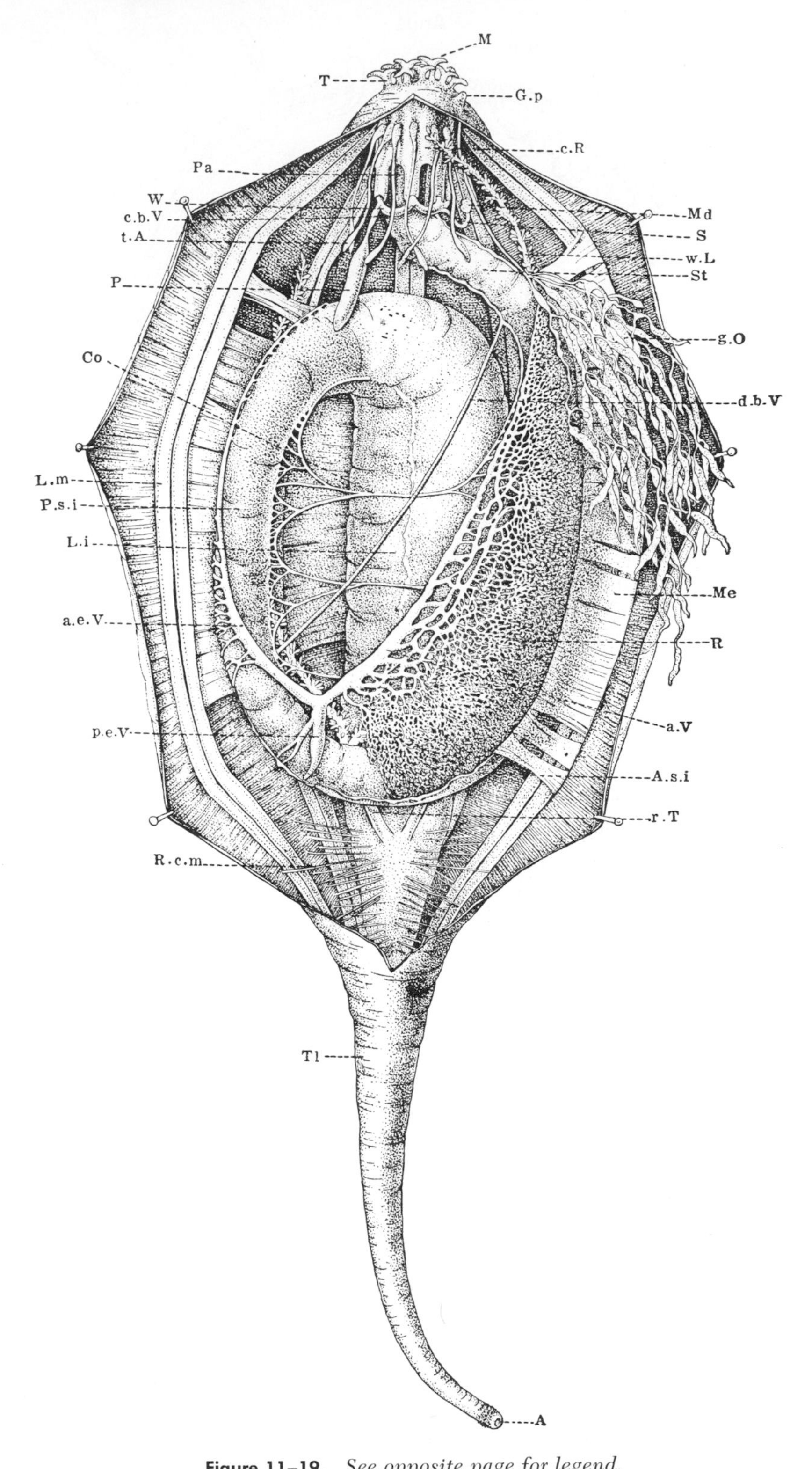

Figure 11–19. *See opposite page for legend.*

nutrients away from the resorbing epithelia and to deliver fresh, nutrient-free medium.

Certain compounds, notably some sugars and *l*-amino acids, are actively transported. Techniques employed in experiments designed to investigate this are shown in Figs. 11–20 and 11–21. For these compounds, the resorption velocity is largely independent of the concentration gradients; in fact, they can be transported even against concentration gradients (although under natural conditions, this is rare). Active transport across the wall of intestines has been studied largely on mammalian preparations (Verzar andMcDougall, 1936; Cori, 1925, 1926; Barany and Sperber, 1939; Wiseman, 1953, 1954, 1956).

The ability of the cells of the digestive tract to resorb molecules from the lumen and to deliver them to the body fluids is not limited to those molecules that can be considered as nutrients. Water and inorganic ions are also resorbed and so is oxygen, if present in sufficient concentration. The absorption of water is most pronounced in marine and terrestrial animals (see Chap. 5). The absorption of water is always accompanied by resorption of ions, particularly univalent ions, such as Na^+ and K^+ or Cl^-. Although ion transport follows the concentration gradient, there is, in addition, active transport which pumps ions (notably Na^+ and Cl^-) against concentration gradients. This has been demonstrated in several Crustacea, insects, fish, and mammals (Ingraham and Visscher, 1936a, b, and 1938; Hendley and Smyth, 1958).

Respiratory Exchange. In a number of animals, portions of the digestive tract serve as a respiratory exchange membrane. The hindgut in certain aquatic insect larvae (*Aeschna*, dragonfly) serves as a respiratory organ and actively pumps water in and out of the body to keep the interior lumen well oxygenated. The intestine of Echiuroid worms (*Urechis*) functions similarly (Hall, 1931). The water lungs of holothurians can also be listed in this connection. They consist of branched tubular extensions of the cloaca which, by rhythmic contractions and associated opening and closing of the anus, cause continuous renewal of the sea water from which oxygen is withdrawn (simple diffusion) into the body fluids. In shore gobies (*Periophthalmus*) the highly vascularized mucous membranes of the mouth and pharynx are employed in aerial respiration (Marlier, 1938). Similar respiratory functions of the oral cavity have been reported for the electric eel (Langley, 1949) and are well known for many amphibians.

Figure 11–19. General anatomy of a holothurian, *Caudina chilensis.* Note the elaborate rete mirabile (*R*). *A*, anus; *a. e. V*, anterior efferent vessel; *A. s. i*, anterior small intestine; *a. V*, afferent vessel; *c. b. V*, circular blood vessel; *Co*, commissure; *c. R*, calcareous ring; *d. b. V*, diagonal blood vessel; *g. O*, genital organ; *G. p*, genital papilla; *L. i*, large intestine; *L. m*, longitudinal muscle; *M*, mouth; *Md*, madreporite; *Me*, mesentery; *P*, polian vesicle; *Pa*, pharynx; *p. e. V*, posterior efferent vessel; *P. s. i*, posterior small intestine; *R*, rete mirabile; *R. c. m*, radial cloacal muscle; *r. T*, respiratory tree; *S*, stone canal; *St*, stomach; *T*, tentacle; *t. A*, tentacular ampulla; *Tl*, tail; *W*, circular water canal; *w. L*, part of respiratory tree. (From Kawamoto, N.: The anatomy of Caudina chilensis [J. Müller] with especial reference to the perivisceral cavity, the blood and the water vascular systems in their relations to the blood circulation. Tohoku Sci. Rep., Ser. 4, 2:239–264, 1927.)

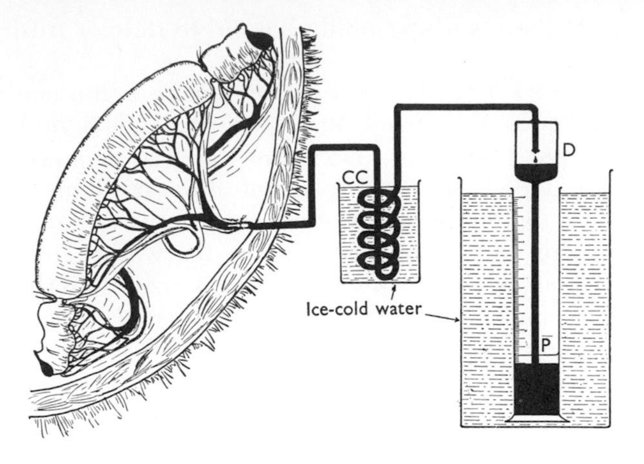

Figure 11–20. Arrangement used for collection of venous blood from a loop of intestine (dog) in experiments designed to study transport of glucose across the wall of the intestine. The loop of the intestine has an intact arterial blood supply, but the venous blood leaving the loop passes through a cooling coil (*CC*) and then a dropping chamber (*D*), and is collected in a cylinder under a layer of liquid paraffin (*P*). (From Atkinson, R. M., B. J. Parsons, and D. H. Smyth: The intestinal absorption of glucose. J. Physiol. *135*:581–589, 1957.)

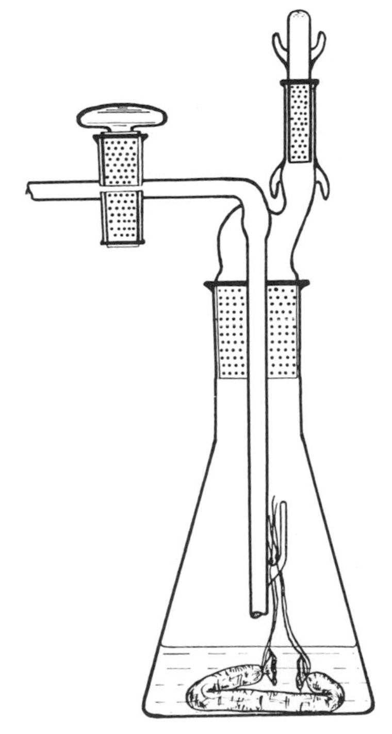

Figure 11–21. Arrangement used in a study of glucose transport across the wall of the mammalian intestine (dog). A loop of intestine is everted and ligatured at both ends and tied to a glass hook to permit easy removal of the "sac" at the end of the incubation period. Since the inside of the gut is now outside, the bathing solution is in contact with it. Substances transferred to the other (outer, or serosal) side of the intestine appear in the lumen of the preparation. At the end of the incubation period the loop of intestine is lifted out of the bath and opened. The contained fluid is analyzed chemically. The stopcocks permit gassing with an atmosphere of 5 per cent CO_2 and 95 per cent O_2 to insure adequate buffering (bicarbonate) and respiration. The method could be easily adapted for studies on intestines of invertebrates. (From Parsons, B. J., D. H. Smyth, and C. B. Tayler: The action of phlorizin on the intestinal transfer of glucose and water in vitro. J. Physiol. *144*:387–402, 1958.)

THE DIGESTIVE GLANDS

All digestive glands function as *exocrine glands*; that is, they deliver their products of secretion to the outside of the body (the lumen of the digestive system must be considered as "outside"). However, some digestive glands also function as *endocrine glands*, producing *hormones* that are released into the blood stream or other body fluids.

The four patterns of exocrine secretion are:

(1) Secretion products are transferred across the apparently intact cell membrane. (2) The top part of the gland cell is sloughed off after the secretion products have been transferred to it. This is known as *apocrine* secretion (typical example: midgut gland of gastropod molluscs). (3) The top portion of the gland cell, after having filled up with secretion products, is pinched off. This is called *merocrine* secretion and occurs in arthropods and annelids, among others. (4) The entire gland cell moves out, or is cast off, into the lumen of the digestive gland or digestive tract. This, called *holocrine* secretion, has been observed in lamellibranch molluscs, certain insects, and myriapods.

Actually more than one of these types of secretion may occur within the same organism, and closely related genera or families may show entirely different modes of secretion. A diagrammatic representation of different types of secretion is given in Figure 11–22.

It was thought for a long time that the secretion, particularly types 3 and 4, releases enzymes into the digestive tract. There is accumulating evidence, however, that much of the secretion consists of excretory products derived from food previously ingested and digested by the secretory gland cells. We may thus assume that secretion is preceded by intracellular digestion (often in food vacuoles). Of course, as the cell apex (merocrine secretion) or cell (holocrine secretion) disintegrates, it releases not only excretory products but also digestive enzymes which can then function in extracellular digestion. Examples are given in Figures 11–22 and 11–23.

Particularly merocrine and apocrine secretion require continuous growth of the secreting cell. The parts that are lost must be replaced. For a number of species it has been reported that secretion is accompanied by a high mitotic rate: the cells not only grow but also divide, and old cells are replaced by new ones. Periods of feeding are often associated with periods of increased mitoses of enzyme-secreting glandular epithelium of the digestive system.

The chief morphological types of digestive glands are: (1) the salivary glands, (2) gland cells within the epithelium of the digestive tract, and (3) midgut glands (variously named *hepatic caeca, hepatopancreas, liver,* and *pancreas*, depending on function and morphology and on the taxonomic position of the organism).

Salivary Glands

Salivary glands occur in practically all phyla of the higher Metazoa (*bilateria*). Their primary function, as mentioned, is the secretion of lubricating mucus, but in most animal forms they also secrete digestive enzymes. In the

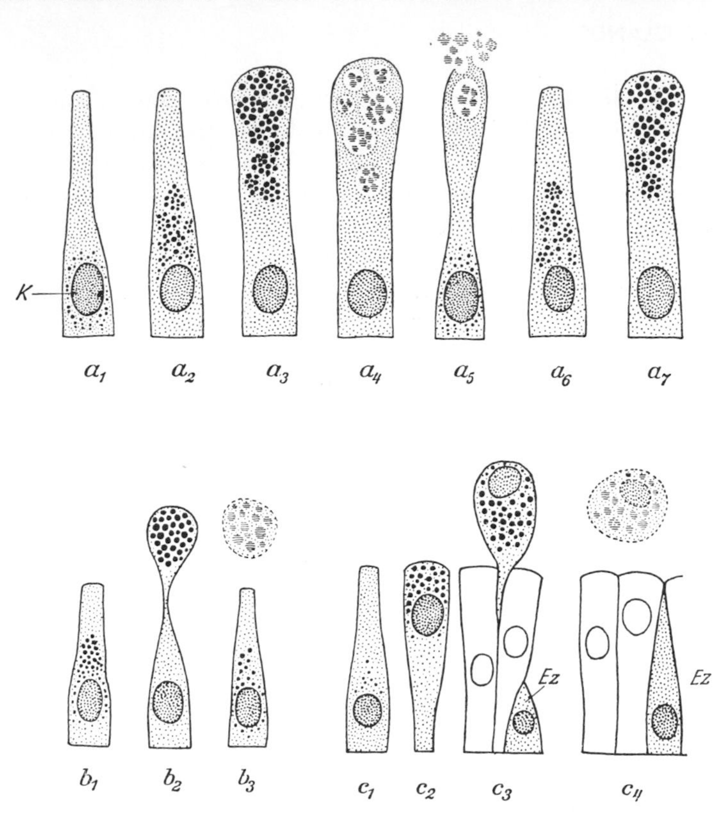

Figure 11–22. Three types of secretion by digestive glands, corresponding to types 2, 3, and 4 mentioned in the text. **a**, apocrine, **b**, merocrine, and **c**, holocrine secretion. Note the production and "upward" transport of secretion granules and the breakdown of the released cells or cell portions. *Ez*, replacement cell; *K*, nucleus. (From Kuehn, A.: Grundriss der allgemeinen Zoologie, 12th Ed. Georg Thieme Verlag, Stuttgart, 1957.)

Turbellaria, gland cells in the pharynx secrete only mucus; digestion in these forms is entirely intracellular (for a detailed discussion see Hyman, 1951, Vol. II, pp. 203–207). Digestion in the other flatworms is almost unexplored, but there is general agreement that these animals absorb nutrients through the body surface. Digestive glands or digestive enzymes are unknown in Trematoda and Cestoda. The digestive physiology of Acanthocephala (also parasitic) is likewise almost unknown, but absorption of nutrients through the body surface is recognized. The rotifers (Phylum Aschelminthes) have two to seven salivary glands with ducts that open near the mouth. Their function has not been explored.

The esophageal glands of parasitic Nematoda appear to secrete a proteolytic enzyme. The ducts of these glands open into the pharynx, near the mouth, and can be classed as salivary glands; the secretions have digestive properties. In carnivorous nematodes the secretion is passed through the stylus into the prey and causes paralysis due to a toxin. Pharyngeal salivary glands occur in annelids (Polychaeta, Oligochaeta, and Hirudinea). They are not known to

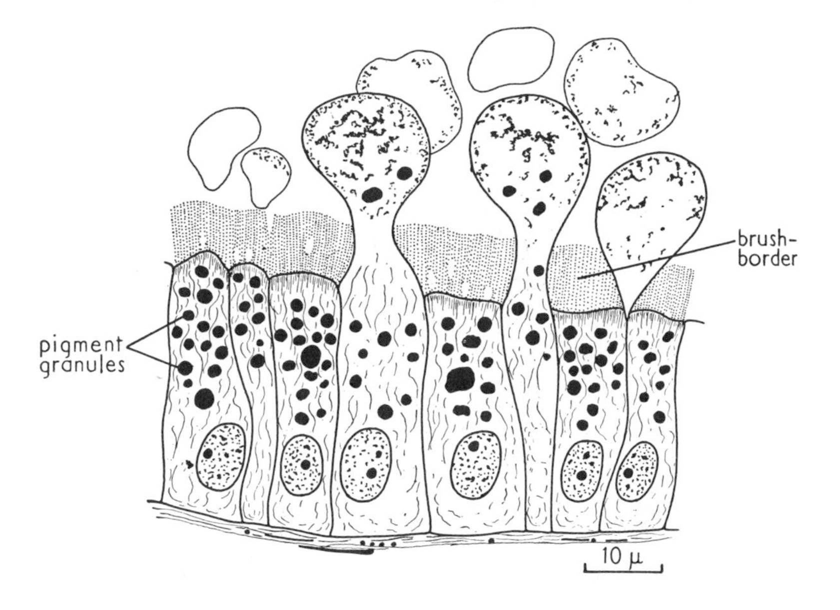

Figure 11–23. Typical example of holocrine secretion: cells of the epithelium of the main digestive diverticula of the lamellibranch *Nucula sulcata* during the "extrusion" phase. The dark granules (yellowish green in life) are considered to be excretory products. (From Owen, G.: Observations on the stomach and digestive diverticula of the Lamellibranchia. II. The Nuculidae. Quart. J. Micr. Sci. 97:541–568, 1956.)

produce digestive enzymes. The gland cells that are clustered around the mouth of blood sucking leeches secrete a blood anticoagulant. The terrestrial Onychophora, Chilopoda, and Diplopoda possess salivary glands. Those of Onychophora are known to secrete amylase and protease enzymes (Fig. 11–4).

Among the arthropods, salivary glands are little developed in the Crustacea, but are prominent in many insects: their *labial* salivary glands secrete various digestive enzymes—those of *Drosophila* larvae produce a *peptidase*, those of aphids a *pectinase*, and some Homoptera inject a *diastase* into the plants they feed on. *Anticoagulants* are secreted by the salivary glands of blood sucking mosquitoes. There are other glands of insects that can be called salivary glands—mandibular, oral, and pharyngeal glands—but these do not seem to secrete digestive enzymes.

Among the arachnids, the scorpions are known to produce a protein-digesting saliva which liquefies the digestible proteins of the prey. The saliva in these animals may, in fact, be the sole source of extracellular digestive enzymes (Vachon, 1953).

Salivary glands are rather prominent in the molluscs. An esophageal gland, known as the *sugar gland*, of chitons (*Cryptochiton*) produces α-amylase and maltase. The published study of these enzymes is a model of a careful, modern analysis and should be studied, as an example, by anyone interested in contributing to the field of digestive physiology and digestive biochemistry (Meeuse and Fluegel, 1958).

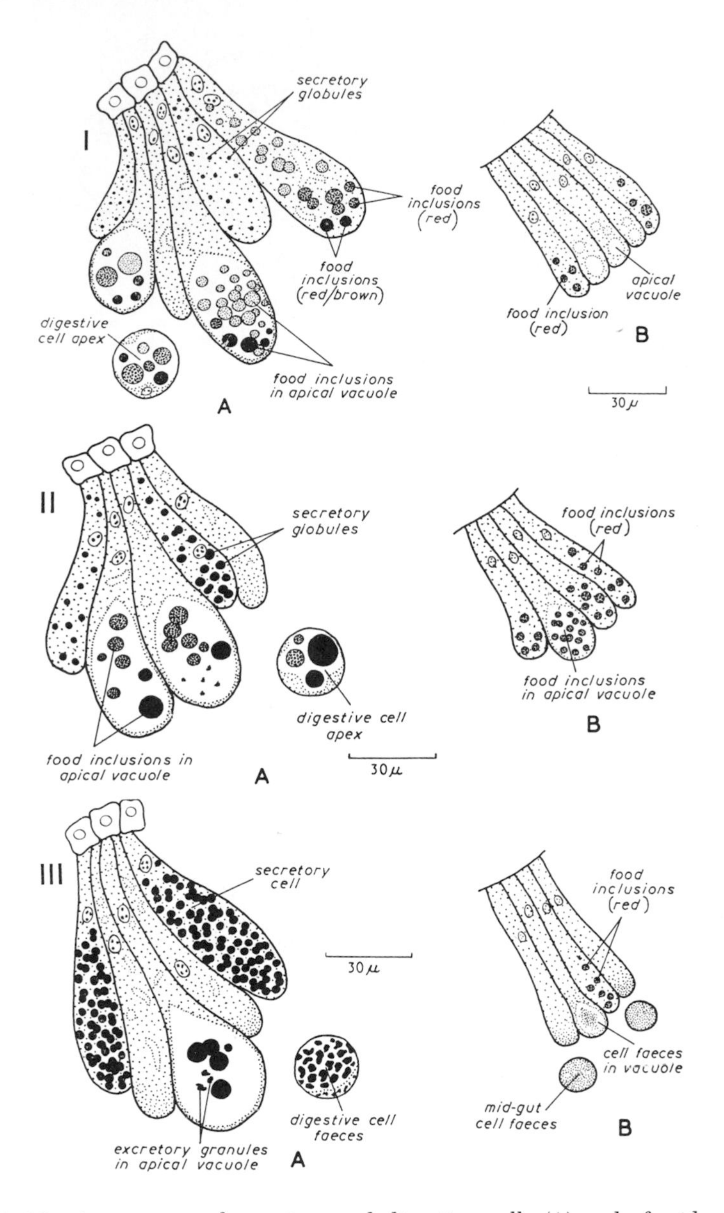

Figure 11–24. Appearance of secretory and digestive cells (**A**) and of midgut cells (**B**) of *Mitopus morio.* (See Fig. 11–15 for general morphology of the digestive system of this animal.) **I**, 6 hours, **II**, 18 hours, and **III**, 48 hours after feeding. The tissues were stained with hemalum, acid fuchsin, metanil yellow, and light green. Note the two types of cells in the diverticula: secretory cells which, in response to feeding, release accumulated secretory granules (enzyme?), and digestive cells which ingest food particles and cut off their apex which contains a large food vacuole. The partially digested contents of the food vacuole are then transferred to midgut cells where they are further processed in apical vacuoles. The midgut cells and some of the diverticular digestive cells release indigestible material as feces. (From Phillipson, J.: Histological changes in the gut of Mitopus morio [Phalangiidae] during protein digestion. Quart. J. Micr. Sci. *102*:217–226, 1961.)

In herbivorous gastropods, salivary glands produce amylase (*Helix*) in addition to mucus. Among the lamellibranch molluscs, salivary glands are generally missing, but in wood-boring forms, such as *Teredo* and *Bankia*, *foregut glands* (analogues of salivary glands) produce a cellulase. Two pairs of salivary glands are found in cephalopods. The possible enzyme contents of their secretions have been only scarcely investigated. According to Ghiretti (1950), the posterior salivary glands produce a trypsin-like protease.

There are no publications that establish extra-intestinal or pre-oral digestion, but this is assumed to happen, at least, in Octopoda. The posterior salivary glands of various Octopoda have been found to contain a toxin of high molecular weight ("*cephalotoxin*") (Ghiretti, unpublished), which rapidly paralyzes crabs if injected into their blood stream (Bacq and Ghiretti, 1951). In addition, these glands contain conspicuous amounts of *tyramine, octopamine, 5-hydroxytryptamine, taurine, acetylcholine,* and *histamine.* Not all these compounds are found in all cephalopod species: 5-hydroxytryptamine, which occurs in quantities of up to 800 μg/gm in the posterior salivary glands of *Octopus vulgaris*, is entirely absent from the same organs of *Octopus macropus*. 5-Hydroxytryptamine, tyramine, and octopamine are not present in the posterior salivary glands of *Sepia officinalis* (Ghiretti, 1960). It can be assumed that the posterior salivary glands have important *incretory* functions: electrical stimulation of the nerve supply of these glands causes the release into the blood stream of a secretion that contains the physiologically active compounds just mentioned (Ghiretti, 1953).

Salivary glands or their equivalents are absent in the echinoderms, and of the group Deuterostomia they appear only among the vertebrates (amphibia, reptiles, birds, and mammals). Fishes do not have salivary glands. Digestive enzymes (amylase) are found only in the saliva of certain mammals; the saliva of man has probably the highest known amylase activity. The chief function of vertebrate salivary glands is the production of lubricating mucus. In secondarily aquatic forms, this function is greatly reduced or even absent.

Gland Cells Within the Epithelium of the Digestive Tract

Exocrine Function. Gland cells within the epithelium of the digestive tract are common. They are the only type of digestive gland found in the coelenterates. In the flatworms, such glandular epithelia do not exist: digestion takes place intracellularly. However, according to von Buddenbrock (1956), "it is certain" that in those forms which possess a plicate pharynx (many polyclads and terrestrial planarians), digestion is extraintestinal, but that the origin of the (proteolytic) enzymes is unknown.

Enzyme secretion by gland cells of the intestinal epithelium has been described for nematodes and representatives of the annelid groups. In one fresh-water oligochaete, *Nais*, gland cells of the stomach secrete acid, but secretion of enzymes by stomach cells has not been described (Nirenstein, 1922; Szarski, 1936).

Nothing definite is known about enzyme secretion and digestive processes in the nemerteans. Digestive gland cells occur in the midgut of insects and in the intestines of various molluscs, but at least in the gastropod and cephalopod molluscs and in the arthropods (other than insects), digestive gland cells are usually restricted to the midgut gland epithelium (see below). In numerous species of pelecypod (lamellibranch) molluscs, the stomach extends into a tubular, blind organ: the *style sac*. The cells of this secrete an amylase-containing material that forms a translucent rod, the *crystalline style* (Fig. 11–10); in other forms, such a style is found in a ciliated groove of the intestine. The style extends into the stomach and its tip is pressed against a chitinous plate, the *stomach shield*. The style is rotated continuously by the action of ciliated epithelia in the stomach and style sac. Enzymes are liberated from the style by erosion.

The intestine of echinoderms (echinoids, holothurians) does not secrete digestive enzymes (Bonnet, 1924, and others). In the echinoids, digestive enzymes are derived from glandular crypts in the esophagus or pharynx. In the holothurians, the digestive enzymes are manufactured by the coelomic epithelium of the *rete* (see Fig. 11–19); they are carried into the gut by amebocytes (Schreiber, 1932; Krukenberg, 1882).

Starfish have a short but branched digestive tract. The esophagus leads into a rather large stomach, usually divided into *cardiac* and *pyloric* portions. The intestine is short, but usually has blind-ending caeca or diverticula. The pyloric stomach usually extends into blind-ending pairs of *pyloric caeca*. Glandular cells (secreting mucus and digestive enzymes) occur predominantly in the pyloric caeca, but are also found in the epithelium of esophagus, intestine, and intestinal caeca. The stomach of ophiuroids does not have pyloric caeca; its glandular epithelium produces the digestive enzymes.

In the vertebrates, glandular epithelia of the digestive tract are usually restricted to the stomach and intestine, but in amphibia, even the esophagus has gland cells which secrete proteolytic enzymes (Swiecicki, 1876; Friedman, 1937). In the frog (*Rana*), the protease secreted in the esophagus becomes active only after it reaches the acid-secreting stomach. The pH in the esophagus is not low enough.

In fishes, digestive enzymes are secreted by gland cells in the stomach and intestine. Several groups of fishes (the carps, for instance), lack a stomach. In these forms, it appears that there is no secretion of pepsin. Other proteinases as well as lipase and amylase are present, however, even in fish without a stomach.

Gland cells in the wall of the stomach of amphibia and higher vertebrates secrete *hydrochloric acid*. In spite of earlier speculations that the low pH of the digestive juices in the stomach of certain vertebrates might be due to the secretion of organic acids, this has never been confirmed, and the general agreement of all pertinent findings indicates that HCl is the universal acidifying agent. The acid is secreted by active hydrogen transport carried out by specialized gland cells (see Chapter 27).

Endocrine Function. Glandular cells within the epithelium of stomach and intestine function also as endocrine glands. They release hormones into the blood stream which control the functioning of the digestive system. Over the past few decades, a rather complex hormonal control system has been uncovered in mammals. At least parts of this have also been recognized in other vertebrate groups. The following is an account of the situation in mammals:

Gland cells in the pyloric region of the stomach produce a hormone, *gastrin*, which stimulates the so-called *oxyntic cells* of the cardiac region of the stomach to produce acid. This acid secretion is inhibited by another hormone, *enterogastrone*, which is released by gland cells in the wall of the duodenum (a segment of the small intestine). The duodenal mucosa also secretes other hormones: *secretin*, which stimulates the flow of the pancreatic secretion, *pancreozymin* (see below), which stimulates enzyme production and secretion by pancreatic gland cells, *duocrinin*, which acts on *Brunner's glands* (they secrete enterokinase, amylase, lipase, and a pepsin) in the duodenum itself, and *cholecystokinin*, which causes evacuation (by contraction) of the gallbladder. *Enterocrinin* is a hormone secreted by unidentified gland cells in the mucosa of the jejunum and ileum. It stimulates the secretion by other gland cells in the same parts of the intestine of digestive enzymes and mucus (this secretion is termed *succus entericus*).

The stimuli that elicit the secretion of these various hormones are the following: Distention of the muscular wall of the stomach stimulates secretion of gastrin. This hormone causes production of acid. Acid, in turn, is the stimulus that causes secretion of secretin and duocrinin. Fat in the intestinal contents stimulates the release of enterogastrone and cholecystokinin, while the products of protein digestion stimulate the secretion of pancreozymin and enterocrinin.

The total picture of the interaction of hormones in the control of digestive functions is shown in Figure 11–25.

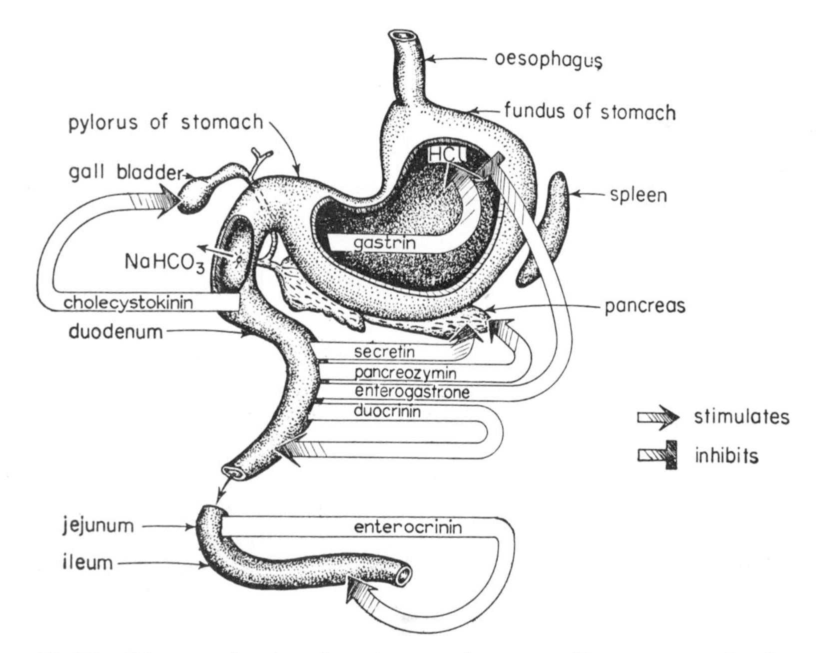

Figure 11–25. Diagram showing the origins and actions of hormones in the digestive tract of mammals (see the text). (Modified after Turner, 1955, from Jenkin, P. M.: Animal Hormones, A Comparative Survey. Part I. Kinetic and Metabolic Hormones. Pergamon Press, New York, 1962.)

Midgut Glands

Large, branched and ducted digestive glands (midgut glands), which serve in enzyme production as well as resorption of nutrients, occur in several phyla, notably the molluscs, crustaceans, and vertebrates. Among the annelids, only *Aphrodite* is known to possess a similar organization: blind-ending caeca of the gut secrete enzymes and resorb digested food after this has passed through filters situated near the orifice of the caeca. These filters prevent larger food particles from entering the lumen of the digestive caeca (Fordham, 1927).

The large, branched midgut gland of higher Crustacea (Malacostraca), often referred to as the *hepatopancreas*, is the chief site of secretion of digestive enzymes and bile acids, and is the site of resorption of nutrients. Although some digestion may take place in the muscular stomach, this organ serves chiefly in mechanically disrupting the food ("gastric mill") (Vonk, 1947; Waterman, 1960; Mansour-Bek, 1932; Degkwitz, 1957; Krueger and Graetz, 1928).

Tryptic and catheptic proteases, esterases (lipases), and various carbohydrases have been detected in the digestive juices of the crustaceans investigated. Insects do not possess well-developed midgut glands, although in several forms there are midgut caeca with digestive function (cockroach). The epithelium of the midgut of insects is the chief site of enzyme secretion, digestion, and resorption. A special gland at the beginning of the midgut of dipteran insects secretes the so-called *peritrophic membrane*, a thin membrane which separates the lumen contents from the digestive epithelium. This membrane is produced continuously; it is permeable to enzymes and to the end products of digestion. Its chief function seems to be mechanical protection of the delicate midgut epithelium from the coarse food material ingested.

The midgut epithelia of insects do not produce mucus (Schildmacher, 1954; Waterhouse, 1954, 1957). Other insect groups also have a peritrophic membrane, but this is secreted by the epithelial cells all along the midgut.

Molluscan midgut glands are most extensively developed in the cephalopods, but in all of them this organ is the site of enzyme secretion, digestion, and resorption. Only small particles and liquefied food material can enter the gland, however. Larger material must be broken down and predigested within the digestive tract.

In the tunicates, the midgut gland consists of a widely ramified system of glandular tubes within the wall of the gut.

Vertebrates usually have two major digestive glands associated with the intestine: the liver and pancreas. The *liver* secretes *bile acids* and *bile salts* (collected in the *gallbladder*; this enlargement of the major bile duct is missing in several mammals, such as the horse and rat, but is generally present in all representatives of the other vertebrate groups, including fish). The liver is connected with the intestinal epithelium by a special hepatic circulatory system (see the diagram in Fig. 10–22). Fats and fatty acids, amino acids, and carbohydrates are transported to the liver, where they are metabolized extensively: fats are broken down or resynthesized, amino acids are transformed into proteins or carbohydrates, carbohydrates into fats, fats into carbohydrates. In short, the liver is *the* chemical laboratory of the body. It is also an important storage site for glycogen.

The liver releases *glucose* into the blood stream and controls the *blood sugar* level. It is also engaged in excretory processes. The *hemoglobin* of dying red blood cells is metabolized there to *bile pigments* (*bilirubin* and *biliverdin*) etc. *Ammonia* and *urea* (or *uric acid*, as the case may be) are produced there and carried by the blood stream to the kidneys. Liver cells take up water whenever water is absorbed into the organism. They swell under such circumstances and later release this water into the circulation to be excreted by the kidneys.

Prothrombin and *fibrinogen*, important proteins in blood clotting mechanisms, are produced in the liver, as is *heparin*, the enzyme that prevents blood clotting.

The *pancreas* secretes several digestive enzymes—proteases, carbohydrases, and esterases. In addition, the islet cells serve as an incretory gland, secreting *insulin*, the hormone that controls carbohydrate metabolism of the various body cells by making the cell membranes permeable to glucose, and *glucagon*, another hormone involved in the control of carbohydrate metabolism. The function of both hormones is discussed in the following chapter (Nutrition).

The midgut gland of decapod crustaceans and of cephalopod molluscs combines the function of the liver and hepatopancreas, because it secretes enzymes and serves in the resorption and storage of nutrients (fat, glycogen), is involved in the metabolism (synthesis) of blood pigment (hemocyanin), and produces *bile acids* (in decapod Crustacea). In this connection, it is interesting that in hemoglobin-containing *Daphnia*, the hepatopancreas serves in the synthesis and breakdown of hemoglobin.

Incretory functions of invertebrate midgut glands are, as yet, unknown.

REFERENCES

Ammon, R., and M. Jaarma (1950) Enzymes hydrolyzing fats and esters. *In* The Enzymes, Vol. 1, pp. 390–442. (J. B. Sumner and K. Myrbäck, eds.) Academic Press, New York.

Bacq, Z. M., and F. Ghiretti (1951) La sécrétion externe et interne des glandes salivaires postérieures des Céphalopodes octopodes. Bull. Acad. Roy. Belg. Cl. Sci., Ser. 5, *37*:79–102.

Bárány, E., and E. Sperber (1939) Absorption of glucose against a concentration gradient by the small intestine of the rabbit. Scand. Arch. Physiol. *81*:290–299.

Barrington, E. J. W. (1962) Digestive enzymes. *In* Advances in Comparative Physiology and Biochemistry, Vol. 1, pp. 1–67. (O. E. Lowenstein, ed.) Academic Press, New York.

Berrill, N. J. (1929) Digestion in ascidians and the influence on temperature. Brit. J. Exp. Biol. *6*:275–292.

Beutler, R. (1926) Beobachtungen an gefütterten Hydroidpolypen. Z. vergl. Physiol. *3*:737–775.

Beutler, R. (1927) Die Wasserstoffkonzentration im Magen von *Hydra*. Z. vergl. Physiol. *6*:473–488.

Bodansky, M. (1924) Comparative studies of digestion. III. Further observations on digestion in coelenterates. Amer. J. Physiol. *67*:547–550.

Bonnet, A. (1924) Recherches sur l'appareil digestif et absorbant de quelques Echinides réguliers. C. R. Acad. Sci. *179*:846–848.

Boyer, P. D., H. Lardy, and K. Myrbäck, eds. (1959–1963) The Enzymes, 2nd Ed., 8 vols. Academic Press, New York.

Buchs, S. (1954) Die Proteolyse im Tiermagen. Z. vergl. Physiol. *36*:165–175.

von Buddenbrock, W. (1956) Vergleichende Physiologie, B. III. Birkhäuser Verlag, Basel.

Cori, C. F. (1925) The rate of absorption of hexoses and pentoses from the intestinal tract. J. Biol. Chem. *66*:691–715.

Cori, C. F. (1926) The rate of absorption of a mixture of glucose and galactose. Proc. Soc. Exp. Biol. Med. *23*:290–291.

Dean, D. (1958) New property of the crystalline style of *Crassostrea virginica*. Science *128*:837.

Degkwitz, E. (1957) Ein Beitrag zur Natur der proteolytischen Verdauungsfermente bei verschiedenen Crustaceenarten. Veroff. Inst. Meeresfschg. Bremerhaven 5:1–13.

Evans, W. A. L. (1958) Studies on the digestive enzymes of the blowfly *Calliphora erythrocephala*. I. The carbohydrases. Exp. Parasitol. 5:191–206.

Florkin, M., and F. Lozet (1949) Origine bactérienne de la cellulase du contenu intestinal de l'escargot. Arch. Int. Physiol. 57:201–207.

Fordham, M. G. C. (1927) *Aphrodite aculea*. L.M.B.C. Mem. No. 27, Liverpool University Press, Liverpool.

Friedman, M. H. F. (1937) Oesophageal and gastric secretion in the frog (*Rana esculenta*). J. Cell. Comp. Physiol. *10*:37–50.

Ghiretti, F. (1949) Action of extracts of the posterior salivary glands of octopods on Crustacea. Boll. Soc. ital. biol. sper. *25*:1304–1305.

Ghiretti, F. (1950) Enzimi delle ghiandole salivari posteriori dei Cefalopodi. II. Attivita proteolitica del secreto gange. Boll. Soc. ital. biol. sper. *26*:559.

Ghiretti, F. (1953) Les excitants chimiques de la sécrétion salivaire chez les Céphalopodes octopodes. Arch. Int. Physiol. *61*:10–21.

Ghiretti, F. (1960) Toxicity of octopus saliva against Crustacea. Ann. N. Y. Acad. Sci. *90*:726–741.

Gottschalk, A. (1950) Alpha-D-glucosidases. *In* The Enzymes, Vol. 1, pp. 551–582. (J. B. Sumner and K. Myrbäck, eds.) Academic Press, New York.

Greenfield, L. J., and C. E. Lane (1953) Cellulose digestion in *Teredo*. J. Biol. Chem. *204*:669–672.

Hall, V. E. (1931) The muscular activity and oxygen consumption of *Urechis caupo*. Biol. Bull. *61*:400–416.

Hendley, E., and D. H. Smyth (1958) Active transport of sodium by the intestine in vitro. J. Physiol. *139*:27P–28P.

Holter, H., and Lovtrup, S. (1949) Proteolytic enzymes in *Chaos chaos*. C. R. Lab. Carlsberg, Ser. chim. *27*:27–62.

Hyman, L. H. (1951) The Invertebrates, Vol. II: Platyhelminthes and Rhynchocoela. The Acoelomate Bilateria. McGraw-Hill Book Co., New York.

Ingraham, R. C., and M. B. Visscher (1936a) The influence of various poisons on the movement of chloride against concentration gradients from intestine to plasma. Amer. J. Physiol. *114*:681–687.

Ingraham, R. C., and M. B. Visscher (1936b) The production of chloride-free solution by the action of the intestinal epithelium. Amer. J. Physiol. *114*:676–680.

Ingraham, R. C., and M. B. Visscher (1938) Further studies on intestinal absorption with the performance of work. Amer. J. Physiol. *121*:771–785.

Jeuniaux, C. (1950) Recherche de la chitinase dans les tissus glandulaires digestifs de l'escargot (Helix pomatia) Arch. Int. Physiol. 58:354–355.

Jeuniaux, C. (1954) Sur la chitinase et la flore bactérienne intestinales des mollusques gastéropods. Acad. Roy. Belg. Cl. Sci. Mém. *28*:1–45.

Kilian, E. F. (1952) Wasserstroemung und Nahrungsaufnahme beim Suesswasserschwamm *Ephydatia fluviatilis*. Z. vergl. Physiol. *34*:407–447.

Kohler, A. (1882) Beitrag zur Kenntnise der Land—und Süsswasser—Conchylien in der Umgegend von Darmstadt. Notizbl. Ver. Erdk. Darmstadt *IV*:1–6.

Krijgsman, B. J. (1936) Vergleichend-physiologische Untersuchungen ueber den Stoffwechsel von *Trypanosoma evansi* im Zusammenhang mit der Anpassung an das Wirtstier. Z. vergl. Physiol. *23*:663–711.

Krijgsman, B. J., and F. H. Talbot (1953) Experiments on digestion in sea anemones. Arch. Int. Physiol. *61*:277–291.

Krueger, P., and E. Graetz (1928) Die Fermente des Flusskrebsmagensaftes. Zool. Jahrb., Allg. Zool. Physiol. Tiere, *45*:463–514.

Krukenberg, C. F. W. (1882) Nachtrag zu den Untersuchungen über den Ernährungsvorsang bei Coelenteraten und Echinodermen. Untersuchungen aus dem Physiologischen Institute der Universität Heidelberg, Vol. 2. C. Winter, Heidelberg.

Langley, L. L. (1949) Respiration of the electric eel. Amer. J. Physiol. *159*:578.

Lasker, R., and A. C. Giese (1956) Cellulose digestion by the silverfish *Ctenolepisma lineata*. J. Exp. Biol. *33*:542–553.

Lowenstein, O. (1962) Frontiers of knowledge in the study of sensory function. Advan. Sci. *19*: 222–235.

Mansour, K., and J. J. Mansour-Bek (1934) On the digestion of wood by insects. J. Exp. Biol. *11*: 243–256.

Mansour-Bek, J. J. (1932) Die proteolytischen Enzyme von *Maja squinado* Latr. Z. vergl. Physiol. *17*:153–208.

Marlier, G. (1938) Considérations sur les organes accessoires servant à la respiration aérienne chez les Téléostéens. Ann. Soc. Zool. Belg. *69*:163–185.

Meeuse, B. J. D., and W. Fluegel (1958) Carbohydrate-digesting enzymes in the sugar gland juice of Cryptochiton stelleri Middendorff (Polyplacophora, Mollusca). Arch. Neerl. Zool. *13*:301–313.

Morton, J. E. (1958) Observations on the gymnosomatous pterod *Clione limacina (Phipps)*. J. Mar. Biol. Assn. U. K. *37*:287–297.

Newell, B. S. (1953) Cellulolytic activity in the lamellibranch crystalline style. J. Mar. Biol. Assn. U.K. *32*:491–495.

Nicholls, A. G. (1931) Studies on *Ligia oceanica*. II. The processes of feeding, digestion and absorption. J. Mar. Biol. Assn. U.K. *17*:675–707.

Nirenstein, E. (1922) Ueber das Vorkommen freier Säure im Verdauungstrakt von Oligochaeten. Pflügers Arch. ges. Physiol. *196*:60–65.

Norris, E. R., and D. W. Elam (1940) Preparation and properties of crystalline salmon pepsin. Contr. Oceanogr. Lab. Univ. Wash. *95*:443–454.

Northrop, J. H. (1922) The mechanism of the influence of acids and alkalies on the digestion of proteins by pepsin or trypsin. J. Gen. Physiol. *5*:263–274.

Pinhey, K. G. (1930) Tyrosinase in crustacean blood. J. Exp. Biol. *7*:19–37.

Prosser, C. L., and F. A. Brown, Jr. (1961) Comparative Animal Physiology, 2nd Ed. W. B. Saunders Co., Philadelphia.

Ray, D. L., and J. R. Julian (1952) Occurrence of cellulase in Limnoria. Nature *169*:32–33.

Rössler, M. E. (1955) Uber eine bakterielle Vorverdauung und eine proteolytische Hauptverdauung im Darm der Nashornkäferlarve (*Oryctes nasicornis* L.) Experientia *11*:357–358.

Rössler, M. E. (1961) Ernährungsphysiologische Untersuchungen an Scarabaeidenlarven (*Oryctes nasicornis* L., *Melolontha melolontha* L.) J. Insect Physiol. *6*:62–80.

Sawano, E. (1938) Studies on the proteolytic system in the Ciliata, *Paramecium caudatum*. Sci. Rep. Tokyo Bunrika Daigaku *3*:221–241.

Schildmacher, H. (1954) Darmkanal und Verdauung bei Stechmücken. Biol. Zbl. *69*:390–438.

Schlottke, E. (1936) Untersuchungen ueber Verdauungsvermente von Infusorien aus dem Rinderpansen. Sitz. Ber. Naturf. Ges. Rostock, 3rd Folge, *6*:59–81.

Schreiber, B. (1932) Un singolare tipo di rigenerazione fisiologica nelle Aloturie Il ciclo di secrezione nelle reti mirabili. Arch. Zool. Torino *17*:387–399.

Shinoda, O. (1926) Contributions to the knowledge of intestinal secretion of insects. J. Mem. Col. Sci. Kyoto *2*:93–116.

Smith, H. G. (1936) Contributions to the anatomy and physiology of *Cassiopeia frondosa*. Pap. Tortugas Labor. *31*:17–52.

Sprissler, S. P. (1942) An investigation of the proteinase of the gastric mucosa of shark. Contr. Ciol. Lab. Cathol. Univ. Amer. *42*:1–52.

Stone, B. A., and J. E. Morton (1958) The distribution of cellulases and related enzymes in Mollusca. Proc. Malac. Soc. Lond. *33*:127–141.

Swiecicki, H. (1876) Untersuchungen ueber die Bildung und Ausscheidung des Pepsins bei den Batrachiern. Pflügers Arch. ges. Physiol. *13*:444–452.

Szarski, H. (1936) Studies on the anatomy and physiology of the alimentary canal of worms belonging to the Naididae family. Bull. Acad. Polon. Sc. Lett. Crocow. pp. 387–409.

Tallan, H. H., and S. Buchs (1947) Die Biologie des Magenkathepsins. S. Karger, Basel.

Tallan, H. H., M. E. Jones, and J. S. Fruton (1952) On the proteolytic enzymes of animal tissues. X. Beef spleen cathepsin C. J. Biol. Chem. *194*:793–805.

Tracey, M. V. (1951) Cellulase and chitinase of earthworms. Nature *167*:776–777.

Tracey, M. V. (1955) Cellulase and chitinase in soil amoebae. Nature *175*:815.

Vachon, M. (1953) Biology of scorpions. Endeavor *12*:80–89.

Verzar, F., and E. J. McDougall (1936) Absorption from the Intestine. Longmans, Green and Co., New York.

Vonk, H. J. (1937) The specificity and collaboration of digestive enzymes in metazoa. Biol. Rev. *12*:245–284.

Vonk, H. J. (1947) La présence d'acides biliaires et la résorption des acides gras chez les invertébrés. Bull. Soc. Chim. Biol. *29*:94–96.

Vonk, H. J. (1960) Digestion and metabolism. *In* The Physiology of Crustacea, Vol. 1, pp. 291–340. (T. H. Waterman, ed.) Academic Press, New York.

Vonk, H. J., and A. Heyn (1929) Das Optimum des Trypsins umd die Reaction des Darminhaltes. Proc. Roy. Acad. Amsterdam *32*:440–443.

Vonk, H. J., and H. P. Wolvekamp (1929) Faktoren, welche die Trypsinenverdauung im Darme beeinflussen. Z. Physiol. Chem. *182*:175–200.

Waterhouse, D. F. (1954) Rate of production of the peritrophic membrane in some insects. Austral. J. Biol. Sci. *7*:59–72.

Waterhouse, D. F. (1957) Digestion in insects. Ann. Rev. Entomol. *2*:1–18.

Waterman, T. H., ed. (1960) The Physiology of Crustacea, Vol. 1: Metabolism and Growth. Academic Press, New York.

Weidenhagen, R. (1940) Carbohydrases. *In* Handbuch der Enzymologie, Akademische Verlagsgesellschaft Becker & Erber Kom. Ges. Leipzig.

von Widmark, E. M. P. (1911) Über die Gastrovascularströmungen bei *Aurelia aurita* L. und *Cyanea capillata* Eschz. Zool. Anz. *38*:378–382.

Wiseman, G. (1953) Absorption of amino-acids, using an *in vitro* technique. J. Physiol. *120*:63–72.

Wiseman, G. (1954) Preferential transference of amino-acids from amino-acid mixtures by sacs of everted small intestine of the golden hamster (*Mesocrisetus auratus*). J. Physiol. *127*:414–422.

Wiseman, G. (1956) Active transport of amino-acids by sacs of everted small intestine of the golden hamster (*Mesocrisetus auratus*). J. Physiol. *133*:626–630.

Woodman, H. E. (1930) The role of cellulose in nutrition. Biol. Rev. *5*:273–295.

Yonge, C. M. (1937) Evolution and adaptation in the digestive system of the Metazoa. Biol. Rev. *12*:87–115.

Yonge, C. M., and A. G. Nicholls (1930) Digestive enzymes. Sci. Rep. Great Barrier Reef Expedition. Brit. Museum *I*, pp. 59–81.

12 NUTRITION

This chapter is concerned to a limited degree with the qualitative food requirements and concentrates on the quantitative food requirements of animal organisms and on the mechanisms of nutrient storage and utilization. *Food*, in this context, means *nutrients*—chemicals that are resorbed by the digestive tract, by the digestive glands, and by the body wall, and that are utilized by the body cells for synthesis of body constituents and for energy metabolism. Since the typical pattern of animal energy metabolism is *oxidative* degradation of certain kinds of amino acids, lipids, and carbohydrates and their derivatives, such a discussion includes the role of oxygen.

In addition, it is customary to consider among the nutrients two categories of substances: (1) inorganic compounds and ions that are indispensable constituents of the cells and of the body fluids: H_2O, NaCl, KCl, $CaCl_2$, $MgCl_2$, Fe^{++}, and Cu^{++}, and several other trace elements; (2) steroids, vitamins, and other organic compounds that cannot be synthesized in the organism and which serve as coenzymes or in certain rate-controlling roles, the precise nature of which is not always understood.

From all we know, it appears that the nutritional requirements are similar throughout the Animal Kingdom. The metabolic pathways are almost interchangeable, and the nutrients, on the whole, are interchangeable too; what is food for one animal can easily serve as food for another, even if this belongs to an entirely different phylum: a sea anemone can live on shrimp and crabs, and so can an octopus. Different food habits are not necessarily the result of differences in nutritional requirements but more often of inborn behavior patterns which allow each species to occupy a separate niche of the environment. For example, the caterpillars of butterflies and moths live on leaves; each species is usually specialized and eats only the leaves of one, or at most a few, species of plants. If the behavior pattern that leads to the selection of the particular plant is circumvented, other food sources can be substituted.

Whenever the food consists of plant or animal matter, it contains proteins, as well as carbohydrates and fats and their derivatives. Animals that live on an exclusive diet of protein, of carbohydrate, or of lipid, are rare. Even wood-boring animals (wood-boring larvae of beetles and moths, wood-boring isopods such as *Limnoria*, and molluscs, such as *Teredo*) have some protein and lipid in their diet, although the chief foodstuff is cellulose. The exceptional food specialists, however, are truly remarkable because they thrive practically exclusively on only one kind of chemical: the larvae of the waxmoth, *Galleria*, can live on a diet of beeswax. Several species of beetles and the clothes moths (*Tineola*) thrive on keratin, a structural protein of hair, feathers, or horns. Digestion of keratin requires a special enzyme, a cysteine disulfhydrase which breaks the sulfate bridges between neighboring cysteine groups by which the folds or helical turns of the keratin molecule are held together (Linderstrøm-Lang and Duspiva, 1935; Powning, 1954).

Even in these extreme cases, however, there is no certainty that no other intake of additional nutrients in involved. Also, the activity of intestinal bacteria should not be forgotten.

Whether the predominant nutrients are protein, lipids, or carbohydrates, their derivatives (amino acids, fatty acids, monosaccharides, etc.) are inter-convertible, and every animal organism is equipped to transform one into the other.

Nutrients are required for two basic functions: (1) growth and replacement of the organized substance of the animal and (2) energy production to perform work, such as: chemical synthesis, movement, molecular and ionic transport, and heat production.

STORAGE AND MOBILIZATION

Nutrients are not usually converted directly into organized body substance and energy. A large amount is stored in the form of reserve nutrients, such as glycogen and fat. This storage can take place within the various body cells themselves, but usually certain organs specialize in storage and release of reserve nutrients. The most prominent among them are the various forms of midgut glands or liver, the gonads, the fat tissues (fat bodies of insects), and often the muscles. Specialized sites for protein storage are as yet unknown. It is likely that utilizable protein is distributed uniformly throughout the body cells. A certain amount of reserve material (mainly carbohydrate and protein) is present within the circulating body fluids, particularly in organisms with a hemocoel or with a closed vascular system. In starving animals, the carbohydrate ("blood sugar") and protein content of hemolymph and blood declines.

The storage of special nutrients makes possible a continuous supply of utilizable molecules even if the food supply is discontinuous. It is not surprising, therefore, that storage functions of certain organs are particularly prominent in animals that feed discontinuously.

Not only the nutrients proper, but also the vitamins and inorganic ions can be stored and held in reserve. Midgut glands and livers are known to contain large amounts of vitamins (e.g., cod liver oil). Inorganic ions are stored in the form of insoluble crystalline deposits within endoskeletons (bone, spicules, cartilage), exoskeletons, and calcareous shells.

It is possible that the chitin of the arthropod exoskeleton serves a function as stored carbohydrate. Like glycogen, chitin is a polysaccharide (Fig. 11–1). That the chitin of the exoskeleton can be readily mobilized is seen in crayfish just prior to molting: the inner (ventral) portions of the skeleton of the chelae become eroded, and in several places the skeleton disappears altogether, thereby forming an opening through which the animal can withdraw the limbs from the exoskeleton it is about to shed. Unfortunately, nothing definite is known about the changes in composition of exoskeletons of arthropods during starvation.

So far, comparative physiology has failed miserably in providing quantitative data which permit an evaluation of the role of storage and mobilization of reserve nutrients, ions, and vitamins in the majority of animal groups. We lack much of the basic information concerning the mechanisms by which the reserves are used and the incorporation of nutrients into storage depots is controlled. Vertebrates, in particular the mammals, have been well investigated in this regard.

The important problems are not the questions concerning the *kinds* of storage material (glycogen, galactogen, fats, oils, etc.), or the *site* of storage, or even the relative *amounts* of such stores at various times during the life cycle of an organism. The real problems are: What are the mechanisms that control the deposition of nutrients in the form of reserve compounds? What are the mechanisms that are put into operation when reserves are to be mobilized?

To bring these problems into focus, we must realize that storage sites are usually removed from the sites where the mobilized products of storage substances are to be utilized: For example, glycogen in the midgut gland is mobilized in the starving crayfish, and the glucose derived from it is utilized, among others, by the muscles of the legs and of the heart for energy production (muscle contractions). The glycolytic enzymes are present in both muscle and the midgut gland. Why is glucose deposited as glycogen in the midgut gland and why is it not metabolized there? How do the cells in the midgut gland "know" that the glycogen or glucose stores of the muscles are exhausted? Why does increased supply of nutrients not lead to a proportional increase in metabolism and energy liberation?

In the recent reviews of crustacean metabolism and nutrition (Marshall and Orr, 1960; Vonk, 1960), these questions have not been discussed, for the simple reason that there is little experimental work in this connection.

As mentioned, satisfactory information is available from research in vertebrates, and from this derives the following discussion of general principles:

1. Nutrients taken up through the resorptive membranes of the digestive system (and the body wall) enter the circulating body fluids. Unless active transport is involved, the amount of nutrients moving into the body fluids is proportional to the concentration gradient across the resorptive membrane.

2. Circulating nutrients are now subject to passive and active transport across cell membranes into the various types of body cells. For the sake of this discussion, these can be divided into four groups: cells of the so-called

excretory organs (emunctoria, nephridia, kidneys), cells of the exchange membranes of the body wall (epidermis, gills, etc.), cells of storage organs (midgut glands, gonads, fat body, etc.), and the rest of the body cells.

The entry of circulating nutrients into these various types of body cells is called *storage by inundation* (Cannon, 1929).

3. The nutrients that have entered the body cells are in part metabolized directly; that is, they are degraded with concomitant energy liberation. In part, however, they are transformed into storage compounds—lipids and fatty acids into fats, amino acids into proteins, and glucose and other simple sugars (fructose, galactose, lactose, etc.) into glycogen (in certain invertebrates, notably molluscs, *galactogen* may, at least in part, take the place of glycogen.

The conversion into storage forms has been named *storage by segregation* (Cannon, 1929). The advantages of this form of storage are: (1) The storage molecules are insoluble in water; therefore, they change only insignificantly the intracellular osmotic concentration, even if they accumulate in large amounts. (2) By the transformation or, better, incorporation into storage molecules, the intracellular concentration of the particular nutrient is reduced so that a large concentration gradient across the cell membrane can be maintained which drives more nutrient into the cell. (3) The water-insoluble storage molecules are also indiffusible; that is, they cannot diffuse into all the compartments of the cell. They are thus protected from attack by the metabolic enzymes situated in other compartments of the cell.

4. The chief storage organs (liver, midgut gland) are strategically located. In the vertebrates, the blood coming from the digestive tract first passes through the intricate vascular system of the liver (see Chap. 10, Fig. 10–22), where the nutrients have every chance of entering the liver cells and of becoming stored there. In Crustacea and Mollusca, to name two prominent phyla, nutrients are resorbed within the digestive gland itself. The cells of the digestive gland, then, have the first chance to take up and store nutrients. Only what is not taken up by the storage organ passes into the general circulation.

5. The cells of the kidney tubules of vertebrates contain a transport system for sugars (glycogen, fructose, etc.), which carries all sugar molecules that enter these cells right out again into the circulating body fluids. This prevents loss of nutrients into the urine which would occur if there were no mechanism to counteract the passive diffusion through the tubular epithelial cells. Only when the transport system becomes overloaded do sugar molecules diffuse into the urine. The phenomenon of sugar loss into urine is called *glycosuria*. Similar mechanisms as those involved in sugar transport exist for transport of amino acids and other important nutrients.

6. In vertebrates, the pancreas produces two hormones: *insulin* and *glucagon*, which control the fate of glucose (and other simple sugars).

Insulin (discovered by the Canadians Banting and Best and the Frenchman Paulesco in 1921) increases the transfer of glucose (and similar sugars) across cell membranes. This results in increased glycogen synthesis in the liver and increased glucose utilization (glycogenesis, glycolysis, conversion to fat). The amount of insulin released controls the intensity of glucose transfer and, consequently, the amount of glucose (blood sugar) circulating in the blood. (The condition of an abnormally high blood sugar level is called *hyperglycemia*; that of an abnormally low concentration of blood sugar is called *hypoglycemia*.)

In the liver, insulin inhibits the action of glucose-6-phosphatase (*hexokinase*): since this enzyme transforms glucose-6-phosphate into glucose (see Figs. 7–1 and 7–2), when it is inhibited by insulin the amount of glucose liberated from liver cells is reduced. (Since the literature on this topic is extensive, refer to the reviews of Turner; von Buddenbrock; and Nocenti in Bard.) Insulin secretion is stimulated by increased blood sugar levels; it is decreased when the blood sugar is low (Grafe and Meythaler, 1927).

Glucagon, like insulin a polypeptide, causes increased production of glucose from liver glycogen and a concomitant increase in blood sugar. It is released when blood sugar levels are low. The mechanism of action of glucagon seems to be that of activation of liver phosphorylase (muscle phosphorylase is unaffected) (Foa, Galasino, and Pozza, 1957).

Insulin and glucagon are produced in two different cell types. The two types are found in the islands of Langerhans, wherever these occur, but in the absence of discrete "islands," they are distributed throughout the pancreatic tissues or occur even outside—for instance, in the intestinal mucosa (larval lampreys [Langerhans, 1873]) or as separate bodies, called "principal islands" (*Lophius, Ameiurus* [Bowie, 1924]). The two cell types are known as alpha and beta cells. Alpha cells produce glucagon, beta cells insulin. Mammals and lizards possess both types, amphibians only beta cells, and reptiles and birds largely alpha cells. The effects of removal of the pancreas (pancreatectomy) are therefore quite different in the various vertebrate groups: the syndromes are predominantly those of lack of insulin (hyperglycemia) or of lack of glucagon (hypoglycemia) (Barrington, 1953; De Robertis and Primavesi, 1939; Fischer, 1912; Nagelschmidt, 1939; Thomas, 1942; Houssay, 1958; Miller and Wurster, 1958; Root, 1956).

7. Secretion of a hormone, *somatotropin*, from the anterior pituitary of mammals antagonizes the action of insulin; that is, it causes a rise in blood sugar, most likely because it stimulates conversion of proteins or fats into sugar (De Bodo and Sinkoff, 1953).

8. The *adrenal glands* secrete steroid hormones and adrenalin; both of these types of hormones affect carbohydrate metabolism: *11-oxy-steroids (glucocorticoids)* produced by the *adrenal cortex* prevent utilization of glucose (blood sugar) by tissues and prevent incorporation of amino acids into proteins. As a result, amino acids are transformed into sugars (see Fig. 7–7) and these sugars diffuse into the blood stream (Ingle, Beary, and Purmalis, 1953). The elevated blood sugar level leads to urinary excretion of sugar, since the tissues cannot utilize it.

Adrenaline, produced by the *adrenal medulla*, stimulates formation of glucose from liver glycogen and stimulates glycolysis in tissues without enhancing oxidative metabolism. Adrenaline, consequently, leads to an increase in lactic acid in both tissues and blood. The blood lactic acid is then, secondarily, transformed into glycogen in the liver.

9. The *thyroid gland* secretes a hormone, *thyroxine*, which generally speeds up catabolic metabolism, particularly oxidative metabolism. Both glycogen and

protein are broken down. In the liver, glucose production from glycogen is increased and this leads to a rise of the blood sugar level.

10. Hormone secretion from the pituitary gland is controlled by the brain, particularly by the release from neurosecretory cells in the hypothalamus of neurohumors (as yet unidentified), that is, substances that diffuse into the blood vessels which carry blood from the hypothalamus to the anterior pituitary gland where these substances act on the gland cells, causing hormone release. Thus, the brain controls the release of somatotropin.

The release of adrenaline is caused by the action of the sympathetic nerves that supply the adrenal glands. The sympathetic nervous system, in turn, is under the control of the central nervous system.

Release of steroid hormones from the adrenal cortex is controlled by a hormone from the anterior pituitary gland, *adrenocorticotropic hormone* (ACTH). The released steroids, in turn, inhibit the release of ACTH (negative feedback). The release of thyroxine is controlled by a pituitary hormone, *thyrotropin*; the level of thyrotropin secretion, in turn, depends on the level of thyroxine in the blood: increased secretion of thyroxine causes a reduction in thyrotropin release (negative feedback).

11. Nerve centers at the floor of the fourth ventricle of the mammalian brain control the blood sugar level by activating the sympathetic nerves that innervate the adrenal glands and by causing release of adrenaline. This was first shown by the famous French physiologist Claude Bernard (1849), and was analyzed in more detail (including adrenalectomy) by Donhoffer and MacLeod (1932) (MacLeod, 1934).

12. Stimulation of sensory neurons along the vagus nerve or in the crural or sciatic nerve, causes an increase in blood sugar level. Stimulation of the crural and sciatic nerves is ineffective, though, if the adrenal glands are removed (Griffith, 1923; Britton, 1925). It appears likely that this effect is mediated by the center in the floor of the fourth ventricle.

It is well known that the majority of the sensory axons in the sciatic nerve carry impulses from muscle receptor organs to the central nervous system. The receptor organs are activated by the actual movements of the muscles in which they are situated. The reflex mobilization of adrenaline secretion makes glucose available to the working muscles and, in addition, stimulates muscle glycolysis.

The complex interactions of hormones and nervous system are summarized in Figure 12–1.

Endocrinology of invertebrates is far behind that of vertebrates, particularly in regard to hormones involved in the control of metabolism. Numerous publications deal with metabolic pathways of invertebrates and with quantitative studies of the amounts of different metabolites during various phases of the organism's life. Many papers have described changes in metabolism and in amounts of various compounds (glycogen, galactogen, fats, protein, amino acids) associated with molting cycles in arthropods, hibernation in terrestrial gastropods, or feeding and starvation in a number of animal types. As yet, however, we lack definite knowledge of the role of specific hormones. In fact, we do not even know the identity of one single hormone that might be involved

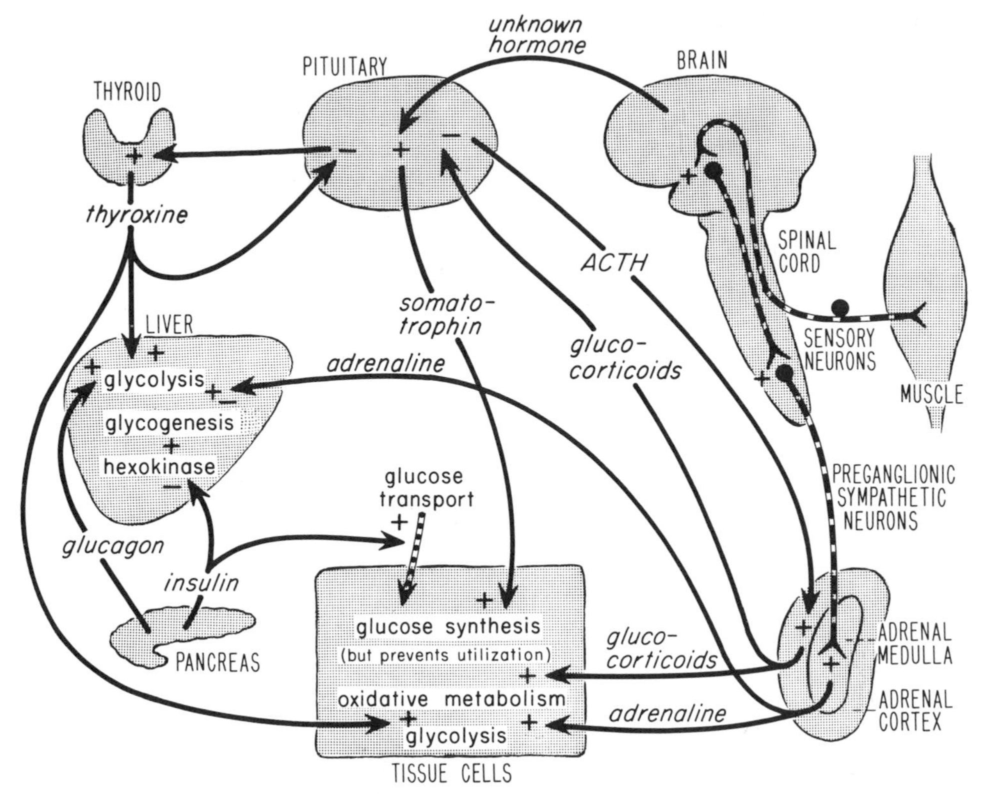

Figure 12–1. Nervous and hormonal control of carbohydrate metabolism in mammals.

in the control of invertebrate metabolism. There is suggestive evidence, however, that products of neurosecretion are directly or indirectly responsible for drastic alterations in metabolic pattern as they occur during molting cycles of Crustacea or during metamorphosis of insects. Such information derives from studies of the effects of removal of crustacean eyestalks or brains, and removal of insect brains, or their associated neurosecretory glands (the corpora allata and corpora cardiaca), and from studies of the effects of implantations or injections of extracts of such organs. The crudeness of the approach can be appreciated when one imagines this employed in experiments on vertebrates: Ablation of eyestalks in Crustacea may be equivalent to removal of the whole pituitary gland plus the hypothalamus.

Only after it has become possible to separate the hormones produced by the neurosecretory apparatus of the eyestalks or of other structures with incretory function, will it be feasible to conduct intelligible investigations. The task, of course, is formidable, if for no other reason than the minute size of the neurosecretory or incretory organs, and the fact that neurosecretory cells are often diffusely located within the central nervous system. On the other hand, the prospects are brightened by the recent development of most effective devices for the separation and purification of biochemicals on a micro-scale, in particular, the improved techniques for small scale chromatography, ion exchange procedures, and electrophoresis.

QUANTITATIVE ASPECTS OF NUTRITION

Several years ago a large whale was pursued by a whaling ship and finally was harpooned. The charge on the harpoon did not explode, and the furious giant dragged the whaler behind him for several hours at no less a velocity than 12 knots—in spite of the fact that the ship's engines were running full speed in reverse! The ship's engines were rated at 250 horsepower (h.p.) and could move the ship forward at a maximal speed of 12 knots. The efficiency of the ship's propeller can be taken to have been about 70 per cent. This means that it took 158 h.p. to move the ship forward at 12 knots.

The whale did not simply propel the ship forward at 12 knots with a power of 158 h.p., but had to overcome the full force of the reversed engines. In reverse, a propeller's action is not quite as efficient as in forward gear, thus with the engines in full speed in reverse, the resistance of the ship was about 95 h.p.

In addition to moving the ship, the whale's muscles had to move the huge body of the whale itself. At a velocity of 12 knots, or 5.5 m/sec, this required at least 50 h.p. The total power required to move both whale and ship (with its engines racing in reverse) amounted to no less than 158 + 95 + 50 = 303 h.p. Since the whale's "engine," the fluke (or tail fin), has an efficiency of 60 to 70 per cent, it must have performed with a force of about 460 h.p. when it moved the whale and resisting ship forward at 12 knots/hour.

The energy for muscular work is derived from chemical reactions. The efficiency of the energy transfer is generally rated at 20 to 30 per cent. Even at the higher figure, this means that 3.3 times as much energy must be made available through chemical reactions within a muscle than finally appears in the work output. In the case of the whale, this means that the chemical energy needed for a performance of 460 h.p./hour was no less than that equivalent to 1518 h.p./hr. One h.p. is equivalent to 75 kilogram-meters (kg-m) per second; 427 kg-m is equivalent to 1 kilocalorie (Cal). The whale must, therefore, have produced 267 Cal/sec, or 16,020 Cal/min, or 960,200 Cal/hr.

This great quantity of energy must have been liberated in chemical reactions consisting of catabolism of carbohydrate (glucose), fat, and protein. As explained below, 1 kg of carbohydrate yields 4000 Cal, 1 kg of fat 9500 Cal, and 1 kg of protein 5700 Cal. The whale could, therefore, have sustained its great effort with a carbohydrate consumption of 260 kg of glucose, 180 kg of fat, or about 100 kg of protein per hour, assuming that this amount was actually being oxidized completely. The oxygen required for this (regardless of whether carbohydrate, fat, or protein was utilized) amounted to about 192,000 liters/hour (measured at standard temperature and pressure), or 19.2m^3.

Whales do not pull whaling ships every day, but the example given here emphasizes the problem that concerns us now: the work done by an animal must be sustained and compensated for by an adequate food supply if this organism is to maintain its weight, and more food (or nutrients) if the organism is still in its growing phase and must increase in weight.

The example just presented is taken from a forgotten publication of the German physiologist August Pütter on "the physiology of giant animals"

(1923). In previous publications, Pütter emphasized a quantitative approach to comparative physiology in which he applied thermodynamic principles to studies of respiration, circulation, and nutrition in a manner that pointed the way to a fruitful extension of physiology into ecology. His efforts were not much understood in his day, and his approach has not been discussed in any of the great books of comparative physiology or of general physiology; in fact Pütter's name is hardly mentioned at all. In part, at least, this is due to the devastating critique which August Krogh, a famous Dane, applied to one of Pütter's favorite theses, namely, that many aquatic animals resorb a large percentage of the required nutrients through the gills. It was this contention of Pütter's that had been more widely discussed, usually quite out of context. When Krogh refuted—rightly or wrongly—the need of aquatic animals to utilize dissolved organic matter, even that part of Pütter's work was soon forgotten. It is only within most recent years that Pütter's star began to rise again, after several investigators showed conclusively that at least certain animals can resorb dissolved organic substances through their body wall and that this mechanism provides a large percentage of their energy requirements.

This section of this chapter is intended to be a tribute to the work of August Pütter, and it is hoped that it will stimulate a fruitful application of his original approach. In several places it will be necessary to replace the older values of heats of combustions, caloric values, etc. with more recent data. These are largely taken from the excellent book of Max Kleiber, The Fire of Life: An Introduction to Animal Energetics (1961). Before going into the discussion proper, it is necessary to introduce and define the necessary terminology.

Hess' law, formulated in 1840, states that *the total heat evolved in a chemical reaction is independent of the velocity of the chemical reaction or of the intermediary pathways by which the change is achieved.*

Robert Mayer, in 1851, established the *heat equivalent of work* and the mechanical equivalent of heat and formulated his law of the conservation of energy, later known as the first law of thermodynamics. Basically, his calculations and deductions are as follows:*

To raise the temperature of 1 mole of an ideal gas from 0° C to 1° C requires 2.980 calories of heat if the gas *volume* is kept constant, and 4.967 cal if the gas *pressure* is kept constant. Mayer assumed that the extra heat required in the latter case (4.967 − 2.980 = 1.987 cal) is transformed into work (expansion of the gas from a volume of 22.414 liters by 22.414/273 = 0.082 liter). Now, if the gas is allowed to expand only into a vertical tube with an inner diameter of 1 cm^2 and is provided with a movable, frictionless piston, it will push the piston up, against the atmospheric pressure (1.033 kg/cm^2), by 82.1 cm, or 0.821 meter. The work performed by the expanding gas is, therefore, 0.821 × 1.033 = 0.848 kilogram-meter (kg-m), and this is equivalent to 1.987 cal. One cal then is equivalent to 0.427 kg-m; 1 kg-m is equivalent to 2.34 cal.

Complete oxidation of a given chemical is called combustion. The heat of combustion is measured with special instruments, called calorimeters. The measured heat of combustion is expressed in terms of calories per mole

*This is a modernized version based on the presentation in Kleiber (1961).

or per gram of substance oxidized, and the number of calories is termed the *caloric equivalent*, or *caloric value*, of the oxidized substance.

Complete combustion of 1 mole of glucose to 6 moles CO_2 and 6 moles H_2O yields 673,000 cal, or 673 kilocalories (Cal) of heat. In this chemical reaction, 6 moles of O_2 is consumed. Once the caloric equivalent of glucose is known, one can calculate the heat produced by an unknown amount of glucose from data of the measured oxygen consumption of the reaction. The amount of CO_2 evolved, likewise, is a measure of the heat produced in the reaction.

The determination of heat production of oxidative chemical reactions by measuring O_2 consumption or CO_2 production is known as *indirect calorimetry*. The amounts of O_2 or CO_2 are usually given in milliliters normal temperature and pressure (N.T.P.), but some authors prefer to use milligrams of gas.

With few exceptions, animal energy metabolism is an oxidative metabolism in which carbohydrates, fats, and proteins (amino acids) are transformed into carbon dioxide and water, and—in the case of proteins—into ammonia, uric acid, urea, etc. According to *Hess' law*, the caloric equivalent of the oxidative metabolism of these substances within animal cells is identical with that determined in a calorimeter, even though the combustion proceeds along much more complex paths of chemical transformation in the animal than it does in the calorimeter.

Proteins and amino acids are an exception to the rule insofar as animals do not completely oxidize proteins but excrete portions of these molecules in the form of ammonia, urea, uric acid, etc. The caloric value of proteins metabolized by animals is, therefore, lower than that determined in a calorimeter, in which proteins are oxidized completely. One gram of protein oxidized in the calorimeter yields 5.7 Cal, but if metabolized in an animal only 4.8 Cal is released—the rest remains within the excretory products and is lost to the animal. Of course, animals also consume less O_2/mole of protein metabolized than does a calorimeter.

Oxygen consumption, then, is a direct measure of the actual amount of energy (heat, calories) liberated during oxidative metabolism.

Table 12–1 gives values for animal heat production resulting from oxidative metabolism of fat, protein, and carbohydrate.

Table 12–1

Substance Metabolized	*Energy (in Kilocalories) Produced per Liter of O_2*	*per Mole of O_2*
Fat	4.7	105
Protein	4.5	101
Carbohydrate (starch)	5.0	112

From Kleiber, M.: The Fire of Life: An Introduction to Animal Energetics. John Wiley & Sons, New York, 1961.

It is permissible to speak not only of the caloric value of the nutrients, but also of the caloric value (caloric equivalent) of the consumed oxygen. The figures given in Table 12–1, therefore, give the *caloric value of oxygen* in fat, protein, and carbohydrate metabolism.

In general, the oxygen consumption is a measure of the intensity of an animal's metabolism or of its *metabolic rate*. From the oxygen consumption one can calculate the amount of organic substance oxidized because the caloric value of the oxygen consumed is roughly identical with the caloric value of the food or nutrients oxidized. If 1 gram of carbohydrate upon oxidation yields 4 Cal, while 0.8 liter of oxygen is consumed, it is equally true that the consumption of 0.8 liter of oxygen liberates 4 Cal while 1 gram of carbohydrate is used up. Similar arguments apply to the utilization of fats and proteins.

If the oxygen consumption is known, the food requirements of the animal are known, because it can be assumed that the organic matter that is oxidized must be replaced if the animal is not to diminish in substance (and weight). Of course, the situation is not so simple, because the food requirements are, at first, known only in terms of grams (or kilograms) or moles of "carbohydrate," "fat," or "protein." Animal food, however, is not simply carbohydrate, fat, or protein, but fish, meat, vegetables, plankton, grass, wood, etc., and consists also of other types of compounds.

The caloric values of the various animal foods can be determined by chemical analysis and by direct calorimetry. Table 12–2 lists a number of values taken from various sources. These are maximal values. Animals cannot utilize these foods completely; a certain fraction of the food always remains undigested, and another amount is excreted in the form of urea, ammonia, uric acid, methane, etc.

Another useful measure of the nutritional significance of organic nutrients is the *oxygen capacity*, defined as the number of milligrams of oxygen used up in the oxidation of a given quantity of organic matter.

If the kind of food is known, the oxygen consumption can be used to calculate the minimum food supply. For instance, if a certain animal lives on copepods (e.g., *Calanus*) and the caloric value of an average *Calanus* is known, the oxygen consumption of the animal can be used to calculate how many

***Table 12–2.* Energy Yield of Various Foodstuffs upon Combustion (Expressed in Kilocalories/100 gm)**

Food	kcal/100 gm	Food	kcal/100 gm
Apples	58	Butter	716
Bananas	94	Lard	884
Cherries	60	Eggs	158
Cabbage	25	Cow's milk	65
Dandelion leaves	52	Beef meat	200–350
Radishes	20	Rabbit, medium fat	175
Turnips	32	Cod	70
Walnuts	702	Herring	136
Barley	346	Lobster	86
Cane sugar	384	Oyster	50
Honey	319		

Data from Documenta Geigy; Scientific Tables, 5th Ed. S. Karger Basle, New York, 1959.

Table 12–3.

Animal Species	Volume μ^3	Number Oxidized by 1 mg O_2
Algae		
Coscinodiscus concinnus	800,000	4,700
Peridinium divergens	250,000	15,000
Ceratium tripos	100,000	37,500
Ceratium fusus	37,000	100,000
Pleurosigma	10,000	375,000
Rhizosolonia	5,500	680,000
Nitschia longissima	1,000	3,750,000
Sceletonema costatum	150	25,000,000
Calycomonas gracilis	10	375,000,000
Copepoda		
Temora	26,000,000	153
Calanus	731,000,000	5.4
Temorella	20,000,000	200
Paracalanus	6,000,000	670
Larval stages *(Nauplii)*	1,000,000	4,000
Entomostraca	organic substance in mg	
Daphnia	0.0272	22
Cyclops	0.00308	194
Diaptomus	0.00449	132

From Pütter, A.: Die Ernährung der Wassertiere und der Stoffhaushalt der Gewasser. G. Fischer Verlag, Jena, 1909.

Calanus the animal has to eat, say in one day, in order to account for this oxygen consumption.

For a number of planktonic organisms, Pütter has calculated the caloric value per organism and converted his figures to indicate the numbers of individuals of any one species oxidized by 1 mg of oxygen. Table 12–3 lists some of his data.

In the case of aquatic animals, if the number of food animals per unit volume of water is known, one can determine the volume of water that must be available exclusively to the particular animal in order to provide the necessary food. Examples are given in Table 12–4.

Complications arise when the consumed nutrients are not completely oxidized, but are metabolized, at least in part, anaerobically. If that is the case, the oxygen consumption indicates a lower metabolic rate than actually occurs

Table 12–4.

Species	O_2 Consumption (in mg/hr/animal)	Volume of Animal (in cm^3)	Volume of Plankton-containing Water Required to Satisfy Food Requirement (in ml/hr)
Collozoum	0.111	0.1	760
Adamsia	0.205	11.0	1,400
Rhizostoma	0.808	80.0	5,580
Pterotrachea	0.700	57.0	4,800
Ciona	0.244	10.0	1,670

From Pütter, A.: Die Ernährung der Wassertiere und der Stoffhaushalt der Gewasser. G. Fischer Verlag, Jena, 1909.

Table 12–5.

Species	*Oxygen Capacity of Total Metabolized Substances* (mg)	*Oxygen Consumption* (mg)	*Oxygen Consumption in % of Oxygen Capacity*
Suberites	585	30	5.1
Helix (15° C)	119	38	32.0
Hirudo (25° C, after meal)	578	460	80.0
(18.8° C, starved)	218	118	54.0
(11° C, starved)	131	42	32.0
Astacus (14° C)	135.5	88	66.0
(20° C)	216.4	165	76.2
Goldfish	510	535	105.0
Stickleback	192	202	95.0
Carp	1300	1285	99.0

From Pütter, A.: Vergleichende Physiologie. G. Fischer Verlag, Jena, 1911.

and the calculated nutritional requirements are too low. The completeness of oxidations can be measured if the oxygen capacity of the metabolized organic matter is compared with the actual oxygen consumption during the observation period. For this purpose, the protein, fat, and carbohydrate content of control animals is determined at the outset of the experiment, and that of experimental animals at the end of a starvation period. During the same period, the oxygen consumption is measured. Table 12–5 shows Pütter's data.

These data reveal that many animal forms must consume more food than is indicated by their oxygen consumption in order to maintain their weight. The increased proportion of anaerobic metabolism at lower temperatures is interesting and significant in connection with food requirements.

In the chapter on respiration, it was explained that the oxygen consumption gm/hr decreases with increasing weight of the organism. Or, the other way around: the smaller an organism, the larger its relative oxygen consumption. Voit, and subsequently Pütter and many others, emphasized the proportionality of the surface area of an animal and its oxygen consumption. Even if the relationship does not strictly hold true, the argument that the area of exchange surface determines the amount of oxygen that can diffuse through it is logical (see the discussion in Chap. 9, p. 166 ff.). It must be recognized, however, that even if all exchange membranes available for diffusion of oxygen were of uniform thickness and composition, the amount of oxygen is proportional not only to the surface area of the membrane, but also to the concentration gradient across this membrane. In addition, the concentration gradient itself depends on the velocity with which external and internal media pass over the membrane.

In spite of such complications, however, the oxygen consumptions are indeed rather closely related to the surface area (see Chap. 9). Since oxygen consumption is a measure of metabolic rate, and the metabolic rate is an index of the food requirements, it follows that per unit weight, smaller animals have greater food requirements than larger ones. Pütter composed a theoretical table (Table 12–6) in which he relates volume to oxygen consumption, food requirement per kilogram live weight and food requirement in per cent of the dry weight. The calculated figures are based on the following assumptions: One

Table 12–6.

Volume	*Oxygen Consumption* (per kg and hour in mg)	*Food Requirement* (per kg live weight per day in gm)	*Food Requirement* (in per cent of own dry substance per day)
μ^3			
1	2,340,000	45,400	30,300
10	1,080,000	21,000	14,000
100	500,000	9,800	6,520
1000	230,000	4,500	3,030
10^4	112,000	2,080	1,400
10^5	52,000	970	650
10^6	24,000	450	303
10^7	11,500	208	140
10^8	5,620	97	65
mm^3			
1	2,600	45	30
10	1,200	21	14
100	560	10	6.5
cm^3			
1	260	4	3.0
10	120	2	1.4
100	56	0.97	0.65
1000	26	0.45	0.30

From Pütter, A.: Die Ernährung der Wassertiere und der Stoffhaushalt der Gewasser. G. Fischer Verlag, Jena, 1909.

gm of food has an average caloric value of 4.1 Cal and an oxygen capacity of 1.2 g/g. The dry weight of the animal amounts to 15 per cent of the live weight. The oxygen consumption is 500 mg/m² body surface (actually a rather low value).

Considerable deviations have been observed, but they are still amazingly close to the calculations based on the figure presented in Table 12–6. Pütter lists a number of data which are given in Table 12–7.

Table 12–7.

Species	*Volume*	*Food Requirement* (in per cent of own dry weight per day) *Calculated*	*Found*
Cyclocypris	0.01 mm^3	140	58
Anopheles	0.05 "	82	140
	0.13 "	60	47
Calanus	0.73 "	34	42
Gorgonia	1 cm^3	3.0	0.74
Pennatula	20 "	1.1	0.13
Blaps	0.49 "	3.75	3.75
Heliastes	0.16 "	5.5	6.8
	1.30 "	3.2	3.7
Hippocampus	1.75 "	2.5	2.5
Scorpaena	13 "	1.3	2.1
Sparrow	22 gram	5.5	75
Elephant	3500 kg	0.023	2.0
Homo	75 kg	0.07	2.7

From Pütter, A.: Vergleichende Physiologie. G. Fischer Verlag, Jena, 1911.

The most conspicuous exceptions are the colonial coelenterates *Gorgonia* and *Pennatula* and the mammals. In the latter, this is explained by the disproportionate increase in body surface (lungs) relative to the volume.

Surface area is only one of the variables affecting oxygen (and food) consumption, but from the available data it is obvious that there is an important relationship.

If there is such a relationship between body size (surface area) and metabolic rate (oxygen and food consumption), we can expect that larger animals can survive without food longer than smaller ones. This relationship is well known for warm blooded vertebrates: a mouse or a small bird cannot survive more than one or two days without food, whereas a man may live 20, 30, or even 40 days without a single meal. As a first approximation, death occurs when about 50 per cent of the body substance has been metabolized. If this were always the case, the lifetimes would be correlated with the metabolic rate as shown in Table 12–8.

Even though the assumption that death occurs if 50 per cent of the body substance has been metabolized is arbitrary, the relationship between body size, metabolic rate, and maximum period of starvation is valid. Large reptiles (20 to 30 kg), for instance, can indeed live without food for up to two years, whereas a frog (50 gm) at 20° C could not survive for more than three months without food.

The preceding discussion may have given the impression that small animals live much less efficiently than large ones because they require so much more food per unit body weight. The question immediately arises: What do they do with all the extra energy they gain through their food? According to the laws of thermodynamics, no energy is ever lost. Energy taken up in the form of nutrients of a given caloric value must appear either as stored chemical energy (storage of nutrients, synthesis of body substance), as mechanical or electrical work (concentration work in transmembrane transport, movement, changes in electric potential), or as heat (see Fig. 12–2).

The ratio of chemically stored (synthesis) and work energy to the energy

Table 12–8.

Organic Matter Utilized in One Day (in % original dry weight)	*Time in Days Until Original Weight Is Reduced to 50%*	
0.1	700	= 1.92 years
0.5	139	= 4.65 months
1.0	70	= 2.34 "
2.0	34.4	= 1.17 "
5.0	14	
10.0	7	
50.0	1.4	
100.0	0.69	= 16.6 hours
200.0	0.34	= 8.3 "
300.0	0.23	= 5.5 "

From Pütter, A.: Die Ernährung der Wassertiere und der Stoffhaushalt der Gewasser. G. Fischer Verlag, Jena, 1909.

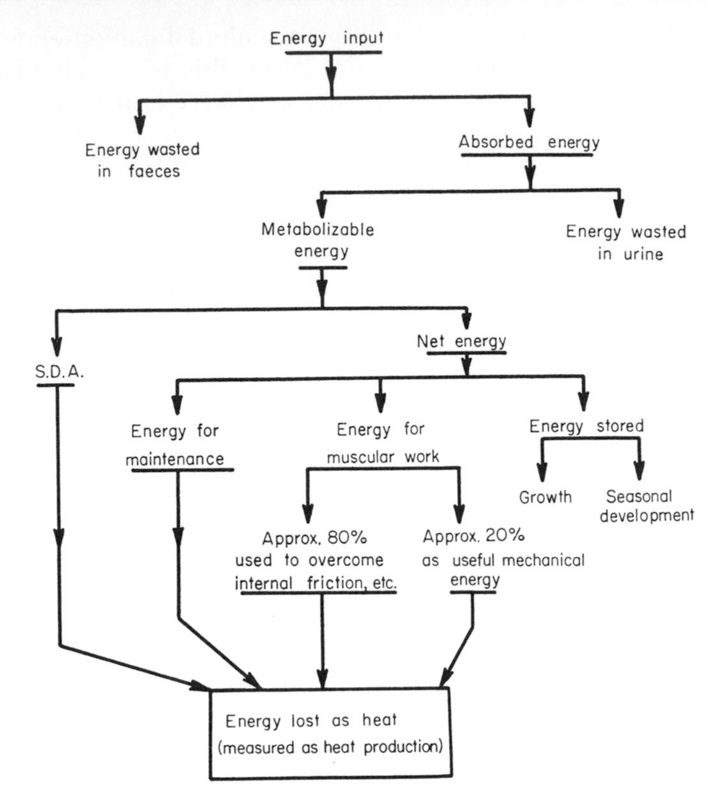

Figure 12–2. Energy flow sheet describing the fate of releasable chemical energy contained in the food taken in by an animal organism (goldfish). The specific dynamic action (*S.D.A.*) is the "energy cost" of assimilation (the energy expended in transporting nutrients into the cell, etc.). (From Davies, P. M. C.: The energy relation of Carassius auratus L. I. Food input and energy extraction efficiency at two experimental temperatures. Comp. Biochem. Physiol. *12*:67–79, 1964.)

lost as heat is called the *efficiency of the metabolizable energy*, or the *energy efficiency*, or *efficiency of utilization of digested energy*, and is expressed in per cent of the total "digested" energy, that is, in per cent of the total metabolizable energy taken in with the digested food. These terms are not to be confused with the energy efficiency of food utilization, which refers to the percentage of metabolizable energy which a given organism can derive from the total energy (as determined by direct calorimetry) of its food. A balance sheet which illustrates this is given in Table 12–9. In this particular example, the energy efficiency of food utilization is $11.64 \times 100/22.14 = 52.6$ per cent.

Now, how is the metabolizable energy used by the organism? How is the efficiency of the metabolizable energy related to body size? The results of many investigations—largely by Kleiber and coworkers (1933, 1941, 1945, etc.) and Brody and coworkers (1928, 1932, 1945)—indicate that the efficiency of the metabolizable energy decreases with increasing body weight and is proportional to the 3/4 power of the body weight. This means that small animals grow faster than large ones; it also means that small animals are relatively stronger than large ones (e.g., no mammal can jump as high as a flea—if the jumps are related to each animal's height).

***Table 12–9.* Energy Balance Sheet of a Cow Fed on Sudan Hay**

	Megacals
The daily intake of 5.27 kg hay contained	22.14
The cow excreted in feces daily	7.25
Thus she digested daily	14.89
The organic substances excreted daily in the urine had a heat of combustion of	1.43
The cow excreted 191 liters of methane equivalent to	1.82
That left metabolizable chemical energy equivalent to	11.64

From Kleiber, M.: The Fire of Life: An Introduction to Animal Energetics. John Wiley & Sons, New York, 1961.

From the amusing illustration shown in Figure 12–3 (Kleiber, 1961), we learn that 300 rabbits are equal in weight to one steer, but they eat 1 ton of hay in 30 days, whereas the steer can live on the same amount of food for no less than 120 days. The steer gains just as much weight in four months as all the rabbits gain in one month—imagine the number of rabbits at the end of four months if further tons of food were provided. If mice lived on hay, an even more striking example could be given.

If small and large animals compete for the same food, the small ones win. After 30 days the steer would have consumed 1/4 of the original ton of hay, but if the 300 rabbits would have been let loose at the same hay, they would have finished it by then. The steer would have had no food even before then, but even if he had been allowed an extra 1/4 ton of hay, to begin with, he would have gained only about 25 kg, whereas during the same time the rabbits would have increased their total mass by 100 kg.

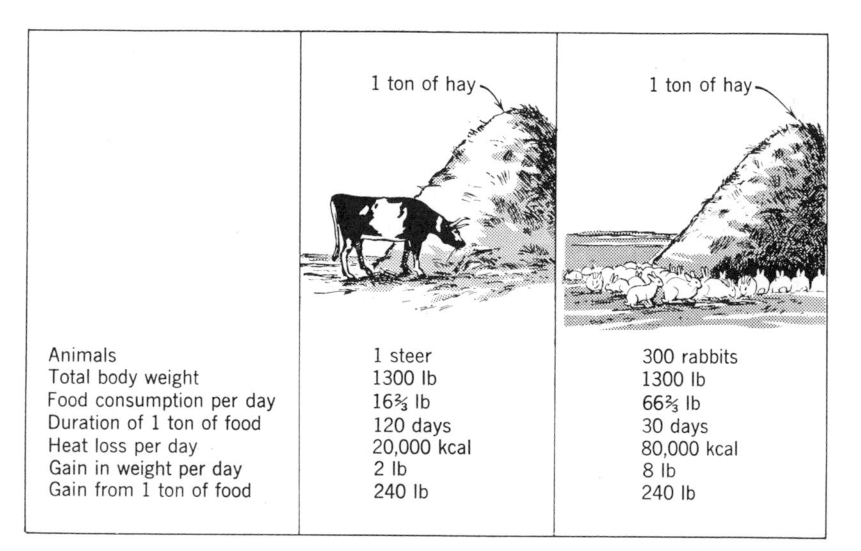

Figure 12–3. What happens when one steer and a group of 300 rabbits are given each 1 ton of hay. The total mass of rabbits gains weight four times faster than the steer, even though rabbits lose four times as much energy in the form of heat as does the steer. (From Kleiber, M.: The Fire of Life. An Introduction to Animal Energetics. John Wiley & Sons, New York, 1961.)

For the sake of argument, let us assume that the steer is a carnivorous animal that feeds on rabbits. Let us further assume that there is an abundance of hay. Let us add to the menagerie a carnivorous cow to ensure reproduction. A simple calculation will show that the rabbits will always outnumber the cattle and will assume a far greater total mass, even though both rabbits and cattle are provided with abundant food.

When the names "cattle" and "rabbits" of the preceding example are replaced by more realistic species names, the argument becomes immediately applicable to the actual situation in nature: within a given living community the total mass (and number) of small animals is always greater than that of the large ones—and the total mass of each species is larger the smaller the species.

Of course, there are exceptions to this rule, but they do not invalidate it. In regard to the statement that small animals grow faster than large ones, we may ask: Why is it, that large animals have evolved and that the body size of species and phyla generally increases with the rise on the evolutionary scale? What, in fact, is the selective value of large body size? The answer is rather simple: When the food supply is low, large animals, because of their slower metabolism, can survive longer (see Table 12–7).

For further discussions of quantitative aspects of metabolism and for additional terminology, refer to Max Kleiber's book, The Fire of Life (1961), and to Brody's Bioenergetics and Growth (1945).

For the purpose of this chapter, it is important to discuss briefly another aspect of nutrition, also stressed by Pütter, which concerns the quantitative relationship between actually measured (or measurable) metabolism or energy requirements and the observed rate of food uptake. From such considerations, Pütter was forced to conclude that aquatic animals derive much of their nutrients from dissolved organic matter which they resorb through their body surface. Although his data were criticized, his quantitative approach is sound and should serve as an example for further investigations. Some of his experiments, unfortunately conducted on small numbers of animals, cannot be ignored and definitely need to be repeated.

Here is one of his calculations:

A salmon, migrating up a river, loses considerable weight. A 9.77 kg specimen lost 2.39 kg in 330 days while the percentage of dry substance changed from 34.6 to 21.8 per cent. The organic matter on day 1 amounted to 3.38 kg, on day 330, 1.62 kg. Therefore, in 330 days the animal lost 1.76 kg of organic matter.

The average live weight of the animal is 8.6 kg, and the average weight of the dry organic matter is 2.4 kg. The average loss of organic substance amounts to 5.3 gm/day, of which 3.59 gm is protein and 1.89 gm is fat. The protein yields 14.4 Cal, the fat 15.7. The metabolized energy thus amounts to 30.1 Cal. If 80 per cent of this energy (a high estimate) is transformed in the animal's muscles, the muscles would have 24 Cal available per day. Assuming an efficiency of 40 per cent (very high estimate), we find that 9.6 Cal would be mechanical energy available for work. The mechanical equivalent of this energy is 4100 kg-m/day, or 0.0475 kg-m/sec.

The salmon moves against the streaming water of the river which flows with a velocity of 4 to 5 m/sec. The frictional resistance of the fish is considerable, and the energy required for the fish to move against the water current is calculated to be 1.32 kg-m/sec (Pütter, 1909). Even if only half this value were accepted, the energy required to maintain the fish in the stream is far greater than can be accounted for by the energy derived from the organic matter which the fish uses up.

Pütter then calculated the oxygen consumption of the fish, and from the caloric value of oxygen found that the amount of respired oxygen indicates an energy liberation of 5.45 cal/sec. If it is again assumed that 80 per cent of this is available to the muscles and that the efficiency of the muscles is 40 per cent, 1.74 cal should be mechanical energy, that is, 0.76 kg-m/sec.

From the measured oxygen consumption, it is obvious that the fish can meet the energy requirement, but the loss of body substance accounts for less than 1/12 of this. Migrating fresh-water salmon do not feed. But if the fish consumed oxygen, it must have metabolized organic matter, and if only part of this organic matter came from the fish itself, the rest must have been acquired from the outside. If the fish did not eat any formed food and (as is well known) did not even swallow, the extra organic matter that was metabolized must have entered the body by a route other than the digestive tract. Pütter concluded that dissolved organic matter entered through the gills.

Pütter's critics emphasized that there is much less organic matter dissolved in river water than Pütter had assumed, and that the organic substances hardly qualify as nutrients. Still, nobody has disproved Pütter's calculations, although they have been disputed (Krogh, 1931; Bond, 1933).

There is now recent direct evidence for the utilization of organic matter dissolved in the aquatic environment (Allee and Frank, 1948, 1949; Provasoli and Shiraishi, 1959; Stephens and Schinske, 1957; Stephens, 1960).

REFERENCES

Allee, W. C., and P. Frank (1948) Ingestion of colloidal material and water by goldfish. Physiol. Zool. *21*:381–390.

Allee, W. C., and P. Frank (1949) The utilization of minute food particles by goldfish. Physiol. Zool. *22*:346–358.

Barrington, E. J. W. (1953) The relationship of the A and B cells of the pancreatic islet tissue of the grass snake (*Natrix natrix*). Quart. J. Micr. Sci. *94*:281–291.

Bernard, C. (1849) Influence de la section des pédonculés cerebelleux moyens sur la composition de l'urine. C. R. Soc. Biol. (Paris) *1*:14.

Best, C. H., R. E. Haist, and T. A. Wrenshall (1955) The pancreas, insulin and glucagon. Ann. Rev. Physiol. *17*:393.

Bond, R. M. (1933) A contribution to the study of the natural food-cycle in aquatic environments, with particular consideration of micro-organisms and dissolved organic matter. Bull. Bingham Oceanogr. Coll. *4*:1–89.

Bourne, G. H., and G. W. Kidder, eds. (1953) Biochemistry and Physiology of Nutrition. 2 vols. Academic Press, New York.

Bowie, D. J. (1924) Cytological studies on the islets of Langerhans in a teleost, *Neomaenis griseus*. Anat. Rec. *29*:57–73.

Britton, S. (1925) Studies on the conditions of activity in endocrine glands. XVII. The nervous control of insulin secretion. Amer. J. Physiol. *74*:291–308.

Brody, S. (1945) Bioenergetics and Growth, with Special Reference to the Efficiency Complex in Domestic Animals. Reinhold Publishing Corp., New York.

Brody, S., J. E. Comfort, and J. S. Matthews (1928) Growth and development. Further investigations on surface area with special reference to its significance in energy metabolism. Montana Res. Bull. *115*.

Brody, S., and R. C. Procter (1932) Growth and development with special reference to domestic animals. Further investigations of surface area in energy metabolism. Montana Res. Bull. *116*.

von Buddenbrock, W. (1950) Vergleichende Physiologie, Vol. IV: Hormone. Birkhäuser Verlag, Basel.

Calugareanu, D. (1907) Die Darmatmung von *Cubitis fossilis*. Pflügers Arch. ges. Physiol. *118*:42–51; *120*:425–450.

Cannon, W. B. (1929) Organization for physiological homeostasis. Physiol. Rev. *9*:399–431.

Ciba Foundation Colloquia on Endocrinology (1953) VI. Hormonal Factors in Carbohydrate Metabolism. J. & A. Churchill, London.

Ciba Foundation Colloquia on Endocrinology (1956) IX. Internal Secretions of the Pancreas. Little, Brown and Co., Boston.

De Bodo, R. C., and M. W. Sinkoff (1953) Anterior pituitary and adrenal hormones in the regulation of carbohydrate metabolism. Recent Progr. Hormone Res. *8*:511–563.

De Robertis, E., and L. Primavesi (1939) Las celulas de los islet de Langerhans del *Bufo arenarum* (Hensel). Rev. Soc. Argent. Biol. *15*:434–481.

Donhoffer, C., and J. J. R. MacLeod (1932) Studies in the nervous control of carbohydrate metabolism. I. The position of the center. Proc. Roy. Soc. B, *100*:125–141.

DuVigneaud, V. (1956) Trail of sulfur research: from insulin to oxytocin. Science *123*:967–974.

Fischer, H. (1912) Ueber die Langerhansschen Inseln im Pankreas von Amphibien. Arch. mikr. Anat. *79*:276–306.

Foa, P. P., G. Galasino, and G. Pozza (1957) Glucagon, a second pancreatic hormone. Recent Progr. Hormone Res. *13*:473–503.

Gilmour, D. (1960) The Biochemistry of Insects. Academic Press, New York.

Grafe, E., and Meythaler, F. (1927) Beiträge zur Kenntnis der Regulation der Insulinproduktion. I. Mitteilung: Der Traubenzucher als Hormon für die Insulinabgabe. Arch. Exp. Path. Pharmacol. *125*:181–192.

Grafe, E., and Meythaler, F. (1928) II. Mitteilung: Die Wirkung von Kohlenhydraten causser. Traubenzucker auf die Insulinabgabe. Arch. Exp. Path. Physiol. *131*:80–91.

Griffith, F. R. (1923) A study of the carbohydrate mobilization effected by afferent crural, sciatic, and vagus stimulation. Amer. J. Physiol. *66*:618–658.

von Holt, C. (1955) Glucagon: das Hormon der A Zellen der Langerhanschen Inseln. Z. Vitamin Hormon Fermentforsch *7*:138–152.

Houssay, B. A. (1958) Comparative physiology of the endocrine pancreas, pp. 638–667. *In* Comparative Endocrinology. (A. Gorbman, ed.) John Wiley & Sons, New York.

Ingle, D. J., D. F. Beary, and A. Purmalis (1953) Comparison of the effects of 11-ketoprogesterone, 11-alphahydroxyprogesterone and 11-betahydroxyprogesterone upon the glycosuria of the partially depancreatized rat. Endocrinology *53*:221–225.

Kleiber, M. (1933) Tiergrösse und Futterverwertung. Tierernährung. *5*:1–12.

Kleiber, M. (1945) Dietary deficiencies and energy metabolism. Nutr. Abstr. Rev. *15*:207–222.

Kleiber, M. (1961) The Fire of Life: An Introduction to Animal Energetics. John Wiley & Sons, New York.

Kleiber, M., M. D. D. Boelter, and D. M. Greenberg (1941) Fasting catabolism and food utilization of magnesium deficient rats. J. Nutr. *21*:363–372.

Kleiber, M., and T. H. Jukes (1942) Metabolism and food utilization of riboflavin-deficient chicks. Proc. Soc. Exp. Biol. Med. *49*:34–37.

Kleiber, M., and S. W. Mead (1941) Body size and milk production. J. Dairy Sci. *24*:127–134.

Kleiber, M., W. M. Regan, and S. W. Mead (1945) Measuring food values for dairy cows. Hilgardia *16*:511–571.

Kleiber, M., and A. H. Smith (1940) Eating habit and fasting metabolism of rats. Proc. Soc. Exp. Biol. Med. *45*:630–632.

Krogh, A. (1931) Dissolved organic substances as food of aquatic organisms. Biol. Rev. *6*:412–442.

Levine, R., and M. S. Goldstein (1955) On the mechanism of action of insulin. Recent Progr. Hormone Res. *11*:343–375.

Linderstrøm-Lang, K., and Duspiva (1935) Beiträge zur enzymatischen Histochemie. XVI. Die Verdauung von Keratin durch die Larven der Kleidermotte. Z. Physiol. Chem. *237*:131–158.

MacLeod, J. J. R. (1934) The control of carbohydrate metabolism. Bull. Johns Hopkins Hosp. *54*:79–139.

Marshall, S. M., and A. P. Orr (1960) Feeding and nutrition. *In* The Physiology of Crustacea, pp. 227–258. (T. H. Waterman, ed.) Academic Press, New York.

Miller, M. R., and D. H. Wurster (1958) The morphology and physiology of the pancreatic islets in urodele amphibians and lizards. *In* Comparative Endocrinology, pp. 668–680. (A. Gorbman, ed.) John Wiley & Sons, New York.

Nagelschmidt, L. (1939) Untersuchungen ueber die Langerhanschen Inseln der Bauchspeicheldruese bei den Voegeln. Z. Mikr. Anat. Forsch. *45*:202–232.

Nocenti, M. R. (1961) Endocrine functions of the pancreas. *In* Medical Physiology, 11th Ed., pp. 883–906. (P. Bard, ed.) C. V. Mosby Co., St. Louis.

Powning, R. F. (1954) A study of cystein desulfhydrase in certain insects. Austr. J. Biol. Sci. *7*: 308–318.

Provasoli, L., and K. Shiraishi (1959) Axenic cultivation of the brine shrimp, *Artemia salina*. Biol. Bull. *117*:347–355.

Pütter, A. (1909) Die Ernährung der Fische. Z. allg. Physiol. *9*:147–242.

Pütter, A. (1923) Zur Physiologie der Riesentiere. Zool. Jahrb., allg. Zool. Physiol. Tiere *40*:217–240.

Root, M. A. (1956) Effect of glucagon on glycogen in rats and rabbits. Endocrinology *59*:340–346.

Stephens, G. C. (1960a) The mechanism of glucose uptake by the coral, *Fungia*. Anat. Rec. *137*:395.

Stephens, G. C. (1960b) Uptake of glucose from solution by the solitary coral, *Fungia*. Science *131*:1532.

Stephens, G. C., and R. A. Schinske (1957) Uptake of amino acids from sea water by ciliary mucoid filter feeding animals. Biol. Bull. *113*:356–357.

Thomas, T. B. (1942) The pancreas of snakes. Anat. Rec. *82*:327–347.

Turner, C. D. (1966) General Endocrinology, 4th Ed. W. B. Saunders Co., Philadelphia.

Vonk, H. J. (1960) Digestion and metabolism. *In* The Physiology of Crustacea, pp. 291–316. (T. H. Waterman, ed.) Academic Press, New York.

Weymouth, F. W., J. Field, II, and M. Kleiber (1942) Relationship between body size and metabolism. Proc. Soc. Exp. Biol. Med. *49*:367–370.

Young, F. T., W. A. Broom, and W. F. Wolff, eds. (1960) The Mechanism of Action of Insulin. Charles C Thomas, Springfield, Ill.

13 EXCRETION AND STORAGE OF METABOLIC END PRODUCTS

The significance of excretion can be best understood by first reviewing nutrition and metabolism. We remember that there are two aspects of metabolism: *catabolism* and *anabolism.* Catabolism consists in energy-yielding reactions during which certain compounds are oxidatively degraded and the entropy of the reaction system increases. Anabolism consists in synthesis of higher order compounds, such as proteins, nucleoproteins, and complex lipids; it is accompanied by a decrease in entropy of the reacting system.

Catabolism is often called "energy metabolism." It provides the energy not only for anabolic processes (chemical work), but also for the mechanical and electrical work of the organism. The energy made available by catabolic reactions is only partially converted into "useful" energy; the larger part of it is lost in the form of heat. The percentage of the total energy yield of a catabolic process (e.g., oxidation of glucose) that is "useful" energy is known as the *efficiency* of the process. This is usually less than 50 per cent. Since the energy required for anabolic (synthetic) processes is derived from catabolism, catabolism must be much more intensive than anabolism. This relation is further enhanced by the fact that catabolism must also provide the energy necessary for all the electrical work (maintenance of electric potentials) and mechanical work (movement) of the organism and its parts.

In an animal that maintains a constant weight, anabolism is minimal. It is just sufficient to replace compounds that have been used up or degraded. But to maintain such a condition, catabolism must proceed at a considerable rate because it is responsible not only for the minimal synthesis that goes on, but also for all the other energy-requiring processes.

Since, during catabolism, compounds are continuously used up, they must be replaced at the same rate. The metabolizing cells must be continuously supplied with nutrients. As shown in Chapter 12 on Nutrition (pp. 268–279), this amount of nutrients can be estimated from data on oxygen consumption (assuming that all catabolic reactions lead to a final oxidation of the oxidizable compounds produced). Now, if the organism does continuously acquire nutrients that can be catabolized and anabolized but does not gain weight, it must lose substance at about the same rate that it gains substance in nutrition.

As a rule, the organism excretes those molecules from which it cannot derive energy. This does not necessarily mean that these molecules do not contain releasable energy, but only that the organism has no facility to release it. Urea is an example. This molecule appears as a product of protein catabolism in many higher animals. If oxidized in a calorimeter, urea yields 153 Cal/mole. Animal cells cannot perform this operation, and thus excrete the compound.

Although a variety of compounds are utilized in catabolism, they do not yield chemical energy directly but must first be transformed into suitable molecules. Glucose, for instance, must be phosphorylated and split into two phosphorylated trioses before energy can be derived from it (by dephosphorylation). The trioses are then further transformed to pyruvate, which is processed in a reaction sequence known as the citric acid cycle. This sequence liberates three molecules of CO_2 and three pairs of hydrogen ions. Energy is derived from the stepwise oxidation of the hydrogen ions (to water) and, in what is known as *coupled phosphorylation*, this energy is incorporated into high energy phosphate compounds.

If proteins are utilized, they are first broken down into amino acids. These amino acids are then deaminated and transformed until they can be oxidized within the citric acid cycle sequence. Fats are likewise changed into smaller molecules which fit the citric acid cycle pattern.

A study of the metabolic patterns of transformation leads to the conclusion that the significant energy yields of oxidative catabolic reactions are obtained from compounds consisting only of carbon, hydrogen, and oxygen. In the preliminary transformation, the more complicated compounds are not only reduced to the smaller size required, but also lose any other atoms, or radicals, such as sulfur (sulfate), phosphorus (phosphate), and nitrogen (ammonia). Sulfur is derived from certain amino acids, such as cysteine, taurine, cystine, cysteic acid, and methionine, whereas phosphorus is derived from many nucleotides and nucleoproteins, which are too numerous to mention here. Ammonia is formed whenever an amino group is removed from an amino acid or other amino compound.

Metabolizing cells contain an abundance of ammonia, sulfate, and phosphate. In addition, they produce water (oxidation of hydrogen) and CO_2. These molecules—or radicals—are all that is left of the metabolized (or better: catabolized) compounds.

Nitrogen-containing compounds may lose their nitrogen in a more complicated way: instead of appearing in the form of ammonia, nitrogen may appear in the form of more complex nitrogen-containing bases, such as *guanine, uric acid* or *urea*. In these cases, the amino groups are first transferred to another

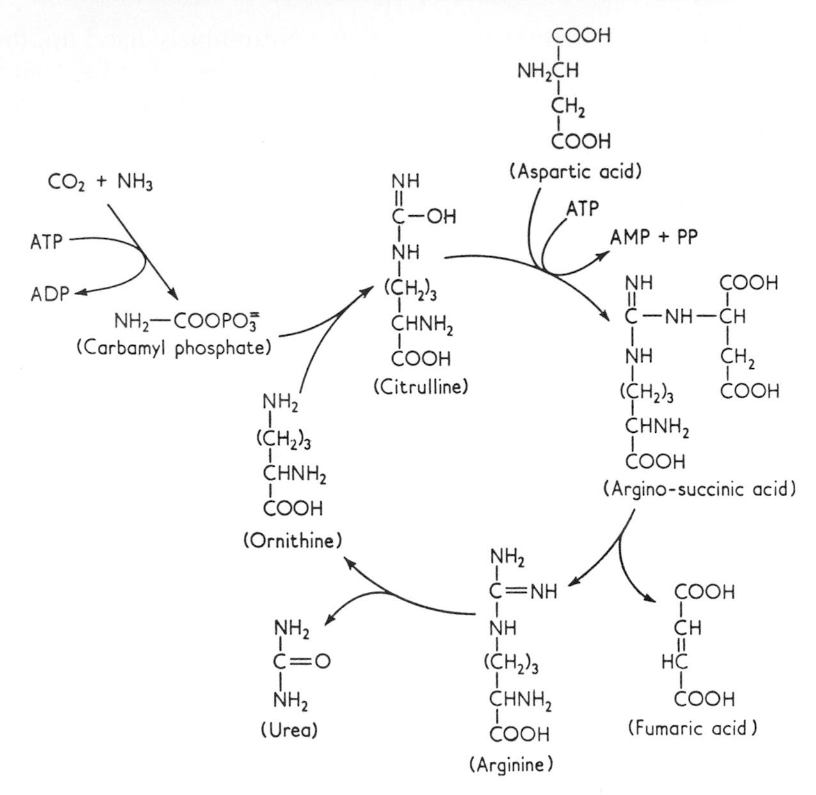

Figure 13–1. The ornithine cycle. With CO_2 and ammonia, ornithine forms citrulline (this requires ATP). The addition of another amino compound (amino acid) gives rise to a nitrogen-free compound (succinic acid), which can enter the citric acid cycle (see Chap. 7) and arginine, a compound containing four nitrogen atoms. Two of these nitrogens are released as urea. (From Gilmour, D.: The Biochemistry of Insects. Academic Press, New York, 1961.)

molecule and the aminated molecule is then split into a metabolizable unit and a nitrogen-containing base. The pathways of these transformations are not always known in detail. One such pathway, which occurs in the vertebrate liver (exception: birds and reptiles), has, however, been well investigated. It is known as the *ornithine cycle,* explained in Figure 13–1. This reaction sequence yields urea. The significance of such a complex reaction sequence lies in the fact that the removed amino groups have no chance to become ammonia, but are trapped into a reaction with another compound which, later, is split, yielding the nitrogen-containing base urea and a unit that can be utilized in energy-liberating catabolism.

During catabolism, molecules are broken down into smaller units: glucose into six molecules of water and six molecules of CO_2, proteins into hundreds, if not thousands, of units (*amino acids*), and these into many times more molecules, such as water, ammonia, sulfate, and CO_2. This raises the osmotic concentration and establishes a steep concentration gradient across the cell wall. Particularly water, ammonia, and CO_2 follow this gradient and diffuse out of the cells into the extracellular body fluids. Sulfate and phosphate are also eliminated by the cells, possibly by simple diffusion but more likely by an active transfer.

In aquatic animals, these molecules diffuse from the body fluids out through the body surface (exchange membranes). The driving force is the concentration gradient across these cellular membranes that cover the body (gills, epidermis, gut, cellular wall of "kidneys"). Outward diffusion into the surrounding water through the body surface is thus the chief route of excretion of metabolic end products.

Secondary aquatic animals (insects, reptiles, and mammals) usually have a highly impermeable body surface. Their excretory pattern, therefore, is similar to that of terrestrial animals. Gaseous end products (CO_2, some ammonia, water) are lost by outward diffusion (and evaporation) across respiratory membranes (lungs, gills, tracheae). Water may actually be secreted by sweat glands in the epidermis (mammals only) and evaporates from there. The chief route of excretion, however, is by way of the kidneys (in insects, by the malpighian tubules), and involves filtration of body fluid into kidney tubules with subsequent reabsorption of compounds that are still required inside the body.

It is not surprising, therefore, that the transition from aquatic to terrestrial life has been accompanied by a metabolic adjustment which permits excretion of nitrogen and phosphorus in the form of compounds that can be tolerated in the circulating body fluids (ammonia is quite toxic) should their concentration build up (the example is urea), or that have a low water solubility so that they crystallize out—for example, uric acid (other compounds with similar properties are guanine, hypoxanthine, and pterins).

Ammonotelic animals excrete nitrogen predominantly in the form of ammonia, *ureotelic* animals excrete nitrogen predominantly as urea, and *uricotelic* animals excrete it as uric acid.

An interesting comparative study by Needham (1935) revealed that marine snails excrete ammonia and that their nephridia contain only traces of uric acid; terrestrial snails, on the other hand, excrete largely uric acid, and their "kidneys" are at times literally filled with this compound. Many fresh-water snails (*Limnea, Viviparus*) excrete uric acid, which has been explained by the assumption that these species are derived from terrestrial forms.

Within the lifetime of an animal, the pattern of nitrogen excretion can change. A classic example of this is the chicken, as studied by Needham (1931) (Fig. 13–2). Amphibia show similar patterns: the aquatic larvae excrete ammonia but as they metamorphose and adapt to terrestrial life, they excrete nitrogen predominantly as urea. A particularly interesting case in point is a newt, the red eft (*Triturus*), which in its terrestrial phase excretes 87 per cent of the excretory nitrogen as urea, but when the mature animal returns to the water in order to breed, urea excretion diminishes in favor of ammonia excretion (Nash and Frankhauser, 1959).

Whales, by the way, excrete urea, like all other mammals.

Owing to its insolubility in water, uric acid, the chief excretory product of reptiles, birds, and adult insects, is excreted in concentrated, often crystalline form. Nitrogen excretion proceeds here without concomitant loss of water.

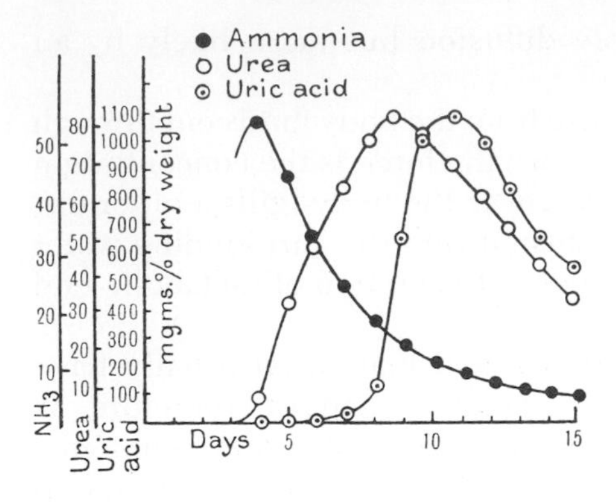

Figure 13–2. Pattern of nitrogen excretion in the developing chick. During the first days of life ammonia is the chief excretory product; later urea predominates until it is overtaken by the production of uric acid. Note that the data are given as mg/gm dry weight. On this basis the total amount of excreted nitrogen decreases with the age of the embryo. The absolute amounts, however, show a continuous increase. (From Needham, J.: Chemical Embryology, Vol. 2. Cambridge University Press, London, 1931.)

Much has been made of this fact. Uric acid excretion has been related to the need of animals to conserve water. It has also been stated to be a prerequisite for flying, since the animal does not need to carry extra water that would be used only as a vehicle for excretion. For discussions of this type, particularly concerning the relationship of water to excretion, refer to Prosser (1961), Baldwin (1960), and Florkin (1949).

INTRACELLULAR EXCRETION

The term "intracellular excretion" is rather awkward and seems contradictory. Yet it is short and descriptive. A better term, perhaps, is phagocytosis; however, this implies the engulfment of large particles, whereas the process we are concerned with here may well involve only the uptake of dissolved, nonparticulate matter.

We are concerned here with the action of specialized cells which take up body substances that are no longer useful or are even harmful. Many of these cells are migratory and move throughout the body spaces, not only within the preformed channels of blood vessels or sinus but also in between tissue cells. Others are fixed in position and take up substances or particles that pass by them.

Particularly the older literature contains innumerable references to intracellular excretion. One gains the impression that it must have been a favorite pastime of zoologists to inject India ink or carmine suspensions into various animal species and to follow, histologically, the fate of the injected particles. Invariably, it was observed that these were rapidly taken up by certain cells which either stored them or transported them to the outside. The latter mode of excretion could take two forms: either the ingested particles were transferred to the lumen of excretory organs ("kidneys") and released into the urine, or the cells that carried the particles migrated through the body wall and disintegrated (see Fig. 13–3). In describing the latter process in his famous book, Ascaris (1922), Goldschmidt recalled a scene in a Mediterranean harbor town: Every evening, after sundown, a procession of women silently walked toward the rocky shore. Each carried a large pail on her head, the aromatic contents of which was emptied into the sea. "To do justice to the comparison with the excretory cells, the pailbearers as well would have had to plunge into the ocean."

It is hardly likely that carbon or carmine particles or vital dyes ever appear in the body fluids of an animal. In most cases, it is not really known what the excretory cells normally ingest if no carmine or carbon particles are offered. However, one can assume that they consume bacteria, should they appear in the body fluids. In addition, they can be expected to carry away the debris of decaying body cells. Body cells, like organisms, have a definite life span, which may be shorter than that of the organism to which they belong. A good deal is known about life spans of mammalian body cells: red blood cells, for instance, live only a few weeks; cells in the intestinal mucosa of the small intestine live only about one day. These cells are continuously replaced by new cells. The dead cells are removed by white blood cells (exception: epidermal cells that are sloughed off directly to the outside). Similar situations are likely to occur in all animals. The removal of the debris of dead cells is probably one of the chief functions of the excretory cells.

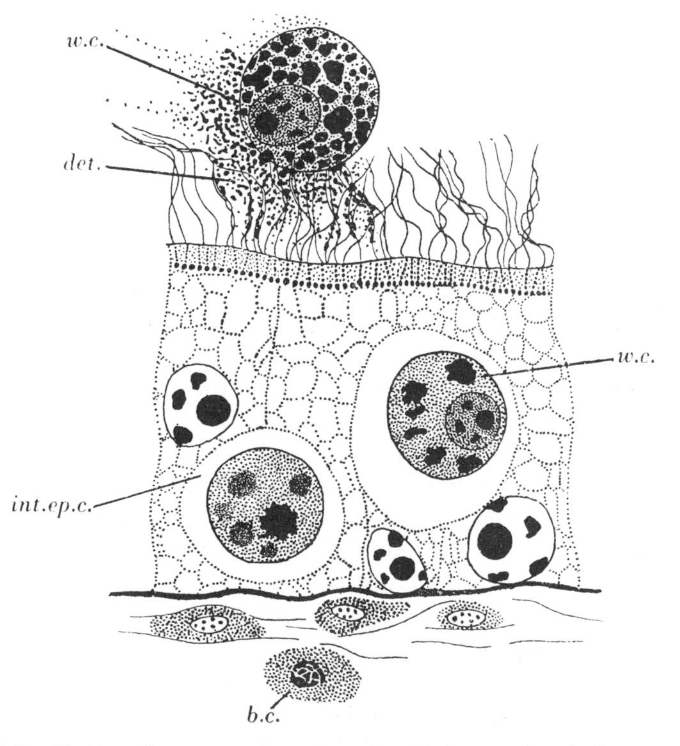

Figure 13–3. Portion of a transverse section of epithelium and underlying tissue of the midgut of a nudibranchiate mollusc, *Aeolidia papillosa*, showing wandering cells. These are ameboid blood cells that pick up effete material and transfer it from tissues and blood stream into the interior of the gut, thus serving an excretory function. ***b.c.***, blood cells; ***det.***, particles of detritus; ***int.ep.c.***, intra-epithelial space; ***w.c.***, wandering cell. (From Millott, N.: On the structure and function of the wandering cells in the wall of the alimentary canal of nudibranchiate Mollusca. J. Exp. Biol. *14*:405–412, 1937.)

More refined physiological zoologists injected dissolved vital dyes and followed their uptake and concentration in certain excretory cells. Such cells, which absorb and concentrate dissolved substances, are called *athrocytes*. (This term is always misspelled. Correctly, it would be "atrocytes.") The compounds absorbed by athrocytes appear then in the form of conspicuous crystalline or granular deposits, known as *concrement*, or as pigment mass. The pigment may well represent a transformation product of the original molecules.

It is impossible to generalize further. It is better to discuss individual cases.

Among sponges, "solids" are excreted predominantly by way of mesoglea cells: when loaded with granular material, these cells migrate through the body surface and discharge their contents as they decay. The classic description of this is by Masterman (1894): Xanthine crystals are often observed in the septal filaments of anthozoans, and in hydrozoans and scyphozoans there are pores toward the outside near the base of tentacles. The pores communicate with the radial canals. The endoderm cells surrounding the pores are filled with brown, highly refractive granules (guanine?) which are eliminated into the pore lumen and discharged to the outside (Claus, 1881). In siphonophores, there occurs under the "float" a peculiar organ (called "liver" by Koelliker), which is permeated by gastrodermal canals and lined with endodermal epithelial cells filled with crystalline granules and needles (Koelliker, 1853; Bedot, 1885).

Turbellarian pigments may be excretory products. Those of the Acoela reflect light and may be related to guanine (von Graff, 1904). Unfortunately, no biochemical investigations into the precise chemical nature of these pigments have been made. Löhner (1911) observed in *Convoluta* that had been immersed in a neutral-red solution that the absorbed dye accumulated in red droplets that progressively moved toward the pharynx and eventually were excreted through the mouth. They were produced and carried by mesenchyme cells (the Acoela have no intestine). Turbellaria excrete pigment that first appears in mesenchyme cells through fine pore canals in the epidermis (Luther, 1904) or accumulate pigment in mesenchyme and epidermal cells, so that the older the animal, the more pigmented it becomes (Vogt and Yung, 1882–1892).

Annelids have a peculiar tissue, known as *excretophore tissue*. Its cells are derived from the coelomic lining of the gut or of blood vessels. In Oligochaetes, they are called *chloragog cells*, or *chloragocytes*, and the tissue which they form and which surrounds the gut and often extends into the heart (Figs. 13–4 and 13–5) is known as chloragogen tissue (Morren, 1826), but should be called *chloragog tissue* (Rosa, 1903), since the name should not imply production of a chloragog (Gr. green carrying tissue).

In the Hirudinea, the chloragocytes form an extensive network, surrounding the numerous capillaries and sinus of the coelomic blood system. The whole tissue is called *botryoidal tissue* (Figs. 13–6, 13–7, 13–8, and 13–9). It fills the space between the gut and muscular body wall. In polychaetes, the excretophore cells are found surrounding blood vessels and, usually in the case of the pulsat-

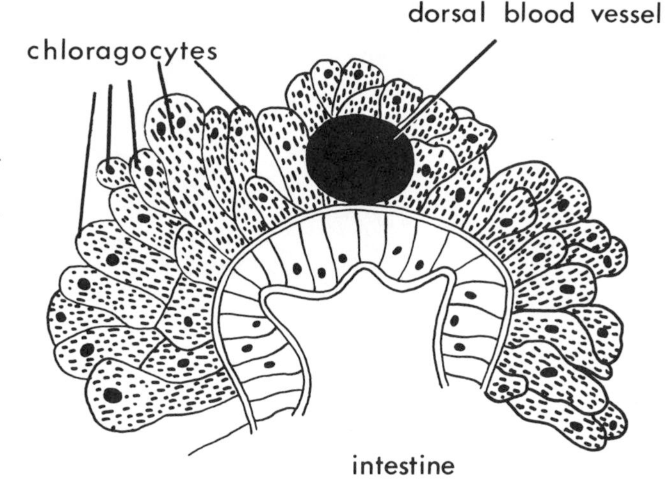

Figure 13–4. Cross section through the upper half of the intestine and the dorsal blood vessel of the fresh-water oligochaete *Tubifex*, showing the chloragog tissue. (Redrawn from Kuekenthal, W.: Ueber die lymphoiden Zellen der Anneliden. Jena. Z. Naturw. *18*:319, 1885.)

ing dorsal vessel, inside of blood vessels in the form of the so-called "heart body," shown in Figs. 13–4 and 13–5 (this also occurs in certain oligochaetes, such as *Lumbricus*).

All these excretophore cells are characteristically green or brown, due to liquid or granular inclusion bodies.

Related to these tissues are the remarkable *urns* of sipunculids: these are ciliated, cup-shaped structures that float in the coelomic fluid (*Sipunculus*) or are stationary. Ciliated "phagocytic" organs (Figs. 13–8 and 13–9) are also found in the body fluids of many annelid groups (Glyceridae, *Nephthys*, Hirudinea): they are the ciliated funnels, attached to the nephridia. All these structures collect, by ciliary currents, coelomocytes (or the fragments of disintegrated coelomocytes) and agglutinate them.

The agglutinated masses which contain colored granules of excretory

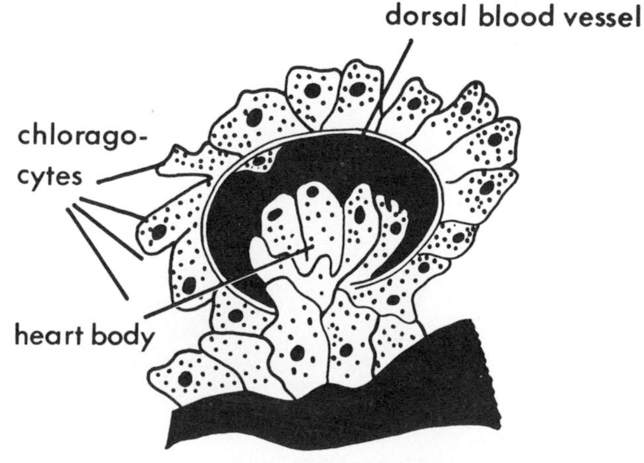

Figure 13–5. Cross section through the dorsal blood vessel (heart) of the oligochaete *Lumbriculus*, showing the chloragog tissue, notably the "heart body." (Redrawn from DeBock, M.: Le corps cardiaque et les amibocytes des Oligochètes limicoles. Rev. Suisse Zool. *8*:107–166, 1900.)

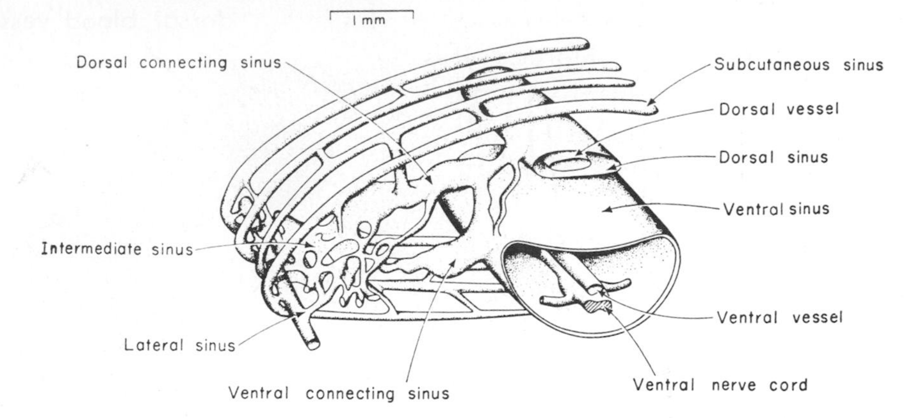

Figure 13–6. Reconstruction of part of the coelomic sinus system of the leech *Glossiphonia complanata.* Branches of the ventral sinus contain the "funnels" of the nephridium shown in Figure 13–16. The coelomic sinus system is similar to that in other Hirudinea; parts of these are shown in Figures 13–8 and 13–9. (After Oka, A.: Beitraege zur Anatomie der Clepsine. Z. wiss. Zool. 58:79–151, 1894. From Mann, K. H.: Leeches [Hirudinea]. Pergamon Press, New York, 1962.)

products are deposited as "brown bodies," either in each segment or in the posterior part of the body. They are, apparently, stored permanently.

Cells of the excretophore tissues, once packed with excretory granules, are released into the body fluid, where they are thought to disintegrate. The remnants are then transferred by other free cells (coelomocytes) to storage sites (pigmented epidermis, for instance) or to the epithelial cells of nephridial tubules or the gut. Where open ended nephridia are present, the fragments of

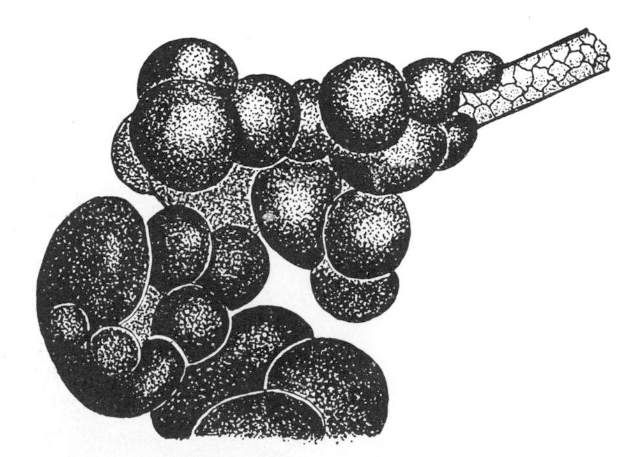

Figure 13–7. Botryoidal tissue of the leech *Hirudo medicinalis*, as seen in a preparation of connective tissue which was spread on a microscope slide and not compressed. The swelling of the cells and their origin from a thin-walled capillary can be seen. The swollen cells are filled with a pigment, much of which is bile pigment, derived from digested blood (hemoglobin). (From Bradbury, S.: The botryoidal tissue and vaso-fibrous tissue of the leech Hirudo medicinalis. Quart. J. Micr. Sci. *100*:483–498, 1959.)

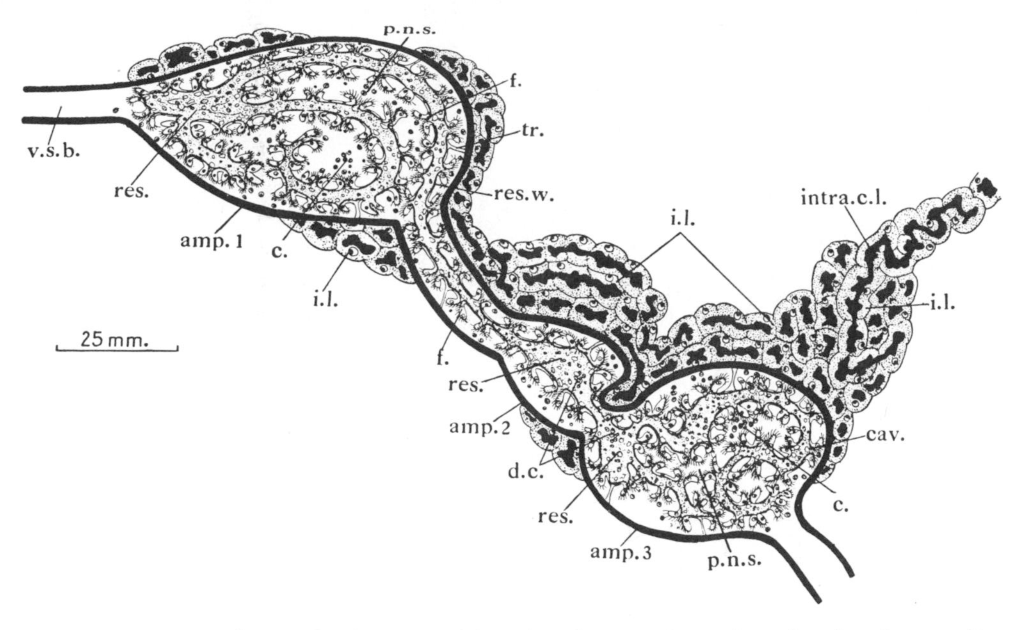

Figure 13–8. A longitudinal section of the ciliated organ of *Hirudo* enclosed in the ampullae of the perinephrostomial sinus. The initial lobe mass is seen surrounding the ampullae. *amp.1.2.3.*, perinephrostomial sinus ampullae; *c.*, corpuscles; *cav.*, cavity in the central mass; *d.c.*, dividing corpuscles; *f.*, funnel; *i.l.*, initial lobe; *intra.c.l.*, intracellular lumen; *p.n.s.*, perinephrostomial sinus; *res.*, reservoir; *res.w.*, reservoir wall; *tr.*, trabeculae; *v.s.b.*, branch of ventral sinus. (From Bhatia, M. L.: Quart. J. Micr. Sci. *81*:28–80, 1938.)

disintegrating excretophore cells are swept by the ciliary current into the tubular lumen and passed on to the outside.

Figure 13–10 gives a diagrammatic view of the modes of excretion of granular material by excretophore and coelomic cells.

The chemical identity of the granular material has not been established. It is assumed that it is formed from material that has been concentrated by the excretophore cells.

Excretophore cells and tissue are also prominent in echinoderms. These marine animals have no "kidneys."

Practically all echinoderms contain phagocytic coelomocytes of various types (see Fig. 13–11) that can ingest injected dye or carbon particles. They may normally be engaged in the elimination of bacteria and cell debris or of certain compounds. Such coelomocytes have been seen to leave the body through the thin epithelia of the respiratory papillae of many types of echinoderms, and they have been observed frequently between epithelial cells of the respiratory tree of holothurians. Some workers have noted that the whole mesentery epithelium (coelom) can ingest foreign particles.

A peculiar tissue, the *axial gland*, which in echinoids and asteroids is a brownish or purplish strand of vascularized connective tissue near the esophagus, contains in its spongy meshwork numerous coelomocytes or amebocytes that are filled with colored, granular material. An excretory function is usually

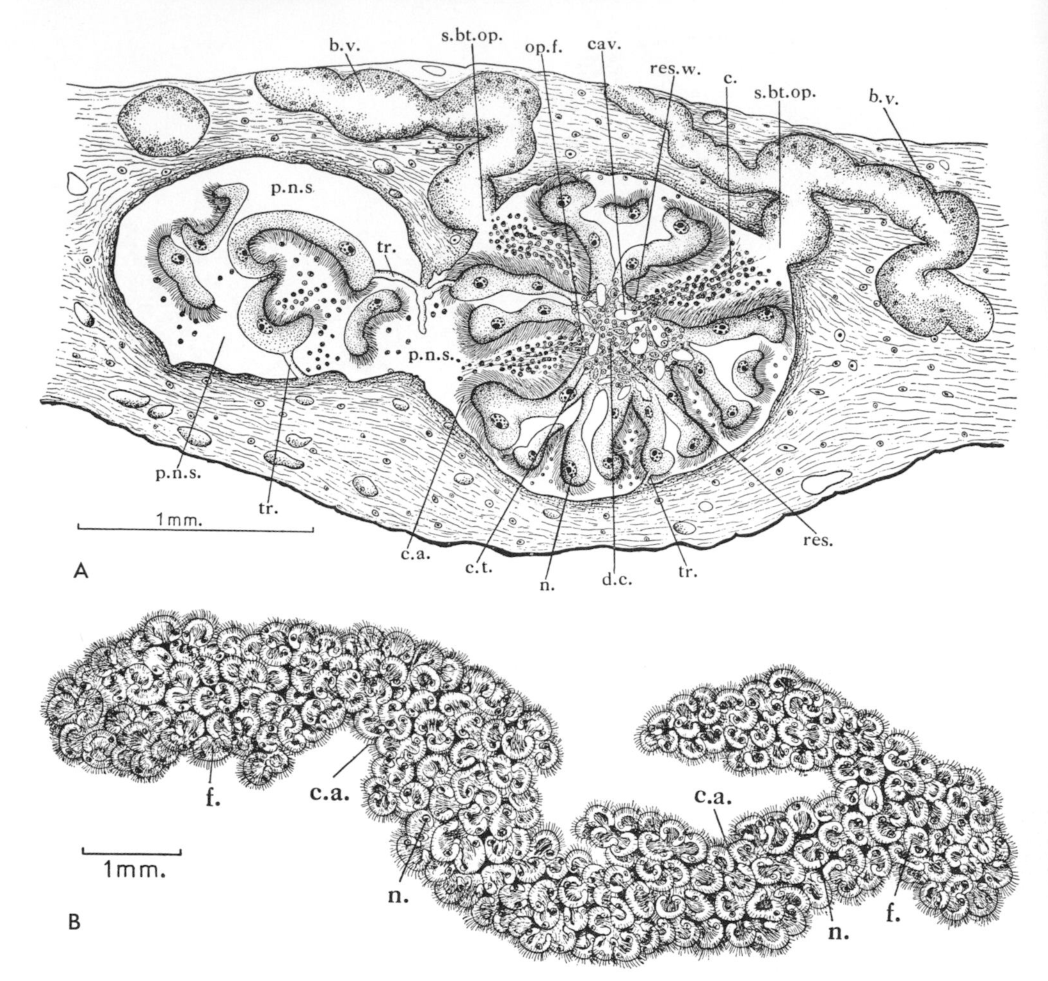

Figure 13–9. A, a transverse section through the ciliated organ of Hirudinaria enclosed in the perinephrostomial sinus. The sinus is seen communicating with the botryoidal vessels at two places. *b.v.*, botryoidal vessel; *c.*, corpuscles; *c.a.*, cilia; *cav.*, cavity in the central mass; *c.t.*, connective tissue; *d.c.*, dividing corpuscles; *n.*, nucleus; *op.f.*, opening of the funnel into the reservoir; *p.n.s.*, perinephrostomial sinus; *res.*, reservoir; *res.w.*, reservoir wall; *s.bt.op.*, sino-botryoidal openings; *tr.*, trabeculae. **B**, the entire ciliated organ of Hirudinaria taken out of the perinephrostomial sinus, showing innumerable independent ciliated funnels. *c.a.*, cilia; *f.*, funnel; *n.*, nucleus. (From Bhatia, M. L.: Quart. J. Micr. Sci. *81*:28–80, 1938.)

ascribed to them, and the organ itself is supposed to be a site of origin of coelomocytes. In the holothurians, the axial gland is not well developed or is even missing. Among these animals, are forms (e.g., Apoda) that possess special coelomic organs, the *ciliated urns*. Some species have whole trees of urns. These strange, bent funnels are attached to mesenteries. By ciliary action they collect aggregated coelomocytes and, after agglutination, release them as "brown bodies" which lie loosely in the coelomic spaces. The situation is reminiscent of that described for sipunculids.

In the molluscs there are, again, extensive developments of excretophore

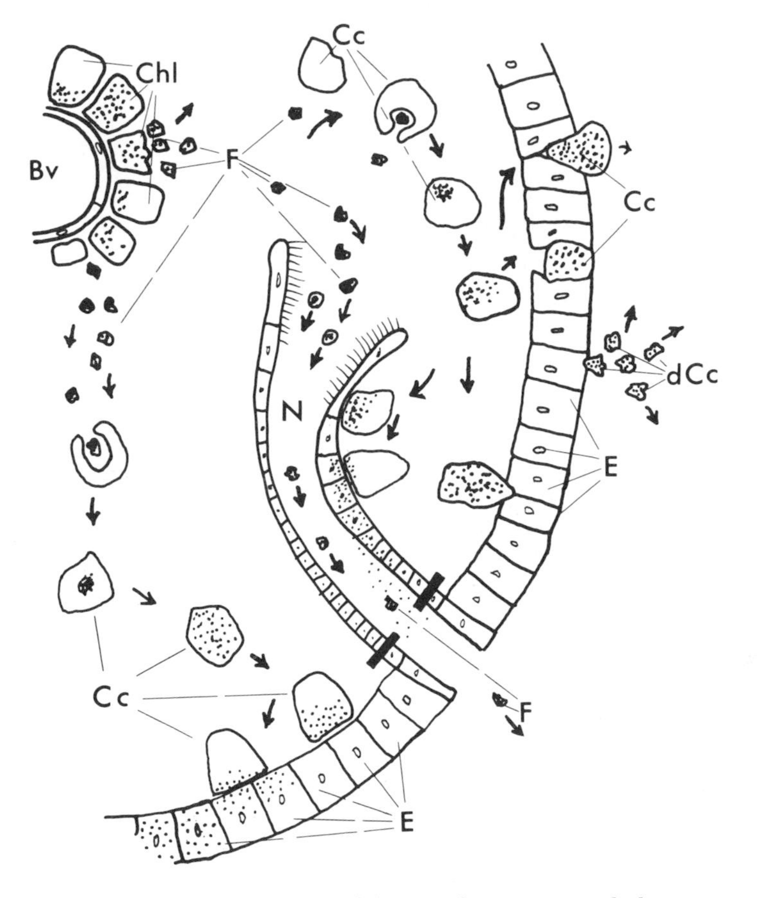

Figure 13–10. Idealized representation of the transfer, storage, and elimination of excretory products (concrement). The diagram shows coelomocytes (*Cc*) ingesting fragments (*F*) of chloragocytes (*Chl*). These phagocytic coelomocytes, loaded with concrement, then either migrate through the epidermis (*E*) and disintegrate (*dCc*) or transfer the concrement to the cells of the nephridium (*N*), which, in turn, release the concrement into the tubular lumen. Fragments of disintegrated chloragocytes are being swept upward by the ciliary current of the nephridium. Some coelomocytes transfer concrement to epidermal cells (*E*), which act as storage sites. *Bv*, blood vessel.

tissue. In lamellibranchs and cephalopods these are found in connection with the pericardium and the gill hearts, respectively. Cells filled with concrement occur inside the auricles of many lamellibranchs (*Arca, Pinna, Ostrea, Pecten,* etc.) and are responsible for the brown color of the auricles. They often form cell strands that traverse the auricular musculature and connect with the pericardium. The gill hearts of cephalopods are muscular organs of spongy consistency. The venous lumen sends numerous fine branches into it. Its cells are filled with dark purple granules.

In opisthobranchs, the genus *Cyclostoma* is conspicuous because of a strikingly white "gland" that surrounds the gut, particularly its dorsal aspect. Its cells are filled with bacteria and concrement. There is evidence that the concrement contains urea, xanthine, and hypoxanthine. Many cells of the connective tissue (e.g., of the mantle) of many mollusc groups contain granular or crystalline concrement.

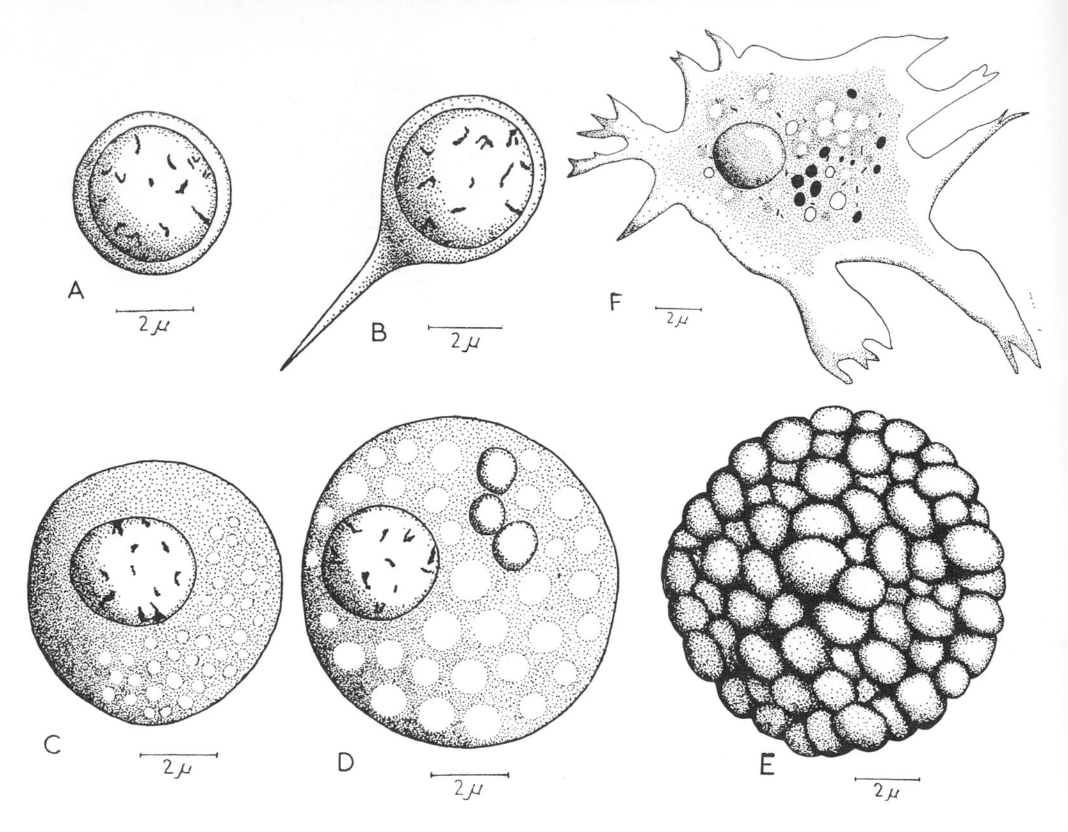

Figure 13–11. Coelomocytes of an echinoderm (*Holothuria leucospilata*). **A–D**, amebocytes. **C**, an early stage of transition to morula-shaped cell. **D**, a later stage, showing vacuoles and globules. Seventy per cent of the cells are morula-shaped (**E**), about 10 per cent are phagocytes of the type shown in **F**. (From Endean, R.: The coelomocytes of Holothuria leucospilata. Quart. J. Micr. Sci. 99:47–60, 1958.)

In addition, molluscs possess numerous migrating phagocytes. They have been observed to move into the lacunae and sinus below the body surface, penetrate the basal membrane of the epidermis, and finally migrate to the outside.

The nephridial cells of molluscs contain concrement. This is either stored (hibernating terrestrial snails), transferred to neighboring tissue (mantle tissue of some lamellibranchs may contain large concrement masses, up to several millimeters in diameter), or secreted into the nephridial lumen to be passed to the outside through the nephridiopore.

For further details, refer to the articles by Burian and Strohl in Winterstein's Handbuch der vergleichenden Physiologie, Vol. 2, Part 2 (1924) and to Hyman's monumental treatises on The Invertebrates (1940–1959).

The material just covered is rarely considered in physiology texts, and it must be admitted that the morphological, descriptive approach far outweighs physiological and biochemical analyses. The older literature contains numerous reports on attempts of chemical identification, but at the time of these investigations, microchemical techniques were not sufficiently advanced. Many of the reported compounds need to be re-examined in light of modern techniques. However, there is every indication that what is described as concrement is, among others, nitrogenous substance. Consequently, intracellular excretion by concrement formation and excretion or storage of it may well be considered a mechanism of fundamental importance. In view of the fact that nitrogen can be excreted in the form of highly diffusible ammonia, this is, perhaps, surprising. On the other hand, ammonia is not the only form in which nitrogen appears. Several metabolic pathways lead to such nitrogen-containing compounds as urea, uric acid, xanthine, purine, and pterines. These are less soluble and less diffusible. In addition other substances need to be excreted.

More recent studies have shed new light on the function of excretophore tissue and excretophore cells. They show that these structures may not simply collect and concentrate circulating nitrogenous compounds, such as urea or uric acid, but *produce* them. Their function thus, is similar to that of vertebrate liver cells: deamination of amino acids and transaminations leading to nitrogen-free compounds and nitrogenous bases (urea, uric acid, etc.) There is circumstantial evidence that oligochaete chloragog cells can "operate" the ornithine cycle. Only citrulline has not yet been detected, but if it is supplied by the experimenter, urea appears. An alternative type of ornithine cycle, by-passing citrulline, has also been suggested. Suffice it here to say that the chloragog cells may be considered, as Heidermanns (1937) expressed it, "the central organ of urea metabolism." Some aspects of the metabolic function of chloragocytes are represented in Fig. 13–12.

Excretophore cells may thus be considered as little metabolic "engines" which prepare metabolizable compounds and remove the nonusable portions of those molecules which the organism takes in through its digestive system. The usable compounds (they are quite soluble, as a rule) are passed on to the circulating body fluids and can be absorbed by the body cells. The nonusable end products accumulate and are passed on to the storage sites or, after dis-

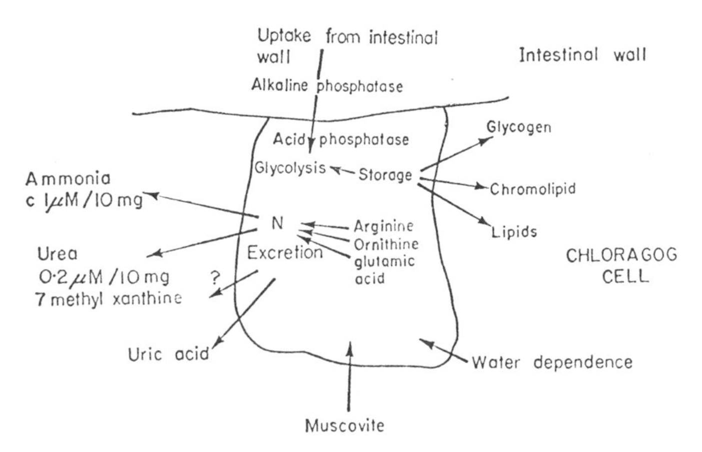

Figure 13–12. Diagram of the role of a chloragocyte in metabolism of the earthworm. (From Laverack, M. S.: The Physiology of Earthworms. Pergamon Press, The Macmillan Co., New York, 1963.)

integration of the excretophore cell, are swept out by the ciliary funnels of nephridia. The excretophore cells then save the other body cells the "effort" of having to deal with excretory problems.

From such considerations, the position of excretophore tissue near the gut or in immediate contact with blood or coelomic channels becomes significant.

The analogy of excretophore cells with liver cells goes even further because both cell types serve—in addition to their excretory function—as storage sites for nutrients, in particular for fats and glycogen. Numerous publications attest to this.

In turn, livers and midgut glands have important functions as excretory organs. They can operate in two ways: (1) They transform nutrients (example: amino acids) into useful, metabolizable compounds (example: α-ketoglutarate, succinic semialdehyde, succinate) and release the unusable by-products (example: urea) into the circulating body fluids from where they are excreted via the kidneys—or by diffusion through the body surface. (2) They take up cell debris and complex compounds of dead body cells and, after breaking them down into smaller molecules, secrete them into the lumen of the digestive tract. The vertebrate liver does this with the dying red blood cells: their hemoglobin is transformed into bile pigment and this is secreted in the bile juice through the gall ducts into the intestine.

The excretory function of invertebrate midgut glands (molluscs, crustaceans) has been suggested repeatedly, but if one combines all the available evidence, no definite conclusions can be drawn. One thing is certain: both crustaceans and molluscs contain concrement in their midgut gland cells. But we do not know whether this (definitely nitrogen containing) material is stored there, excreted into the lumen or released—perhaps via phagocytes—into the circulating body fluids.

Insects and arachnids and crustaceans possess cell systems engaged in intracellular excretion. Circulating athrocytes have been observed in all groups. In addition, there are cell masses with obvious excretory function: in insects, the cells of the so-called *fat body* store nitrogenous compounds, in particular uric acid. There also is evidence for an excretory function of the midgut in many insects and arachnoids. The integument may serve as a depot of excretory products. A famous example is the white scales of butterflies (Pieridae): they are filled with pterines (formerly thought to be uric acid).

Many Crustacea possess peculiar glandular cell masses ("head glands," "gill glands," etc.). They usually surround hemal sinus and are filled with colored, granular material.

The so-called pericardial cells of insects appear to have excretory functions. Recent evidence shows that they are engaged in deamination reactions involving amino acids.

Perhaps the most peculiar form of excretion occurs in the tunicates. With the exception of the salps, in which the intestinal epithelium excretes accumulated concrement, there are no mechanisms developed for the elimination of concrement. However, dissolved excretory products may well be excreted by simple diffusion through the body wall. The highly developed vascularization of the pharynx may contribute to this. Concrement accumulates in connective tissue cells around the viscera (Cionidae, Synascidia), in storage vesicles (Cynthiidae, Ascidiidae), or in one large storage vesicle (Molgulidae) that grows with the age of the animal. The storage vesicles consist of an outer connective tissue sheath, the inside of which is covered by a columnar epithelium of a structure reminiscent of the epithelial cells of nephridial tubules of other phyla. These cells contain concrement and release this into the center of the storage vesicle.

This rather brief and sketchy description of intracellular excretion is intended to point out the almost universal occurrence of the phenomenon.

It may have become obvious to the reader that the biochemistry and physiological significance of "concrement" is still rather obscure. Yet it must play an important part in the life of animal organisms. The deposition of concrement within the organism must represent a factor that limits the life span. One must ask, however, whether the production of apparently insoluble concrement is the chief function of excretophore cells. The real challenge for the physiologist lies in the question: Are the excretophores of a given animal engaged in preliminary metabolism and does the appearance of concrement merely represent the end products arising from it? In the older literature, concrement production has been viewed only as a form of extra-renal or extra-nephridial excretion whereby the excretophore cells take up and concentrate dissolved excretory products from the body fluids and deposit them as insoluble concrement. The new approach considers the possibility that the substances out of which concrement is formed arise within the excretophore cells themselves. The primary function of these cells, however, is then not the production of concrement, but the liberation of nutrient molecules from ingested food matter. The nonutilizable nitrogenous molecules then become deposits of "concrement" or are excreted as urea, uric acid, etc.

EXCRETION THROUGH "NEPHRIDIA"

With few exceptions, metazoans possess highly specialized tubular organs which control the composition of the body fluids. They may be called *nephridia*. As a rule they communicate with the coelom if such exists, through *nephrostomes* or *ciliated funnels* (annelids, molluscs). In arthropods, Onychophora, and in *vertebrate* kidneys, in which the coelom is greatly reduced, the tubules begin with a sac or capsule (coelomosac, Bowman's capsule) that is, in fact, identical with a reduced coelom. In the primitive vertebrate condition a tubule may communicate with a common ceolomic space by way of ciliated funnels (*pronephridia*).

In flatworms, many annelids, the Kinorhyncha, Rotifera, Nemertinea, and even *Amphioxus (Branchiostoma)*, the nephridia are of the type known as *protonephridia*. These are blind-ending tubes that open to the outside by way of a pore, called a *nephropore, nephridial pore*, or *excretory pore*. The organs are either segmentally repeated or form a common system of a large, branched tube. The blind ends are made up of *flame bulbs* (flatworms, rotifers; Figs. 13–13 and 13–14) or *solenocytes*. In either case, a specialized cell closes off a particular

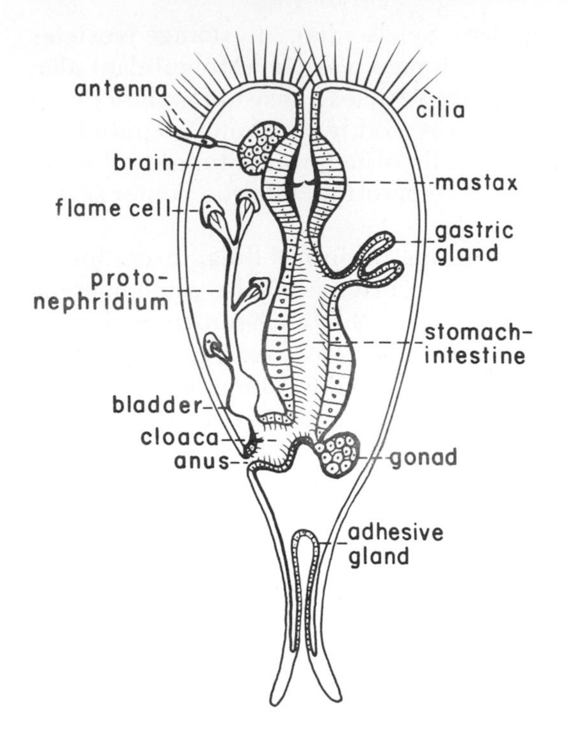

Figure 13–13. Diagram of the anatomy of a rotifer. Note the rather extensive excretory organ. The bladder empties rhythmically. The excretory organ serves, among others, in osmoregulation (see Chap. 5). (Modified after Stempell, W.: Zoologie im Grundriss. G. Borntraeger, Berlin, 1926.)

tube and extends one (solenocyte) or more (flame bulb) cilia into the lumen of the tube.

Protonephridia are probably the original type of nephridium. They are replaced in certain animal types (molluscs, crustaceans, vertebrates) by metanephridia – in some animal types, they coexist with metanephridia or nephridia.

The transition from one form of excretory organ to the other can best be gleaned from a study of annelid morphology, if one follows the guidance of the work of Goodrich (1898–1946). Because the coelom includes the gonads, removal of egg and sperm cells requires an opening to the outside environment. This is provided by the coelomoduct, a funnel-shaped organ (coelomostome) provided with a duct (coelomoduct proper) that leads to the body wall and opens to the outside (genital pore). The duct fuses either with that of the protonephridium to form a *protonephromixium*, or with a modified nephridium, the metanephridium, which is open to the coelom. In the latter case, a *metanephromixium* is formed. (Fig. 13–15). In cases in which the fusion is so complete that the coelomostome becomes, as it were, the nephrostome, one speaks of a *mixonephridium*. In some annelids (*Nereis*, for example), no fusion takes place; instead the coelomoduct becomes transformed into a *ciliophagocytal organ*. This serves in the accumulation and collection of phagocytes loaded with excretory products, or with fragments of disintegrated excretophore cells. To get an impression of the variety of nephridial structures encountered in the annelids, refer to Figures 13–16 through 13–20.

Although molluscan larvae (trochophora) possess protonephridia (as did, presumably, the ancestral molluscs), coelomoducts – in various modified forms –

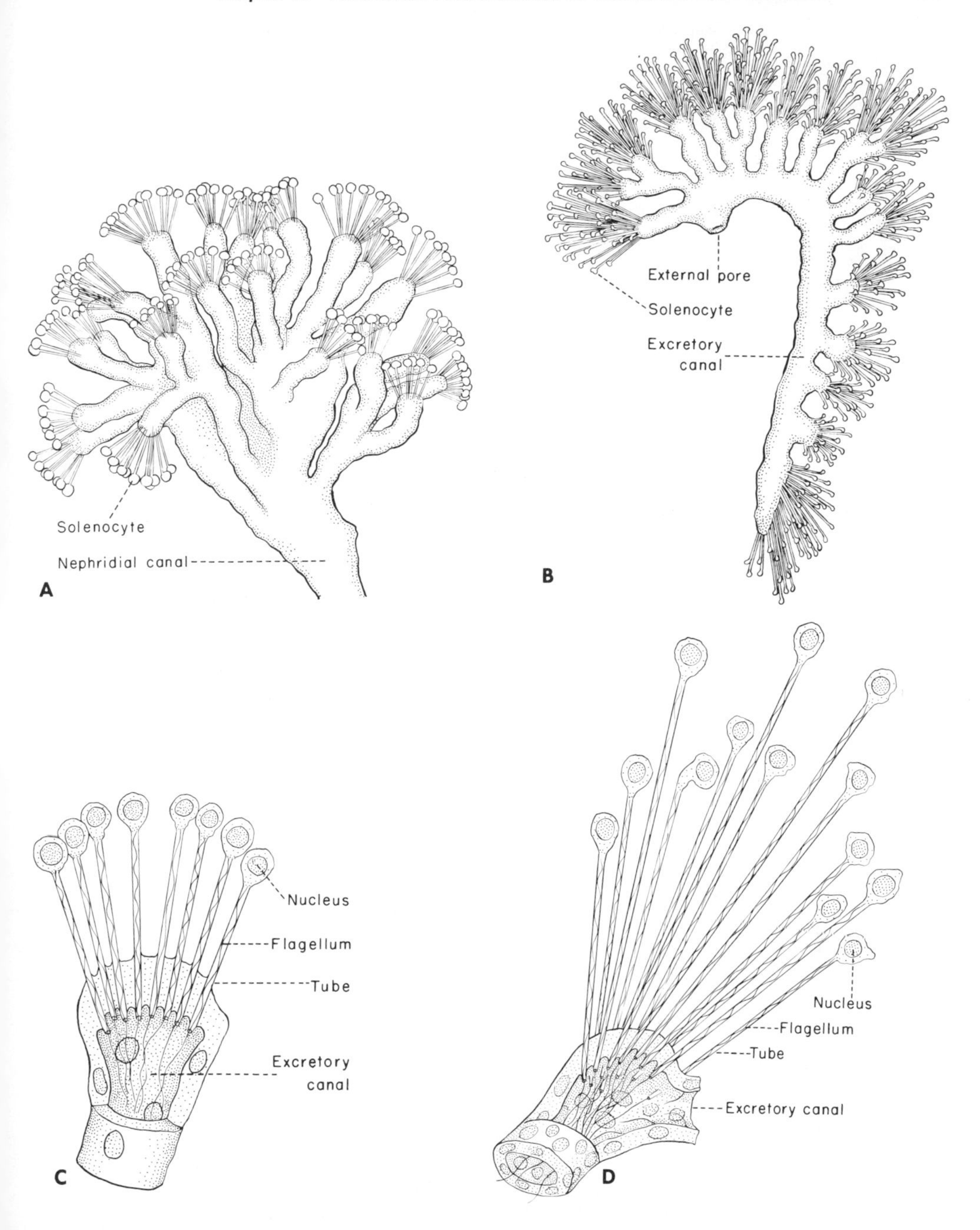

Figure 13-14. Enlarged views of excretory organs of *Amphioxus* and of a polychaete *Phyllodoce paretti*. Both have solenocytes. Goodrich, who discovered this, concluded that the excretory organs of the representatives of these two phyla are homologous. ". . . All we need to assume is, not that the vertebrates have been evolved from the polychaetes, but that the remote common ancestor of these now highly differentiated phyla was of more elaborate structure than most authors have been hitherto inclined to suppose." **A**, excretory organ of *Phyllodoce*, **B**, excretory organ of *Amphioxus*. **C** and **D**, semidiagrammatic views of portions of the excretory organs of *Phyllodoce* and *Amphioxus*, respectively. (From Goodrich, E. S.: On the structure of the excretory organs of Amphioxus. Quart. J. Micr. Sci. *45*:493–501, 1902.)

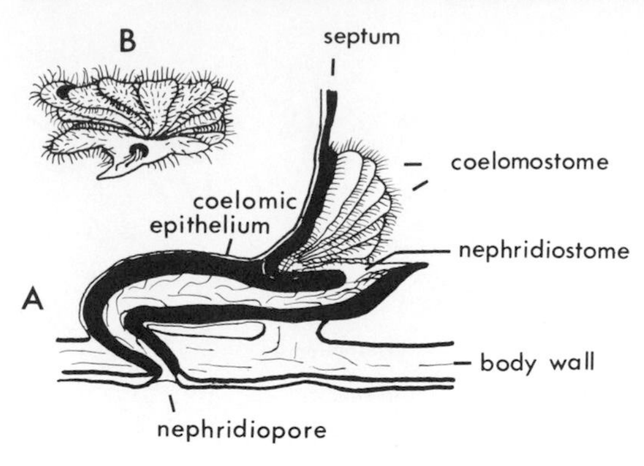

Figure 13–15. Metanephromixium of an annelid of the family Syllidae, *Odontosyllis enopla.* **A**, lateral view of the semisected left metanephromixium. **B**, front view of the organ. Although the coelomostome ends blindly in a pocket, its opening is almost fused with that of the nephridiostome. (Redrawn from Goodrich, E. S.: The study of nephridia and genital ducts since 1895. Quart. J. Micr. Sci. *86*:1–392, 1946.)

are the only type of "nephridium" found in molluscs (Figs. 5–15, 10–18, 13–21, and 13–22). According to Goodrich (1945), it is to be assumed that the excretory organs of crustaceans (Fig. 13–23), the antennal glands or the maxillary glands (each is paired—some Crustacea have only one or the other, others have both), derive from segmentally repeated coelomoducts. In all modern forms the one or two remaining pairs are associated with a small remnant of the coelom, the *coelomosac* (see Fig. 13–24).

In *Amphioxus*, considered the most primitive vertebrate by some, the nephridia (Fig. 13–14) lie between ectoderm and coelom. They have solenocytes. There is no communication with the coelom.

The typical vertebrate kidneys (Fig. 13–25) consist of many nephridia which are assumed to derive from "more or less funnel-shaped paired outgrowths from the wall of the coelomic somites" (Goodrich, 1945) and are homol-

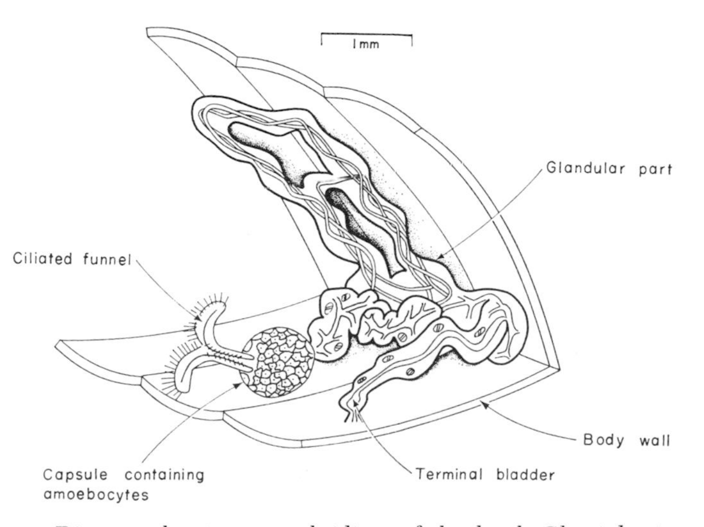

Figure 13–16. Diagram showing a nephridium of the leech *Glossiphonia complanata*, in situ. (After Oka, A.: Beitraege zur Anatomie der Clepsine. Z. wiss. Zool. 58:79–151, 1894. From Mann, K. H.: Leeches [Hirudinea]. Pergamon Press, New York, 1962.)

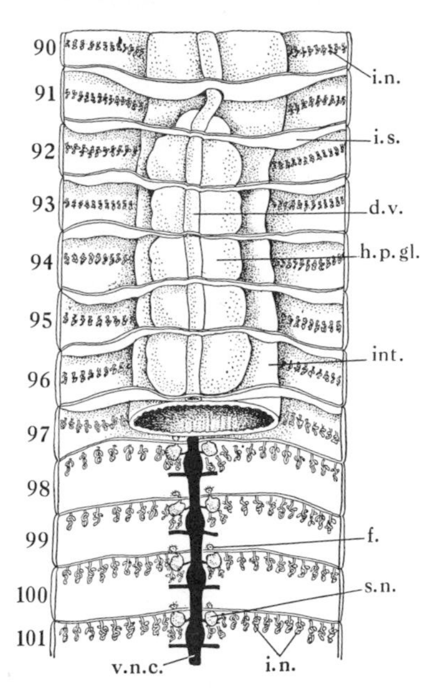

Figure 13–17. Semidiagrammatic representation of the nephridial system of the oligochaete *Eutyphoeus foveatus*. Region of the hepatopancreas and behind. *d.v.*, dorsal blood vessel; *f.*, funnel of a septal nephridium; *h.p.gl.*, hepatopancreatic glands; *i.n.*, close integumentary nephridia (see Fig. 3–19); *int.*, intestine; *i.s.*, intersegmental septum; *s.n.*, open septal nephridia (see Fig. 3–18); *v.n.c.*, ventral nerve cord; *90–101*, serial numbers of segments. (From Bahl, K. N.: Quart. J. Micr. Sci. *83*:423–449, 1942.)

ogous with the coelomoducts just referred to. Their structure is explained in Figures 13–26 and 13–27.

This historical approach to morphology—and with it to physiology—is a triumph of the concept of evolution.

Since the kidney structure is best explained in illustrations, refer to the diagrams in Chapter 3 and to Figure 13–24. Notice that, except in the protonephridia, a coelomic space always connects to a tubule, and this, in turn, often opens into a bladder. The organs are bilateral, often multiple. The walls of the

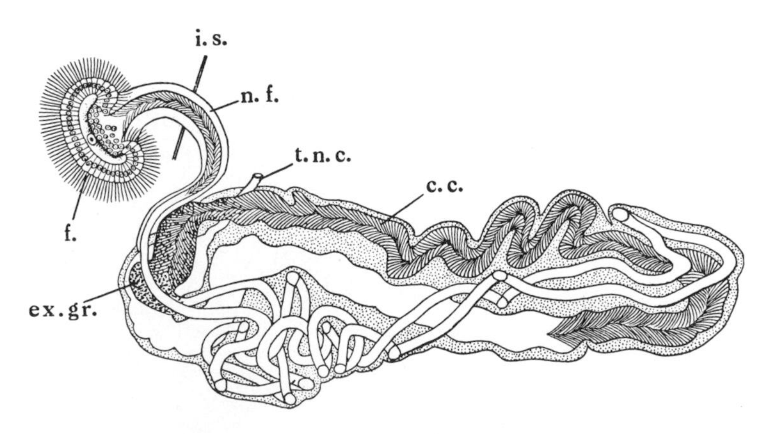

Figure 13–18. Open septal nephridium of *Eutyphoeus foveatus* (see Fig. 13–17). *c.c.*, long ciliated tract of the nephridial canal; *ex.gr.*, excretory granules in the walls of the canal; *f.*, preseptal funnel; *i.s.*, intersegmental septum; *n.f.*, neck of the funnel with the ciliated tubule; *t.n.c.*, terminal part of the nephridial canal opening on the body wall through the nephridiopore. (From Bahl, K. N.: Quart. J. Micr. Sci. *83*:423–449, 1942.)

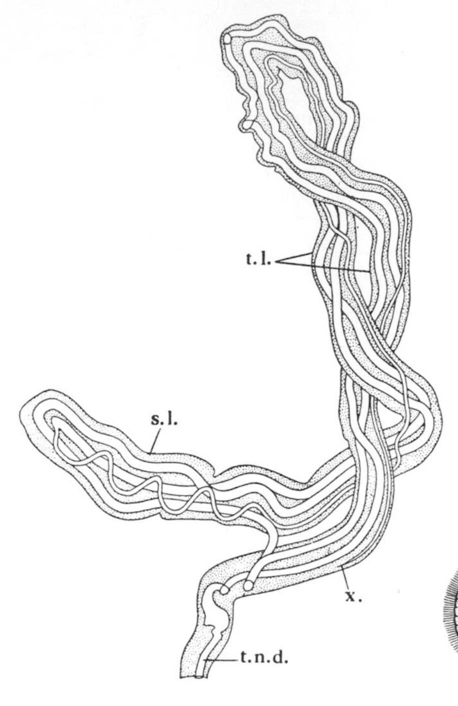

Figure 13–19. Closed integumentary nephridium of *Eutyphoeus foveatus* (see Fig. 13–17). *s.l.*, straight loop; *t.l.*, twisted loop; *t.n.d.*, terminal nephridial duct; *x.*, initial blind end of the nephridial canal. (From Bahl, K. N.: Quart. J. Micr. Sci. 83:423–449, 1942.)

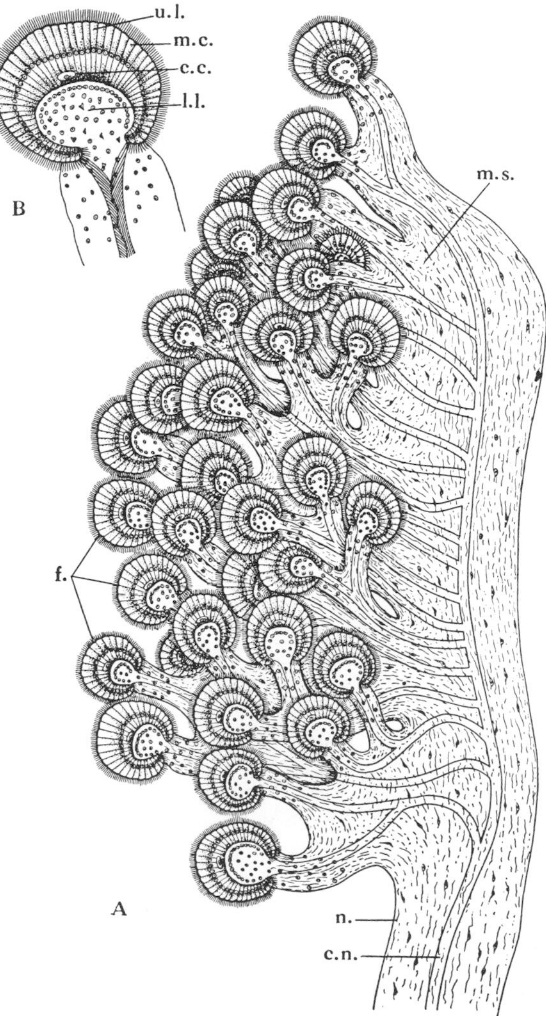

Figure 13–20. Multiple funnels of a nephridium of the oligochaete *Thamnodrilus crassus*. **A**, preseptal portion of one nephridium. **B**, one of the funnels enlarged. *c.c.*, central cell of the upper lip; *c.n.*, canal of the neck; *f.*, funnels; *l.l.*, lower lip; *m.c.*, marginal cells of the upper lip; *m.s.*, membranous shelf of the funnels; *n.*, neck of the funnels; *u.l.*, upper lip. (From Bahl, K. N.: Quart. J. Micr. Sci. 83:450–454, 1942.)

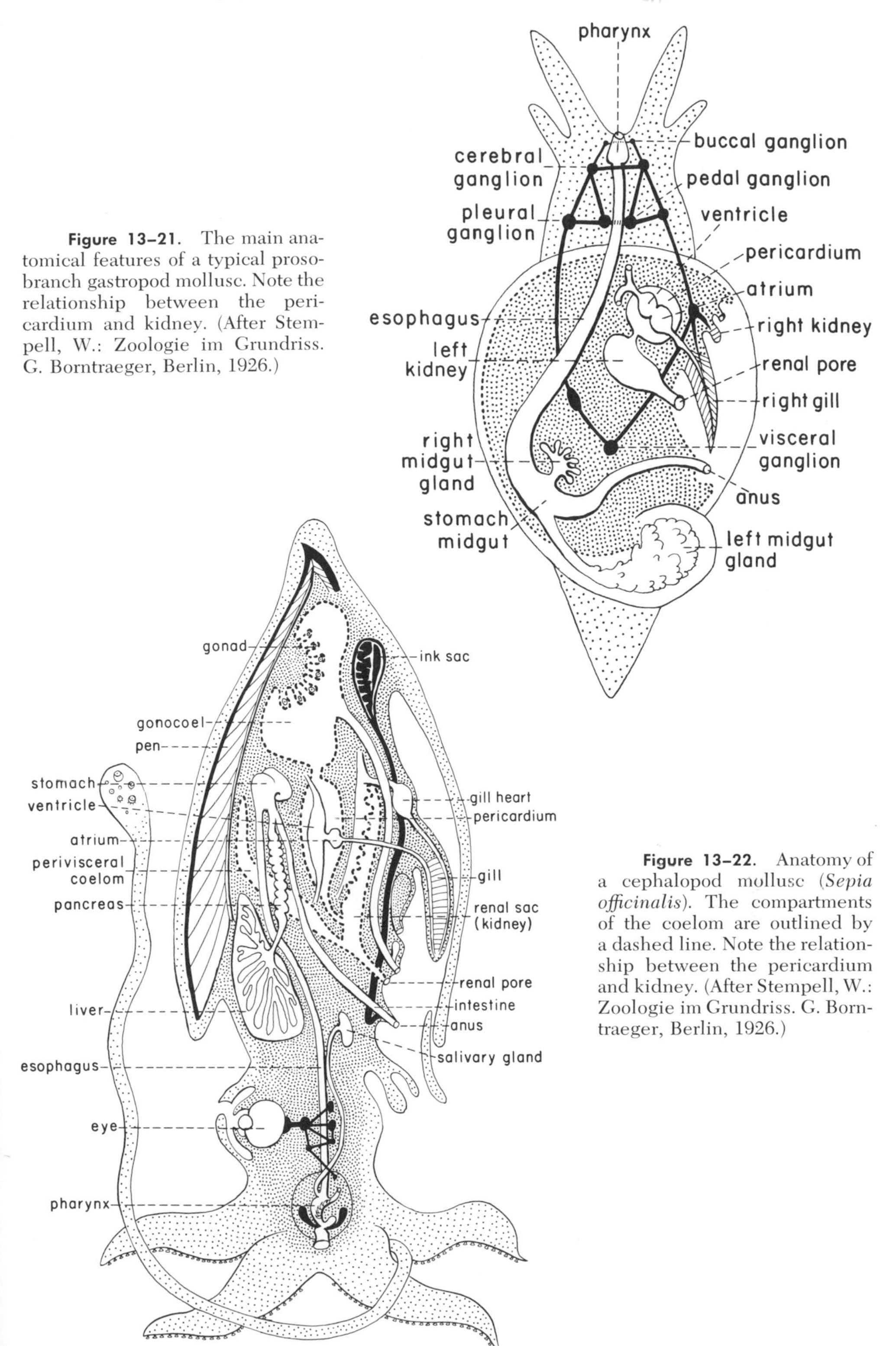

Figure 13–21. The main anatomical features of a typical prosobranch gastropod mollusc. Note the relationship between the pericardium and kidney. (After Stempell, W.: Zoologie im Grundriss. G. Borntraeger, Berlin, 1926.)

Figure 13–22. Anatomy of a cephalopod mollusc (*Sepia officinalis*). The compartments of the coelom are outlined by a dashed line. Note the relationship between the pericardium and kidney. (After Stempell, W.: Zoologie im Grundriss. G. Borntraeger, Berlin, 1926.)

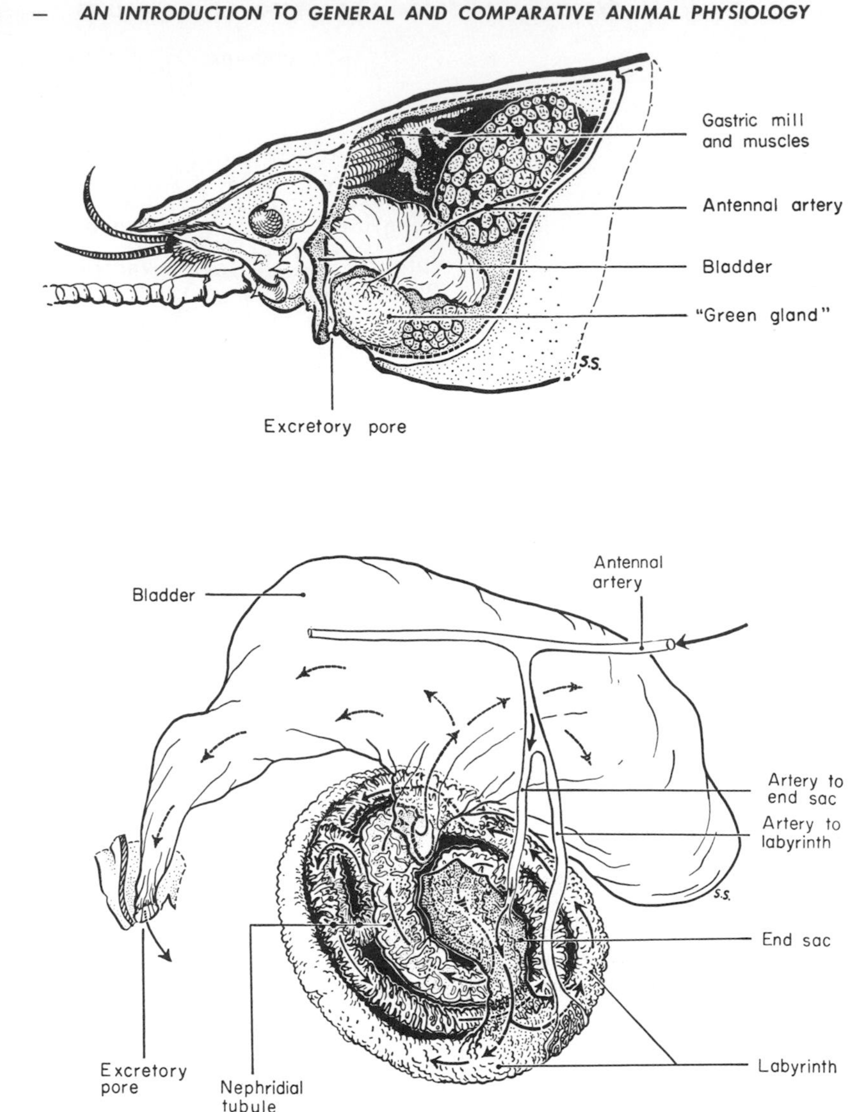

Figure 13–23. Location and structure of the renal organ (kidney) of a crayfish (*Astacus pallipes*). The organ is known as the "green gland." Its structure, when unraveled, is shown in Figure 5–13. It receives arteries which appear to provide the hydrostatic pressure that is necessary for filtration into the end sac (coelomosac). (From Potts, W. T. W., and G. Parry: Osmotic and Ionic Regulation in Animals. Pergamon Press, Oxford, 1964.)

tubule usually consist of a single layer of epithelial cells. These have the function of secreting compounds into the tubules and of reabsorbing others from the tubules. Different portions of the tubules transport different compounds or ions. Such transport concerns by no means only "dissolved" molecules; there is also considerable secretion of granular concrement. In fact, the tubular cells of many kidneys have been described as functioning just like other excretophore cells.

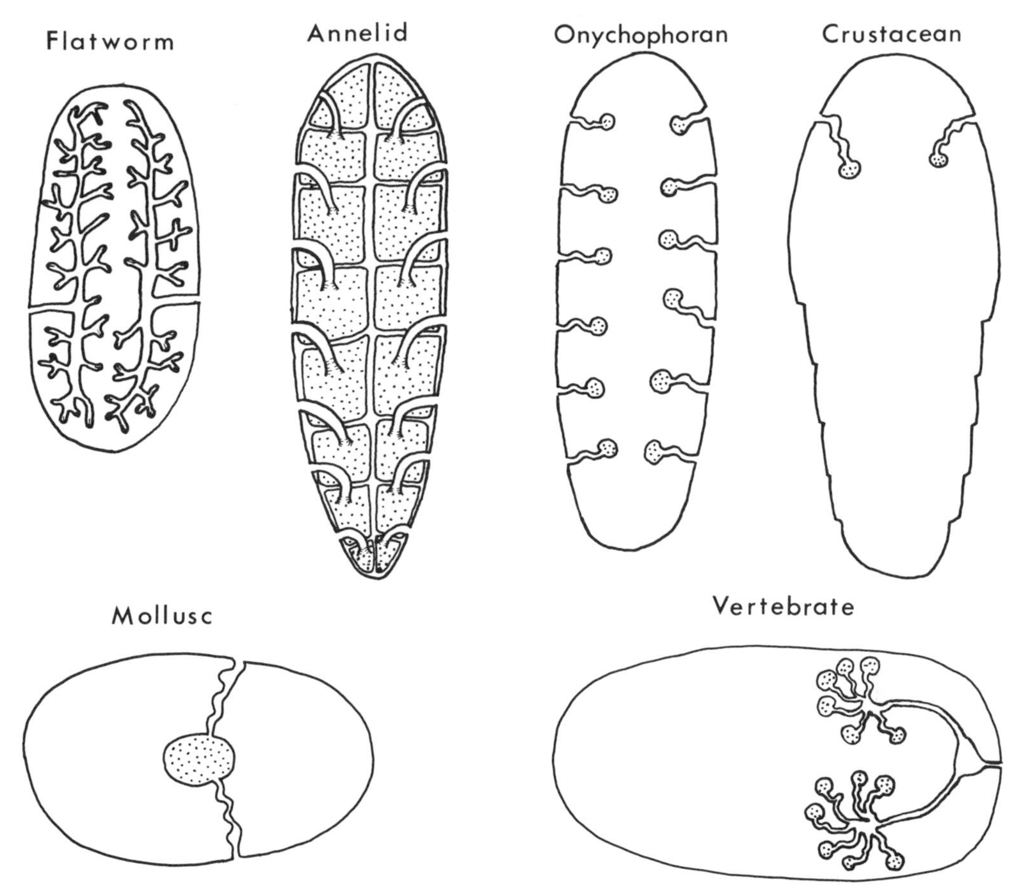

Figure 13–24. Abstractions of various types of nephridium, showing the relation to the coelom (indicated in stipple). This is an idealized version of the physiologist's concept and in no way represents the true morphology. This is particularly true of the annelid. Note the coelomic remnants that form the first part of the extractory structures (nephridia) of onychophorans, crustaceans, and vertebrates. The coelomic cavity of molluscs represents the pericardium (the heart is not shown).

Examples of the transfer of molecularly dispersed (dissolved) substances across cells of the tubular epithelium are described in Chapter 5 (Ionic Regulation) and Chapter 27. Excretion as such is not the chief function of kidneys. Only in terrestrial animals have the kidneys, of necessity, assumed the role of chief excretory organ, since there is no acquatic environment into which excretory products might diffuse through the body wall. *Kidneys*, as mentioned before, are *organs that regulate the composition of the body fluids.* This is done by passive as well as active transport of molecular species into, as well as out of, the kidney tubules or their equivalent structures. When active transport is involved, the first process is called *active secretion*, the second, *active reabsorption*.

Kidneys cannot function properly unless fluid flows continuously through the tubule. This fluid is processed as on an assembly (perhaps better "disassembly"?) line; components are added here and taken away there, until the

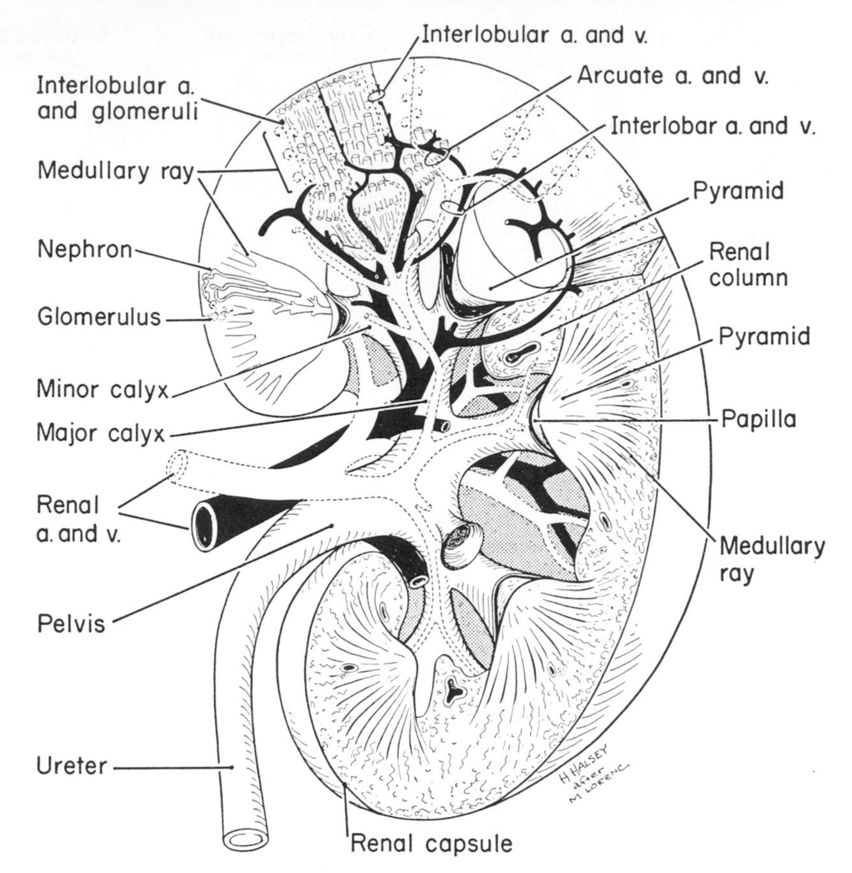

Figure 13–25. Gross structure of the human kidney. Only one of the innumerable nephrons is shown. *a.*, arteries (or arterioles); *v.*, veins (or venules). The structure of individual nephrons is shown in Figure 13–27. (After Smith, H. W.: Principles of Renal Physiology. Oxford University Press, 1956.)

final product, the urine, is allowed to pass to the outside. Just as production in a factory breaks down when the belt on the assembly line stops, so does the kidney stop functioning if there is no movement of the tubular fluid.

Several mechanisms are employed to drive fluid through the kidneys. In the protonephridia, the flame bulb, or solenocyte(s), provides the motor in the form of continuously moving cilia or flagella. Where the tubule is open to a coelomic space, the hydrostatic pressure of the coelom forces fluid through the tubule. This pressure is generated by the tonus of the muscular body wall and is convincingly demonstrated whenever an animal is injured: body fluid and even parts of the internal organs are forced out of the opening of the wound by this internal pressure. Since the kidney tubules communicate with the outside world, their internal pressure tends to be similar to the outside pressure.

Figure 13–26. Simplified diagrams representing kidneys and reproductive organs of vertebrates. (Modified after Stempell, W.: Zoologie im Grundriss. G. Borntraeger, Berlin, 1926; and Kuehn, A.: Grundriss der allgemeinen Zoologie, 12th Ed. Georg Thieme Verlag, Stuttgart, 1957.)

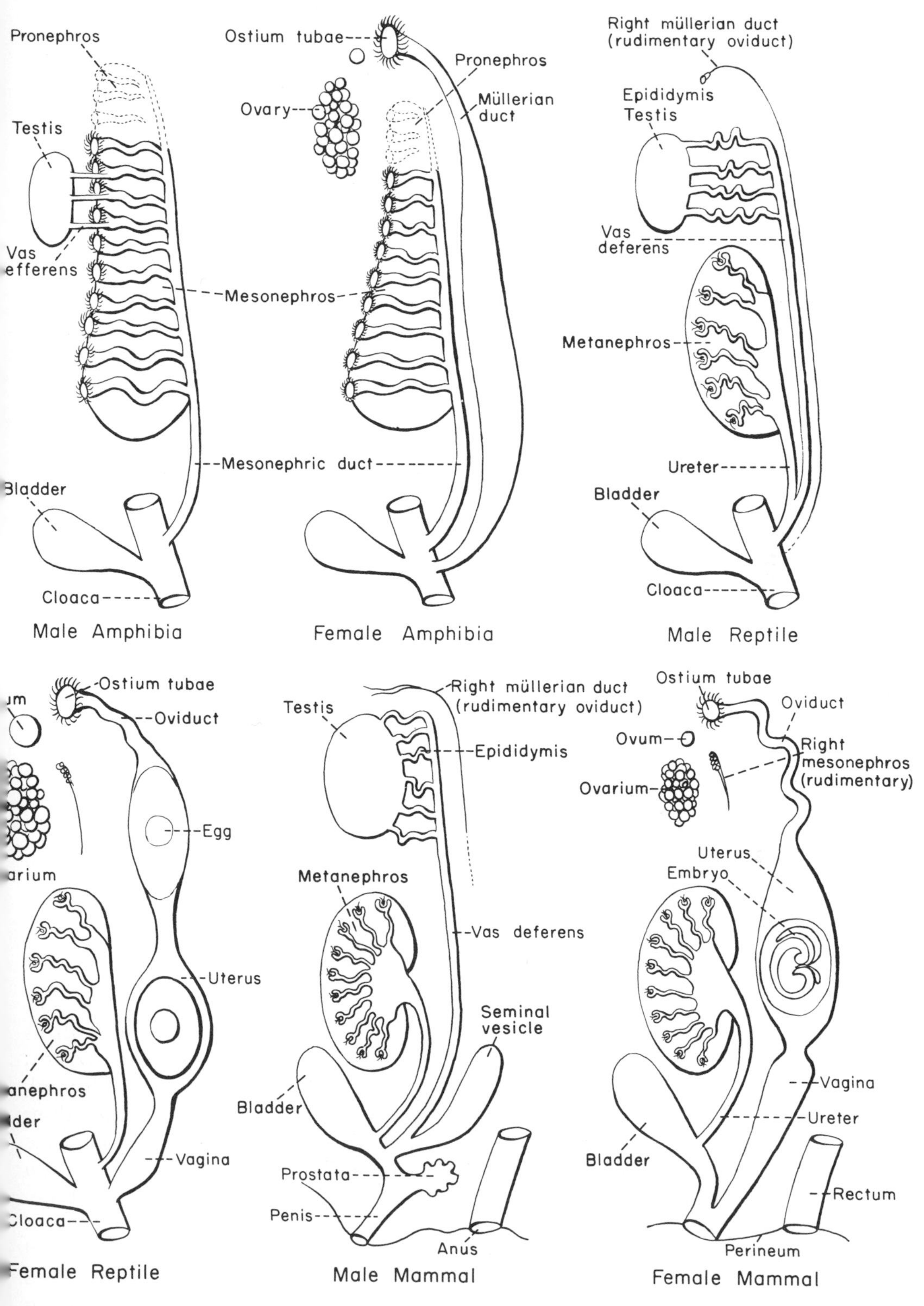

Figure 13–26. *See opposite page for legend.*

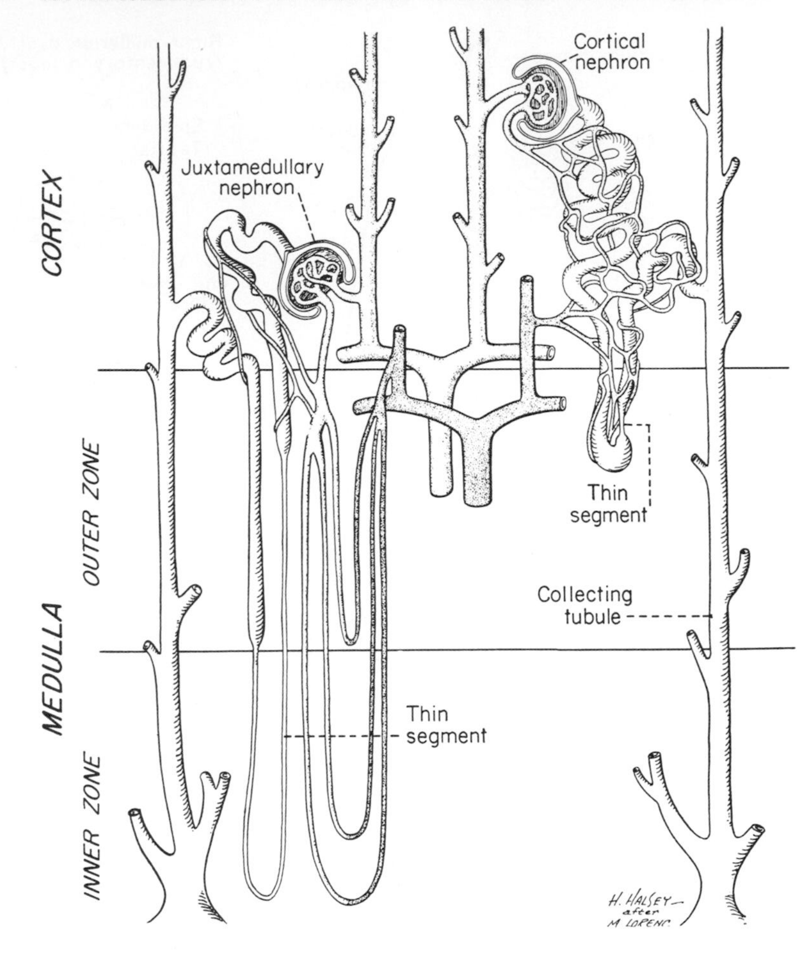

Figure 13–27. Structure of two types of nephron found in the human kidney. Both consist of a capsule (Bowman's), shown in section, and three segments of a tubule, the lumen of which communicates with that of the capsule. The segments are named: proximal convoluted tubule, thin segment, and distal convoluted tubule. Note the glomerulus inside the capsule. This is the site of filtration. (After Smith, H. W.: The Kidney, Its Structure and Function in Health and Disease. Oxford University Press, New York, 1951.)

The internal pressure of the organism acts, therefore, on the tubular wall as well as on the internal opening of the tubules, forcing fluid through the tubules.

Where a coelom communicates with the tubule (nephropore, ciliated funnel, etc.), the coelomic pressure can be expected to be lower than that of the other, closed body compartments. Consequently, there will be a pressure difference across the coelomic epithelium. Such a pressure difference gives rise to *filtration* of body fluids into the coelomic space that communicates with the tubule. Although the sum of the total internal pressures may remain constant, different regions of an animal may show differences. The pumping action of a heart creates areas of high (arteries) as well as of low (veins) pressure. In localized areas, the blood pressure can thus add considerably to the pressure difference across coelomic epithelia, and can thus increase the rate of filtration. How this is employed in kidney function shall be illustrated with three examples:

In decapod Crustacea, the kidney is represented by the antennal glands (Fig. 13–23): each consists of coelomosac, tubule, and bladder. The heart sends arteries directly to the coelomosac. Hemolymph, then, arrives there under pressure and is filtered into the coelomosac which is already under the general internal pressure of the hemolymph.

In lamellibranchs (Fig. 5–15), the heart is surrounded by a coelomic space (identical with the pericardial space) that communicates with the kidney tubule (known as the organ of Bojanus). The hydrostatic pressure in the heart filters blood through the wall of the heart and the coelomic epithelium into the pericardial coelom from where it passes on to the outside.

In vertebrate kidneys (Fig. 13–25), a mass of arterial capillaries (the *glomerulus*) is enclosed by a double walled coelomic capsule, the inside of which represents coelomic space and is continuous with the tubule (Fig. 13–27). Blood plasma is filtered under pressure (arterial blood pressure) into the space between the capillary wall and the inner wall of the capsule. Since the capsule tightly encloses the "neck" of the capillary glomerulus, this space maintains essentially the same pressure as the capillaries. The filtered fluid is thus filtered again into the coelomic space and passed on to and through the tubule.

It must be asked, of course, why the coelomic space does not collapse if its internal hydrostatic pressure is lower than that acting upon it. The answer is that it is held distended by connective tissue strands. In regard to the tubules, we must assume that their epithelial walls are strong enough to resist the external pressure. In addition, the openings to the outside (nephropore, etc.) are usually provided with valves or muscular sphincters (Fig. 13–28).

If, as is the case, body fluids are filtered into the nephridial lumen, the nephridia must provide mechanisms for the return of important components to

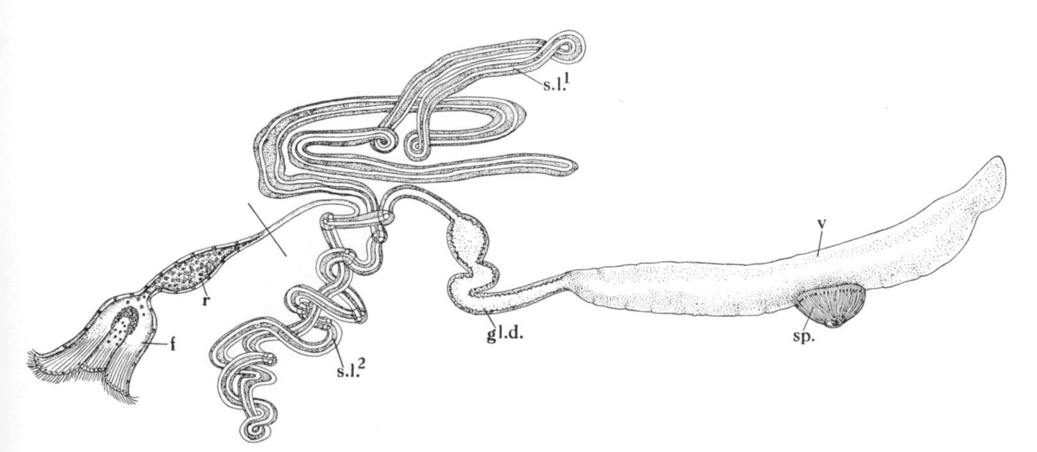

Figure 13–28. Nephridium from a clitellar segment of the oligochaete *Pontoscolex corethrurus*. *f*, funnel; *gl.d.*, glandular duct; *s.l.*[1], *s.l.*[2], first and second supplementary loops; *r*, receptacle; *sp.*, sphincter around the nephridiopore; *v*, vesicle (bladder). (From Bahl, K. N.: Quart. J. Micr. Sci. *84*:1–18, 1942.)

the body—otherwise the nephridia would be useless, a filter that permits loss of body fluids with all they contain, except cellularly or colloidally dispersed components (blood cells, protein).

One may ask: Why is filtration insufficient? Why do the cells of the kidney tubules have to actively secrete certain excretory components of the body fluid into the lumen? The answer is this: (1) Filtration is not sufficient if the components to be excreted accumulate faster than they are filtered out. (2) During filtration, all components of the body fluids are filtered, while it is required for the maintenance of a normal composition of body fluids that certain substances, particularly ions, be excreted at a greater rate than others. (3) Filtration must be thought of as serving primarily the function of providing the necessary flow through the tubules so that there is a vehicle that carries away secreted components. (4) In some kidneys, such as the aglomerular nephridia of fish, filtration does not seem to be prominent.

Before summarizing the function of kidneys, the malpighian tubules of the insects must be mentioned. These excretory structures open into the gut (Figs. 13–29 through 13–32), and are, in fact, considered to be specialized diverticula of it. The situation of excretory tubules opening into the gut, actually, is nothing new. It occurs in some annelids (*Pheretima*, *Megascolex*, Fig. 13–33). Since the lumen of the digestive tract represents the outside of the animal, there is no radical departure from the normal pattern of external kidney openings (nephridiopores). What makes the malpighian tubules so interesting is their mech-

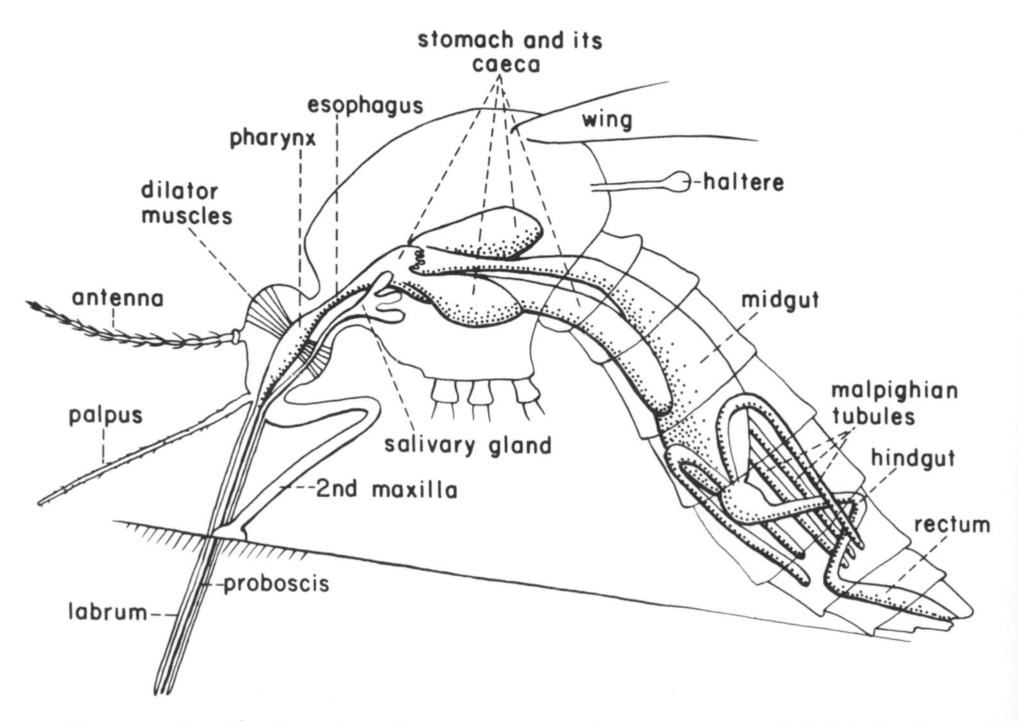

Figure 13–29. The digestive and excretory system of a mosquito (*Anopheles*). (After Stempell, W.: Zoologie im Grundriss. G. Borntraeger, Berlin, 1926.)

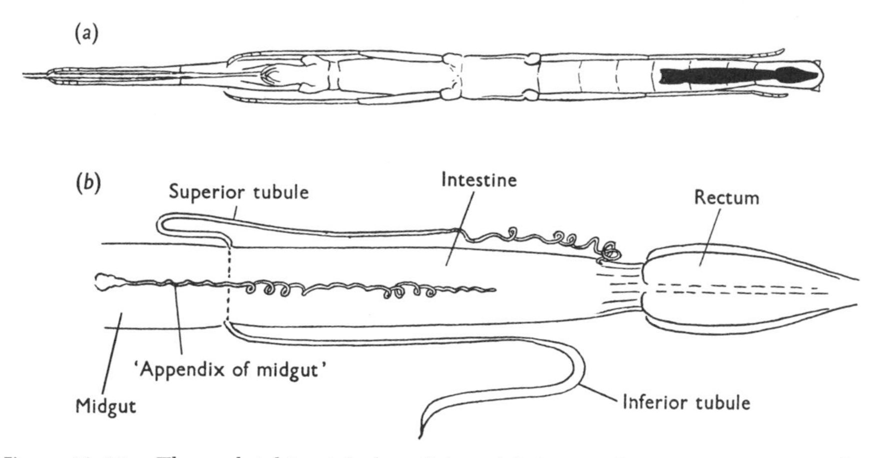

Figure 13–30. The malpighian tubules of the stick insect, *Carausius morosus*. a shows the position within the animal of the region illustrated in **b**. (From Ramsay, J. A.: The excretory system of the stick insect, Dixippus morosus [Orthoptera, Phasmidae]. J. Exp. Biol. *32*:183–199, 1955.)

anism of action, as suggested by Ramsay (1955): Instead of filtration into the tubules, body fluids are drawn into them osmotically. This is achieved by the active secretion of potassium ions into the lumen. As potassium is concentrated in the lumen, chloride ions follow passively. The high concentration of KCl sets up a steep osmotic gradient which draws water (and all small molecules and ions dissolved in it) into the lumen. Later on the water and other components are resorbed, the rest is excreted through the gut.

In summary, then, the principal functions of kidneys are:

1. Accumulation, concentration, and eventual secretion of certain excretory products (concrement) in solid form.
2. Filtration of body fluids into the nephridial lumen.
3. Active secretion of substances adsorbed from body fluids, into the same lumen.
4. Active reabsorption of substances from the fluid inside the lumen and return of these to the body fluids.

Quantitative aspects of this have been worked out in several cases. Before discussing some examples, it is helpful to deal with the concept of *clearance*, because this is widely employed in studies of kidney function.

The term "clearance" was originally developed for vertebrate, glomerular kidneys. It may be defined as *the volume of blood plasma that is completely cleared of a given component during a certain time interval, as it passes through the renal circulation*. The technique of measuring clearance is illustrated in Figure 13–34. Clearance is usually expressed in ml/min. Obviously, the more of a given substance lost to the nephridia, the higher the clearance value. The maximum value is equal to the total volume of blood plasma that has passed through the blood vessels of the kidneys in 1 minute.

If a substance that has entered the nephridial lumen is not reabsorbed by the tubular cells, and if these cells do not actively transfer this substance into the lumen, the amount of this substance that appears inside the lumen—or that

(Text continued on page 314.)

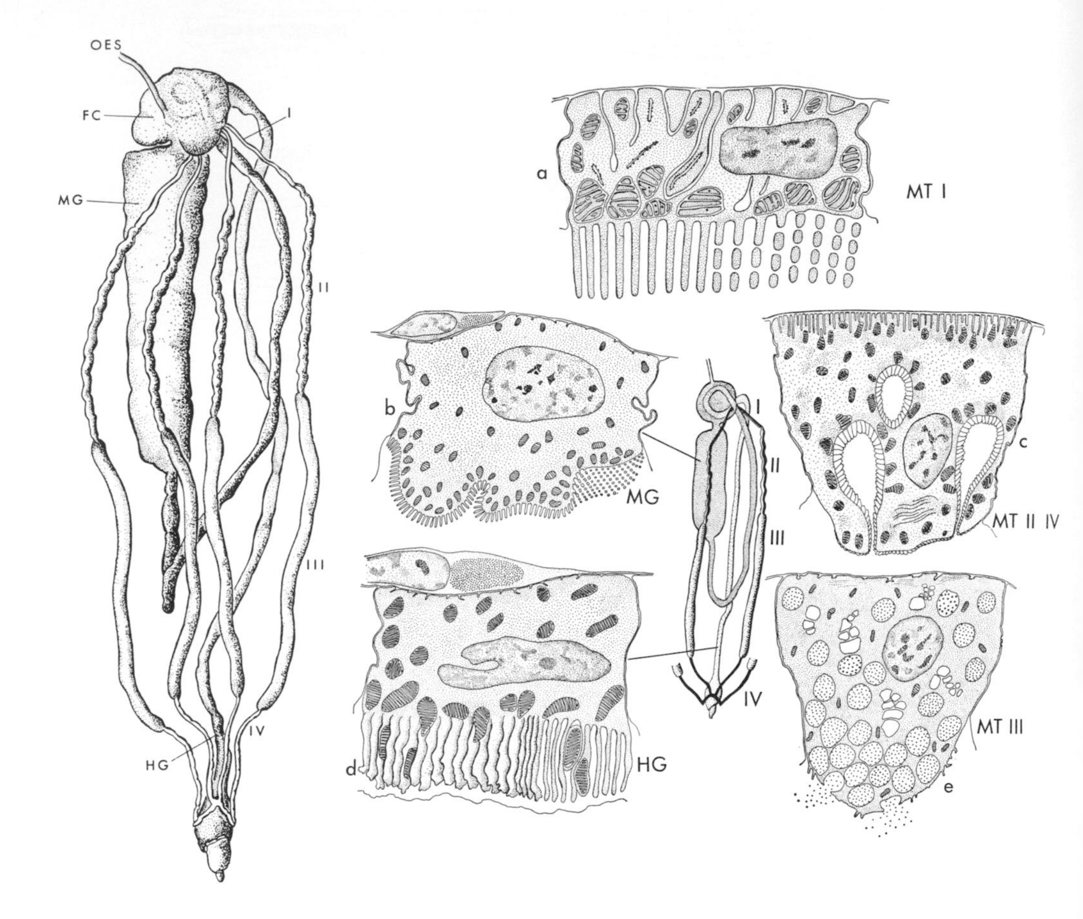

Figure 13–31. Diagram of the digestive tract and malpighian tubules, and the cell types found in them, of a homopteran insect, *Macrosteles fascifrons*. The slender esophagus (*OES*) leads into a dilated sac, the filter chamber (*FC*), which in turn opens into the stomach (*MG*). Both the filter chamber and the stomach are part of the midgut, the thinner part of which turns forward (upward in the diagram). The transition zone between the midgut and the hindgut (*HG*), including the origin of the malpighian tubules (*MT*), extends into the filter chamber. This is found in several insects. The filter chamber provides a shortcut for the passage of water imbibed by the insect, directly from the first to the last part of the midgut. The four malpighian tubules are linked by cross connectives that are in contact with, but not fused to, the dilated rectum. The tubules are formed by a single layer of cells. I to IV, the different regions of the tubules. Note the infolding, or plication, of the external plasma membrane, which provides a large surface area in contact with the extracellular fluid, and the brush border (shown in sagittal and cross sections) of the membrane facing the lumen of MG, MT I, and the membrane folds and lobes of HG. The membrane of MT II facing the lumen shows a flask-shaped infolding and extensive inflection and pleating. It serves, perhaps, in osmoregulatory function; the corresponding membrane in MT I serves, probably, in water absorption. The cells of MT III release excretory granules into the lumen of the tubule. As can be judged by the size of the mitochondria shown, the magnification of the represented cell types differs. (From Smith, D. S., and V. C. Littau: Cellular specialization in the excretory epithelia of an insect, Macrosteles fascifrons, Stål [Homoptera]. J. Biophys. Biochem. Cytol. 8:103–133, 1960.)

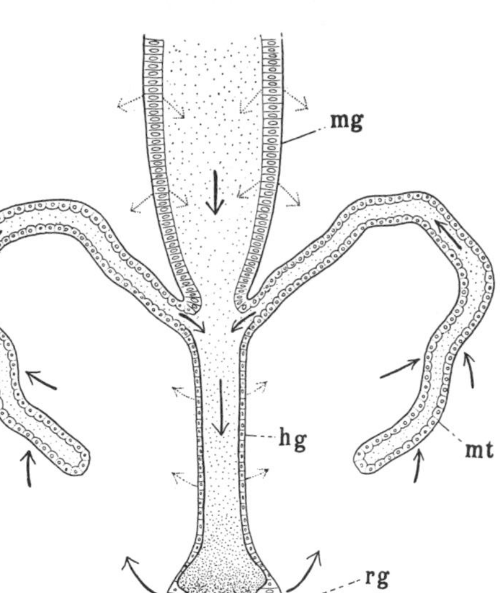

Figure 13–32. Diagram of the course of water movement in the digestive and excretory systems of insects. Fluid is probably both secreted and absorbed in the midgut (*mg.*). Fluid also moves through the malpighian tubules (*mt*) into the hindgut (*hg*) and is reabsorbed in the hindgut, especially in the rectum (rectal glands). *f*, feces, which are often almost dry; *r*, rectum; *rg*, rectal glands. (From Wigglesworth, V. B.: On the function of the so-called "rectal glands" of insects. Quart. J. Micr. Sci. 75:131–150, 1932.)

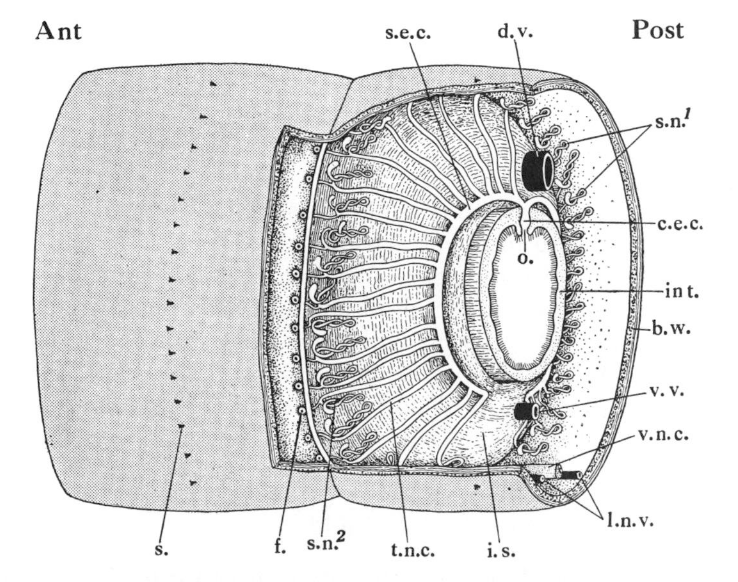

Figure 13–33. Diagrammatic representation of the enteronephric nephridial system as found behind the 74th segment of the oligochaete *Megascolex cochinensis*. *b.w.*, body wall; *c.e.c.*, common excretory canal; *d.v.*, dorsal vessel; *f.*, funnel of one of the septal nephridia; *int.*, intestine; *i.s.*, intersegmental septum; *l.n.v.*, lateral neural vessels; *o.*, opening of the common excretory canal into the lumen of the intestine; *s.*, seta; *s.e.c.*, septal excretory canal; *s.n.*[1], *s.n.*[2], septal nephridia of the right and left sides; *t.n.c.*, terminal nephridial canal; *v.n.c.*, ventral nerve cord; *v.v.*, ventral vessel. (From Bahl, K. N.: Quart. J. Micr. Sci. *84*:18–34, 1942.)

Figure 13–34. Arrangement of a clearance experiment on a rabbit. The animal's body, except the head, is immobilized by being placed inside a wooden box. Inulin, or another compound, is infused from a syringe (*2*) into a peripheral ear vein. The urine produced is collected with the aid of a catheter (*1*). Samples of blood are withdrawn from an artery by another syringe (*3*), and the concentration of the injected substance in the blood plasma is determined. (From Josephson, B., and J. Kallas: Inulin and creatinine clearance of unanaesthetized rabbits. Acta Physiol. Scand. *30*:1–10, 1953.)

is excreted—can have entered only by filtration. Since filtration leaves the concentrations of filterable components of body fluids unchanged, the amount of this substance in urine is a direct measure of filtration rate. Few substances actually behave in this way. Of these, *inulin*, a polysaccharide, is the most reliable.

The inulin clearance can be calculated as follows: it can be assumed that the concentration of inulin in blood plasma before this enters the renal circulation is identical with the inulin concentration in the filtrate produced. Even if the *concentration* of the filtered fluid changes as it passes along the length of the tubule, the *amount* of inulin will not change, since it is one of the few compounds that are left untouched by the tubular cells. Thus, if we know the initial concentration of inulin in bloood plasma and the amount of inulin appearing per minute in the urine, the filtration rate can be computed according to the simple formula:

$$C = \frac{U \cdot V}{B} \qquad (1)$$

where C is the clearance, U is the concentration in urine (in mg/ml), V is the volume (in ml) of urine produced per minute, and B is the concentration of inulin in blood plasma (in mg/ml). The dimension of C is ml/min. To make the resulting data from different organisms comparable, they are given in ml/min/kg.

If the assumption that inulin is neither reabsorbed nor secreted is correct, the inulin clearance gives the filtration rate. An exemplary illustration of this is shown in Figure 13–35.

Substances that give clearance values larger than inulin are *secreted* into the tubules; substances whose clëarance value is below that of inulin are *reabsorbed.* Once this inulin clearance is known, the clearance values of other compounds can be taken as an indicator of the fate of these substances as they pass through the renal circulation. The simple diagram in Figure 13–36 illustrates this.

Clearance can also be calculated for water. By adaptation of Formula 1, one can formulate the osmoregulatory properties of kidneys:

$$C_{osm} = \frac{U_{osm} \cdot V}{P_{osm}} \qquad (2)$$

Here C_{osm} is the osmolar clearance, U_{osm} is the osmolar concentration of urine, and P_{osm} is the osmolar concentration of plasma. The value arrived at represents the number of milliliters of solution formed if the urine excreted during 1 minute is made isosmolar to blood plasma. If water is reabsorbed, the amount (R_{H_2O}) is given by:

$$R_{H_2O} = \frac{U_{osm} \cdot V}{P_{osm}} - V \qquad (3)$$

and has the dimension ml/min. If more water is excreted in the urine than appears as glumerular filtrate ("hypotonic" urine), the R_{H_2O} value will be negative. Such an occurrence is not necessarily due to secretion of water by tubular cells, but may be simply caused by reabsorption of solute.

Where inulin is known to be neither secreted nor reabsorbed, insulin clearance can also be used to calculate the amount of water reabsorbed or secreted. The formula then reads:

$$R_{H_2O} = \frac{U \cdot V}{P} - V \qquad (4)$$

If the resulting value is positive, it gives the amount of water reabsorbed; if negative, it gives the amount of water secreted in addition to that which appears in the final urine as filtrate.

Many authors prefer the symbol B (blood concentration) to P (plasma concentration), particularly for invertebrates in which the number of blood cells is often small and the volume of blood cells negligible compared to the volume of blood or hemolymph.

It is extremely difficult to measure accurately the concentration of any substance in the filtrate before nephridial cells have a chance to reabsorb part of it or to add additional amounts by secretion. With ingenious techniques, a number of physiologists obtained minute quantities of filtrate and chemically analyzed them. In some cases, special microchemical methods had to be devised; most famous, perhaps, are those of Ramsay (1955), which enabled him to determine the ions in only 0.01 ml of fluid.

In large molluscs the kidney structures are relatively large. In a large octopus (about 25 kg), the coelomic portion of a nephridium may have a volume of 60 ml, the tubule 10 ml, and the "bladder," properly called the renal sac, no less than 300 ml. Martin and his collaborators have developed techniques for

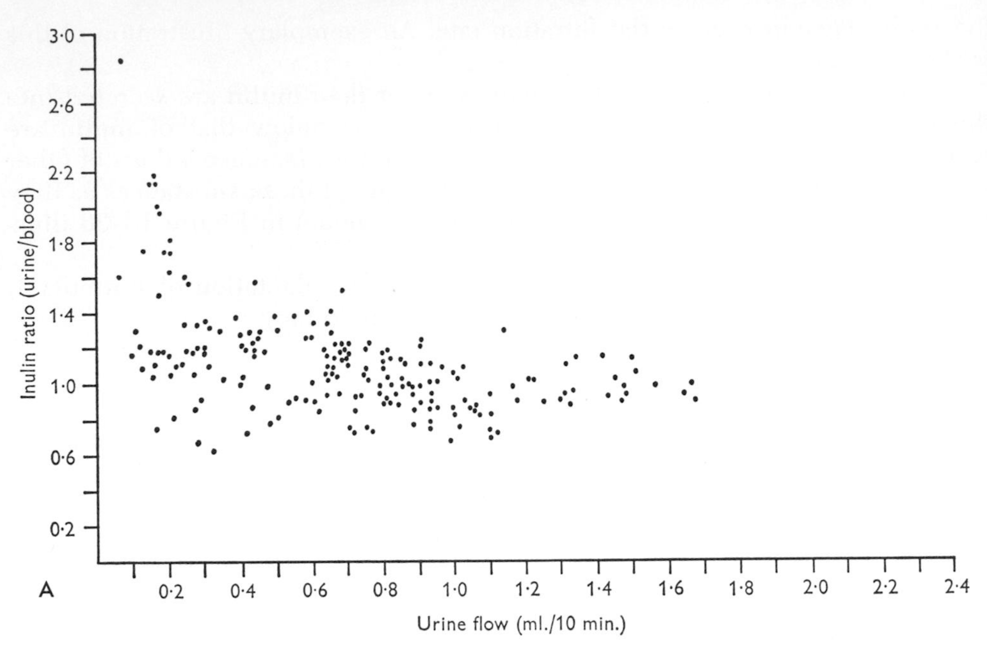

U/B ratios for inulin in relation to the urine flow rates. Results of twelve experiments.

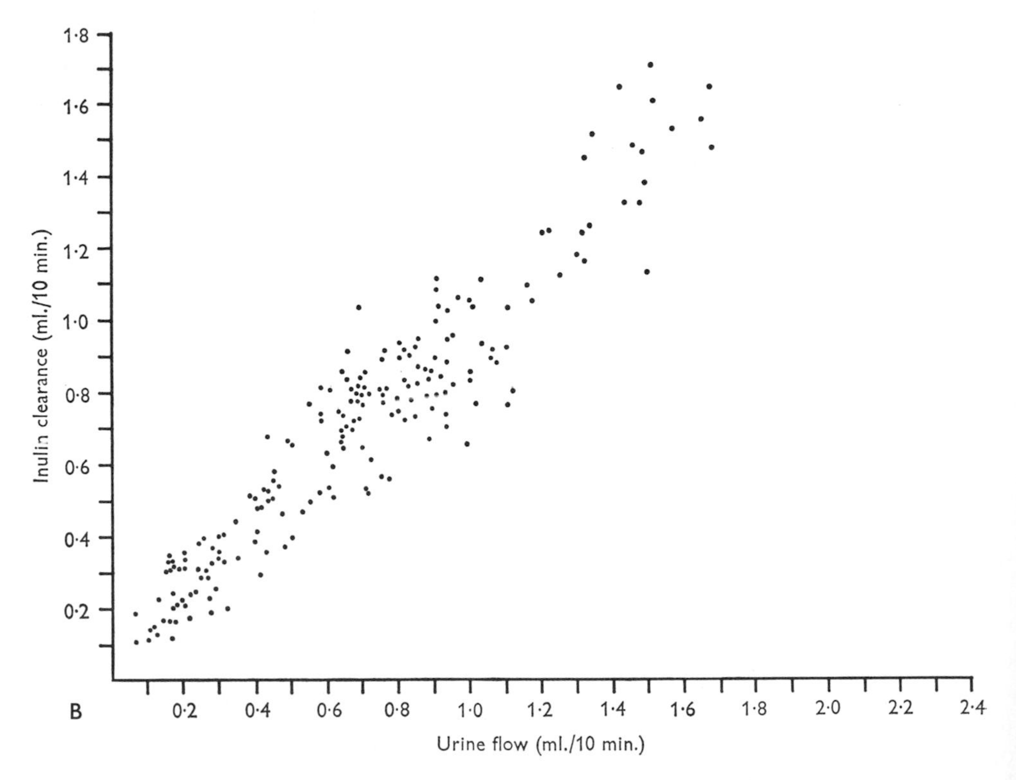

Inulin clearance in relation to rate of urine flow. Results of twelve experiments.

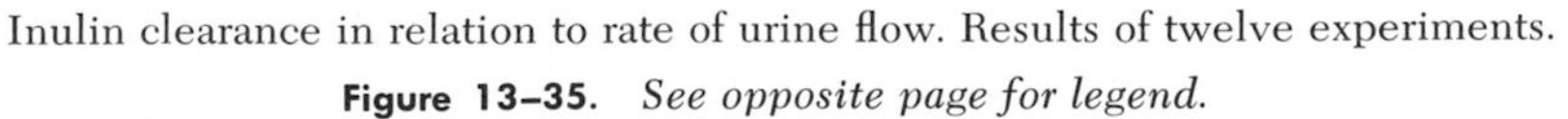

Figure 13–35. *See opposite page for legend.*

Table 13–1.

Animal	Filtration Rate (Inulin Clearance) (ml/min/kg)	Blood Flow Past the Filter Structure (ml/min/kg)	Maximum Rate of Glucose Reabsorption (mg/hr/kg)	Plasma Glucose (mg/100 ml plasma)
Molluscs				
Achatina	2.00	5.58	42.0	140
Haliotis	0.19	10.15	–	–
Octopus	0.044	11.00	–	92
Vertebrates				
Dogfish	0.05	2.25	–	–
Frog	0.66	11.60	35.6	300
Chicken	1.84	50.0	–	–
Rat	6.00	22.00	–	–
Dog	4.29	13.50	672.0	200
Man	1.97	10.00	322.0	300

Data from Martin, A. W., D. M. Stewart, and F. M. Harrison: J. Exp. Biol. *42*:99–123, 1965; Harrison, F. M., and A. W. Martin: J. Exp. Biol. *42*:71–98, 1965; and Smith, H. W.: The Kidney, Structure and Function in Health and Disease, Oxford University Press, New York, 1951.

implanting permanent polyethylene tubes into all the different parts of an *Octopus* kidney and thus can collect fluid samples any time of the day or night. They even succeeded to do the same in the (much smaller) giant African snail, *Achatina*, in the abalone (*Haliotis*) and in a nudibranch (Harrison, 1962; Harrison and Martin, 1965; Martin et al., 1965). These studies on molluscan kidneys have yielded the most complete data in invertebrate renal physiology. In fact, the molluscan preparations offer far greater opportunities for such studies than do vertebrate kidneys, if for no other reason than that of the structural advantage: whereas the vertebrate kidneys employ the principle of multiplication, so that they contain hundreds of thousands of minute nephridia, the molluscs use only two such "nephridia," but each is enormous.

The studies on excretion in molluscs have shown that filtration takes place across the heart wall in archaeogastropods (*Haliotis*) and lamellibranchs, whereas in pulmonate gastropods (*Achatina*), the arterial supply of the kidney seems to provide the filtration pressure. In the *Octopus* filtration takes place across the gill heart appendages that are enclosed by the pericardia (note that in the Octopoda the pericardium is reduced to two sacs that enclose the gill heart appendage on each side of the animal). The data obtained are presented in Table 13–1 together with comparable data from vertebrate animals.

Table 13–1 also contains data on the glucose content of blood (plasma) and on *glucose reabsorption* by the "kidney" tubules, that is, by the renopericardial duct (molluscs) and tubules (vertebrates). Glucose is a rather important con-

Figure 13–35. Two plots of experimental data obtained from the giant African snail *Achatina fulica*. The demonstrate that (**A**) the inulin ratio is close to 1 except at low rates of urine flow when reabsorption of water significantly changes the urine concentration, and that (**B**) the inulin clearance is independent of the rate of urine flow. *B*, inulin concentration in blood; *U*, inulin concentration in urine. (From Martin, A. W., D. M. Stewart, and F. M. Harrison: Urine formation in a pulmonate land snail, *Achatina fulica*. J. Exp. Biol. *42*:99–123, 1965.)

GLUCOSE

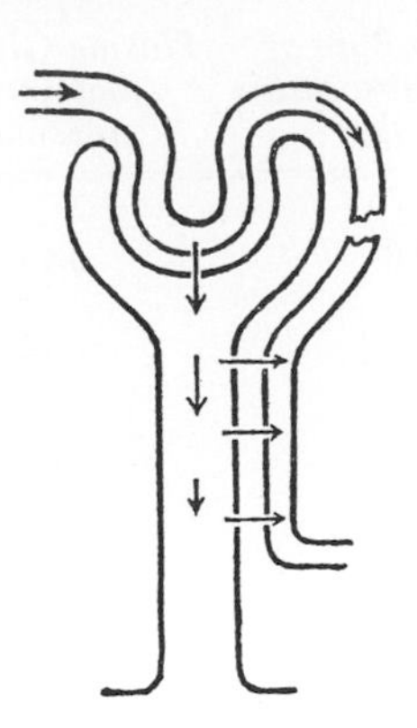

Glucose is completely reabsorbed. Plasma clearance = 0.

WATER

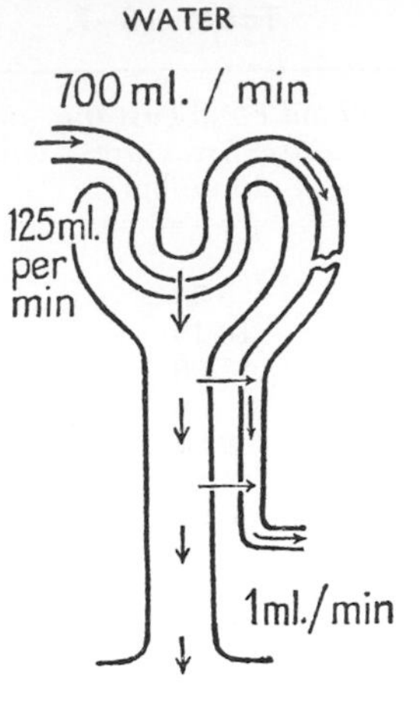

Water is reabsorbed very nearly completely (99 per cent.). Plasma clearance = 1 ml./min.

UREA

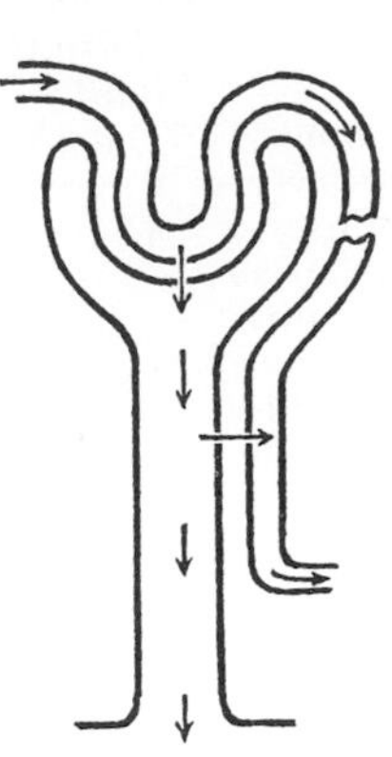

Urea is partially reabsorbed. Plasma clearance = 75 ml./min.

INULIN

Inulin is neither reabsorbed nor excreted by the tubules. Plasma clearance is glomerular filtrate = 125 ml./min.

DIODONE

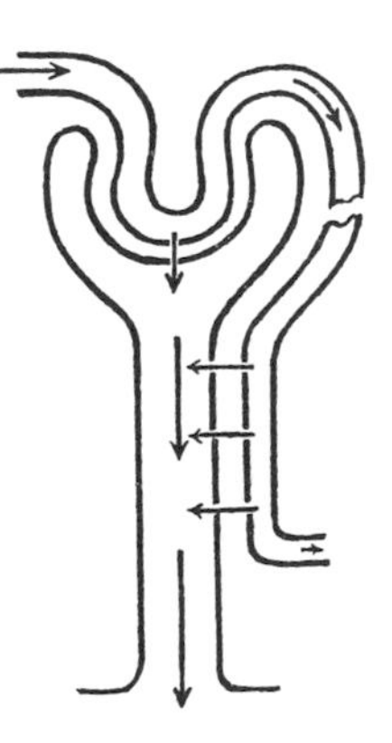

Diodone is filtered at the glomerulus and excreted into the tubules so that only a small amount leaves the kidney in the renal veins. Plasma clearance nearly equals plasma flow = 700 ml./min.

Figure 13–36. Conceptual diagrams to explain the concept of *clearance*. The symbolic representations are of a mammalian nephron with the afferent and efferent glomerular blood vessels and a capillary running alongside the tubule. The arrows show the direction of movement of the substance under discussion and their length indicates the amount that is moving. The middle diagram above shows the amount of fluid passing into the kidney (700 ml/min), the amount filtered at the glomerulus (125 ml/min), and the amount eliminated as urine (1 ml/min). Since the 700 ml of plasma (about 1200 ml of blood) flowing through the glomerulus (this glomerulus representing all the glomeruli of that kidney) per minute carries the red cells, the volume of *blood* flowing through the kidney is 1200 ml/min. (From Bell, G. H., J. N. Davidson, and H. Scarborough: Textbook of Physiology and Biochemistry, 5th Ed. The Williams & Wilkins Co., Baltimore, 1961.)

stituent of blood; this is, in fact, the glucose that is being delivered to the tissues. Because of its small molecular size, glucose is readily filtered, and unless reabsorbed, it is lost to the outside with the urine. Glucose transport (reabsorption) by "kidneys" appears now to be a common, if not universal, feature of kidney function. The carrier system responsible for glucose transport can be poisoned by the compound *phlorhizin*. This is illustrated in Figure 13–37.

"KIDNEYS" AND EXCRETION

The physiological term "kidney" denotes a variety of structures, such as nephridia, protonephridia, the organ of Bojanus, kidneys proper (vertebrates), antennary glands (Crustacea), and even the malpighian tubules of the insects. The term "excretion," likewise, includes many processes, and it is important to realize that, in most animals, the "kidneys" are not the primary organs of excretion. The kidneys, and in particular their tubules and reabsorptive structures, predominantly regulate the composition of body fluids with regard to their organic, as well as inorganic, constituents.

Figures 13–37 to 13–41 show some characteristic examples of regulatory

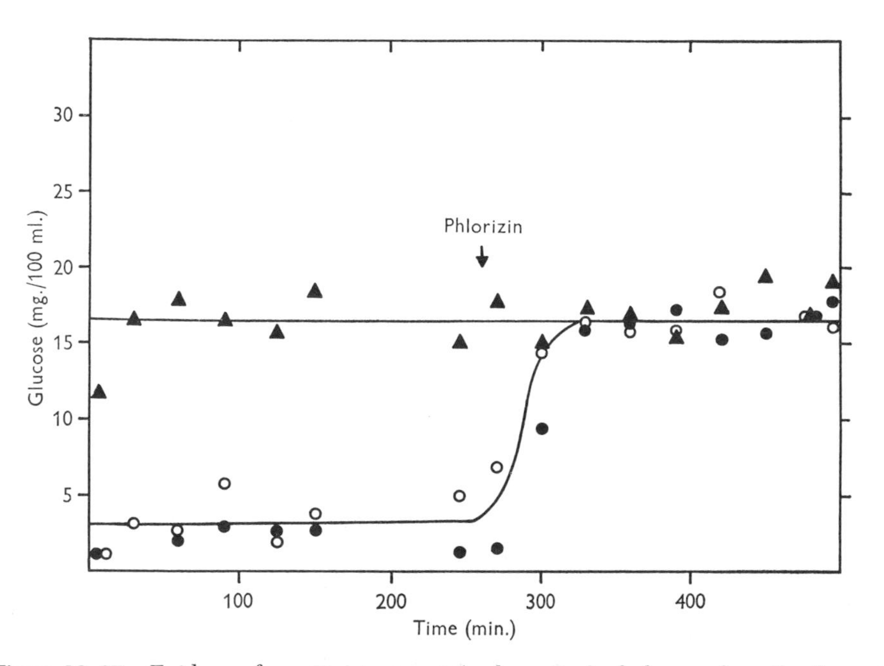

Figure 13–37. Evidence for active transport (reabsorption) of glucose from the "excretory" organs of *Octopus dofleini* and its inhibition by phlorizin. The glucose concentration in the pericardial fluid (○, ●) is normally much lower than that in the blood (▲). Soon after administration of phlorizin (10.3 mg/kg) the concentration gradient disappears and the pericardial fluid contains as much glucose as the blood. *Note*: In contrast to filtration in vertebrates, which takes place at the site of the nephridial glomeruli, filtration in the octopus takes place across the wall of the pericardial heart appendage. The filtrate then passes along the renopericardial canal into the renal sac. Glucose is reabsorbed across the wall of the pericardium and of the renopericardial duct. (From Harrison, F. M., and A. W. Martin: Excretion in the cephalopod, *Octopus dofleini*. J. Exp. Biol. *42*:71–98, 1965.)

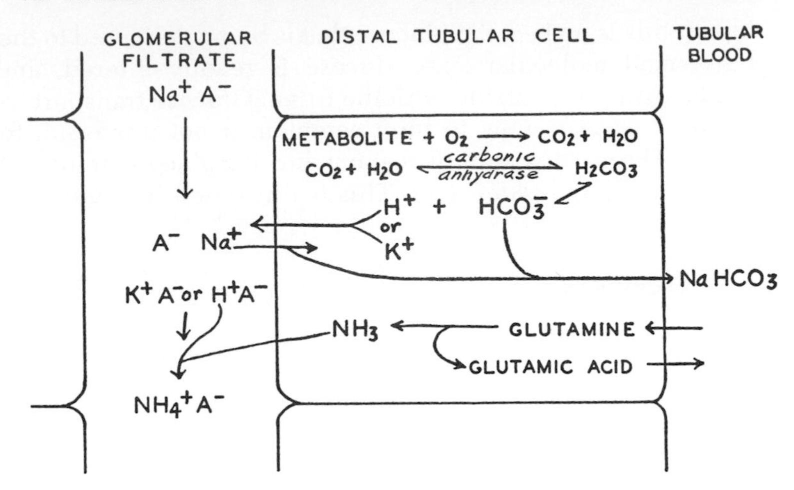

Figure 13–38. Ionic regulation accomplished by kidney tubules (mammals): the normal Na^+ ion concentration of body fluids is conserved in two steps. (1) The Na^+ ions that are filtered into the tubule are exchanged for H^+ ions derived from the dissociation of carbonic acid, which in turn originates from metabolically released CO_2. (2) The resulting acid urine is neutralized by ammonia (NH_3) derived from deamination of amino acids. The resulting ammonium ion (NH_4^+) can combine with organic acids. The reabsorbed Na^+ ions return to the blood stream, together with the bicarbonate ion (HCO_3^-). (After Pitts, 1946, from Cantarow, A., and B. Schepartz: Biochemistry, 3rd Ed. W. B. Saunders Co., Philadelphia, 1962.)

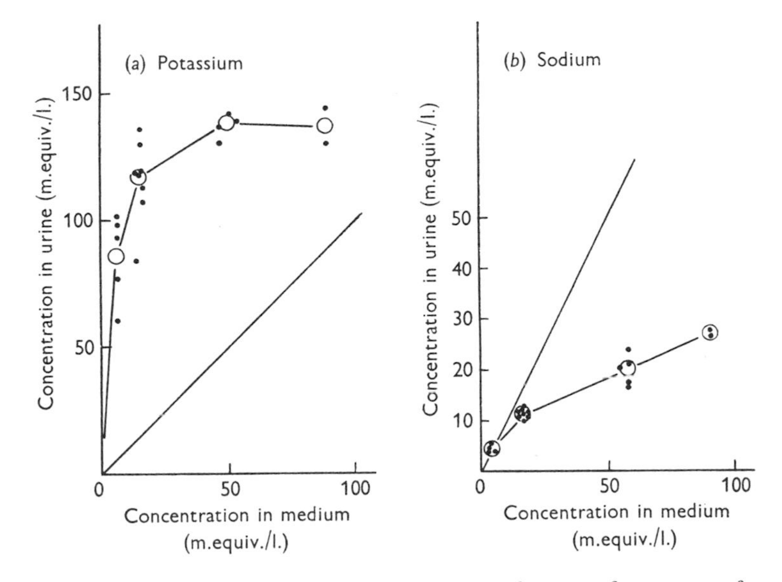

Figure 13–39. In the stick insect *Carausius morosus* the rate of secretion of potassium into the malpighian tubules is 11 times greater than that of sodium. **a**, the potassium concentration in urine as a function of the potassium concentration in the medium bathing the tubules at a sodium concentration of 16 to 17 mEq./l. **b**, the sodium concentration in the urine as a function of the sodium concentration in the medium bathing the tubules with a constant potassium concentration of 15 to 16 mEq./l. The circles represent average values. The straight lines from the origin indicate equal concentration in urine and medium. (From Ramsay, J. A.: The excretion of sodium, potassium and water by the malpighian tubules of the stick insect, Dixippus morosus [Orthoptera, Phasmidae]. J. Exp. Biol. *32*:200–216, 1955.)

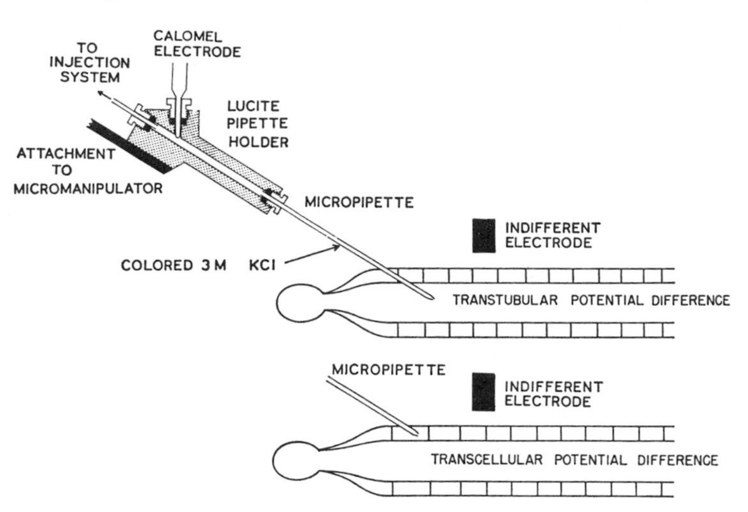

Figure 13–40. Diagram of a set-up that permits injection of substances into a tubular lumen or into tubule cells and simultaneous or subsequent recording of the electric potentials. In this particular case, the kidneys of the amphibian *Necturus maculosus* have been used. (From Whittembury, G.: Ion and water transport in the proximal tubules of the kidney of *Necturus maculosus.* J. Gen. Physiol. *43*(5)Part 2:43–56, 1960.)

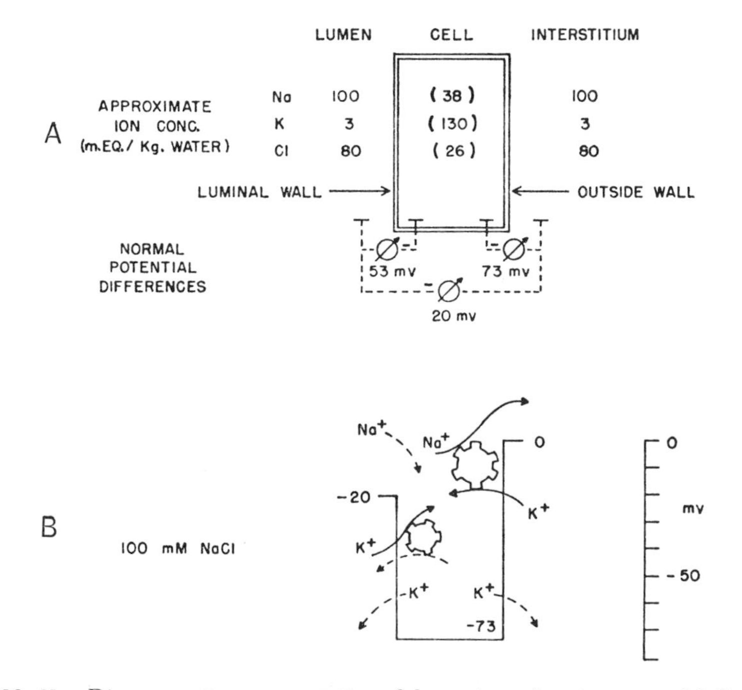

Figure 13–41. Diagrammatic representation of the various electric potential differences measurable in the proximal tubule of the amphibian *Necturus maculosus.* The concentrations of ions inside the tubular cell are given in brackets because they are taken from determinations made on similar cells of the frog (Amphibia). **A** shows the ion concentrations and potentials in relation to the anatomical situation. **B** represents the respective potentials in the form of a mechanical model illustrating up-hill (active) and down-hill (passive) transport of ions. (From Whittembury, G.: Ion and water transport in the proximal tubules of the kidney of *Necturus maculosus.* J. Gen. Physiol. *43*(5)Part 2:43–56, 1960.)

functions. Numerous transport mechanisms are involved, many of them are energy requiring (active transport). Whenever ion transport occurs, electric potentials are generated which can be measured (Figs. 13–40 and 13–41) and which give important clues about the intensity of transport and about the nature of the transport mechanism (see Chaps. 16 and 27).

Excretion of metabolic end products is only partially achieved by "kidneys." Particularly in aquatic animals the nitrogenous end products, especially ammonia, are lost to the outside environment by diffusion across the body wall, and in particular across the gills and analogous exchange membranes. Only part of the metabolic end products are voided through the "kidneys." It is only in the terrestrial animals that the kidneys (vertebrates, gastropods) and analogous structures (malpighian tubules) assume a predominant role in excretion.

REFERENCES

Baldwin, E. (1960) Excretory metabolism of proteins and amino acids. *In* Dynamic Aspects of Biochemistry, 3rd Ed., pp. 251–267. Cambridge University Press, London.

Bedot, M. (1885) Sur l'histologie de la *Porpita mediterranea*. Rec. Zool. Suisse *2*:189–194.

von Buddenbrock, W. (1956) Vergleichende Physiologie, Bd. III: Ernährung, Wasserhaushalt und Mineralhaushalt der Tiere. Birkhäuser Verlag, Basel.

Burian, R. (1924) Die Excretion. *In* Handbuch der vergleichenden Physiologie, Vol. 2, Part 2, pp. 259–900. (H. Winterstein, ed.) G. Fischer Verlag, Jena.

Claus, C. (1881) Beiträge zur Kenntniss der Geryonopsiden und Eucopiden-Entwicklung. Arb. Zool. Inst. Univ. Wien *4*:89–120.

Cohen, P. P., and G. W. Brown, Jr. (1960) Ammonia metabolism and urea biosynthesis. *In* Comparative Biochemistry, Vol. 2, pp. 161–244. (M. Florkin and H. S. Mason, eds.) Academic Press, New York.

Cohen, P. P., and H. J. Sallach (1961) Nitrogen metabolism of amino acids. *In* Metabolic Pathways, 2nd Ed., Vol. 2, pp. 1–78. (D. M. Greenberg, ed.) Academic Press, New York.

Florkin, M. (1949) Biochemical Evolution. Academic Press, New York.

Goldschmidt, R. (1922) Ascaris. Theod. Thomas Verlag, Leipzig.

Goodrich, E. S. (1945) The study of nephridia and genital ducts since 1895. Quart. J. Micr. Sci. *86*:113–392.

von Graff, L. (1904) Marine Turbellarien Orotavis und der Küsten Europas. I. Einleitung und Acoela. Z. wiss. Zool. *78*:190–244.

Harrison, F. M. (1962) Some excretory processes in the abalone, *Haliotis rufescens*. J. Exp. Biol. *39*:179–192.

Harrison, F. M., and A. W. Martin (1965) Excretion in the cephalopod, *Octopus dofleini*. J. Exp. Biol. *42*:71–98.

Heidermanns, C. (1937) Ueber die Harnstoffbildung beim Regenwurm. Zool. Jahrb., Allg. Zool. Physiol. Tiere, *58*:57–68.

Hyman, L. H. (1940–1959) The Invertebrates. 5 vols. McGraw-Hill Book Co., New York.

Koelliker, A. (1853) Nachtrag zu dem "Bericht ueber einige im Herbste 1852 in Messina angestellte vergleichend-anatomischen Untersuchungen" von C. Gegenbauer, A. Koelliker und H. Mueller. Z. wiss. Zool. *4*:299–369.

Laverack, M. S. (1963) The Physiology of the Earthworms. The Pergamon Press, New York.

Löhner, L. (1911) Zum Exkretionsproblem der Acölen. Z. allg. Physiol. *12*:451–484.

Luther, A. (1904) Die Eumesostomien. Z. wiss. Zool. *77*:1–273.

Martin, A. W. (1958) Comparative physiology (excretion). Ann. Rev. Physiol. *20*:225–242.

Martin, A. W., D. M. Stewart, and F. M. Harrison (1965) Urine formation in a pulmonate land snail, *Achatina fulica*. J. Exp. Biol. *42*:99–123.

Masterman, A. T. (1894) On the nutritive and excretory processes in Porifera. Ann. Mag. Nat. Hist. London, ser. 6, *13*:485–496.

Morren (1826) Complete reference unavailable to the author.

Nash, G., and G. Frankhauser (1959) Changes in the pattern of nitrogen excretion during the life cycle of the newt. Science *130*:714–716.

Needham, J. (1931) Chemical Embryology, Vol. 2, pp. 1055–1145. Cambridge University Press, London.

Needham, J. (1935) XXVIII Problems of nitrogen catabolism in invertebrates. II. Correlation between uricotelic metabolism and habitat in the phylum Mollusca. Biochem. J. *29*:238–251.

Nicol, J. A. C. (1960) The Biology of Marine Animals, Chap. 7, pp. 280–304. Interscience Publishers, New York.

Prosser, C. L. (1950) Nitrogen excretion. *In* Comparative Animal Physiology, pp. 187–208. (C. L. Prosser, ed.) W. B. Saunders Co., Philadelphia.

Prosser, C. L. (1961) Nitrogen excretion. *In* Comparative Animal Physiology, 2nd Ed., pp. 135–152. (C. L. Prosser and F. A. Brown, Jr.) W. B. Saunders Co., Philadelphia.

Ramsay, J. A. (1955) The excretion of sodium, potassium and water by the malpighian tubules of the stick insect, *Dixippus morosus* (Orthoptera, Phasmidae). J. Exp. Biol. *32*:200–216.

Rosa, D. (1903) Il cloragogo tipico degli Oligocheti. Mem. Reale Acad. Sci. Torina, *53*:119–144.

Schoenheimer, R. (1946) The Dynamic State of Body Constituents. Harvard University Press, Cambridge.

Smith, H. W. (1951) The Kidney: Structure and Function in Health and Disease. Oxford University Press, New York.

Strohl, J. (1924) Die Exkretion; Mollusken. *In* Handbuch der vergleichenden Physiologie, Vol. 2, Part 2. (H. Winterstein, ed.) G. Fischer Verlag, Jena.

Vogt, C., and E. Yung (1882–1892) Traité de l'Anatomie comparée, Vol. 1, pp. 256. C. Reinwald, Paris.

14 ANIMAL PIGMENTS

Perhaps more than its shape, it is the color pattern exhibited by an animal that appeals to our esthetic senses. The student of animal anatomy will know the delight that accompanies the discovery of the often so richly colored internal organs upon dissection. And many of us have enjoyed the beautiful patterns of butterfly wings and bird feathers.

Color appeals not only to the human eye; many animal species can recognize—and enjoy—colors. Let us, however, not dwell on the psychological aspect of our topic. Only one thing must be mentioned: The perception of color is based on the nature of the photosensitive structures of the eyes. What appears white to us may appear colored to another animal. Bees, for instance, can readily distinguish different kinds of white paint: their receptor cells in the eyes respond to ultraviolet light which is reflected by some but not all "whites." We must recognize that we are subjective in singling out those compounds as pigments which, to us, appear to be colored. Still, to a certain extent, we are justified in this, for the simple reason that these pigments fall into rather well-defined chemical classes of compounds and that their functions, as far as they are known to us, are rather distinct. It must be admitted, however, that there are compounds with similar structure and function which remain invisible to us because they are—to our eyes—colorless and therefore inconspicuous.

Although pigments are often employed for esthetic—and sexual—attraction, they also make animals inconspicuous by imitating the background coloration of the environment. Sometimes external color patterns are "designed" to frighten or visually stun the "enemy"—and in other cases conspicuous colored markings elicit behavior patterns in the approaching "friend" or "foe." Examples are shown in Figures 14–1 and 14–2.

It is unfortunate, but true, that the above-mentioned roles of animal pigments are the concern of the ecologist but not primarily of the physiologist. The subject matter of physiology is restricted to a description and analysis of physicochemical mechanisms within an organism and of the interaction

Figure 14–1. Adaptive coloration. The frogfish (*Histrio histrio*) lives amid the saragassum. Its pigmentation makes it almost invisible. (From Portmann, A.: Animal Camouflage. University of Michigan Press, Ann Arbor, 1959.)

of these mechanisms with the environment, whereby the term "environment" implies abstract chemical and physical properties (e.g., temperature, partial pressure of oxygen, concentration of compounds, light intensity) and not individual constellations of properties as they are given, for instance, by the presence of another organism—or even "inanimate" object. The interaction of

Figure 14–2. Warning display of the mantis *Pseudocreobotra wahlbergi*. The distribution of pigment of the forewings visually stuns a potential aggressor when the wings are suddenly raised. (From Cott, H. B.: Adaptive Coloration in Animals. Oxford University Press, New York, 1940.)

animals—or even of animal mechanisms (as established by the physiologist) with individual constellations of properties or entities as we may call them, or with other organisms—all this is the subject matter of psychology and ethology.

This and the following chapter are concerned with the origin and metabolism of pigments, with their occurrence and position within animals of various species, and with their control and functional role within each organism.

Apart from their overt function in attractive, adaptive, protective, or offensive coloration, animal pigments serve a variety of truly physiological functions: (1) Many serve as "respiratory pigments" in oxygen (and CO_2) transport and oxidative metabolism. (2) Others are involved in photochemical reactions within photoreceptor cells in eyes. (3) Several pigments are precursors of physiologically important compounds, and others are the transformed products of originally highly active hormones. (4) Some pigments can be considered metabolic waste products that are stored in one or the other animal structure (see Chap. 13). (5) Because they can absorb certain wavelengths of light, pigments have important functions as radiation shields; that is, they protect underlying organs from harmful exposure to ultraviolet light.

CAROTENOIDS

Many of the most conspicuous pigments of animals belong to the chemical group of carotenoids. Because of their lipid solubility they are often referred to as *lipochromes*. They are always derived from plant food; animal cells cannot synthesize carotenoids, although they can alter their structure to a certain extent.

Carotenoids are highly unsaturated hydrocarbon compounds consisting of a highly branched chain of carbon atoms, with a cyclic structure at one or both ends (Fig. 14–3).

Carotenes

Perhaps the most widely distributed carotenoid is astaxanthin. Astacin (or astacene), an orange-red compound which was first obtained from lobsters (the genus *Homarus* was formerly called *Astacus*), proved to be an artifact, that is, a variant of the astaxanthin molecule, produced by the chemical isolation procedure (Kühn and Sørensen, 1938). It is likely that wherever the occurrence of astacin has been reported, the naturally occurring form of the pigment is astaxanthin.

Astaxanthin is usually associated with protein. Its original orange-red color is thereby changed: depending on the protein, the pigment can be yellow, orange, red, purple, green, or blue. When the protein is destroyed or denatured, or when the carotenoid separates from the protein, the color changes and the pigment usually appears orange-red. The color change can be observed whenever lobsters, crayfish, or crabs are boiled, but it also occurs naturally in certain cases. Crayfish and lobster eggs, for instance, which are green at first, change to orange-red soon after fertilization. This is due to separation of astaxanthin

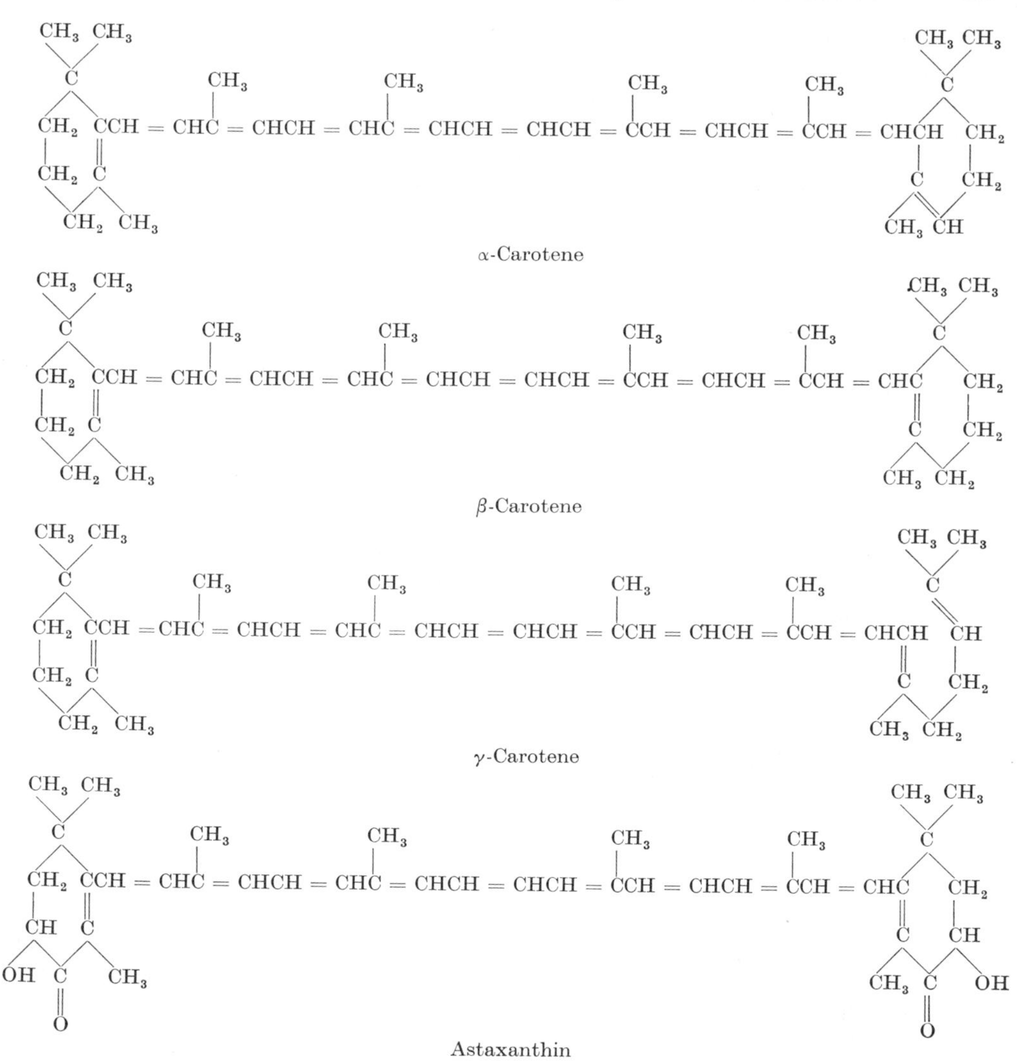

Figure 14–3. Structural formulae of α, β, and γ-carotene and of astaxanthin. (From Gilmour, D.: The Biochemistry of Insects. Academic Press, New York, 1961.)

from protein. The astaxanthin-protein complex of crustacean eggs is known as *ovoverdin*.

Astaxanthin has been identified (often in the form of astacin) in sponges, siphonophores (*Velella*), Actiniaria (*Metridium*), several Bryozoa, asteroid echinoderms (*Echinaster, Ophidiaster*), lamellibranch (*Pleurobranchus*) and gastropod (*Lima*) molluscs, in many species of Crustacea (including entomostracans and malacostracans), insects (*Leptinotarsa, Locusta*), tunicates (*Halocynthia, Dendrodoa*), and a number of vertebrates. The red muscles of the salmon (*Salmo*) and the skin of goldfish (*Carassius*) contain the pigment, and so do the retina of the chicken (*Gallus*), the egg yolk of the laughing gull (*Larus*), and the fat of the flamingo (*Phoenicopterus*).

Astaxanthin, together with α-, β-, and γ-carotene, belongs in the group of carotenes. Most other carotenoids found in animals belong to the group of xanthophylls. The most common of the former is β-carotene, which occurs in sponges, several coelenterates, asteroid and echinoid echinoderms, lamellibranch molluscs, tunicates, fish, amphibia, and mammals. Alpha- and γ-carotene are rare. An echinoderm pigment, echinenone, is a monoketonic γ-carotene.

Xanthophylls

The detailed structure of many xanthophylls is not yet established. They are recognized by their chemical properties and absorption bands. To these belong the *metridioxanthin* (a yellow pigment of the anemone *Metridium*), an "*asteric acid*" from the starfish *Asterias*, pentaxanthin from the sea urchin *Strongylocentrotus*, glycymerin from the scallop *Pectunculus glycymeris*, *pectenoxanthin* from another scallop, *Pecten maximus*, *mytiloxanthin* from the lamellibranch *Mytilus*, *hopkinsiaxanthin* from the nudibranch *Hopkinsia*, and *cynthiaxanthin* from the tunicate *Halocynthia*.

The chemical nature of several carotenoids is still entirely unknown. To these belong *zoonerythrin*, which, according to Verne (1923–1927), represents the major pigment in chromatophores, carapace, and eggs of numerous crustacean species (usually in the form of a protein complex), and certain pigments described by Krukenberg (1882), such as *lacertofulvin* from the lizard *Lacerta* and *lipochrin* from frog skin, as well as the bird-feather pigments *zoofulvin*, *coriosulfurin*, *paradiseofulvin*, and *picofulvin*.

Occurrence and Function of Carotenoids

The blood of many animals, notably insects, contains lipochromes derived from green plants. This gives the blood a yellow, green, or brown color, a fact familiar to anyone who has driven a car in summertime when insects encounter untimely death on the windshield. Carotenoids are stored by certain cells within the integument (many insects, crustaceans, nudibranchs, tunicates) and give it the characteristic color. The carotenoids of Hymenoptera are largely derived from pollen. Often the green color of insects is not due to green pigment but to the presence of a mixture of blue and yellow lipochromes.

In general, carotenoids are found in epidermis or hypodermis and the integument of animals, but conspicuous quantities are also present in gonads (carotenoids are transmitted to the eggs) and in the eyes. Occasionally carotenoids have been detected in nerve fibers (frog, lobster, and horseshoe crab; Monaghan and Schmitt, 1932; Bartz and Schmitt, 1936). Arvanitaki and Chalazonitis (1961) described carotenoid granules in *Aplysia* ganglion cells.

When the eggs are ripening in the ovaries, the blood of female crayfish is distinctly orange-red. This is due to carotenoid pigment which is on its way to the ovary after it has been mobilized from stores elsewhere in the body.

The function of carotenoids in animals is only incompletely understood. It is interesting that a number of carotenoids have been shown to have *vitamin* A activity. In many cases this has been shown to be due to a conversion of these carotenoids to vitamin A (β-carotene, astaxanthin, cryptoxanthin, echinenone, and other xanthophylls are precursors), but there is evidence that certain carotenoids can replace vitamin A without having to be transformed; at least this has been described for the chicken (With, 1946). Fox (1953) argues that this may be a much more widespread functional role of carotenoid pigments. Vitamin A, as is well known, is involved in the maintenance of epithelial tissue, in particular of mucous membranes and secretory epithelia. This may explain the widespread occurrence of carotenoid pigments in epithelial tissue and chromatophores. Nothing is known, as yet, about the mechanism of action of vitamin A or of the carotenoids that take its place.

The aldehyde of vitamin A_1, known as *retinene*$_1$, plays an important role in vision (both in vertebrates and invertebrates). In combination with a protein (*opsin*), it forms *rhodopsin* or "visual purple" (so named by the German physiologist Kühne in 1878). Light causes the dissociation of retinene and opsin. This dissociation is probably a secondary process that results from changes in the rhodopsin molecule when "hit" by a light quantum. The change is recognizable in a shift in the absorption spectrum of this pigment. It is likely to result in a subsequent electron transport process that, somehow, leads to an alteration of the membrane potential of the receptor cell, which results in "excitation" of the nerve cell that is connected with it.

Complex chemical reactions permit the resynthesis of rhodopsin from opsin and transformation products of retinene or vitamin A_1. A diagrammatic representation of these processes, as they have been worked out by the pioneering research of Wald and his coworkers, is shown in Figure 14–4.

The dissociation of retinene$_1$ from opsin is accompanied by a characteristic change in color of the pigment ("bleaching"). Kühne utilized this in a dramatic demonstration of his discovery of the role of photochemical reactions in vision: he kept frogs in the dark and held their heads in a fixed position. When he was certain that all visual purple had regenerated, he turned on the light for a few moments, permitting the frog to see. Then he turned off the light, and killed the frog, and removed the eyes. He then inspected the retina of each eye in the light, and for a few fleeting moments he could see the imprinted negative image of what the frog had seen. He called these images "optograms."

Photochemical reactions, in particular the blackening of silver chloride on exposure to light, have been known since the end of the eighteenth century. Photography was invented by Niepce and Daguerre during the first third of the nineteenth century. Kühne's discovery coincided with the invention of photographic plates using a gelatin emulsion of silver bromide in 1878 by the Englishman Bennet.

Rhodopsin occurs in the outer segments of the rods, which are the highly photosensitive cells in the retina of terrestrial vertebrates and many fishes. The rods of some other fishes and amphibia, and even of the larvae of those frogs in which the adult eyes contain rhodopsin, have another visual pigment, known as *porphyropsin*. This is composed of the protein opsin and the aldehyde of another form of vitamin A, vitamin A_2; this aldehyde is called *retinene*$_2$. Retinene$_1$ in combination with an unnamed protein forms the golden-yellow pigment in the eyes of certain deep-sea fishes. This pigment has been named *chrysopsin*.

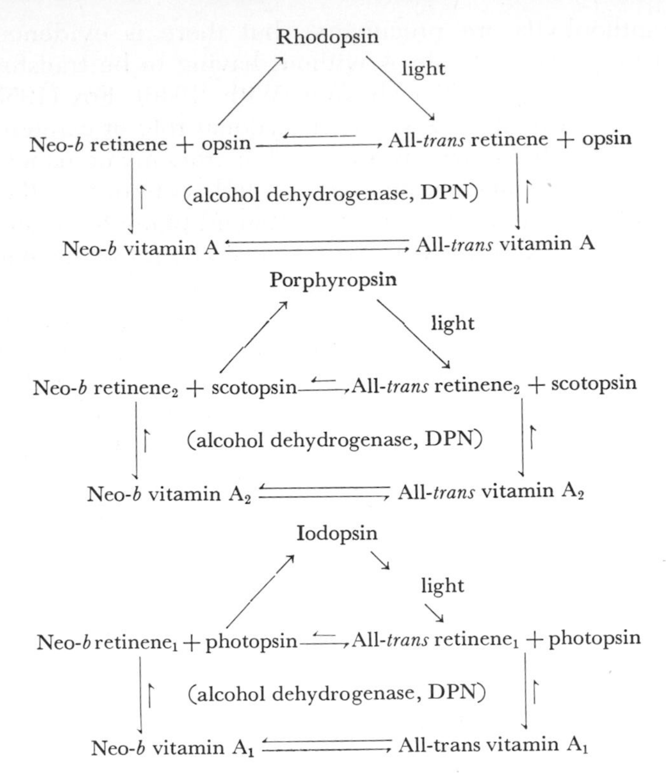

Figure 14–4. Simplified diagram of photochemical reactions occurring in vertebrate rods and cones. The resynthesis of the photosensitive pigment from vitamin A requires activation of this molecule by transformation to an isomere, neo-b vitamin A from which (by oxidation) neo-b retinene is obtained. The latter combines with the appropriate protein to form the reactive visual pigment. (After Wald, G.: The photoreceptor process in vision. *In* Handbook of Physiology, Sec. 1, Vol. I, pp. 671–692, 1959. American Physiological Society, Washington, D.C.)

From the cones of the chicken retina has been extracted a violet pigment, *iodopsin* (the name does not imply an iodine content; it is derived from the Greek word *iōdēs* which means "like a violet"). It is composed of an isomer of retinene and a protein which apparently is not identical with the opsin from the rods of other retinae. To permit a distinction, one calls the one protein *cone opsin*, or photopsin, and the other *rod opsin*, or scotopsin.

According to Wald (1958), there is a conspicuous pattern throughout the vertebrate series of animals with regard to the type of visual pigment found in retinal rods: marine fish and terrestrial vertebrates, including frogs, possess rhodopsin, whereas newts and frog larvae, just like fresh-water fish, have porphyropsin. Euryhaline fishes that inhabit both fresh and salt water (eel, salmon, cyclostomes) contain both pigments, but in the American eel, which spawns in the sea, rhodopsin predominates, whereas in the various species of salmon which spawn in fresh water porphyropsin prevails. Downstream migrants of cyclostomes have rhodopsin, upstream migrants have porphyropsin. The European eel (*Anguilla*) changes from porphyropsin to "deep-sea rhodopsin" (chrysopsin) preparatory to migration into the ocean.

In order to emphasize this pattern, Wald prefers to call the visual pigment of deep-sea fish "deep-sea rhodopsin." It shows maximal sensitivity to much shorter wavelengths of light than do rhodopsin or porphyropsin. Absorption spectra of the visual pigments of a number of vertebrates are shown in Figure 14–5. In general, the maximum absorption corresponds to wavelengths that are shorter the deeper the animal lives. The "fresh-water" porphyropsins show maximum absorption at longer wavelengths than the "sea-water" rhodopsins (including the deep-sea rhodopsins).

Rhodopsin has been extracted from eyes of cephalopods (*Loligo, Sepia, Octopus*) by Bliss (1948), Hubbard and coworkers (1958, 1959), and arthropods (*Limulus, Daphnia, Homarus*) (Hubbard et al., 1958, 1959, 1960; Kampa, 1955). The rhodopsin of cephalopods is remarkable in that it can be regenerated in the light.

A number of photosensitive pigments, probably of carotenoid origin, have been extracted from many invertebrate species, including polychaetes, echinoderms, and coelenterates. They may well be involved in "visual" responses (Peskin, 1951). Certainly not all photosensitive pigments are indicative of visual processes. Yamamoto (1938) described a lemon-yellow pigment in the

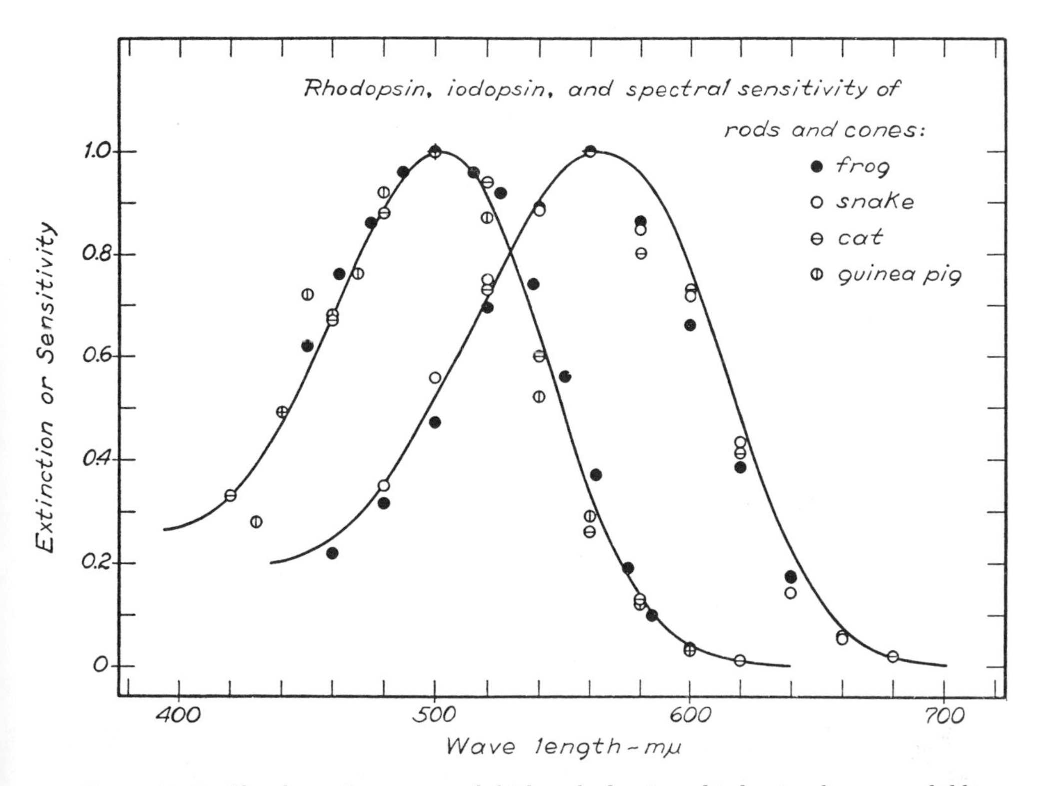

Figure 14–5. The absorption spectra of chicken rhodopsin and iodopsin, shown as solid lines, compared with electrophysiologically measured photopic and scotopic sensitivities of the photoreceptors of various animals. Maximum absorption (*Extinction*) and maximum sensitivity taken as 1.0. (Data from various authors. From Wald, G., P. K. Brown, and P. H. Smith: Iodopsin. J. Gen. Physiol. 38:623–681, 1955.)

eggs of the polychaete *Ceratocephale osawai*. If illuminated, the pigment becomes green, owing to dissociation of a lipochrome from a protein. The process is reversed in darkness; the pigment itself appears to be chemically related to rhodopsin. Surely, we cannot expect these eggs to see!

However, a reasonable method allows a conclusion about the role of photosensitive pigments in vision. Two prerequisites for this method are: (1) it must be established that the animal responds to visual stimulation, and (2) the visual pigment must be available in more or less pure form in solution, so that it can be analyzed in a spectrophotometer. If maximal visual response is elicited at a wavelength that is equal to that which is maximally absorbed by the isolated pigment, it can be assumed that the pigment is involved in vision. Electrophysiological responses of cells within the retina are usually taken as a measure of visual response, rather than behavioral reactions.

Visual responses to bright light, mediated by cones, are called *photopic responses*; visual responses to weak light, mediated by rods, are referred to as *scotopic responses*. The dependence of the magnitude of the visual response on the wavelength of light is called the *spectral sensitivity* of the response. This can be determined in two ways: (1) the reciprocal of the energy content of light which is just sufficient to elicit a response is plotted against the wavelength, or (2) the magnitude of the response to lights of equal energy content is plotted against the wavelength (see Fig. 14–6). In a number of cases it has indeed been shown that the spectral sensitivity of photopic responses and of scotopic responses is nearly identical with the absorption spectra of cone and rod opsins, respectively (Figs. 14–5 and 14–7).

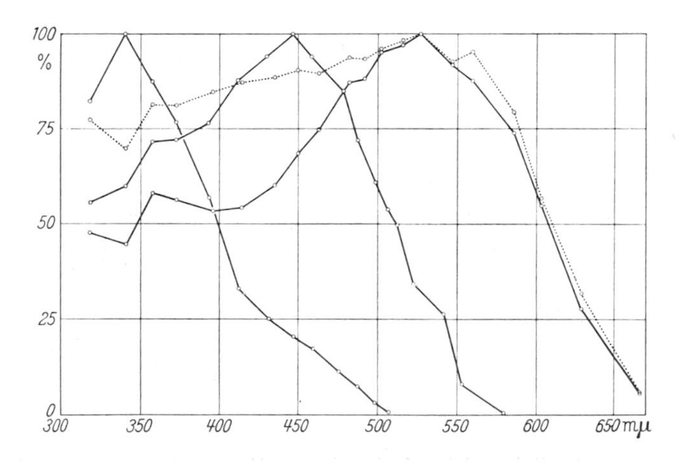

Figure 14–6. Spectral sensitivity of different photoreceptor cells from eyes of male bees (*Apis mellifica*). The height of the initial phase of the generator potential (given in per cent of the maximal height observed) is plotted against the wavelength of light. Near monochromatic lights of equal energy content have been employed. Three types of cells are found, each with a maximum response in a different region of the spectrum, corresponding to an ultraviolet-receptor, a blue-receptor, and a green-receptor. The dotted line represents the behavior of a green receptor with a maximum at 530 mμ and high sensitivity at shorter wavelengths. (From Autrum, H., and V. von Zwehl: Ein Grünreceptor im Drohnen auge [Apis mellifica] Naturwissenschaften *50*:698, 1963.)

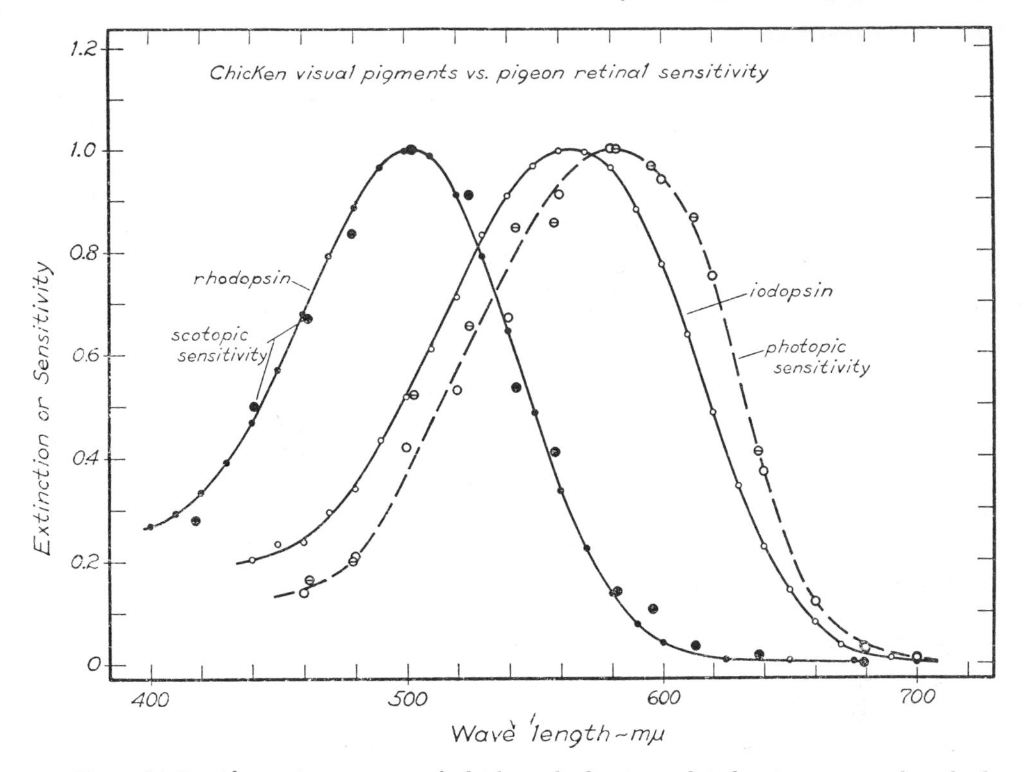

Figure 14–7. Absorption spectra of chicken rhodopsin and iodopsin, compared with the spectral sensitivities of dark- and light-adapted pigeons. The spectral sensitivities were measured electrophysiologically, and are plotted in terms of the reciprocals of the numbers of quanta needed to evoke a constant electric response. Absorption spectra shown as solid lines. Data from various authors. Note that the photopic sensitivity is displaced about 20 millimicrons toward the red from the absorption spectrum of iodopsin, owing to the filtering action of the colored oil globules of pigeon cones. (From Wald, G., P. K. Brown, and P. H. Smith: Iodopsin. J. Gen. Physiol. *38*:623–681, 1955.)

In the retina of many species of vertebrates, in particular of birds, carotenoid pigments are dissolved in oil droplets. These are likely to serve as color filters. They are held responsible for the shift in photopic sensitivity as compared to the spectral sensitivity of the isolated visual pigment. An example is shown in Figure 14–7.

Summary

Only three major functions are known for carotenoids in animals: They (1) act as coloring matter, (2) may give rise to vitamin A_1 or A_2, or may function like vitamins A in maintenance of epithelial tissue, and (3) are precursors of visual pigments.

Although some of the carotenoids found in animal tissues are identical in structure to the carotenoids known from plants, the majority of animal carotenoids differ in structure from the original plant carotenoids from which they are derived; this is particularly true for astaxanthin and the xanthophyll derivatives mentioned in this chapter.

NAPHTHOQUINONES

The naphthalene molecule consists of two benzene rings, fused in ortho-position. Quinone is a benzene ring with two carbonyl groups. Naphthoquinones combine both properties.

In 1883, MacMunn described red, purple, and brownish pigments in perivisceral fluid, tissues, test, and spines of sea urchins, *Echinus* and *Paracentrotus*. He did some spectroscopic examinations and called the pigments *echinochrome*. Similar pigments were later described in eggs of *Arbacia* and shell and spines of *Strongylocentrotus* and *Paracentrotus* and other echinoids. Chemical analyses by a number of investigators have shown that these pigments are naphthoquinones. They were grouped into two classes: *echinochromes* and *spinochromes* (the latter were named after their predominant location in the spines). This distinction has not been maintained, however, since it was found that the chemical differences do not correspond to the location in which the pigments are found. "Echinochrome" is now the group name. The structural formula of one echinochrome is shown in Figure 14–8.

Echinochromes are not found in all echinoderms; they are restricted to the echinoids—and even among these not all species have these pigments, and often it is found that the color of the ovaries, for example, is not due to echinochrome but to carotenoid pigments.

MacMunn assumed that the echinochromes play a role as oxygen-carrying pigments. A number of facts support this: The pigment is often found in sea urchin coelomocytes, just as is hemoglobin in the coelomocytes of certain holothurians (*Cucumaria*); it is readily oxidized and reduced. With sodium hydrosulfite the pigments become reduced and bleach; shaking in air restores their original color, again a behavior reminiscent of respiratory pigments (see pp. 178–189) (Suto, 1938); furthermore, there are indications that echinochrome is normally combined with a protein (Cornman, 1941).

In spite of this, it has never been possible to demonstrate that echinochromes can transport significant amounts of oxygen, and no oxygen dissociation curves have been reported. Most interesting, however, are the observations that echinochrome increases the respiration of sea urchin eggs and of rabbit erythrocytes, and that it activates sea urchin spermatozoa (Friedheim, 1932). These experiments were carried out with unpurified preparations of the pigment. Later studies with crystalline pigment (Tyler, 1939) did not confirm the earlier findings. It is possible that the pigments are active only as long as they are combined with specific protein, and that they lose activity

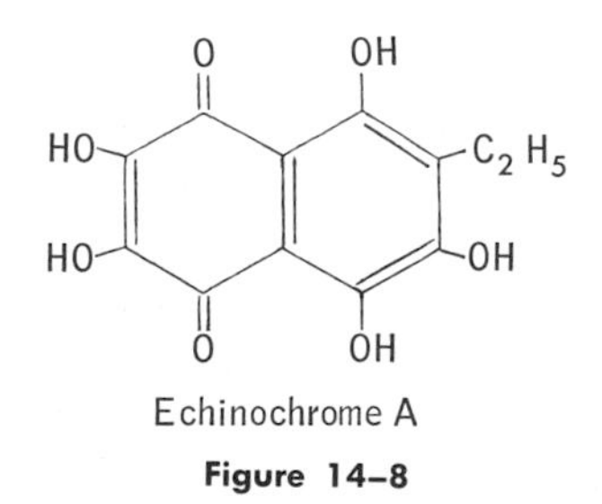

Echinochrome A

Figure 14–8

when, in the process of purification, the protein is lost. A re-investigation of echinochrome function is needed.

MELANIN PIGMENTS

The name "melanin" (Gr. *melas* black) refers to a whole group of pigments. Actually not all of them are black: The colors range from yellow, orange, and red to brown and black.

The melanins are highly polymerized compounds derived from tyrosine or related dihydroxyphenols or *catechols*, such as adrenaline or noradrenaline. The intermediate stages involve the formation of dopa (3,4-dihydroxyphenylalanine) and the oxidation of dopa to dopachrome, an indole derivative. The responsible enzyme is *tyrosinase*, or *phenoloxidase*; it contains copper. Dopachrome is transformed into 5-6,dihydroxyindole (and further to indole-5,6-quinone). This compound then polymerizes to melanin (Fig. 14–9). The sequence is shown in Figure 14–10.

Melanin production ("melanization") is an oxidative process. It takes place in cells, usually derived from ectoderm, designated as melanocytes, or melanophores when they occur in epidermis. The grey, or even dark grey

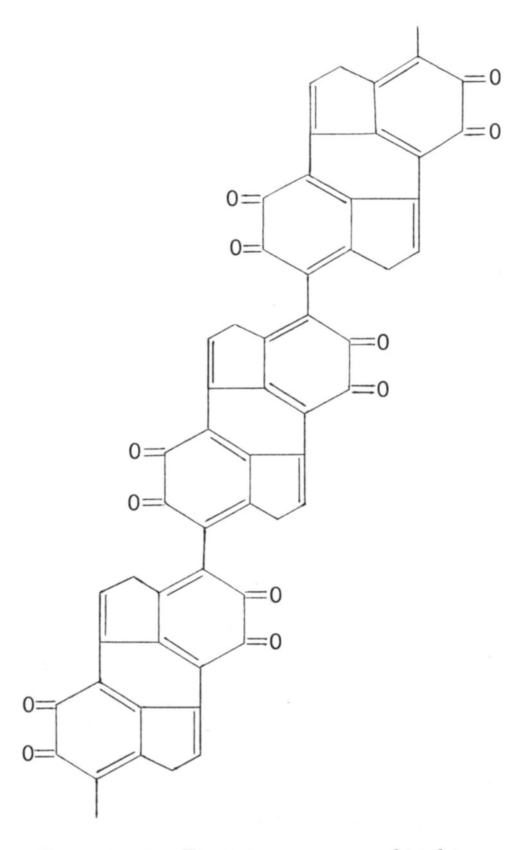

Figure 14–9. Tentative structure of Melanin.

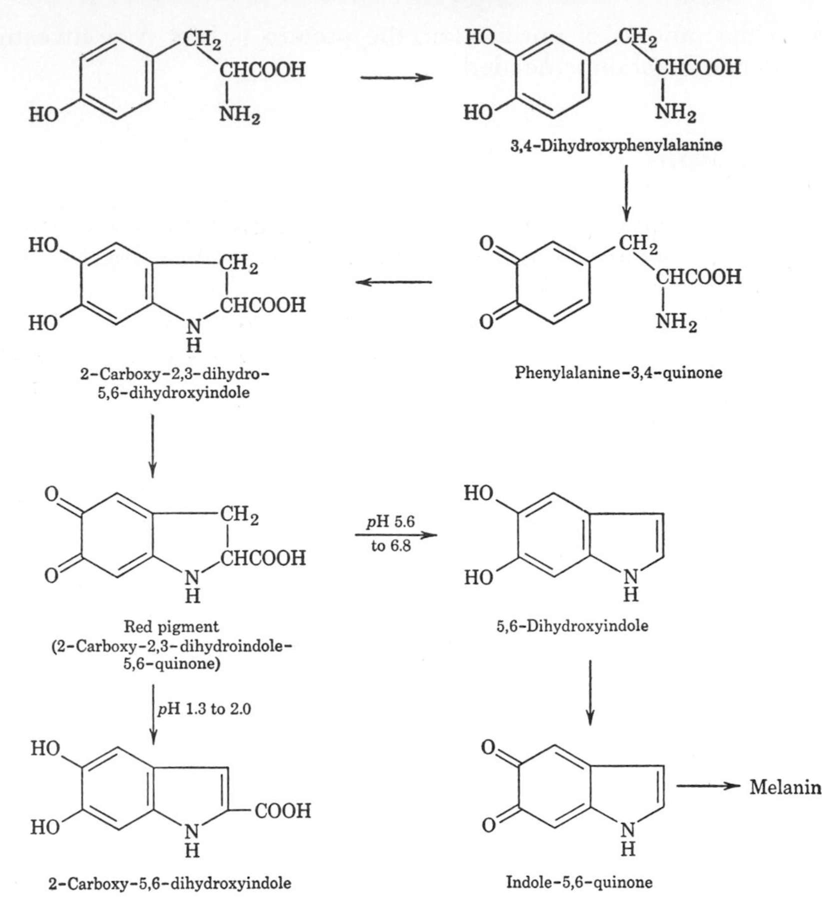

Figure 14–10. Mechanism of melanin formation. (From Fruton, J. S., and S. Simmonds: General Biochemistry, 2nd Ed. John Wiley & Sons, New York, 1958.)

color of certain parts of the vertebrate brain (substantia grisea centralis, substantia nigra) is due to the presence of melanin in their nerve cells. The dark color of adrenal glands is likewise due to melanin. The best known source of melanin is probably the ink sac of cephalopods. The same pigment occurs in hairs and feathers of vertebrate animals, and in the pigment cells of the eyes of vertebrates and of many invertebrates.

Melanin is a conspicuous constituent of many types of tumors, known as *melanomas*. Practically all known tumors of insects are melanomas.

Melanin is often found associated with tissues that show a high mitotic rate, such as epidermis, hair and feathers, or tumors. In this connection, it is interesting that the vertebrate growth hormone, *thyroxine*, is formed from two molecules of diiodotyrosine. In lower vertebrates dibromotyrosine occurs, together with the diiodotyrosine. It is conceivable that some melanins arise from transformed thyroxine.

In the hypobranchial gland of certain marine gastropods (*Murexidae*), there occurs a pigment closely related to melanin, the Tyrian purple, or *royal purple*. In the ancient Mediterranean cultures this pigment was used to dye the robes of kings and emperors. The symbolic red carpet derives its color from it. This pigment is identical with dibromindigo and is possibly derived from two molecules of a 4-bromindoxyl, a compound that is closely related to tyrosine, as shown in Figure 14–11. It is interesting that the hypobranchial gland of several species of marine gastropods contains a pharmacologically highly active indole derivative, 5-hydroxytryptamine (see Chap. 26). The same 5-hydroxytryptamine is found in enormous quantities in tumors. It is not unlikely that the compound serves as a precursor for melanin.

In bringing this speculative section to a close, it might be argued that melanin represents the end product of the chemical inactivation of highly active hormone-like agents, such as adrenaline, noradrenaline, 5-hydroxytryptamine, and thyroxine.

Melanin pigments occur in practically all phyla of the animal kingdom, including coelenterates (*Metridium*). Apart from their possible role as detoxification products, several functions can be assigned to them. Within melanophores (black chromatophores, see Chap. 15), they serve in adaptive or protective coloration. Probably by combining with protein they impart a certain rigidity to structures that contain them. Black hair and feathers are mechanically more resistant than hair or feathers without melanin. This can explain the black wing tips of otherwise white sea birds.

Another function of melanin is the protection from visible and ultraviolet radiation. The melanin formation in human skin ("tanning") is the result of

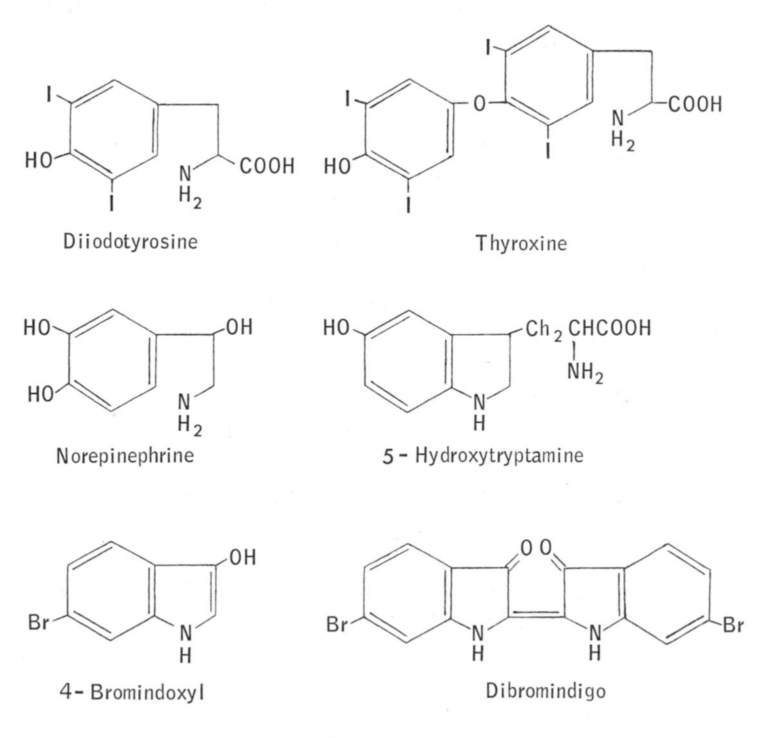

Figure 14–11

activation of the enzyme tyrosinase by ultraviolet light (Fitzpatrick et al., 1950). The presence of small amounts of dopa, either artificially supplied or produced by partially active tyrosinase, catalyzes the activation of tyrosinase and thus stimulates melanin formation.

The presence of melanin in superficial epithelia leads not only to light absorption but also to heat absorption. It may well serve in temperature regulation.

Melanin expelled from the ink sac of cephalopods is often employed as a "smoke screen" behind which the animal can hide, but in a number of squid species the pigment mass does not disperse, rather it stays together as a lump which has a size similar to the animal which leaves it behind while it propels itself backward, having become almost transparent by allowing its melanophores to contract.

TETRAPYRROLES: PORPHINS AND BILINS

Pyrrole is a heterocyclic compound, C_4H_4NH. Four of these rings arranged in a secondary ring structure form the *porphin*-type of tetrapyrroles (Fig. 14–12). A linear arrangement of four pyrrole rings is called a *bilin* structure.

Before going into details concerning the chemical structure and synthesis of these compounds, it is worthwhile to recall the discussion of the origin of life (Chap. 1). In the course of natural selection of organic compounds in the primeval ocean of the earth, porphyrin structures must have been of high "survival" value. It appears that the porphin structure was one of the first "inventions" of life, for these compounds are almost universally distributed throughout the Animal and Plant Kingdoms: hemoglobin, chlorophyll, and cytochromes are representatives of this group of pigments. The appearance of porphin structures, and particulary of porphyrins, must have been one of the principal conditions for the evolution of living matter.

By far the best known, and most common, porphyrin compound is *heme* (haeme, in the British literature). It occurs in the various types of *hemoglobin*, in certain enzymes, such as *catalase* and *peroxidase*, and in *cytochrome b*. Slight modifications of the molecule lead to another type of heme that is found in the pigment *chlorocruorin*, and in cytochromes *a* and *c*.

The biosynthesis of porphyrins is based on the condensation of two molecules of δ-aminolevulinic acid to porphobilinogen, as shown in Figure 14–13. Four of these units form a porphyrin structure in which the four "pyrol rings" are joined by methyl bridges (=CH–). The general structure of the porphyrins follows that of porphin (Fig. 14–12), but hydrogen atoms 1 to 8 are replaced by various radicals. In the case of the protoporphyrins, to which heme belongs, the hydrogens are replaced by 2 vinyl, 4 methyl, and 2 propionic groups. There are 15 possible isomers; number 9 (protoporphyrin IX) is identical with heme (porphin-1,3,5,8-tetramethyl-2,4-divinyl-6,7-dipropionic acid). It is shown in Figure 14–12. If the vinyl group in position 2 is oxidized to a formyl group, the molecule becomes *chlorocruoroporphyrin*, or *chlorocruoro-heme*. In the case of the heme of cytochrome *c*, the vinyl groups are reduced and probably

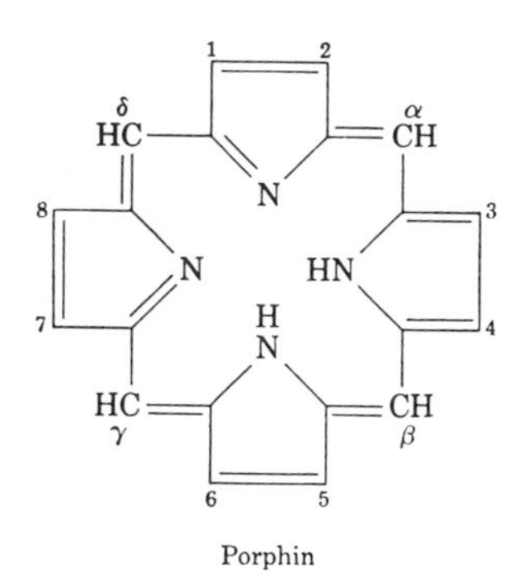

Porphin

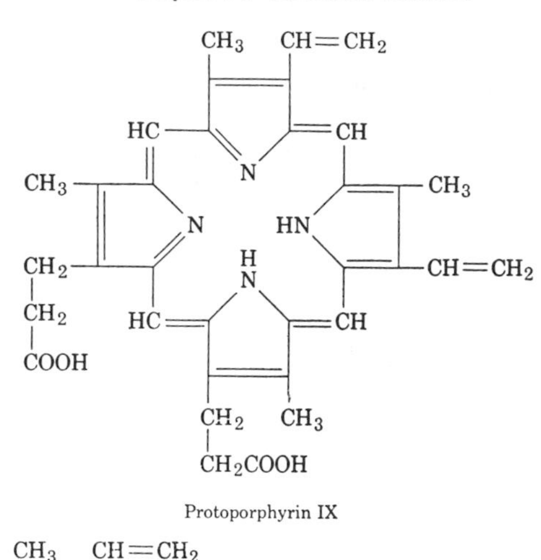

Protoporphyrin IX

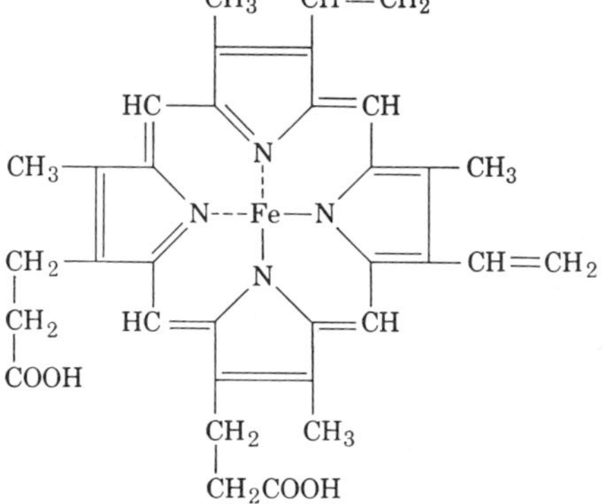

Ferrous protoporphyrin (heme)

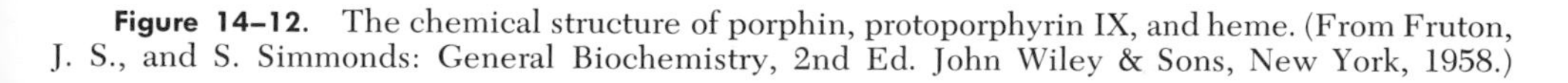
Figure 14–12. The chemical structure of porphin, protoporphyrin IX, and heme. (From Fruton, J. S., and S. Simmonds: General Biochemistry, 2nd Ed. John Wiley & Sons, New York, 1958.)

form thio-ethers with cysteine residues on the protein part of the cytochrome molecule. The heme of cytochrome *a* is similar to that of chlorocruorin.

In the heme molecule the porphyrin structure associates with a ferrous iron ion. Provided the solution is acid, this is accompanied by a loss of two protons from the porphyrin. The resulting negative charge is shared between the four nitrogen atoms and holds, by electrostatic attraction, the ferrous ion in the center. The ferrous ion as it associates with the porphyrin molecule retains two water dipoles.

When heme molecules unite with appropriate proteins to form hemoglobins, cytochromes, etc.; the water dipoles are replaced by nitrogen bases present on the protein.

Hemoglobin is unique in that its ferrous ion retains its four unpaired electrons so that the linkage between heme and protein (globin) is that of electrostatic attraction between the ferrous ion of the heme and the (ionized) imidazole groups of globin. In other complexes between heme and protein (cytochromes,

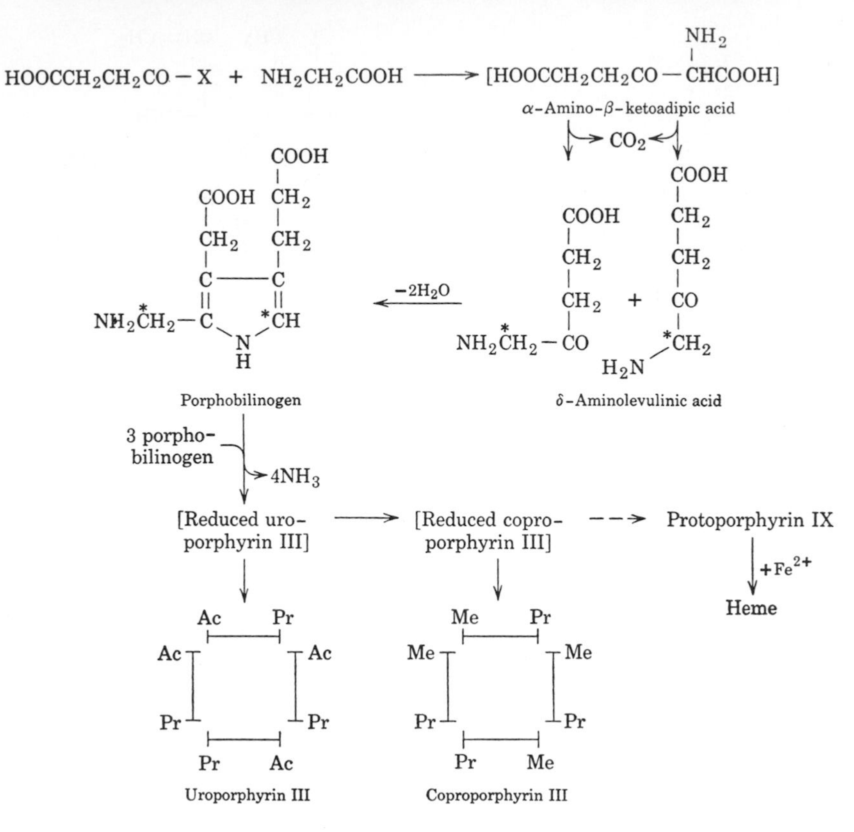

Figure 14–13. The role of δ-aminolevulinic acid and of porphobilinogen in the biosynthesis of heme. (From, Fruton, J. S., and S. Simmonds: General Biochemistry, 2nd Ed. John Wiley & Sons, New York, 1958.)

chlorocruorin, catalase, peroxidase), the electrons are shared between ferrous ion and imidazole groups so that the union between heme and protein is one of covalent bonds.

Hemoglobin can combine with oxygen without being oxidized. Oxygen displaces one of the two imidazole groups and brings about a redistribution of electrons and the formation of covalent bonds, so that the oxygenated hemoglobin molecule has properties similar to those of the other heme-protein complexes. The absorption spectrum of oxyhemoglobin is, therefore, similar to that of the other heme-protein compounds. Carbon monoxide has an action similar to that of oxygen on hemoglobin; in fact, hemoglobin usually has a stronger affinity for carbon monoxide than for oxygen.

All the different heme-protein complexes are known as *hemochromogens*. A great deal is known about the detailed structure of their proteins, but a discussion of this, admittedly fascinating, topic is beyond the scope of this book. If interested, refer to the great treatise on Comparative Biochemistry edited by Florkin and Mason (1960–1964).

The name "hemoglobin" was introduced by Hoppe-Seyler in 1864. The term "*erythrocruorin*," suggested by Ray Lankester, has not found general acceptance, but was adopted by Svedberg and Eriksson (1933) as a general name for all invertebrate heme pigments, and it was in use for many years. The term has meanwhile been discarded, since Keilin and Hartree (1951) pointed out that the variability of molecular weight, isoelectric point, and chemical composition of invertebrate heme pigments does not set them apart from the vertebrate hemoglobins.

Hemoglobin occurs in free solution in circulating body fluids of many animal types. It occurs in blood cells and coelomocytes in others, and it has

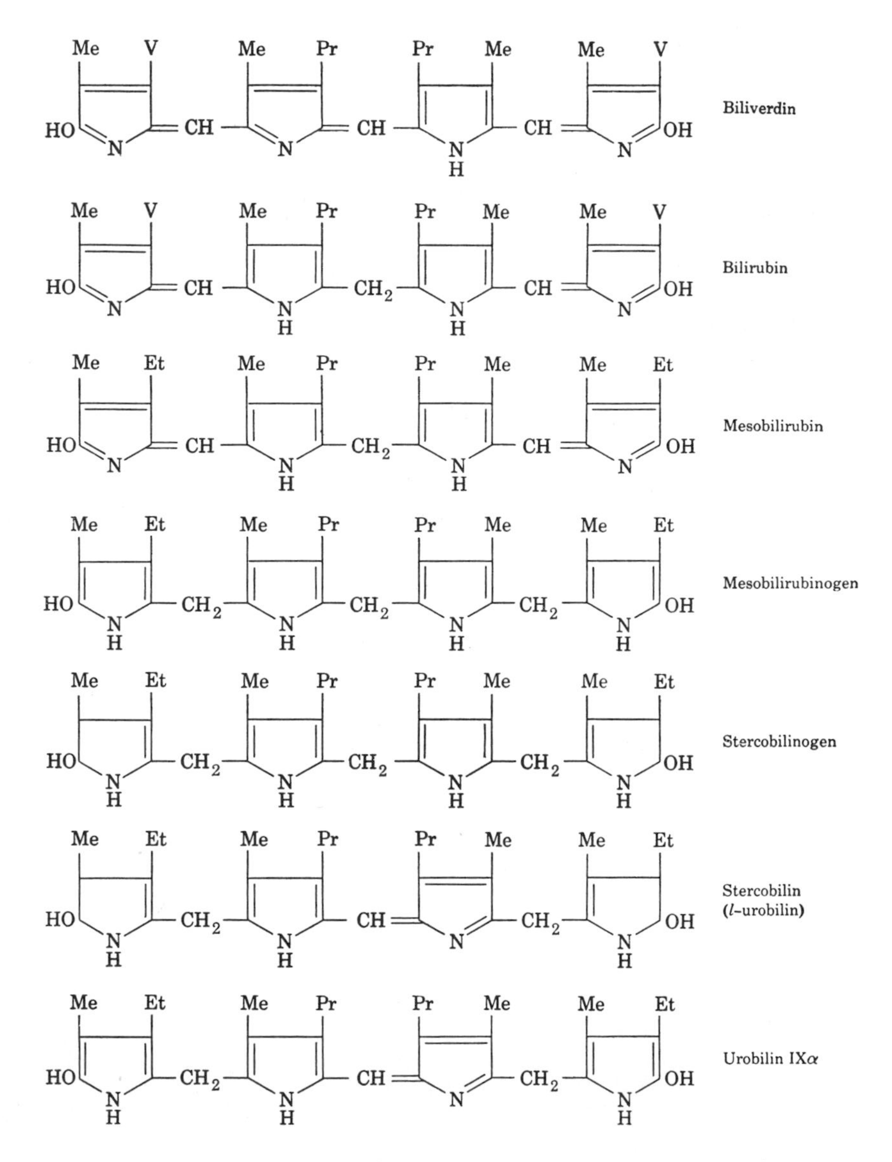

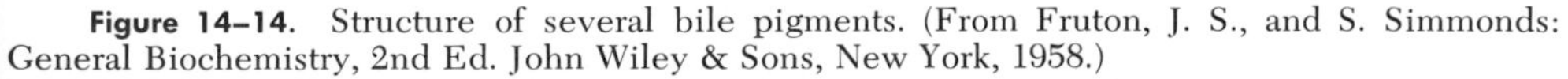
Figure 14–14. Structure of several bile pigments. (From Fruton, J. S., and S. Simmonds: General Biochemistry, 2nd Ed. John Wiley & Sons, New York, 1958.)

been found in muscle of a variety of animals (myoglobin) and in the tissues of many coelenterates (literature in Fox, 1953).

Porphyrins of different types, coproporphyrins and uroporphyrins, occur not only as excretory products in feces (coproporphyrins), but also as coloring matter in molluscan shells, bird egg shells, bones (fox squirrel, *Sciurus niger*), or epidermis (green or brown echinoderms, "worms": most famous, perhaps, is the green body wall of *Bonellia viridis*, a green annelid, which contains "bonellin").

Many porphyrin pigments are derived from plant chlorophyll. This is particularly true for the green or brown pigments found in crustacean and molluscan midgut glands. They may, however, also be derived from ingested hemoglobin.

The nervous system of birds and mammals contains porphyrins. Extensive investigations by Klüver (1944) have led him to assign an important role to this compound in behavior and in the control of reproductive organs. These studies were later extended by Benoit and his associates in France, and by others. They led to the discovery that the influence of the length of day on reproduction is mediated by porphyrin compounds in the nervous system: the optimally effective wavelengths of light coincide with the absorption maxima of porphyrins.

The *bilins* are linear tetrapyrroles and represent degradation products of various porphyrin compounds, including hemoglobin, chlorophyll, and cytochromes. They may arise within the digestive tract, in midgut glands, or (in the case of vertebrates) in the liver from where they enter the gall duct. Examples are shown in Figure 14–14.

Bilins are responsible for much of the yellow or brown color of feces and of urine. Bilins are also present in circulating body fluids and may impart a yellow or even orange color. The yellow or orange color of vertebrate serum derives from bilins. Bilins have no known physiological function but they serve effectively as coloring pigments in the blue or green scales of fishes, the reddish or green shells of clams or gastropods, egg shells of birds, and the orange or red epidermis of slugs or of certain coelenterates. They also occur bound to calcium in the blue skeletons of corals or in the green bones of certain fish.

The purple ink secreted by the ink gland of *Aplysia* contains two bilin compounds. Bilins are also responsible for some of the blue and green pigments in the scales of butterfly wings.

For a more detailed account, refer to D. L. Fox's Animal Biochromes and Structural Colours (1953) and to the treatise on Comparative Biochemistry edited by Florkin and Mason (1960–1964).

REFERENCES

Arvanitaki, A., and N. Chalazonitis (1961) Carotenoid granules in Aplysia ganglion cells. *In* Nervous Inhibition. (E. Florey, ed.) Pergamon Press, New York.

Bartz, J. P., and F. O. Schmitt (1936) Carotene and associated pigments in medullated nerve. Amer. J. Physiol. *117*:280–284.

Bliss, A. F. (1948) Absorption spectra of visual purple of the squid and its bleaching products. J. Biol. Chem. *176*:563–569.
Cornman, I. (1941) Sperm activation by Arbacia egg extracts, with special reference to echinochrome. Biol. Bull. *80*:202–207.
Crescitelli, F., and H. J. A. Dartnell (1953) Human visual purple. Nature *172*:195–197.
Fitzpatrick, T. B., S. W. Becker, Jr., A. B. Lerner, and H. Montgomery (1950) Tyrosine in human skin: Demonstration of its presence and its role in human melanin formation. Science *112*:223–225.
Florkin, M., and H. S. Mason, eds. (1960–1964) Comparative Biochemistry. 7 vols. Academic Press, New York.
Fox, D. L. (1953) Animal Biochromes and Structural Colours. Physical, Chemical, Distribution and Physiological Features of Coloured Bodies in the Animal World. Cambridge University Press, New York, 279 pp.
Friedheim, E. A. H. (1932) Sur la fonction respiratoire du pigment de Bacillus violaceus. Arch. Sci. Phy. et Nat. *14*:125–126.
Hubbard, R. (1958a) Bleaching of rhodopsin by light and by heat. Nature *181*:1126.
Hubbard, R. (1958b) The thermal stability of rhodopsin and opsin. J. Gen. Physiol. *42*:259–79.
Hubbard, R., P. K. Brown, and A. Kropf (1959) Vertebrate lumi- and meta-rhodopsins. Nature *183*:442–446.
Hubbard, R. and A. D. Coleman (1959) Vitamin A content of the frog eye during light and dark adaptation. Science *130*:977–978.
Hubbard, R., and A. Kropf (1958) Action of light on rhodopsin. Proc. Nat. Acad. Sci. (U.S.A.) *44*:130–140.
Hubbard, R., and A. Kropf (1959) Molecular aspects of visual excitation. Ann. N.Y. Acad. Sci. *81*:388–398.
Hubbard, R., and R. C. C. St. George (1958) The rhodopsin system of the squid. J. Gen. Physiol. *41*:501–528.
Hubbard, R., and S. Wald (1960) Visual pigments of the horseshoe crab *Limulus polyphemus*. Nature *186*:212–215.
Kampa, E. M. (1955) Euphausiopsin, a new photosensitive pigment from the eyes of euphausiid crustaceans. Nature *175*:996–997.
Keilin, D., and E. F. Hartree (1951) Relationship between haemoglobin and erythrocruorin. Nature *168*:266–269.
Klüver, H. (1944) Naturally occurring porphyrins in the central nervous system. Science *99*:482–484.
Kropf, A., P. K. Brown, and R. Hubbard (1959) Lumi- and meta-rhodopsins of squid and octopus. Nature *183*:446–448.
Krukenberg, C. F. W. (1881–1882) Vergleichend-Physiologische Studien. Carl Winter's Universitätsbuchhandlung, Heidelberg.
Kühn, R., and N. A. Sørensen (1938) Über astaxanthin und Ovorerdin. Ber. Dtsch. Chem. Ges. *71*, pt. 2:1879–1888.
Kühne, W. (1878–1879) On the stable colours of the retina. J. Physiol. *1*:109–130; 189–192.
Lankester, E. R. (1868) Preliminary notice of some observations with the spectroscope on animal substances. J. Anat. Physiol. *2*:114–116.
MacMunn, C. A. (1883) Studies in animal chromatology. Proc. Bgham. Nat. Hist. Soc. *3*:351–407.
Monaghan, B. R., and F. O. Schmitt (1931) The absorption-spectrum of medullated and of nonmedullated nerves. Proc. Soc. Exp. Biol. Med. *28*:705–708.
Monaghan, B. R., and F. O. Schmitt (1932) The effects of carotene and of vitamin A on the oxidation of linoleic acid. J. Biol. Chem. *96*:387–395.
Peskin, J. C. (1951) Photolabile pigments in invertebrates. Science *114*:120–121.
Suto, R. (1938) Echinochrome, an oxidation-reduction pigment from the sea-urchin, *Anthocidaris crassispina*. Japan. J. Zool. *8*:121–122.
Svedberg, T., and I. B. Eriksson (1933) Molecular weight of erythrocruorin. J. Amer. Chem. Soc. *55*:2834–2841.
Tyler, A. (1939) Crystalline echinochrome and spinochrome: their failure to stimulate the respiration of eggs and of sperm of *Strongylocentrotus*. Proc. Nat. Acad. Sci. (U.S.A.) *25*:523–528.
Verne, J. (1920a) Nature of the red dye of Crustacea. C. R. Soc. Biol. *83*:963–964.
Verne, J. (1920b) The oxidation of carotin from Crustacea and the presence of a substance in the oxidation product which gives a cholesterol reaction. C. R. Soc. Biol. *83*:980–990.
Verne, J. (1923) Essai histochimique sur les pigments tégumentaires des Crustacés décapodes. Gaston Doin et Cie., Paris. 167 pp.
Verne, J. (1925a) Present pigmentary problems. I. Formation of the melanins. Rev. Gen. Sci. *36*:621–643.

Verne, J. (1925b) Present pigmentary problems. II. Relation of pigmentation to digestion. Interpretation of cases of homochromia. Rev. Gen. Sci. *36*:705–711.

Verne, J. (1927) Caroténoïdes d'origine endogène et d'origine exogène dans la carapace de *Carcinus maenas*. C. R. Soc. Biol. *97*:1290–1292.

Wald, G. (1958) Photochemical aspects of visual excitation. Exp. Cell Res. *15*:389–410.

Wald, G. (1959) The photoreceptor process in vision. *In* Handbook of Physiology, Sec. 1, Vol. I, pp. 671–692. (J. Field, ed.) The Williams & Wilkins Co., Baltimore.

Wald, G. (1960) The significance of vertebrate metamorphosis. Circulation *21*:916–938.

With, T. K. (1946) Do carotene and the A-active carotenoids act as provitamin A, or do they unfold their biological action in the organism without previous transformation into vitamin A? Z. Vitaminforsch. *17*:88.

Yamamoto, T. (1935) Photochemical phenomenon in the egg of a polychaete worm, *Ceratocephale osawai*. J. Fac. Sci. Imp. Univ. Tokyo, Ser. IV, *4*:99–110.

15 COLOR CHANGE AND THE CHROMATOPHORES

If we credit Aristotle (384–322 B.C.) with the writing of the first scientific zoological textbook, he was the one who first described the phenomenon of animal color change. He accurately described the patterns of color change of various cephalopods. The reliability of this was pointed out by Henry Lee, director of the Public Aquarium in London, who, in 1875, wrote a charming book on The Octopus or the Devil Fish of Fiction and Fact. Lee observed the rapid fluctuation of coloration in mating cephalopods in the aquarium, and, after ascertaining that this had never been described since Aristotle, frustrates his readers by saying that it would be improper to give details of the sex life of the *Octopus* in a book designed for the general public.

It is amusing that the sixteenth, seventeenth, and even eighteenth century naturalists attribute to fantasy and invention Aristotle's description of rapid color changes in cephalopods, for they did not hesitate to describe mermaids and giant octopuses (kraken) of such enormous dimension that, as they asserted, fishermen mistook them for islands and on occasion met disaster when the "island" on which they had confidently landed to prepare their lunch suddenly submerged.

The first modern treatment of animal color change is a rather thorough study by Bruecke (1852) of the African chameleon. Since then, an enormous number of scientific papers have dealt with many aspects of color change. The last complete survey was by G. H. Parker (1948), in which some 1200 references are listed for the period from 1910 to 1943. Fuchs (1914) lists about 500 references for the period between 1852 and 1914. Since 1943, the literature must have at least doubled.

The topic of color change of animals is the change of external coloration that is caused by an increase or decrease in number of pigmented cells (*chromatophores*) or by pigment movement within pigment cells. The former is known as *morphological color change*, the latter as *physiological color change*. The morphological color change is a slow process that takes days and weeks. It is not the subject of physiology—at least, not at present.

Physiological color change is a more rapid process, requiring minutes, in some cases seconds, and in some only milliseconds. It is most dramatically displayed by cephalopods: A dark squid may, within a fraction of a second, become almost transparent, and a pale *Octopus* may suddenly flush to a dark brown when irritated. Sand-colored shrimp of the genus *Crangon* become almost black if transferred to a black container. Mud shrimp (*Upogebia*) become blue if exposed to light for a few hours. Tree frogs (*Hyla*) change from a bright green to a muddy grey if transferred to a terrarium that provides only rocks. Flatfish (*Pleuronectes*) can imitate a checkerboard in black and white, and if a few orange squares are added, these too are pictured on their scaly backs. The epidermis of several species of sea urchin becomes dark when illuminated, as does that of certain annelids.

These few examples illustrate color change. (Changes of color due to shedding of hair or feathers, molting [insects, Crustacea], or altered patterns of epidermal blood flow are not considered under the heading "Color Change.") The examples were chosen to indicate that the phenomenon occurs in many diverse phyla. In most cases, the color change serves in adaptive coloration, but in those cases in which animals become dark upon illumination, it is possible that the pigment shields sensitive tissues from harmful radiation. The ecological—and biological—significance of color changes of animals is not a topic of physiology proper. However, physiology is concerned with the mechanism that brings about such color changes, that is, with the movement of pigment and the nervous and hormonal control of this.

The subject matter includes not only chromatophores that are engaged in the overt color changes of animals, but also those that are engaged as optical screens or reflectors in the eyes.

CHROMATOPHORES AND THEIR CONTROL

Chromatophores are pigment-containing cells—or clusters of cells—that can reversibly change the position or the distribution of their pigment. They do not form a tissue; rather they are scattered throughout certain epithelia (Fig. 15–1); rarely, they are found even among the cells of organs, such as muscles.

Depending on their color, they are called *melanophores* (black), *erythrophores* (red), *xanthophores* (yellow), *leucophores* (white), *guanophores* and *iridiophores* (iridescent, reflecting). A chromatophore cell always contains only one kind of pigment, but in some cases, cells containing different pigments can form a cluster and give rise to a *chromatosome* which shows two or more colors. *Monochromatic* chromatosomes consist of two or more cells containing

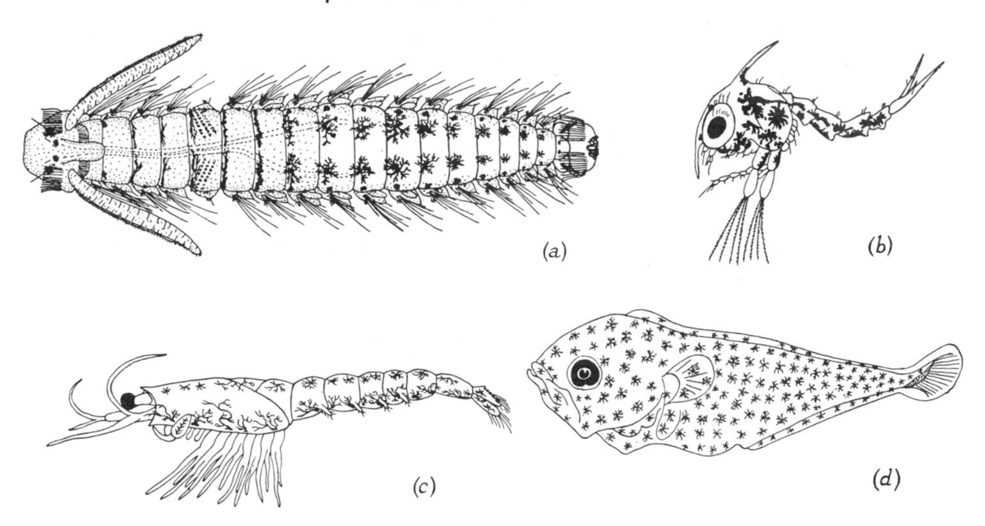

Figure 15–1. Chromatophore patterns: a, larva of the spionid *Polydora hoplura*. b, zoea of the spider crab *Maja squinado*. c, the prawn *Praunus neglecta*. d, the larval turbot *Scophthalmus maximus*. (After (a) Wilson, 1928; (b) Le Bour, 1928; (c) Keeble and Gamble, 1904; (d) Cunningham, 1896; from Nicol, J. A. C.: The Biology of Marine Animals. Interscience Publishers, New York, 1960.)

the same pigment. *Polychromatic* chromatosomes consist of two or more cells, each of which contains a different pigment. In the literature on crustacean chromatophores, the term chromatosome is seldom employed, for it was not always known whether a multicolored pigment spot was represented by a single cell (or syncytium) or by a group of cells. All direct evidence points now to a strict separation of pigments, and the term "polychromatic chromatophore" can be replaced by "polychromatic chromatosome."

Cephalopod Chromatophores

The black, yellow, and red chromatophores in the skin of cephalopods have sets of smooth muscle fibers attached to them (Fig. 15–2). Each chromatophore with its complement of radiating muscle fibers forms a little color organ. The chromatophore is a rather large, pliable cell. It is pulled into various shapes by the action of the attached muscle fibers. When these contract, they tear the chromatophore into a disc, or more commonly an irregular polygonal shape. When the fibers relax, the chromatophore becomes a small sphere. The muscle fibers are under nervous control. Single stimuli applied to the supplying nerves cause twitch-like contractions; repetitive stimulation causes tetanic contractions.

Hormonal control of cephalopod chromatophores has been claimed repeatedly, but the evidence is insignificant. Sereni (1929) is much quoted for experiments in which he cross-perfused two octopods and noted that both animals became pale. However, the animals did not survive the surgical procedure for more than a few hours, and it is well known that dying octopods

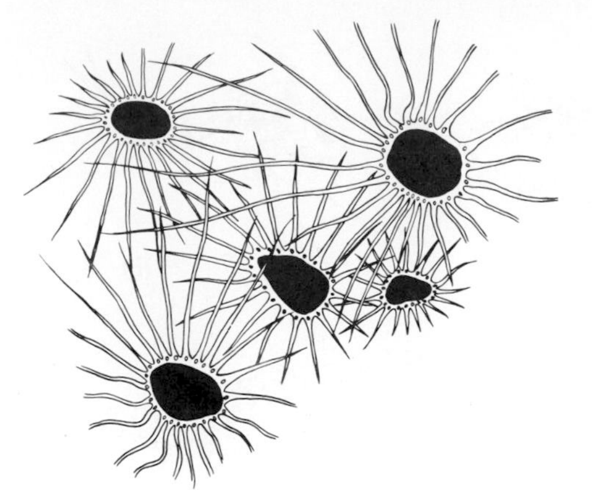

Figure 15–2. Typical picture of cephalopod chromatophores with their radial arrays of muscle fibers whose nuclei lie close to the chromatophore proper. The chromatophores shown here are from the skin of *Loligo vulgaris*. (Redrawn from Hofmann, F. B.: Histologische Untersuchungen über die Innervation der glatten und der ihr verwandten Muskulatur der Wirbeltiere und Mollusken. Arch. mikr. Anat. *70*:361–413, 1907.)

become pale. Sereni's results cannot be taken as proof of a hormonal control of chromatophores or of their muscles.

Numerous studies, in which substances as well as blood samples from light or dark specimens were injected into whole animals, are more or less worthless because they do not permit the distinction between effects on the central nervous system and those on the chromatophore muscles. A new and rigorous investigation of the problem is much needed. The best physiological and morphological studies are those of Hofmann (1907a, b), Kühn and Heberdey (1929), and Bozler (1928, 1931). Bozler concluded that the radial muscle fibers are capable of both tonic (slow) and phasic (fast) contractions. Several authors, including Bozler, have considered (favorably) the possibility that tonic contractions arising "spontaneously" (*autotonus*) in the periphery after connections with the central nervous system have been cut, can be abolished by the action of *inhibitory nerves* (first suggested by Fuchs, 1914). This is an important problem to be solved by a competent physiologist. At present, what Parker said in 1948 is still true: "These several opinions of the way in which the radial muscle fibers of the cephalopod are activated have never been closely scrutinized and carefully tested by experiment."

Chromatophores of the type found in cephalopod skin also occur in another group of molluscs, the pteropods: Gegenbaur, Koelliker, and Mueller described them in 1853 in *Cymbulia radiata*; Gegenbaur (1855) found them in another species of *Cymbulia* and in two species of *Tiedemannia*, and Trojan (1910) saw them in *Phyllirhoe*.

The pigmented epithelial cells of slugs (*Ariolimax, Limax,* etc.) do not have muscle fibers attached to them (Weber, 1923–1924).

The molluscan chromatophores that have muscle fibers attached to them are unique in the Animal Kingdom. In all other chromatophores, pigment concentration and dispersion is effected by a migration of pigment within the chromatophores which may or may not be accompanied by overall changes in the shape of the chromatophores. The most common type of chromatophore is highly branched. This type occurs in many annelids, echinoderms, crustaceans, fishes, amphibia, and reptiles. Examples are shown in Figure 15–1.

Chromatophores of Annelids

Chromatophores of polychaetes (*Nereis dumerilii*) have been studied by von Hempelmann (1939). They show pigment dispersal in response to light. His experiments show that light acts either indirectly through the agency of the eyes (indicating nervous or hormonal control of chromatophores), or directly. Stellate chromatophores which are expanded by light have been described for other polychaetes (*Polydora, Poecilochaetus*) (Lebour, 1942; Wilson, 1928). A direct action of light on chromatophores is not uncommon and has been reported for leeches, fishes, and certain chromatophores of Crustacea. In all these cases, the response consists in expansion of pigment. A nervous control of chromatophores has been demonstrated in the leech *Placobdella parasitica* (Smith, 1942). This animal has red and green chromatophores. The red ones are usually dispersed, but stimulation of the nerve cord causes the pigment to concentrate. In the green chromatophores, pigment expands in response to direct illumination or to nerve stimulation (Janzen, 1932a, b).

Chromatophores of Echinoderms

Chromatophores in echinoids have been described repeatedly. Hartmann (1887) described yellow and red chromatophores in globiferes of *Centrostephanus longispinus*, and purple ones in those of *Sphaerechinus granularis*. The first physiological experiments were reported by von Uexküll in 1896. He found that *Arbacia pustulosa* and *Centrostephanus longispinus* became lighter in color when placed in the dark. Kleinholz (1938a) later confirmed the findings and observed the movement of pigment within the chromatophores. Pigment expansion was caused by light. This occurred even in amputated tube feet. Hormonal control was thus excluded, but it is possible that the local nervous system of the tube feet (they contain several thousand nerve cells) mediates the response, even though a direct action of light on the chromatophores, as reported in so many other cases, is likely.

Chromatophores of Insects

Physiological color change is rare among insects. Nevertheless, there are a few well-known examples. Most prominent, perhaps, are *Carausius (Dixipus) morosus* (stick insect) and *Corethra (Chaoborus) plumicornis* (a chironomid larva).

The epithelial cells in the hypodermis of stick insects contain pigment granules (orange, brown, and green) which change position under the influence of hormones (Fig. 15–3). This was first shown by Giersberg (1928) and Janda (1936). The hormones are released in response to stimulation by the environment. Particularly effective are light and humidity. Light as well as humidity cause the animals to become dark, whereas they become light if kept dry or in the dark. Giersberg demonstrated the nature and chain of events in pigment control of *Carausius* in a simple and striking experiment (see Fig. 15–4): He placed the rear end of the animal into a small, humid chamber and

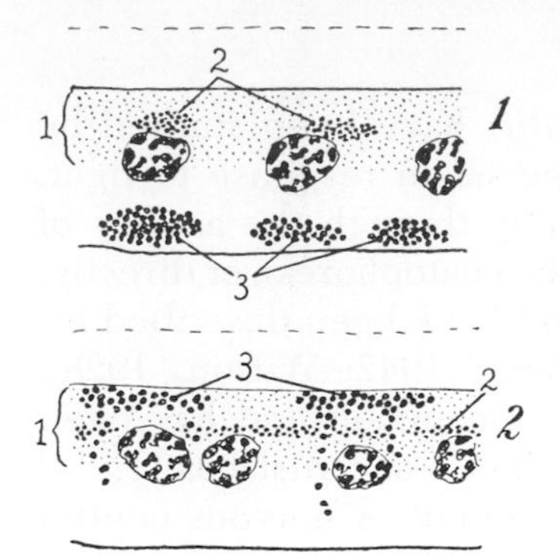

Figure 15–3. Pigment migration in epidermal cells of the stick insect (*Carausius morosus*), and its hormonal regulation. **1**, pigment position when the animal appears light. **2**, pigment position when it appears dark. Pigment granules: *1*, green and yellow; *2*, orange; *3*, brown. (From Giersberg, H.: Über den morphologischen und physiologischen Farbwechsel der Stabheuschrecke *Dixippus* [*Carausius*] *morosus*. Z. vergl. Physiol. 7:657–695, 1928.)

ligated the animal just caudal to the first thoracic segment. The animal, which was light at the beginning of the experiment, became dark on the head and first thoracic segment while the rest of the body remained light. The stimulation responsible for the darkening of the front part of the body came from the humidified rear end. Communication between the rear end and the front end was possible only by way of the nervous system. If the front end showed a response to stimulation of the rear end, the primary effect of the humidity must have been stimulation of nerve elements which in turn excite the central nervous system (brain) forward of the ligature.

Since the stimulated part of the body did not become dark, the nervous system itself must be incapable of causing the animal to darken. That the response stopped just at the ligature, indicates that the ligature prevented transmission of a chromatophore-controlling agent. Since the ligature did not prevent transmission of nerve impulses from one part of the animal to the other, this agent must have been outside the nervous system, presumably in the body fluids. The existence of the agent in the body fluids, however, was caused by nerve impulses arriving in the central nervous system cephalad to the ligature. The experiment, therefore, permits the conclusion that humidity stimulates receptor neurons which activate nerve cells within the head region of the animal. These activated nerve cells cause the release of a "darkening hormone" into the circulating body fluids. The hormone, then, induces the pigment movement in the cells of the hypodermis.

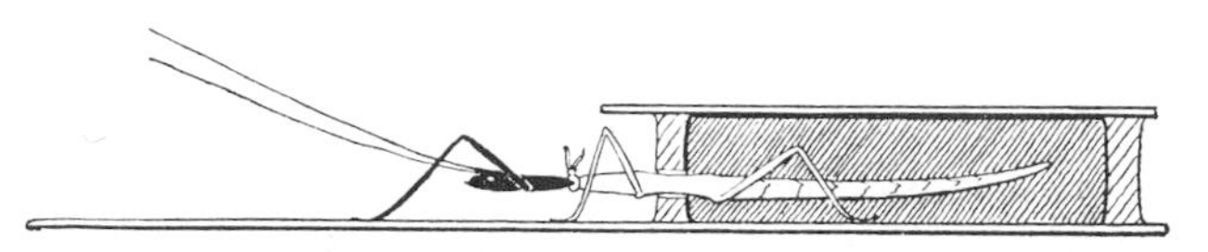

Figure 15–4. Diagrammatic representation of an experiment that proves the hormonal control of the color change: The rear end of the animal is enclosed in a moist chamber. A ligature is placed around the junction between the second and third thoracic segment. The ligature does not interrupt the nervous pathways that carry nerve impulses from abdominal sense organs to the brain; however, it interrupts blood flow so that the color change hormone(s) released from secretory cells controlled by the brain cannot reach the regions behind the ligature. In the absence of the ligature the whole animal would turn dark in response to the moist atmosphere. (From Giersberg, H.: Über den morphologischen und physiologischen Farbwechsel der Stabheuschrecke *Dixippus* [*Carausius*] *morosus*. Z. vergl. Physiol. 7:657–695, 1928.)

DuPont-Raabe (1951, 1952) and later Knowles, Carlisle, and DuPont-Raabe (1955) extracted a melanin-dispersing "hormone" from *Carausius* brains. In addition, the latter authors found a melanine-concentrating agent in the corpora cardiaca (neuroendocrine organs). The hormones have not been identified.

Experiments of DuPont-Raabe (1949a, b) and Kopenec (1949) on *Corethra (Chaoborus)* larvae have yielded similar but, perhaps, more complete results. These animals possess two pairs of tracheal sacs which act as swim bladders. As shown in Figure 15–5, these are covered with ameboid melanophores which

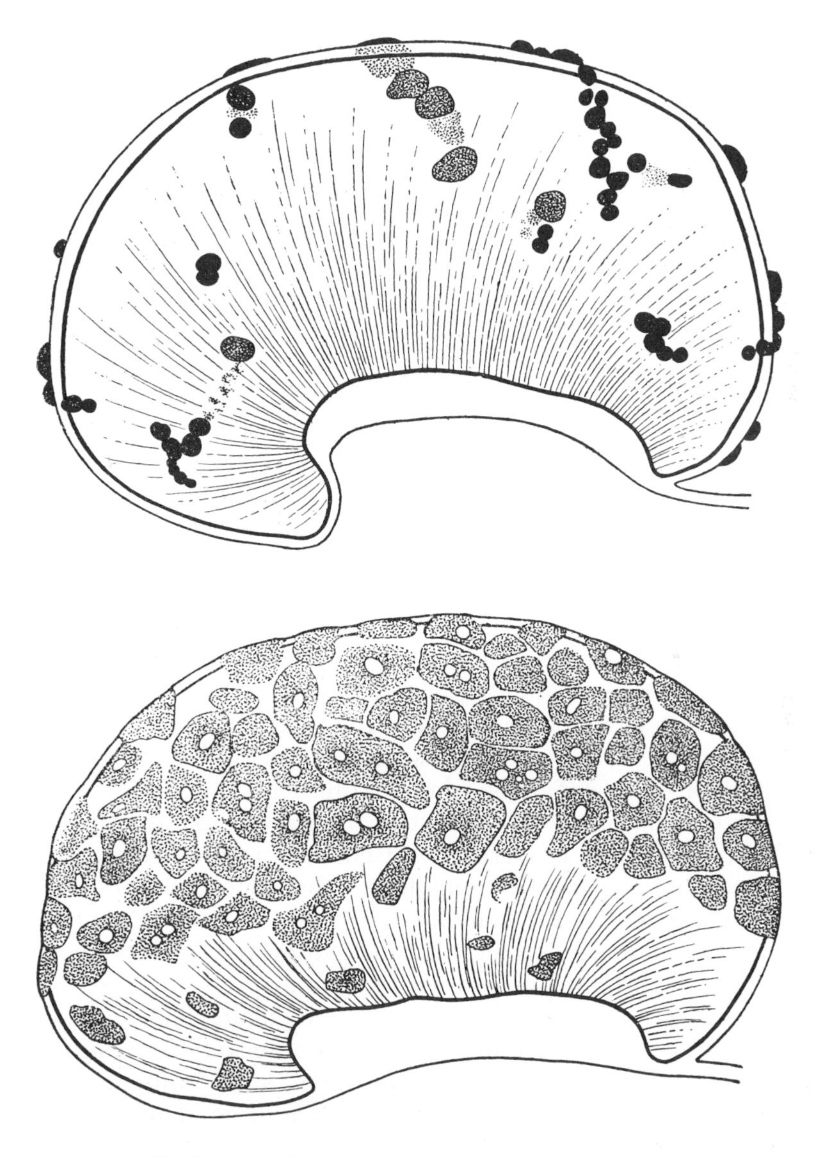

Figure 15–5. Tracheal swim bladder of *Corethra* larva (*Chaoborus plumicornis*), a dipteran insect, showing the melanophores in a state of concentration (**above**) and dispersion (**below**). (From Kopenec, A.: Farbwechsel der Larve von *Corethra plumicornis*. Z. vergl. Physiol. *31*:490–505, 1949.)

may spread out and cover the whole surface of the sacs, or they may contract and migrate all to one side (the apex of the kidney-shaped sacs). Expansion is caused by direct action on the chromatophores of strong light or high temperatures (27 to 28° C), or by hormone(s) circulating in the hemolymph. The hormone is identical with, or related to, *adrenaline*. It is released by the brain when the eyes are illuminated.

Animals on a dark background, even if light shines into their eyes, show maximal expansion of the melanophores. This response is prevented if a ligature is placed behind the head. If the eyes are covered with shellac and lampblack, the melanophores also expand. Normal animals on a white background have concentrated melanophore pigment. It must be concluded that excitation of the nervous elements of the eyes by reflected light leads to an inhibition of the otherwise continuous secretion of melanophore-dispersing hormone (adrenaline).

The suggestive evidence provided by the experiments of Kopenec (1949) that adrenaline or a closely related catecholamine is the melanophore-expanding hormone, has not been considered by other authors who have postulated that this hormone is a peptide (Knowles, Carlisle, and DuPont-Raabe, 1955; Gersch et al., 1960).

Crustacean Chromatophores

Although the chromatophores of crustaceans, in particular of decapods, have been studied most extensively, our knowledge of their structure and function is limited. At present, there is general agreement that pigment dispersion and concentration take place within the confines of each chromatophore and that pigment movement does not involve a change in configuration of the chromatophore itself (see, however, p. 358). This was first suggested by Keeble and Gamble (1906). The assumption that ameboid movement and actual contraction of chromatophores cause pigment concentration (Pouchet, 1872, 1876) was revived when Hanson (1959) showed that in isolated chromatophores of prawns (*Pandalus*) pigment concentration is accompanied by more or less complete withdrawal of cell processes, so that in the final stage of concentration, the chromatophores appear to be almost spherical. Since there is definitive evidence that in several types of crustacean chromatophores pigment moves toward the chromatophore center without changes in the overall configuration of the chromatophore, it must be concluded that ameboid withdrawal of cell processes is not a necessary concomitant of pigment concentration. It is possible, however, that, particularly under extreme conditions which favor pigment concentration, the cell processes are withdrawn also.

Many crustacean chromatophores are polynucleate. There is no evidence, however, that they are multicellular. Even Keeble and Gamble (1906), who portray a chromatophore as a multicellular organ, speak only of compartments separated by denser protoplasm. Figure 15–6 is a good representation of a typical multinucleate chromatophore.

In the older literature, it was assumed that polychromatic chromatophores contain the different pigments in separate compartments of the same chromato-

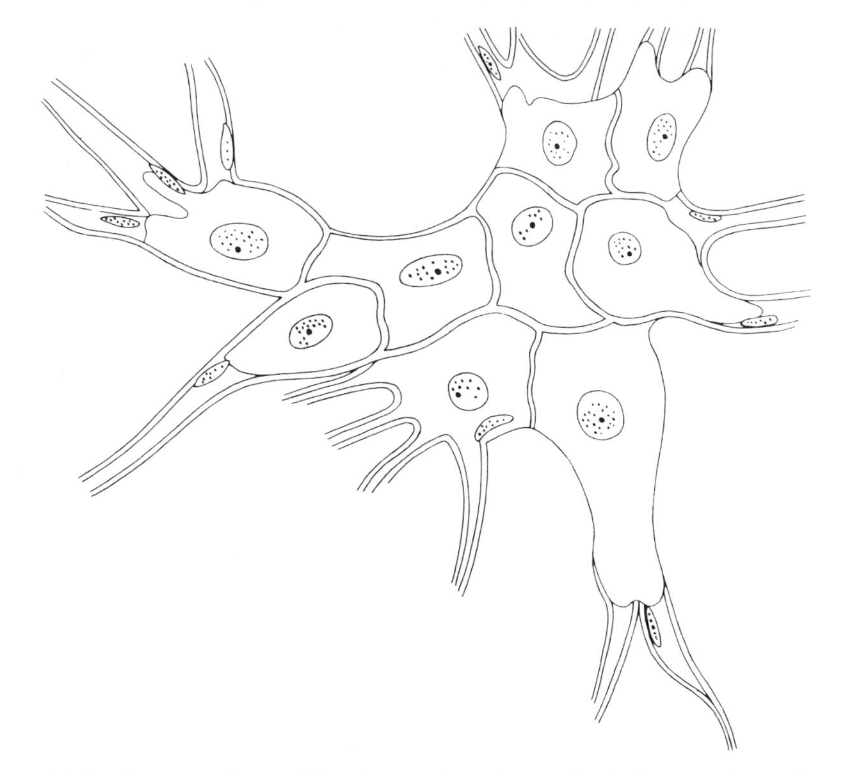

Figure 15–6. Diagram of a multinucleate, compartmentalized chromatophore of a shrimp. (From Keeble, F., and F. W. Gamble: The colour-physiology of higher Crustacea, Part III. Phil. Trans. Roy. Soc. London B, *198*:1–15, 1905.)

phore. This was assumed even when it was known that the different pigments disperse and concentrate independently. Hanson (1959) has shown that polychromatic chromatophores can be resolved into separate chromatophores, each containing a different pigment, by appropriate digestion of the intercellular cement.

It is the general consensus that crustacean chromatophores are not controlled by the nervous system and that there are no synaptic contacts between endings of nerve fibers and chromatophores.

The dominating control over the pigment distribution in chromatophores is, undoubtedly, exerted by hormones produced by neurosecretory cells of the central nervous system. Chromatophore responses have, in fact, become a favorite test object in the study of crustacean hormones (see Chap. 21). However, the extensive literature on crustacean color change has as its prime object not the elucidation of the physiology of chromatophores or the mechanism of hormone action, but the identification of neurohormones. So far, not a single color-change hormone has been identified, although great progress has been made in the chemical separation of active fractions of tissue extracts.

In 1876, Pouchet found that removal of eyestalks in shrimps (*Crangon, Palaemon*) leads to a conspicuous darkening of the animals caused by complete dispersion of the pigment of the dark chromatophores. Koller (1925) showed that blood of light colored *Crangon* (adapted to a white background) caused dark *Crangon* (adapted to a black background) to blanch if injected into their blood stream. Perkins (1928) and Koller (1928) then showed that the blanching hormone could be obtained by extracting eyestalks with water or saline. The darkening caused by eyestalk removal could thus be explained as due to absence of "eyestalk hormone" and inability to concentrate the pigment. The reports of Koller (1928) that extracts of the "rostral region" of the animals caused dispersion of pigment in the dark chromatophores, have never been confirmed by other investigators, in spite of repeated trials.

After the papers of Koller and of Perkins were published there followed an almost explosive increase in research on crustacean color change with the main aim of discovering the nature and source of the color-change hormones. The techniques used were usually unsophisticated, and adequate biochemical methods were not employed until the 1960's. The results, particularly before the 1950's, do not lend themselves to a systematic treatment. It is worthwhile, however, to point out the difficulties and shortcomings of the early experiments: the effects of injected crude extracts were used to identify hypothetical hormones. If an extract caused the telson of *Crangon* to become dark, this was taken to mean that the extract contained a *Crangon* tail-darkening hormone (CTDH); if an extract caused the body of *Crangon* to become light, one spoke of a *Crangon* body-lightening hormone (CBLH), etc. Injecting such extracts into other crustaceans gave rise to names of additional hormones, such as UDH (*Uca* darkening hormone) or PLH (*Palaemon* lightening hormone). The extracts were made from eyestalks or nerve tissues of different crustaceans in an attempt to discover whether different species would produce identical or different hormones. Inevitably, these experiments led to confusing results, which were not improved when attempts were made to separate components of extracts into alcohol-soluble and alcohol-insoluble fractions.

Some promise of progress appeared with the application of electrophoresis. The mobility of different compounds in an electric field permits their separation according to their own electric charges. The more strongly positive, the faster they move toward the cathode, and vice versa. By electrophoresis, Knowles, Carlisle, and DuPont-Raabe (1955) separated from extracts of eyestalks of *Leander serratus* a component which they called the *A′ substance*. This substance caused concentration of white chromatophores and the red pigment of large red chromatophores. Upon standing at room temperature, it changed its properties: it now caused pigment concentration of large and of small red chromatophores but had no effect on white chromatophores. The new substance was named *A-substance*. In unheated samples, the A-substance underwent further transformation, yielding two components with different behavior in the electric field. They concentrated the pigment of the small red chromatophores only and were named *alpha-substances*. The same authors also detected a *B-substance*. It concentrates the pigment of the large red chromatophores but disperses that of the small red chromatophores.

From nerve tissue of *Carausius*, Knowles, Carlisle, and DuPont-Raabe (1955) obtained yet another component, the *C-substance*, which can disperse melanin granules in the hypodermis of *Carausius*. DuPont-Raabe (1956) suggested that this C-substance can be transformed into the A-substance (in the corpora cardiaca of *Carausius*). A German author, Gersch (1956), purified extracts of cockroach (*Periplaneta*) nervous system and tested them on *Corethra (Chaoborus)* melanophores. He described a C and a D substance, later resolved into active fractions C_1 and D_1 and inactive fractions C_2 and D_2. The D-substance was found to cause pigment dispersion in high dilution (10^{-11} gm/ml) and pigment concentration in high concentration.

For the purpose of this introductory text, it appears best to leave the enumeration of experimental detail at this point and refer the interested reader to the reviews by Carlisle and Knowles (1959), Knowles and Carlisle (1956), and Fingerman (1959, 1963).

It is worthwhile, however, to examine critically, if briefly, the logic of the experimental approach reported in the extensive literature.

1. Hormones were identified on the basis of two criteria: chemical (or electrochemical) properties and physiological action.

2. The chemical properties examined were: solubility in water, alcohol, chloroform, or acetone, mobility in an electric field and—sometimes—mobility in paper chromatography. In certain cases, additional tests establish heat resistance, dializability, and sensitivity to the action of certain enzymes (notably trypsin). The A′ and A-substances, for instance, are heat stable (100° C), dializable, and destroyed by incubation with trypsin.

3. The physiological action was determined by injecting the purified agent into certain test animals and observing the response of their chromatophores.

If the procedures, as they have usually been applied, are examined critically, certain faults become obvious:

1. The chemical properties of the "hormone" vary according to the history of the extract. This is well illustrated by the example just mentioned concerning the A′, A-, and alpha-substances. Hormones are often bound to proteins, and the mobility in an electric field may well be that of the hormone still attached to its carrier molecule.

2. The extraction procedure, particularly when organic solvents are employed, may well alter the properties of the "hormone."

3. In many of the published experiments the possibility is not excluded that the injected extract fraction acts indirectly by causing the release (or a modification of ongoing release) of pigment-activating hormone. In addition, it is by no means certain that an action on chromatophore pigment signifies a normal role of the compound in pigment control: cockroaches, from which pigment-activating substances have been extracted, have no chromatophores. Furthermore, it is possible that certain substances that normally never leave the cells in which they occur, have effects on chromatophores, once artificially released.

In order to assure progress in the attempts to identify pigment-activating hormones, it is necessary to adhere to certain minimum rules: 1. Extracts and their fractions should be tested on isolated, chromatophore-containing epidermis and not on whole animals. 2. If extracts of tissues from different species are to be compared, the test chromatophores must be of precisely the same type and obtained from the same species.

From the results of a number of investigations, it appears that crustacean color-change hormones are peptides or polypeptides. This would correspond to the situation in vertebrates in which the pituitary produces melanophorotropic hormones (see p. 360) that is a polypeptide. The structure of the hormone of two mammals (cattle and pig) has been determined: as has been found with other polypeptide hormones, the amino acid sequence of the hormone from the two sources differs somewhat, although the biological action is, for all practical purposes, identical. If crustacean pigment-activating hormones are indeed polypeptides, it may well be that species differences exist which affect the amino acid sequence. It may be assumed that some chromatophores show differential responses to hormones of somewhat different structure whereas others may show identical responses.

Although the more recent reviews do not consider this, adrenaline, noradrenaline, or a related amine might well be a color-change hormone in crustaceans. Beauvallet and Veil (1934) reported that injection of as little as 1 microgram of adrenaline into *Palaemon* causes expansion of melanophore pigment. The experiments were confirmed with *Crangon* (Florey, 1952), and it was shown that this response is rather specific inasmuch as of several structurally related compounds (see Fig. 15–7) only adrenaline and noradrenaline were active. Pautsch (1948) described the melanin-expanding effect of adrenaline

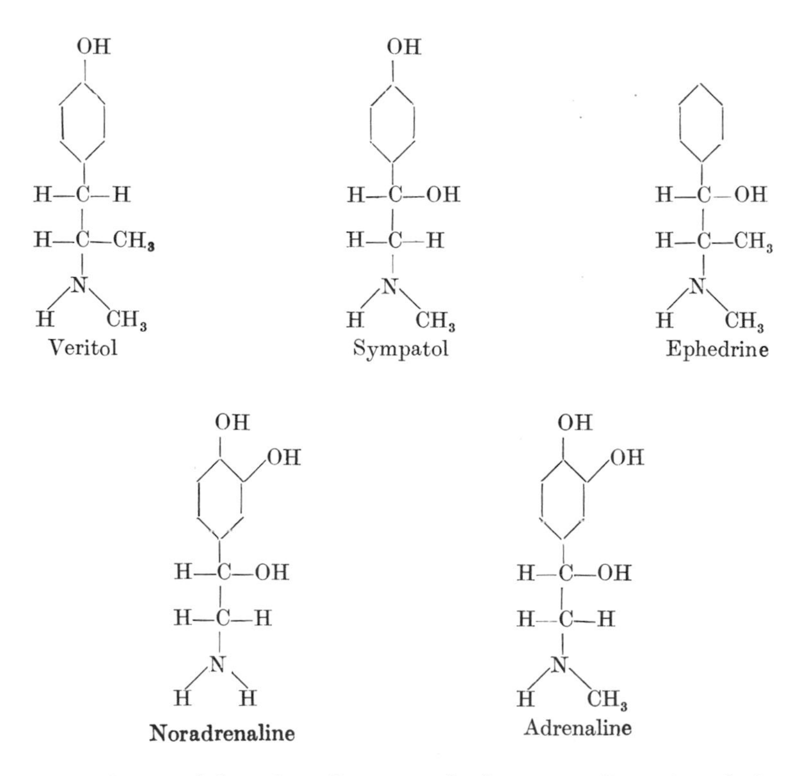

Figure 15–7. Structural formulae of compounds that cause dispersion of pigment in the melanophores of *Crangon vulgaris*. The compounds in the top row act only in rather high concentrations, but adrenaline and noradrenaline are effective even in dilute solution. (After Florey, E.: Untersuchungen über die Natur der Farbwechselhormone der Crustaceen. Biol. Zbl. *71*:499–511, 1952.)

in an isopod, *Idothea tricuspidata*, and Hanson (1959) observed pigment dispersion in red chromatophores of *Pandalopsis dispar*. Östlund and Faenge (1956) found that adrenaline, noradrenaline, and 5-hydroxytryptamine caused pigment dispersion in red chromatophores of *Leander adspersus*.

It is unfortunate that, so far, we have no knowledge of the actual occurrence of catecholamines in crustacean nerve tissue. Attempts to find adrenaline or noradrenaline (Östlund, 1954) in several crustacean species have failed.

The studies with adrenaline-like compounds on *Crangon* yielded an important observation: adrenaline caused concentration of pigment in white chromatophores, noradrenaline did not. Thus a slight change in molecular configuration can determine the pattern of coloration of an animal. This conforms to observations on the transformations of the A′ substance which also alter the pattern of selectivity for different types of chromatophores.

Crustacean color change may be highly complex. Some forms, such as *Crangon*, possess chromatophores of four different colors (black, red, orange, yellow) and can imitate a variety of background colorations. This requires the most delicate adjustment of the state of expansion (or concentration) of the various pigments in the different chromatophores. A multiplicity of hormones may well be involved.

The pigmentary responses of a number of crustaceans to background coloration have been described in detail. A good example are the descriptions given by Koller (1925, 1928) for color adaptations of *Crangon*.

If the performance of individual chromatophores is disregarded and if only the general aspect of the animal's light reflection is considered without regard for color, it is relatively easy to summarize the data in the literature concerning the origin of color-change hormones. In the *Natantia* (Astacura, Anomura, e.g., lobsters, shrimps, prawns), removal of eyestalks causes general darkening (expansion of dark chromatophore pigments) and injection of eyestalk extract causes blanching. In the Brachyura (crabs), eyestalk removal causes blanching, and injection of eyestalk extract, regardless of whether obtained from Natantia or Brachyura, leads to darkening. The exceptions reported by Enami (1951) in the cases of *Sesarma* were explained as due to a direct action of light on the dark chromatophores which overrides the hormone action (Fingerman, Nagabhushanam, and Philpott, 1960, 1961).

A third type is represented by the Isopoda. Injection of eyestalk extracts of Natantia or Brachyura causes darkening, but injection of extracts of isopod heads causes blanching.

Remember, however, that eyestalks (and heads, for that matter) are complex structures and that they are more than likely to produce more than one color-change hormone. Removal of eyestalks and injection of eyestalk extracts reveal only the role of the *dominant* hormone.

Crustacean compound eyes contain pigment cells which act as optical screens (Figs. 15–8 and 15–9). During intense illumination (daylight) the pigment (known as the *distal pigment*) mass lies close to the retinula cells away from the cornea; in dim light the pigment is found surrounding the crystal cones. The retinula cells themselves contain pigment (melanin) that migrates toward the photoreceptive portion of these cells when these are strongly illu-

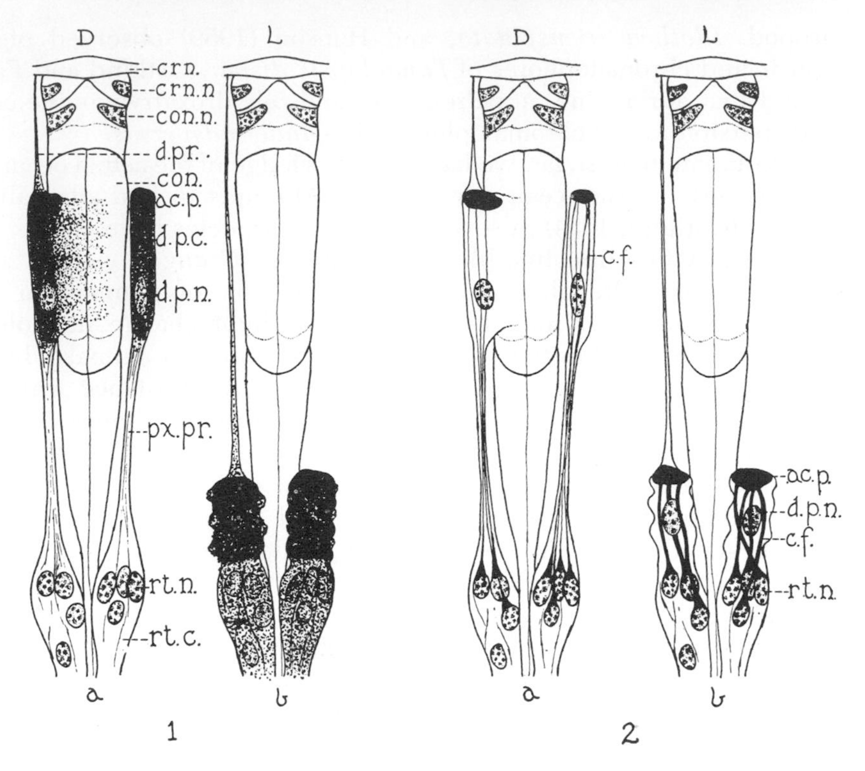

Figure 15–8. Single ommatidium from the compound eyes of the shrimp *Palaemonetes vulgaris*, showing the distal pigment in the condition of light adaptation (**L**) and dark adaptation (**D**). The diagrams show (**1**) the pigment and (**2**) the appearance of the distal pigment cells (*d.p.c.*) and retinula cells (*rt.c.*) after the pigment has been removed. Note the contractile fibrils (*c.f.*). *ac.p.*, accessory pigment; *con.*, cone; *con.n.*, nuclei of cone cells; *crn.*, cornea; *crn.n.*, nuclei of corneal cells; *d.p.n.*, nucleus of distal pigment cell; *d.p.r.*, distal process of distal pigment cell; *px.pr.*, proximal process of distal pigment cell; *rt.n.*, nucleus of retinula cell. (From Welsh, J. H.: The mechanics of migration of the distal pigment cells in the eyes of Palaemonetes. J. Exp. Zool. *56*:459–487, 1930.)

minated, and withdraws to their base during dark adaptation. The phenomenon was analyzed by Welsh (1930). Later, Kleinholz (1934) and others showed that the distal pigment is under the control of hormone(s) produced in the eyestalk which cause it to move toward the retinula cells (light adaptation) (Fig. 15–8). It is likely that dark adaptation is also caused by a hormone, probably from the so-called post-commissural organ (see p. 516).

Surrounding the retinula cells at the level of the basement membrane are guanine-containing light reflecting cells (Fig. 15–9). The guanine retracts below the basement membrane during light adaptation. Under these conditions, light is absorbed by the proximal pigment which is above the basement membrane. During dark adaptation, the reflecting pigment moves above the basement membrane, while the proximal (dark) pigment moves below it. Since it is not screened by dark pigment, the guanine now reflects any light that is

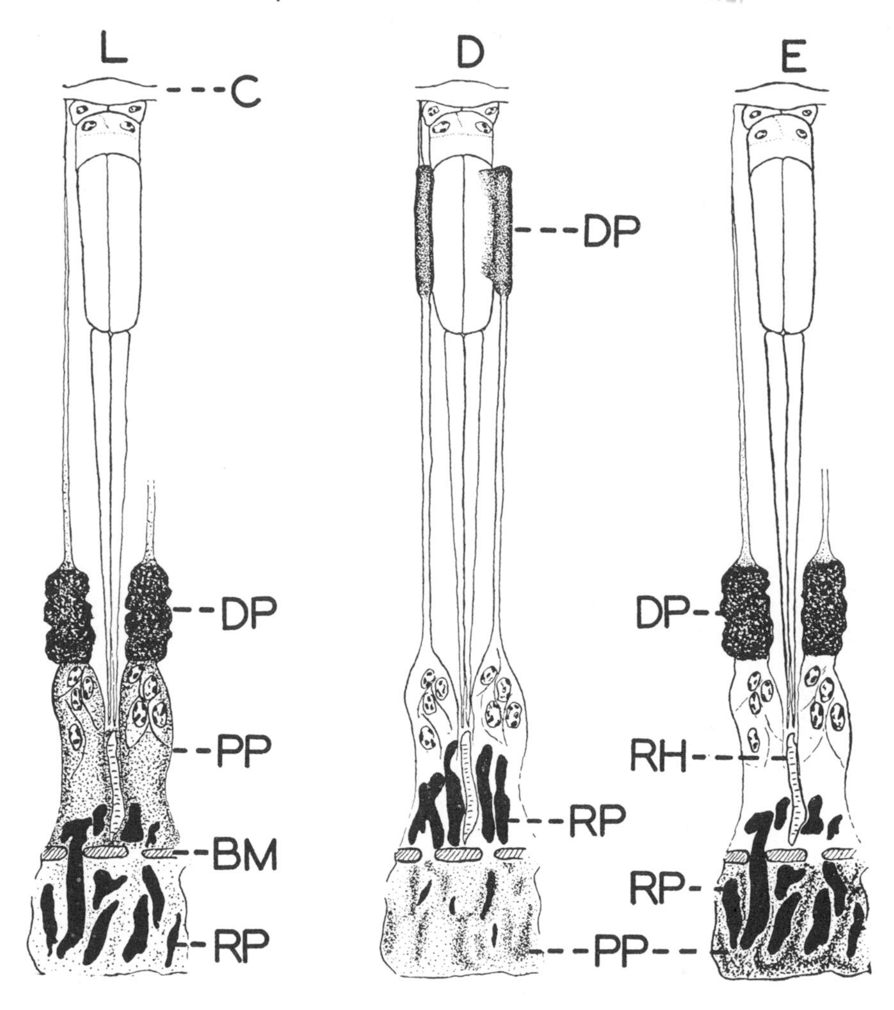

Figure 15–9. Single ommatidium from the compound eyes of the shrimp *Palaemonetes vulgaris*, showing the general structure, and the position of the three types of retinal pigment in the light-adapted (**L**) and the dark-adapted (**D**) eye. **E** shows the pigment position in a dark-adapted animal after injection of "eyestalk hormone" (eyestalk extract). *BM*, basement membrane; *C*, cornea; *DP*, distal pigment; *PP*, proximal pigment; *RH*, rhabdom; *RP*, reflecting pigment. (From Kleinholz, L. H.: Crustacean eye-stalk hormone and retinal pigment migration. Biol. Bull. *70*:159–184, 1936.)

not absorbed by the retinula cells and thus increases the effect of dim light in vision. The bared reflecting pigment is responsible for the brilliant glow which crustacean eyes exhibit at night, when suddenly illuminated. In *Palaemonetes*, injection of eyestalk extract causes movement of reflecting pigment into the position occupied during light adaptation (Kleinholz, 1934).

There is little question but that the migration of all the eye pigments is directly affected by light. Hormones, where they are active, enhance or inhibit this action (under normal conditions, hormone release and hormone effect parallel that produced by light).

Color Change and Chromatophore Responses in Vertebrates

In contrast to the situation in crustaceans (the best investigated invertebrate group, as far as chromatophores are concerned), it is relatively simple to discuss color-change regulation of vertebrates. This is because we know the identity of the color-change hormones, and of the transmitter substances involved.

In contrast to the elasmobranchs, in which a nervous control of chromatophores is probably absent, the chromatophores of teleost fishes are, as a rule, innervated by both sympathetic and parasympathetic nerve fibers (Fig. 15–10), the former causing concentration, the latter dispersion of melanophores (see Fig. 15–11). Parasympathetic supply is not always certain, but it has been definitely established in such widely studied fish as *Phoxinus* (minnow), *Macropodus* (fighting fish) and *Fundulus* (killifish), *Ameiurus* (catfish) and *Anguilla* (eel) (von Frisch, 1911; Giersberg, 1931; von Gelei, 1942; Umrath and Walcher, 1951; Mills, 1932; Kleinholz, 1935; Parker, 1943).

In addition to the control by direct innervation, the chromatophores of fishes respond to hormones released by the adrenal gland (*adrenaline, noradrenaline*), by the pituitary gland (*intermedin, adrenocorticotropic hormone* [ACTH], *melanophore-stimulating hormone* [MSH]), and by the thyroid gland (*thyroxine*). Sex hormones have also been implicated (Umrath, 1959).

Although the melanophores are usually innervated, the erythrophores are often not, and no innervation has been reported for xanthophores.

The innervated chromatophores respond in many species to pituitary hormones so that they are actually under a multiple control. The nerves are then responsible for a more rapid, the pituitary hormones for a slower, change in pigment configuration. Typical examples of such a multiple control are the minnow (*Phoxinus*) and the eel (*Anguilla*), in which the melanophore pigment (melanin) expands in response to activity of parasympathetic nerve fibers and to melanophore-stimulating hormone (*MSH*) and contracts in response to the action of sympathetic nerve fibers and to melanophore-concentrating hormone (*MCH*). In *Ameiurus*, the situation is similar, except that the pituitary hormone for melanin concentration (MCH) is missing. In *Macropodus*, there is no pituitary control of melanophores.

The erythrophores of *Phoxinus* (and most likely those of others as well) show pigment expansion under the influence of intermedin (Giersberg, 1931). Likewise, the melanophores of the elasmobranch fishes appear to be controlled only by pituitary hormones, but in most cases, it is not known for certain whether they are innervated, or whether one or more pituitary hormones are involved.

In all fishes studied, adrenaline causes melanin concentration (Fig. 15–12). The same is true for noradrenaline. *Thyroxine* has been reported to cause melanin expansion in goldfish (*Carassius*).

The melanophores of amphibia (exception: those of *Xenopus*), are, as far as is known, noninnervated and are exclusively controlled by hormones. Pigment concentration is caused by circulating adrenaline (or noradrenaline), expansion by pituitary hormones (intermedin, MSH, or ACTH). The melanophores of *Xenopus* tails are controlled only by the intensity of incident light (Bagnara, 1960; Van der Lek et al., 1958). The rest of the melanophores of

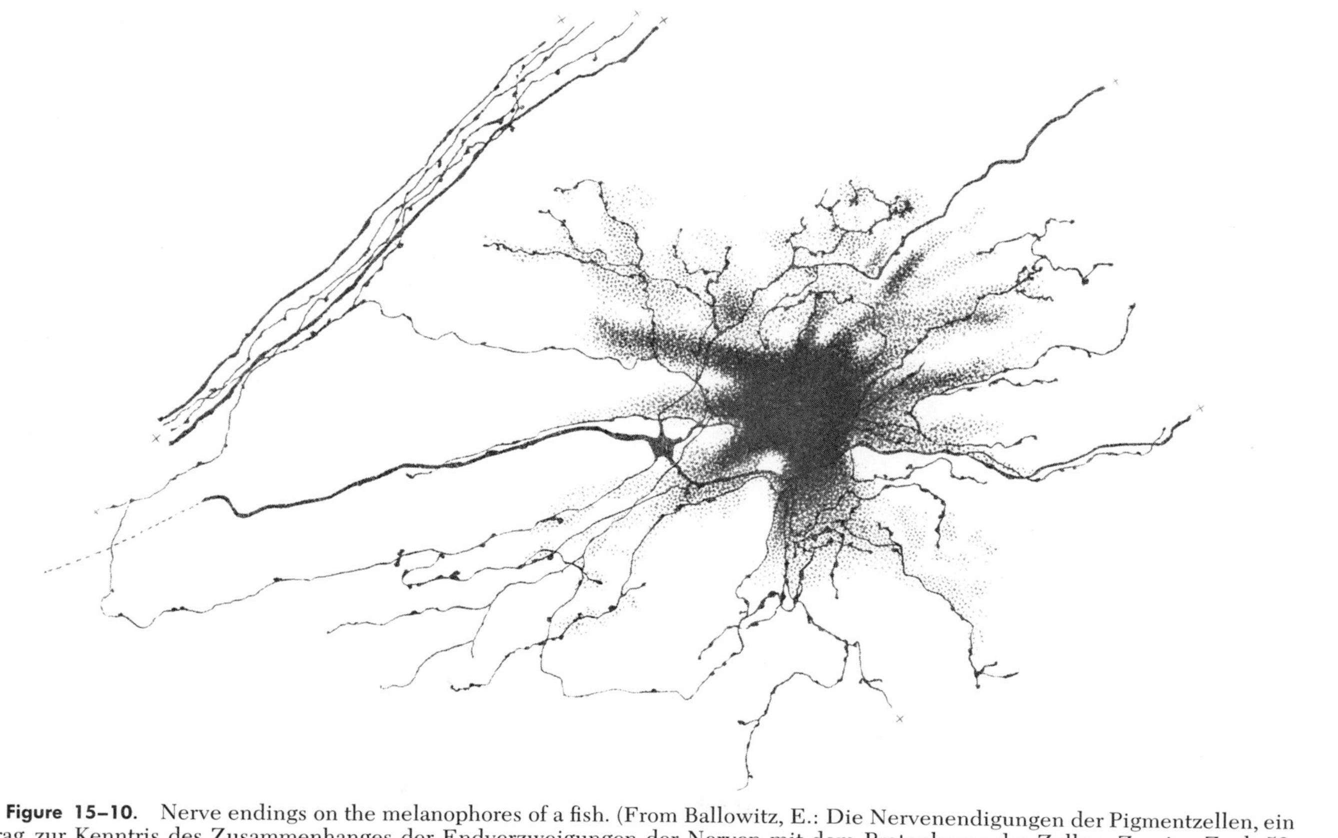

Figure 15–10. Nerve endings on the melanophores of a fish. (From Ballowitz, E.: Die Nervenendigungen der Pigmentzellen, ein Beitrag zur Kenntris des Zusammenhanges der Endverzweigungen der Nerven mit dem Protoplasma der Zellen. Z. wiss. Zool. *56*: 673–703, 1893.)

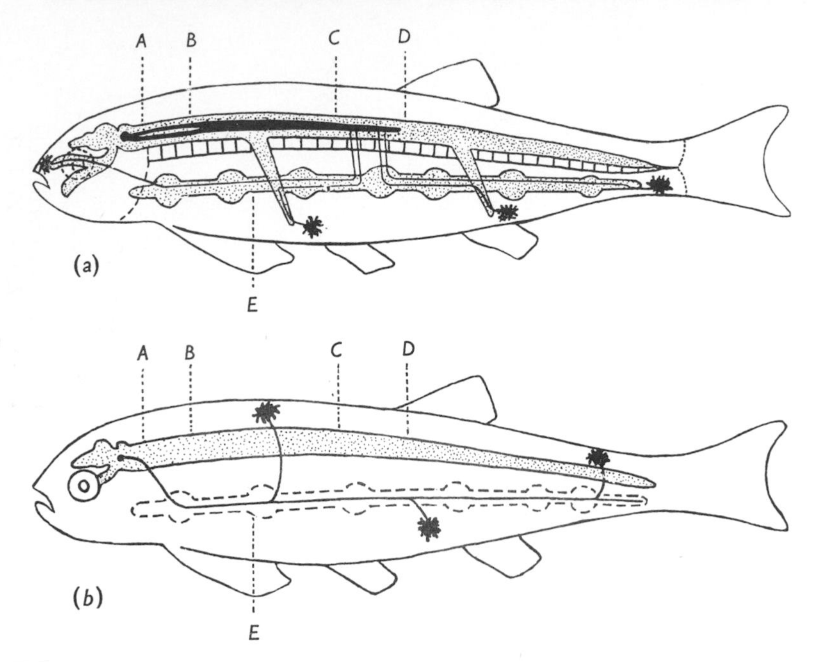

Figure 15–11. Pathways of nervous control of melanophores of the minnow *Phoxinus laevis*. a, pathways of the sympathetic fibers responsible for pigment concentration. The diagram shows the brain, spinal cord, sympathetic ganglion chain, and two spinal nerves (according to von Frisch, 1911). b, pathways of parasympathetic pigment-dispersing nerve fibers (according to von Gelei, 1942). *A* to *E*, levels of experimental transection of the spinal cord and chain of autonomic ganglia in a successful attempt of Healey to confirm the earlier findings of von Frisch and von Gelei. (From Healey, E. G.: The color change of the minnow [Phoxinus laevis AG.]. J. Exp. Biol. *31*:473–490, 1954.)

larval and adult *Xenopus* show pigment dispersion in response to adrenaline and concentration under the influence of pituitary extracts.

Reptilian chromatophores are controlled by nerves (*Chamaeleo*), hormones (*Anolis*), or by both (*Phrynosoma*). The multicolored chromatophores of chameleons, as Bruecke (1852) has shown, are innervated by pigment-dispersing as well as pigment-concentrating fibers. Theirs is the most intricate nervous control system, permitting the most incredible changes of color pattern that conform to background or the mood of the animal. Because of their general distribution throughout the body, hormones would be rather inadequate for independent control of small patches (or even individual) chromatophores.

Anolis, on the other hand, can adapt to background coloration even if the skin innervation has been cut (Kleinholz, 1938b). The horned lizard (*Phrynosoma*) seems to have a melanin-concentrating nerve supply (sympathetic nervous system). Its melanophores show pigment dispersion in response to pituitary extract or MSH, and pigment concentration under the influence of adrenaline (Parker, 1938).

Birds and mammals do not have chromatophores proper, but may have melanin in epidermal cells (melanocytes). It is known, particularly from recent studies (Lerner, Shizume, and Bunding, 1954), that injection of MSH into humans causes a conspicuous darkening of the skin (even if this is alrēady

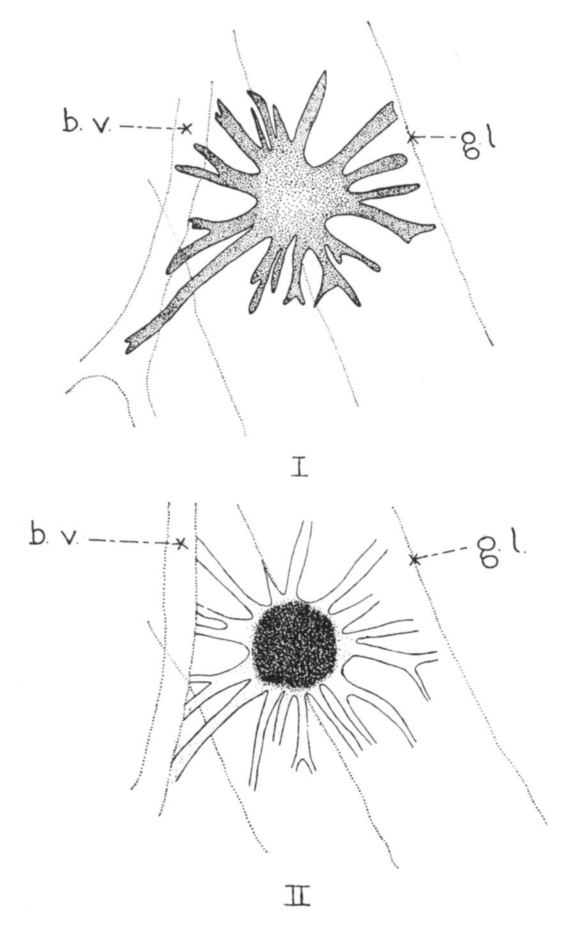

Figure 15–12. Pigment dispersion and concentration in a melanophore of the fish *Fundulus heteroclitus.* The expanded pigment appears to fill the cell processes. When the pigment concentrates (effect of adrenaline), the cell processes appear optically empty. *b.v.*, blood vessel; *g.l.*, growth line of the scale on which the chromatophore is situated. (From Matthews, S. A.: Observations on pigment migration within the fish melanophore. J. Exp. Zool. 58:471–486, 1931.)

pigmented, as in Negroes or sunburned Caucasians). The significance of this effect is discussed in the following section.

The Chemical Constitution of Vertebrate Color-Change Hormones (Chromatophorotropins). *Adrenaline* and *noradrenaline* are released by the adrenal gland. With few exceptions, these compounds cause concentration of melanophore pigment. The structural formula is shown in Figure 14–11. *Thyroxine*, produced by the thyroid, has been reported to activate melanophores of a number of vertebrates. However, its action may be indirect. This has been shown to be the case in tadpoles of *Xenopus*. Injection of thyroxine causes blanching, owing to melanin concentration. Thyroxine does not act directly on the melanophores but causes the release of melanophore-stimulating hormone (MSH). (*Note: Xenopus* melanophores are exceptional in that they concentrate their pigment in response to this pituitary hormone [Chang, 1957]). According to Wright and Lerner (1960), thyroxine antagonizes the darkening action of pituitary MSH in the frog (*Rana*); this must be a direct action on melanophores. Although it is doubtful that thyroxine is a significant factor in pigmentary control, it must be expected to contribute to the actions of other agents on chromatophores. The structure of thyroxine is given in Figure 14–11.

Most interesting is the chemistry of the pituitary hormones involved in chromatophore control. In the older literature, the name *intermedin* is employed to define an unknown agent present in extracts of the intermediary lobe of the pituitary that has pronounced effects on vertebrate melanophores, usually causing pigment dispersion. The agent has also been named melanophore- (or melanocyte-) stimulating hormone, or MSH. It occurs in pituitaries of all vertebrates that have an intermediary lobe—even if these animals have no chromatophores on which the hormone could act.

The chemical analyses of several investigators have now elucidated the structure of intermedin, or MSH. The results lead to the recognition that intermedin and MSH are not the same if obtained from different sources, and that they represent mixtures of two or three different compounds, even if extracted from the same animal. All these compounds are polypeptides. There are two main types: *α-MSH* and *β-MSH*. Alpha-MSH is a basic compound with an iso-electric point between 10.5 and 11.0. Beta-MSH is neutral or acidic and has an iso-electric point between 5.8 and 7.0. Their structure strikingly resembles ACTH (adrenocorticotropic hormone), which also has some chromatophore activity.

As shown in Figure 15–13, there are sequences of amino acids that are identical in all three types of compounds. The differences lie in the substitution of certain amino acids outside of these sequences. Alpha-MSH has identical structure wherever it is found (so far: pig, cow, horse, and monkey). It consists of 14 amino acids. Beta-MSH consists of at least 18 amino acids. The second can be glutamic acid (β-glutamyl-MSH; cow, pig, sheep) or serine (β-seryl-MSH; cow, pig, sheep) (Harris and Roos, 1956; Geschwind, Li, and Barnafi, 1956, 1957a, b; Geschwind and Li, 1957; Burgers, 1961). Human β-MSH consists

ACTH (the active part of the molecule)

. . . ser · tyr · ser · met · glu · his · phe · arg · try · gly · lys · pro · val.

α-MSH

ser · tyr · ser · met · glu · his · phe · arg · try · gly · lys · pro · val.

β-MSH

asp · $\frac{\text{glu}}{\text{ser}}$ · gly · pro · tyr · lys · met · glu · his · phe · arg · try · glu · ser · pro · lys · asp.

Figure 15–13. The common amino acid sequence in adrenocorticotropic hormone (ACTH) and α- and β-melanophore-stimulating hormones (α- and β-MSH) of mammals. *arg*, arginine; *asp*, aspartic acid; *glu*, glutamic acid; *gly*, glycine; *his*, histidine; *lys*, lysine; *met*, methionine; *phe*, phenylarginine; *pro*, proline; *ser*, serine; *try*, tryptophan; *tyr*, tyramine. (After various authors; see text for references.)

of 22 amino acids, of which the first four are an addition to the sequence of 18 amino acids as found in β-glutamyl-MSH (Harris, 1959).

Adrenocorticotropin (ACTH) likewise represents several related compounds. All have in common a sequence of amino acids that is also present in all the different MSH compounds.

The similarity of structure explains why ACTH can have an action similar to that of intermedin (the name is used here as a collective name to denote all types of MSH).

Whether a MSH is basic, neutral, or acidic depends on the substituted amino acids. If serine is replaced by glutamic acid, the iso-electric point changes to a lower value and the compound becomes acidic.

Since the behavior of a compound in electrophoresis depends on its charge (determined by the iso-electric point and the pH of the medium), similar compounds can have quite different mobilities. This means that electrophoresis is a good method to separate closely related compounds, but if compounds can be separated by electrophoresis, this does *not* mean that they are much different.

An important lesson applies to the current state of knowledge of crustacean color-change hormones.

1. If a polypeptide has an effect on chromatophores, this does not mean that its chief role is that of a pigment-regulating hormone—just as the chief function of ACTH is not the control of melanophores. All that can be concluded from such an observation is that the hormone contains an amino acid sequence that is identical (at least similar) to that of an actual chromatophorotropic hormone.

2. For this reason, it is likely that many more hormones have chromatophore activity than are actually engaged in chromatophore control. A key factor may well be concentration: polypeptides with an amino acid sequence that is active on chromatophores are less active if the sequence is surrounded by other amino acids than if the sequence exists alone. Chromatophores are convenient test objects for hormone assay, but their reactions do not provide a clue to the normal role of the hormonal substance tested—only to its structure. Again, ACTH is a good example: its action is not primarily that of a melanin-dispersing agent but—as is well known—that of increasing the production and release of hormones by the adrenal cortex.

DIURNAL AND OTHER RHYTHMS

Many animals capable of physiological color change show a diurnal variation in coloration. In part, this is the direct consequence of the changing pattern of illumination, but now many species are known in which such rhythmic color changes go on even in a constant environment, that is, in conditions of constant light or darkness and constant temperature. The melanophores of the isopod *Ligia* show such a typical 24 hour rhythm, concentrating their pigment at night and expanding it during the day (Kleinholz, 1937; Enami, 1941; Armitage, 1960). A similar 24 hour rhythm is characteristic of the fiddler crab, *Uca* (Abramowitz, 1937). Brown and Webb (1949) have shown that the pattern can be reversed if the animals are illuminated at night and kept in the dark during the daytime.

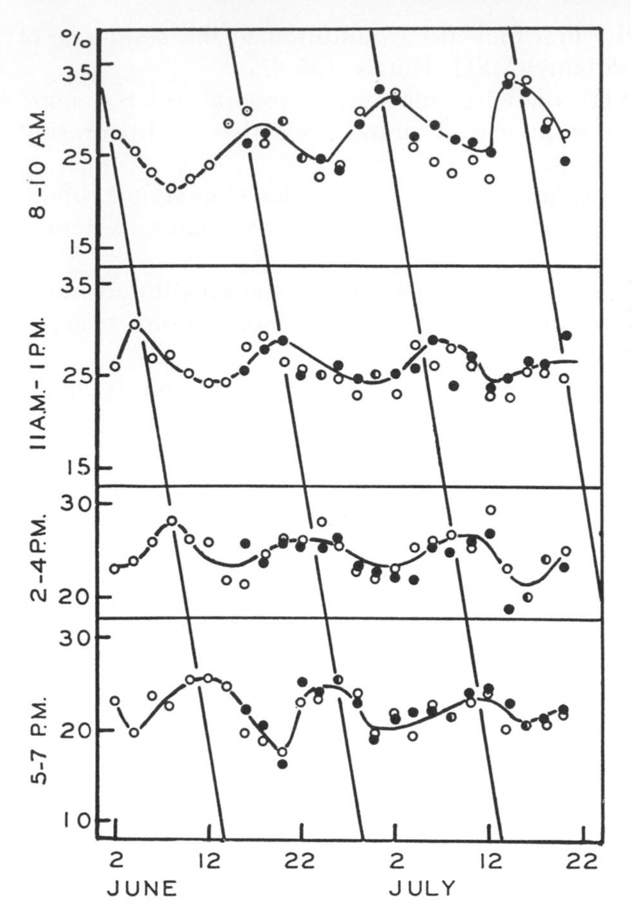

Figure 15–14. Periodic color change of the fiddler crab *Uca pugilator*. During the period of observation (June to July) the state of melanophores was observed four times during each day. The state of pigment expansion is given in terms of "percentage of daily melanin dispersion." Note the tidal maxima passing over the daily periods at a rate of about 50 min/day. A 14.8 day cycle is indicated by the interval between the diagonal lines. (From Fingerman, M.: Phase difference in the tidal rhythms of color change of two species of fiddler crab. Biol. Bull. *110*:274–290, 1956.)

In other crabs, likewise, a dark day phase and a pale night coloration occurs. This has been described for *Uca* and has been extensively studied by F. A. Brown, Jr., and his collaborators because it displays, superimposed upon the 24 hour rhythm, a semilunar rhythm that corresponds to the time of low tide during which additional pigment dispersion above that normally present occurs (see Fig. 15–14, from Fingerman, 1956). Such persistent rhythms are a challenge to the biologist and have in recent years been much discussed. For a discussion of the intricate problems involved, refer to the following publications: Bünning (1964), Cloudsley-Thompson (1961), and Sollberger (1965).

GENERAL PHYSIOLOGY OF CHROMATOPHORES

Whereas the preceding section was concerned chiefly with general descriptions of chromatophore structure and the relation between hormones and nerve action and pigment movements, this section considers the following questions: (1) What precisely does happen when a hormone or the action of a nerve fiber affects a chromatophore? (2) What is the mechanism of pigment movement?

Information concerning these questions is available only for chromatophores of arthropods, cephalopods and vertebrates. Few investigations have been carried out in this regard. The promising early investigations by Keeble and Gamble, Bauer, Degner, Franz, and Perkins and Snook were not continued. It seems that the discovery of a hormonal control of crustacean chromatophores completely diverted attention from chromatophore physiology proper. Only in recent years have there been a few important contributions: those of Hanson (1959) on crustacean chromatophores, of Novales (1959) and Novales and Novales (1961) concerning amphibian melanophores, and those of Kinosita (1953) on fish chromatophores.

Keeble and Gamble (1906) stated that the cytoplasm of chromatophores of *Hippolyte* (prawn) and *Crangon* (shrimp) is differentiated into a firmer, more refractive ectoplasmic wall, and a viscous endoplasm. Similarly, Degner (1912) found that the chromatophores of another prawn, *Praunus*, contain the pigment within more centrally located, membraneless compartments. Keeble and Gamble (1906), and later Perkins and Snook (1932) studying *Palaemonetes*, found that the external, firmer cell structures remained in place when the pigment moved toward the chromatophore center. Similar observations have been made by Matthews (1931) on fish chromatophores (*Fundulus*). Whereas the outline of the chromatophores in the animals studied by Keeble and Gamble and by Matthews remained unaltered, the walls of the tubular branches of chromatophores of *Palaemonetes* were seen to collapse when the pigmented protoplasm withdrew into the chromatophore center.

The older description has been confirmed by Falk and Rhodin (1957) who studied chromatophores of a teleost fish, *Lebistes*, with the electron microscope. They found that a membrane, no thicker than 80 Å (invisible in the light microscope), separated an outer, pigment-free zone from the inner cytoplasm that contains the nucleus, mitochondria, and pigment granules. A thick cell membrane (no less than 1200 Å) surrounds the whole chromatophore. The outer zone is traversed by fibrils which appear to be contractile and form a meshwork around the inner pigmented sac. The fibrils had been described by the earlier investigators (Franz, 1910; Degner, 1912), and in his monumental review in 1914, Fuchs expressed the opinion that they are contractile like myofibrils and responsible for pigment movement. This opinion was again expressed by Falk and Rhodin (1957).

If pigment concentration is brought about by contraction of the filaments, pigment dispersion must represent the resting condition. Pigment movement, according to this interpretation, would be entirely passive: it would be forced toward the chromatophore center when the fibrillar network around the pigment mass contracts, and it would expand into the processes when the network relaxes again.

Assuming this to be the correct interpretation, it would follow that pigment-concentrating hormones induce contraction of the fibrils, pigment-dispersing hormones (or nerve actions) would cause them to relax.

In chromatophores which show only limited branching, this may well be the case. However, many chromatophores are so widely branched that the explanation of pigment movement due to contraction of a fibrillar network surrounding each branch becomes unlikely. In many crustacean chromatophores, the pigment can be seen to clump and concentrate within the peripheral branches before it moves toward the center. Often, individual small pigment masses can be seen to move independently, some staying behind while others move toward the center. Later, the remaining pigment lumps can be seen to move rapidly toward the chromatophore center. This occurs then with considerable force. The pigment mass may be thicker than the tubular process through which it has to pass. The tube must be expanded, a process which, obviously, requires energy and a driving force. Perhaps there are cytoplasmic contractile filaments that are responsible for such movement of pigment masses. Welsh (1930) pictured fibrils in the distal pigment cells of crustacean eyes. He showed that they are shortened and contracted when the pigment has moved toward the base of the cells. He considered the possiblity that they act like muscle fibrils (see Fig. 15–8).

A mechanism of protoplasmatic streaming has been suggested as a possible mechanism of pigment transport (Franz, 1910; Degner, 1912). Matthews (1931) described the independent movement of pigment granules in fish chromatophores, where one granule may move toward the center while another, in the same cell process, moves in the opposite direction.

In the cephalopods, the pigment moves passively as the chromatophores are pulled into various shapes by the associated muscle fibers (see p. 347).

Kamada and Kinosita (1944) have experimented with chromatophores of four species of fish, using microneedles. Their experiments, shown in Figures 15–15 and 15–16, show that it is not the pressure of the central part—nor that of the periphery—that drives the pigment in one or the other direction. They compressed portions of chromatophore branches with the needle, induced pigment concentration—or pigment dispersion—and later released the pressure. Pigment movement on both sides of the pressure block proceeded almost undisturbed. This indicates that the movement of the pigment granules is not caused by a pressure difference between different parts of the chromatophore.

Later, Kinosita (1953) showed that the melanin granules in the chromatophores of the fish *Oryzias* are negatively charged and that their movement is determined by a difference in electric potential between the periphery and center of the chromatophore. Figure 15–16 shows the experimental set-up. It enabled Kinosita to not only measure the membrane potential across the cell membrane of different portions of the cell, but—because two intracellular electrodes were used—also to record differences of potential between two points inside the chromatophore. He found that in the normal condition, when the pigment was expanded, the center was more negative than the periphery, whereas when the pigment was concentrated in the center of the chromatophore, the center was more positive (less negative) than the periphery. The experimental set-up made it possible to apply electric current through the same

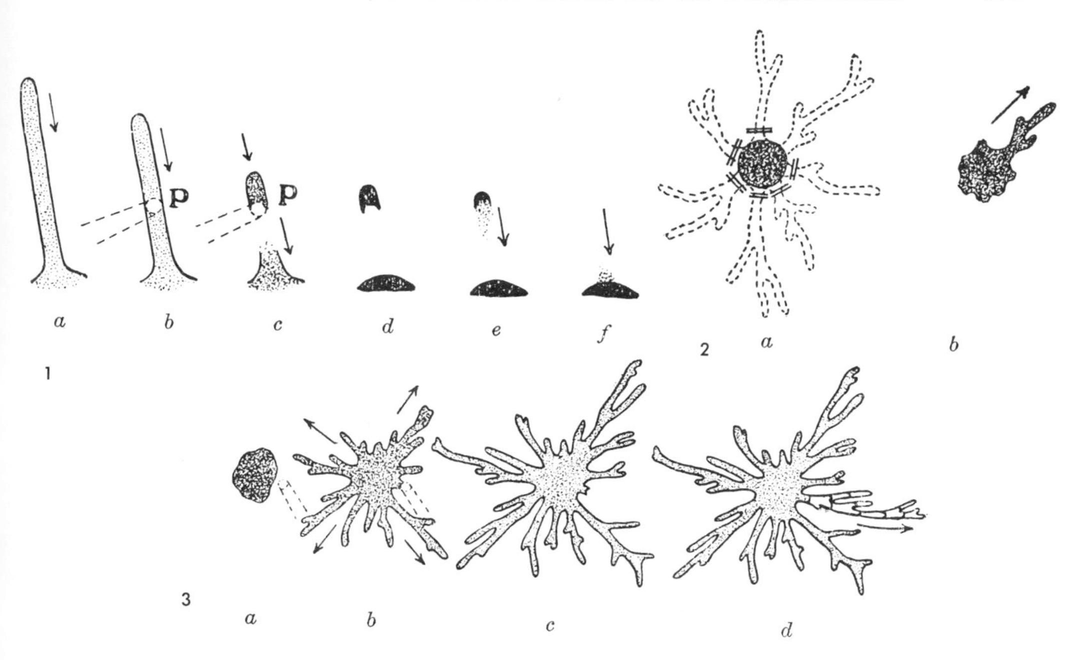

Figure 15–15. Some basic experiments performed on fish chromatophores (*Oryzias latipes*). Pigment concentration is brought about by an increase in the external K concentration; dispersion follows the return to normal saline medium (Ringer's solution). In all the diagrams only the outline of the pigmented protoplasm is shown, not that of the chromatophore and its processes as such.

1, If a branch is pressed at a point *P* with a microneedle so as to halt the migration of pigment granules during "contraction," the granules in the distal part accumulate near the needle tip while the granules in the proximal part migrate, as usual, toward the chromatophore center (centrosphere). If the needle is then removed, the distal granules start toward the centrosphere even after the others have stopped migrating.

2, When in the "contracted" state if all the branches except one are removed and the cut ends thereby sealed, the pigment migrates (after return to Ringer's solution) into the uncut branch, but more slowly than normal. It is therefore highly unlikely that pressure drives the pigment into the distal processes.

3, If one branch of a contracted melanophore is pressed with a microneedle, the centrifugal migration then induced is prevented by the needle. At the moment the needle is removed, the granules move to fill up the distal part of the branch even when the centrifugal migration has stopped in all the other branches.

(From Kamada, T., and H. Kinosita: Movement of granules in fish melanophores. Proc. Imp. Acad. Japan *20*:484–492, 1944.)

intracellular electrodes that were used to record potentials. In this way, the electric potential between two portions of the chromatophore was altered at will. Pigment granules could then be made to move always in the direction of the anode, that, away from the site of the more negative potential.

These results demonstrate the melanin granules in the chromatophore are negatively charged and move electrophoretically in an electric gradient.

Whereas the chromatophores just described are normally more negative at the center and have their pigment dispersed in the "resting" condition, the situation is different in the iridiophores (same animal). These show a normal state of pigment concentration. Miyoshi (1952) has shown that in the iridiophores, the chromatophore center is positive (less negative) compared to the

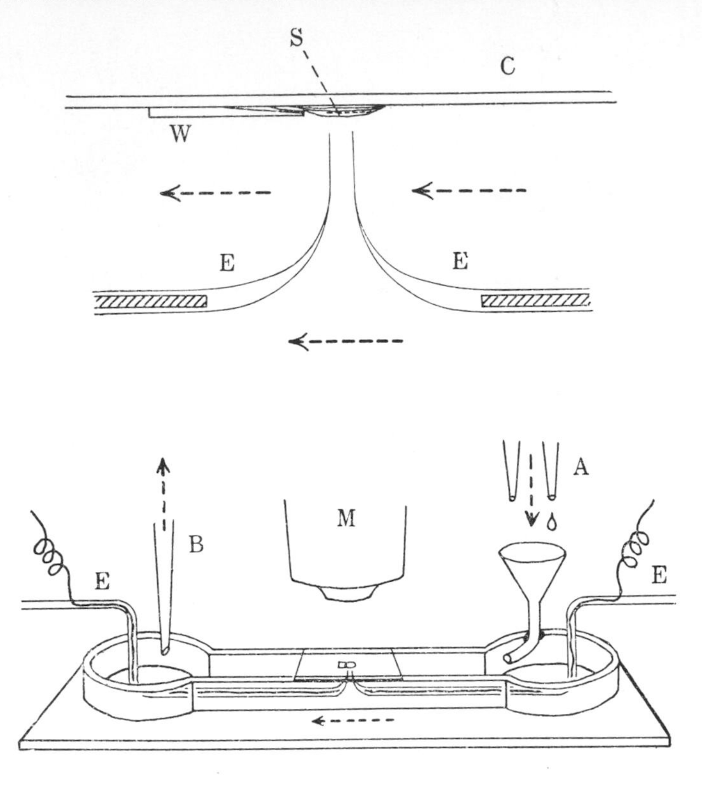

Figure 15–16. Experimental set-up used by Kinosita to induce and measure electric potential differences within chromatophores of the scales of a fish (*Oryzias latipes*). **Above**, lateral view of the scale and the capillary microelectrodes. **Below**, glass trough constructed for the determination of the electric potentials by the capillary microelectrodes inserted into the melanophore under the effect of various external solutions. *A*, inflow siphons connected with the solution reservoirs, furnished with stoppers and screw cocks; *B*, outflow pipet connected with suction pump; *C*, cover glass; *E*, quartz capillary microelectrodes connected with micromanipulators; *M*, microscopic lens; *S*, single piece of scale; *W*, wedge-shaped piece of cover glass to hold the scale in position; arrows in broken lines indicate the flowing directions of experimental solutions. (From Kinosita, H.: Studies on the mechanism of pigment migration within fish melanophores with special reference to their electric potentials. Annot. Zool. Jap. *26*:115–127, 1953.)

more distal parts. Like the melanin granules, the guanine particles are negatively charged.

Electrophoresis explains only the pigment movement, not the phenomenon of pigment aggregation in the chromatophore center. If the pigment granules are negatively charged, it is unlikely that they would fuse or coalesce into a common pigment mass, since equally charged particles tend to repel each other. Kinosita pointed out that in the condition of pigment concentration, the pigmented plasm is a gel, whereas pigment dispersion is accompanied by solation (liquefication) of the cytoplasm. This change in the physical condition of chromatophore cytoplasm has been observed repeatedly by many authors. It is possible that the pigment granules lose their charge when gelation occurs, and that this is the prerequisite for the clumping of pigment in the final phase of pigment concentration.

According to the theory expressed here, changes in pigment configuration of chromatophores involves two steps: (1) gel-sol transformation with charging and simultaneous dispersion of pigment granules and (2) movement of charged pigment granules in an electric field.

According to the theory, pigment dispersion is not necessarily accompanied by unidirectional movement of the charged pigment granules. Such movement would occur only in an electric field. If no field exists, the granules would simply separate (disperse) randomly.

Earlier investigators as well as recent students of chromatophore physiology have observed that pigment in chromatophore branches that had been severed from the main body of the chromatophore does respond to color-change hormones. The pigment, however, no longer moves in the direction of the chromatophore center. Hanson (1959) described the responses of branches of red chromatophores of *Pandalus* whose main central portion had been destroyed. When eyestalk extract was added, the pigment in each of the isolated branches became concentrated, and later dispersed again when the hormone was washed out. From these observations, it can be concluded that hormonal control affects the condition of the pigment-containing cytoplasm. If melanin granules were negatively charged in the dispersed state, they must be assumed to lose this charge before they finally clump together. Prior to coalescing, however, the pigment granules move away from the ramifications of the branches toward the thicker portion of each branch. If the granules remain dispersed in the normal, resting condition of the chromatophore and move under the influence of a hormone, the hormone must act by altering the internal potential of the chromatophore branches in such a way as to make the finer branches more negative than the thicker (more central) ones. Even on purely geometric ground, this is likely: the surface area, if compared with the volume, is larger the thinner the branch. Any agent that affects the chromatophore either on its surface membrane or after diffusion through it will thus have a more profound effect on the interior the larger (relative to volume) the surface area, or the thinner the chromatophore branch.

REFERENCES

Abramowitz, A. A. (1937) The comparative physiology of pigmentary responses in the Crustacea. J. Exp. Zool. *76*:407–422.

Armitage, K. B. (1960) Chromatophore behavior of the isopod *Ligia occidentalis* Dana, 1853. Crustaceana *1*:193–207.

Bagnara, J. T. (1960) Tail melanophores of *Xenopus* in normal development and regeneration. Biol. Bull. *118*:1–8.

Bauer, V. (1914) Zur Hypothese der physikalischen Wärmeregulierung durch Chromatophoren. Z. allg. Physiol. *16*:191–212.

Bauer, V., and E. Degner (1913) Ueber die allgemein-physiologische Grundlage des Farbenwechsels bei den decapoden Krebsen. Z. allg. Physiol. *15*:363–412.

Beauvallet, M., and C. Veil (1934) Chromatophores de poisson (*Carassius vulgaris*) et chromatophores de Crustacés (*Palaemon squilla*). C. R. Soc. Biol. *116*:688–690.

Bozler, E. (1928) Ueber die Tätigkeit der einzelnen glatten Muskelfaser bei der Kontraktion. II. Mitteilung: die Chromatophorenmuskeln der Cephalopoden. Z. vergl. Physiol. 7:379–406.

Bozler, E. (1931) Ueber die Tätigkeit der einzelnen glatten Muskelfaser bei der Kontraktion.

3. Mitteilung: Registrirung der Kontraktionen der Chromatophorenmuskelzellen von Cephalopoden. Z. vergl. Physiol. *13*:762–772.

Brown, F. A., Jr., and H. M. Webb (1949) Studies of the daily rhythmicity of the fiddler crab, *Uca*. Modifications by light. Physiol. Zool. *22*:136–148.

Bruecke, E. (1852) Untersuchungen über den Farbwechsel des afrikanischen Chamaeleons. Denkschr. Akad. Wiss. Wien *4*:179–210.

Bünning, E. (1964) The Physiological Clock. Academic Press, New York.

Burgers, A. C. J. (1961) Occurrence of three electrophoretic components with melanocyte-stimulating activity in extracts of single pituitary glands from ungulates. Endocrinology *68*:698–703.

Carlisle, D. B., and F. G. W. Knowles (1959) Endocrine Control in Crustaceans. Cambridge University Press, London.

Chang, C. Y. (1957) Thyroxin effect on melanophore contraction in *Xenopus laevis*. Science *126*:121.

Cloudsley-Thompson, J. L. (1961) Rhythmic Activity in Animal Physiology and Behaviour. Academic Press, New York.

Degner, E. (1912) Ueber Bau und Funktion der Krusterchromatophoren, eine histologisch-biologische Untersuchung. Z. wiss. Zool. *102*:1–78.

DuPont-Raabe, M. (1949a) Les chromatophores de la larve de Corethre. Arch. Zool. Exp. et Gen. *86*:22–29.

DuPont-Raabe, M. (1949b) Réactions humorales des chromatophores de la larve de Corethre. C. R. Acad. Sci. *228*:130–132.

DuPont-Raabe, M. (1951) Etude expérimentale de l'adaptation chromatique chez le phasme, *Carausius morosus*, Br. C. R. Acad. Sci. *232*:886–888.

DuPont-Raabe, M. (1952) Contribution a l'étude du rôle endocrine du cerveau et notamment de la pars intercerebralis chez les phasmides. Arch. Zool. Exp. et Gen. *89*:128–138.

DuPont-Raabe, M. (1956) Mise en évidence sur les phasmides d'une troisième paire de nervi corporis cardiaci, voie possible de cheminement de la substance chromative tritocérèbrale vers les corpora cardiaca. C. R. Acad. Sci. *243*:1240–1243.

Enami, M. (1941) Melanophore response in an isopod crustacean, *Ligia exotica*. I. General responses. Japan. J. Zool. *9*:497–514.

Enami, M. (1951) The sources and activities on two chromatophorotropic hormones in crabs of the genus *Sesarma*. I. Experimental analysis Biol. Bull. *100*:28–43.

Falk, S., and J. Rhodin (1957) Mechanism of pigment migration within teleost melanophores. *In* Electron Microscopy: Proceedings of the Stockholm Conference. (F. S. Sjöstrand and J. Rhodin, eds.) Academic Press, New York.

Fingerman, M. (1956) Phase difference in the tidal rhythms of color change of two species of fiddler crab. Biol. Bull. *110*:274–290.

Fingerman, M. (1959) The physiology of chromatophores. Int. Rev. Cytol. *8*:175–211.

Fingerman, M. (1963) The Control of Chromatophores. The Macmillan Co., New York.

Fingerman, M., R. Nagabhushanam, and L. Philpott (1960) The responses of the melanophores of eyestalkless specimens of *Sesarma reticulatum* to illumination and endocrines. Biol. Bull. *119*:315.

Fingerman, M., R. Nagabhushanam, and L. Philpott (1961) Physiology of the melanophores in the crab *Sesarma reticulatum*. Biol. Bull. *120*:337–347.

Florey, E. (1952) Untersuchungen über die Natur der Farbwechselhormone der Crustaceen. Biol. Zbl. *71*:499–511.

Franz, V. (1910) Zur Struktur der Chromatophoren bei Crustaceen. Biol. Zbl. *30*:424–430.

von Frisch, K. (1911) Beiträge zur Physiologie der Pigmentzellen in der Fischhaut. Pflügers Arch. ges. Physiol. *138*:319–387.

Fuchs, R. F. (1914) Der Farbenwechsel und die chromatischen Hautfunktionen der Tiere. *In* Handbuch der vergleichenden Physiologie, Bd. III, pp. 1189–1652. (H. Winterstein, ed.) G. Fischer Verlag, Jena.

Gegenbaur, C., A. Koelliker, and H. Mueller (1853) Bericht über einige im Herbste 1852 in Messina angestellte vergleichend-anatomische Untersuchungen. Z. wiss. Zool. *4*:299–369.

Gegenbaur, K. (1855) Untersuchungen ueber Pteropoden und Heteropoden. Leipzig.

von Gelei, S. (1942) Zur Frage der Doppelinnervation der Chromatophoren. Z. vergl. Physiol. *29*:532–540.

Gersch, M. (1956) Untersuchungen zur Frage der hormonalen Beeinflussung der Melanophoren bei der Corethra-larve. Z. vergl. Physiol. *39*:190–208.

Gersch, M., F. Fischer, H. Unger, and H. Koch (1960) Die Isolierung neurohormonaler Faktoren aus dem Nerven system der Küchenschabe *Periplaneta americana*. Z. Naturforsch. *15*B:319–322.

Geschwind, I. L., and C. H. Li (1957) The isolation and characterization of a melanocyte-stimulating hormone (beta-MSH) from hog pituitary glands. J. Amer. Chem. Soc. *79*:615–620.

Geschwind, I. L., C. H. Li, and L. Barnafi (1956) Isolation and structure of melanocyte-stimulating hormones from porcine pituitary glands. J. Amer. Chem. Soc. *78*:4494–4495.

Geschwind, I. L., C. H. Li, and L. Barnafi (1957a) The isolation and structure of a melanocyte-stimulating hormone from bovine pituitary glands. J. Amer. Chem. Soc. *79*:1003–1004.
Geschwind, I. L., C. H. Li, and L. Barnafi (1957b) The isolation, characterization and amino acid sequence of a melanocyte-stimulating hormone from bovine pituitary glands. J. Amer. Chem. Soc. *79*:6394–6401.
Geschwind, I. L., C. H. Li, and L. Barnafi (1957c) The structure of the beta-melanocyte-stimulating hormone. J. Amer. Chem. Soc. *79*:620–625.
Giersberg, H. (1928) Ueber den Zusammenhang zwischen morphologischem und physiologischem Farbwechsel der Stabheuschrecke *Dixippus (Carausius) morosus*. Z. vergl. Physiol. *7*:657–695.
Giersberg, H. (1931) Ueber den Zusammenhang von morphologischem und physiologischem Farbwechsel. Nach Untersuchungen an Insekten und Fischen. Arch. Zool. (Ital.) Napoli, *16*:363–370.
Hanson, D. (1959) Studies on the physiology of crustacean chromatophores. Thesis, University of Washington, 155 pp.
Harris, J. I. (1959) Structure of a melanocyte-stimulating hormone from the human pituitary gland. Nature *184*:167.
Harris, J. I., and P. Roos (1956) Amino-acid sequence of a melanocyte-stimulating peptide. Nature *178*:90.
Hartmann, O. (1887) Beitraege zur Histologie der Echinodermen. 3 Heft. G. Fischer Verlag, Jena.
von Hempelmann, F. (1939) Chromatophoren bei Nereis. Z. wiss. Zool. *152*:353–383.
Hofmann, F. B. (1907a) Gibt es in der Muskulatur der Mollusken periphere kontinuierlich leitende Nervennetze bei Abwesenheit von Ganglienzellen? I. Untersuchungen an Cephalopoden. Pflügers Arch. ges. Physiol. *118*:375–412.
Hofmann, F. B. (1907b) Histologische Untersuchungen ueber die Innervation der glatten und der ihr verwandten Muskulatur der Wirbeltiere und Mollusken. Arch. mikr. Anat. *70*:361–413.
Janda, V. (1936) Ueber den Farbwechsel transplantierter Hautstücke und künstlich verbundener Körperfragmente bei Dixippus morosus (Br. et Redt.) Zool. Anz. *115*:53–57. Find here a quotation of the previous publication (1934) in Mem. Soc. Boheme, Cl. Sci.
Janzen, R. (1932a) Der Farbwechsel von *Piscicola geometra L.* I. Beschreibung des Farbwechsels und seiner Elemente. Z. Morph. Okol. *24*:327–341.
Janzen, R. (1932b) Ueber das Vorkommen eines physiologischen Farbwechsels bei einigen einheimischen Hirudineen. Zool. Anz. *101*:35–40.
Kamada, T., and H. Kinosita (1944) Movement of granules in fish melanophores. Proc. Imp. Acad. Tokyo *20*:484–492.
Keeble, F. W., and F. W. Gamble (1906) The colour-physiology of higher Crustacea, Part II. Phil. Trans. Roy. Soc. B, *198*:1–15.
Kinosita, H. (1953) Studies on the mechanism of pigment migration within fish melanophores with special reference to their electric potentials. Annot. Zool. Jap. *26*:115–127.
Kleinholz, L. H. (1934) Eye-stalk hormone and the movement of distal retinal pigment in *Palaemonetes*. Proc. Nat. Acad. Sci. (U.S.A.) *20*:659–661.
Kleinholz, L. H. (1935) The melanophore-dispersing principle in the hypophysis of *Fundulus heteroclitus*. Biol. Bull. *69*:379–390.
Kleinholz, L. H. (1937) Studies in the pigmentary system of Crustacea. I. Color changes and diurnal rhythm in *Ligia bandiniana*. Biol. Bull. *72*:24–36.
Kleinholz, L. H. (1938a) Color changes in echinoderms. Pubbl. Staz. Zool. Napoli *17*:53–57.
Kleinholz, L. H. (1938b) Studies in reptilian color changes. III. Control of the light phase and behavior of isolated skin. J. Exp. Biol. *15*:492–499.
Knowles, F. G. W., and D. B. Carlisle (1956) Endocrine control in the Crustacea. Biol. Rev. *31*:396–473.
Knowles, F. G. W., D. B. Carlisle, and M. DuPont-Raabe (1955) Studies on pigment activating substances in animals. I. The separation by paper electrophoresis of chromactivating substances in arthropods. J. Mar. Biol. Assn. U.K. *34*:611–634.
Koller, G. (1925) Ueber den Farbwechsel bei *Crangon vulgaris*. Verh. dtsch. Zool. Ges. *30*:128–132.
Koller, G. (1927) Ueber Chromatophorensystem, Farbensinn und Farbwechsel bei *Crangon vulgaris*. Z. vergl. Physiol. *12*:632–667.
Koller, G. (1928) Versuche ueber die inkretorischen Vorgaenge beim Garneelenfarbwechsel. Z. vergl. Physiol. *8*:601–612.
Kopenec, A. (1949) Farbwechsel der Larve von *Corethra plumicornis*. Z. vergl. Physiol. *31*:490–505.
Kühn, A., and R. F. Heberdey (1929) Über die Anpassung von *Sepia officinalis* L. an Helligkeit und Farbton der Umgebung. Verh. dtsch. Zool. Ges. *4*:231–237.
Lebour, M. V. (1942) Stellate chromatophores in the Polychaeta. Nature *15*:209.
Lee, H. (1875) The octopus or the devil fish of fiction and of fact. Chapman & Hall, London.

Lerner, A. B., K. Shizume, and I. Bunding (1954) The mechanism of endocrine control of melanin pigmentation. J. Clin Endocr. *14*:1463–1490.

Matthews, S. A. (1931) Observations on pigment migration within the fish melanophore. J. Exp. Zool. *58*:471–486.

Mills, S. M. (1932) Double innervation of fish melanophores. J. Exp. Zool. *64*:231–244.

Miyoshi, S. (1952) Response of iridocytes in isolated scales of the Medaka (*Oryzias latipes*) to chlorides. Annot. Zool. Jap. *25*:21–29.

Novales, R. R. (1959) The effects of osmotic pressure and sodium concentration on the response of melanophores to epinephrine and intermedin. Physiol. Zool. *32*:15–28.

Novales, R. R., and B. J. Novales (1961) Sodium dependence of intermedin action on melanophores in tissue culture. Gen. Comp. Endocr. *1*:134–144.

Östlund, E. (1954) The distribution of catechol amines in lower animals and their effect on the heart. Acta Physiol. Scand. *31*, Suppl. 112:5–67.

Östlund, E., and R. Faenge (1956) On the nature of the eyestalk hormone which causes concentration of red pigment in shrimps (Natantia). Ann. Des. Sc. Nat., Zool. Ser. 11, *18*:325–334.

Parker, G. H. (1938) The color changes in lizards, particularly in *Phrynosoma*. J. Exp. Biol. *15*:48–73.

Parker, G. H. (1943) Animal color changes and their neurohumors. Quart. Rev. Biol. *18*:205–227.

Parker, G. H. (1948) Animal Color Changes and Their Neurohumors. Cambridge University Press, London.

Pautsch, F. (1948) The influence of vertebrate hormones on the melanophores of some Baltic Isopoda. Preliminary note. Bull. Inst. Mar. & Trop. Med., Med. Acad. Gdańsk, Poland, *1*:3.

Perkins, E. B. (1928) Color changes in crustaceans, especially in *Palaemonetes*. J. Exp. Zool. *50*:71–105.

Perkins, E. B., and T. Snook (1932) The movement of pigment within the chromatophores of *Palaemonetes*. J. Exp. Zool. *61*:115–128.

Pouchet, G. (1872) Sur les rapides changements de coloration provoques expérimentalement chez les crustacés et sur les colorations bleues des poissons. J. de l'Anat. et de la Physiol., Paris *8*:401–407.

Pouchet, G. (1873) Recherches anatomiques sur la coloration bleue des crustacés. J. Anat. (Paris) *9*:290–304.

Pouchet, G. (1876) Le changements de coloration sous l'influence des nerfs. J. Anat. (Paris) *12*:1–90; 113–165.

Sereni, E. (1929) Sui cromatofori dei cephalopodi. Z. Verg. Physiol. *8*:488–600.

Smith, R. I. (1942) Nervous control of chromatophores in the leech *Placobdella parasitica*. Physiol. Zool. *15*:410–417.

Sollberger, A. (1965) Biological Rhythm Research. Elsevier Publishing Co., New York.

Trojan, E. (1910) Ein Beitrag zur Histologie von *Phyllirhoe bucephala* Peron u. Lesueur mit besonderer Berücksichtigung des Leuchtvermögens des Tieres. Arch. mikr. Anat. *75*:473–518.

von Uexküll, J. (1896) Vergleichend-sinnesphysiologische Untersuchungen. II. Der Schatten als Reiz fuer *Centrostephanus longispinus*. Z. Biol. N. F. *34*:319–339.

Umrath, K. (1959) Ueber den Einflus des adrenaocorticotropen Hormons auf die Färbung und über die Auslösbarkeit des Hochzeitskleides bei einigen Fischen. Z. vergl. Physiol. *42*:181–191.

Umrath, K., and K. Walcher (1951) Farbwechselversuche an *Macropodus opercularis* und ein Vergleich der Geschwindigkeit der Farbänderung bei Macropoden und Elritzen. Z. vergl. Physiol. *33*:129–141.

Van der Lek, B., J. De Heer, A. C. J. Burgers, and C. J. Van Oordt (1958) The direct reaction of the tail-fin melanophores to light. Acta physiol. pharmacol. neerl. *7*:409–419.

Weber, R. (1923–1924) Di Chromatophoren von *Limax agrestis*. L. Eine morphologisch-physiologische Untersuchung. Zool. Jahrb., Allg. Zool. Physiol. Tiere *40*:241–292.

Welsh, J. H. (1930) The mechanics of migration of the distal pigment cells in the eyes of *Palaemonetes*. J. Exp. Zool. *56*:459–487.

Wilson, D. P. (1928) The larvae of *Polydora ciliata* Johnston and *Polydora hoplura* Claparede. J. Mar. Biol. Assn. U.K. *15*:567–603.

Wright, M. R., and A. B. Lerner (1960) Action of thyroxine analogues on frog melanocytes. Nature *185*:169.

16 BIOELECTRICITY

A knowledge of the electrical behavior of living systems is fundamental to the understanding of the functioning of nervous systems and muscles. Bioelectric phenomena are not restricted to nerve and muscle cells alone: electric charges play an important role in every aspect of an organism's life.

The concept of "animal electricity," which dates back to the days of the Italian physiologist Luigi Galvani (1737–1798), has been so influential that even today many a student of biology feels that bioelectricity is a mystic and unique phenomenon peculiar to nerves and muscles. It must, therefore, be emphasized that electricity is a fundamental property of all matter and that wherever ionized molecules appear there are electric charges and consequently electric potentials. The existence of electric tension and of electric currents is by far not as miraculous as situations in which no electric phenomena are observable.

The electric phenomena in living systems are associated, almost exclusively, with the electric charges carried by ionized molecules and ions. Practically all electric potential differences within organisms—and between organisms and their environment—are due to differences in the concentration of ions. All electric currents in living systems are ionic currents in which the charges that move are carried by ions.

Practically all kinds of molecules within a living organism are—to varying degrees—dissociated. These molecules are highly ordered and oriented, forming the internal and external structures of cells and organs. Whenever a molecule dissociates, an electric potential develops between its ions. Arrays of ionized molecules have an electric potential with respect not only to other ions in their vicinity but also to other arrays of ionized molecules. The mechanical, optically recognizable morphology of an organism therefore has an electric counterpart: an electric morphology which can be detected with electrostatic and electronic recording devices.

In an organism there are not only interacting electric fields, but also electric currents. Currents occur whenever ions move. These movements are determined by the electric fields and also by concentration gradients. Complex equilibria occur where osmotic and diffusional forces are balanced by electric forces acting in the opposite direction. Wherever diffusion of ions occurs, it is likely that electric potentials are generated and that electric currents flow. If oppositely charged ions move together, the net current is zero, but as soon as they move with different velocities, a potential difference results and current flows.

For purely technical reasons it is impossible to measure directly the electric potential differences between individual ions or even those between the organelles of a cell. Undoubtedly there are electric potentials, for instance, between the surface of mitochondria and the surrounding cytoplasm, but there is no recording system small enough to measure them. We can, however, imitate the situation in a model, making certain assumptions and increasing the scale.

At present electrophysiology permits only the experimental determination of electric potentials and currents between large organizational units, such as those between whole cells and their environment or between different portions of a tissue or organ system. There are many physicochemical theories based on experiments with large model systems of simple composition, so that we have a good theoretical understanding of the electric phenomena that must occur even at the molecular level of the living organism. Although electrophysiology is concerned almost exclusively with membrane potentials and the electric behavior of membranes, it is necessary, by way of introduction to the modern theories of membrane potentials and membrane behavior, to discuss first the physicochemistry of two important modes of generation of electric potentials: (1) the diffusion of ions (diffusion potentials) and (2) the distribution of ions in adjacent but different solvents (phase-boundary potentials).

DIFFUSION POTENTIALS

Assume a container that is divided into two compartments by a removable partition. Compartment I is filled with a concentrated solution of an electrolyte, compartment II with a dilute solution of the same electrolyte. The ions produced by the electrolyte can be symbolized as A^- (anion) and C^+ (cation).

When the partition is carefully removed so as to avoid mixing of the two solutions, the highly concentrated ions of compartment I tend to diffuse into compartment II where the concentration of ions is lower. A^- and C^+ are likely to have somewhat different diffusion velocities due to the differences in size and mass. Assuming that C^+ moves faster than A^-, it is easy to see that as the ions move into compartment II the two species of ions separate: the faster C^+ ions move ahead of the slower A^- ions. Such a separation of ions means a separation of electric charges. Owing to the advancing front of C^+ ions, compartment II has a positive potential, while the lagging A^- particles establish a negative potential in compartment I. The potential difference can be measured if appropriate electrodes are dipped into the two solutions and connected through a potentiometer (voltmeter) as shown in Figure 16–1.

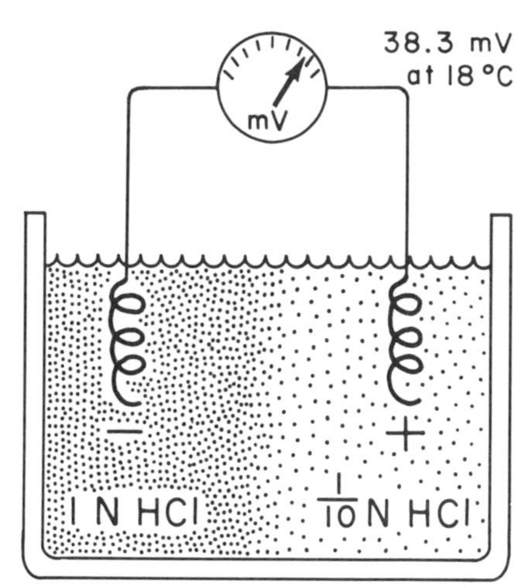

Figure 16–1. Conceptual diagram of diffusion potential. The hydrogen ions diffuse faster than the chloride ions so that there is an advancing front of positively charged ions (cations) followed by negatively charged ions (anions). The H^+ ions are actually retarded by the following Cl^- ions while the latter are accelerated by the advancing H^+ ions. The measured potential difference in the two parts of the compartment closely corresponds to that predicted by the equation (first formulated by Nernst) given in the text.

The electric potential difference that develops is called the *diffusion potential.* Its magnitude depends on the difference in diffusion velocity (mobility) of the two ions, the concentration differences between the two compartments, and the temperature. The greater the concentration difference, the *more* ions move; the higher the temperature, the *faster* both types of ions move and, therefore, the more pronounced is the separation of charges. The amount of increase per degree Kelvin is expressed by the constant R (the universal gas constant, p. 81).

Diffusion potentials are expressed in terms of volts or millivolts. The quantities of electric charges involved are given in coulombs (1 gram-ion carries approximately 96,500 coulombs, which is equal to 1 Faraday [F]). According to the Swedish physicist W. Nernst (1888, 1889), the diffusion potential can be calculated as follows:

Since the electric effects are caused by the diffusion, which in turn is caused by the difference in concentration, the electric work must be equal to the osmotic work (concentration work). The physicist expresses electric work by the formula $E \cdot zF$, where E is the electromotive force (or the potential), z is the valency of the ion, and F is the Faraday. The osmotic work (see p. 80) follows the equation

$$RT \cdot \ln \frac{C_1}{C_2} \qquad (1)$$

A complication arises from the fact that oppositely charged ions of an electrolyte usually have different diffusion velocities, so that the change in concentration differs for each of the two ions. The total osmotic work done by the diffusing electrolyte amounts to

$$\frac{u - v}{u + v} \cdot RT \ln \frac{C_1}{C_2} \qquad (2)$$

where u and v are the diffusion velocities under unit force of the cation and anion, respectively. Now, if

$$E \cdot zF = \frac{u - v}{u + v} \cdot RT \ln \frac{C_1}{C_2} \tag{3}$$

it follows that the diffusion potential E obeys the formula

$$E = \frac{u - v}{u + v} \cdot \frac{RT}{zF} \ln \frac{C_1}{C_2} \tag{4}$$

If the gas constant R is given in the dimension of electrostatic units (8.3 joules), the potential E has the dimension of volts.

If the natural logarithm is divided by 0.4343, the logarithm to the base of 10 (log) is obtained. A more convenient formula is thus obtained which reads:

$$E = \frac{u - v}{u + v} \cdot 0.0002 \cdot T \cdot \log \frac{C_1}{C_2} \text{ volts} \tag{5}$$

The relative mobilities (at 18° C) of several ions of physiological importance are given in Table 16–1.

The diffusion potential of a system in which compartment I contains 10 times more KCl than compartment II would, therefore, be equal to

$$\frac{64.7 - 65.4}{64.7 + 65.4} \cdot 0.0002 \cdot (273 + 18) \log 10 \text{ volts}$$

$$= \frac{0.7}{130.1} \cdot 0.0002 \cdot (291) \cdot 1 = 0.0054 \cdot 0.058 = 0.00031 \text{ volts} = 0.31 \text{ mV}$$

If compartment I contains 10 times more NaCl than compartment II, the resulting diffusion potential (at 18° C) is equal to

$$\frac{43.5 - 65.4}{43.5 + 65.4} \cdot 0.058 = 0.2 \cdot 0.058 = 0.0116 \text{ volts} = 11.6 \text{ mV}$$

PHASE-BOUNDARY POTENTIALS

Whereas diffusion potentials develop within a system of *miscible* solutions, electric potential differences can also develop at the boundary of two *immiscible* solutions. A diffusion potential is produced by an imbalance of ion concentrations within the same solvent system. It is abolished as soon as equilibrium

Table 16–1.

u		v	
H^+	318	OH^-	174
Na^+	43.5	Cl^-	65.4
K^+	64.7		

After Kohlrausch, F. W. G.: Praktische Physik Zum Gebrauch für Unterricht, Forschung und Technik, 2 vols. B. G. Teubner Verlagsgesellschaft, Stuttgart, 1956.

(equalization of concentrations throughout the system) is reached. A phase-boundary potential, on the other hand, may exist even when the two immiscible solutions (or phases) are in equilibrium. By equilibrium is meant the distribution of solute in the two solvents according to the *solubility coefficients* of the solute.

Assume that the solvent of compartment I is water, that of compartment II is an oil. Both contain a solute CA. Its solubility coefficients under the experimental conditions may be 3 (water) and 5 (oil). The two phases then are in equilibrium if the concentrations of solute are related 3:5. If CA is nonionized in either compartment, the potential difference between the two phases is zero. If CA ionizes, it must be assumed that C^+ as well as A^- have their own solubility coefficients and that, therefore, unequal amounts of C^+ and A^- tend to be dissolved in compartments I and II, respectively. This results in a separation of ions, and consequently in a separation of charges. The resulting potential difference opposes the tendency of each ionic species to distribute according to the respective solubility coefficients. An equilibrium condition results in which the potential difference balances the diffusion tendency of the ions. According to Beutner (1920), the phase-boundary potential can be calculated for each species of ion common to both phases: it is equal to

$$R \cdot T \cdot \ln \frac{C_1}{C_2} + K \tag{6}$$

where C_1 and C_2 are the molar concentrations of the ion and K is a constant, specific for the particular compound CA.

In contrast to the diffusion potential, which is the result of diffusion and ends as soon as all the ions are equally distributed, the phase-boundary potential is a steady potential which can be described as an equilibrium potential. Since at equilibrium no ions move, no current—and, therefore, no work—can be derived from the system.

Phase-boundary potentials are likely to exist wherever an aqueous medium borders on a nonaqueous one. In living systems such situations are frequent and must occur at most internal and external membranes of cells as well as at the borders of lipid inclusion bodies. In the absence of information concerning the solvent characteristics of membrane lipids and lipid inclusion bodies, the role and dimension of phase-boundary potentials are, at present, difficult to assess. It is of considerable interest, however, that a number of alkaloids and drugs that have known pharmacological actions, strongly affect phase-boundary potentials of certain artificial systems (for a summary of available information, see Beutner, 1944).

MEMBRANE POTENTIALS

As pointed out in the discussion of Donnan equilibrium (Chap. 4, pp. 84–87), a semipermeable membrane that separates two compartments can be the cause of a potential difference between the two if one compartment contains a nondiffusible or nonpermeating ion and if there are diffusible ions present in both compartments. At equilibrium conditions no work is done by the system, and the energy difference derived from the concentration gradient of each species of diffusible ion is equal to the energy difference represented by the separation of charges. The chemical composition of the membrane is of little concern in such a discussion which relies on the physical properties (diffusion barriers) of the membrane.

Now, the *concentration gradient energy difference* is identical with the osmotic work required to achieve an equal concentration difference. In the case of a diffusible cation C^+, this is, therefore, equal to $R \cdot T\,(\ln [C^+]_i - \ln [C^+]_o)$, if $[C^+]_i$ is the concentration of C^+ in the compartment that contains an indiffusible or nonpermeating anion. $[C^+]_o$ in this case is the concentration of C^+ in the other compartment. R is the gas constant, here represented by 8.3 joules, and T is the absolute temperature (see also Chap. 4, pp. 80–82).

For a diffusible anion A^- in the same system, the formula $RT\,(\ln [A^-]_o - \ln [A^-]_i$ applies. The reversal of the position of the subscripts o and i takes care of the need to express all potential differences in the same manner, that is, as either positive or negative voltage.

At equilibrium, this *concentration gradient energy difference* must be equal to the *electric potential energy difference*. The latter can be expressed as $z \cdot F \cdot E_{C^+}$ ($= z \cdot F \cdot E_{A^-}$), where E_{C^+} and E_{A^-} represent the potential difference due to C^+ and A^-, respectively, z is the valency of the ion, and F is the Faraday (equal to 96,500 coulombs).

Therefore, equilibrium exists if

$$R \cdot T \cdot (\ln [C^+]_i - \ln [C^+]_o) - E_{C^+} \cdot z \cdot F = 0 \tag{7}$$

or

$$R \cdot T \cdot \ln \frac{[C^+]_i}{[C^+]_o} - E_{C^+} \cdot z \cdot F = 0 \tag{8}$$

Since the values of z and F are known, the value of T can be determined readily. If, in addition, the molar concentrations of C^+ within the two compartments can be determined, it is possible to calculate (in volts) the membrane potential caused by the unequal distribution of C^+ in the two compartments by transforming equation 8 to read

$$E_{C^+} = \frac{R \cdot T}{z \cdot F} \cdot \ln \frac{[C^+]_i}{[C^+]_o} \tag{9}$$

Assuming that C^+ is a monovalent cation and that the temperature is 20° C (293° K), we find that

$$E_{C^+} = \frac{8.3 \cdot 293}{1 \cdot 96{,}500} \cdot \ln \frac{[C^+]_i}{[C^+]_o} = 0.025 \ln \frac{[C^+]_i}{[C^+]_o} \text{ volts} \tag{10}$$

Dividing the natural logarithm (ln) by 0.4343, we obtain the logarithm to the base of 10 ($\log_{10}$, or simply log). The equation now reads:

$$E_{C^+} = 0.058 \cdot \log \frac{[C^+]_i}{[C^+]_o} \text{ volts} = 58 \cdot \log \frac{[C^+]_i}{[C^+]_o} \text{ mV} \tag{11}$$

This equation has become the famous *Nernst equation.* It applies to each diffusible ion of the system, that is, to each ion that distributes according to a Donnan equilibrium. For this reason the potential difference, calculated for each diffusible ion species, is called the *equilibrium potential* of that particular ion. The membrane potential, as actually measured, is the sum of all the equilibrium potentials (see, however, p. 386).

The Resting Potential

When a voltmeter is connected with a suitable electrode inserted into a living cell and with another electrode placed into the aqueous medium that surrounds the cell, a steady difference of potential in the order of several tens of millivolts (mV) is indicated. Examples are listed in Table 16–2. This steady potential is usually called the resting potential of the cell. For a number of cell types, in particular certain nerve and muscle cells, the resting potential can be altered artificially by changing the concentration of certain ions (especially K^+ and Cl^-) in the external medium. From the available data concerning the intracellular concentrations of these ions, it has been calculated that the potential change follows approximately the logarithm of the ratio of the inside and outside concentrations of these two ions. An example of such measurements is given in Figure 16–2.

Furthermore, it has been shown for a number of cells that the ratio of the

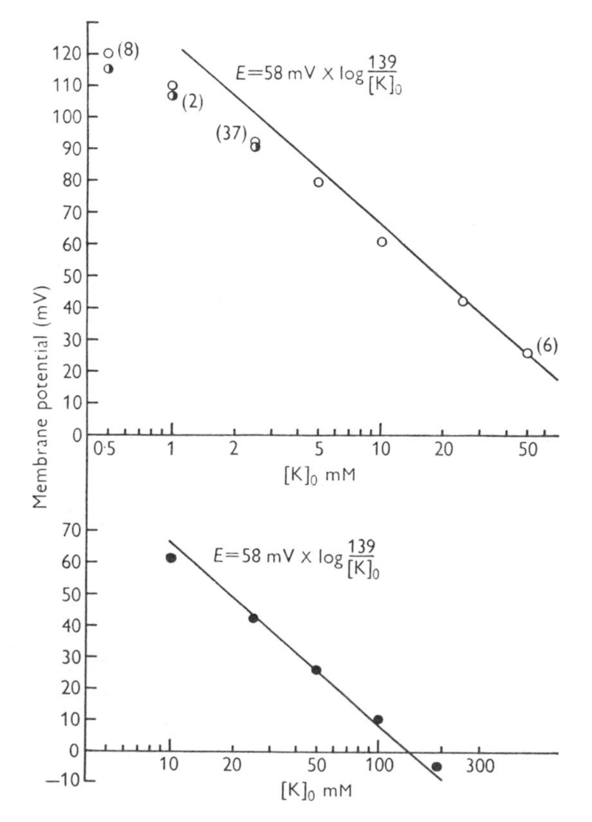

Figure 16–2. The effect of changes in the external K concentration on the membrane potential (resting potential) of fibers of the musculus sartorius of the amphibian *Rana temporaria* (frog). Abscissa: K concentration in mM/l (logarithmic scale). Ordinate: membrane potential in mV. ○, membrane potential in Cl solutions; ●, membrane potentials in SO_4 solutions; ◑, membrane potentials in Cl solutions with half the normal concentration of NaCl. Unless indicated otherwise (numbers in brackets), each point is the average of four muscles. The solid lines are drawn according to the Nernst equation. Note that there is a slight deviation from the calculated curve at the lower K concentrations. The internal K concentration is assumed to be constant at 139 mM/l. (From Adrian, R. H.: The effect of internal and external potassium concentration on the membrane potential of frog muscle. J. Physiol. *133*:631–658, 1956.)

Table 16–2. Resting Potentials of Nerve and Muscle Fibers

	mV
Striated muscle	
Cat, tenuissimus	55–70
Rana (frog) sartorius	80–90
Oxya (insect) wing muscle	50–70
Locusta (insect) wing muscle	47
Platypleura (insect) sound muscle	61
Periplaneta (insect) leg muscle	60
Smooth muscle	
Guinea pig, intestine	51
uterus	27–66
Man, uterus	21–31
Cat, uterus	29
Rabbit, uterus	32–52
Vertebrate heart muscle	
Cat, auricle	60
Dog, Purkinje fiber	94
Sheep, Purkinje fiber	98
Giant nerve fiber	
Loligo (squid)	61
Sepia (cuttlefish)	62
Periplaneta (insect)	70
Nerve fibers	
Homarus (lobster)	62,73
Carcinus (crab)	71–94
Rana (frog)	71
Cat, sympathetic neurons	50–80
motoneurons	60–80

Data from many publications, as compiled by Ridge, M. A. P., and R. J. Walker: Bioelectric Potentials. *In* Problems in Biology, Vol. 1 (G. A. Kerkut, ed.) Pergamon Press, Oxford, 1963; and Narahashi, T.: The properties of insect axons. Adv. Insect Physiol. *1*:175–256, 1963.

Cl^- concentrations is similar to the reciprocal of the ratio of the K^+ concentrations. Table 16–3 gives two examples.

It was found that changes in the external Na^+ concentration did not significantly affect the resting potential and that the ratio of external to internal Na^+ showed no relation to the existing resting potential.

From such findings it was concluded that the resting potential must be determined largely by the difference in the concentrations of K^+ and Cl^- of the extra- and intracellular media. (See the important papers of Boyle and Conway, 1941; Curtis and Cole, 1942; Hodgkin and Keynes, 1955; Adrian,

Table 16–3. **Ion Concentrations Inside and Outside a Nerve Fiber and a Muscle Fiber (Giant Axon of *Loligo*, Sartorius Fiber of *Rana*)**

	K_i	K_o	K_i/K_o	Na_i	Na_o	Na_i/Na_o	Cl_i	Cl_o	Cl_o/Cl_i
Nerve	410	22	19	49	440	0.11	40	560	14
Muscle	125	2.6	48	15	110	0.14	1.2	77	64

Data from Hodgkin, A. L.: The ionic basis of electrical activity in nerve and muscle. Biol. Rev. *26*:339–409, 1951.

1956.) Since it had been assumed that the cell membrane is impermeable to Na^+, earlier explanations employed the Donnan equilibrium: the presence in the cells of nonpermeating anions (proteins and other organic compounds) was held responsible for the fact that the intracellular concentration of K^+ is greater than that of Cl^-. The resting potential was thus considered a Donnan potential, for K^+ and Cl^-. The resting potential was thought to result from the peculiar permeability characteristics of the membrane. That the cells contained considerably more K^+ than the extracellular fluid was explained by Bernstein (1902; summarized in his famous book Elektrobiologie, 1911) as due to the inability of Na^+ to penetrate the membrane so that the K^+ ions to which the membrane is permeable must assume the job of neutralizing the negative charges of the nonpermeating internal anions, according to the Donnan hypothesis.

Although a satisfactory explanation and interpretation of many experimental results, the Bernstein hypothesis met with difficulties when it was discovered that animal cells actually are permeable to Na^+ ions, even though this permeability is low compared with that to other ions, such as K^+ or Cl^-. The discovery was made possible by the use of the then newly available radioisotopes (see the early summary of results by Hevesy, 1948). Most important was the finding that Na^+ ions left the cells at the same rate as they entered.

The permeability of cell membranes to Na^+ demanded a completely new theoretical treatment of the resting potential. That given by Hodgkin and Huxley (1952a–d) has found wide acceptance by physiologists. It was summarized by Hodgkin (1957),* and is discussed within an even wider theoretical framework by Woodbury (1965).

To understand the new theory, one must first realize that if the resting potential were due to the Donnan ratio of all diffusible ions, it should, according to the new findings, be caused by the concentration differences not only of K^+ and Cl^- but also of Na^+. However, as known from earlier studies, the resting potential is close to the equilibrium potentials of K^+ and Cl^- and far from the "equilibrium potential" of Na^+. The latter, in fact, would require the inside of the cell to be positively charged and the outside of the membrane to be negatively charged, which is exactly the opposite of the normal situation. Since

*This Croonian Lecture (Proc. Roy. Soc. B, *148*, 1957) should be read by every physiology student.

a resting potential exists which is quite different from the equilibrium potential of Na^+, it follows that the Na^+ distribution across the membrane is not an equilibrium distribution and the inward and outward movement of Na^+ ions does not represent an equilibrium. An equilibrium *would* exist if the *concentration gradient energy difference* for Na^+ were balanced by the *electric potential energy difference* (see p. 380), this is not the case.

The inward movement of Na^+ is purely passive and can be explained by the concentration gradient and by the direction of the electric potential. The outward movement of Na^+ against the concentration gradient and against the electric potential difference (against the resting potential) must be an active process requiring the expenditure of energy. Since Na^+ enters the cells continuously, the cell must do work continuously in order to expel Na^+ at the same rate. It appears that the energy expended is derived from oxidative metabolism, because so-called metabolic inhibitors, such as cyanide, dinitrophenol, or azide, cause the efflux of Na^+ to stop so that the cells accumulate sodium.

The work that must be done to expel enough Na^+ per unit time to maintain the concentration difference must be equal to the sum of the concentration gradient energy difference and the electric potential energy difference per mole multiplied by the number of moles of Na^+ transported per unit time (second), or

$$\dot{W} = \left(E_r \cdot z \cdot F + R \cdot T \cdot \ln \frac{[Na^+]_i}{[Na^+]_o}\right) M_{Na^+} \tag{12}$$

where $\dot{W}$ has the dimension of energy per second and mole of Na^+. E_r is the resting potential, z is the valency of the Na^+ ion, F equals 96,500 coulombs/mole of charge, R is the universal gas constant, T is the absolute temperature in degrees Kelvin, $[Na^+]_i$ and $[Na^+]_o$ are the inside and outside concentrations of Na^+, respectively, and M_{Na^+} is the number of moles of Na^+ transported per second. W may be expressed in watts (joules/second) per mole of Na^+ transported, but this can also be transformed into calories, since 1 joule = 0.239 cal (1 cal = $4.186 \cdot 10^7$ ergs = 4.186 joules = 0.427 kilogram-meter).

Of course, as soon as it must be assumed that the Na^+ distribution across the cell membrane is *not* an equilibrium distribution, but one that is maintained by an active transport system, it becomes clear that the Nernst equation (11) does not apply to Na^+ at all. This equation is valid only when the concentration gradient energy difference is equal to (and acting in the opposite direction from) the electric potential energy difference.

Much energy is required to transport Na^+ out of the cell against the resting potential and against the concentration gradient. According to measurements by Keynes and Maisel (1954) on frog muscle, this amounts to up to 15 per cent of the total energy yield of the oxidative metabolism of the cells. Since metabolically driven "engines," like all engines, have an efficiency considerably below 100 per cent, a considerable fraction of the total energy expenditure of muscle cells would have to be utilized for Na^+ extrusion. If muscle cells are as efficient in this as they are in the utilization of metabolic energy for mechanical work (for which they are designed), about 75 per cent of the energy derived from oxidative metabolism of resting muscle would have to be used for Na^+ transport. A good deal of evidence supports the view, however, that Na^+ transport may be coupled with an inward transport of K^+ (this is known as *exchange diffusion*). If this occurs, the energy expenditure is reduced by one half.

The preceding sections have dealt with the membrane potential as recognized in many nerve and muscle cells. Experimental evidence for this has been obtained from numerous investigations on such cells taken from diverse species of several phyla, notably the vertebrates, molluscs, and crustaceans.

Microelectrodes small enough to be inserted into animal cells were first made and employed by Peterfi (1925) in Prague, Czechoslovakia, to measure resting potentials in *Amoeba*. However, the potentials he measured were much too low and variable. His technique was improved and publicized by Gicklhorn, also from the German University in Prague. Figure 16–3 is taken from one of his publications. Umrath brought the technique of pulling glass microelectrodes by hand to Graz, Austria, where he employed it for his studies on membrane potentials of large plant cells (*Nitella, Chara*) in the early 1930's. After a visit with Umrath, Gerard brought the technique to the United States and with Graham and Ling improved it further to make it suitable for membrane potential measurements of the much smaller cells of animals. The main innovation was not so much in the thinness of the electrode tips (the new ones had

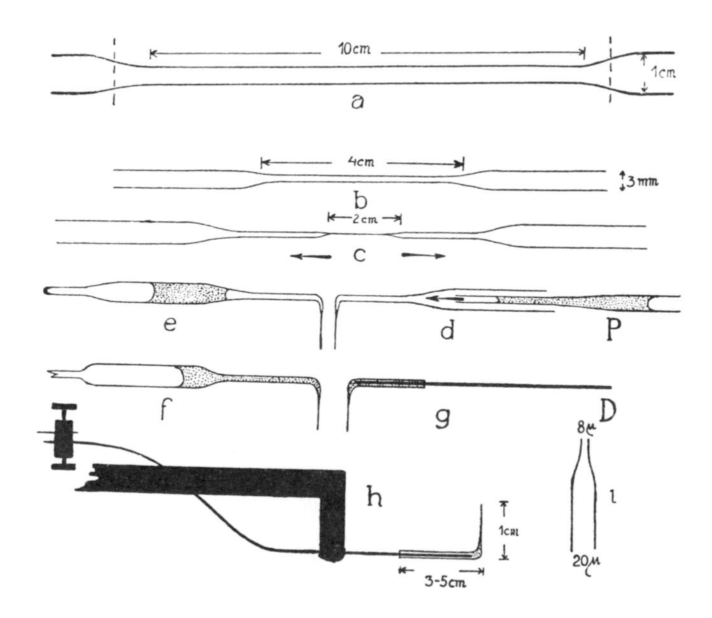

Figure 16–3. Diagrams showing the steps involved in pulling microelectrodes by hand and filling them. The figure was published in 1929. At that time the finest electrode tips were still several microns wide. The modern electric microelectrode pullers achieve tip diameters of a fraction of a micron (invisible to the light microscope, even at the highest possible magnification). The electrodes shown here were filled with a solution of 1/10 M KCl and 2 per cent agar in water. The modern electrodes used for intracellular recording are usually filled with 3 M KCl. The technique of filling, shown in diagrams *d* to *f*, also works with the modern, much finer electrodes. (From Gicklhorn, J.: Die Herstellung von Mikroelektroden zur Potentialmessung. Kolloidchem. Beihefte 28: issues 7–10, 1929.)

diameters down to one tenth of those employed by Umrath), but in the electronic circuits that permitted recording through electrodes of extremely high impedance (several megohms). The decisive publications of Graham and Gerard, and Ling and Gerard, appeared in 1946 and 1949, respectively. Since then, the technique of using electrolyte-filled glass microelectrodes has revolutionized electrophysiology.

Membrane potentials of animal origin were first measured directly just before World War II—in 1939 by Hodgkin and Huxley and in 1940 by Curtis and Cole, using somewhat larger metal (AgAgCl) and glass capillary electrodes which were inserted into the now famous giant axons of squid (*Sepia, Loligo*). In larger squid, these axons may have diameters up to 1 mm (or even more).

The refined technique introduced after World War II made it possible to measure membrane potentials of a large variety of cells, in particular muscle and nerve cells, and to compare these with the results of chemical analyses of the ion content of these cells. It soon became evident that membrane potentials are usually slightly lower than would be predicted from the Nernst equation applied to K^+ and Cl^- ions. This means that the normal membrane potential of these cells does not completely correspond to the equilibrium potential of these ions and that a more complicated situation exists that requires a more complex mathematical formulation than that provided by the Nernst equation.

As pointed out, the membrane potential is always found to be far from the equilibrium potential for Na^+ that could be described by the equation:

$$E_{Na^+} = \frac{RT}{zF} \cdot \ln \frac{[Na^+]_i}{[Na^+]_o} \tag{13}$$

Also, the distribution of Na^+ across the membrane is not an equilibrium distribution but the result of active outward transport of as many Na^+ ions as enter the cell per unit time. Now, if the membrane is permeable to Na^+ ions, as has been shown to be the case, it follows that Na^+ ions must influence the membrane potential.

The quantitative treatment of this is given by a modification of Goldman's constant field equation (1943), as developed by Hodgkin and Katz (1949):

$$E_M = \frac{RT}{zF} \ln \frac{P_K[K^+]_i + P_{Na}[Na^+]_i + P_{Cl}[Cl^-]_o}{P_K[K^+]_o + P_{Na}[Na^+]_o + P_{Cl}[Cl^-]_i} \tag{14}$$

in which the membrane potential (E_M) is considered equal to the sum of the ratios of K^+, Cl^-, and Na^+ concentrations inside and outside the cell, but each ratio is multiplied by the relative permeability of the membrane to the particular ion. The relative permeability, P, is related to the permeability constant inasmuch as it expresses the ratio of the respective permeability constants, taking that of K^+ as the standard (numerical value therefore 1.0). For vertebrate muscle (striated amphibian muscle), the permeability of the muscle fiber membrane to Na^+ is 1/100 that to K^+; thus the relative permeability of the membrane to Na^+ is 0.01 (Hodgkin, 1957).

Other data for the relative permeabilities of frog muscle fiber membranes to K^+, Na^+, and Cl^- were given by Jenerick (1953) and by Harris and Martins-Ferreira (1955) as 1 : 0.027 : 0.23 and 1 : 0.015 : 0.17, respectively.

There are other cells in which the interior contains considerable amounts of Na^+ and small amounts of K^+. These are certain blood cells and glia cells. Unfortunately, no data are available concerning the membrane potentials of these cells. Only with a knowledge of the membrane potentials would it be possible to estimate the activities of the Na^+ pumps of each system. At present we do not know to what extent the outward movement of Na^+ in these cells is due to "active" pumping.

The resting potential of muscle and nerve cells is usually of considerable magnitude; values up to 90 mV are common. A flashlight battery produces 1.5 V, an electromotive force only about 17 times larger than that produced by living cells. The comparison with the dimensions of everyday life gives even more striking results if we consider that the distance of the two "poles" of the living battery (the internal and external media) are separated by an extremely thin membrane, probably 60 to 100 Å. The calculated voltage gradient across this membrane amounts to no less than 100,000 volts/cm. This leads one to believe that the molecules and ions in the membrane are exposed to extremely strong electric forces. The behavior of such electrically stressed membranes may differ considerably from that of "ordinary" membranes.

THE ELECTRIC PROPERTIES OF CELL MEMBRANES

In the discussion of the resting potential it became evident that the cell membrane is electrically polarized and that this polarization is maintained constant in spite of the fact that ions (electric charges) move continuously from one side to the other. It is indeed possible to consider the membrane as a condenser, charged on each side with ions of opposite sign. According to widely accepted views, the "plates" (the inner and outer surfaces of the membrane) of the condenser are charged by the diffusible ions which penetrate the membrane, following the concentration gradients.

The capacitance of the membrane depends on thickness, surface area, and the dielectric constant of the material of which the membrane is composed. Considering how thin they are, the cell membranes have amazingly high capacitance. It is about a million times higher than that of industrial cables. On the other hand, the resistance of the cell membrane is usually not so very great; the values range from 1000 to 12,000 ohms for 1 cm^2.

In its electric behavior the cell membrane resembles a condenser with a resistor in parallel, as shown in Figure 16–4. The resistor permits a continuous charging, but also discharging, of the condenser. In actual fact, however, the membrane charges remain unchanged during the resting condition of the cell. This means that there are processes going on which keep the membrane charged in spite of a continuous drain of charges across the membrane resistance (the resistor in Figure 16–4). In a circuit diagram, such a charging device is represented by the symbol for a battery. The equivalent circuit diagram for a cell membrane can therefore be presented as in Figure 16–5.

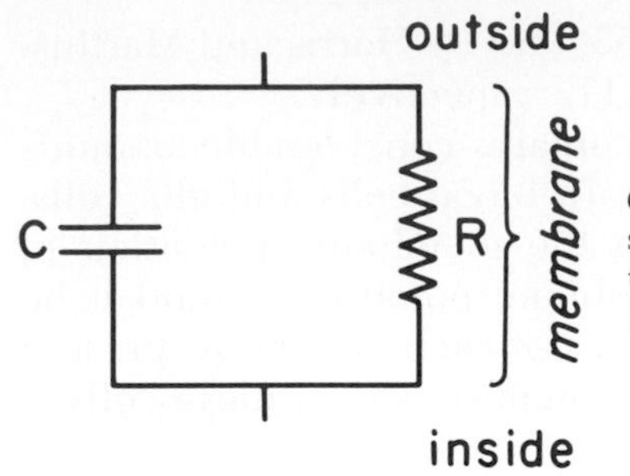

Figure 16–4. Equivalent circuit of a cell membrane. *C*, condenser, representing membrane capacitance; *R*, resistor, representing membrane resistance. C is usually of the order of several microfarads/cm^2; R is of the order of 1000 ohm – cm^2 (see Table 16–4).

The resistor in the membrane circuit represents membrane resistance. Since electric currents flow through the membrane in the form of ions, the resistance of the membrane is nothing else but an expression of its ion permeability. The permeability of the membrane to ions is usually referred to as *conductance.* A high membrane resistance means low ion conductance, a low resistance, a high conductance. Thus, membrane resistance is the reciprocal of the conductance of the membrane. If resistance is given in ohms, conductance is given in 1/ohms, or mhos (ohm spelled backward).

As discussed (p. 383), the cell membrane is not equally permeable to all ions. In particular, the permeability to Na^+ is much lower than that to K^+ or Cl^-. The membrane resistance must therefore be the product of the combined resistances to the passage of K^+, Cl^-, and Na^+.

The battery in the equivalent circuit, as shown in Figure 16–5, is likewise composed of several elements. We may assume a separate battery for each species of ion, each battery representing the unequal numbers of ions of one species on the two sides of the membrane. Thus we have a K^+ battery (with the positive pole outside, the negative pole inside the cell), a Cl^- battery (positive outside, negative inside), and a Na^+ battery (positive inside, negative outside). The electromotive force of each battery is determined by the difference in number of the ions of any species on the two sides of the membrane. Thus the voltage of each battery is identical with the equilibrium potential referred to on p. 381).

The K^+ battery is being charged, indirectly, by the "sodium pump"

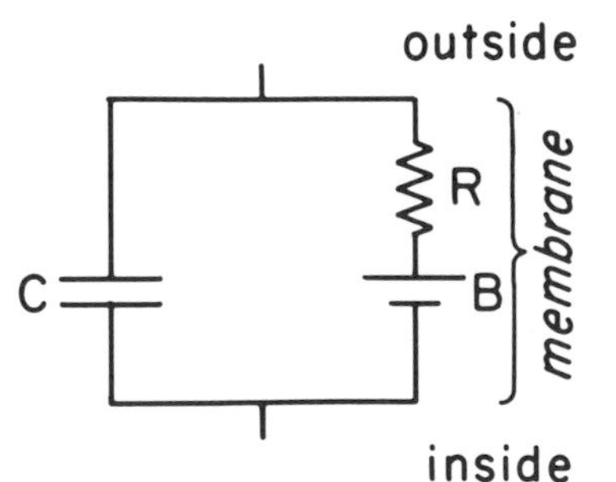

Figure 16–5. Equivalent circuit of a cell membrane incorporating a battery, *B*. Other symbols as in Figure 16–4. B is of the order of 0.1 volt.

inasmuch as this pump prevents accumulation of Na^+ inside the cell so that the K^+ ions to which the membrane is relatively permeable (and which may be "pumped" into the cell by an active transport mechanism), become the chief cation in the cell—in contrast to the extracellular medium in which the chief cation is Na^+.

The Cl^- battery is being kept charged by the Cl^- ions that are distributing according to a Donnan equilibrium. The Na^+ battery is being charged by the Na^+ pump. The sodium conductance of the resting membrane is so low, however, that Na^+ ions contribute comparatively little to the charging of the membrane condenser. For this reason, the overall membrane potential is much closer to the equilibrium potentials for K^+ and Cl^- than to the Na^+ equilibrium potential. The appropriate mathematical formulation is given on p. 386.

The condenser in the equivalent circuit (Fig. 16–5) is usually not thought of as representing several condensers, since it represents the capacitance of the membrane. This is simply determined by the surface area and the dielectric properties of the membrane. Its value is always the same, regardless of the kinds of ions that charge the membrane. A more useful diagram of an equivalent circuit of a cell membrane is shown in Figure 16–6.

Electric constants for a number of cells are given in Table 16–4.

Do not confuse the distribution of charges on both sides of the membrane with the distribution of ions in the two compartments separated by the membrane. Figure 16–7 emphasizes the difference.

PASSIVE AND ACTIVE CHANGES OF THE MEMBRANE POTENTIAL OF LIVING CELLS

As shown in preceding discussions, the membrane potential of living cells is the result of interactions between the intra- and extracellular media. Many types of cells are known to maintain a resting membrane potential for extensive periods of time, provided the environmental conditions remain unchanged and

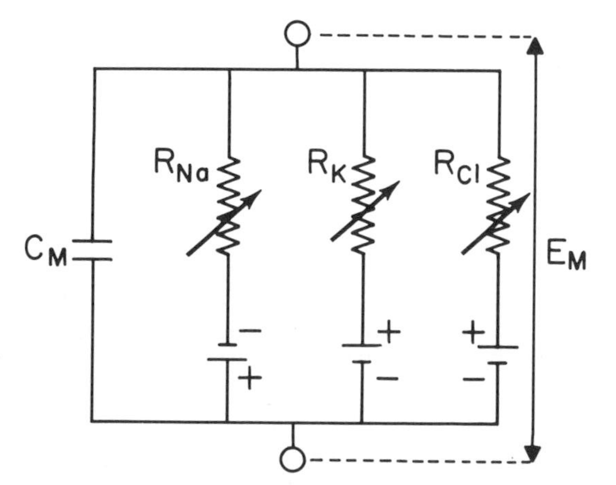

Figure 16–6. Equivalent circuit of a cell membrane according to Hodgkin. C_M, membrane capacitance; E_M, membrane potential. R_{Na}, R_K, and R_{Cl} represent the reciprocal of the membrane permeability to Na, K, and Cl ions. The three batteries correspond to the equilibrium potentials of Na, K, and Cl. (After Hodgkin, A. L.: Ionic movements and electrical activity in giant nerve fibres. Proc. Roy. Soc. London B, *148*:1–37, 1957.)

Table 16–4. Electric Constants of Nerve Fibers, Cell Bodies, and Muscle Fibers

Nerve or Muscle	*Diameter or Area*	*Membrane Capacity* μF/cm²	*Membrane Resistance* ohm cm²	*Space Constant* mm	*Time Constant* msec
Sepia giant axon	200 μ	1.2	9200	2–5	6.2
Loligo giant axon	500 μ	1.1	1500 (rest) 25 (active)	2.5	0.7–1.6
Carcinus leg nerve		1.1	3000–7000	2.0	6.2
Carcinus leg nerve fibers		0.72–1.75	2940–3700	1.6–1.8	2.1–5.5
Homarus leg nerve	75 μ	1.3	2290	1.6	2.3
Frog A fibers	node	3–7	8–20		0.06
	internode	0.005	100,000		
Aplysia ganglion cells	600 μ	23	2200		50
Puffer supramedullary cells	250 μ		500–1000	4–6	
Puffer supramedullary cells		5–15	400–1000		
Toad motoneuron	6×10^{-5} cm²	17.5	270		4.3
Cat motoneurons	5×10^{-4} cm²	6	400–600		2.5
Mytilus retractor		3.3	61,400	2.4	92.0
Crustacean muscle		20	1000		
Portunus muscle		40	100		
Frog sartorius		5–8	1180–2080	0.55–0.8	10.3
Frog adductor magnus	75 μ	5	1500	0.65	9
Frog extensor digitorum	45 μ	5	4300	1.1	18.5
Cat muscle		2–5	1200–1600		

Data compiled from numerous publications, from Prosser, C. L., and F. A. Brown, Jr.: Comparative Animal Physiology, 2nd Ed. W. B. Saunders Co., Philadelphia, 1962.

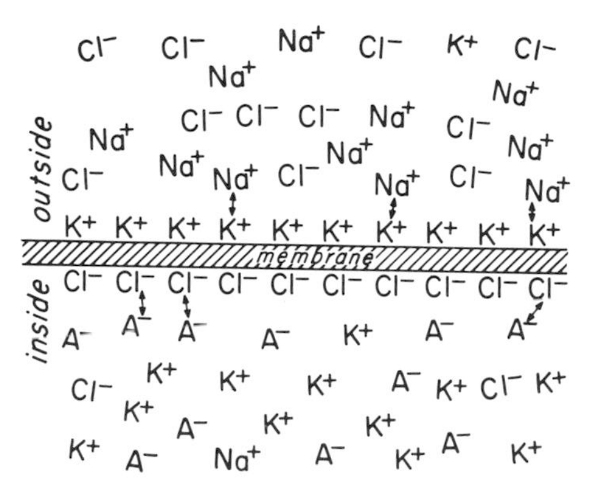

Figure 16–7. Conceptual diagram of the electric charges held to the cell membrane by the membrane potential. *Note*: this electrical double layer is not the cause of the potential difference but the result of it. The cause of the large potential difference is the Na pump, which favors selective accumulation of K ions inside the cell by excluding Na. The maintenance of the large K concentration gradient is due to the nonpermeating organic anions: the electric energy difference is balanced by the concentration energy difference; thus the concentration difference is a measure of the electric potential that exists across the cell membrane. K ions can be expected to exchange secondarily with other cations in the external medium; the electrically "adsorbed" Cl ions will exchange with other (organic) anions (A^-).

are normal. Any change in the ionic composition, in particular of the K^+ and Cl^- content of the external medium, however, causes an immediate alteration of the membrane potential. So does any change in temperature. The Nernst equation (see p. 380) which describes the membrane potential shows this clearly.

There are other environmental changes that likewise cause an alteration of a cell's membrane potential. Mechanical deformation, stretching, or compressing of the membrane itself alters its properties sufficiently to cause a potential change. Stretching of the membrane usually leads to depolarization. Addition of various chemicals results in membrane potential changes, in particular if they react chemically with the membrane or alter the pH of the external or internal medium of the cell. From the standpoint of the experimenting biophysicist, the most important method of altering membrane potentials is by changing the electric field that surrounds the cell. This is usually achieved by the controlled application of electric current by means of electrodes.

Stimulus and Stimulation

Any change in the immediate environment of a cell that causes a change of the membrane potential is called a *stimulus* (plural: *stimuli*). In order to be effective there must be a minimal rate of change, a minimal extent or amplitude of change, and a minimal duration of change. Therefore, *a stimulus must be defined by all three parameters: rate, amplitude, and duration.*

The act of applying a stimulus or a series of stimuli is called *stimulation.*

In many types of physiological experiments, particularly when they are concerned with the function and interaction of nerve and muscle cells, stimulation is achieved by application of brief electric pulses. Conveniently these are produced in the form of "square pulses" with a rate of change so great that the change is effected within a few microseconds. The electric properties of the immediate environment of the cell area to be stimulated are thus changed

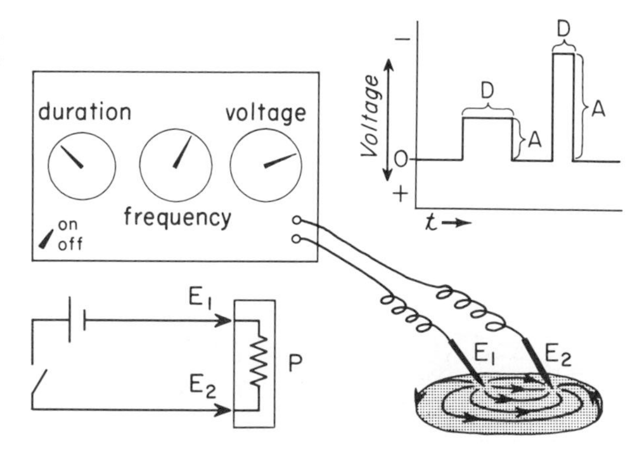

Figure 16–8. Diagram of an electronic stimulator used to electrically stimulate tissues by passing a current through the tissue. Most stimulators allow the experimenter to vary duration (D), frequency, and voltage (amplitude, A) of the stimulating pulses. The configuration of such pulses is shown in the upper right diagram. An elementary equivalent circuit of the stimulator including the two electrodes (E_1 and E_2) and the physiological preparation (P) is shown in the lower left. The current flow through the tissues of the preparation (indicated in stipple) is shown by arrows.

almost instantly and the rate of change does not need to be considered. Still, even in this ideal situation where square pulses can be used as stimuli, it is absolutely necessary to define the stimulus in terms of magnitude (voltage) and duration (usually given in milliseconds).

Electric pulses are usually applied with the aid of electrodes which are connected with a pulse generator, called a *square pulse generator* or *stimulator*. If the instrument is good, no electric current flows in between pulses. Each pulse, however, represents a certain current which flows out one electrode and returns through the other. The stimulator always has two electrodes connected with it and stimulation always requires two electrodes even though, as we shall see, only one of them elicits the action potential. The electromotive force, or voltage, of the pulse is determined by the stimulator, and so is its duration. The *amount* of current that flows between the electrodes, however, is determined by the resistance of the medium between the electrodes, as shown in Figure 16–8.

To be sure the student understands the relation between current, potential, resistance, and conductivity, Ohm's law shall be recapitulated here:

$$\text{current} = \frac{\text{potential difference}}{\text{resistance}}$$

$$\text{current} = \frac{1}{\text{resistance}} \times \text{potential difference}$$

$$\text{current} = \text{conductance} \times \text{potential difference}$$

Electrotonus

If both electrodes are attached to a nerve fiber or muscle fiber, one reduces and the other raises the membrane potential during an electric pulse delivered by a stimulator. The cathode (negative electrode) acts as the stimulating electrode while the other serves to return the current to the generator. The second electrode, therefore, does not have to be in direct contact with the cell; it need only be connected with it by way of a conducting medium, such as blood, tissue fluid, or saline. With the latter arrangement, the second electrode is usually made rather large (Fig. 16–9). The current density is then greatest at the cathode and the current flows from there in many directions toward the

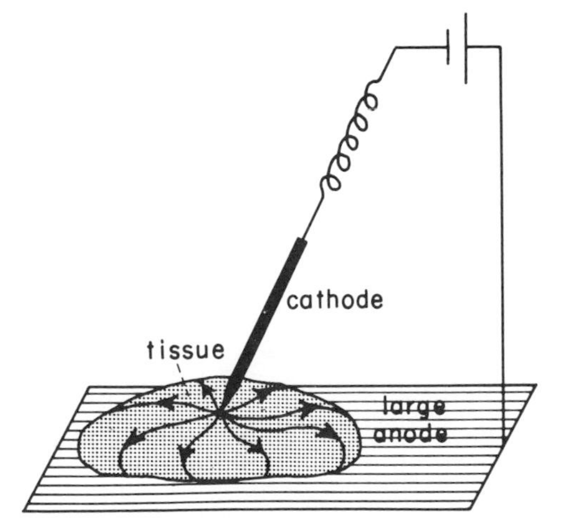

Figure 16–9. Current flow from a stimulating electrode (cathode) when the other electrode (anode) is large. The current flow is most dense near the cathode.

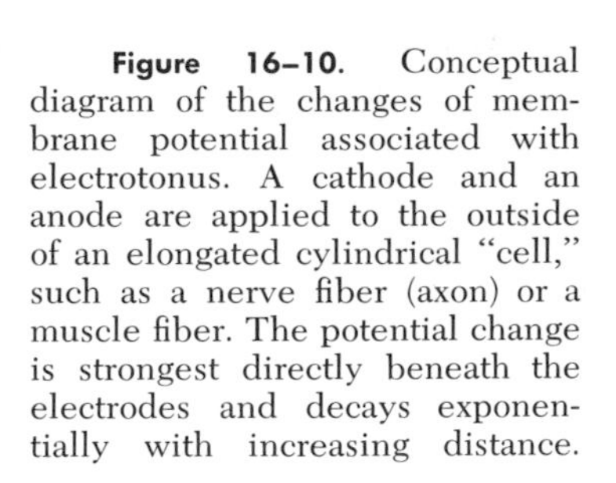

Figure 16–10. Conceptual diagram of the changes of membrane potential associated with electrotonus. A cathode and an anode are applied to the outside of an elongated cylindrical "cell," such as a nerve fiber (axon) or a muscle fiber. The potential change is strongest directly beneath the electrodes and decays exponentially with increasing distance.

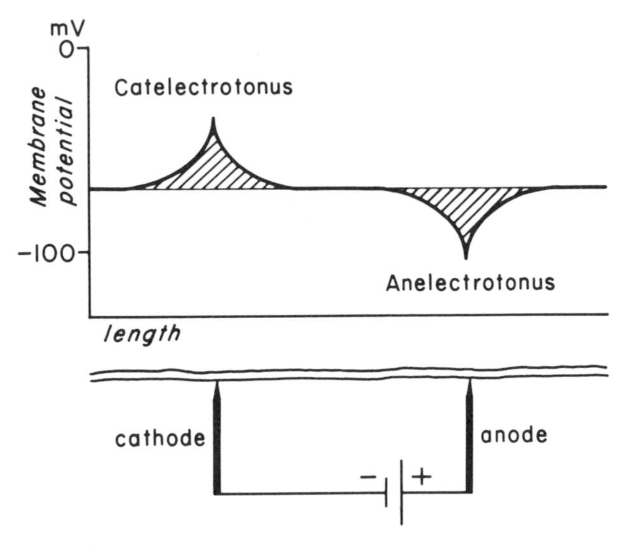

large anode. In this way no localized increase in membrane potential takes place.

The altered membrane potential under the stimulating electrodes is referred to as *electrotonus*. The membrane depolarization at the cathode is known as *catelectrotonus*, and the increased membrane potential at the anode (in case this is in contact with the cell also) is called *anelectrotonus*. The pattern of membrane potential is shown in Figure 16–10.

Length Constant

Although maximal at each electrode, electrotonus extends to membrane regions outside of this area of contact. Its intensity and pattern depend on the current distribution. The pattern is determined by the resistance in the medium surrounding the cell, by the resistance across the cell membrane, and by the resistance of the protoplasm inside the cell. Figure 16–11 illustrates how the current flows through external and internal media and how the density of the lines of current flow are distributed. Since the current density falls off exponentially to both sides of the electrode, the electrotonus likewise diminishes exponentially with the distance from the electrodes until, as it reaches zero, only the resting membrane potential is left.

According to Rushton (1937), it is possible to calculate (for cylindrical cells) the membrane potential P at a distance x from the point of application of the electrode where the membrane potential assumes the value P_o by the formula

$$P = P_o \exp - \frac{x}{\sqrt{\dfrac{R_m}{R_i + R_o}}} \qquad (15)$$

The expression $\sqrt{\dfrac{R_m}{R_i + R_o}}$ is called the *characteristic length, length constant,*

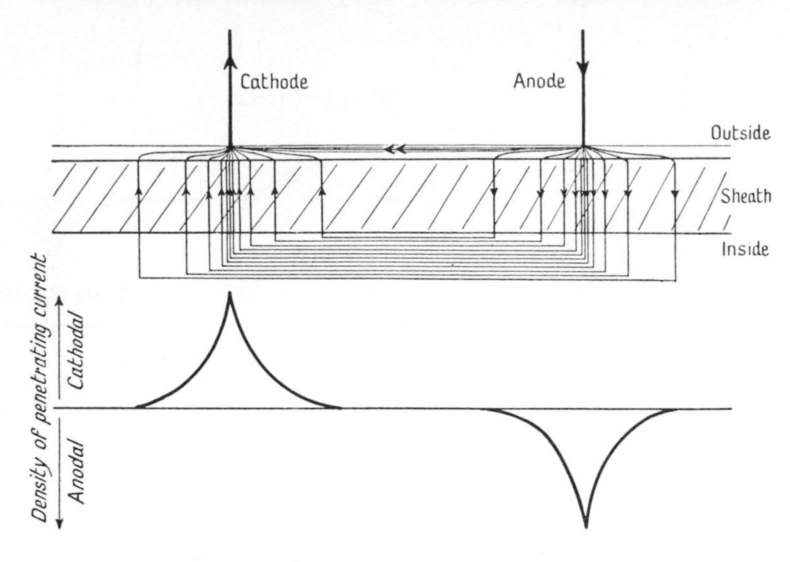

Figure 16–11. Lines of current flow and density of current flowing between two electrodes (cathode and anode connected with a suitable generator) applied to a living cell. For "sheath" read *membrane.* (From Katz, B.: Electrical Excitation in Nerve. Oxford University Press, London, 1939.)

or *space constant*, and is assigned the Greek letter λ (pronounced lambda). Here R_m is the membrane resistance, R_i the internal and R_o the external resistances of the cell. The resistances are usually given in ohms, whereby R_m is the resistance across a 1 cm length of membrane, and R_i and R_o are the respective internal and external resistances of a 1 cm length of cell (usually measured on elongated cell structures, such as nerve or muscle fibers). The length constant, or space constant, therefore, has the dimension of centimeters. That of skeletal muscle fibers (100 μ diameter) of frogs is about 0.25 cm or 25 mm.

Time Constant

When current flows through the electrodes which are applied to a nerve or muscle cell as shown in Figure 16–11, the membrane potential changes and assumes a pattern described under the heading "Electrotonus" and depicted in Figure 16–10. This pattern of electrotonus does not appear at the instant the current starts flowing; rather it develops with a characteristic time course. Initially the current consists in a charging (at the anode) and discharging (at the cathode) of the membrane capacity, but gradually more and more current flows through the membrane. The charging of the membrane capacity is most rapid immediately at the electrodes; the voltage change thus is established soonest at the electrodes whereas it takes longer and longer for the new voltage to be established the farther the membrane region is from the electrode.

Since the current flow through the membrane is greatest immediately at the electrode and diminishes exponentially with the distance, less and less of the total current flowing through the electrodes is available for charging the membrane areas as the distance from the electrode contacts increases. The farther away from the electrodes, the slower is the charging process and the smaller is the finally established voltage change.

To conclude: *the amount of electrotonus is directly proportional, and the time for its establishment is inversely proportional to the distance from the electrodes.*

The spread of electrotonus thus involves not only space but also time. The time course of *electrotonic spread* is characterized by the time constant τ (pronounced tau), which is equal to the product of membrane resistance R_m and membrane capacity C_m.

$$\tau = R_m \cdot C_m \tag{16}$$

If R_m is expressed in ohms · cm² and C_m in farads/cm, then τ has the dimension of seconds.

When the current passing through the electrodes is turned off, the electrotonus does not cease instantly but decays with a time course that is the mirror image of that of its appearance. Where the capacity had been discharged by the cathode, it is now recharged by the previously unaffected portions of the membrane which act, as always, as batteries. Where the membrane had been charged by the anode, the charges leak off through the resistance of the membrane or equalize with those present everywhere on their side of the membrane.

The diagrams in Figure 16–12 summarize the concepts of space and time constants.

In many ways the electric properties of cells are similar to those of electric cables (core conductors). The biophysical theories concerning the electric behavior of cell membranes are therefore known collectively as the *core-conductor* theory, and the electric properties of the membrane are often referred to as its *cable* properties.

Local Potentials

The events associated with the establishment and breakdown of electrotonus occur in typical form only within a rather limited range of applied currents. If the currents are larger, the membrane potential change follows a course that deviates from that predictable from the static cable properties of the cell.

This is particularly true for the membrane behavior under the active cathode: from a certain amount of depolarization on, the membrane potential changes more than would be predictable from a knowledge of membrane resistance and capacity during the resting condition. This additional change is called the *local potential.* It is best seen when the applied current is of rather short duration. The situation is best explained in the form of a diagram (Fig. 16–13). The local potential is considered to be a "response" of the cell to the externally applied current. The term "local" potential indicates that

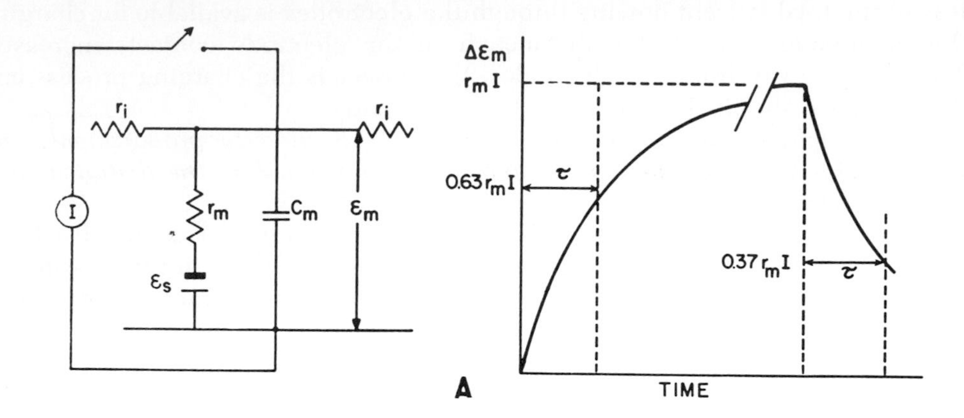

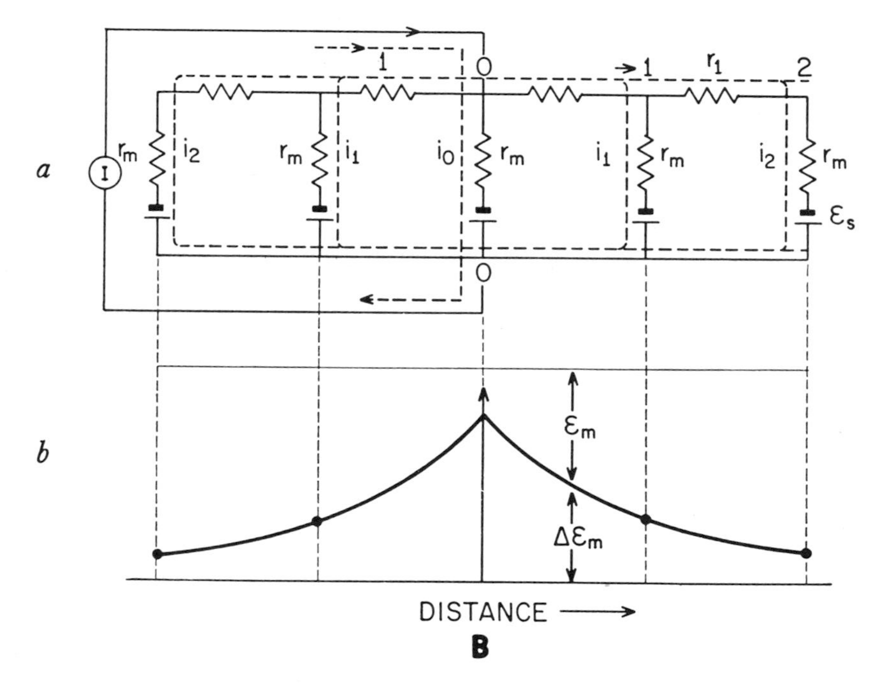

Figure 16–12. A, time constant; properties of a resistance-capacitance (RC) circuit. *Left*, the equivalent circuit of a segment of membrane and the means for switching on or off an external current source (I). *Right*, the time course of voltage change ($\Delta E_m = E_m - E_s$) across capacity when the switch is closed and then, after a long time, opened. The time constant (τ) of the membrane is the time in milliseconds during which the voltage has changed to 0.63 of the maximum change achieved.

B, space constant. **a**, the equivalent circuit of an axon with membrane capacity removed. The current flow in a circuit with capacitors is the same, after a long time, as the current flow in this circuit at any time. The arrows show the various paths of applied current, I. The longer the current flow path, the greater the resistance and hence the smaller the proportion of current flowing in that branch. **b**, graph of membrane voltage as a function of the distance from the point of current application (marked 0 in the circuit diagram). The space constant is that distance (measured in mm) at which the recorded voltage is 0.37 of the voltage change just below the current passing electrodes.

(From Woodbury, J. W., and A. M. Gordon: Action potential; cable and excitable properties of the cell membrane. *In* Physiology and Biophysics, 19th Ed. Ruch, T. C., and H. D. Patton, eds. W. B. Saunders Co., Philadelphia, 1965.)

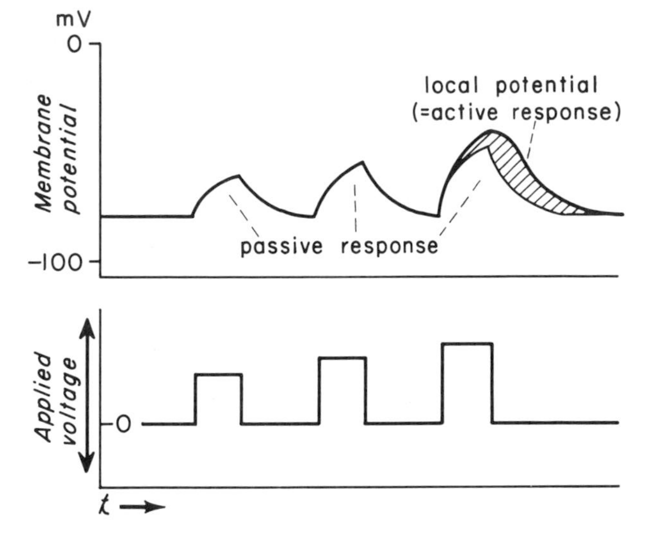

Figure 16–13. Conceptual diagram to explain the difference between passive and active membrane responses. The stimulating pulses are thought to be of a duration of a few milliseconds. Local potentials or active responses can also be elicited by much shorter pulses, provided these have a larger amplitude. In such cases the local potential would still have the same duration as shown here.

this potential change is localized and does not extend very far outside the area of contact with the cathode.

The larger the applied current, the larger the local potential. The latter is therefore called a *graded response*. Figure 16–14 shows a series of local potentials which demonstrates the increase in size of these potentials with increasing applied current.

The occurrence of local potentials implies that the application of current causes an alteration of membrane properties, namely, resistance. Since resistance here means permeability to ions, such a change indicates the transient alteration of membrane permeability to one or more ions.

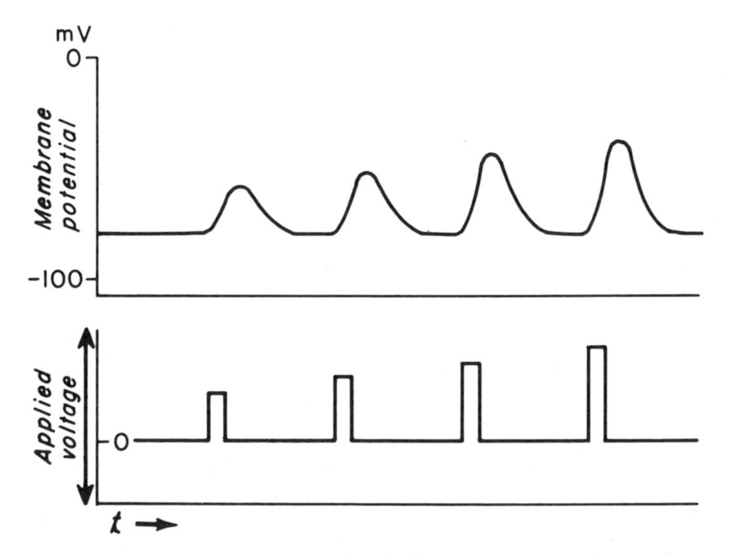

Figure 16–14. A series of local potentials elicited by a series of stimulating pulses of increasing amplitude. Local potentials are not of a fixed size; they are *graded responses*.

The word "potential" as used here in the term "local potential" means "time course and distribution in space of deviation from the resting potential or from the purely electrotonic potential." In the term "membrane potential" the word "potential" stands for "difference of potential across the membrane at a certain instant."

Action Potential

When catelectrotonus and/or associated local potential reaches a certain value, a rather conspicuous further deviation from predictable membrane behavior sets in: as soon as a characteristic level of depolarization (the *threshold depolarization*) is reached, the membrane potential diminishes further rapidly. In most instances the membrane potential reverses in polarity. In most nerve and muscle cells this breakdown (or inversion) of membrane potential is quickly reversed and the membrane potential rises again toward the level determined by the applied current. If plotted on a system of coordinates representing membrane potential and time, the shape of the transient potential change is that of a spike. For this reason, one calls this event a *spike potential*, or simply a *spike*. A cell that is undergoing such a potential change is said to *fire*. The critical level of membrane potential that must be reached in order to induce such a *spike discharge* or *firing* is called also the *firing level* or *threshold* of the membrane potential. This level may be considered constant. The situation is explained in Figure 16–15.

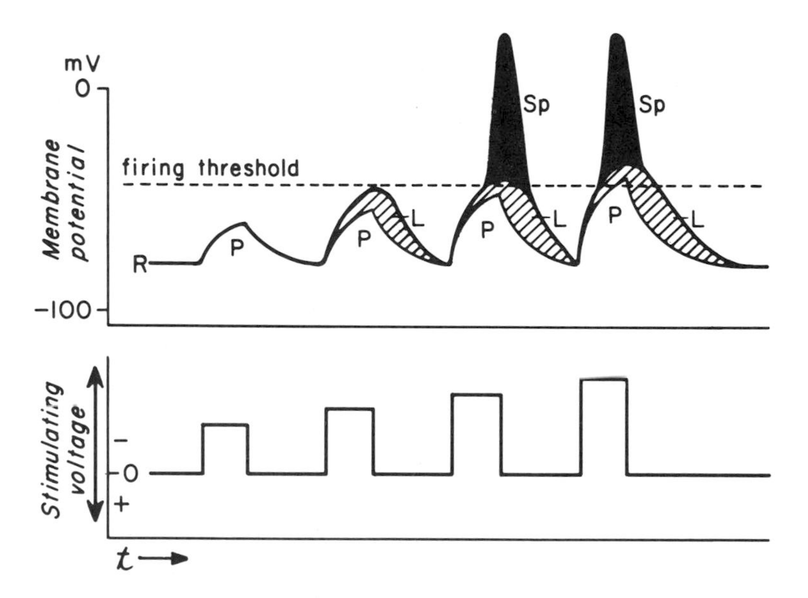

Figure 16–15. Conceptual diagram of the relationship of passive membrane response (*P*), local potential (*L*), and spike potential (S_p). *R* = resting potential. *Note*: the steeper the rise of the local potential, the sooner the spike appears. The configuration of the falling phase of the spike (including the falling phase of the local potential) is simplified. The permeability changes associated with a spike discharge actually give this phase a somewhat different slope. In the case of synaptic activation of cells, the local potential is called synaptic potential or, more commonly now, *postsynaptic potential.*

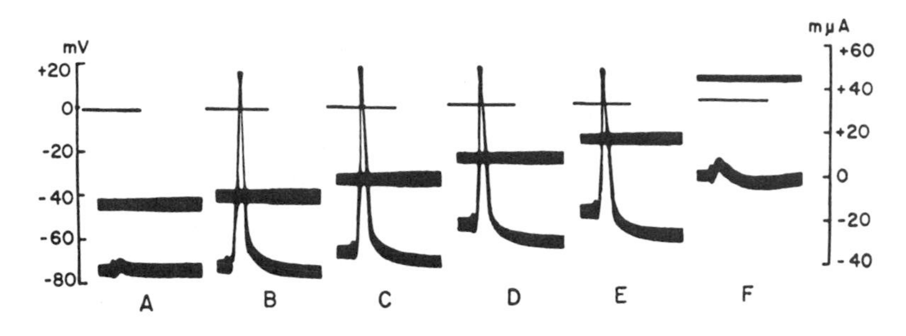

Figure 16–16. Demonstration that spike potentials always reach the same peak potential even though they start from different levels of membrane potential. The responses were recorded with a microelectrode from a motoneuron in the spinal cord of a cat. A second microelectrode, inserted into the same cell, was used to alter the cell's membrane potential by passing a current across the membrane. The current scale is shown on the right; the current actually passed is indicated by the horizontal bar of each record. Note that no current is applied in record *C*. The spike here rises from the resting membrane potential of 65 mV. Preceding each spike is a small vertical deflection signaling the moment of stimulation. In *A* the stimulus is not strong enough to elicit a full grown action potential; in *F* the spike response is greatly diminished because of the strong depolarization of the membrane, a phenomenon known as *cathodal block*. (From Eccles, J. C.: The Physiology of Nerve Cells. Johns Hopkins Press, Baltimore, 1957.)

Once started, a spike potential continues to its maximum before the original membrane conditions begin to be restored. Spike potentials are therefore said to follow the *all-or-none law*. To be precise, however, it is better to state that the spike potential always reaches a certain level of membrane potential which is usually in the order of 0 ∓ 40 mV. The size of the action potential, that is, the actual dimension of the membrane potential change, varies with the level of depolarization produced by the stimulus. This is illustrated in Figure 16–16.

The value of membrane potential attained at the peak of the action potential of many types of cells is surprisingly close to the equilibrium potential of Na^+, i.e., the potential at which net Na^+ flux is zero. It has indeed been demonstrated that the permeability of the membrane to Na^+ increases greatly (up to 1000 times the resting value) during the initial phase of the action potential and that Na^+ ions move rapidly into the cell. These conditions approximate those necessary for reaching the Na^+ equilibrium potential. As further evidence for this, no action potentials occur if the external medium surrounding the cell contains no Na^+ ions, and the peak of the action potential approaches the equilibrium potential of Na^+ for a wide range of external Na^+ concentrations (Figs. 16–17 through 16–20). The equivalent circuits of resting and excited membranes are shown in Figure 16–21.

The descending phase of the action potential is ascribed to a delayed increase in K^+ permeability and an outward movement of K^+ ions. Later phases of the action potential, referred to as *after-potentials*, are probably due, in part, to K^+–Na^+ exchange (Na^+ pump) which leads to the restoration of original conditions. The general configuration of an action potential and the terminology applied to its components are shown in Figure 16–22.

The movements of Na^+ and K^+ have been observed indirectly by an

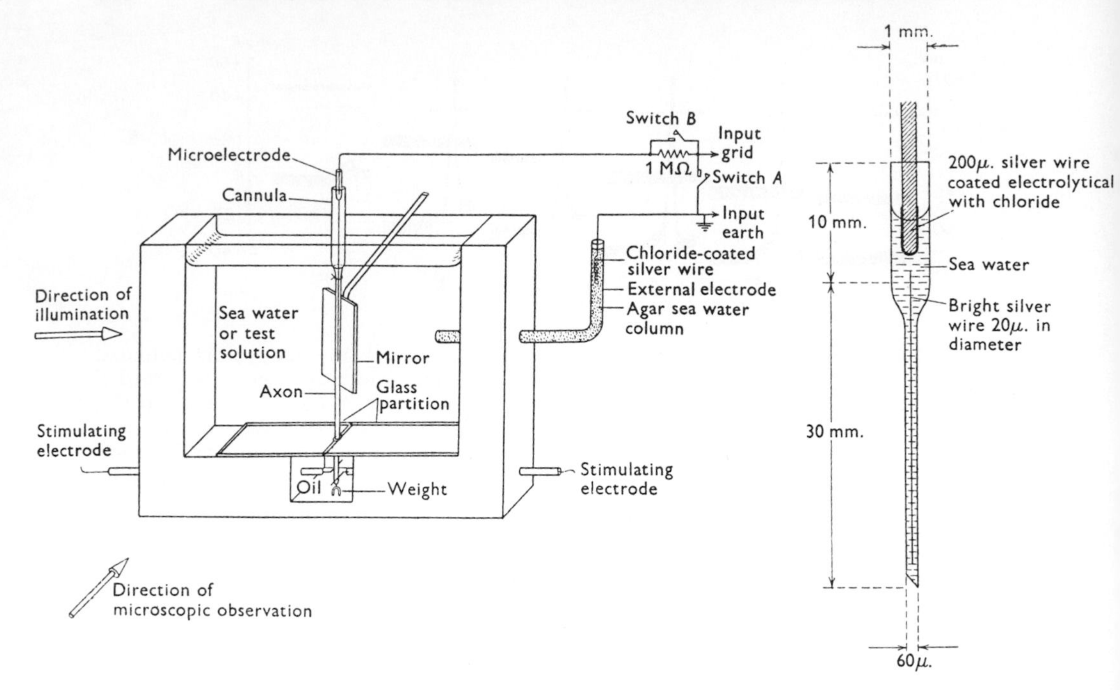

Figure 16–17. Simplified diagram of the experimental set-up used by Hodgkin and Katz to record membrane potentials and action potentials from squid giant axons (see Fig. 16–18). (From Hodgkin, A. L., and B. Katz: The effect of sodium ions on the electrical activity of the giant axon of the squid. J. Physiol. *108*:37–77, 1949.)

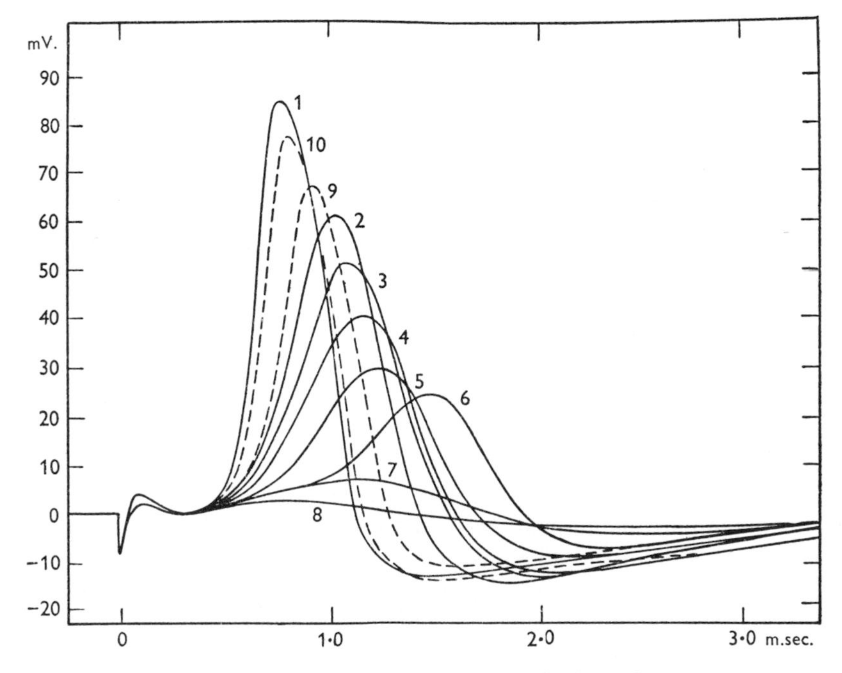

Figure 16–18. *See opposite page for legend.*

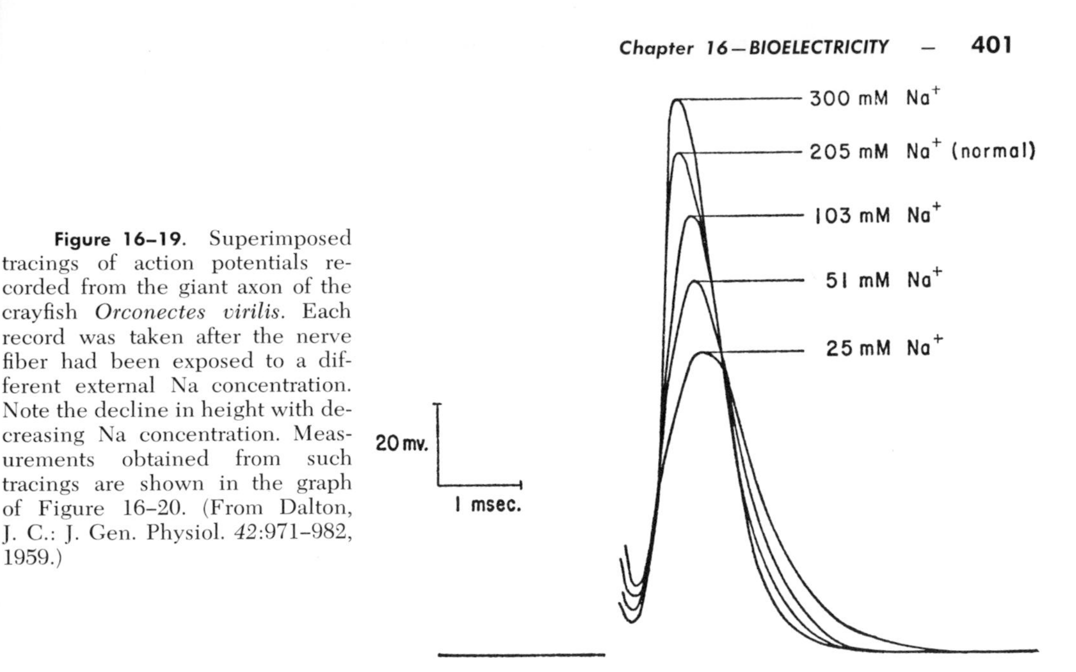

Figure 16–19. Superimposed tracings of action potentials recorded from the giant axon of the crayfish *Orconectes virilis*. Each record was taken after the nerve fiber had been exposed to a different external Na concentration. Note the decline in height with decreasing Na concentration. Measurements obtained from such tracings are shown in the graph of Figure 16–20. (From Dalton, J. C.: J. Gen. Physiol. *42*:971–982, 1959.)

ingenious technique, called *voltage clamp*, invented in 1949 by Cole and by Marmont. Experiments using this method are not only the basis of the ion exchange hypothesis developed by Hodgkin, Huxley, and others, but have also been used to test this hypothesis rigorously. For a discussion of this, see Eccles (1953) and Woodbury and Patton (1965).

The technique consists in stabilizing the membrane potential by electronic feedback and recording the current required to do this while the potential tends to change. The current that has to be applied to the membrane in order to counteract a change in membrane potential is exactly equal to that ionic current which actually flows across the membrane.

Figure 16–18. Superimposed oscilloscope tracings of action potentials recorded from giant axons of squid (see Fig. 16–17) to show the effect on the action potential of decreasing the sodium concentration to zero. Sodium chloride was replaced by dextrose. While records *1* to *8* were taken, the external Na^+ concentration fell to zero. Records *9* and *10* were taken 30 and 500 msec after the original, normal sodium concentration was reestablished. (From Hodgkin, A. L., and B. Katz: The effect of sodium ions on the electrical activity of the giant axon of the squid. J. Physiol. *108*:37–77, 1949.)

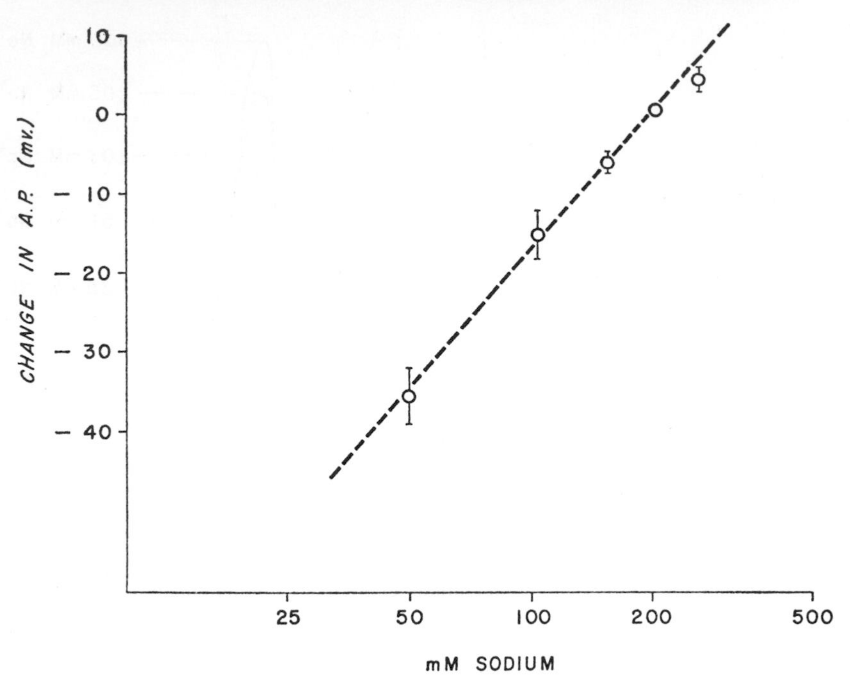

Figure 16–20. Giant axon of the crayfish *Orconectes virilis*: changes in action potential (*A.P.*) magnitude as a function of the external Na concentration (the latter is given on a logarithmic scale in mM/l on the x axis). The experiments were carried out at 9 to 12° C. The dashed line has a slope of 58 mV/ten-fold change in Na concentration as predicted by the Nernst equation. Mean data from six axons, showing one standard deviation on either side of each experimental point. (From Dalton, J. C.: J. Gen. Physiol. *42*:971–982, 1959.)

It has been demonstrated that during the passage of an action potential, current flows first inward and then outward, and that the inward current stops if Na^+ is removed from the outside medium (it is replaced by choline in the experiment) or if the membrane is artificially polarized to such an extent that the new membrane potential balances the tendency of Na^+ ions to follow their concentration gradient. Since the concentration gradient was known, the opposing potential could readily be calculated using the Nernst equation (see p. 380). The experiments of Hodgkin and Huxley (1952) have shown that at precisely this (artificially increased) membrane potential, the inward current ceases while the outward current keeps its time course (Figs. 16–23 and 16–24).

With the aid of radioactive sodium and potassium it has been shown that stimulated (excited) nerve and muscle fibers accumulate Na^+ and lose K^+. This takes place, presumably, during the action potentials. Techniques and resulting data are shown in Figures 16–25 through 16–29.

The outflow of K^+ ions during the later phase of the action potential has been observed more directly in experiments on heart muscle: Wilde (1957) and coworkers cannulated the coronary artery of turtle hearts that had previously been "saturated" with a radioactive isotope of potassium, ^{42}K. In these

(Text continued on page 407.)

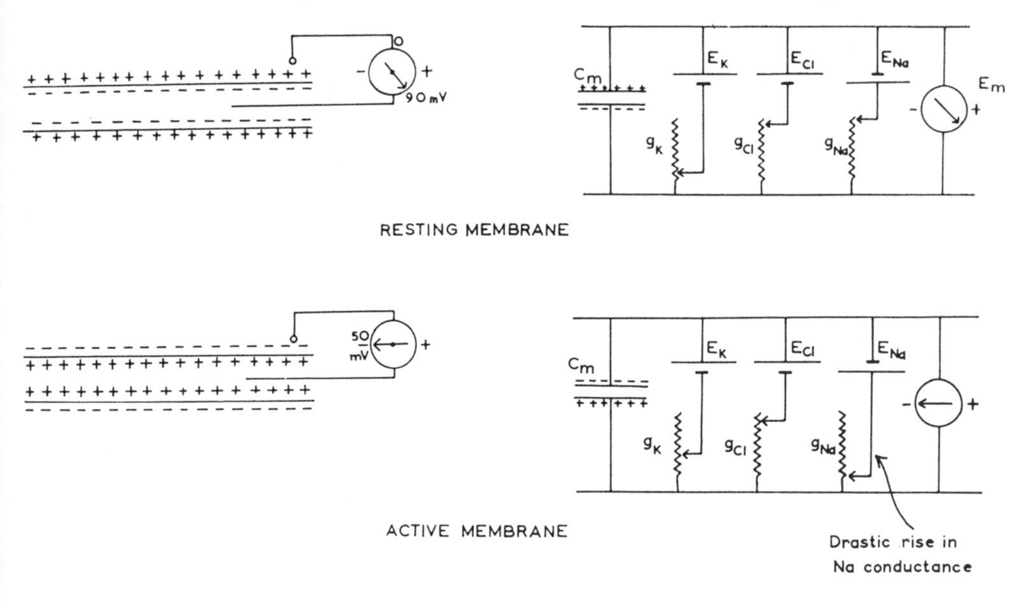

Figure 16–21. Conceptual diagrams and equivalent circuits of resting and active membranes. The "ion batteries" underlying electrical activity. At rest the potassium battery (E_K) dominates the membrane potential (E_m), owing to a relatively high potassium conductance (g_K). Following excitation the sodium conductance (g_{Na}) undergoes a drastic rise and so the sodium battery (E_{Na}) comes instead to determine the membrane potential. An increase in chloride conductance (g_{Cl}) would act in the opposite direction to sodium. (From Hoyle, G.: Comparative physiology of conduction in nerve and muscle. Amer. Zoologist 2:5–25, 1962.)

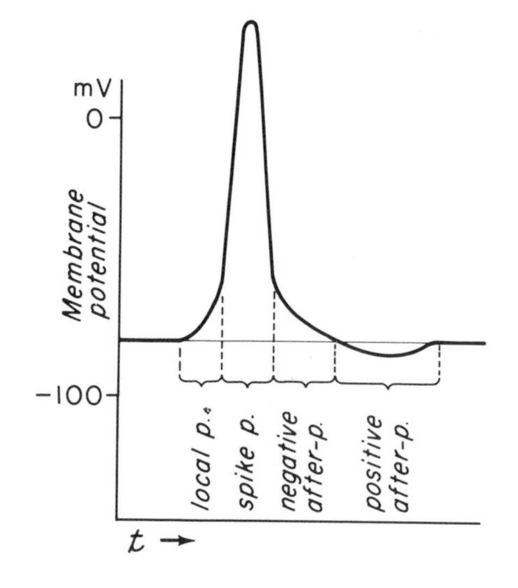

Figure 16–22. Configuration and terminology of the action potential as commonly observed in nerve cells. In muscle cells the positive after-potential is usually missing and the negative after-potential is pronounced. The terms "negative" and "positive" were coined in the earlier years of electrophysiology when only extracellularly applied electrodes were used. Under such conditions no resting membrane potential can be recorded and the action potential appears as a negative wave that has, in general, the configuration of the intracellularly recorded positive action potential, except that its amplitude is smaller due to the short-circuiting action of the extracellular fluid. With extracellular electrodes one records indeed a positive after-potential. With intracellular electrodes, however, this is "seen" as a stronger negativity (hyperpolarization), as is evident in this figure.

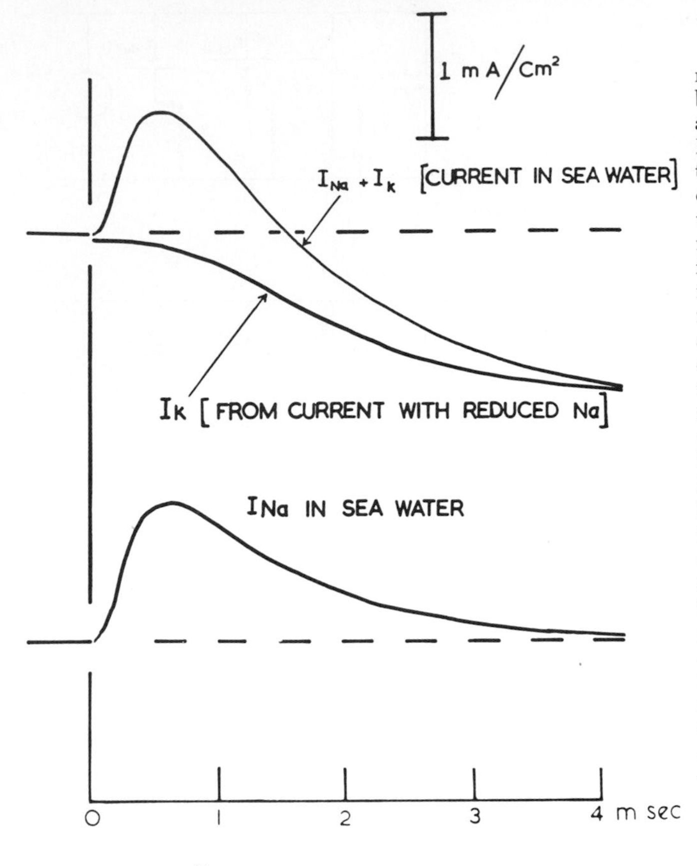

Figure 16–23. Ionic currents across the excited membrane of the squid giant axon, as measured by Hodgkin and Huxley with the voltage-clamp technique, when the nerve was depolarized steadily. When sea water was used as the external medium the measured current followed the upper curve (first negative, then positive). The middle curve was obtained in a Na^+ free medium. The third curve is obtained by subtracting the second from the first. With sea water as the external medium, the current is carried by Na^+ (inward) *and* K^+ (outward). In the absence of Na^+ only the K^+ current (I_K) takes place. The third curve represents the Na^+ current alone. Note that, in spite of maintained depolarization, the Na^+ current is transient. (From Hodgkin, A. L., and A. F. Huxley: Properties of nerve axons. I. Movement of sodium and potassium during nerve activity. Cold Spr. Harb. Symp. Quant. Biol., 1952, pp. 43–52.)

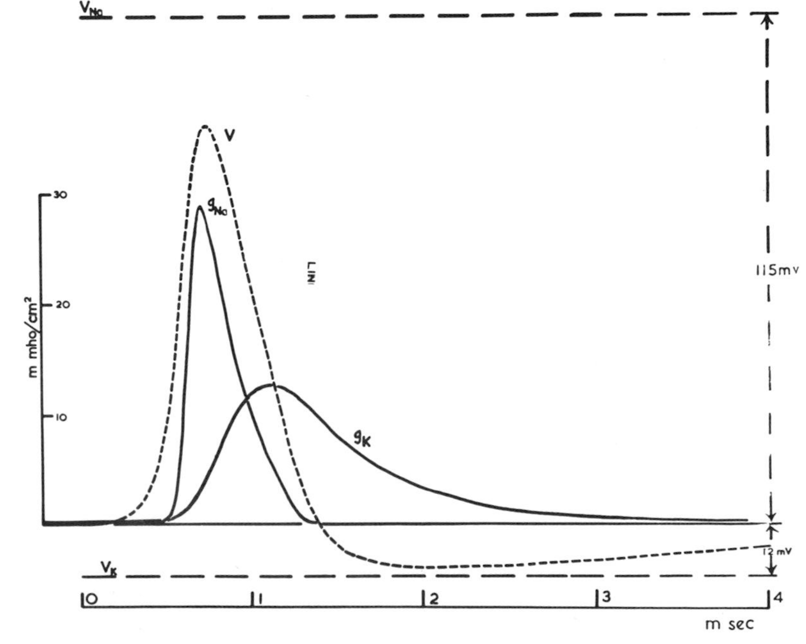

Figure 16–24. *See opposite page for legend.*

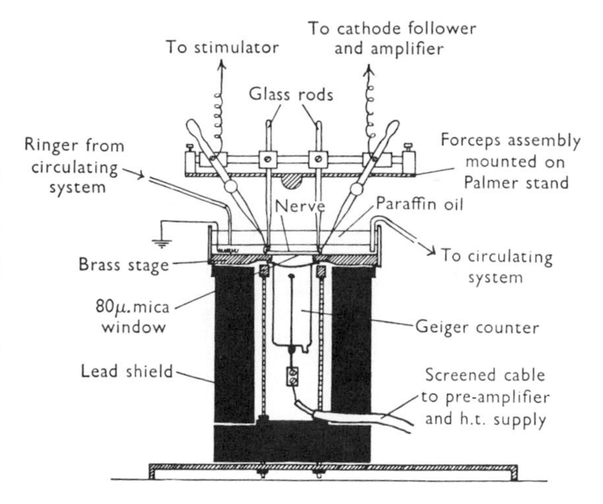

Figure 16–25. Simplified diagram of the experimental arrangement used in studies on movement of radioactive K across nerve fiber membranes. The holding forceps served as stimulating and recording electrodes. (From Keynes, R. D., and P. R. Lewis: The resting exchange of radioactive potassium in crab nerve. J. Physiol. *113*:73–98, 1951.)

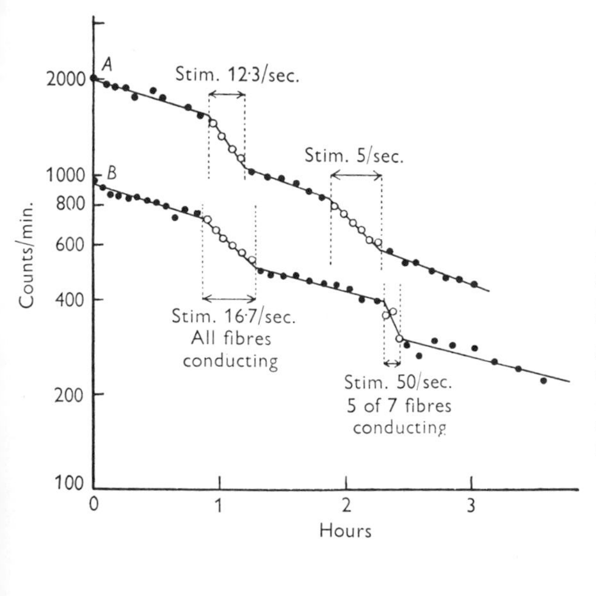

Figure 16–26. Leakage of ^{42}K from a peripheral nerve of the crab *Carcinus maenas* (Crustacea) during stimulation and at rest, in normal saline. Ordinate: counts per minute (logarithmic scale); abscissa: time. *A*, whole nerve; *B*, bundle of seven fibers of 30 micron diameter. The fiber was previously soaked in a saline medium containing ^{42}K. The set-up used was similar to that shown in Figure 16–25. (From Keynes, R. D.: The leakage of radioactive potassium from stimulated nerve. J. Physiol. *113*:99–114, 1951.)

Figure 16–24. Theoretical action potential and conductance changes as they occur in giant axons of squid, according to Hodgkin and Huxley. g_{Na} and g_K are the Na^+ and K^+ conductances, respectively. They are expressed in terms of the reciprocal of the membrane resistance. The action potential travels along the axon and is assumed to be recorded at a region away from its origin. The conductance changes, likewise, are assumed to be recorded at the same region. The action potential curve shown, therefore, is not caused by the conductance change where it is recorded, but by current flow originating in the neighboring, previously excited region. The initial depolarization of the action potential is, in fact, responsible for the conductance changes which, in turn, enhance the action potential and terminate it. (From Hodgkin, A. L., and A. F. Huxley: Properties of nerve axons. I. Movement of sodium and potassium during nerve activity. Cold Spr. Harb. Symp. Quant. Biol. 1952, pp. 43–52.)

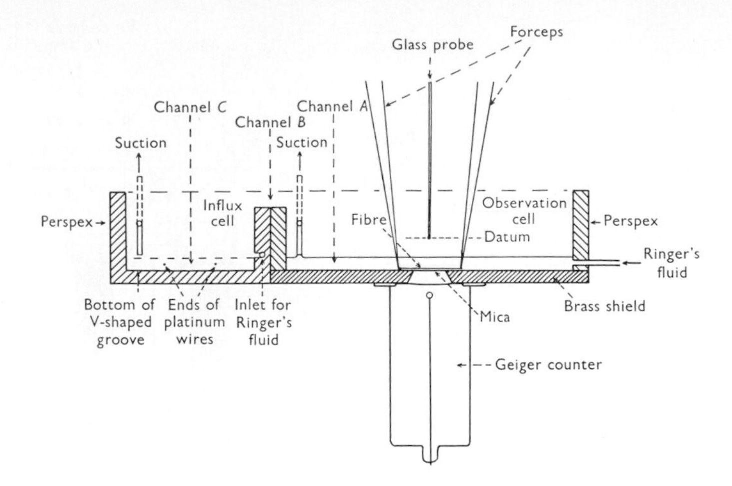

Figure 16–27. Simplified diagram of the apparatus used to measure ion movements across the membrane of single muscle fibers. The fiber is held by micromanipulated forceps. It is first exposed to a saline solution with radioactive ^{42}K or radioactive ^{24}Na in the left-hand chamber (influx cell). At intervals the fiber is transferred to the right-hand chamber (observation cell) and accurately placed over a mica window. A glass probe serves as a reference point to permit repeated positioning in identical location. The fluid level is held constant by suction tubes. The fiber is so delicate that it would be injured if it were carried through the surface of the saline medium. The fluid level is therefore raised before each transfer which involves moving the fiber through Channel B. The section through the assembly as shown is cut through the plane of the channels so that only their bottoms are shown. The platinum wire serves for electric stimulation. The stimulator, the micromanipulator, the shutter above the Geiger counter, and the lead shield are not shown. (From Hodgkin, A. L., and P. Horowicz: Movements of Na and K in single muscle fibers. J. Physiol. *145*:405–432, 1959.)

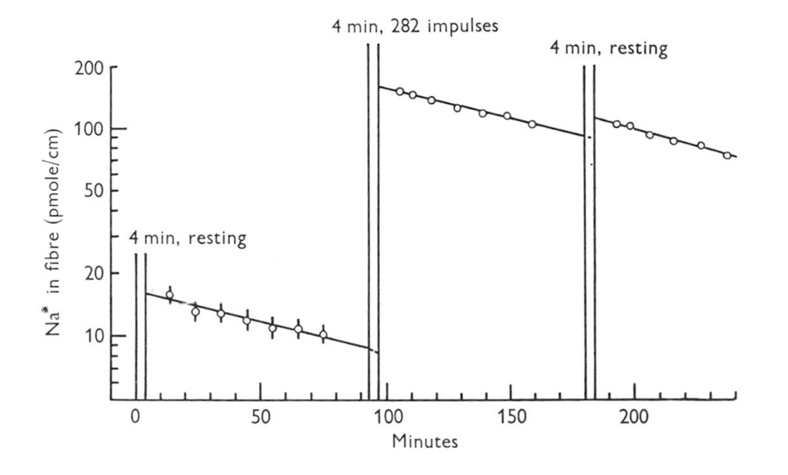

Figure 16–28. Effect of stimulation on entry of ^{24}Na into a single muscle fiber semitendinosus of frog. Abscissa: time. Ordinate: quantity of ^{24}Na per centimeter of fiber (logarithmic scale). The vertical lines define 4 minute periods during which the fiber was exposed to the tracer. In the second period the fiber was stimulated 1.56 times per second for 3 minutes. Note the large increase in ^{24}Na content after stimulation (consider that the scale of the ordinate is logarithmic). The experimental arrangement used is that shown in Figure 16–27. (From Hodgkin, A. L., and P. Horowicz: Movements of Na and K in single muscle fibers. J. Physiol. *145*:405–432, 1959.)

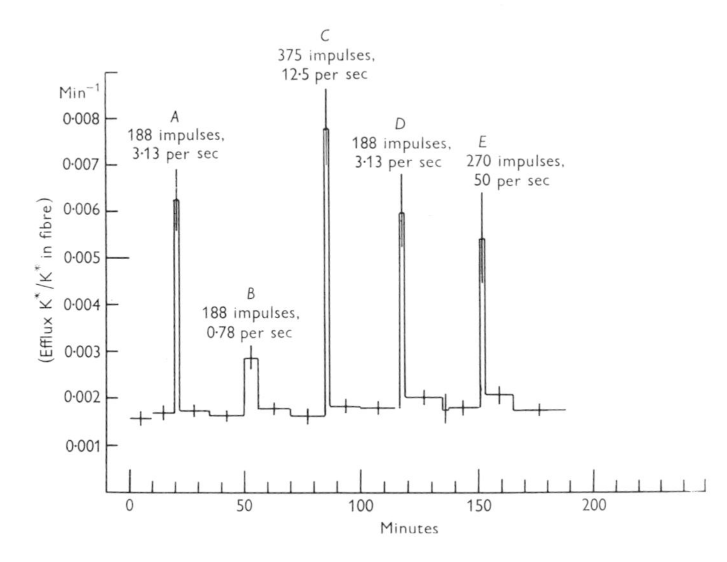

Figure 16–29. Effect of stimulation on K efflux from single muscle fibers (musculus semitendinosus of frog. Abscissa: time. Ordinate: fraction of ^{42}K lost per minute. The frequencies of stimulation and the total number of impulses are shown on the graph. The durations of the collecting periods and of the stimulation were as follows: *A*, 120 sec collection, 60 sec stimulation; *B*, 360, 240; *C*, 120, 30; *D*, 120, 60; *E*, 120, 5.4. (From Hodgkin, A. L., and P. Horowicz: Movements of Na and K in single muscle fibers. J. Physiol. *145*:405–432, 1959.)

hearts the action potentials last very long, those of the muscle fibers of the ventricle about 2 seconds (see also Fig. 16–30d). The onset of depolarization is indicated by the "S" wave in the electrocardiogram shown in Figure 16–31; the repolarization phase more or less coincides with the "T" wave. Radioactive K^+ appears in the perfusion fluid simultaneously with the beginning of the "T" wave, as shown in the lower part of Figure 16–31. This experiment probably represents the first and only direct proof for the outward movement of K^+ during the falling phase of the action potential.

The action potential of each type of cell has its own characteristic shape and time course. In most nerve cells and the striated muscle cells of vertebrates action potentials usually last not more than a few milliseconds; in some nerve fibers the whole process is over in less than 1 millisecond. Vertebrate heart muscle cells exhibit action potentials of longer duration. In certain hibernating squirrels they may last several seconds. Examples of action potentials are represented in Figure 16–30.

Action potentials are considered as consisting of two portions: the spike potential proper and the series of after-potentials. Frequently two such after-potentials are seen: before the potential returns to a value equal to that at which the spike started, the rate of change diminishes in certain case more or less abruptly so that the potential returns more slowly. This phase is called the *negative* (or *depolarizing*) *after-potential*. Then the potential changes further and the membrane potential temporarily increases beyond the value from which the spike started. This second phase is known as *positive* (or *hyperpolarizing*) *after-potential*. The terms "negative" and "positive" have no significance

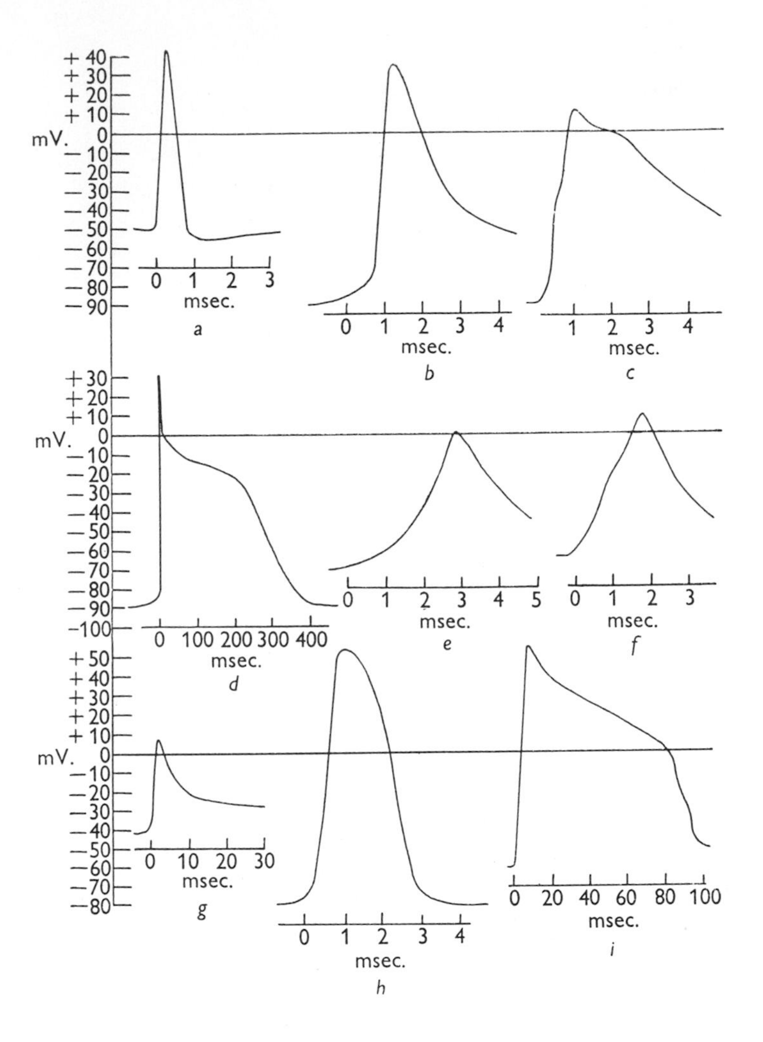

Figure 16–30. Action potentials recorded with intracellular electrodes. Many of them include rather large local potentials. Note the great variation in time course. **a**, squid giant axon; **b**, sartorius muscle fiber of frog; **c**, same, but recorded at end plate region; **d**, muscle fiber of dog heart; **e**, muscle fiber of crab (*Carcinus*); **f**, muscle fiber of cockroach (*Periplaneta*); **g**, muscle fiber of stick insect (*Carausius*); **h**, electroplax of electric eel (*Electrophorus*); **i**, *Carcinus* muscle fiber in saline medium in which Na ions are replaced by tetraethylammonium ions. (After various authors, from Hoyle, G.: Comparative physiology of the nervous control of muscular contraction. Cambridge University Press, London, 1957.)

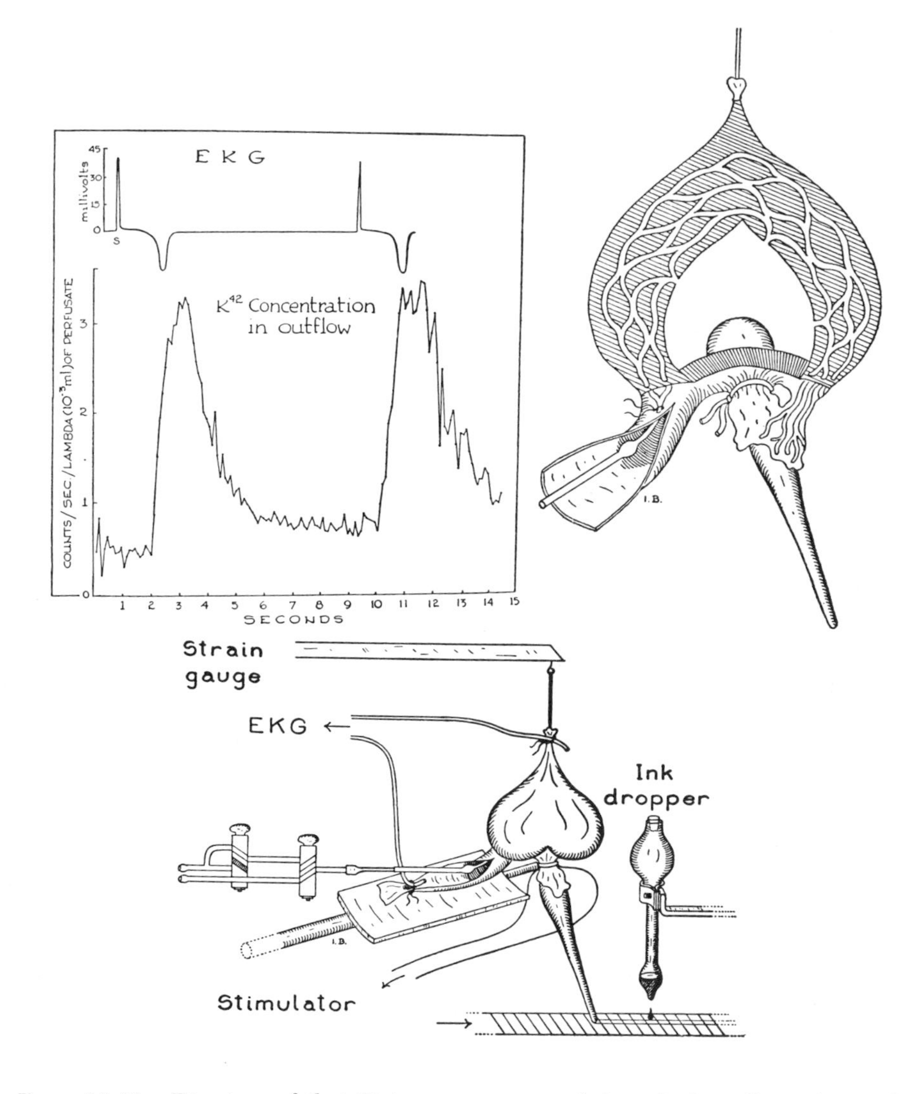

Figure 16–31. Direct proof that K^+ ions move outward through the cell membrane during the later phase of the action potential. A turtle heart is used for this experiment. The coronary artery which supplies the ventricle is cannulated. Through it the heart muscle is first loaded intensely with radioactive ^{42}K ions by allowing its nonradioactive ^{40}K to exchange with the radioactive ^{42}K provided. The heart muscle is then perfused with normal, nonradioactive saline solution (blood substitute). The auricle with the cut effluent veins is draped over a glass stylus that allows the perfusate to drip onto a strip of fast moving filter paper. The heart muscle is stimulated electrically. Suitable electrodes are placed on two areas of the heart tissue to permit recording of the action potentials (in the form of an electrocardiogram, *EKG*). Portions of the filter paper strip are fed into a Geiger-Müller counter to determine the amount of radioactive ^{42}K present. The record is then correlated with the EKG as shown in the upper left diagram. (From Wilde, W. S.: Discussion on "Ionic transfer in muscle and nerve," pp. 157–167 of Metabolic Aspects of Transport across Cell Membranes. G. R. Murphy, ed. University of Wisconsin Press, Madison, 1957.)

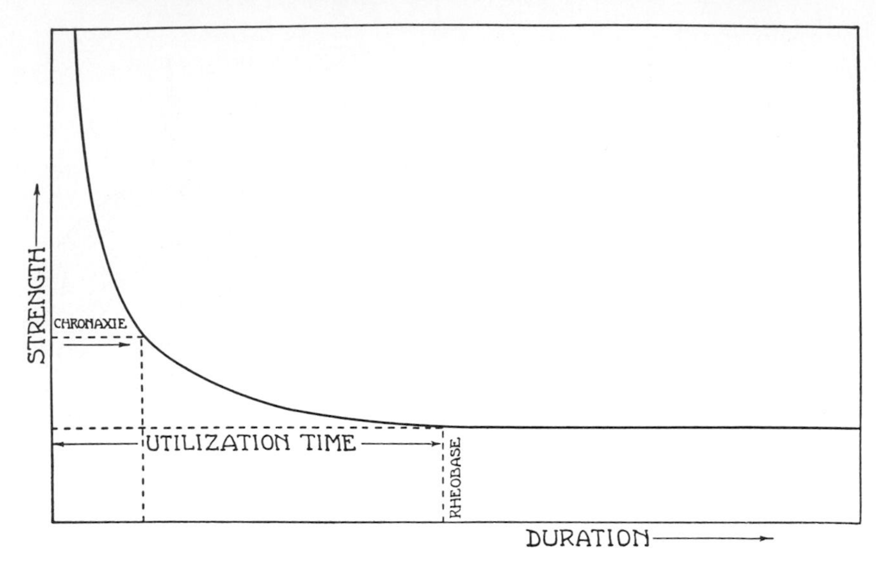

Figure 16–32. Strength-duration curve, which expresses the relation between the least strength of an applied current and the least time during which it must flow in order to reach threshold. There is a minimal current density below which excitation does not occur, but strength-duration curves do not express subliminal events. Since utilization time is difficult to measure accurately, Lucas, Lapicque, and others have taken as a measure of excitability the time during which current twice rheobase must flow in order to excite. This time interval is called *chronaxy* (chronaxie) or *excitation time.* (From Woodbury, J. W., and H. D. Patton: Action potential; cable and excitable properties of the cell membrane. *In* Medical Physiology and Biophysics, 18th Ed. Ruch, T. C., and J. F. Fulton, eds. W. B. Saunders Co., Philadelphia, 1960, pp. 32–65.)

with regard to the actual membrane potential. They are derived from experiments employing external electrodes in which the recording instrument indicates the steady membrane potential as 0 mV (whether this is the resting potential or an induced membrane potential). The positive after-potential is often several times longer than the spike potential. Its time course is liable to change during an experiment and is much more variable than the spike potential. The terminology of after-potentials is explained in Figure 16–22.

Chronaxy

In 1892 Nicola Tesla, in England, invented an electric circuit that permitted the generation of high voltage currents of extremely high alternation rate. It soon became known that such high frequency alternating currents are harmless if allowed to flow through human beings, even if their electromotive force amounts to thousands of volts. The so-called "Tesla currents" have been employed widely by amusement park exhibitors to produce the startling effect of lighting an electric light bulb in the hands of a person by simply connecting the person to a Tesla generator.

Experiments have shown that alternating current stimulates muscle or nerve cells only if the curent flows for a sufficient length of time in one and the same direction. It was soon recognized that it is not the current as such but the charging action of the current that matters: Only if the current flows long enough to cause a certain change in the total charge of the cell membrane can it bring about nerve or muscle action potentials. The minimum time required for the current to flow before it elicits an action potential depends on the electric properties of the cell membrane. This figure, therefore, represents a characteristic that can be used to indirectly describe the properties of this membrane and its excitability.

The minimum current-duration that excites a cell (elicits an action potential) has been called "Nutz-Zeit" (utilization time) by the German physiologists. Although not used in modern literature, the term and its meaning should be known to anyone who finds it necessary to study the original literature in this rather rapidly advancing field of physiology.

That a current must also have a sufficient strength (voltage) before it can excite, has, of course, been known for a long time. For the minimum strength of an applied current pulse, the term *rheobase* has been introduced.

The minimum duration of current flow is effective only if the current is much greater than rheobase, and conversely, the current of rheobase strength is effective only at durations considerably longer than the minimum duration or utilization time.

The French physiologist Lapicque has studied this extensively. He has shown how the minimum duration diminishes with increasing voltage and vice versa. The curve relating voltage and duration (see Figure 16–32b) has the shape of a hyperbolical curve which reaches infinity of voltage along the line of minimum duration, and infinite duration along the line of minimum voltage. The point on the curve which corresponds to twice that of the minimum voltage (rheobase) he named "*chronaxie*" (English: chronaxy).

Lapicque, and many physiologists after him, believed that the chronaxy is an important characteristic of excitable cells, and innumerable determinations of chronaxies have been published. The original concept of a functional hierarchy of cells within an organism, based on their respective chronaxies, has not materialized, and today the term chronaxy has only historical value. However, the shape of the strength-duration curve, and the arguments leading to the hypothesis connected with chronaxy, are important for the general theory of the phenomena of bioelectricity.

Conduction of Action Potentials

In contrast to electrotonic and local potentials, which are confined to a restricted region of the cell membrane, action potentials are *self-propagating*. They represent such large changes in membrane potential (depolarization) that they act as a stimulus which induces an action potential in the neighboring membrane region. Thus the process of temporary increase in Na^+ permeability spreads over the whole membrane. This gives the appearance of a movement (or change in position) of the action potential, and may be compared to the movement of a wave over a water surface. Just as the water particles move only up and down and are not carried in the direction of the wave, there is no net movement of electric charges (ions) along the extent of the cell membrane during the propagation of an action potential. The propagation, or *conduction* as it is called, of an action potential over the entire length of a nerve or muscle cell is completely different from the conduction of electricity (electrons or ions) through a conductor.

It is, therefore, totally misleading if the conduction of action potentials along nerve fibers is compared with the conduction of an electric current along a wire or other conductor. Conduction is made possible by the dramatic membrane conductance changes that result from threshold depolarizations, as explained in the section on the action potential. The cable properties of the cell would permit only a limited electrotonic spread of the produced transmembrane potential change (the action potential).

The currents that flow across the membrane during the action potential (the action current) are not confined to the cross-sectional area of the active membrane. Only the region over which the potential difference is *measured* is confined. The lines of current extend over a certain distance in either direction of the membrane and on the outside as well as the inside. These lines of current actually form loops (see Fig. 16–33) or small circuits. They are therefore known as *eddy currents*, or *local circuits*. In fact, these local circuits are held responsible for the potential change in the vicinity of an action potential, and thus for the induction of an action potential in these neighboring regions. These currents are supposed to act in the same manner as the current flowing from stimulating electrodes.

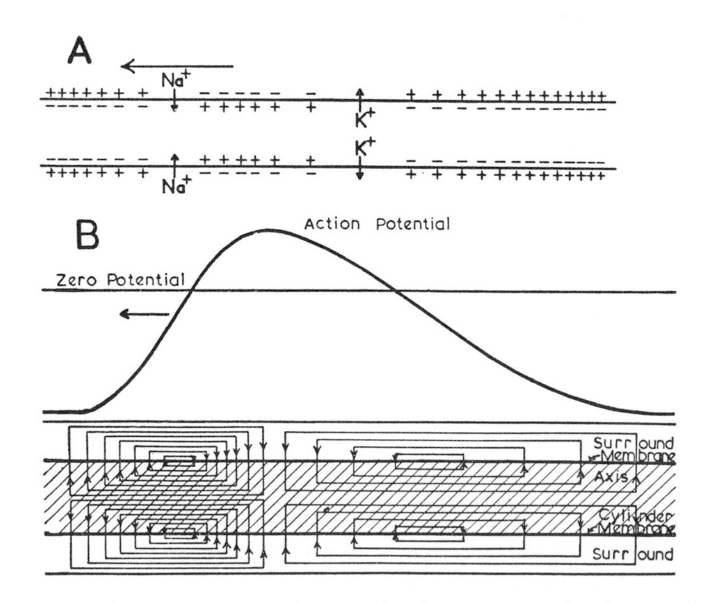

Figure 16–33. A, diagram showing the postulated movement of sodium and potassium ions across the membrane during an impulse advancing in the direction of the arrow, and the resulting alteration of charge on the membrane and its recovery. **B**, the upper part shows the potential distribution of impulse along the nerve fiber or muscle fiber, while the lower part shows the resulting flow of electric current both in the external medium and within the fiber. The lower part shows the resulting flow of electric current both in the external medium and within the fiber. Note the reversal of membrane potential during the spike. B is drawn so that the impulse is at approximately the same position as in A. (From Eccles, J. C.: The Neurophysiological Basis of Mind. The Clarendon Press, Oxford, 1953.)

According to this *local circuit theory*, the action current which flows during the action potential is far greater than the minimum current required to elicit an action potential in the adjacent, inactive membrane. Thus the biophysical mechanism of the propagation of action potentials operates with a considerable safety factor.

An action potential can propagate in all directions from its point of origin over the whole membrane of the cell—provided the membrane has properties adequate to permit this response. As shown in Chapter 17 (pp. 447, 448), dendrites and parts of the cell body of certain nerve cells have a special functional type of membrane in which action potentials do not normally arise and which may not even conduct action potentials arising in other parts of the cell membrane. A similar situation is found with many muscle cell membranes.

The axons of nerve cells, and vertebrate striated muscle fibers, can propagate action potentials. The process is usually referred to as *conduction*. Conduction of action potentials can be defined as the propagation of a wave consisting of a transient change of membrane potential which progresses without diminution of amplitude.

For any given temperature the velocity of conduction is constant. It is strictly proportional to the length constant (see p. 393) of the membrane (see Pumphrey and Young, 1938; and Rushton, 1951). The greater the length constant, the greater the velocity. The magnitude of the length (or space) constant depends on: the membrane resistance R_m, the internal resistance R_i, and the external resistance R_o. Increasing R_m or decreasing R_i and/or R_o leads to an increase in conduction velocity. With increasing cell diameter, R_m increases and R_i decreases. The conduction velocity therefore increases in proportion to the cell diameter (see Fig. 16–34). Thick nerve fibers conduct faster than thin ones. If the external resistance is raised, the conduction velocity is decreased; thus cells placed in mineral oil (as is done in many experiments in order to isolate them electrically) conduct more slowly than cells in saline medium.

Temperature also affects the conduction velocity: nerves conduct faster at higher temperature; therefore we find higher conduction velocities for nerve fibers of mammals than for those of amphibians, although the diameters are similar.

Accommodation

Several times our discussion has involved the effects of applied currents. So far we have considered only those of rather short duration. Interesting complications arise if such currents are allowed to flow for prolonged periods of time.

To simplify the situation, we will consider an excessively long square pulse, applied through a cathode and anode, both in contact with the same cell. When the current is first applied, it charges the membrane and this shows as a change in membrane potential as discussed (p. 393, Fig. 16–11). A depolarization (catelectrotonus) develops under the cathode, a hyperpolarization (anelectrotonus) under the anode. But, although the current remains unaltered, the membrane potential returns again in the direction of the previous, resting

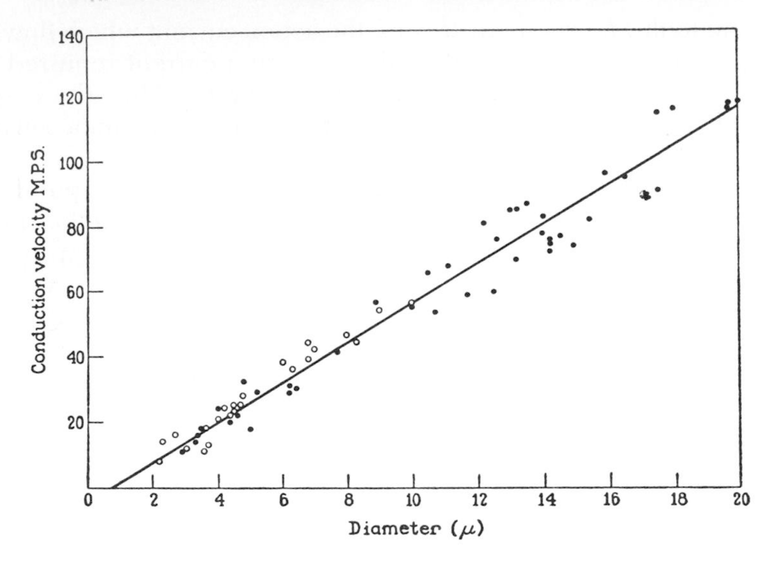

Figure 16–34. Linear relation between conduction rate and diameter of mammalian myelinated nerve fibers. Slope of line is approximately 6 m. per second per μ of diameter. (After Hursh, from Gasser, Ohio J. Sci., 1941, *41*:145–159.)

condition. It will, in fact, fall rather rapidly at first and then level off to a new steady state. If now the current is suddenly turned off, the potential swings in the opposite direction; at the cathode the membrane behaves as if an anodic current were applied, at the anode it depolarizes as if activated by a cathode. In fact, as the current is turned off the membrane behaves as if a pulse in the opposite direction had been applied.

The change in membrane potential which appears to be due to a secondary reaction of the cell membrane to the long-lasting pulse is referred to as *accommodation.* The cell is said to accommodate to the stimulus. Figure 19–5 illustrates the phenomenon and the term.

Unfortunately, accommodation is much misunderstood. In fact, no curve of the type reproduced in Figure 19–5 has ever been experimentally determined. The experiments on accommodation as originally carried out by Erlanger and Gasser (1937) consist in the application of brief electric pulses at various intervals after a constant current is allowed to charge (or discharge) the membrane over extended periods of time. The constant current is kept below rheobase strength. Then one determines the amount of additional current (measured as voltage) that must be applied during the brief additional pulse in order to elicit a conducted response. In this way the time course of threshold excitability can be determined. Figure 16–35 illustrates the experiment and its explanation.

The accommodation has been related to the inactivation of the sodium conductance (see Eccles, 1953; Woodbury, 1960), by the prolonged action of the applied depolarizing current, or activation by the hyperpolarizing current. However, this cannot be the only explanation.

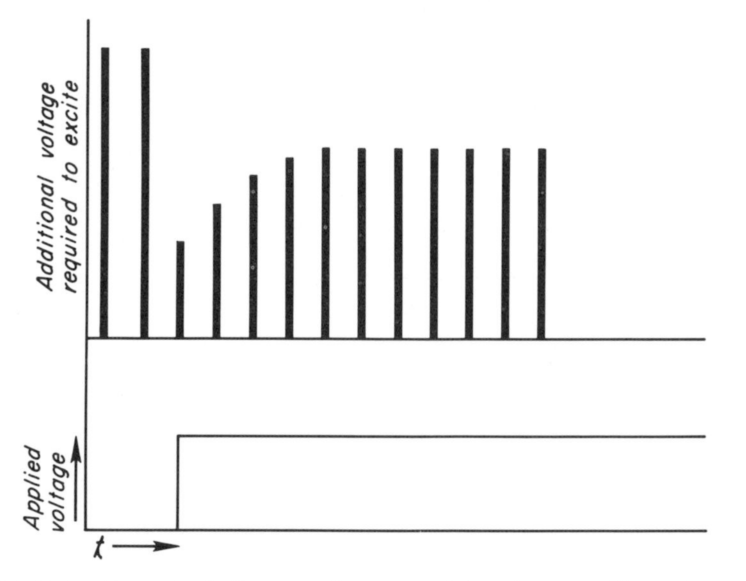

Figure 16–35A. Conceptual diagram of accommodation in nerve fibers. Immediately after the onset of the stimulus the excitability increases sharply as indicated by the lower voltage required to excite the membrane to produce an action potential. In the older literature this was referred to as a "lowering of the threshold." As explained in Figure 16–35B, the firing threshold always remains the same; what changes is only the threshold voltage (or threshold strength of the stimulus) which is just sufficient to excite. While the stimulus persists, the excitability rises again, as shown by the increasingly larger additional voltage needed to excite.

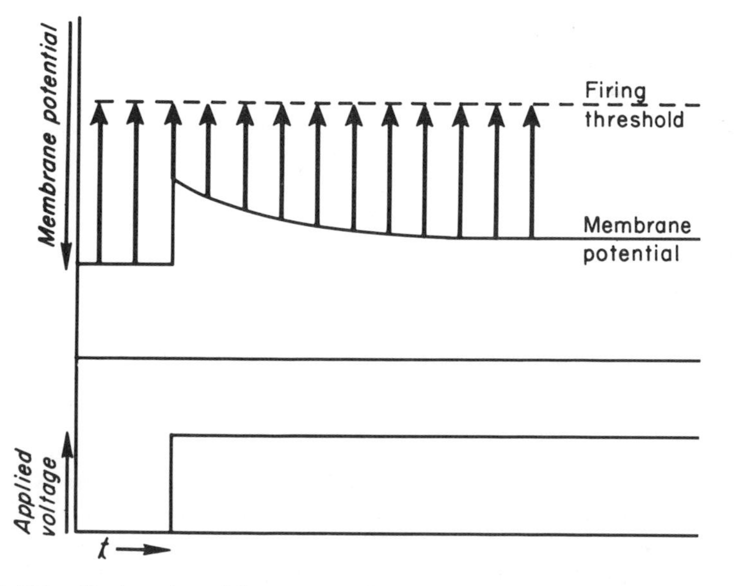

Figure 16–35B. Explanation of the accommodation phenomenon described in Figure 16–35A. The change in excitability of the nerve cell is causally related to the difference between the membrane potential and the firing threshold: the closer the membrane potential is to the firing threshold the less additional depolarization is required to excite the membrane to produce an action potential.

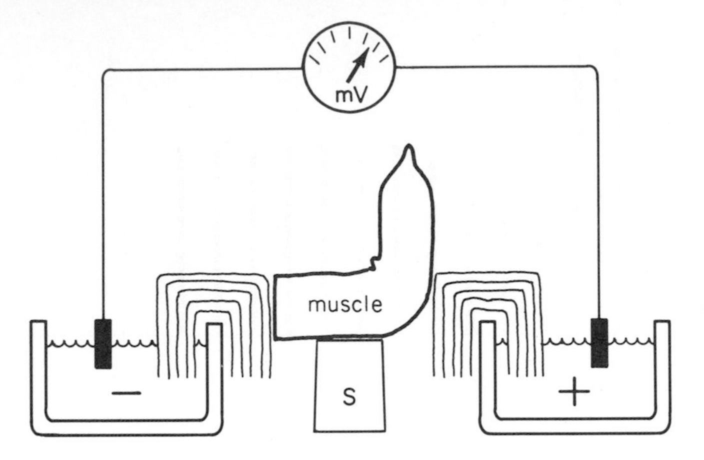

Figure 16–36. Experiment for the detection of injury current or demarcation potential of frog gastrocnemius muscle. A transverse cut has been made through the freshly dissected muscle. The cut end is held against a wad of filter paper dipped on one side into a glass vessel filled with NaCl solution. A similar wad of filter paper touches the uninjured side of the muscle. Nonpolarizable electrodes dip into the two saline-filled vessels and are connected with a galvanometer. S, a support made of insulating material. The diagram is based on figures published by Emil DuBois-Reymond in 1848 in his pioneering "Untersuchungen über die thierische Elektrizitaet."

INJURY POTENTIALS AND INJURY CURRENTS

Only a functionally intact cell membrane can maintain a normal resting potential. Wherever these conditions are disturbed, abnormal membrane potentials result. Destruction or injury of the membrane usually leads to a reduction or abolition of the potential difference between the inside and outside of the membrane.

Local reduction of the membrane potential can be the cause of excitation (generation of local potentials and action potentials) in neighboring regions of the membrane. Injury or partial destruction of the cell membrane, therefore, often acts as a powerful stimulus.

During the first decades of electrophysiology (much of it would today be called biophysics), intentional injury of part of the cell membrane was the only means of determining the magnitude of the resting potential. Most of the early experiments were done on frog muscles (gastrocnemius). The muscle was simply cut by a smooth cross section, and suitable electrodes were placed against the injured region and against an intact portion of the same muscle (Fig. 16–36). In order to avoid any possible change of the potential difference with time, ingenious experimenters used bone teeth, soaked with saline, as electrodes which could record the potential while they were used to literally bite through the muscle. The significance of these experiments is readily explained. The muscle cells are lying more or less parallel. Their outsides are in electric contact with each other, and therefore can be assumed to be of the same potential level (positive with regard to their inside). As the muscle is cut, the tooth electrode destroys the membrane of all cells lying across the section and at the same time makes contact with the interior of these cells which has a different potential (negative with respect to the outside).

The modern methods make use of microelectrodes inserted into the interior of single cells. These electrodes are so thin at their tips that it can be assumed they do not injure the membrane significantly. In this way membrane potentials can be recorded much more accurately, since the short circuits that result when the cell interior is exposed by injury are avoided.

The term "injury potential" actually means the potential difference between the injured region of a cell and the outer surface of its membrane. Since the potential difference arises at the point of demarcation between the normal and injured regions of the cell or a group or bundle of cells, this potential difference has also been named the *demarcation potential.*

Injury potentials often persist for many hours. They are accompanied by electric currents, the *injury current.* This consists of moving ions which follow the potential gradients and concentration gradients.

Nerve fibers with a normal resting potential close to the firing level may exhibit prolonged repetitive spike discharges after they are cut. This is obvious in arthropods: legs which are cut off can be seen to move for a considerable time after they are severed from the animal. This is due to the activation of motor nerve fibers by injury potentials.

SECRETION POTENTIALS, RESORPTION POTENTIALS, AND TRANSPORT POTENTIALS

Cell membranes are not destroyed only by injury. In certain cells parts of the cell membrane are periodically dissolved or cast off. This is the case with secretory cells, particularly those of the apocrine type (Fig. 11–23). Such actively secreting cells develop a potential difference between the secretory surface and the intact membrane. The secreting region becomes negative with respect to the intact outside surface of the cell. An active glandular epithelium thus develops a potential difference across it.

Even where the secretion process does not involve any obvious destruction of the cell membrane, profound alteration in the membrane structure of the secretory portion of the cell must be assumed, and differences in membrane potential between this and normal regions of the cell membrane are likely to result.

The same is true for cells that are active in resorption, that is, in the uptake of substances into the cell interior. Examples are the resorptive cells in the epithelia of the digestive tract and of "kidney" tubules.

Of greatest interest are the relations between membrane potential and ion and water transport. As pointed out in Chapter 5, the cells in gills and "kidneys" are often very active in the absorption or active excretion of salts. This ion transport undoubtedly leads to the development of potential differences between the two sides of the active cells, and between the two surfaces of the secretory—or excretory—epithelia. On the other hand, the existence of membrane potentials may well cause the ion transport. The same is true for the transport of water by electro-osmosis.

Few experimental data are available which go beyond the early experiments summarized by Biedermann (1895), Bernstein (1912), and Beutner (1944). However, there has been some argument about these problems recently. For a good starting point, refer to Ussing (1957) and Rehm and Dennis (1957). For a discussion of electric potentials generated by active ion transport see Chapter 27.

REFERENCES

Adrian, R. H. (1956) The effect of internal and external potassium concentration on the membrane potential of frog muscle. J. Physiol. *133*:631–658.

Bernstein, J. (1902) Untersuchungen zur Thermodynamik der bioelektrischen Stroeme. Erster Theil. Pflügers Arch. ges. Physiol. *92*:521–562.

Bernstein, J. (1912) Elektrobiologie. Vieweg Verlag., Braunschweig.

Beutner, R. (1920) Die Entstehung elektrischer Ströme in lebenden Geweben und ibre künstliche Nachahmung durch synthetische organische Substanzen. Experimentelle Untersuchungen. Mit einen Geleitwort von R. Höber. Ferdinand Enke, Stuttgart.

Beutner, R. (1944) Bioelectricity. *In* Medical Physics, Vol. 1, pp. 35–88. (O. Glasser, ed.) Year Book Publishers, Chicago.

Biedermann, W. (1895) Elektrophysiologie. G. Fischer Verlag, Jena.

Boyle, P. J., and E. J. Conway (1941) Potassium accumulation in muscle and associated changes. J. Physiol. *100*:1–63.

Cole, K. S. (1949) Dynamic electrical characteristics of the squid axon membrane. Arch. Sci. Physiol. *3*:253–258.

Curtis, H. J., and K. S. Cole (1940) Membrane action potentials from the squid giant axon. J. Cell. Comp. Physiol. *15*:147–157.

Curtis, H. J., and K. S. Cole (1942) Membrane resting and action potentials from the squid giant axon. J. Cell. Comp. Physiol. *19*:135–144.

Davies, H., and A. Forbes (1936) Chronaxie. Physiol. Rev. *16*:407–441.

Eccles, J. C. (1953) The Neurophysiological Basis of Mind. The Clarendon Press, Oxford.

Erlanger, J., and H. S. Gasser (1937) Electrical Signs of Nervous Activity. University of Pennsylvania Press, Philadelphia.

Gicklhorn, J. (1929) Die Herstellung von Mikroelektroden. *In* Elektrostatik in der Biochemie. (W. Ostwald, ed.) Sonderausgabe Kolloidchemische Beihefte *28*:208–390; 252–258.

Goldman, D. E. (1943) Potential, impedance and rectification in membranes. J. Gen. Physiol. *27*:37–60.

Graham, J., and R. W. Gerard (1946) Membrane potentials and excitation of impaled single muscle fibers. J. Cell. Comp. Physiol. *28*:99–117.

Harris, J. E., and H. Martins-Ferreira (1955) Membrane potentials in the muscles of the South American frog, *Leptodactylus ocellatus*. J. Exp. Biol. *32*:539–546.

Hevesy, G. C. (1948) Radioactive Indicators. Interscience Publishers, New York.

Hodgkin, A. L. (1951) The ionic basis of electrical activity in nerve and muscle. Biol. Rev. *26*:339–409.

Hodgkin, A. L. (1957) Ionic movements and electrical activity in giant nerve fibres. Proc. Roy. Soc. B, *148*:1–37.

Hodgkin, A. L., and A. F. Huxley (1939) Action potentials recorded from inside a nerve fiber. Nature *144*:710–711.

Hodgkin, A. L., and A. F. Huxley (1952a) A quantitative description of membrane current and its application to conduction and excitation in nerve. J. Physiol. *117*:500–544.

Hodgkin, A. L., and A. F. Huxley (1952b) Currents carried by sodium and potassium ions through the membrane of the giant axon of *Loligo*. J. Physiol. *116*:449–472.

Hodgkin, A. L., and A. F. Huxley (1952c) The components of membrane conductance in the giant axon of *Loligo*. J. Physiol. *116*:473–496.

Hodgkin, A. L., and A. F. Huxley (1952d) The dual effect of membrane potential on sodium conductance in the giant axon of *Loligo*. J. Physiol. *116*:497–506.

Hodgkin, A. L., and B. Katz (1949) The effect of sodium ions on the electrical activity of the giant axon of the squid. J. Physiol. *108*:37–77.

Hodgkin, A. L., and R. D. Keynes (1955) Active transport of cations in giant axons from *Sepia* and *Loligo*. J. Physiol. *128*:28–60.

Huxley, A. F. (1954) Electrical processes in nerve conduction. *In* Ion Transport across Membranes, pp. 23–39. (H. T. Clarke and D. Nachmansohn, eds.) Academic Press, New York.
Jenerick, H. P. (1953) Muscle membrane potentials, resistance and external potassium chloride. J. Cell. Comp. Physiol. *42*:427–448.
Keynes, R. D., and G. W. Maisel (1954) The energy requirements for sodium extrusion from a frog muscle. Proc. Roy. Soc. B, *142*:383–392.
Lapicque, L. (1926) L'excitabilité en fonction du temps; la chronaxie, sa signification et sa mesure. Presses Universitaires de France, Paris.
Ling, G. N., and R. W. Gerard (1949) The membrane potential and metabolism of muscle fibers. J. Cell. Comp. Physiol. *34*:413–438.
Marmont, G. (1949) Studies on the axon membrane. I. A new method. J. Cell. Comp. Physiol. *34*:351–382.
Narahashi, T. (1963) The properties of insect axons. Adv. Insect Physiol. *1*:175–256.
Nernst, W. (1888) Zur Kinetik der in Lösung befindlichen Körper. Z. physik. Chem. *2*:613–637.
Nernst, W. (1889) Die elektromotorische Wirksamkeit der Ionen. Z. physik. Chem. *4*:129–181.
Peterfi, T. (1925) Data presented by R. Keller. Die Elektrizität der Zelle, 2nd Ed. Verlag Julius Kittls Nachfolger Keller and Co., Maehrisch-Ostrau.
Pumphrey, R. J., and J. Z. Young (1938) The rates of conduction of nerve fibers of various diameters in cephalopods. J. Exp. Biol. *15*:453–466.
Rehm, W. S., and W. H. Dennis (1957) A discussion of theories of hydrochloric acid formation in the light of electrophysiological findings. *In* Metabolic Aspects of Transport across Cell Membranes, pp. 303–330. (Q. R. Murphy, ed.) University of Wisconsin Press, Madison.
Ridge, M. A. P., and R. J. Walker (1963) Bioelectric potentials. *In* Problems in Biology, Vol. 1, pp. 91–126. (G. A. Kerkut, ed.) Pergamon Press, Oxford.
Rushton, W. A. H. (1937) Initiation of the propagated distrubance. Proc. Roy. Soc. B, *124*:210–243.
Rushton, W. A. H. (1951) A theory of the effects of fibre size in medullated nerve. J. Physiol. *115*:101–122.
Umrath, K. (1930) Potentialmessungen an *Nitella mucronata* mit besonderer Berücksichtigung der Erregunserscheinungen. Protoplasma 9:576–597.
Umrath, K. (1956) Elektrophysiologische Phaenomene. *In* Encyclopedia of Plant Physiology, Vol. II, pp. 747–778. (W. Ruhland, ed.) Springer-Verlag, Berlin.
Ussing, H. H. (1957) General principles and theories of membrane transport. *In* Metabolic Aspects of Transport across Cell Membranes, pp. 39–56. (Q. R. Murphy, ed.) University of Wisconsin Press, Madison.
Wilde, W. S. (1957) Discussion remarks *in* Metabolic Aspects of Transport across Cell Membranes, pp. 157–167. (Q. R. Murphy, ed.) University of Wisconsin Press, Madison.
Woodbury, J. W. (1965) The cell membrane: ionic and potential gradients and active transport. *In* Medical Physiology and Biophysics, pp. 1–25. (T. C. Ruch and H. D. Patton, eds.) W. B. Saunders Co., Philadelphia.
Woodbury, J. W. (1965) Action potential: properties of excitable membrane. *In* Medical Physiology and Biophysics, pp. 26–58. (T. C. Ruch and H. D. Patton, eds.) W. B. Saunders Co., Philadelphia.

17 THE NERVOUS SYSTEM

No other organ system has received as much attention as the nervous system. Neurophysiology is the largest branch of physiology. The study of the nervous system is so fascinating because it touches on the innermost problem of biology: behavior and mind.

Within the animal organism the nervous system is the chief coordinating agency. Almost every organ function is controlled and continuously regulated by it. And almost all the operations of organs are continuously monitored by sensory nerve systems. The nervous system is the most extensive and elaborate control system known to man.

The endocrine system which controls organ growth and function by bloodborne hormones is not only controlled by the nervous system, but is to a large degree a part of it. The hormones elaborated by the neurohypophysis of vertebrates, by the X-organ and sinus gland complex of decapod crustaceans, and by the corpora allata-cardiaca system of insects are secretory products of nerve cells (see Chapter 21).

On the other hand, more and more evidence accumulates which indicates that hormones act on the nervous system itself, so that we must consider the nervous system as an immense control system which operates by positive and negative feedback not only through impulse conducting channels (nerves and nerve fibers) but also through hormones.

Nervous systems are today understood as transducer and amplifier systems with negative and positive feedback circuits. Central nervous systems are treated as analytical computers.

As a functional system a nervous system not only consists of nerve tissue but shows an intricate organization involving many other types of tissues as well.

Ganglia, nerves, and often the individual nerve fibers are usually covered with layers of connective tissue. These give the rather tender and fragile nerve cells the necessary mechanical support and protection. Examples of such protective coverings are shown in Figures 17–1 through 17–5.

Ganglia, as well as connectives and even nerves, are often found to lie within special body compartments or sinuses which contain a fluid (Fig. 17–6). The composition of the fluid is in most cases unknown, but in larger vertebrates, in which the fluid is known as *cerebrospinal fluid* or *liquor,* it is found to be similar to the interstitial fluid that fills the so-called extracellular space between body cells. Nevertheless, it is conspicuous that even in the vertebrates there is no direct communication between the cerebrospinal fluid and the fluid of the extracellular body space outside the nervous system.

The enclosure of the fluid that surrounds the major portion of the nervous system in other phyla is an indication that nerve tissue requires a special environment and that, perhaps, it needs to be protected from substances that circulate through the blood stream, coelomic spaces, and interstices of the other organs. The vertebrate cerebrospinal fluid not only bathes the outside of

(Text continued on page 425.)

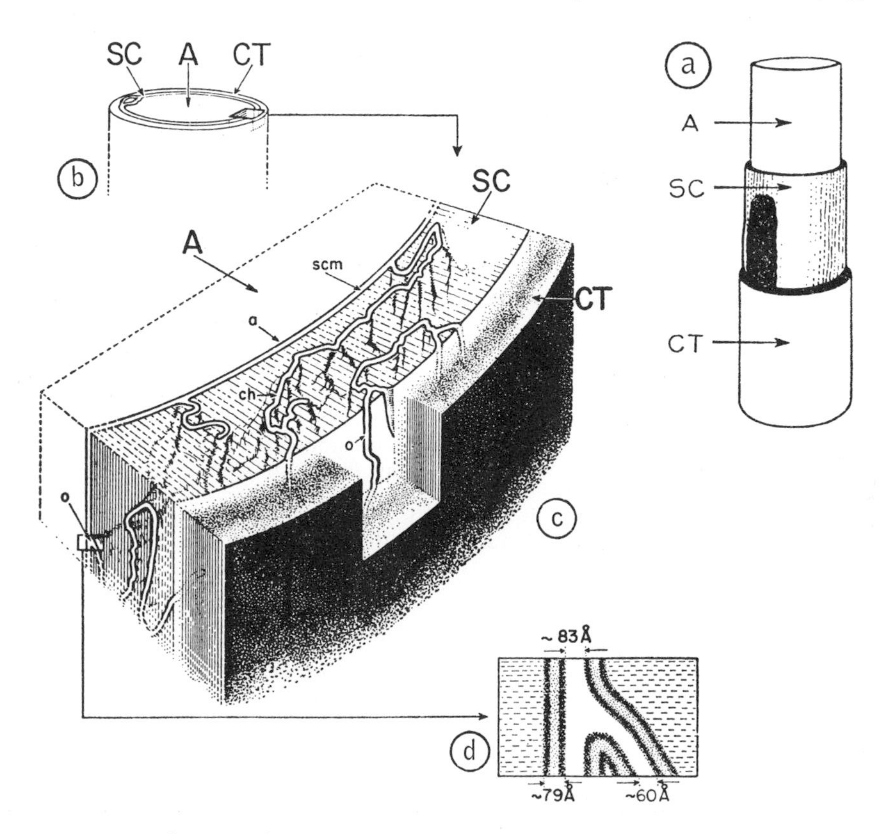

Figure 17–1. Schematic drawing of a giant nerve fiber from the first stellar nerve of the squid (Cephalopoda) *Dorytheuthis plei.* **a** and **b** show the relation between axon (*A*), Schwann cell (*SC*), and connective tissue (*CT*). **c** shows an enlarged portion of the fiber in which channels (*ch*) are shown as slits crossing the Schwann cell from the outer surface to the axonal surface. *a,* axonal membrane (axolemma); *o,* opening of the channel. **d** shows a highly enlarged view of one of the channel openings in which the continuity of the channel walls with the Schwann cell membrane (*scm*) is demonstrated. (From Villegas, R., and G. Villegas: Characterization of membranes in the giant nerve fiber of the squid. J. Gen. Physiol. *43*:73–104, 1960.)

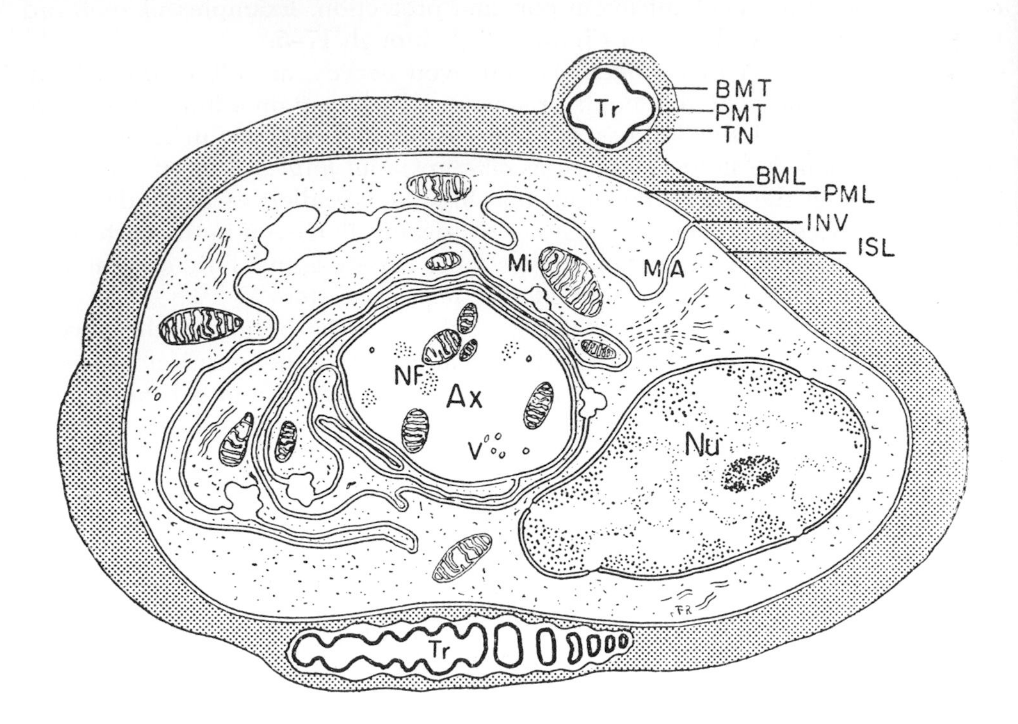

Figure 17–2. Diagram of a sheathed nerve (actually only a single axon) from the leg of a wasp. Arthropod connective tissue, unlike that of other animal phyla, contains no fibroblasts or fibrils; it consists of merged basement membranes derived from tracheoblasts. The lemnoblast is the same kind of cell which, elsewhere, would be called Schwann cell. The accompanying tracheolar (*Tr*) intima (*TN*) is enclosed within the plasma membrane (*PMT*), and basement membrane (*BMT*) of the tracheoblast. The latter membrane merges with the thick basement membrane (*BML*) of the lemnoblast. The lemnoblast plasma membrane (*PML*), separated by an interspace (*ISL*) from the basement membrane, invaginates (*INV*) to form the mesaxon (*MA*). The mesaxon meanders through the cytoplasm, finally forming a loose mantle of membranes around the axon. The lemnoblast shows a typical nucleus (*Nu*), mitochondria (*Mi*), and membrane-bound profiles. The axon (*Ax*) typically contains mitochondria, neurofilaments (*NF*), and a few vesicles or membrane-bound profiles (*V*). (Drawing by Frank Reed.) (From Edwards, G. A., H. Ruska, and E. deHarven: Electron microscopy of peripheral nerves and neuromuscular junctions in the wasp leg. J. Biophys. Biochem. Cytol. *4*:107–114, 1958.)

Figure 17–4. Diagram to explain the relation of subarachnoid space, blood vessels, and nerve tissue proper. Note that the small blood vessel (artery) and its side branch are surrounded by subarachnoid space. The space around the capillaries is labeled "perivascular space" and is shown continuous with a space around nerve cells ("perineural space"); this represents an interpretation of the brain structures as seen with the light microscope. The electron microscope (see Figs. 17–7 and 17–8) reveals that these spaces contain processes of glia cells which form a barrier between blood vessels and nerve tissue (*blood-brain barrier*). (From Ranson, S. W., and S. L. Clark: The Anatomy of the Nervous System, 10th Ed. W. B. Saunders Co., Philadelphia, 1959.)

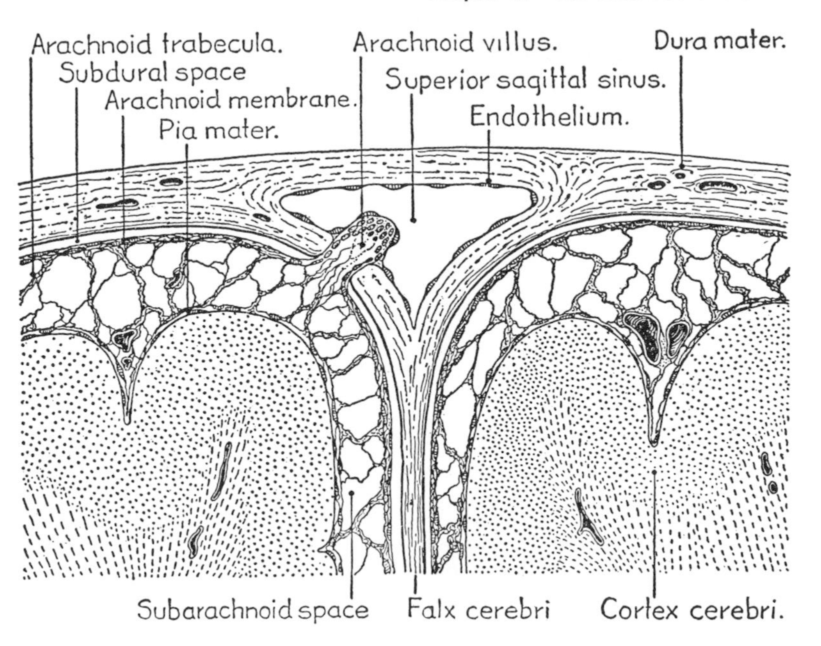

Figure 17–3. Diagram to explain the position and relation of the connective tissue layers or membranes that cover the central nervous system of vertebrates. These membranes are called *meninges*. The outer one is the thickest and strongest, known as *dura mater*. Below it is the delicate *arachnoid membrane*, which forms the outer covering of the so-called *subarachnoid space* which is filled with cerebrospinal fluid. The third layer, the *pia mater*, separates the subarachnoid space from the nerve tissue proper. Blood vessels and blood sinus lie within the dura mater and in the subarachnoid space (see also Figs. 17–4 and 17–5). The *falx cerebri*, a continuation of the dura mater, forms a septum that separates the two cerebral hemispheres. Arachnoid and pia mater are connected by processes called arachnoid *trabecula*. (From Weed *in* Ranson, S. W., and S. L. Clark: The Anatomy of the Nervous System, 10th Ed. W. B. Saunders Co., Philadelphia, 1959.)

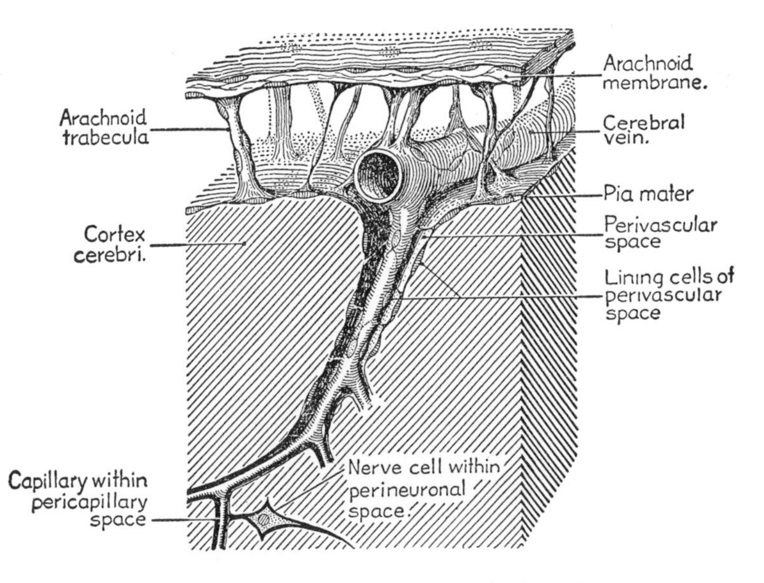

Figure 17–4. *See opposite page for legend.*

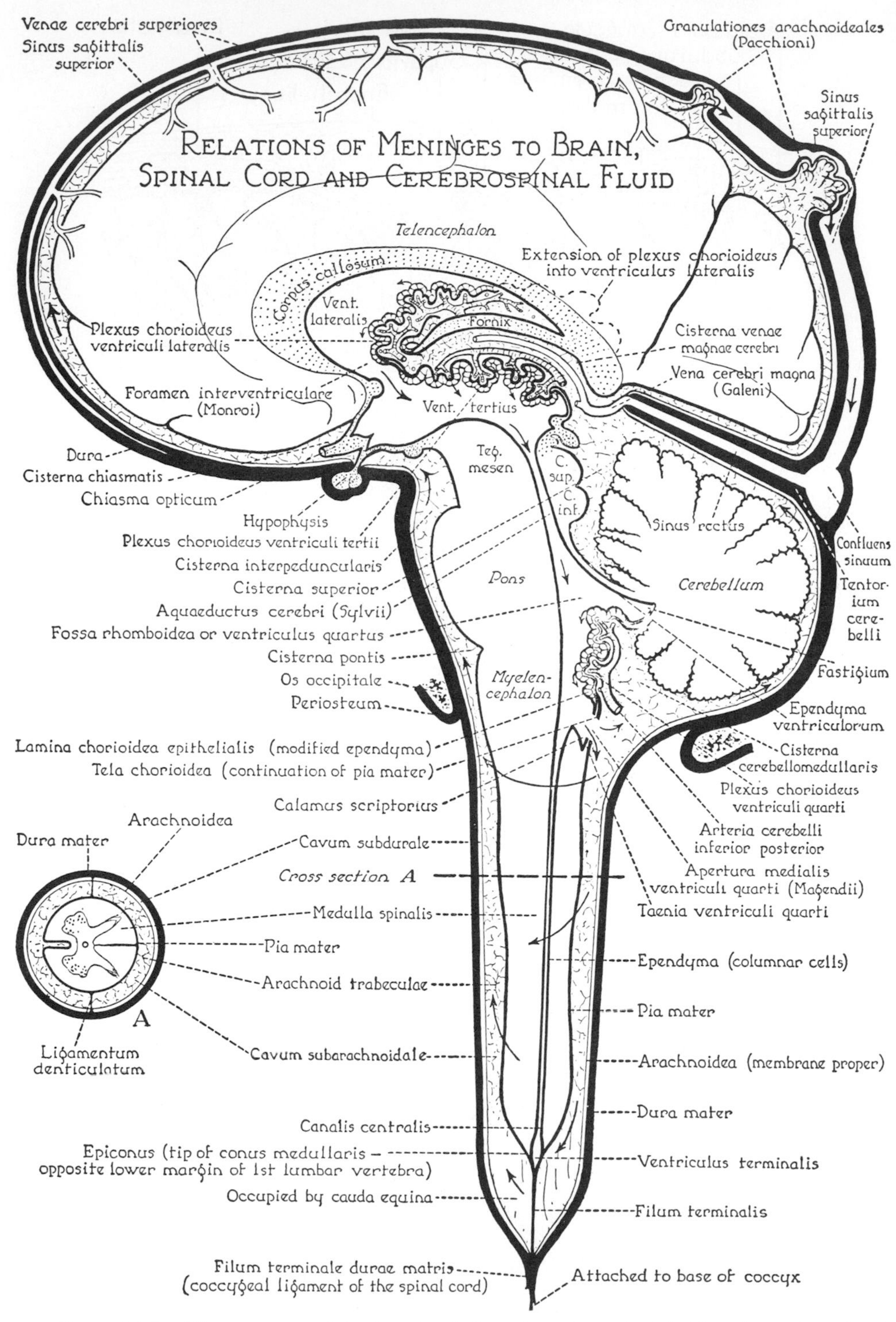

Figure 17–5. Diagram to explain the circulation of cerebrospinal fluid within subarachnoid spaces and brain ventricles. The fluid is formed by the *plexus chorioideus* and is absorbed by the arachnoid *villi* (see Fig. 17–3) and *granulationes*. (After Rasmussen, A. T.: The Principal Nervous Pathways, 4th Ed. By permission of the Macmillan Co., Publishers, 1952.)

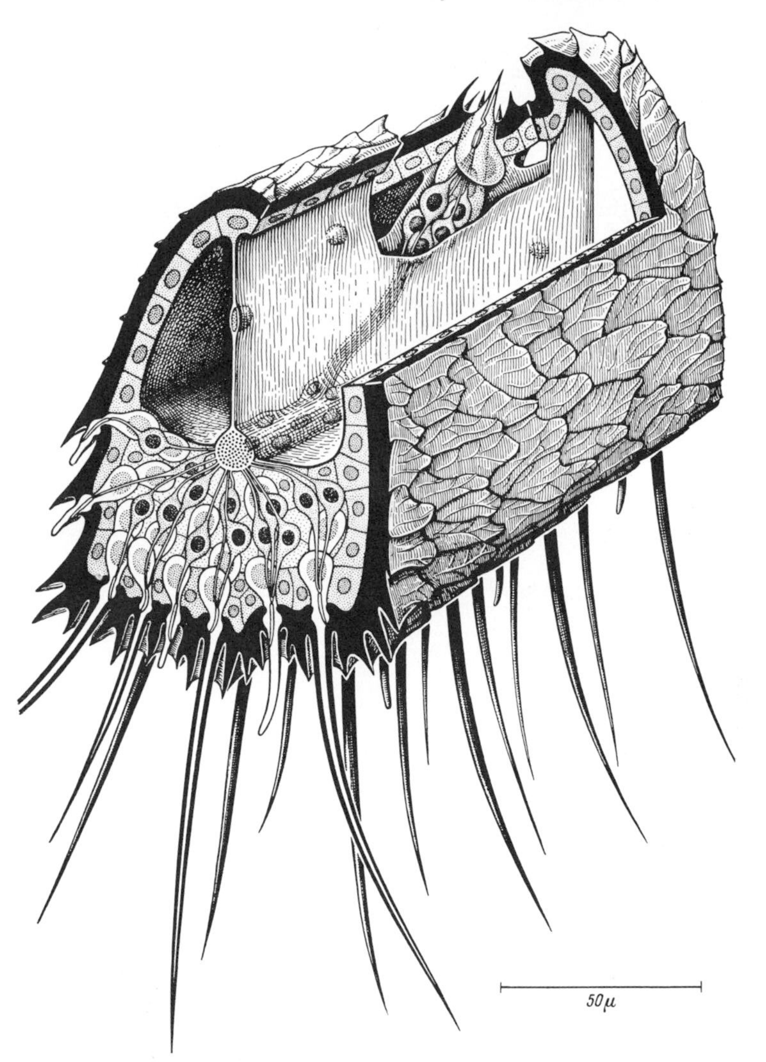

Figure 17–6. Three-dimensional representation of the structure of a side branch of one antenna of the moth (Insecta) *Bombyx mori* (see Fig. 25–2). Note the double septum which, together with the basal membrane and the neurilemma, separates all tissues, in particular the nerve cells and nerves from the hemolymph space. The diagram also shows the numerous sensory hairs and a nerve branch going to an olfactory sense organ. (From Schneider, D., and K. E. Kaissling: Der Bau der Antenne des Seidenspinners Bombyx mori, L. III. Das Bindegewebe und das Blutgefäss. Zool. Jahrb. Abt. Anat. Ontog. d. Tiere 77:11–132, 1959.)

the mass of central nerve tissue, but is contained within cavities of the brain (known as ventricles) and the spinal cord (known as the spinal canal), as shown in Figure 17–5.

In animals in which blood or hemolymph is pumped through a vascular system, the nervous system, and in particular the central nervous system, receives a conspicuous supply of arteries and capillaries. In the vertebrates the capillaries within the central nervous system are surrounded by special glia cells (Figs. 17–7 and 17–8). Any exchange of materials across the capillary wall, therefore, is between the blood and the intracellular medium of glia cells.

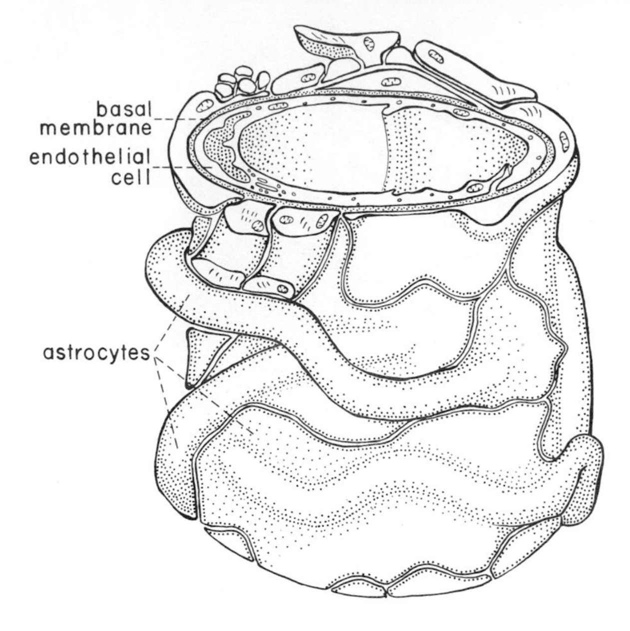

Figure 17–7. A capillary in the mammalian cerebral cortex, surrounded by densely applied processes of glia cells of the type known as astrocytes. These processes form a sheath around the capillary and completely modify its permeability characteristics, thus forming the well known blood-brain barrier. (Redrawn after Wolff, J.: Beiträge zur Ultrastruktur der Kapillaren in der normalen Grosshirnrinde. Z. Zellforsch. *60*:409–431, 1963.)

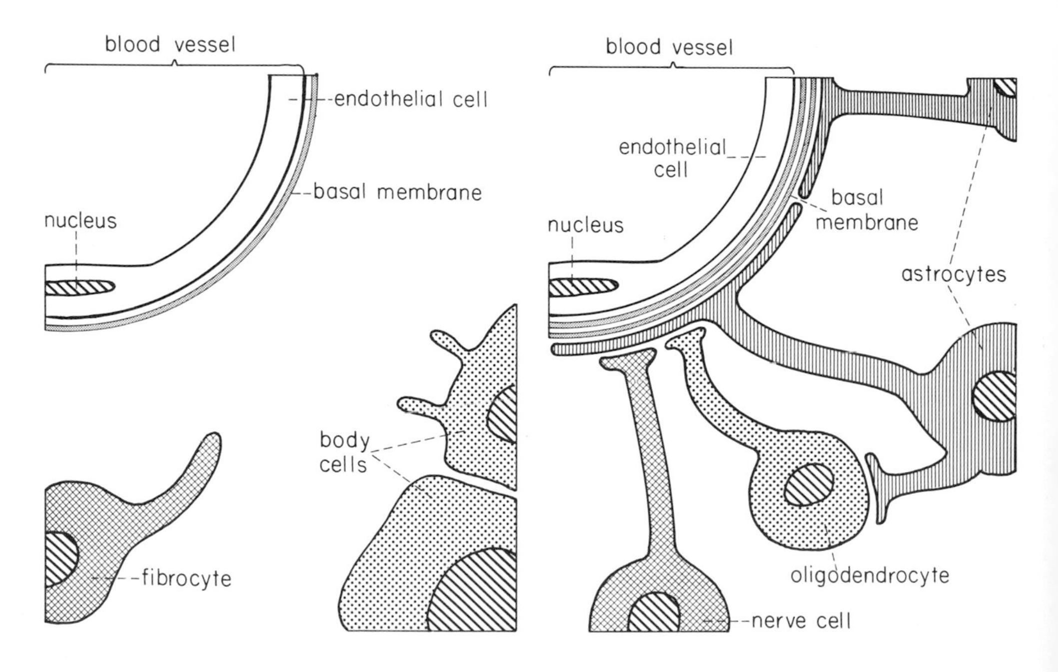

Figure 17–8. Relation between the blood capillaries and extracellular space in body tissues (**left**) and in brain tissue (**right**). Astrocyte processes form a barrier around brain capillaries. Note also the double basement membrane. (Diagrams based on drawings of Wolff, J.: Beiträge zur Ultrastruktur der Kapillaren in der normalen Grosshirnrinde. Z. Zellforsch. *60*:409–431, 1963.)

There appears to be no direct exchange between blood and the cerebrospinal fluid. For this reason one speaks of a *blood-brain barrier* which prevents the ready diffusion of substances from the blood stream into the cerebrospinal fluid and vice versa. It is believed that selective transport of nutritional material is accomplished by the glia cells. Much has to be learned about the mechanisms of gas exchange and transfer of hormones and of excretory products.

In the Crustacea the situation is not so very different. Hemolymph flows by way of arteries and capillaries into extensive sinuses which are enclosed by sheaths of dense connective tissue. This is also the case in insects. There, however, at least the problem of gas exchange is solved in a comprehensible manner: air-filled tracheal tubules enter the nervous system, penetrate the sheaths, and end among the nerve cells and fibers.

The significance of the separation of "extracellular fluid" of the nervous system and that of the rest of the body and blood or hemolymph is nowhere so obvious as in the herbivorous insects. Plants contain extremely little sodium—in fact, sodium is not a necessary constituent of a plant's nutrition. A caterpillar feeding on leaves thus has only traces of sodium in its diet. Its blood is found to contain almost no sodium. Yet the nerve cells require a considerable Na^+ ion concentration in their external environment for the production of nerve impulses. It is indeed found that there are considerable amounts of Na^+ present in the nervous system. There is good evidence that a layer of large glia cells which surround the core of nerve cells is responsible for the accumulation of Na^+ ions (Thornton, 1963). In a way, the glia cells may be considered as extracellular space as far as the nerve cells are concerned. They are likely to be quite permeable to ions, and we may assume that their intracellular aqueous medium is in a sort of diffusion equilibrium with whatever little true extracellular space (see Fig. 17–9) exists between them and the true nerve cells.

We may safely forgo a discussion of the situation in other phyla since little more is known than the anatomical fact that the central nervous system is usually enclosed within a fluid-filled sinus or a system of sinuses.

STRUCTURE

Nervous Systems

Nervous systems are organized into three main structures; their morphological characteristics recur in practically all animal groups (exceptions: Protozoa, Porifera, Coelenterata, and certain parasites). The structures are: ganglia, nerves, and nerve nets.

Ganglia. Ganglia are groups of nerve cells and nerve cell bodies surrounded by glia cells and enclosed by sheaths of connective tissue (Fig. 17–10). Ganglia that contain the terminations of sensory neurons and the cell bodies of motor fibers (which control the locomotion of the animal), and that are concerned with the elaboration of the overt behavior of the animal, are collectively called the *central nervous system*. This term includes, however, the *commissures* and *connectives* which are composed of cell processes (axons) and connect

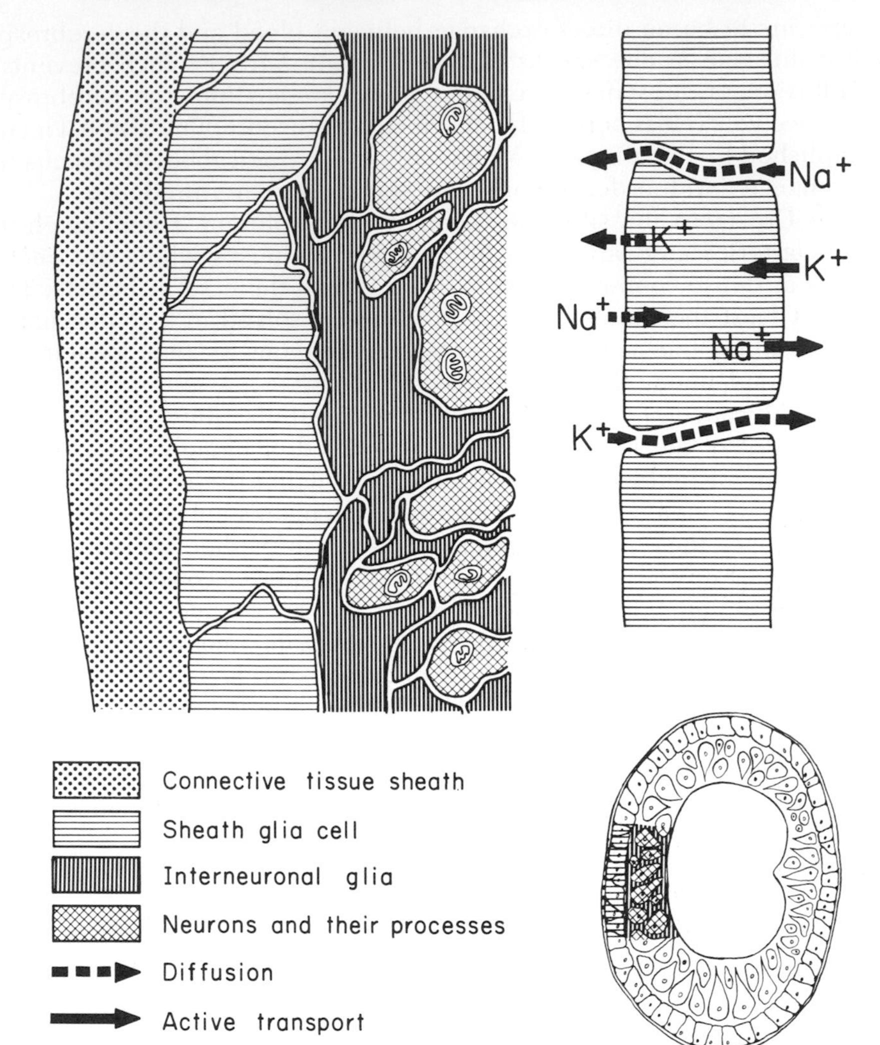

Figure 17–9. Cross section through a ganglion of the central nervous system of a larva of the sphinx moth *Ceratomia* (lower right) and ultrastructure of part of this (upper left). Note the layer of large sheath glia cells and the interneuronal glia cells that fill the entire space between the nerve cells and their processes, leaving only a gap of about 200 Å for extracellular fluid. The suggested function of the sheath glia cells in ion transport is shown at the upper right. (Based on diagrams of Thornton, J. W.: The relationship of the low sodium, herbivorous diet of Sphingidae to the ionic composition of their hemolymph and the activity and histology of their central nervous system. Thesis, University of Washington, Seattle, 1963.)

ganglia belonging to the central nervous system. Examples are shown in Figures 17–11 and 17–12.

In many organisms certain ganglia are situated outside the central nervous system. They are collectively called *peripheral ganglia*. Often these are named after the location in which they are found or after the organ which they control. Examples are the *cardiac* ganglia, which control heartbeat, and the *visceral*

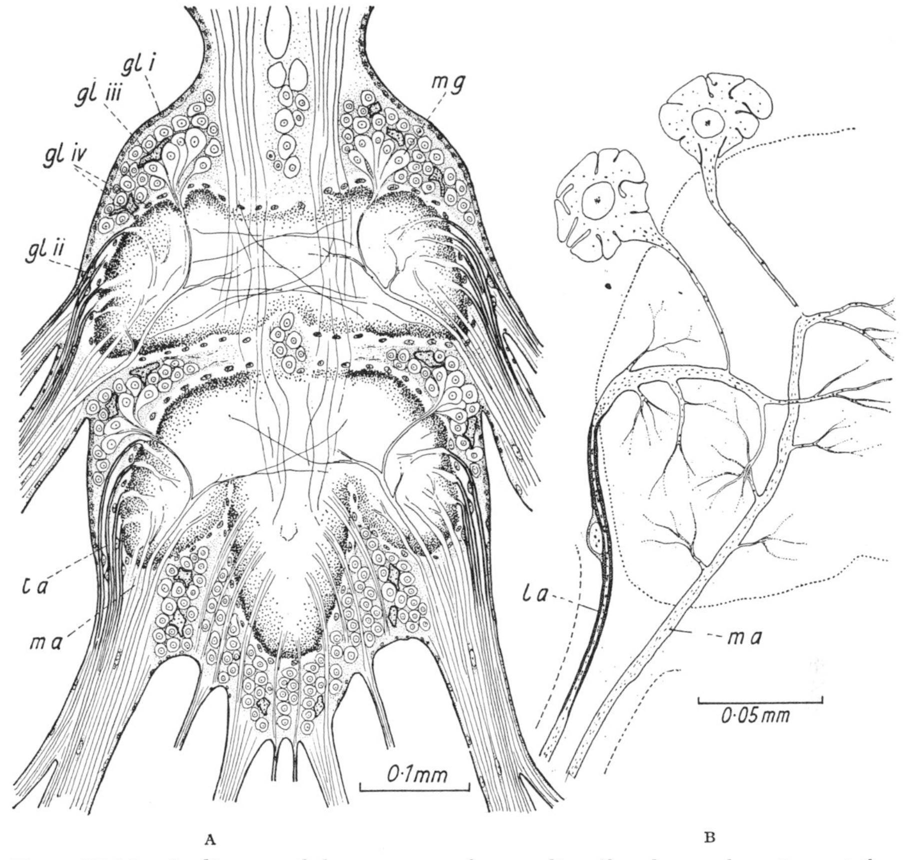

Figure 17–10. A, diagram of the structure of a ganglion (fused mesothoracic, metathoracic, and abdominal ganglia) of the hemipteran insect *Rhodnius,* showing the relation of glia and nerve cells. Note the absence of cell bodies in the neuropile region. *gl i,* perineurium; *gl ii,* glial cells forming sheaths of lateral motor axons; *gl iii,* nucleus of giant glial cell; *gl iv,* nuclei of glial cells surrounding the dark neuropile; *la,* lateral motor axons; *ma,* medial motor axons; *mg,* motor ganglion cells.

B, semischematic scale drawing of a typical lateral motor axon (*la*) and medial motor axon (*ma*). The dotted lines mark the boundaries of the nerve and of the dark neuropile.

(From Wigglesworth, V. B.: Histology of the nervous system of an insect, *Rhodnius prolixus* [Hemiptera]. Quart. J. Micr. Sci. *100*:299–313, 1959.)

ganglia, which control the digestive tract. As a rule, *reflex connections between afferent and efferent neurons do not occur in peripheral ganglia.*

Nerves. Nerves are tubular structures composed of long processes of nerve cells, the cell bodies of which may be situated in sense organs or tissues, or in ganglia. Nerves also contain glia cells or modified glia cells (*Schwann cells*) which surround the nerve fibers (Figs. 17–13 and 17–14), and connective tissue cells which form a sheath around individual axons or axon bundles (Fig. 17–2). Usually the nerve fibers and nerve fiber bundles are enclosed in a common nerve sheath.

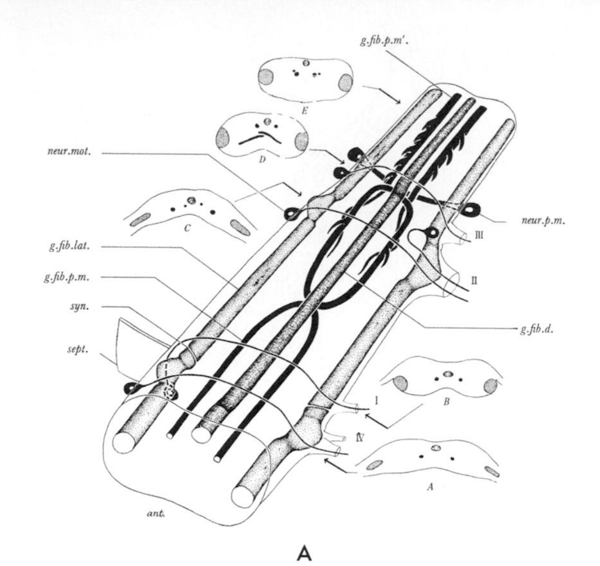

A

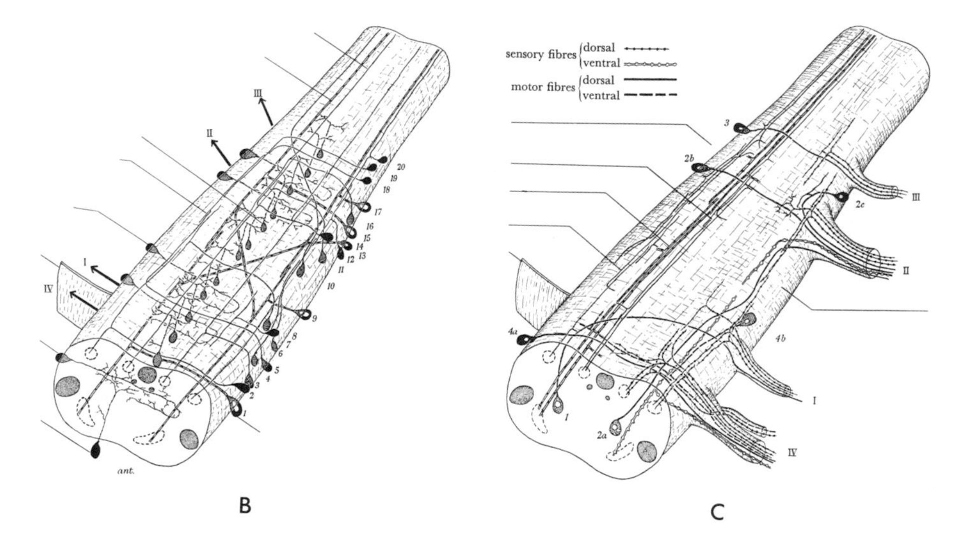

B C

Figure 17–11. Stereograms of a ganglion in the ventral nerve cord of the annelids *Nereis diversicolor* and *Platynereis dumerilii.* The general arrangement of nerve cells in the two species is similar. Imagine all three diagrams superimposed to get an impression of the complexity of the organization of the annelid central nervous system. Four systems of neurons are shown: **A**, the giant neurons; **B**, interneurons; **C**, sensory and motoneurons. The nerve roots are indicated in roman numerals. The part of a septum (*sept.*) shown indicates the boundary between two body segments. There are five giant neurons: one dorsal (*g.fib.d.*), two paramedial (*g.fib.p.m.*), and two lateral (*g.fib.lat.*). The soma, or perikaryon, of the lateral giant fibers is not known, but these neurons are not longer than one segment: they form a wedge-shaped synapse (*syn.*) with the corresponding neuron of the next ganglion. The paramedial giants likewise reach only from one ganglion to the next; the two cross twice, then make synaptic contact with the corresponding cells in the next, anterior ganglion. The cell body or bodies of the dorsal giant fiber are situated in the subesophageal ganglion. This fiber runs uninterruptedly the whole length of the nerve cord. Certain motor neurons (*neur.mot.*) make synaptic contact with the lateral giant fibers. The neuropile is not shown in the diagrams. (From Smith, J. E.: The nervous anatomy of the body segments of nereid polychaetes. Phil. Trans. Roy. Soc. London B, *240*:135–196, 1957.)

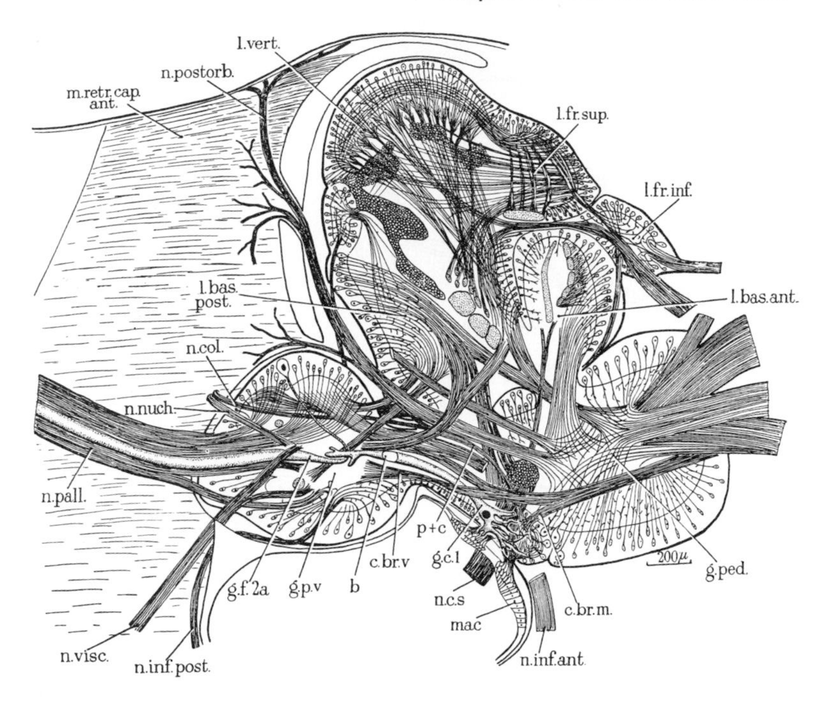

Figure 17–12. Semidiagrammatic view of a sagittal section through the lateral portion of the central nervous system of a cephalopod mollusc (*Loligo*) as seen from the inner side, anterior part on the right. Note the orderly arrays of cell bodies and axons in vertical, superior and inferior, and anterior and posterior basal lobes and in the pedal ganglion (*g.ped.*) and palliovisceral ganglion (*g.p.v*). Note the fiber tracts that connect the different parts of the central nervous system. The neuropile is not shown.

Find the first order giant neuron (*g.c.1*) and the second order giant neuron (*g.f.2a*) that leaves the palliovisceral ganglion through the pallial nerve (*n.pall.*) to join the stellate ganglion where it synapses with third order giant neurons (see Fig. 20-8). There are two first and two second order giant neurons; the former form a connection at *b*.

b, interaxonic bridge; *c.br.m.*, brachio-magnocellular connective; *c.br.v.*, brachio-palliovisceral connective; *g.c.1*, first-order giant cell; *g.f.2a*, second-order axon running to stellate ganglion and making distal synapses; *g.ped.*, pedal ganglion; *g.p.v.*, palliovisceral ganglion; *l.bas.ant.*, lobus basalis anterior; *l.bas.post.*, lobus basalis posterior; *l.fr.inf.*, lobus frontalis inferior; *l.fr.sup.*, lobus frontalis superior; *l.vert.*, lobus verticalis; *mac.*, macula of the statocyst; *m.retr.cap.ant.*, musculus retractor capitus anterior; *n.col.*, nervus collaris; *n.c.s.*, nervus cristae staticae; *n.inf.ant.*, nervus infundibuli anterior; *n.inf.post.*, nervus infundibuli posterior; *n.nuch.*, not nervus nuchalis, but a part of n. collaris; *n.pall.*, nervus palliallis; *n.postorb.*, nervus postorbitalis; *n.visc.*, nervus visceralis; *p.+c.*, branches of n. postorbitalis and n. collaris leading to l. magnocellularis.

(From Young, J. Z.: Fused neurons and synaptic contacts in the giant nerve fibres of cephalopods. Phil. Trans. Roy. Soc. 229:465–503, 1939.)

Nerves usually do not contain nerve cell bodies, and the length of a nerve is nearly identical with the length of the individual cell processes contained within them. Nerves may connect ganglia or run directly to effector organs, such as muscles or glands.

Nerves that run from a central ganglion to a peripheral ganglion are referred to as *preganglionic nerves*; nerves that run from a peripheral ganglion to an effector organ are called *postganglionic nerves.* A nerve containing only sensory

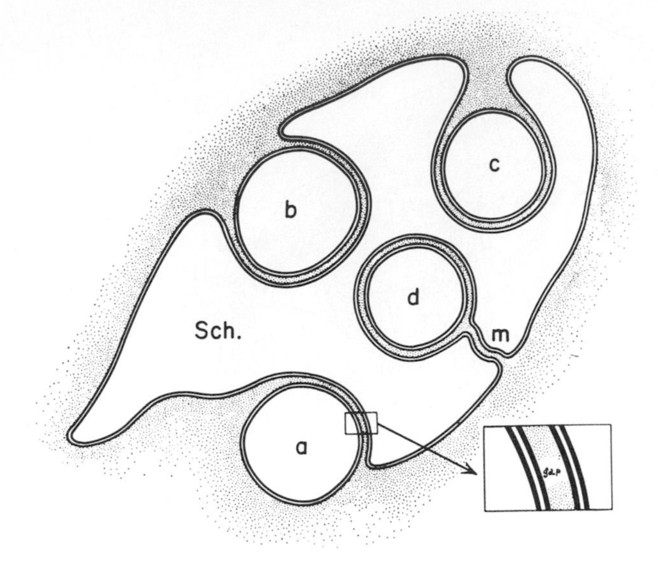

Figure 17–13. Diagram of a cross section through a "satellite" Schwann cell in which four "non-myelinated" axons are imbedded. *a* to *d*, the four axons; *Sch.*, Schwann cell. Where the two lips of the Schwann cell meet around axon *d* they form a paired membrane structure known as the *mesaxon* (*m*). A segment of the axon-Schwann membrane is enlarged at the lower right to show the gap between the two unit membranes. (From Robertson, J. D.: New unit membrane organelle of Schwann cells. *In* Biophysics of Physiological and Pharmacological Actions. A. M. Shanes, ed. Amer. Assn. Adv. Sci., Washington, D.C., pp. 63–96, 1961.)

fibers is called a *sensory nerve*; a nerve containing only motor fibers is a *motor nerve*. If both sensory and motor fibers are present, one speaks of *mixed nerves*. The total of all sensory, motor, and mixed nerves of an animal is referred to as the *peripheral nervous system*.

The peripheral ganglia, together with their pre- and postganglionic nerves, are often called the *autonomic nervous system*.

Nerve Nets. Nerve nets are two-dimensional arrays of bipolar and multipolar nerve cells; that is, they are composed of singly placed nerve cell bodies which are connected by cell processes. Nerve nets are characteristic of organs or organisms consisting of hollow muscle sheaths or tubes. Examples are: coelenterates, tube feet and external musculature of echinoderms, the body wall of adult tunicates, and the muscular portion of the intestine of almost all coelomate animals. An example of a nerve net and details of its structure are shown in Figure 17–15.

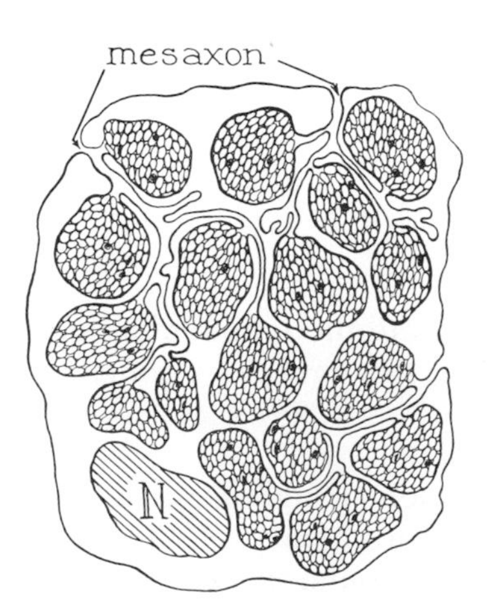

Figure 17–14. Schematic representation of the relation of the olfactory nerve fibers to the Schwann cell (olfactory nerve of rabbit). Groups of naked axons are surrounded by the infolding Schwann cell membrane. The infolding is called the *mesaxon*. Note the enormous size of the Schwann cell and its nucleus (*N*). (From DeLorenzo, A. J.: Electron microscopic observations of the olfactory mucosa and olfactory nerve. J. Biophys. Biochem. Cytol. 3:839–850, 1957.)

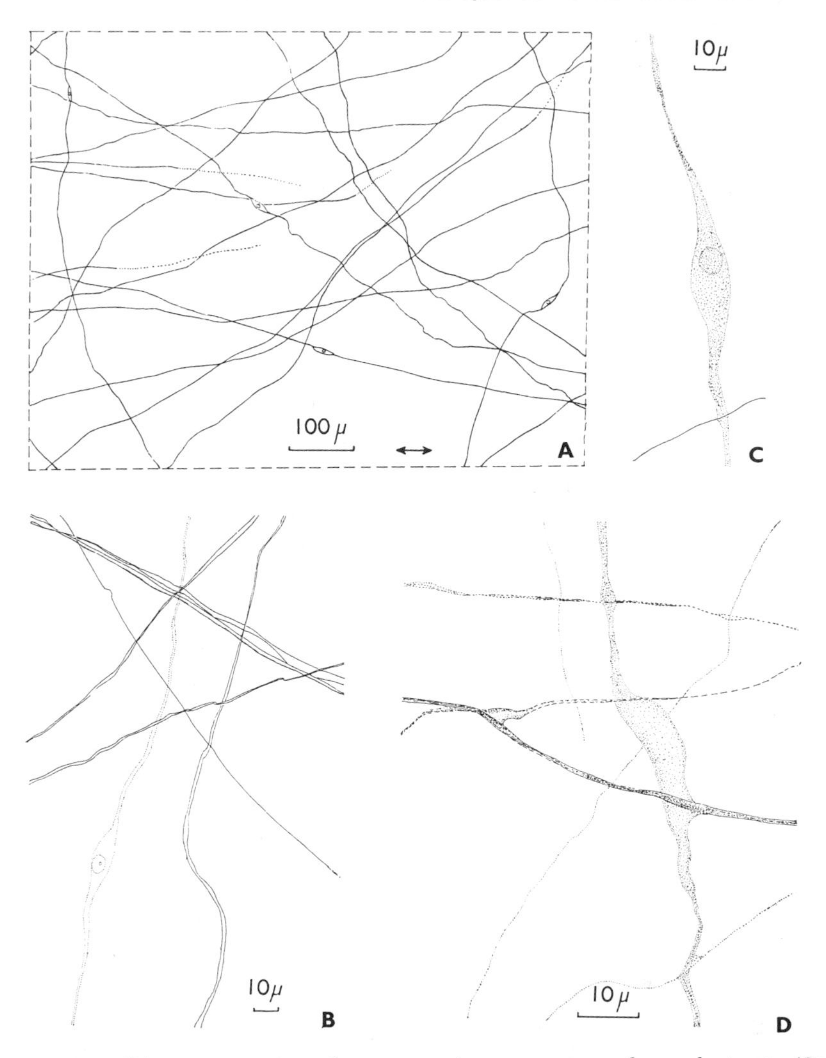

Figure 17–15. Silver preparation of nerve net in a mesentery of a coelenterate (*Stomphia*, the swimming sea anemone). A representative area is shown in **A**. The arrows indicate the direction of the retractor muscle fibers. **B**, **C**, and **D** show enlargements of some of the bipolar nerve cells, their axons and various forms of connections. The latter may be synapses or true fusions of cell processes. In the absence of specific information the connections are simply termed "junctions" implying that they are capable of impulse transmission and that they may show such properties as summation, facilitation, and subthreshold excitation, just as synapses do, even though they may not be true synapses. (From Robson, E. A.: The nerve-net of a swimming anemone, Stomphia coccinea. Quart. J. Micr. Sci. *104*:535–549, 1963.)

Coelenterates have no central nervous system proper but their nerve nets often exhibit elaborate organization. Some species have portions of their nerve nets condensed to ganglion-like structures, others to nervelike strands, known as through-conducting nets. An excellent survey of the known features of coelenterate nerve-net structure and function can be found in the treatise of Bullock and Horridge (1965). Coelenterate nerve nets are capable of elaborate response patterns and can give rise to complex behavior. A good example is shown in Figure 17–16.

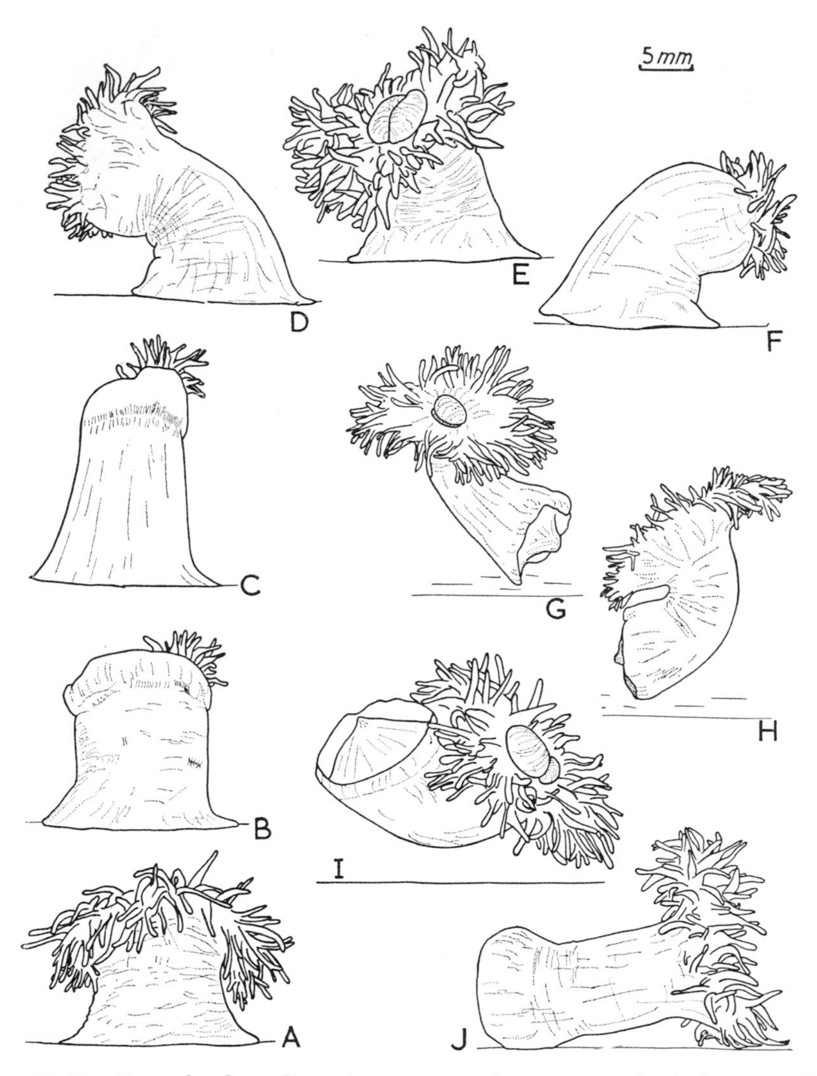

Figure 17–16. Example of coordinated movements of an organism that lacks a central nervous system: the swimming sea anemone (Anthozoa) *Stomphia coccinea.* **A**, normal appearance of *S. coccinea.* **B**, specimen responding to stimulation by starfish. The oral disk is partly retracted and the sphincter is contracting. **C**, extension of the column after contraction of the column. The oral disk is beginning to expand. Both actions are due to contraction of the circular muscle sheet of the column. **D**, lateral bending movement caused by rapid contraction of limited area of parietobasilar muscles. **E**, lateral bending toward the observer. Note the folds of gullet protruding through the mouth as a result of increased internal pressure. **F**, lateral bending. Note the raised edge of the pedal disk. **G**, swimming. The specimen is free from substratum and is actively swimming. **G**, **H**, and **I** illustrate the side-to-side bending movements. **H**, swimming. **I**, swimming. Note the conical shape of the pedal disk. **J**, anemone during the period of inactivity after swimming. Note that the oral end of the animal is supported by the turgid oral disk and tentacles. (From Sund, P.: A study of the muscular anatomy and swimming behavior of the sea anemone, *Stomphia coccinea.* Quart. J. Micr. Sci. 99:401–420, 1958.)

Nervous Tissue

Nervous tissue proper consists of two kinds of cells: *nerve cells* (neurons) and *glia cells*. Nerve cells are always associated with glia cells, they are never alone. Glia cells accompany them to their farthest extensions. Several instances are known in which glia cells actually indent the nerve cells (Fig. 17–17). All electron microscope studies of nerve tissue have shown that the cells within ganglia and nerves are so tightly packed that there is little extracellular space between them (see, for example, Fig. 17–9). Nerve cells and glia cells are in close contact, their membranes being separated only by a narrow gap of perhaps 200 Å; this is the only space available for extracellular fluid (see Fig. 17–18). There are few exceptions to this.

It is characteristic of any nervous system that every nerve cell is in contact with another nerve cell and that no nerve cell is isolated from the rest of the nervous system. Wherever a nerve cell is found, there is a nerve fiber in contact with it which can be followed to another nerve cell body or branch that is in contact with another neuron, and so forth.

The Neuron. Neurophysiology is concerned almost exclusively with the action and interaction of nerve cells. The functions that are discussed in the following sections of this chapter are all carried out by nerve cells (neurons). If glia cells play a direct role in this, we have no knowledge of it.

Nerve cells are the functional units of every nervous system. There is quite a variety of types. Within the human brain alone, hundreds of different kinds of nerve cells have been described and named.

It is characteristic of all neurons that they possess numerous branches. Of these there are three kinds: *dendrites*, *axons*, and *collaterals*.

Dendrites, supposedly, are those branches that under normal conditions permit spread of excitation toward the cell body, whereas *axons* carry excitatory processes away from the cell body. The distinction between dendrites and axons on the basis of this type of function is, however, not practical and applies only to a limited number of nerve cell types (e.g., mammalian motoneurons). It is better to distinguish dendrites and axons on the basis of morphological characteristics: dendrites show extensive branching which usually commences close to the cell body proper and exhibits the pattern of a tree (Gr. *dendros* tree). Axons, on the other hand, are slender, long processes; usually not more than one such process emerges from the cell body. This may branch later on, usually by bifurcation.

Collaterals are side branches of axons which make contacts with branches of other nerve cells. Near their point of origin they divide into a group of terminals.

Axons possess specialized end structures. In many cases the terminal portion of the axon branches and each branch ends with a knob-like structure, the *synaptic knob, terminal knob,* or *bouton terminal* (Figs. 20–2 and 20–3). In other cases the axons end with ribbon-like filaments, or they form only one end structure, such as the *motor end-plate* found on vertebrate skeletal muscle fibers (Fig. 20–12).

Many types of axons have no obvious morphological end structures, although these must be assumed to be functionally present. Such axons and

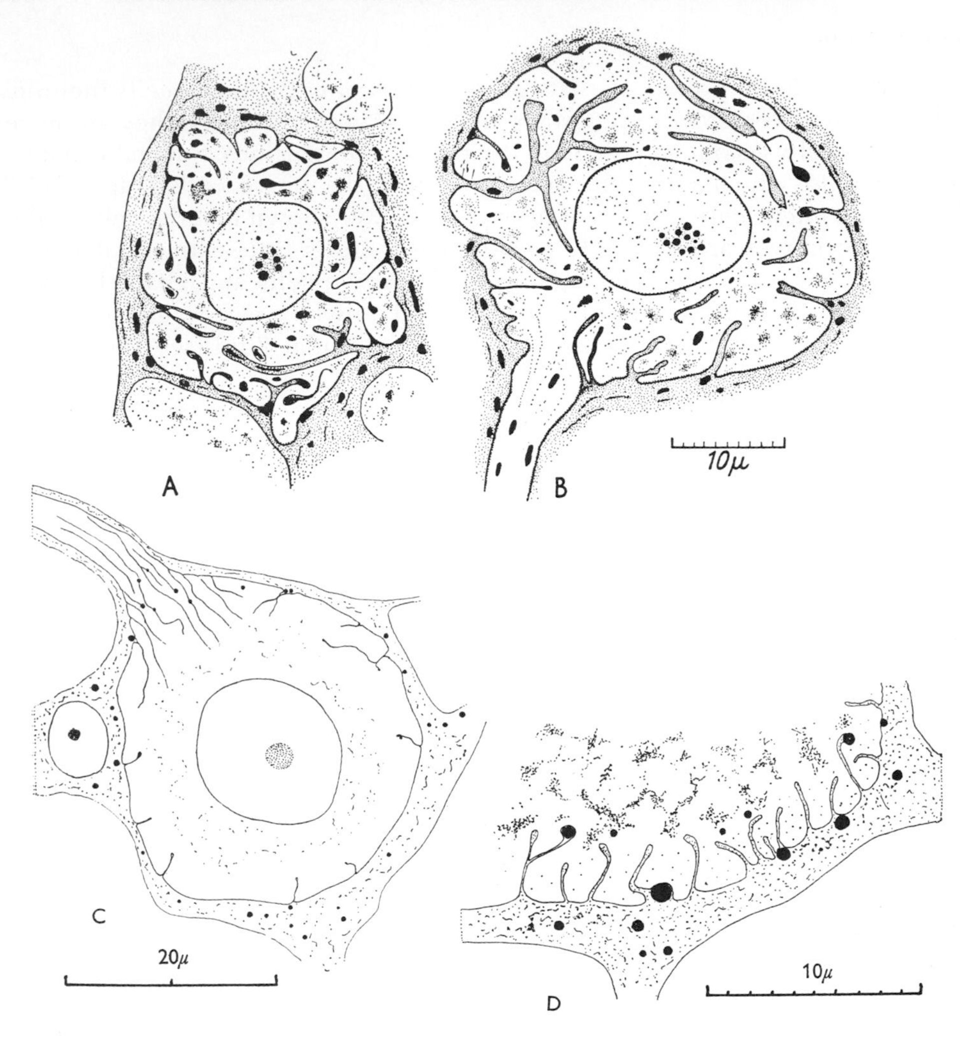

Figure 17–17. Drawings of motor ganglion cells surrounded by glial cytoplasm containing mitochondria and fat droplets. Note the numerous invaginations of the plasma membrane of the nerve cells. **A** and **B**, from the central nervous system of the hemipteran *Rhodnius*. **C** and **D** from the central nervous system of the cockroach *Periplaneta*. (From Wigglesworth, V. B.: Histology of the nervous system of an insect, *Rhodnius prolixus* [Hemiptera]. Quart. J. Micr. Sci. *100*:299–313, 1959, and The nutrition of the central nervous system in the cockroach, Periplaneta americana L. The role of perineurium and glial cells in the mobilization of reserves. J. Exp. Biol. *37*:500–512, 1960.

their branches simply end as thin filaments. In the case of sensory axons these are referred to as *free nerve endings* (Fig. 17–19).

The portion of a neuron that surrounds the nucleus is called the *pericaryon* or, more commonly, the *soma*. The structure of such a soma, or cell body, is shown in Figure 17–20.

A number of types of nerve cells are illustrated in Figure 17–21.

Glia Cells and Sheath Cells. Nerve cells are usually surrounded by glia cells. These are in intimate contact with the nerve cells; within ganglia

(Text continued on page 439.)

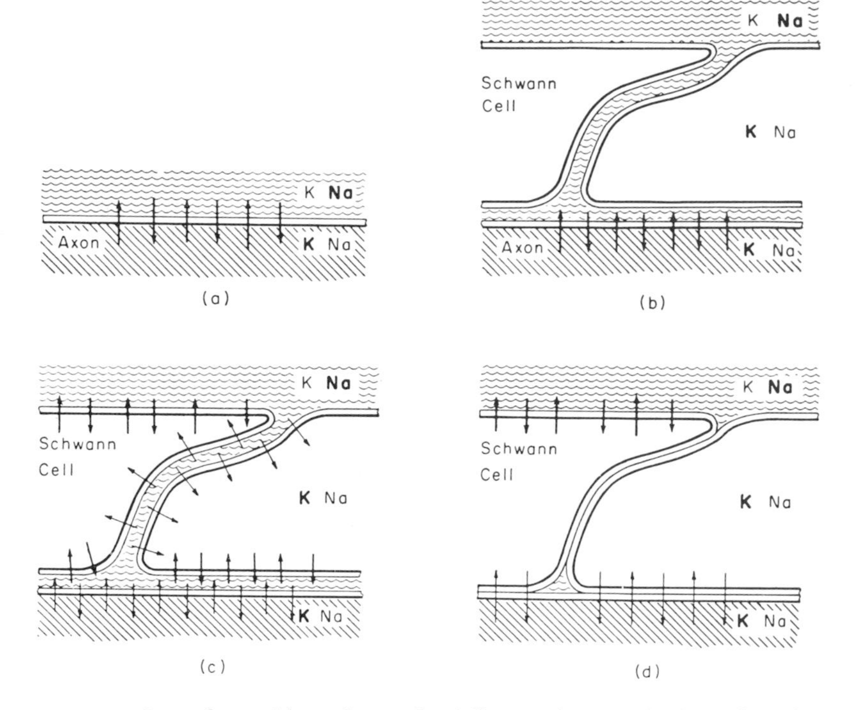

Figure 17–18. Several possible pathways for diffusion of ions and other solutes between the extracellular fluid and the intracellular medium of nerve fibers. K^+ and Na^+ gradients are indicated by boldness of type. The actual concentrations of ions inside satellite (Schwann) cells are not known. In a the bare axon membrane is directly exposed to bulk extracellular fluid. In **b** the axon is covered everywhere by satellite cells, but all membranes are separated by a space of 150 to 200 Å filled with extracellular fluid. Schwann cells act as diffusion barriers. **c**, same as b except that exchange occurs across all membranes. Schwann cells participate in processes involving interchange between axon and extracellular space. In **d** the axon membrane and the Schwann cell membrane are in direct contact. Exchange occurs through protoplasm of satellite cells which, effectively, represents the extracellular medium of the axon. (From Schmitt, F. O.: Axon-satellite cell relationships in peripheral nerve fibers. Exp. Cell Res., Suppl. 5:33–57, 1958.)

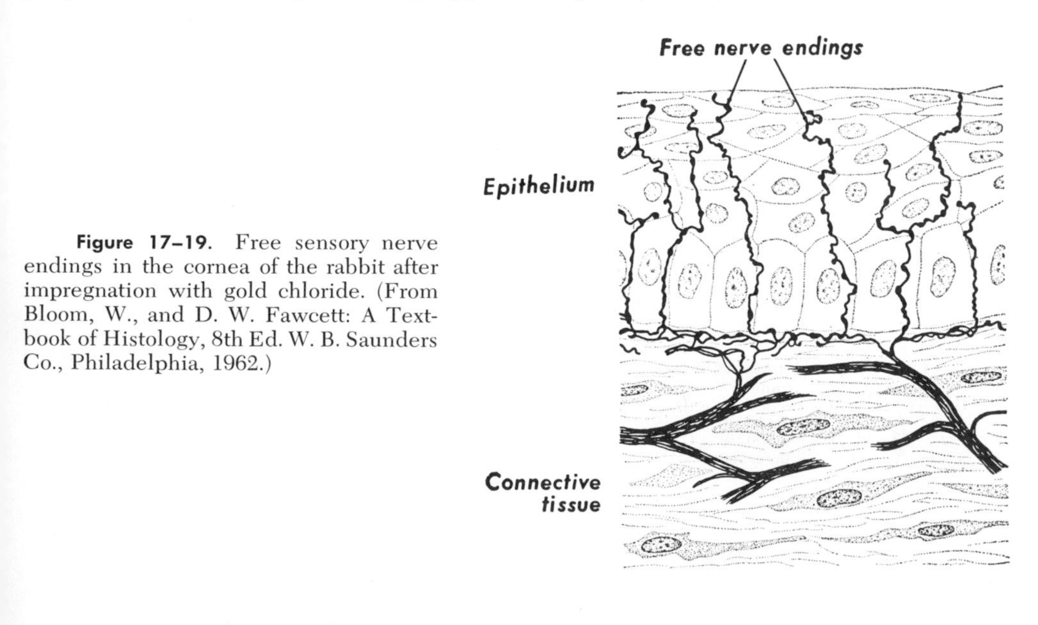

Figure 17–19. Free sensory nerve endings in the cornea of the rabbit after impregnation with gold chloride. (From Bloom, W., and D. W. Fawcett: A Textbook of Histology, 8th Ed. W. B. Saunders Co., Philadelphia, 1962.)

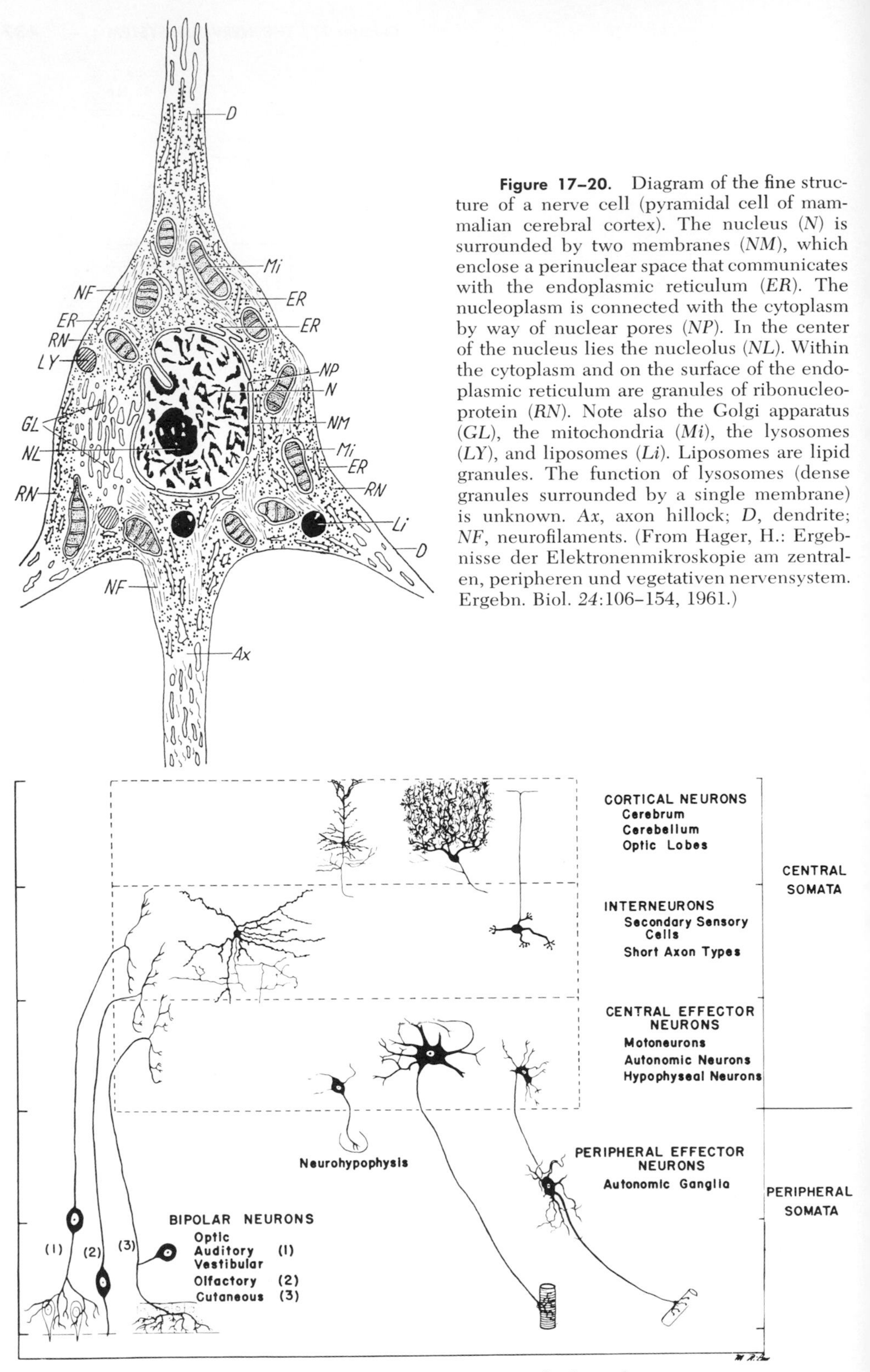

Figure 17–20. Diagram of the fine structure of a nerve cell (pyramidal cell of mammalian cerebral cortex). The nucleus (*N*) is surrounded by two membranes (*NM*), which enclose a perinuclear space that communicates with the endoplasmic reticulum (*ER*). The nucleoplasm is connected with the cytoplasm by way of nuclear pores (*NP*). In the center of the nucleus lies the nucleolus (*NL*). Within the cytoplasm and on the surface of the endoplasmic reticulum are granules of ribonucleoprotein (*RN*). Note also the Golgi apparatus (*GL*), the mitochondria (*Mi*), the lysosomes (*LY*), and liposomes (*Li*). Liposomes are lipid granules. The function of lysosomes (dense granules surrounded by a single membrane) is unknown. *Ax*, axon hillock; *D*, dendrite; *NF*, neurofilaments. (From Hager, H.: Ergebnisse der Elektronenmikroskopie am zentralen, peripheren und vegetativen nervensystem. Ergebn. Biol. *24*:106–154, 1961.)

Figure 17–21. *See opposite page for legend.*

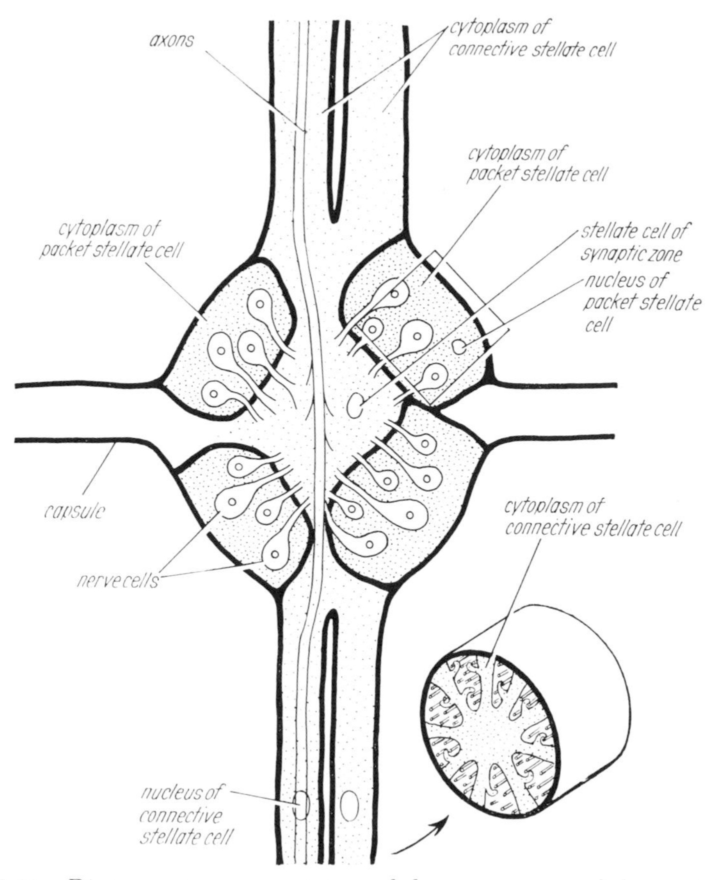

Figure 17–22. Diagrammatic representation of the organization of the ventral nerve cord of the leech *Hirudo medicinalis* (Hirudinea). The nerve cell bodies lie in six packets (four of which are shown) around a central synaptic zone into which their processes extend. These processes have to pass through a fibrous lamina that surrounds each "packet." Each packet consists of a large glia cell ("packet stellate cell"). The synapsing nerve fibers are surrounded by the somata of two large glia cells ("stellate cells of the synaptic zone"), which fill the central portion of each ganglion. The connectives are occupied each by one large glia cell ("connective stellate cell") between whose septa lie the axons. The area enclosed by the rectangle is represented at higher magnification in Figure 17–23. (From Gray, E. G., and R. W. Guillery: An electron microscopical study of the ventral nerve cord of the leech. Z. Zellforsch. *60*:826–849, 1963.)

and central nervous systems, they continuously fill the space between them, as shown in Figures 17–9, 17–22, and 17–23.

Some glia cells have branches and assume a configuration reminiscent of nerve cells. The chief difference between these and nerve cells proper is the absence of axons and of specialized terminal structures as well as the different straining reactions when they are subjected to histological techniques.

Figure 17–21. Neuron types in the mammalian nervous system. (From Bodian, D.: Introductory survey of neurons. Cold Spr. Harb. Symp. Quant. Biol. *17*:1–13, 1952.)

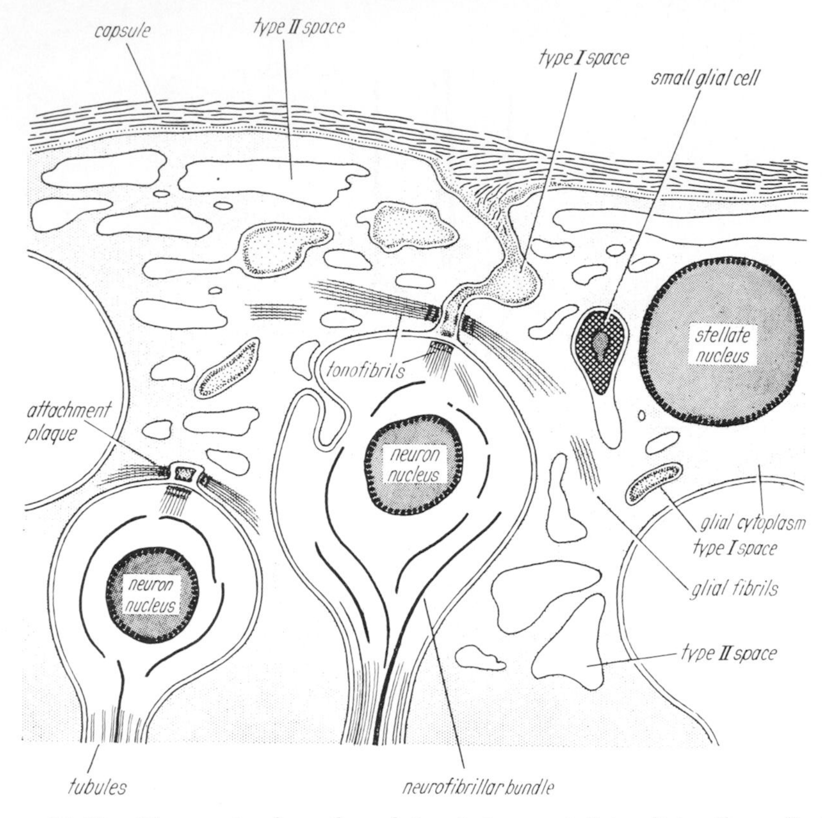

Figure 17–23. Diagram to show the relation between stellate glial cell, small glial cells, nerve cells, and extracellular spaces in the central nervous system of the leech *Hirudo medicinalis*. See also Figure 17–22. (From Gray, E. G., and R. W. Guillery: An electron microscopical study of the ventral nerve cord of the leech. Z. Zellforsch. *60*:826–849, 1963.)

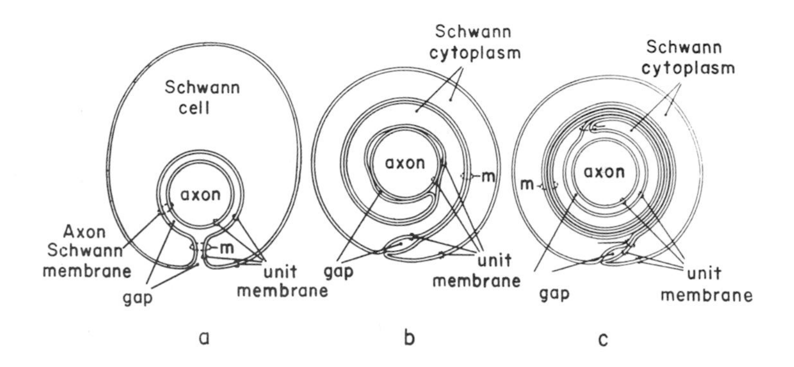

Figure 17–24. Diagram summarizing the formation of the myelin sheath around a vertebrate "myelinated" nerve fiber. The myelin itself consists of the lipid layers of concentrically arranged cell membranes, the structure of which is symbolized in Figure 17–26. In **a** a single Schwann cell with a short mesaxon (*m*) surrounds an axon. This type of fiber is called a protofiber. In **b** the gap between the unit membranes and the mesaxon is obliterated and the mesaxon is elongated in a spiral around the axon. This type of fiber is called an intermediate fiber. In **c** the mesaxon loops have come together along their cytoplasmic surfaces to make the major dense lines of compact myelin. This type of fiber is designated by the term "myelinated." (From Robertson, J. D.: New unit membrane organelle of Schwann cells. *In* Biophysics of Physiological and Pharmacological Actions. A. M. Shanes, ed. Amer. Assn. Adv. Sci., Washington, D.C., 1961, pp. 63–96.)

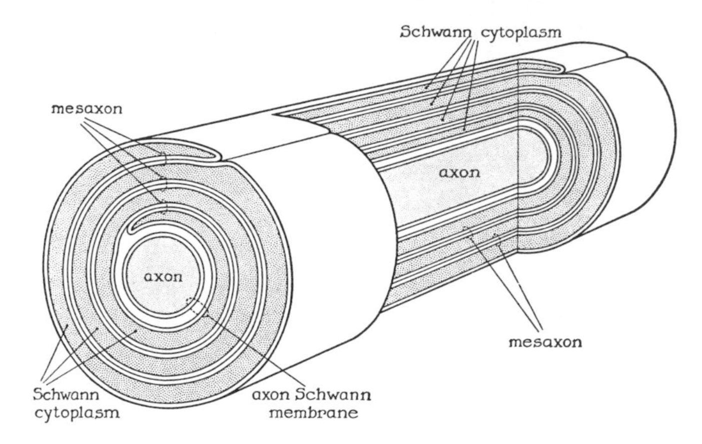

Figure 17–25. Three-dimensional diagram of an internodal segment of an immature, myelinated peripheral nerve fiber (vertebrate). The Schwann cell wraps itself around the axon several times. The double membranes thus formed are referred to as *mesaxon.* During maturation most of the cytoplasm intervening between subsequent layers of the Schwann cell disappears, leaving the concentric layers of membrane in immediate contact. (From Robertson, J. D.: The ultrastructure of Schmidt-Lanterman clefts and related shearing defects of the myelin sheath. J. Biophys. Biochem. Cytol. *4*:39–46, 1958.)

Several kinds of glia cells, particularly those that accompany and surround peripheral axons, are known under the name of *Schwann cell, lemnoblast,* and *teloglia.*

In vertebrate peripheral and central nervous systems, Schwann cells give rise to the *myelin sheath* of nerve fibers (axons). The myelin is composed of lipids present in the plasma membrane of Schwann cells. How it is laid down is explained in Figures 17–24 and 17–25. The detailed structure of the repeating unit membrane of vertebrate myelin is shown in Figure 17–26. Schwann cells do not behave like that everywhere: even in vertebrates there occur many types of nerve fibers that are "*unmyelinated*" or "*nonmyelinated.*"

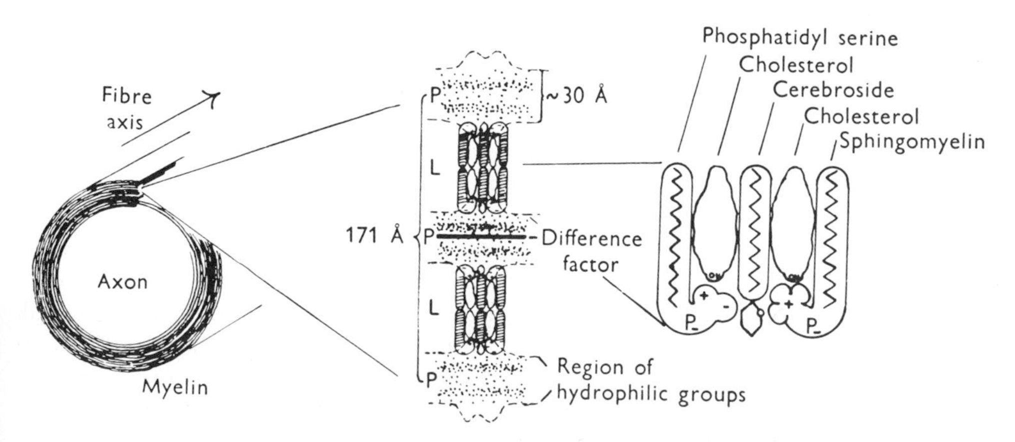

Figure 17–26. Conceptual diagram of the molecular organization of the repeating unit in nerve myelin. Two bimolecular leaflets of lipid are shown, the polar surfaces of which are each bounded by a monolayer of protein. (From Finean, J. B.: X-ray diffraction studies on the myelin sheath in peripheral and central nerve fibers. Exp. Cell Res., Suppl. 5:18–32, 1958.)

Even these, however, have a sheath composed of glia (or Schwann) cells, as shown in Figures 17–1, 17–2, 17–13, and 17–14.

FUNCTION OF THE NERVOUS SYSTEM

Perception

The nervous system is concerned with the perception of the mechanical, thermal, chemical, and electrical qualities of the environment. "Environment" in this connection is everything external to the nervous system itself, including non-nervous tissue and body fluids. In fact, the environment that is external to the organism is largely perceived through alterations in the body structure resulting from environmental changes. Only certain nerve cells are affected directly, as, for example, chemoreceptors or photoreceptors.

The term "perception," as employed here, is to be distinguished from the term "sensation." The latter presupposes a conscious mind and therefore cannot be part of physiological theory. "Perception" involves not only excitation of receptor nerve cells but also the subsequent analysis of primary sensory data.

Responses

The nervous system elaborates response patterns to certain sensory *information*. Information, in this sense, consists of primary receptor responses as transmitted to other nerve cells, and of the whole range of nerve cell activities which result from such primary receptor responses and which are part of the analysis of sensory data. The response patterns involve one or more of the following processes:

1. The reactivity of groups of nerve cells is altered, depressing or enhancing their "readiness" to become activated. The alteration may involve only a part of each nerve cell's structure, thus affecting not all of its possible reactions and activities. Examples range from suppression of simple, monosynaptic reflexes (see later) to the modification of complex behavioral responses. Learning must also be included.

Responses to information involve not only such organs as muscles or glands but also other portions of the nervous system; in fact, many response patterns are restricted to changes in the nervous system itself.

2. By way of excitation of efferent nerve fibers, effector organs are activated or inhibited. In the most simple case where anatomical connections and physiological disposition of the cells involved make this a fixed response, we speak of a reflex. However, *the term "reflex" should be reserved for situations in which only few cells are involved in an easily recognizable reaction sequence with involves excitation of a sensory (or afferent) neuron, excitation of an efferent neuron* (example: motoneuron or neuron of the vagus nerve), *and activation or inactivation of an effector cell* (examples: striated muscle or heart muscle cells).

Reflexes are the result of rigid anatomical relationships of the elements involved and of considerable safety factors which assure direct impulse transmission from one unit to the other. Pure reflexes seldom, if ever, occur in the living, intact animal. They can be studied only in isolation after interactions from other parts of the nervous system are excluded (this is usually a surgical procedure). For example: physiologists who are interested in studying pure spinal reflexes in the cat always decerebrate their experimental animals or transect the spinal cord. In the intact animal the nerve cells involved in reflexes are controlled by other nerve cells. It is precisely this control that is involved in many reaction patterns that are elaborated in response to sensory information.

Spontaneous Actions

The nervous system not only reacts to sensory information, but also develops action patterns independently and autonomously. In fact, the nervous system is not driven by the environment and is usually provided with mechanisms that isolate it from the impact of "sensory input." An example illustrates this: When, during the day, we open our eyes, hundreds of thousands of sensory cells are excited by light. A stream of nervous activity passes through the optic nerves into our brain. As soon as we close the eyes, all this activity ceases abruptly. Yet we experience no striking changes in our "inner dispositon," in our thinking, or in our reactions; if we do this while walking, our gait does not change.

Coordination

The nervous system coordinates the various organ systems. An example illustrates this: a hungry octopus sees a crab, moves toward it, catches it, devours its contents, and releases the empty shell while it digests. The term "hungry" implies a definite condition of the nervous system, brought about by sensory information derived from receptors responding to conditions of the digestive system, and possibly by direct effects of the altered nutritional state of its cells. In the hungry animal various groups of nerve cells are disposed in a certain way so that the response pattern of "following" is elicited as soon as the information signifying "moving crab" arrives in the brain. Then the diverse muscles of all eight arms are coordinated: their contractions and relaxations are the result of controlled activity in the diverse motor nerve fibers. The activity pattern is adjusted according to visual information. As soon as the mechanoreceptors in the tip of one tentacle signal contact with the crab, the response pattern changes abruptly as the octopus leaps over its prey and engulfs it in the web that stretches between the base of its arms. How involved the processes of the generation of sensory information are can be appreciated when one considers that a distinction has to be made between tactile and chemical stimuli derived from the ground on which the animal "walks," with its crevices and rocks, and those stimuli produced by the crab. (The eyes are not essential in this; even a blind octopus can catch crabs.) What matters here is the space-time pattern of excitations of the receptor neurons.

As soon as the prey is "in the bag" (literally speaking), other nerve fibers are activated which in turn bring about a release of deadly saliva which not only paralyzes the victim but dissolves its inner organs. Now the mouth parts of the octopus begin to suck in the juices. Again the complex of muscular contractions and relaxations of the mouth parts is the result of coordinated nervous action which also controls the musculature of the esophagus, stomach, and intestine. If we could record and measure the activity of the octopus' respiratory and circulatory system, we would find that during the extra activity of the hunt and capture, the respiratory movements and heart activity increase greatly. Both are controlled by the nervous system. The specific nervous mechanisms involved here are not known. In man, such increased respiratory and circulatory action would be brought about in the following way: increased muscular activity accelerates metabolism. This means greater production of CO_2. In turn, carbonic acid is formed in the blood and the increased acidity stimulates chemoreceptors located in certain blood vessels. Excitation of these receptor neurons alters the excitability of the nerve cells in the brain stem which are responsible for elaborating motor control of respiratory muscles, and of other nerve cells which give rise to excitation of the sympathetic nervous system which causes acceleration of the heartbeat.

To return to the octopus: As the animal satisfies his need for nutrients, the reactivity of certain cell groups in his nervous system is altered. This goes to the extent of inhibiting reflex responses to tactile stimulation of the "suckers." Only in this way can the animal get rid of the empty "shell" of the crab. The changes in the nervous system are so profound that the perception of another crab fails to elicit another hunt.

What has been described here is only the barest outline of the complexity of nervous function. Nothing has been said about the specific mechanisms involved in bringing about analysis of sensory data, transmission of information, elaboration of the response pattern, and activation or inactivation of effectors. All this is the subject matter of the following sections of this chapter.

Control by Hormones

The nervous system responds not only to the activation pattern of its receptor neurons. Its overall activity, and that of specifically disposed neurons, is also controlled by hormonal factors and the chemical conditions of the body fluids with which the nerve cells are in contact. Sex hormones are known to elicit characteristic behavior patterns, apparently by directly influencing nerve cells. Not much is known about the mechanism of hormone action on nerve cells, but it is likely that the phenomenon is widespread and important. The pH of extracellular fluid is of considerable influence; a rise in pH usually increases excitability, a fall in pH usually decreases excitability. The ionic composition of the extracellular fluid can vary. If it does, excitability changes are bound to result.

Endocrine Function

In the nervous system of many species of different phyla, groups of nerve cells have been detected which show evidence of secretory function. One speaks of *neurosecretory cells*. This is the subject of Chapter 21. Here it is sufficient to mention that the release of hormones from nerve cells has been established in several cases. In fact, this is a most important aspect of hormone production. Interestingly enough, some of these hormones appear to be involved in the control of nervous activity.

Trophic Function

Another important function of the nervous system lies in the ability of certain efferent nerve fibers to maintain the organs which they innervate. The term "trophic function" of nerve cells is, however, misleading (Gr. *trophein* to nourish). Nerve cells do not nourish other cells. There is evidence, however, that they produce and release a substance (or substances) which is necessary for the maintenance of normally innervated cells. So far, the evidence is indirect; no *trophic substance* has yet been found. All we know is that when nerve fibers degenerate, the previously innervated organ then degenerates.

REFERENCES

Autrum, H. (1959) Nonphotic receptors in lower forms. *In* Handbook of Physiology, Sec. 1, Vol. I, pp. 369–385. (J. Field, ed.) The Williams & Wilkins Co., Baltimore.

Bass, A. D., ed. (1959) Evolution of Nervous Control from Primitive Organisms to Man. Amer. Assn. Adv. Sci., Washington, D.C.

Bethe, A. (1903) Allgemein Anatomie und Physiologie des Nervensystems. Georg Thieme Verlag, Leipzig.

Bodian, D. (1952) Introductory survey of neurons. Cold Spr. Harb. Symp. Quant. Biol., *17*:1–13.

Bullock, T. H., and G. A. Horridge (1965) Structure and Function in the Nervous Systems of Invertebrates, 2 vols. W. H. Freeman & Co., San Francisco.

Carthy, N. D. (1958) An Introduction to the Behaviour of Invertebrates. Macmillan & Co., London.

de Castro, F. (1950) Die normale Histologie des peripheren vegetativen Nervensystems. Verh. dtsch. path. Ges. *34* Tagung:1–52.

Cold Spring Harbor Symposium on Quantitative Biology (1952) The Neuron. Long Island Biol. Assn., New York.

Fernández-Morán, H. (1958) The Submicroscopic Organization and Function of Nerve Cells. Exp. Cell Res., Suppl. 5. Academic Press, New York.

Galambos, R. (1961) The glial-neural theory of brain function. Proc. Nat. Acad. Sci. (U.S.A.) *47*:129–136.

Geren, B. B., and F. O. Schmitt (1954) The structure of the Schwann cell and its relation to the axon in certain invertebrate nerve fibers. Proc. Nat. Acad. Sci. (U.S.A.) *40*:863–870.

Glees, P. (1957) Morphologie und Physiologie des Nervensystems. Georg Thieme Verlag, Stuttgart.

Hagbarth, K. E. (1960) Centrifugal mechanisms of sensory control. Ergebn. Biol. *22*:47–66.

Herrick, C. J. (1931) Introduction to Neurology. W. B. Saunders Co., Philadelphia.

Hoyle, G. (1957) Comparative Physiology of the Nervous Control of Muscular Contraction. Cambridge University Press, London.

Hyman, L. H. (1940–1959) The Invertebrates. 5 vols. McGraw-Hill Book Co., New York.

Kappers, C. U. (1929) The Evolution of the Nervous System. de Erven F. Bohn, Haarlem.

Kappers, C. U., G. C. Huber, and E. C. Crosby (1936) The Comparative Anatomy of the Nervous System of Vertebrates, including Man. 2 vols. The Macmillan Co., New York.

Koshtoyants, K. S. (1957) Fundamentals of Comparative Physiology, Vol. II. Comparative Physiology of the Nervous System (in Russian). Acad. Sci., Moscow.

Kuntz, A. (1934) The Autonomic Nervous System. Lea & Febiger, Philadelphia.

Pantin, C. F. A. (1952) The elementary nervous system. Proc. Roy. Soc. B, *140*:147–168.

Parker, G. H. (1918) Some underlying principles in the structure of the nervous system. Science *45*:619–626.

Parker, G. H. (1919) The Elementary Nervous System. J. B. Lippincott Co., Philadelphia.

Prosser, C. L. (1954) Comparative physiology of nervous systems and sense organs. Ann. Rev.

Physiol. *16*:103–124.

Ramón y Cajal, S. (1952) Histologie du Système Nerveux de l'Homme et des Vertébrés. Inst. Ramón y Cajal, Madrid.

Rasmussen, A. T. (1947) Some Trends in Neuroanatomy. Brown, Dubuque, Iowa.

Thornton, J. W. (1963) The relationship of the low sodium, herbivorous diet of Sphingidae to ionic composition of their hemolymph and the activity and histology of their central nervous system. Thesis, University of Washington, Seattle.

Young, J. Z. (1938) The evolution of the nervous system and of the relationship of organism and environment. *In* Evolution; Essays presented to E. S. Goodrich. (G. R. deBeer, ed.) Oxford University Press, London.

18 NERVE CELLS: IMPULSE GENERATION AND IMPULSE CONDUCTION

In spite of their incredible diversity in size, anatomical position, and structure, practically all nerve cells have three functionally distinct regions: the *generator region*, the *conductile region*, and the *transmissional region*. The generator region is usually restricted to dendrites and soma, and in many cases to certain collaterals. The conductile region can be identified with the main portion of the axon (or axons, in case a cell has more than one), and the transmissional region comprises the nerve endings or nerve terminals. A conceptual diagram of these functional regions is shown in Figure 18–1.

IMPULSE GENERATION

The experimenting physiologist can induce propagating nerve impulses at practically any point of the conductile portion of a nerve cell. From the point where he stimulates the axon, the resulting action potential is conducted toward the transmissional region (the nerve endings) as well as toward the soma and dendrites. The action potential that propagates along the axon toward the nerve terminals is called *orthodromic*, the one that moves toward the soma or dendrites is known as the *antidromic action potential*.

Under natural conditions the nerve impulse always arises at the initial portion of the conductile region of the nerve cell and is conducted orthodromically. The cause of this conducted nerve impulse is a physiological process in

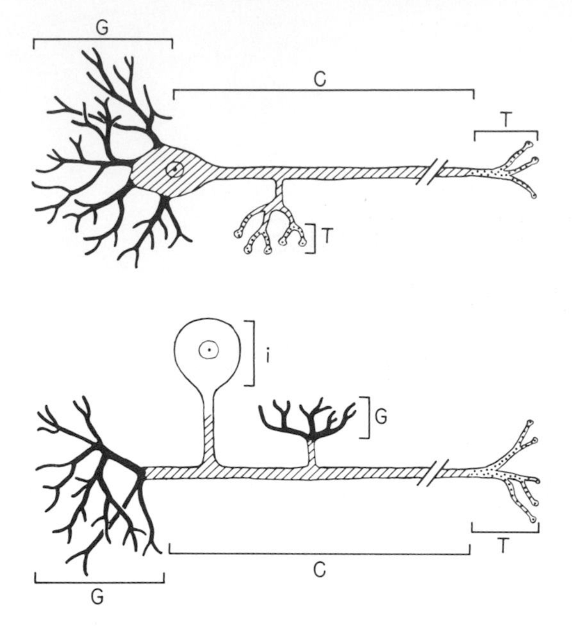

Figure 18–1. Conceptual diagrams showing the three functional regions of nerve cells: *G*, generator region; *C*, conductile region; *T*, transmissional region. **Above**, a typical vertebrate nerve cell or a primary receptor nerve cell (invertebrates). **Below**, a typical neuron of invertebrates (invertebrates comprise over 90 per cent of all animal species; thus this is the most common type of nerve cell). The cell body, or soma, does not usually participate in the electrical activity (exception: *Aplysia* ganglion cells); it is therefore marked *i*, meaning "inexcitable." Collateral branches are shown on both types of neuron, but on the upper one they bear transmissional terminals, on the lower one they are represented as the generator region. This is an arbitrary assignment even though it corresponds to the more common situations; both types of neuron may have "transmissional" and "generator" collaterals.

the adjacent generator region. The site where the full-blown conducted action potential (the nerve impulse) first appears is not the same as that where the process that generates this action potential takes place. Some applications of the terms "orthodromic" and "antidromic" are shown in Figure 18–2.

There is evidence that the membrane of the generator region is functionally quite different from that of the conductile portion of the axon. For one thing, it is difficult to excite this region with electric current. Grundfest and his school at Columbia University have given numerous examples of "electrical inexcitability" of the generator region of diverse types of nerve cells. Other neurophysiologists, however, believe that the peculiar properties of the generator region are not due to different characteristics of the cell membrane but to the special configuration of this cell portion and to the fact that this region is covered by innumerable endings of other nerve cells.

The generator regions of *receptor* nerve cells are activated by a variety of chemical, mechanical, thermal, and other stimuli. Their anatomical position usually exposes them to a selected range of external agents and their morphological fine structure disposes them to be even more specifically excited by only certain kinds of stimuli. Photoreceptors in mammals, for instance, are located in the retina of the eyes, where they are protected from mechanical or thermal changes and exposed to specially collected and directed light. They also possess the elaborate laminated and pigmented structures (Fig. 18–3) that enable them to capture photons and to utilize them for the generation of nerve impulses. Additional discussion of photoreceptor physiology is given in Chapters 14 and 25.)

The activity of all other (nonreceptor) cells may be modified and modulated by the same agents that excite receptor neurons, but the main control of impulse

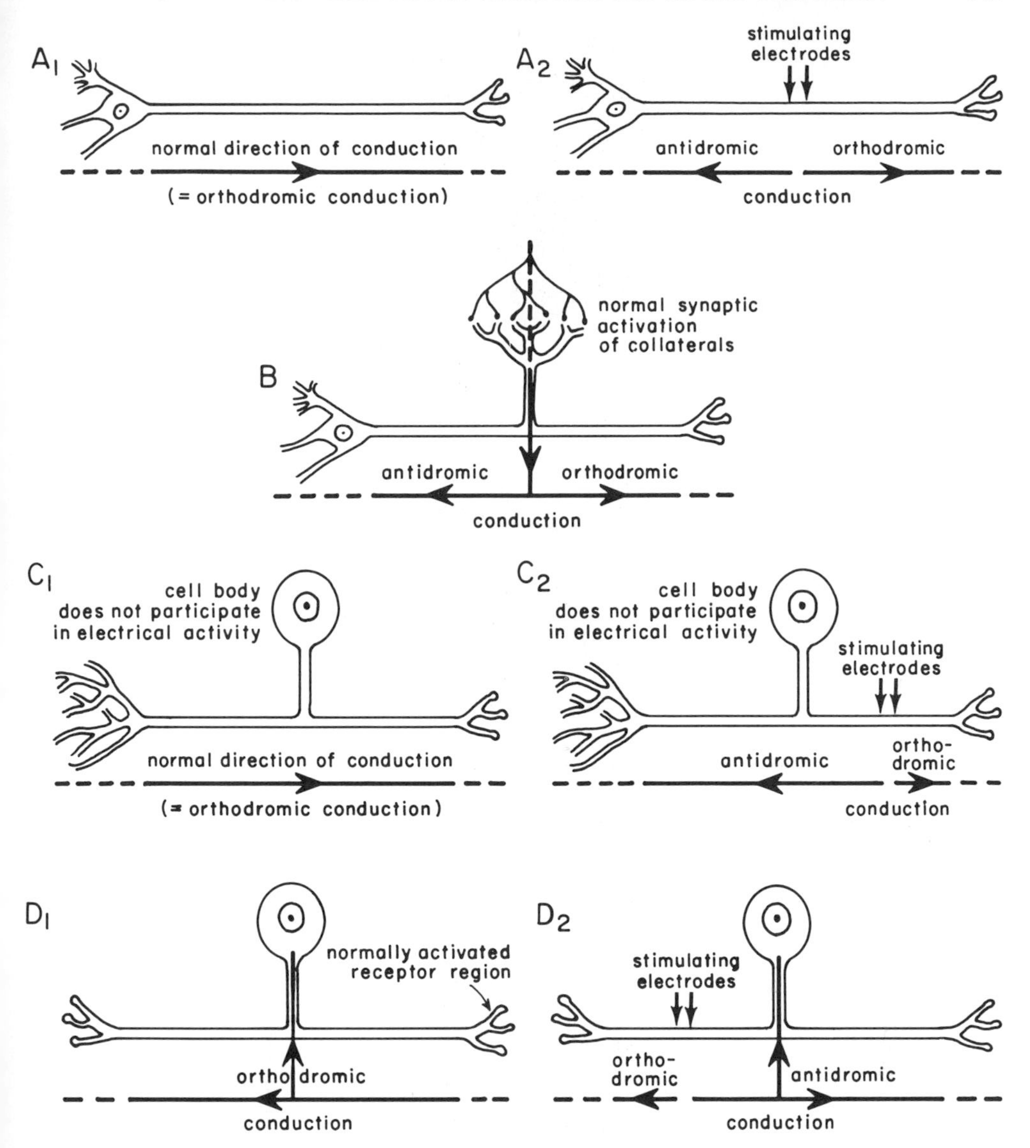

Figure 18–2. Conceptual diagram to explain the meaning of the terms "orthodromic" and "antidromic." Several types of nerve cell are shown.

generation is by *synaptic transmission*. A *synapse* is a specialized region of contact between transmissional portions of one nerve cell (the *presynaptic* cell) and the membrane of the generator region of another cell (the *postsynaptic* cell). Synaptic transmission is the process by which one nerve cell affects the excitability of another cell. It is always initiated by the arrival of a nerve impulse (action potential) in the presynaptic transmissional region, and it causes a transient change in excitability in the postsynaptic cell. If the excitability is increased, the generator region of the postsynaptic cell may set up one or

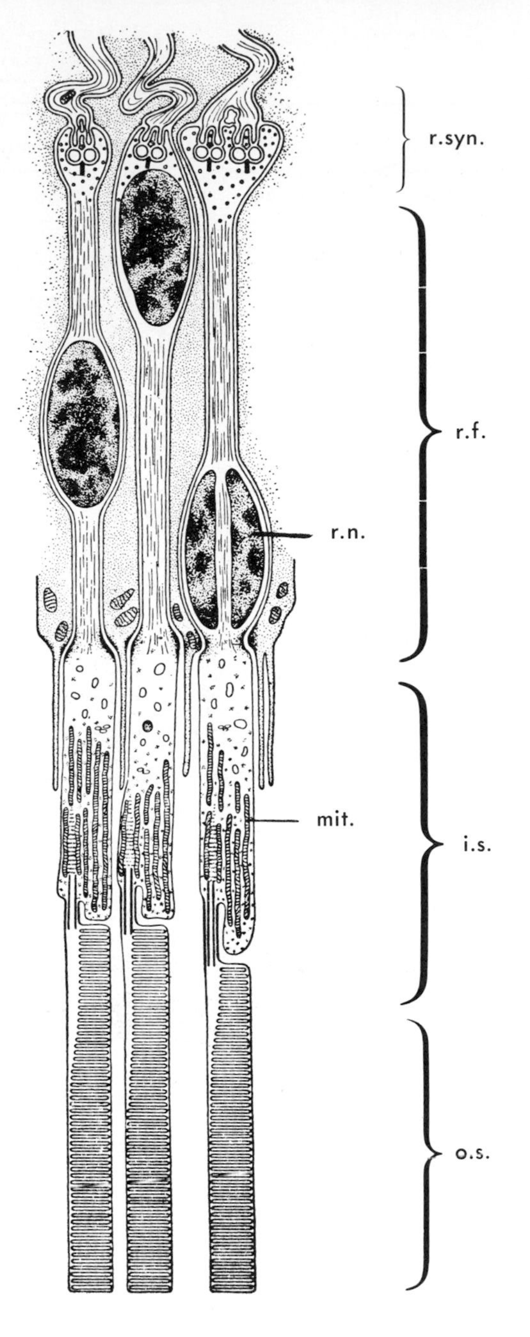

Figure 18–3. Diagrammatic representation of the structure of rods in the guinea pig retina. Note the lamellated structure of the outer segments (*o.s.*). The inner segments (*i.s.*) are filled with mitochondria (*mit.*). *r.f.*, rod fiber; *r.n.*, rod nucleus; *r.syn.*, synapse between rod cell and sensory nerve fiber. It is important to realize that light has to penetrate several layers of ganglion cells and the entire rod structure before it can be absorbed by the photosensitive pigment located in the lamellae of the outer segments of the rod cells. (Modified after Sjöstrand, F. S.: Int. Rev. Cytol. 5:455–533, 1956. G. H. Bourne and J. F. Danielli, eds. Academic Press, New York.)

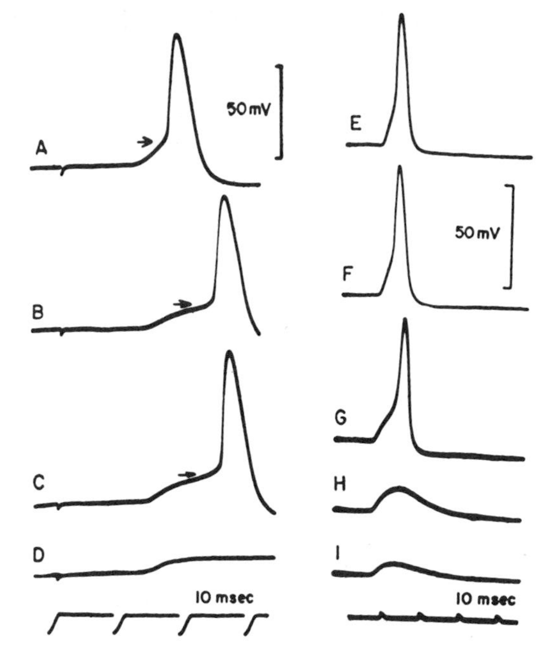

Figure 18–4. Records obtained with intracellular microelectrodes inserted into the soma of postganglionic neurons in a sympathetic ganglion (rabbit, superior cervical ganglion). (If unfamiliar with the anatomical terminology, refer to Fig. 20–26.)

The neurons receive many endings from several presynaptic nerve fibers. Records **A** to **D** show the results of synaptic activation with progressively fewer synapses. In the sequence **E** to **I** the number of activated synapses remained constant but their effectiveness was progressively diminished by the application of a chemical (dihydro-β-erythroidin). Note that the spike potential (action potential proper) occurs later and later as the local potential (the synaptic potential) develops more slowly and reaches the firing level later and later. In *D* and *I* only the synaptic potential remains. (After R. M. Eccles, from Eccles, J. C.: The Physiology of Nerve Cells. Johns Hopkins Press, Baltimore, 1957.)

more propagated nerve impulses or action potentials. The mechanism of transmission is the subject of Chapter 20 (Synaptic Transmission).

Each type of synapse behaves in a somewhat different manner. Perhaps the simplest case is that in which the postsynaptic cell responds to each presynaptic nerve impulse with one propagated action potential. Here it would *appear* as if a nerve impulse were actually transmitted across the synapse. What actually happens is that the presynaptic impulse starts the synaptic transmission; this in turn leads to a permeability change in the postsynaptic membrane and causes a local potential change in the generator region which then may set up a conducted action potential in the conductile portion (the axon) of the postsynaptic cell. The local potential change is often called "synaptic potential" or "postsynaptic potential" (psp). Situations of this kind have been described for many synapses between sensory and motor neurons. Other examples are shown in Figure 18–4.

Generator Potential and Synaptic Potential

Whatever the exciting agent, generator regions of all nerve cells respond in a similar manner, namely, by a change in "membrane" permeability. The permeability change is followed by a migration of ions (usually Na^+, K^+, or Cl^-, or two, or even all three of them). This, of course, represents an electric current. The energy of this current flow is much greater than the energy that acts on the generator region. The generator region of a neuron thus acts as an amplifier—and since this amplifier in most cases responds with a change in electric current to chemical, thermal, or mechanical energy, it is called a *trans-*

ducer, that is, a structure that "translates" or transduces one kind of energy state or flow into a flow of energy of another type.

There is one important difference between *synaptic* activation of nerve cells and stimulation by other changes in the environment as they might affect a receptor nerve cell: synaptic transmission is of rather short duration since the presynaptic impulse and the concomitant transmitter action last no longer than 1 or a few milliseconds. Postsynaptic potentials are therefore of short duration. Properties of the environment which affect nerve cells may change and remain in the changed condition for extended periods of time; the potential change thus produced may last for a long time. When they are depolarizing, these often long-lasting potential changes are called *generator potential* (this usage of the term was introduced by Granit, 1947). Although it is sometimes assumed that the postsynaptic potentials are only a special case of generator potential, it is best to reserve the term "generator potential" for the potential changes in the generator portions of *receptor* neurons and for longer-lasting graded responses of the generator regions of other nerve cells.

Both generator and postsynaptic potentials are local, graded, and non-conducted responses (see Chap. 16) which spread electrotonically, that is, with exponentially diminishing magnitude, to neighboring membrane regions of the same neuron.

The mechanism by which permeability changes in the generator regions of nerve cells are effected is unknown. It is certain, however, that submicroscopic structural changes of the "membrane" are involved. The most widely held view is that membrane pores are opened, or enlarged, thereby permitting or facilitating the passage of ions. The concept that pores are the basis of permeability rests on the observation that permeability is definitely related to the size of the (hydrated) ions and not to their chemical properties. If ions are sorted into two groups according to whether or not they permeate the membrane, it is found that the ones that penetrate are smaller, and those that do not penetrate are larger than a certain critical size, regardless of charge.

The generator potential, like the postsynaptic potential, is greatest in the immediate region of its origin and diminishes exponentially with increasing distance from this point. How much it diminishes depends on the capacitance of the membrane and the electric resistance of the membrane and axoplasm (see the discussion of *space constant*, p. 394). Capacitance and membrane resistance are responsible for the characteristic time of decay of the voltage change produced by the ionic current (see the discussion on *time constant*, p. 394).

In some types of neuron, generator potentials or synaptic potentials spread over larger distances than in others. In any case, the significance of such depolarizing potentials lies in the fact that they can change the membrane potential of the conductile region of the neuron to a degree where the "threshold" depolarization" is reached that leads to the development of a full-blown action potential.

Impulse generation can thus be summarized as follows: The generator region cannot develop an action potential across its own membrane. However, it serves as an amplifier which responds with relatively strong electric currents to relatively small changes in environmental conditions. Although the potential change thus produced decays with increasing distance from the location of the amplifier membrane, the membrane potential change thus produced in the initial region of the conductile portion of the neuron may be great enough to reach the firing ("threshold") level of the conducting membrane. When this happens a full-blown nerve impulse arises.

Should the generator potential persist beyond the duration of the action potential, a second action potential may occur, and in many cases action potentials are generated as long as the generator potential persists in sufficient magnitude. In such cases the neuron is said to *fire repetitively.*

Any of the following can cause repetitive firing (see Fig. 18–5):

1. Persistence of the environmental condition that produces large current flow through the generator region and thereby maintains the generator potential.

2. A long time constant of the decay of generator potential (slow accommodation).

3. A large space constant (mainly due to low resistance in axoplasm, as is

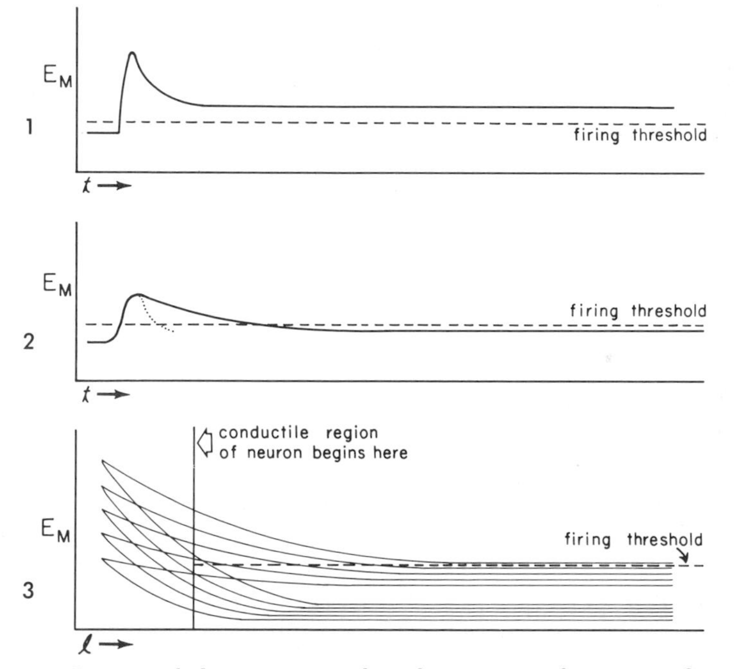

Figure 18–5. Conceptual diagrams to explain three causes of repetitive firing: (1) a large generator potential, even if it drops off with time because of accommodation, remains below the firing level, thus causing repetition of action potentials; (2) a slow time course of accommodation so that even a small generator potential can be maintained for a prolonged time (if accommodation had the same time course as in the upper diagram, indicated here in stipple, the cell would fire only briefly); (3) a large space constant so that the decaying generator potential (the decay, due to accommodation, is indicated by the series of curves below the top one) extends into the conductile region of the neurons for an extended time. With a shorter space constant, firing would cease much earlier, as indicated by the lower set of curves. E_M = membrane potential, increasing negativity downward. Note that the abscissa indicates length. The concept of space constant is explained in Figure 6–12.

the case with cells of large diameter), permitting more of the "above threshold" voltage to extend over the conductile region of the neuron, thus exposing the initial portion of it to this depolarization for a longer time.

Many types of nerve cell are known that are *spontaneously active.* Such cells generate propagated impulses, usually at regular intervals, without apparent external cause. In these cases recurrent, transient local potential changes occur in the generator region (this is usually restricted to dendrites or soma), and if they reach—or transgress—a certain minimal value, they trigger a full-blown action potential in the conductile portion of the cell: one action potential follows each of these *local* potentials. Since the latter are not caused by synaptic activation, they cannot be called synaptic potentials. The name *prepotentials* is sometimes employed to describe this particular type of transient generator potential.

We must assume that the "spontaneous activity," wherever it occurs, is the result of special internal conditions as well as of the conditions of the external environment of these cells. The interaction of both sets of circumstances results in such a high level of excitability that recurrent generator activity goes on and produces action potentials in the conductile portion of the neuron.

Environmental changes that are of sufficient magnitude to act as "stimuli" alter the frequency of spontaneous discharges—that is, they cause the interval between the "spontaneous" nerve impulses to shorten (*excitatory stimuli*) or to lengthen (*inhibitory stimuli*). Such environmental changes are involved in the application of mechanical stress, in the application of light, or in the change in concentration of chemicals in the external medium that surrounds the generator region. To the latter type belong also processes of synaptic transmission, since these involve chemical interactions between pre- and post-synaptic cells.

To summarize: Under experimental conditions nerve impulses can be generated at any region of the conductile portion of the cell, but electric stimulation is most effective at the conductile portion of the neuron. Under normal functional conditions within the organism, however, impulses always arise as a consequence of local activity in the generator region (the generator potential, synaptic potential, or prepotential); they always start in that portion of the conductive membrane immediately bordering the generator region.

IMPULSE CONDUCTION

Once a full-blown action potential has arisen in the soma or axon of a nerve cell, it propagates over the whole extent of the conductile membrane of the cell. The velocity of propagation is proportional to the length constant of the particular cell structure (see Chap. 16, p. 393). For cylindrical forms it increases with increasing diameter; thus, in general, thick axons conduct impulses faster than thin ones. The conduction velocity also increases with increasing temperature. Conduction in warm-blooded animals is therefore more rapid than in cold-blooded ones.

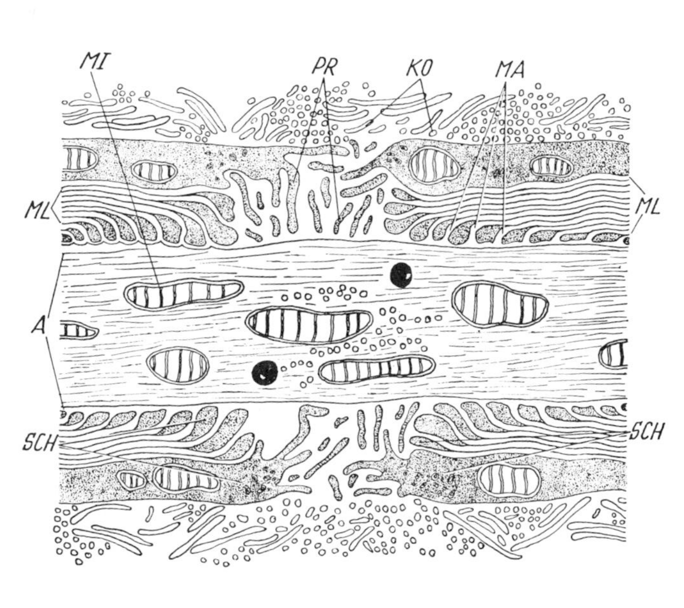

Figure 18–6. Diagram of the ultrastructure of a node of Ranvier (myelinated, peripheral nerve fiber of frog) representing a longitudinal, sagittal section. The axon (*A*) contains neurofibrils and mitochondria (*MI*) and is bounded by a membrane. It is surrounded by a Schwann cell (*SCH*) that envelops the axon with concentric layers of myelin (*ML*); the ends of these layers or lamellae give access to the spaces between them, known as mesaxon (*MA*). Between two adjacent Schwann cells the axonal membrane is not covered by myelin. These regions are known as "nodes." They are loosely covered by finger-like protrusions (*PR*) of the Schwann cells. The outside of Schwann cells is covered by collagen fibrils (*KO*). (From Hagen, H.: Ergebnisse der Elektronenmikroskopie am zentralen, peripheren und vegetativen Nervensystem. Ergebn. Biol. *24*:106–154, 1961.)

In the vertebrates many nerve fibers, particularly those of the peripheral nervous system, possess segmented sheaths of myelin. This complicates the otherwise simple picture of impulse conduction: The transverse resistance of the axon membrane follows the pattern of the myelin sheath; it is rather high (10^5 ohm · cm^2) under the myelin segments and relatively low (10 ohm · cm^2) at the nodes of Ranvier (Fig. 18–6) which separate the segments. Therefore, membrane current largely follows the path of lowest resistance and traverses the membrane almost exclusively at the nodes, as illustrated in Figure 18–7. Conduction is therefore not continuous, but leaps, as it were, from node to node: whenever an action potential arises it is restricted to the nodal membrane. The action current then flows to—and through—the membrane of the adjacent node and induces an action potential there. Figure 18–8 demonstrates this quite clearly (Huxley and Stämpfli, 1949 a, b). This is known as *saltatory conduction* (L. *saltare* to leap).

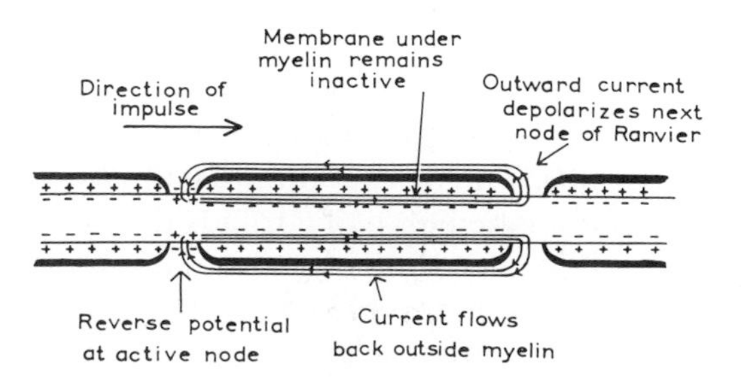

Figure 18–7. Conceptual diagram of saltatory conduction in a myelinated peripheral nerve fiber (vertebrate). Only the membrane in the nodal region becomes active (see Fig. 18–6). Current flows from the next nearest resting node back over the outside of the myelin sheath and returns in the core of the fiber. (From Hoyle, G.: Comparative physiology of conduction in nerve and muscle. Amer. Zoologist 2:5–25, 1962.)

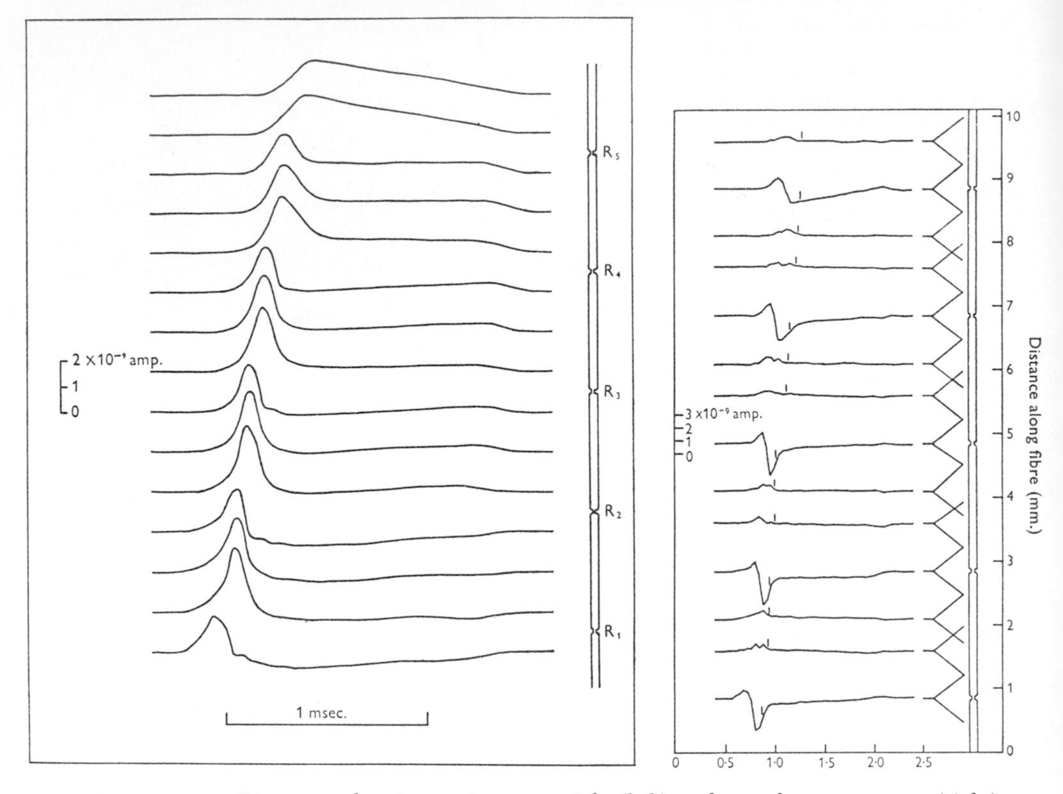

Figure 18–8. Diagrams showing action potentials (**left**) and membrane currents (**right**) as recorded with electrodes positioned at various points along a single, myelinated amphibian nerve fiber. The recorded action potentials appear simultaneously over a given internodal distance, but suddenly later when the electrode position is changed to a new segment of the fiber. This is evidence that conduction here is not continuous but that excitation "jumps" from node to node. This is even more convincingly demonstrated by the current record which shows that currents flow only across the nodal membrane. The structure of myelinated nerve fibers is explained in Figures 17–25 and 18–6. (From Huxley, A. F., and R. Stämpfli: Evidence for saltatory conduction in peripheral myelinated nerve fibres. J. Physiol. *108*:315–339, 1949.)

Examples of conduction velocities of a number of different kinds of nerve fiber are given in Table 18–1.

Action potentials are usually so large that they can be detected even if the active nerve fiber is in the center of a whole nerve and the recording electrodes are applied to the outside of this nerve. Usually more than one nerve fiber is active at any time. The potential changes recorded by the electrodes are therefore rather complex. Action potentials (belonging to different axons) that follow each other closely in time cannot be resolved as single impulses; rather, they give rise to a *compound action potential* (also known as a *summated action potential*). This is explained in Figure 18–9.

If a sciatic nerve of a frog is dissected free and electrically stimulated at one end while recording electrodes are moved from the stimulated end toward the other end of the nerve, the recorded pattern of the compound action potential undergoes a predictable change: since the impulses generated by the stimuli are

Table 18–1. Conduction Velocities of Nerve Fibers

Organism	*Fiber Type*	*Velocity m/sec*	*Diameter μ*	*Temperature °C*
Coelenterates				
Aurelia	nerve net	0.5	6–12	
Metridium	nerve net	0.13		27
Annelids				
Lumbricus	ganglionic cord	0.025		
	median giant fiber	30.0	50–90	22
	lateral giant fiber	11.3	40–60	
Myxicola	giant fibers	3.2–21	90–996	20
Megascolex	giant fiber	20	20	
Neanthes	giant fiber	5	30–37	
Harmothoe	giant fiber	2–4.5		
Molluscs				
Ariolimax	nerve fibers	5.5	30–35	
Sepia	giant fiber	7	200	17
Loligo	giant fiber	20	400	23
Arthropods				
Cambarus	claw opener axon	8	36	
	claw slow closer axon	10	41	
	claw fast closer axon	20	58	
	median giant fiber	18–20	90–180	
	lateral giant fiber	10–15	70–150	
Homarus	leg nerve fiber	14–18	60–80	
	giant fibers	11.7	121	
Vertebrates				
Ameiurus	Mauthner fiber	50–60	22–43	10–15
Cyprinus	Mauthner fiber	55–63	55–65	
	lateral nerve fiber	47	20	
Protopterus	Mauthner fiber	18.5	45	
Trout	lateral nerve fiber	50	22	
Frog	A fibers	30	15	
	B fibers	3–4.5		
Cat	A fibers	78–102	13–17	37
	B fibers	24–48	4–8	37
	skin nerve fibers	0.7–2.3	0.43–1.17	37

Selected values from the literature, from a larger list by Prosser, C. L., and F. A. Brown, Jr.: Comparative Animal Physiology, 2nd Ed. W. B. Saunders Co., Philadelphia, 1961.

propagated at different velocities, the slower ones separate more from the faster ones the farther they travel. This was first demonstrated rather elegantly by Erlanger and Gasser (1937); Figure 18–10 illustrates their experiment.

ACCOMMODATION

When a nerve is stimulated electrically with linearly increasing voltage, the threshold voltage at which action potentials begin to appear is inversely proportional to the rise time of the stimulating voltage. In other words, a slowly rising stimulating voltage must reach a much higher value before it triggers

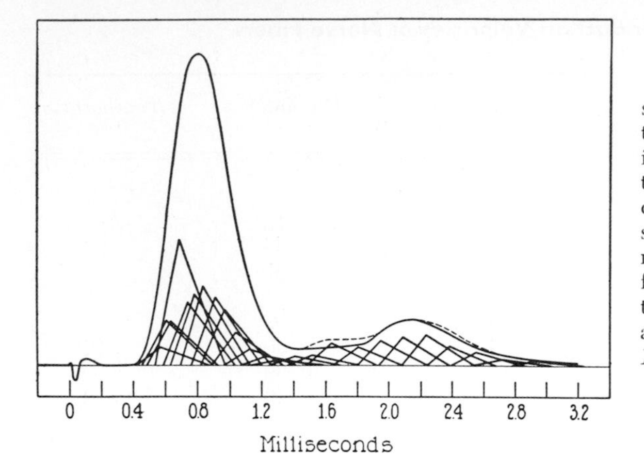

Figure 18–9. Diagrammatic representation of a compound action potential (cat saphenous nerve) and of the individual action potentials (shown as triangles) that contribute to it. The dashed line shows the deviation of the sum of the triangles from the actually recorded wave form. The initial deflection near 0 millisecond represents the stimulus artifact. (After Gasser, H. S., and H. L. Grundfest, Amer. J. Physiol. *127*:393–414, 1939.)

action potentials than a fast rising voltage. This was first investigated by Nernst (1908), who assumed that nerve fiber excitability decreases during application of an electric stimulus. He called this decrease in excitability *accommodation*. Hill (1926) investigated this further and studied the time course of accommodation and defined it by the accommodation constant λ (pronounced lambda), that is, the rise time of a stimulating voltage at which the threshold of excitation is twice the rheobase (rheobase is defined on p. 411). The mechanism of accommodation remained unknown however. Tasaki and Sakaguchi (1950)

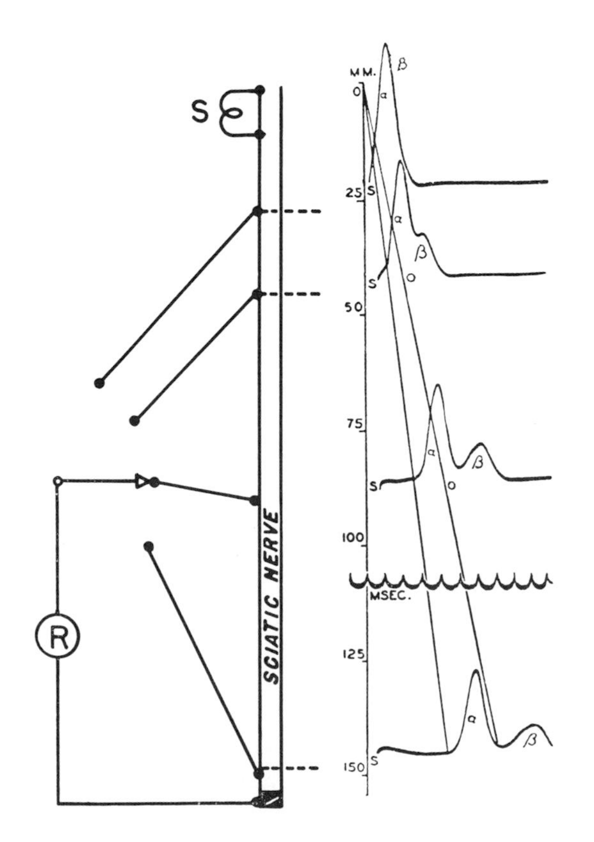

Figure 18–10. The compound action potential as recorded at various points along a sciatic nerve (frog) after the nerve was electrically stimulated. On the left is a diagram of the recording set-up: electrodes from the stimulator (*S*) are attached to one end of the nerve. A switch connects the recording device (*R*) with any one of four recording electrodes placed along the nerve. The indifferent reference electrode is attached to the cut end of the nerve. The numbers along the vertical line represent the length of nerve (in millimeters). The nerve contains numerous fibers of various diameters and, consequently, of various conduction velocities. The diameters and velocities are grouped, giving rise to peaks within the compound action potential, as explained in Figure 18–9. Only the two major groups, α and β, are shown. Note that with increasing distance, α and β become more and more separated in time. (After Erlanger, J., and Gasser, H. S.: Electrical Signs of Nervous Activity. University of Pennsylvania Press, Philadelphia, 1937.)

and Diecke (1954) showed that the phenomenon, as observed by Nernst and Hill, is caused by the large capacitance of the nerve sheaths. Isolated single nerve fibers do not show the changes in excitability that they exhibit while still enclosed within the nerve sheath.

It was found, however, that even single nerve fibers show a change in excitability when subthreshold currents are applied to them for some time. The change in excitability then is comparable to that occurring during electrotonus (see p. 415).

The concept of accommodation can be legitimately applied here, even if the term was originally applied to a phenomenon that can now be explained by the charging and polarizing of large capacitance of nerve sheaths. Originally the concept of accommodation was based on the assumption that the excitability change represents a time-dependent reaction of the nerve fibers themselves. This assumption is still valid, only the pattern and time course of the excitability change of the isolated nerve fibers differs. While the nerve sheath still surrounds the fibers, stimulating voltages that rise slower than a certain value (characteristic for a given nerve) never excite the nerve fibers. With isolated nerve fibers, the threshold of excitation changes with time while stimulating currents (or voltages) are applied, but even if these are made to rise very slowly, they eventually excite the fibers to respond with action potentials (see Wright and Adelman, 1954; Sato, 1951; Niedergerke, 1953).

The difference in behavior of sheathed and desheathed nerve fibers is shown in Figure 18–11.

Using isolated nerve fibers (or nerve cell bodies, for that matter), one can observe accommodation even when a constant and persistent stimulating voltage is applied. The excitability decreases asymptotically to a new level. Excitability here is measured by adding short electric pulses to the steady

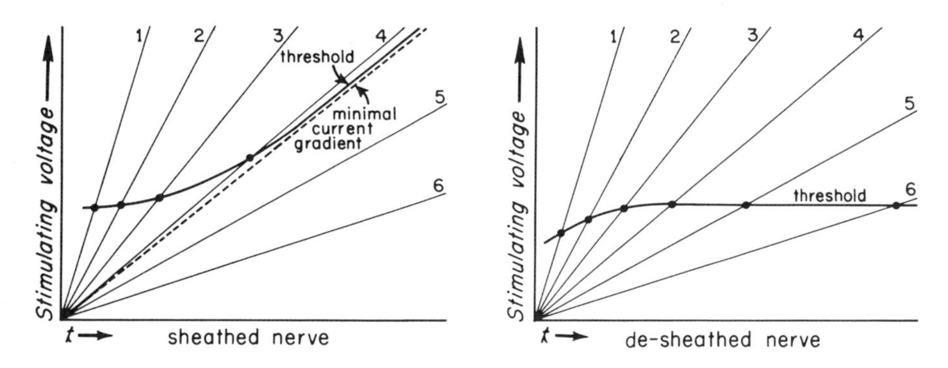

Figure 18–11. The phenomenon of accommodation as observed in a normal nerve with its sheath intact, and in a de-sheathed nerve (frog sciatic). The lines numbered *1* through *6* represent different slopes of rising stimulating voltage; the dots mark the time at which the action potentials are generated in the large motor fibers and indicate the threshold voltage (to be read off on the ordinate). The dots are connected by a curve (labeled "threshold"). In both cases it can be seen that the threshold is lower the faster the voltage rises, but while the threshold remains constant with the longer rise times in the de-sheathed nerve, the threshold rises sharply in the case of the sheathed nerve and excitation never occurs if the rise time of the voltage is greater than a certain minimal gradient.

voltage applied and by determining at successive intervals the minimal additional voltage required to elicit action potentials (Fig. 16–35).

With the use of microelectrodes, one can observe directly the events underlying accommodation: a constant, depolarizing voltage causes immediate depolarization, but this depolarization diminishes with time and asymptotically declines to a new level. Excitability can be defined in terms of the magnitude of the stimulus required to depolarize the membrane to the firing threshold. The farther the membrane potential is from the firing threshold, the stronger must be the stimulus. Thus the decline in depolarization during accommodation brings about a decrease in excitability. It is thought that the decline in depolarization is caused by a decrease in Na permeability of the membrane (referred to as *Na inactivation*) (Eccles, 1957).

REFERENCES

See also the References to Chapter 19.

Bullock, T. H., and G. A. Horridge (1965) Structure and Function in the Nervous Systems of Invertebrates. 2 vols. W. H. Freeman and Co., San Francisco.

Diecke, F. P. J. (1954) "Akkommodation" des Nervenstammes und des isoltierten Ranvierschen Schnürringes. Z. Naturforsch. 9B:717.

Eccles, J. C. (1957) The Physiology of Nerve Cells. The Johns Hopkins Press, Baltimore.

Erlanger, J., and H. S. Gasser (1937) Electrical Signs of Nervous Activity. University of Pennsylvania Press, Philadelphia.

Gernandt, B., and R. Granit (1947a) Inhibition and the polarity of the retinal elements. Nature *159*:806.

Gernandt, B., and R. Granit (1947b) Single fibre analysis of inhibition and the polarity of the retinal elements. J. Neurophysiol. *10*:295–301.

Granit, R. (1947) Sensory Mechanism of the Mammalian Retina. Oxford University Press, London.

Granit, R., and A. Lundberg (1947) Heat- and cold-sensitive mammalian nerve fibers. Some somatic reflexes to thermostimulation. Acta Physiol. Scand. *13*:334–346.

Hill, A. V. (1926) Excitation and accommodation in nerve. Proc. Roy. Soc. B, *119*:305–355.

Huxley, A. F., and R. Stämpfli (1949a) Evidence for saltatory conduction in peripheral myelinated nerve fibres. J. Physiol. *108*:315–339.

Huxley, A. F., and R. Stämpfli (1949b) Saltatory transmission of the nervous impulse. Arch. Sci. Physiol. *3*:435–448.

Huxley, A. F., and R. Stämpfli (1951) Direct determination of membrane resting potential and action potential in single myelinated nerve fibres. J. Physiol. *112*:476–495.

Nernst, W. (1908) Zur Theorie des elektrischen Reizes. Pflügers Arch. ges. Physiol. *122*:275–314.

Niedergerke, R. (1953) Elektrotonus und Akkommodation an der markhaltigen Nervenfaser des Froschs. Pflügers Arch. ges. Physiol. *258*:108–120.

Sato, M. (1951) Comparative measurements of accommodation in two nerve fibers of different sizes. Japan. J. Physiol. *1*:309–315.

Tasaki, I., and M. Sakaguchi (1950) Electrical excitation of the nerve fiber. II. Excitation by exponentially increasing currents. Japan. J. Physiol. *1*:7–15.

Wright, E. B., and W. J. Adelman (1954) Accommodation in three single motor axons of the crayfish claw. J. Cell. Comp. Physiol. *43*:119–132.

19 RECEPTOR NEURONS

CLASSIFICATION OF RECEPTORS

Not all sensory cells have an axon. The so-called *secondary sensory cells*, often situated in epidermal tissue, are not even nerve cells. They are innervated by nerve cells and mediate between the stimulating agent and the excitation of the innervating nerve cell. Secondary sensory cells are found only in vertebrates: examples are the cells of the taste buds of the tongue and the neuromast cells of the vertebrate acoustico-lateralis system (Fig. 19–1). Sometimes the rods and cones of the vertebrate retina are regarded as secondary sensory cells rather than nerve cells.

Primary sensory cells are neurons possessing at least one axon. Their generator region acts as a transducer which can translate certain changes in the environment of the neuron into a change in the frequency of nerve impulses which are generated by the neuron. Primary sensory cells are also known as *receptor neurons*. This latter term is used throughout the following discussions. An example of a receptor neuron is shown in Figure 19–2.

Receptor neurons may be grouped into mechanoreceptors, chemoreceptors, thermoreceptors, photoreceptors, and electroreceptors, depending on the environmental condition to which they respond predominantly. These categories represent the five classes of properties of the environment of an organism or a cell. In fact, all physical and chemical properties of the universe can be described in terms of these five properties, that is, by mechanical condition, chemical composition, temperature, emission or absorption of light, and electric properties.

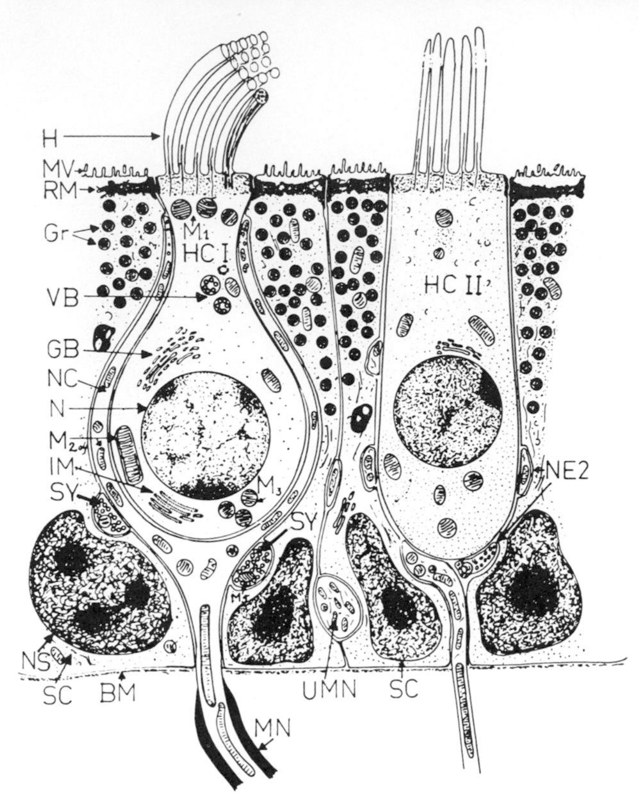

Figure 19–1. Schematic diagram of the two types of secondary sensory cells (hair cells) found in the macula of the inner ear of the guinea pig. The hairs are covered by a jelly-like material containing calcite crystals. Note the relationship between sensory cells and sensory nerve endings. *BM*, basilar membrane; *GB*, Golgi complex; *Gr*, granules in a supporting cell (*SC*); *H*, hairs; *HC I*, hair cell of type I; *HC II*, hair cell of type II; *IM*, intracellular granulated membranes; M_1, subcuticular mitochondria; M_2, mitochondria in the nerve chalice; M_3, subnuclear mitochondria; M_4, mitochondria around the nucleus; *MN*, myelinated nerve; *MV*, microvilli; *N*, nucleus; *NC*, nerve chalice; *NE2*, granulated nerve ending at the base of a hair cell of type II; *NS*, nucleus of a supporting cell; *RM*, reticular membrane; *SC*, supporting cell; *SY*, granulated synapse; *UMN*, unmyelinated nerve; *VB*, vesiculated bodies. (From Engström, H., and J. Wersäll: The ultrastructural organization of the organ of Corti and of the vestibular sensory epithelia. Exp. Cell Res., Suppl. 5:460–492, 1958.)

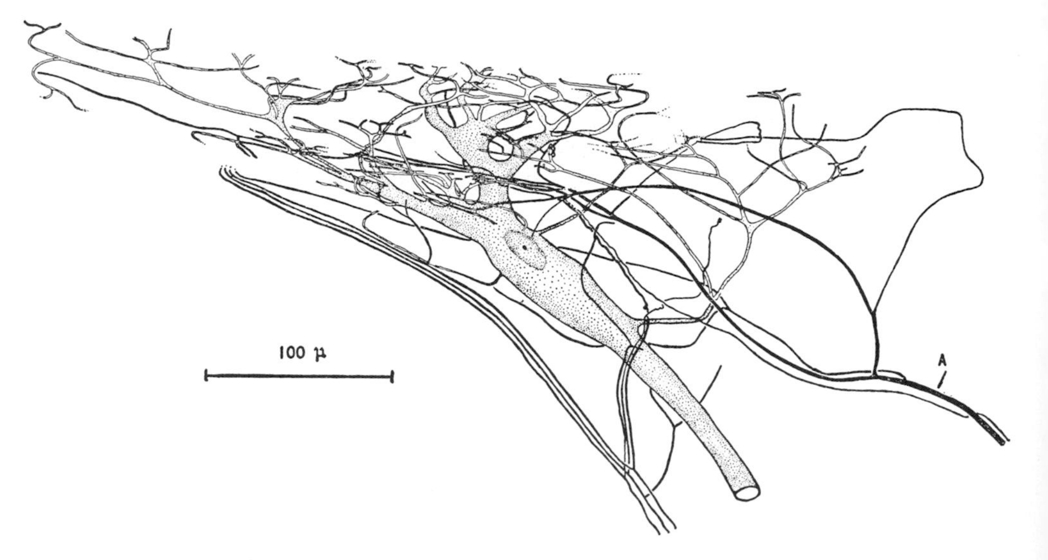

Figure 19–2. Drawing of a silver impregnated primary sensory neuron: a stretch receptor cell from a receptor organ within the abdominal extensor musculature of a crayfish (*Astacus*). The fiber labeled *A* is an efferent inhibitory neuron which, when activated, depresses the excitability of the sensory cell. The bundle of three axons running parallel with the sensory axon represents the motor supply of the muscle strand of the receptor organ (not shown). Flexing of the crayfish tail results in stretching of the receptor organ's muscle strands. This stretch is transmitted to the sensory dendrites where a generator potential is set up. (From Florey, E., and E. Florey: Microanatomy of the abdominal stretch receptors of the crayfish (Astacus fluviatilis L.). J. Gen. Physiol. 39:69–85, 1955.)

RESPONSE AND STIMULUS

Receptor neurons and the environment are in continuous interaction. In this the receptor neurons are in no way different from other nerve cells, or any other body cell. We have discussed in some detail the interactions that result in the membrane potential of cells, and the more obvious interactions that are the basis of cellular respiration or of osmotic pressure.

Whenever cell properties change as a consequence of an environmental change, we call this a *response* of the cell. We distinguish two types of responses: *passive responses*, which are physical and chemical changes that can be predicted on the assumption that the physicochemical characteristics of the cell do not change. *Active responses* are secondary reactions of cells to their own passive responses. They consist of changes in the physicochemical characteristics of the cell. Examples of passive and active membrane responses are discussed in Chapter 16.

If the oxygen tension in the medium around a mammalian red blood cell is lowered by a certain amount, the oxygen content of the cell will be reduced in a predictable manner. If an external electric field is applied to a muscle cell, the membrane potential of this cell will change predictably according to the physicochemical characteristics of the cell membrane, e.g., its capacitance and resistance. These are passive responses. If, on the other hand, as a result of such passive responses the electric resistance of the cell membrane changes, a secondary change in cell behavior results—for instance, an action potential. Synaptic potentials and generator potentials are, at least to a large extent, active responses.

The definition of "response" must, however, contain an additional statement: the reaction must be reversible. Otherwise, the definition would apply to the irreversible reactions of cell damage or death.

Any environmental change that elicits an active response is a *stimulus* (plural: *stimuli*). Depending on whether the change is mechanical, thermal, chemical, photic, or electrical, we speak of mechanical, thermal, chemical, photic, or electrical stimuli, respectively. The response of the generator region of a receptor neuron can be either a depolarization (a transient decrease of the membrane potential) or a hyperpolarization (a transient increase of membrane potential). A stimulus that causes depolarization is called an *excitatory stimulus*; a stimulus that causes hyperpolarization is an *inhibitory stimulus*.

One and the same environmental change can cause depolarization of one type of receptor neuron and hyperpolarization of another. For example, there are temperature receptors that respond to a lowering of the environmental temperature with a depolarization, and there are others that respond to the same temperature change with hyperpolarization. This is described in more detail on p. 632.

If environmental conditions change sufficiently to act as a stimulus to a receptor cell and then change back to the original conditions, the second change again acts like a stimulus. If the first change caused excitation, the second causes inhibition; and if the first change caused hyperpolarization (inhibition), the return to the previous condition results in depolarization (excitation).

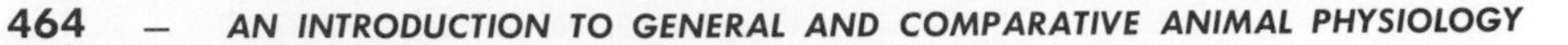

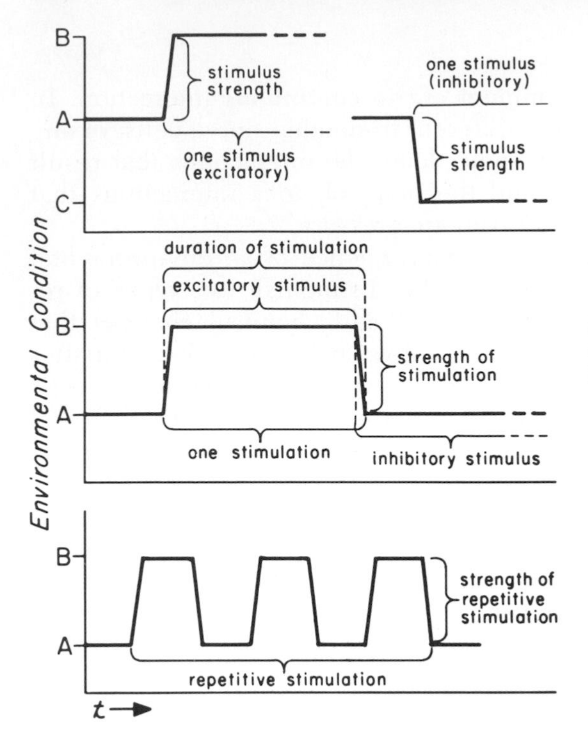

Figure 19–3. The concept of *stimulus* and *stimulation.* x axis: time; y axis: strength of stimulus. The letters *A*, *B*, and *C* define arbitrary levels.

One is used to calling the application of a brief electric pulse to a nerve or muscle a "stimulus." Actually, this pulse consists of two stimuli, but only the depolarizing stimulus causes excitation—the hyperpolarizing effect usually remains unnoticed since it does not elicit a nerve action potential or a muscle contraction. A change of environmental conditions in one direction, followed by a return to the original condition, should appropriately be called *stimulation*. If this sequence of events is repeated, the term *repetitive stimulation* applies.

To summarize: Change from condition A to condition B represents a stimulus and so does the return from B to A. The sequence of changes A–B–B–A is stimulation, and a sequence A–B — B–A — A–B — B–A — A–B — B–A is repetitive stimulation. This statement is represented graphically in Figure 19–3.

The extent to which the environment changes when it causes a response is called the *strength of the stimulus*, *stimulus strength*, or *stimulus intensity*.

The Nature of the Response

The depolarization and hyperpolarization caused by stimuli occur primarily in the generator region of the receptor neurons. These are the parts of the nerve cells that act as transducers. The electric responses are graded and represent local potentials (see Chap. 16). At present nothing is known about the mechanism by which changes in the receptor's environment produce these potential changes, but it must be assumed that the membrane structure is ultimately affected.

A receptor responds by (1) being immediately affected by the stimulus and (2) modifying this effect by opposing it. Thus it is found that the apparent effect of the stimulus diminishes with time: depolarizations as well as hyperpolarizations diminish while the new environmental condition persists. The phenomenon of a reduction of the immediate response is identical with *accommodation* (see Chap. 16).

Accommodation develops with time and becomes stronger the longer the new environmental action lasts—until it has reached its maximum. At this point environmental action and the reaction of accommodation reach an equilibrium, known as a *steady state*. If the environmental change is so slow that its time course is the same as that of accommodation, a steady change in membrane condition results and the immediate or primary response cannot be seen. If, on the other hand, the change is rapid, the primary effect of the stimulus outruns, as it were, the accommodation process; it will therefore be much greater than the steady state response.

From this we learn that *the effect of a stimulus depends not only on stimulus strength, but also on the rate of change of the stimulus*. Given sufficient time, the final effect (steady state) is the same regardless of the rate of change, but the initial action of the stimulus is greater the greater the rate of change. This is illustrated in Figure 19–4.

Since stimulation always consists of two stimuli acting successively in opposite directions, accommodation occurs twice: first during the situation A–B—B and then during B–A—A. Thus *even under normal, resting conditions, a receptor must be considered as having accommodated to the "normal" environmental condition and that it is in a steady state*. Figure 19–5 illustrates this.

It is now easy to fit the term "generator potential" into the schema as presented in Figure 19–5 and to derive its meaning: *a generator potential*

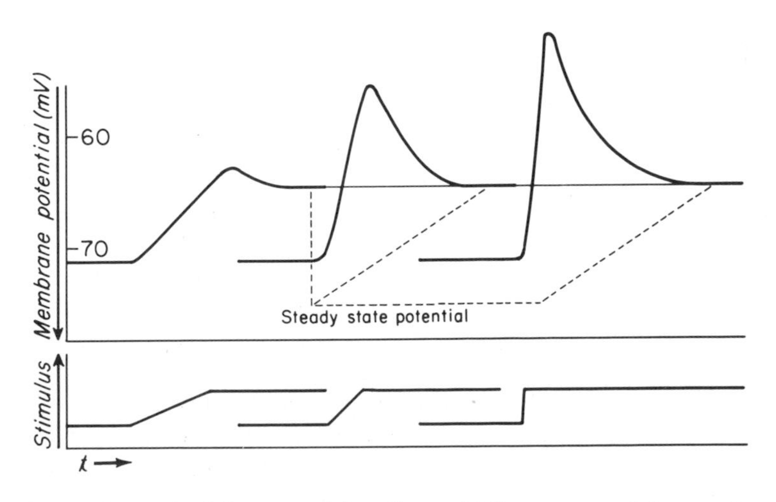

Figure 19–4. Conceptual diagram of the effects of different rates of change of environmental conditions (stimulus) on the configuration of the change in membrane potential. The first, or dynamic, phase is the more prominent the greater the rate of rise of the stimulus.

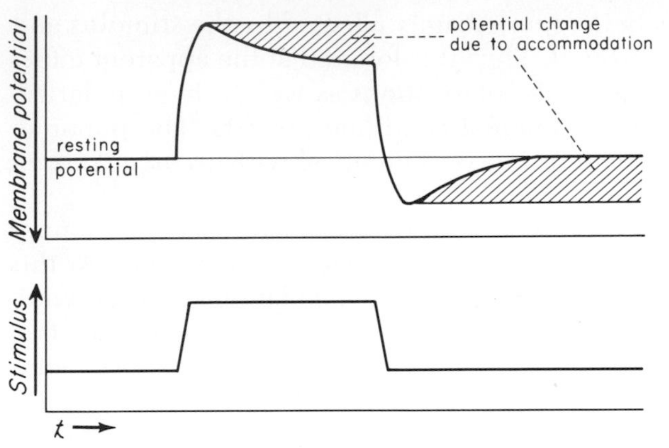

Figure 19–5. The concept of accommodation (see the text).

is a depolarizing response of the generator region which, if of sufficient magnitude, can set up (generate) one or more (full-blown) conducted, action potentials in the conductile portion of the receptor neuron.

The mechanism by which action potentials are generated is most likely the following: the generator depolarization causes a transient increase in Na^+ permeability. If the depolarization is sufficient and the depolarized area large enough, a sufficient amount of electric current flows to induce an action potential of the "all-or-none" type in the conductile part of the cell. The duration of the induced permeability change, in particular the time course of spontaneous recovery from it while stimulation persists, depends on the amount of depolarization—the amount of current that flows depends on the magnitude of the depolarized area. As soon as this transient permeability change is over, it can start anew. Thus it is possible that a generator potential produces a series of transient permeability changes with concomitant transient depolarization which summate with the generator potential. The stronger the depolarization (generator potential), the shorter the interval between successive permeability changes. The terminology applied to generator potential and resulting action potentials is explained in Figure 19–6.

Such transient depolarizations, riding, as it were, on top of the generator potential, are known as *prepotentials* (see Fig. 19–6). The intensity of the prepotentials, and the rate of their initial depolarization (their *rise time*), increase with increasing generator area. If a sufficiently large membrane area is affected by the stimulus, the prepotential can become so intense that it reaches the firing threshold and grows into a full-blown spike or action potential, which then is conducted along the length of the axon of the receptor neuron.

Unless the prepotentials grow into spikes, they remain local potentials, restricted to the generator region of the receptor neuron.

The fact that the interval between prepotentials decreases with increasing generator potential has a functionally most important consequence: *the frequency of prepotentials increases with increasing generator potential* (provided, of course, that the generator potential lasts sufficiently long). Thus, if the generator potential involves a sufficiently large membrane area (and in receptor

(Text continued on page 469.)

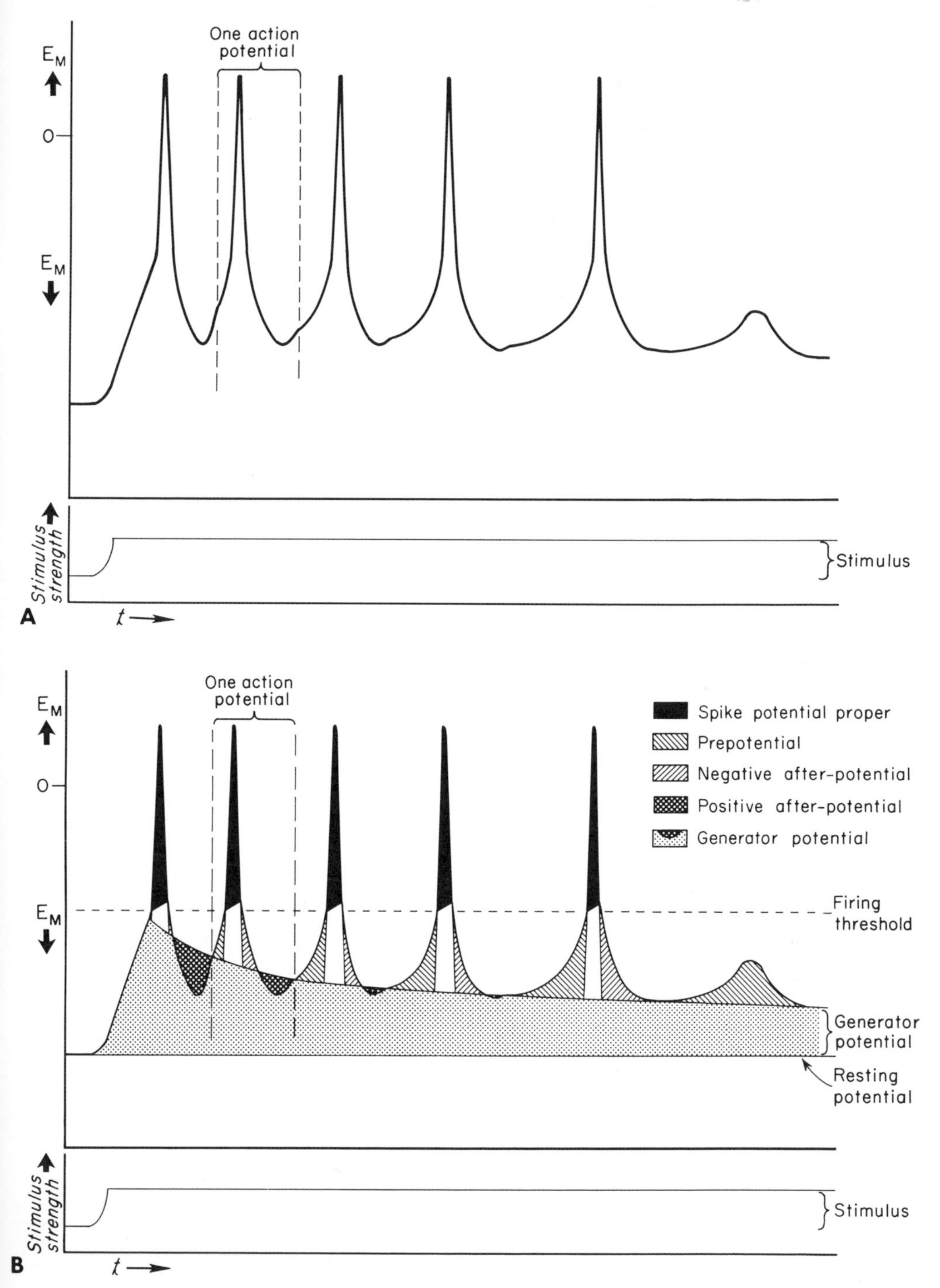

Figure 19–6. Electrical membrane responses of a receptor neuron near or at the generator region. The diagram in **A** shows the responses to a stimulus as they are actually recorded by a microelectrode inserted into the cell. The terms assigned to the different phases of the response pattern are shown in diagram B. E_M = membrane potential.

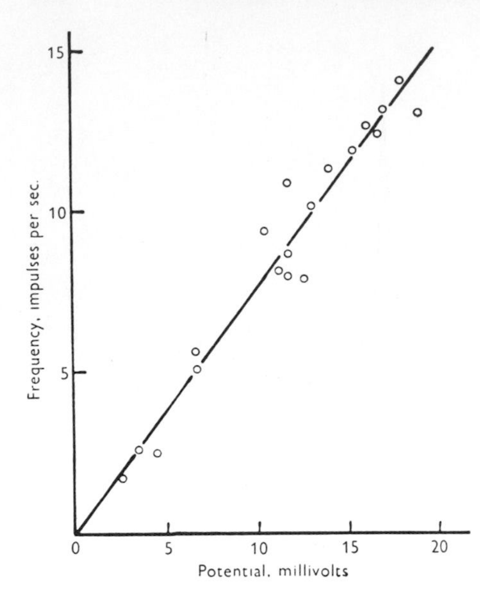

Figure 19–7. Relation between magnitude of generator potential and impulse frequency recorded from a photoreceptor neuron in the eye of *Limulus*. Note that this is a strictly linear relationship. The same has been found for other types of receptors. (From MacNichol, E. F., Jr.: Subthreshold excitatory processes in the eye of Limulus. Exp. Cell Res., Suppl. 5:411–425, 1958.)

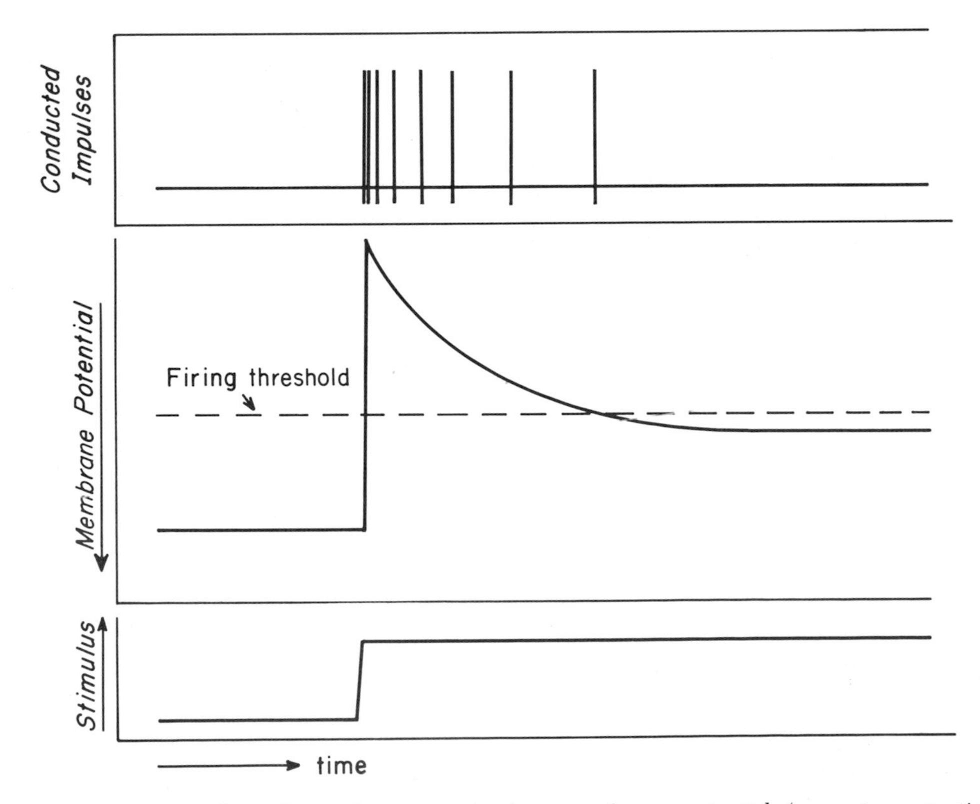

Figure 19–8. The relation between stimulus, membrane potential (generator potential) at the generator region, and impulse frequency of the axon of a receptor neuron.

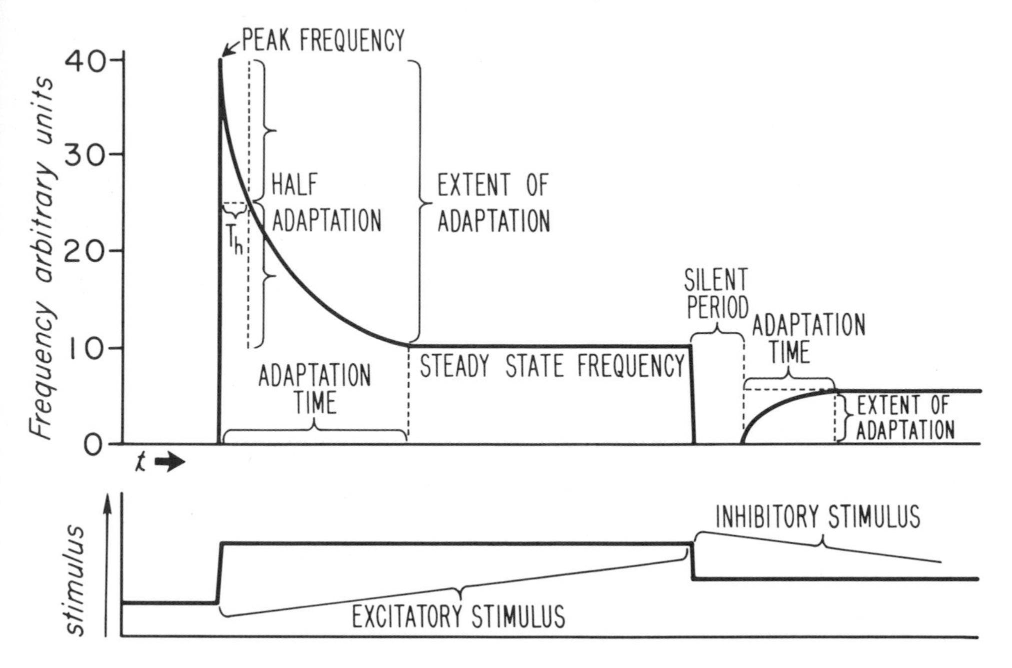

Figure 19–9. Terminology of adaptation, as applicable to a diagram that relates frequency of firing to time. T_h = half adaptation time. (This is an extension of the terminology used by Burkhardt, 1959.)

neurons this is normally the case), *the frequency of generated nerve impulses* (spike potentials which travel along the axon) *is directly proportional to the amount of generator potential.* An example of this is given in Figure 19–7.

The time course of the generator potential, which changes because of the concomitant accommodation, is reflected in the characteristic frequency change of the nerve impulses, known as *adaptation*: while the changed environmental conditions remain unaltered, the frequency of receptor nerve impulses elicited as a response to the stimulus diminishes. Figure 19–8 illustrates this. Just as the generator potential reaches a steady state when accommodation balances the effect of the stimulus, so does the impulse frequency reach a steady state which, in the case of an excitatory stimulus, is a lower frequency than that initially reached immediately after the onset of the stimulus.

Following the precise terminology of Burkhardt (1959), we can describe the frequency response of a receptor neuron to an excitatory stimulus by a set of terms which are explained in Figure 19–9.

PHASIC AND TONIC RECEPTORS

Many kinds of receptor neurons do not generate spike potentials unless they are activated by excitatory stimuli. There are others, however, that generate nerve impulses continuously even under normal environmental conditions. The former are called *phasic receptors*, the latter *tonic receptors*. Tonic receptors are often referred to as *slow(ly) adapting* receptors, whereas some phasic receptors are called *fast adapting* receptors.

Although they usually differ in structure, the two types function according to the same principles. The chief difference lies in the firing level of their membrane (see Chap. 16). In fast adapting, or phasic, receptors the resting membrane potential is considerably greater than the potential at which the conductile membrane fires. In tonic (slowly adapting) receptors, on the other hand, the "resting potential" is close to the potential level necessary for firing so that, in fact, the resting neuron fires at a steady rate. Between these two extremes, there are many possible intermediates.

In the case of typical tonic receptors, the term "generator potential" is insufficient to describe the relationship between the membrane potential of the generator region and the resulting impulse frequency. For this reason it is better to simply remember that *the impulse frequency is always proportional to the membrane potential as long as the membrane potential stays below the firing level of the initial conductile portion of the receptor neuron.* This means that in a tonic receptor the impulse frequency not only follows the pattern of depolarization (generator potential) but also that of the polarization and hyperpolarization which is caused when environmental conditions change in a direction opposite to that which causes depolarization.

Stimulation (A–B–B–A) applied to a tonic receptor neuron results therefore in a frequency pattern that differs considerably from that of a phasic receptor responding to the same stimulation. Both patterns are shown in Figure 19–10.

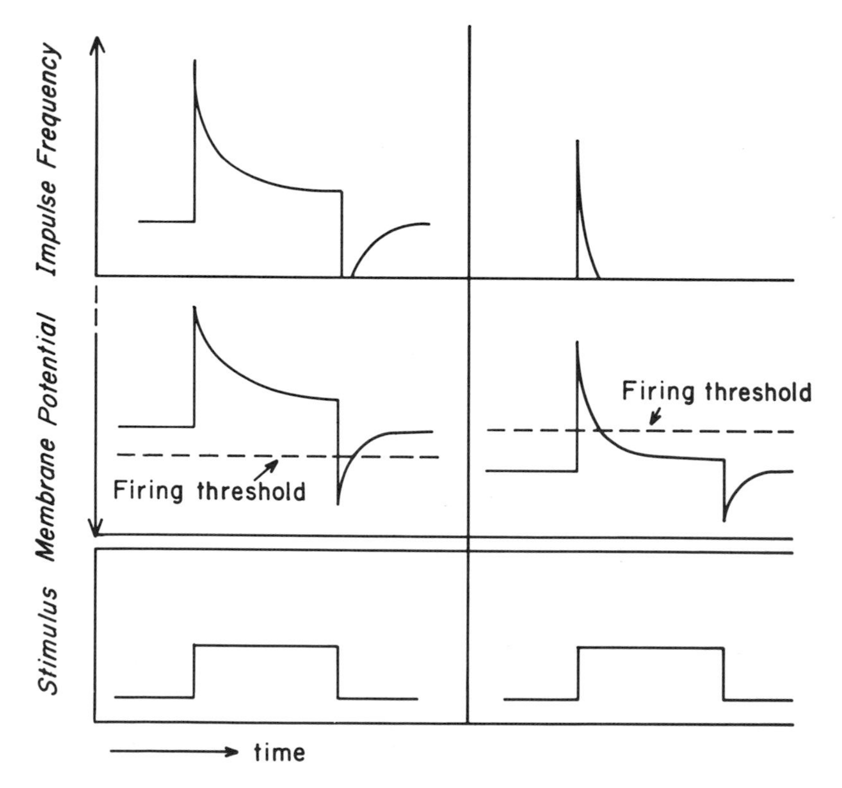

Figure 19–10. The difference between a tonic ("spontaneously active") and phasic ("fast adapting") receptor neuron, as explained in the text.

Now, there is no rule that stimulation must proceed in the order: excitatory stimulus–inhibitory stimulus. Environmental conditions may well change the other way around. When that happens the frequency pattern again reflects the changing membrane potential. In the case of phasic receptors this has a most important consequence: while no impulses are generated during the hyperpolarization phase, impulses arise immediately when the depolarization crosses the firing level: thus the phasic receptor can generate impulses at the end of stimulation. Such a response is called an *"off" response*, in contrast to the *"on" response* of a receptor that generates impulses during the depolarizing response to stimulation which causes first excitation, then inhibition. The diagrams of Figure 19–11 explain this.

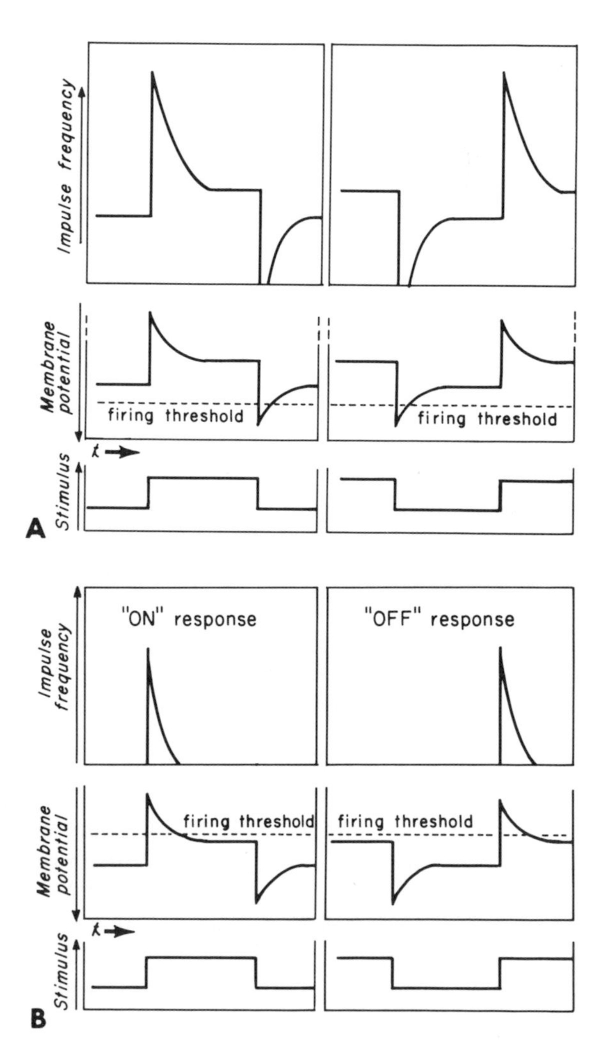

Figure 19–11. "On" and "off" effects in a tonic receptor (**A**) and a phasic receptor (**B**).

SYNAPTIC CONTROL OF RECEPTOR NEURONS

Many receptor neurons receive synaptic contacts from other nerve cells. It is possible that this is a general feature of receptors. The synaptic endings are derived from: (a) collaterals of other, usually similar, receptor neurons that are located nearby and (b) efferent neurons whose cell soma is located within the central nervous system.

In all known cases, the synapses are inhibitory. Examples for inhibitory collaterals from nearby receptors are the photoreceptors in the compound eyes of *Limulus*; examples for inhibitory endings of efferent neurons are found in the stretch receptor neurons of decapod Crustacea. These situations are discussed in Chapter 20 (pp. 487–489) and Chapter 25 (p. 641).

The effect of synaptic inhibition is a suppression of potential changes in response to the natural, specific stimuli. This is achieved by forcing the membrane potential toward the equilibrium potential for K^+ and/or Cl^-. The process is discussed in Chapter 20 (Synaptic Transmission).

INTERACTION OF STIMULI OF DIFFERENT MODALITIES

Although receptor neurons are specialized (by position or structure) to respond predominantly to only one modality of stimulation, they do respond also to changes of other parameters of the environment. Mechanoreceptors are known to respond to temperature changes, photoreceptors respond to pressure (this is responsible for the sensation of light when we compress our eyeballs), and temperature receptors respond to drugs (e.g., menthol).

Only the experiment can tell whether increase or decrease of temperature excites a certain mechanoreceptor, or whether a particular photoreceptor is activated or inactivated by pressure. But it is a general rule that all excitatory stimuli, regardless of their nature, have qualitatively the same effect as the adequate excitatory stimulus. The same, with opposite sign, is true for inhibitory stimuli.

Looking at the pattern of the impulse frequency of a receptor, one cannot tell what kind of environmental change caused it.

How stimuli of different modality interact on a receptor neuron may be illustrated as follows: a crayfish stretch receptor neuron (tonic receptor) responds with excitation to stretching, but also to cooling and to the application of acetylcholine. Inhibition (that is, momentary reduction of impulse frequency) is produced by relaxing the receptor muscle and by warming, or by suddenly removing previously applied acetylcholine. If the receptor muscle is suddenly stretched to a new level of tension, the impulse frequency immediately rises to a peak value and then declines (adaptation) to a steady state level. Then if the organ is suddenly warmed, inhibition results, the frequency suddenly drops and then rises gradually (adaptation) to a low steady state level. Application of acetylcholine induces the typical pattern of excitation, and if, finally, the receptor muscle is allowed to relax suddenly to the initial tension, inhibition once more results and during adaptation a steady state frequency is reached which corresponds to the combined effects of mechanical tension, concentration

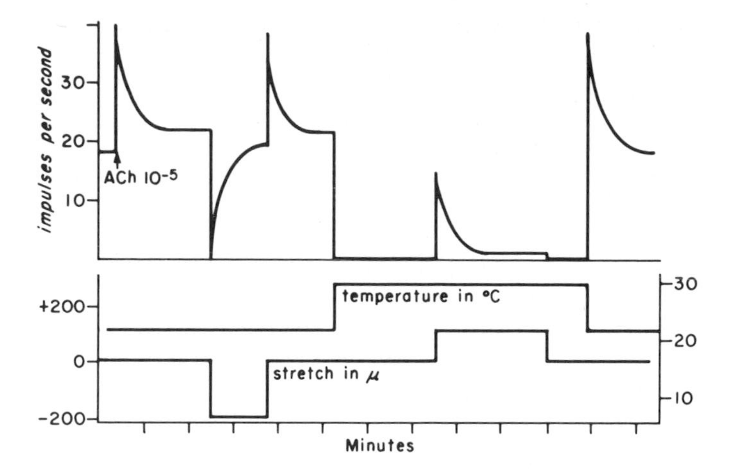

Figure 19–12. Interactions of three modes of stimulation (chemical, thermal, and mechanical) on a crayfish stretch receptor neuron. The response pattern is similar to that obtainable if only one modality is varied. ACh = acetylcholine.

of acetylcholine, and temperature. The experiment is illustrated in abstract form in Figure 19–12.

REFERENCES

Adrian, E. D. (1928) The Basis of Sensation. The Action of Sense Organs. Christophers, London.

Adrian, E. D. (1959) Sensory mechanisms—Introduction. *In* Handbook of Physiology, Sec. 1, Vol. I, pp. 365–367. (J. Field, ed.) The Williams & Wilkins Co., Baltimore.

Adrian, E. D., and Y. Zotterman (1926) The impulses produced by sensory nerve-endings. Part 2. The response of a single end-organ. J. Physiol. *61*:151–171.

Alanis, J., and B. H. Matthews (1952) The mechano-receptor properties of central neurones. J. Physiol. *117*:P59–P60.

Arvanitaki, A., and N. Chalazonitis (1961) Excitatory and inhibitory processes initiated by light and infrared radiations in single identifiable nerve cells (giant ganglion cells of *Aplysia*). *In* Nervous Inhibition, pp. 194–232. (E. Florey, ed.) Pergamon Press, Oxford.

Barlow, H. B. (1961) The coding of sensory messages. *In* Current Problems in Animal Behaviour. (W. H. Thorpe and O. L. Zangwill, eds.) Cambridge University Press, London.

Bernard, C. G., and R. Granit (1946) Nerve as model temperature organ. J. Gen. Physiol. *29*:257–265.

Bing, A. I., and A. P. Skouby (1950) Sensitization of cold receptors by substances with acetylcholine effect. Acta Physiol. Scand. *21*:286–302.

von Buddenbrock, W. (1930) Untersuchungen über den Schattenreflex. Z. vergl. Physiol. *13*: 164–213.

Bullock, T. H., ed. (1957) Physiological Triggers. American Physiological Society, Washington, D.C.

Bullock, T. H. (1959) Initiation of nerve impulses in receptor and central neurones. *In* Recent Advances in Invertebrate Physiology. (B. T. Scheer, ed.) University of Oregon Press, Eugene.

Burkhardt, D. (1959) Die Erregungsvorgänge sensibler Ganglienzellen in Abnängigkeit von der Temperatur. Biol. Zbl. *78*:22–62.

Burkhardt, D. (1960) Die Eigenschaften und Funktionstypen der Sinnesorgane. Ergebn. Biol. *22*:226–267.

Davis, H. (1961) Some principles of sensory receptor action. Physiol. Rev. *41*:391–416.

Eccles, J. C. (1957) The Physiology of Nerve Cells. Johns Hopkins Press, Baltimore.

Erlanger, J., and E. A. Blair (1938) Comparative observations on motor and sensory fibers with special reference to repetitiousness. Amer. J. Physiol. *121*:431–453.

Erlanger, J., and H. S. Gasser (1937) Electrical Signs of Nervous Activity. University of Pennsylvania Press, Philadelphia.

Eyzaguirre, C., and S. W. Kuffler (1955a) Further study of soma, dendrite and axon excitation in single neurons. J. Gen. Physiol. *39*:121–153.

Eyzaguirre, C., and S. W. Kuffler (1955b) Processes of excitation in the dendrites and in the soma of single isolated sensory nerve cells of the lobster and crayfish. J. Gen. Physiol. *39*:87–119.

Florey, E. (1955) Untersuchungen über die Impuls-Entstehung in den Streckreceptoren des Flusskrebses. Z. Naturforsch. *10B*:591–597.

Florey, E. (1956) Adaptationserscheinungen in den sensiblen Neuronen der Streckreceptoren des Flusskrebses. Z. Naturforsch. *11B*:504–513.

Florey, E. (1957) Chemical transmission and adaptation. J. Gen. Physiol. *40*:533–545.

Florey, E. (1961) Excitation, inhibition and the concept of the stimulus. *In* Nervous Inhibition, pp. 136–143. (E. Florey, ed.) Pergamon Press, Oxford.

Frank, K., and M. G. F. Fuortes (1960) Accommodation of spinal motoneurons of cats. Arch. Ital. Biol. *98*:165–170.

Granit, R. (1944) Stimulus intensity in relation to excitation and pre- and post-excitatory inhibition in isolated elements of mammalian retinae. J. Physiol. *103*:103–108.

Granit, R. (1952) Aspects of excitation and inhibition in the retina. Proc. Roy. Soc. B, *140*:191–198.

Granit, R. (1955) Receptors and Sensory Perception. Yale University Press, New Haven.

Granit, R., and C. R. Skoglund (1943) Accommodation and autorhythmic mechanism in single sensory fibres. J. Neurophysiol. *6*:337–348.

Gray, J. A. B. (1959) Initiation of impulses at receptors. *In* Handbook of Physiology, Sec. 1, Vol. I, pp. 123–145. (J. Field, ed.) The Williams & Wilkins Co., Baltimore.

Hartline, H. K. (1959) Receptor mechanisms and the integration of sensory information in the eye. *In* Biophysical Science—A Study Program. (J. L. Oncley, ed.) John Wiley & Sons, New York.

Hartline, H. K., F. Ratliff, and W. H. Miller (1961) Inhibitory interaction in the retina and its significance in vision. *In* Nervous Inhibition. (E. Florey, ed.) Pergamon Press, Oxford.

Hensel, H. (1952) Physiologie der Thermoreception. Ergebn. Physiol. *47*:165–368.

Hensel, H., and Y. Zotterman (1951) The response of mechanoreceptors to thermal stimulation. J. Physiol. *115*:291–319.

Katz, B. (1950a) Action potentials from a sensory nerve ending. J. Physiol. *111*:248–260.

Katz, B. (1950b) Depolarization of sensory terminals and the initiation of impulses in the muscle spindle. J. Physiol. *111*:261–282.

Kolmodin, G. M. (1957) Integrative processes in single spinal interneurones with proprioceptive connections. Acta Physiol. Scand. *40*:1–89.

Kolmodin, G. M., and C. R. Skoglund (1958) Slow membrane potential changes accompanying excitation and inhibition in spinal moto- and interneurons in the cat during natural activation. Acta Physiol. Scand. *44*:11–54.

Kuffler, S. W. (1953) Discharge patterns and functional organization of mammalian retina. J. Neurophysiol. *16*:37–68.

Lorente de Nó, R. (1947) A Study of Nerve Physiology. Rockefeller Institute, New York.

Morita, H. (1959) Initiation of spike potentials in contact chemosensory hairs of insects. III. D.C. stimulation and generator potential of labellar chemoreceptor in *Calliphora*. J. Cell. Comp. Physiol. *54*:189–204.

Terzuolo, C. A., and Y. Washizu (1962) Relation between stimulus strength, generator potential and impulse frequency in stretch receptor of Crustacea. J. Neurophysiol. *25*:56–66.

20 SYNAPTIC TRANSMISSION

STRUCTURE

The points of contact between terminal (transmissional) portions of neurons and the generator region of another neuron or an effector (muscle) cell are called *synapses* (Foster and Sherrington, 1897; Sherrington, 1906). The cell contributing the terminals is called the *presynaptic* neuron; the cell that contributes the generator region is called the *postsynaptic* cell. The part of the cell membrane of the presynaptic terminal that is applied to the generator region of the postsynaptic cell is called the *presynaptic membrane*; that part of the generator region of the postsynaptic cell which is directly underneath the presynaptic membrane is called the *subsynaptic* membrane, while the membrane of the generator region surrounding and including this subsynaptic membrane is generally known as the *postsynaptic* membrane. The situation is explained in Figure 20–1.

Many morphological types of synapses are known. The most common one consists of contacts between rather small (1 μ) knob-like terminals with dendrites or soma of postsynaptic neurons. The knobs are often referred to as *boutons terminaux* (terminal knobs), as first described by Cajal. Typical examples are pictured in Figures 20–2 and 20–3. These are probably the most common synapses in the vertebrate central nervous system. In vertebrate autonomic ganglia knob-like endings have also been found. What is often seen, however, is a dense intermingling of fine, terminal branches of presynaptic axons and postsynaptic dendrites, forming a "synaptic basket." There may well be no fixed apposition between presynaptic and subsynaptic membranes. One peculiar type of autonomic synapse, the *calyciform synapse* in the ciliary ganglion of the chick (Fig. 20–4), has become of great importance in physiological studies of synaptic transmission; it is discussed below.

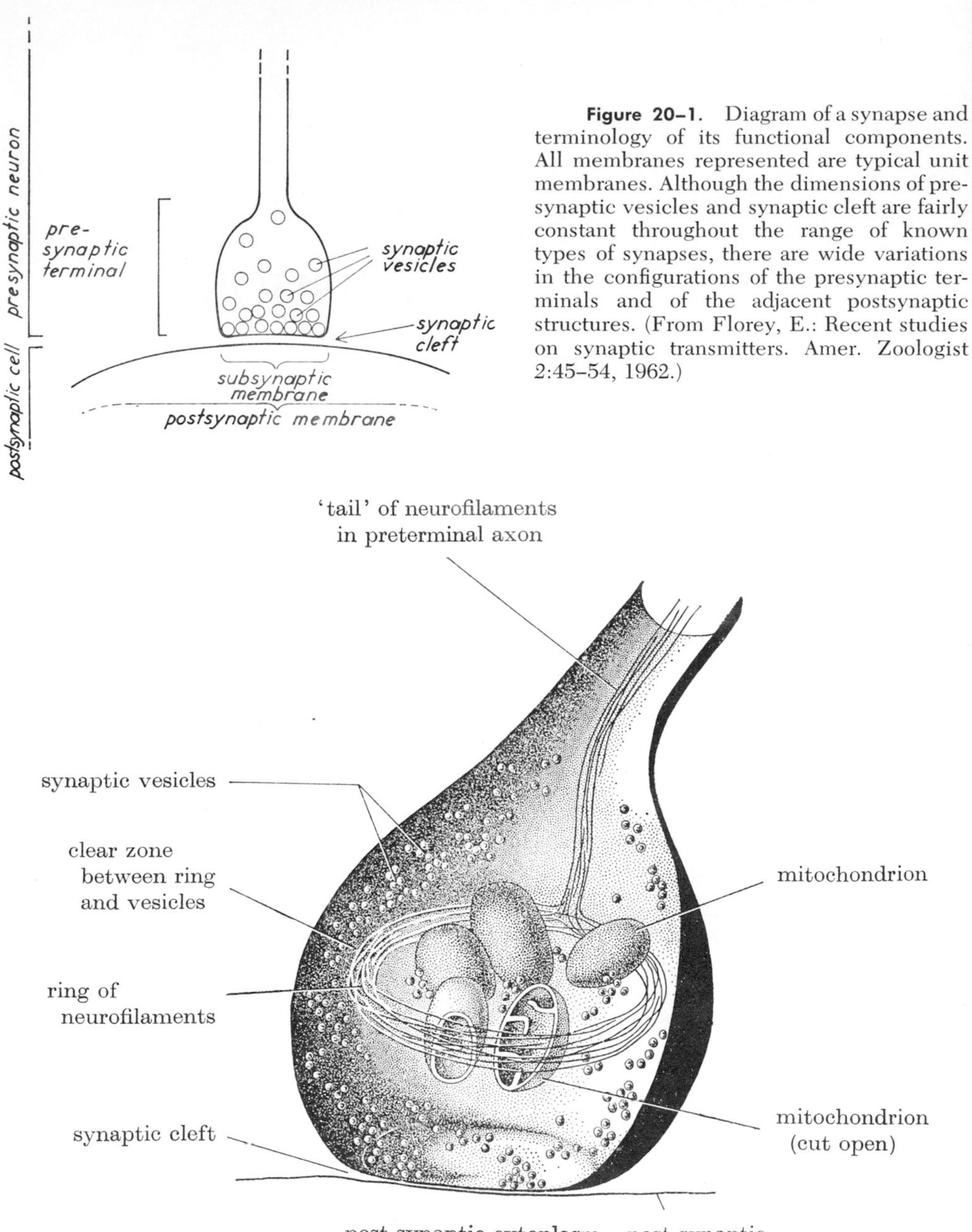

Figure 20–1. Diagram of a synapse and terminology of its functional components. All membranes represented are typical unit membranes. Although the dimensions of presynaptic vesicles and synaptic cleft are fairly constant throughout the range of known types of synapses, there are wide variations in the configurations of the presynaptic terminals and of the adjacent postsynaptic structures. (From Florey, E.: Recent studies on synaptic transmitters. Amer. Zoologist 2:45–54, 1962.)

Figure 20–2. Schematic three-dimensional representation of a bouton terminal (presynaptic nerve ending), opened on one side to show the internal structure. It is based on electron microscope studies of synaptic structures in the brain of the lizard (Reptilia) *Lacerta viridis*. The diameter of such endings reaches 5 microns. Each contains synaptic vesicles (about 500 Ångstrom units in diameter) and a bundle of neurofilaments (each about 100 Å in diameter), usually oriented in the form of a ring. A "tail" of neurofilaments is sometimes observed extending up the axon from the ring. The synaptic cleft is about 200 Å across. The synaptic vesicles form aggregates near the presynaptic membrane bounding the cleft. The membrane thickenings that are present at these regions have been omitted since their three-dimensional appearance is unknown. (From Boycott, B. B., E. G. Gray, and R. W. Guillery: Synaptic structure and its alteration with environmental temperature: a study by light and electron microscopy of the central nervous system of lizards. Proc. Roy. Soc. B, *154*:151–172, 1961.)

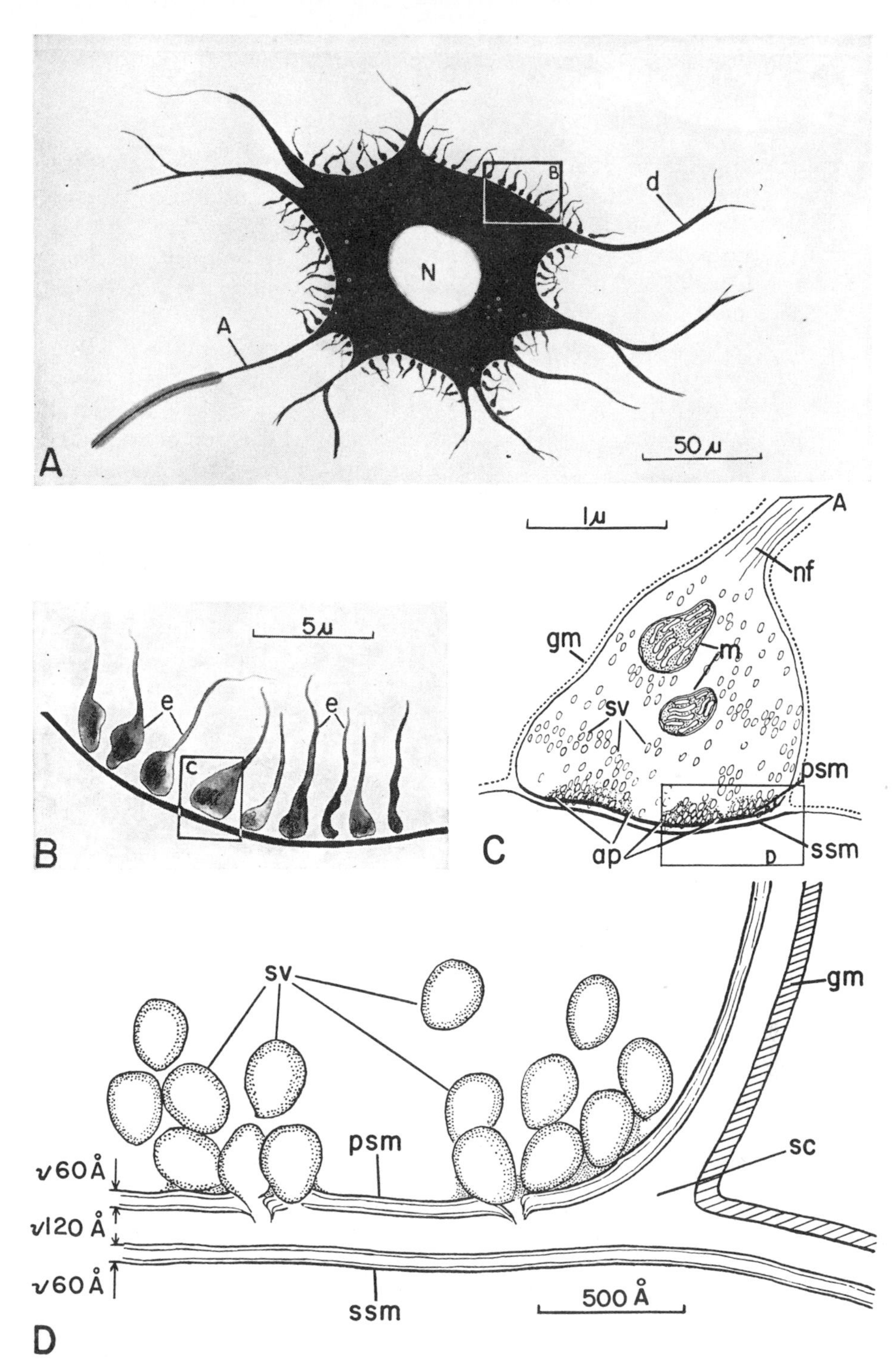

Figure 20–3. Diagram showing synapses between bouton-like nerve endings and a mammalian spinal motoneuron at different magnifications with the light microscope and the electron microscope. **A**, a motoneuron as seen at medium power with the light microscope. *A*, axon; *d*, dendrites; *N*, nucleus. Note the numerous nerve endings on the cell body which, having a surface area of about 10,000 μ^2, is covered by no less than 2000 such boutons. The enclosure B is magnified about 10 times more in **B**. *e*, nerve endings. Enclosure C is magnified six times further (electron microscope) in **C**. *A*, axon; *ap*, active areas of synapse; *gm*, glial membrane; *m*, mitochondria; *nf*, neurofilaments; *psm*, presynaptic membrane; *ssm*, subsynaptic membrane; *sv*, synaptic vesicles. Enclosure D is magnified 20 times more in **D**, which is an imaginative interpretation. (From De Robertis, E.: Submicroscopic morphology of the synapse. Int. Rev. Cytol. 8:61–96, 1959.)

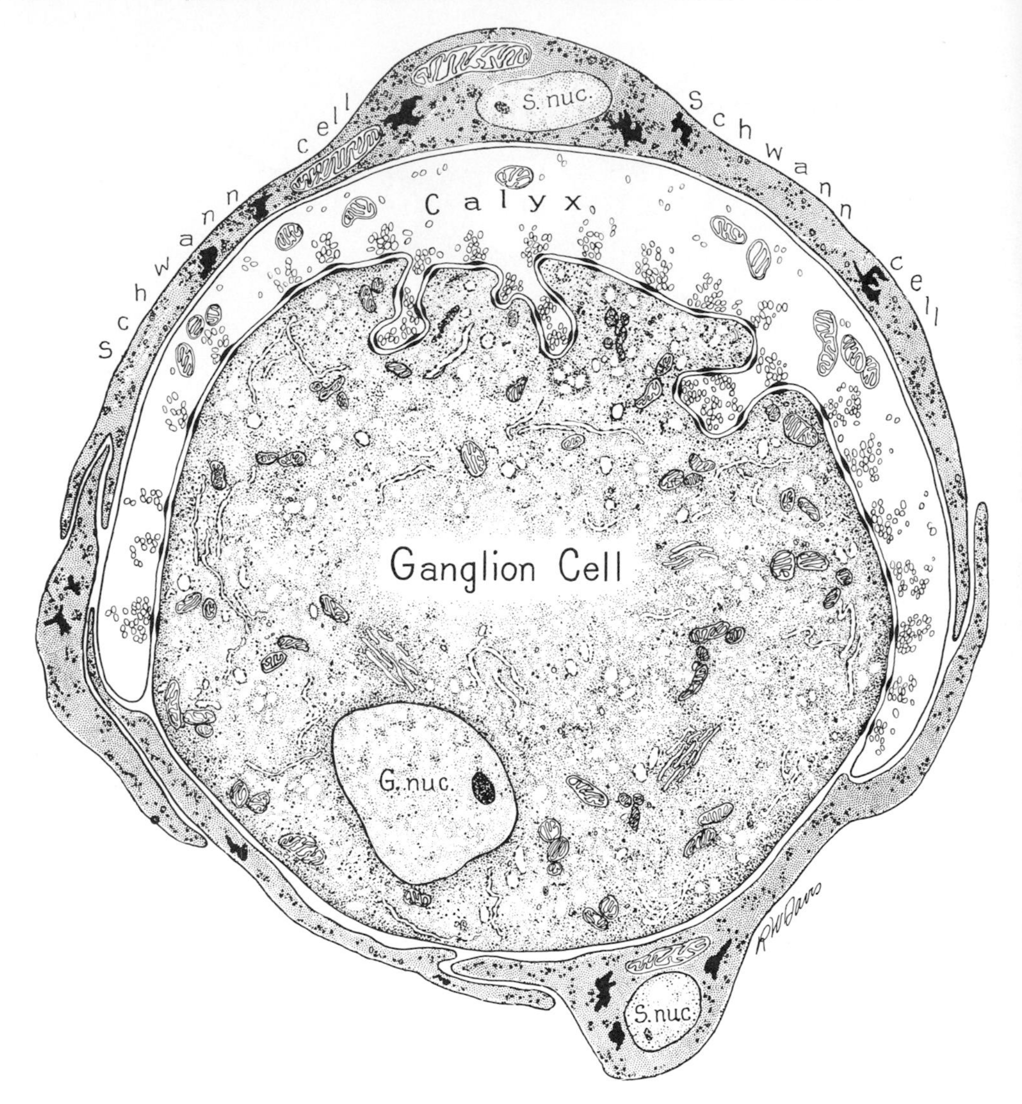

Figure 20–4. Diagrammatic representation of a cross section through a calyciform synapse in the ciliary ganglion of a chick. The presynaptic fiber has a cup-shaped ending (*calyx*), which contacts a large area of the ganglion cell (axon not shown). The synaptic cleft is 300 to 400 Ångstrom units wide. Note the synaptic vesicles and mitochondria within the presynaptic ending. This is a synapse capable of both electrical and chemical synaptic transmission. *G. nuc.*, nucleus of ganglion cell; *S. nuc.*, nucleus of Schwann cell. (From DeLorenzo, A. J.: The fine structure of synapses in the ciliary ganglion of the chick. J. Biophys. Biochem. Cytol. 7:31–36, 1960.)

The synapses in the central nervous system and in peripheral ganglia of invertebrate animals are largely unknown, with the exception of those involving giant neurons. In the central ganglia, synaptic transmission takes place in the *neuropile* (see Fig. 17–10), a structure in which the presynaptic terminal nerve endings are densely interwoven with collaterals of postsynaptic cells. Figure 20–5 illustrates the situation.

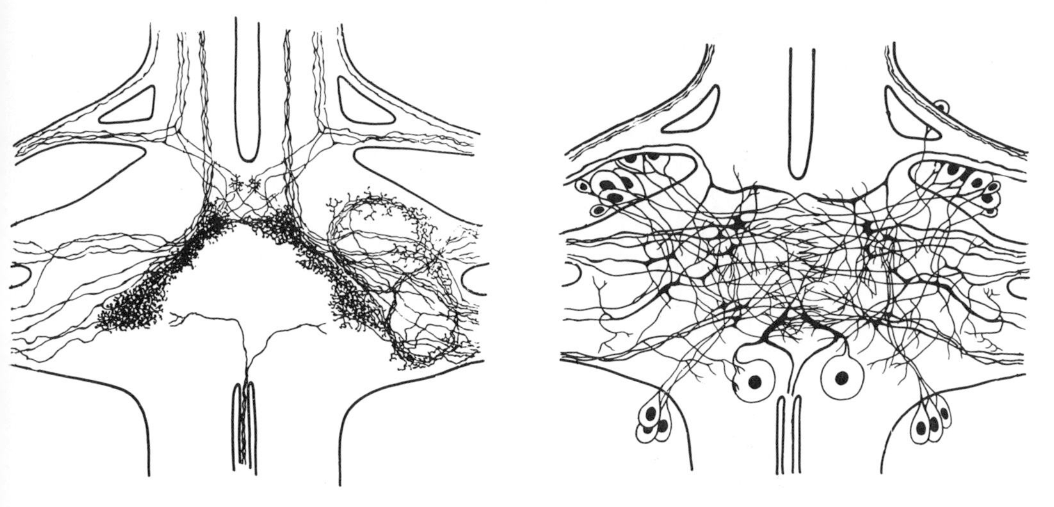

Figure 20–5. Two diagrams representing the sensory (**left**) and motor (**right**) arborizations and branches which, together, form the neuropile. This is the core of the ganglion where the synaptic contacts are made between sensory and motor neurons and between either of them and interneurons. The nerve cell bodies are situated in the periphery of the ganglion. This situation is typical of most invertebrate phyla. This figure represents the situation in a ganglion of the abdominal nerve cord of a larva of a dragonfly (*Aeschna*). (After Zawarzin, 1924, from Horridge, G. A.: The organization of the primitive central nervous system as suggested by examples of inhibition and the structure of neuropile. *In* Nervous Inhibition. E. Florey, ed. Pergamon Press, New York, 1961.)

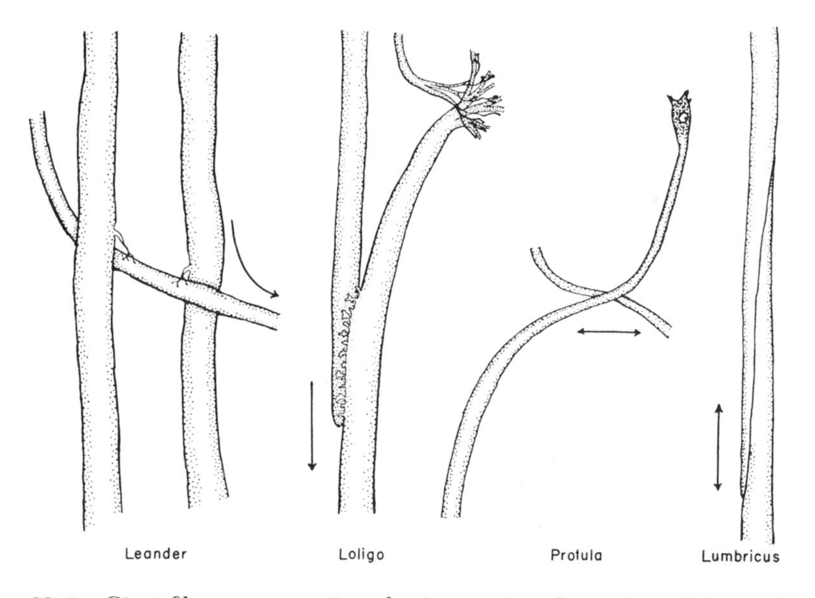

Figure 20–6. Giant fiber synapses. *Leander* (a prawn), redrawn from Holmes, showing two of the four central giant synapses upon a large segmental motor fiber in an abdominal ganglion. *Loligo*, redrawn from Young, showing the second order giant and accessory giant prefibers above, the third order giant postfiber below, in the stellate ganglion. *Protula*, a serpulid polychaete, redrawn from Bullock, showing the decussational synapse of paired giants in the brain. *Lumbricus*, after Stough, showing the oblique septal synapses of central giants. The arrows indicate the direction of transmission. (From Bullock, T. H.: The invertebrate neuron junction. Cold Spr. Harb. Symp. Quant. Biol. *17*:267–273, 1952.)

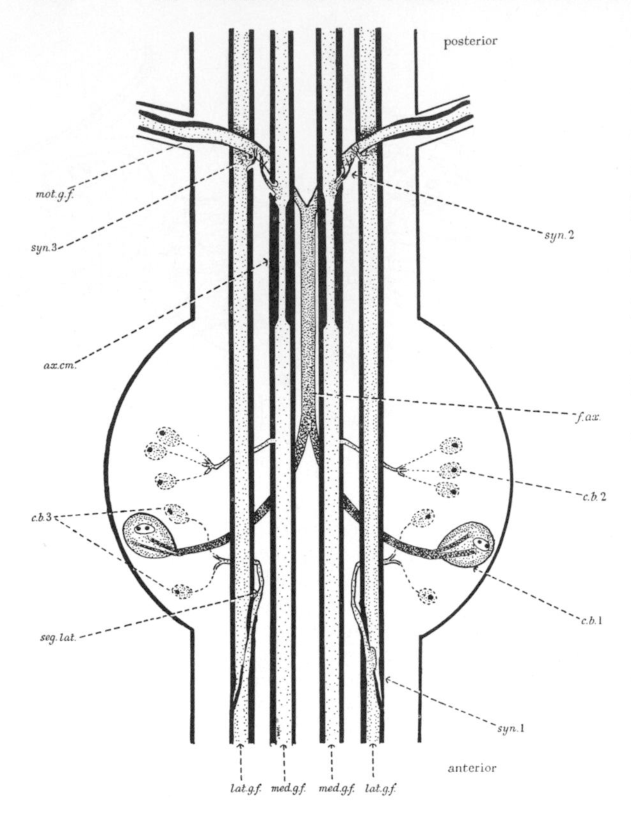

Figure 20–7. Diagrammatic dorsal view of the arrangement of the giant fibers in an abdominal ganglion of the central nervous system of *Leander serratus*. The myelin sheaths of the fibers are represented as dense black lines; the axoplasm is stippled. The number and location of the cell bodies of the median and lateral fibers is hypothetical, and their connections with the fibers, which have not been demonstrated, are represented by broken lines. *ax.cm.*, segmental constriction of the axon of the median giant fiber; *c.b.*1, cell body of the motor giant fiber; *c.b.*2, cell bodies of the median giant fiber; *c.b.*3, cell bodies of the lateral giant fiber; *f.ax.*, single axon produced by the fusion of the motor giant fibers; *lat.g.f.*, lateral giant fiber; *med.g.f.*, median giant fiber; *mot.g.f.*, motor giant fiber; *seg. lat.*, the lateral giant fiber arising in the segment; *syn.*1, synapse between two successive lateral giant fibers; *syn.*2, synapse between a median and a motor giant fiber; *syn.*3, synapse between a lateral and a motor giant fiber. (From Holmes, W.: The giant myelinated nerve fibers of the prawn. Phil. Trans. Roy. Soc. B, *231*:293–311, 1942.)

The synapses between giant neurons are better understood, largely, of course, because of their conspicuous size. Some giant neurons are joined to form long giant fibers; these neurons have large cylindrical axons, the ends of which attach to the ends of other cylindrical giant axons, thus forming a segmented, or *septate*, fiber. Such septate giant fibers are found in annelids (*Lumbricus*) and decapod Crustacea. Examples are shown in Figures 20–6 and 20–7. In the case of such septate giant fibers, the synapses consist of interdigitating pre- and subsynaptic membranes.

Giant neuron synapses that have been well investigated physiologically include not only the examples of synapses "within" septate giant fibers, but also the synapses between second and third order giant fibers of certain species of squid (Figs. 20–8 and 20–9), and the synapses between giant fibers in the nerve cord of crayfish (*Procambarus, Astacus*) and the giant motor axon supplying certain leg muscles of these animals (Figs. 20–10 and 20–11). The structure of these synapses has been investigated with the aid of electron microscopes (Fig. 20–11).

Since the vast majority of animals are invertebrates, and since most of their central synapses are of the neuropile type, only a small fraction of all the diverse synapses is structurally known. Indeed, the synapses from which we derive our knowledge of synaptic transmission are limited in number.

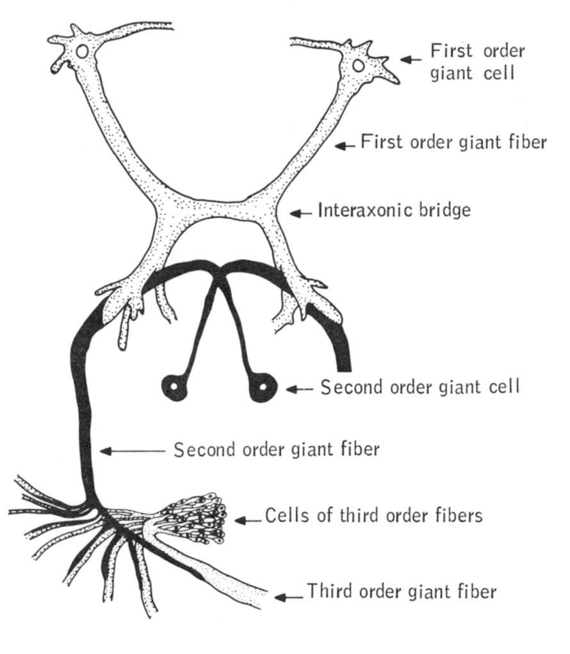

Figure 20–8. Drawing composed of several figures originally published by J. Z. Young (1939), showing the sequence of first, second, and third order giant neurons in the squid (*Loligo pealii*). See also Figure 17–12. The synapse between the second and third order giant fibers has been the one particularly studied. Note that the axons of the third order giant fibers arise by fusion of cell processes of several neurons. (Adapted from Young, 1939, by McLennan, H.: Synaptic Transmission. W. B. Saunders Co., Philadelphia, 1963.)

Synapses between efferent neurons and effector cells, in particular with muscle fibers, are among the most widely studied. Again, the number of structurally known synapses is limited. Best known are the synapses between "fast" motor axons and striated muscle fibers, the motor end-plates, as they occur in vertebrates. Their structure is pictured in Figures 20–12 and 20–13. Neuromuscular synapses have also been described for a few other kinds of muscle, notably of insects (Fig. 20–14).

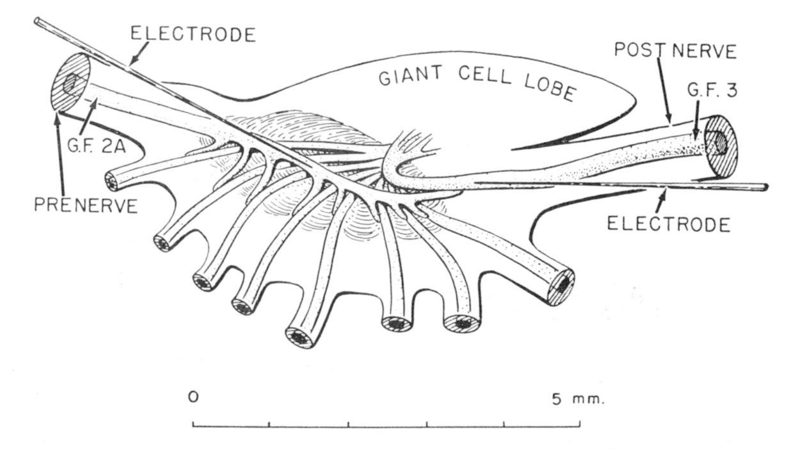

Figure 20–9. Diagrammatic representation of the stellate ganglion with the "giant synapse" between the second order giant fiber (G.F. 2A) and the third order giant fibers (G.F. 3) of the squid (Cephalopoda) *Loligo pealii.* Microelectrodes are shown inserted into the presynaptic fiber and into one of the postsynaptic fibers. (From Bullock, T. H., and S. Hagiwara: Intracellular recording from the giant synapse of the squid. J. Gen. Physiol. *40*:565–577, 1957.)

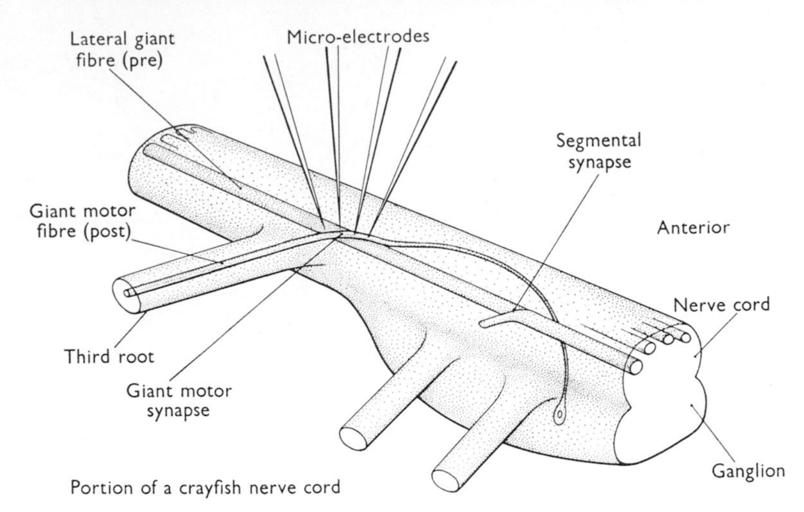

Figure 20–10. Semidiagrammatic drawing of a portion of the abdominal nerve cord of a crayfish (*Astacus*), showing one ganglion and its three nerve roots (right side). One of the four giant axons forms a synapse (segmental synapse) with the giant axon (originating in the ganglion of the next segment) that forms its continuation. This in turn makes synaptic contact with a large motor axon, the so-called giant motor fiber. The structure of this axo-axonal synapse is shown in Figure 20–11. Four microelectrodes are shown, two each in the presynaptic giant fiber and the postsynaptic motor axon respectively. One of each pair records the membrane potential, the other passes current in order to adjust the membrane potential of each fiber to any desired value. With this technique Furshpan and Potter established the rectifier properties of this synapse; they demonstrated that this is an electrically transmitting synapse. (From Furshpan, E. J., and D. D. Potter: Transmission at the giant motor synapses of the crayfish. J. Physiol. *145*:289–325, 1959.)

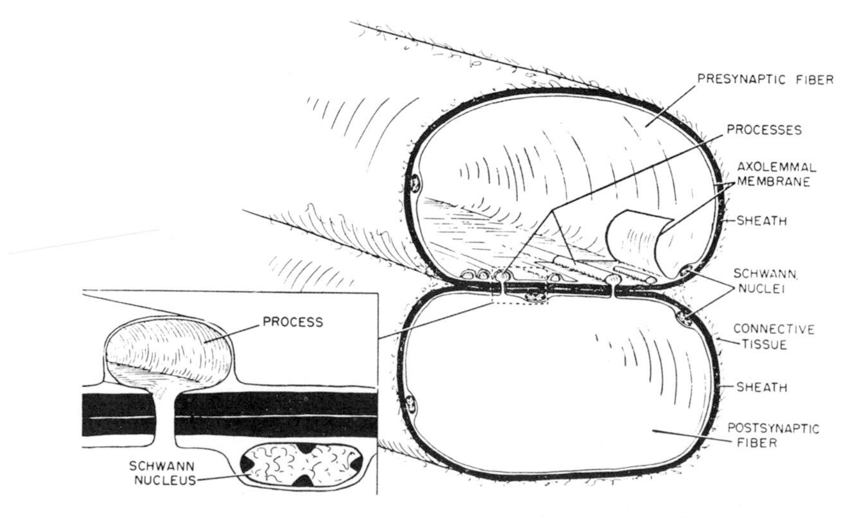

Figure 20–11. Ultrastructure of a giant synapse (see Fig. 20–10) of crayfish nerve cord. The postsynaptic motor fiber is shown below the giant axon. A flap of the presynaptic axonal membrane (called axolemmal membrane in the diagram) is reflected to show two postsynaptic cell processes. One of these and the overlying fold of presynaptic membrane are shown in the insert at higher magnification. The axons are surrounded and separated by a sheath produced by Schwann cells. (From Robertson, J. D.: Ultrastructure of two invertebrate synapses. Proc. Soc. Exp. Biol. Med. 82:219–223, 1953.)

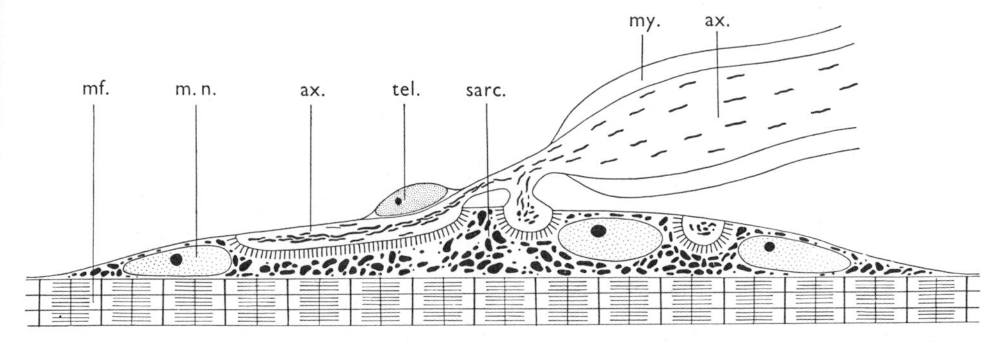

Figure 20–12. Diagrammatic representation of a motor end-plate as found in the skeletal muscle of a reptile (the American chameleon *Anolis carolinensis*). *ax.*, axoplasm with its mitochondria; *mf.*, myofibrils; *m.n.*, muscle nuclei; *my.*, myelin sheath; *sarc.*, sarcoplasm with mitochondria; *tel.*, teloglia (terminal Schwann cells). The terminal nerve endings lie in "synaptic gutters" or "troughs" (see Figs. 20–13 and 20–23). (Based on the work of Robertson, 1952, from Couteaux, R.: Morphological and cytochemical observations on the post-synaptic membrane at motor endplates and ganglionic synapses. Exp. Cell Res., Suppl. 5:294–322, 1958.)

Wherever synaptic structures have been analyzed by electron microscopy, it has been found that the pre- and subsynaptic membranes are in close apposition, the distance between them being 0.02 to 0.03 μ. This narrow gap between the two membranes is known as the *synaptic cleft.*

Rather special membrane configurations are known in which the subsynaptic membrane is deeply folded whereas the presynaptic membrane is smooth. Examples are the motor end-plates of vertebrate striated muscle (Fig. 20–13).

PHYSIOLOGICAL ASPECTS

In a number of cases, particularly crustacean and insect muscles, the physiological knowledge of synaptic events is extensive, in spite of rather inadequate morphological data. In other instances, for example, the autonomically innervated cardiac muscle and visceral smooth muscle of vertebrates, morphological knowledge of synaptic structure by far exceeds the physiological experience.

The physiological study of synaptic events requires placement of recording electrodes in the immediate vicinity of the subsynaptic membrane or penetration of subsynaptic membranes by microelectrodes. In a few ideal situations (giant fiber synapses), it has been possible to insert electrodes below the subsynaptic membrane as well as below the presynaptic membrane (Figs. 20–9 and 20–10).

Electrical Synaptic Transmission

Synapses in which the current flow through the activated presynaptic membrane directly affects the subsynaptic membrane so that a nerve impulse

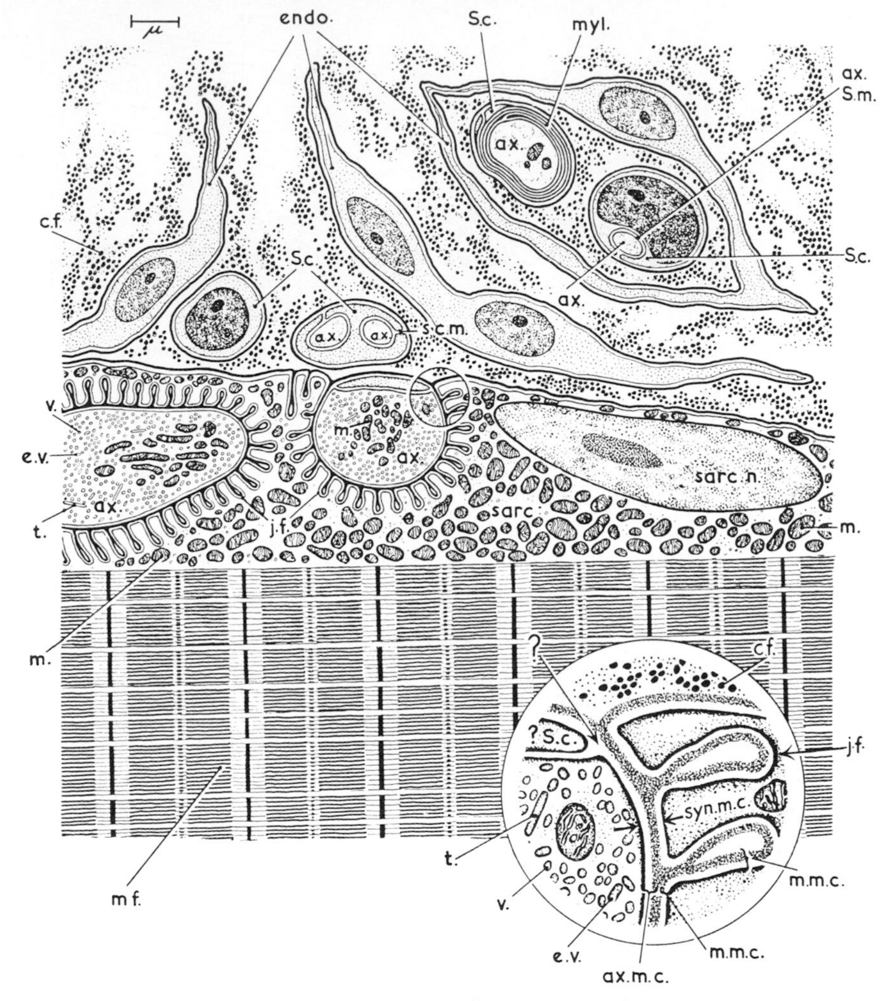

Figure 20–13. Diagrammatic representation of a neuromuscular junction on a striated skeletal muscle fiber of a reptile (*Anolis*). The diagram also shows (upper right quadrant) the axon (*ax*) of another motoneuron imbedded in a Schwann cell (*S.c.*) and surrounded by a cell of the endoneurium (*endo.*). Note the infolding of the sarcoplasmic membrane that surrounds (or almost surrounds) the motoneuron terminals. The latter are characterized by numerous vesicles (*v.*) and elongate vesicles (*e.v.*), as well as by many mitochondria (*m.*). Note also the numerous mitochondria in the vicinity of the synapse. Compare this diagram with the more abstract and schematic Figure 20–12; the latter does not show the endoneurial sheath cells.

The region marked by the circle is shown enlarged in the lower right quadrant to show in more detail the junctional folds (*j.f.*), the muscle membrane complex (*m.m.c.*), and the nerve membrane complex *(ax.m.c.)*. *c.f.*, Collagen fibrils; *mf.*, myofibrils; *myl.*, myelin; *sarc. n.*, sarcoplasmic nucleus; *s.c.m.*, surface connecting membrane (=mesaxon); *ax. S. m.*, axon Schwann membrane; *t.*, tubule. (From Robertson, J. D.: The ultrastructure of a reptilian myoneural junction. J. Biophys. Biochem. Cytol. 2:381–393, 1956.)

can effectively travel across the synaptic cleft are rare. The primary requirement for such an occurrence is a synaptic area of sufficient size: membrane resistance is of the order of magnitude of 1000 ohm/cm^2. A membrane of 1 mm^2 would have a resistance of 100×1000 ohms, a membrane of 1 μ^2 would have a resistance of $1{,}000{,}000 \times 100 \times 1000$ ohms, or 10^{11} ohms. The extracellular medium which is supposed to permeate even the synaptic cleft has a resistance many

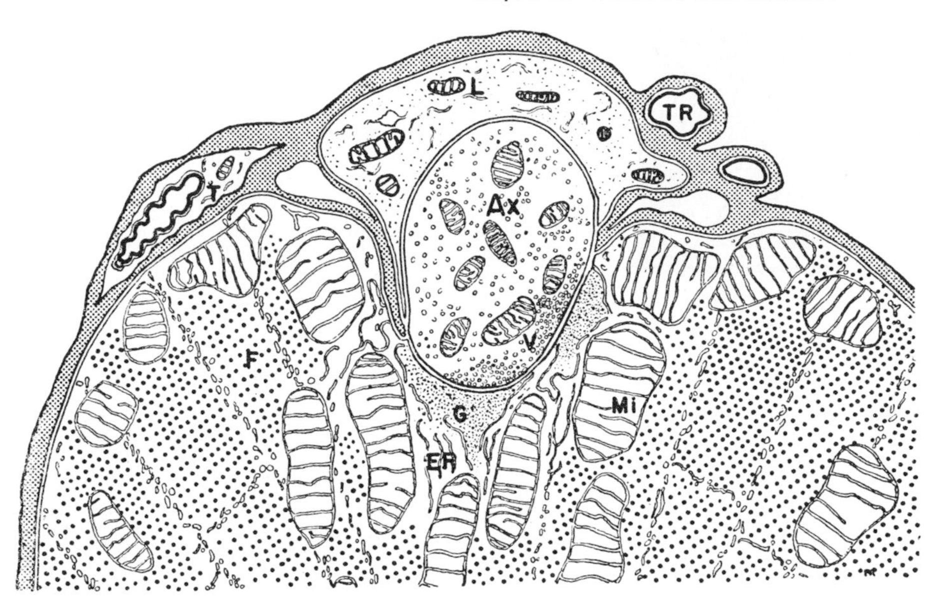

Figure 20–14. Neuromuscular junction in a wasp leg. Note that it is completely enclosed. Tracheoles *(Tr)*, with or without accompanying tracheoblast cytoplasm *(T)*, are numerous in the contact region. The synapsing axon *(Ax)* in the muscle cell groove is essentially two-thirds covered externally by the lemnoblast *(L)*. The basement membranes of the tracheoblast, lemnoblast, and muscle are merged. The final synapse involves apposition of the plasma membranes of axon and muscle fiber. The synaptic region is characterized by numerous mitochondria and synaptic vesicles (*V*) in the axon and by aggregates of mitochondria (*Mi*), augmented endoplasmic reticulum (*ER*), and aposynaptic granules (*G*) in the muscle. In nonsynaptic regions the band-shaped myofibrils (*F*) and tubules of the reticulum are more regularly arranged. (Drawing by Frank Reed.) (From Edwards, G. A., H. Ruska, and E. DeHerven: Electron microscopy of peripheral nerves and neuromuscular junctions in the wasp leg. J. Biophys. Biochem. Cytol. *4*:107–114, 1958.)

orders of magnitude lower, and even in a synaptic cleft 0.02 μ thick and 1 μ^2 in area the external resistance would be about 1/1000 that of either presynaptic or postsynaptic membrane. As the synaptic area increases, the synaptic membrane resistance decreases in proportion, while the extracellular resistance of the cleft (assuming that this remains of constant width) increases. Consequently there is a critical size of the synaptic area above which current flows predominantly through the subsynaptic membrane rather than out through the cleft.

Synaptic transmission by electric current can take place whenever the synaptic area is large enough so that the current flowing through the subsynaptic membrane reaches the minimal strength required to elicit an active response in the postsynaptic membrane. In the absence of complicating features, such synapses can transmit impulses in both directions: from pre- to postsynaptic neuron and vice versa. Typical examples are the septal synapses of septate giant fibers of certain annelids and crustaceans. The cross-sectional area in these cases is well above 1000 μ^2.

Another well-documented case of electrical synaptic transmission is that of the ciliary ganglion of the chicken, where it occurs in the calyciform synapses which have such a conspicuously large synaptic area (Fig. 20–4).

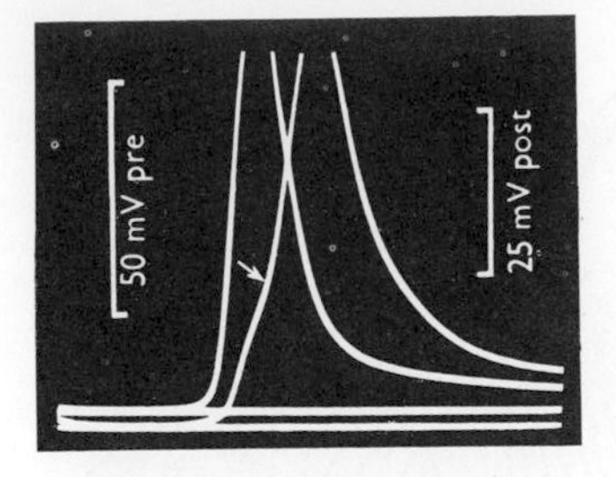

Figure 20–15. Action potentials recorded by means of intracellular electrodes from a giant synapse in a crayfish nerve cord (Fig. 20–10) during synaptic transmission. Note that the postsynaptic potential (lower channel) starts almost as soon as the presynaptic action potential begins. At the arrow it reaches the firing level of the postsynaptic membrane potentials and elicits an all-or-nothing spike. This is the characteristic behavior of an electrically transmitting synapse. (From Furshpan, E. J., and D. D. Potter: Transmission at the giant motor synapse of the crayfish. J. Physiol. *145*:289–325, 1959.)

More complicated is transmission across the so-called giant synapses in thoracic ganglia of crayfish. Although the synaptic area is large and electrical transmission takes place from presynaptic giant fiber to postsynaptic giant motoneuron, this transmission goes only in this one direction: the strong rectifying properties of the presynaptic membrane prevent current flow into the presynaptic fiber. Electrical records and a diagram of the experimental set-up are shown in Figures 20–10 and 20–15.

Electrical synaptic transmission is of the all-or-nothing type: every presynaptic action potential evokes a postsynaptic action potential. This is a rather rapid process, and the *synaptic delay*, that is, the time between arrival of the presynaptic impulse and the departure of the postsynaptic impulse, is less than 0.1 msec.

All known instances of electrically transmitting synapses involve transmission of nerve impulses from one neuron to another. Neuromuscular transmission is not known to occur by electrical interaction.

The requirement of a large area of synaptic contact does not have to be met if the resistance of the synaptic membrane is lower than the normal membrane resistance. Particularly among muscles there are certain types where excitation spreads from one muscle fiber to the other by what could be called electrical transmission. This is accomplished by areas of contact that offer unusually low resistance to current flow. Vertebrate cardiac muscle and certain types of smooth muscle show this kind of behavior.

Chemical Synaptic Transmission

Although still in use, the term "synaptic transmission" is rather unfortunate, for it implies the transmission of a nerve impulse from a presynaptic cell to a postsynaptic cell. This kind of transmission is the exception. More often than not *no* postsynaptic impulse is generated by the synaptic action of a presynaptic impulse; instead, this sets up a transient local response in the postsynaptic cell. Only in specialized kinds of synapses is the sum of all local postsynaptic responses to a presynaptic impulse large enough to generate one—or even a sequence—of postsynaptic action potentials.

The postsynaptic responses to a presynaptic nerve impulse are known as *postsynaptic potentials.* These are active local responses consisting of a transient decrease of membrane resistance (increase in membrane conductance) and a concomitant transient depolarization or hyperpolarization.

The synaptic areas are usually small, small enough at any rate to prevent a significant amount of current flow across subsynaptic membranes during presynaptic action potentials. In those synapses that have been amenable to experimental analysis (particularly the giant synapses in the squid stellate ganglion (see Fig. 20–9) there is no electrical interaction (electrophysiologists call it "electrical coupling") between pre- and postsynaptic membranes. For a postsynaptic reaction to occur, a booster mechanism is necessary. This is provided by a complex biochemical chain reaction which is initiated by the arriving presynaptic nerve impulse. This chain reaction is known as *chemical transmission*. Before describing it in more detail, it is advantageous to discuss the nature of the postsynaptic response.

Two types of postsynaptic response are known: the excitatory postsynaptic potential (e.p.s.p.), or excitatory junction potential (e.j.p.), and the inhibitory postsynaptic potential (i.p.s.p.), or inhibitory junction potential (i.j.p.). (The terms "excitatory" or "inhibitory junction potential" are used in connection with neuromuscular transmission only.)

Both are caused by a transient resistance change, as mentioned. But whereas the resistance change, in the case of e.p.s.p.'s, is due to a permeability increase to all ions, in particular Na^+, K^+, and Cl^-, the permeability change in the case of i.p.s.p.'s consists in a permeability change to only K^+ and Cl^-, often only K^+.

In the case of e.p.s.p.'s this causes the membrane potential to shift toward the Na^+ equilibrium potential and to approach a value between this and the equilibrium potentials for K^+ and Cl^-. Under normal physiological conditions this always means a depolarization. If, under experimental conditions, the membrane potential of the postsynaptic cell is greatly reduced or even reversed, the e.p.s.p.'s are reduced and may even reverse, as shown in Figure 20–16.

I.p.s.p.'s, on the other hand, tend to approach the K^+ or Cl^- equilibrium potential. Since this is usually somewhat greater than the resting potential of a cell, the i.p.s.p.'s in most cases consist in a hyperpolarization. In cases (physiological or experimental) in which the postsynaptic membrane potential is larger than this equilibrium potential, the i.p.s.p.'s are reversed and depolarize the postsynaptic membrane (Fig. 20–17).

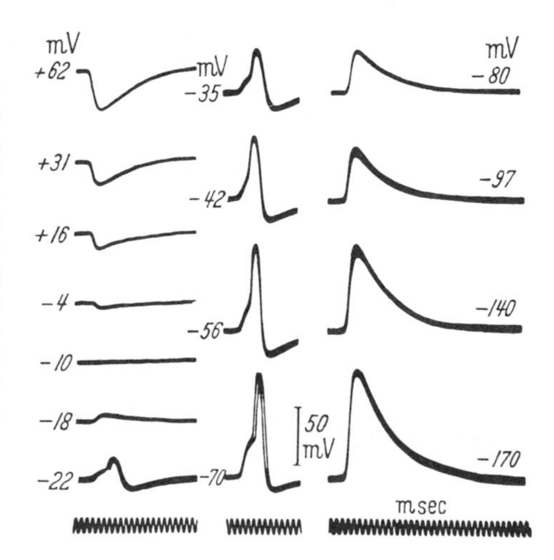

Figure 20–16. Excitatory postsynaptic potentials (e.p.s.p.'s) recorded from a sympathetic ganglion cell of a frog. The membrane potential, normally −70 mV, was artificially altered to the values shown with each record. The reversal potential is at −10 mV. At a membrane potential of −22 to −70 mV the e.p.s.p. is followed by a spike potential. Note that the e.p.s.p. is hyperpolarizing at membrane potentials more positive (looking from the inside of the cell) than the reversal potential. For a graphic explanation of the terms "reversal potential" and "postsynaptic potential" see Figure 20–18. (After Nishi and Koketsu, 1962, from Eccles, J. C.: The mechanism of synaptic transmission. Ergebn. Physiol. *51*:300–430, 1961.)

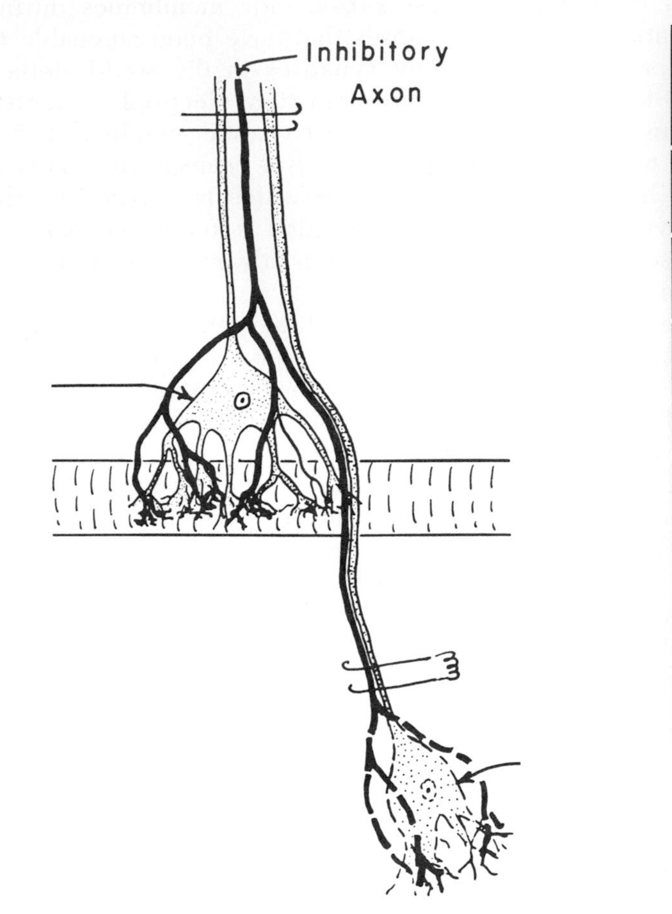

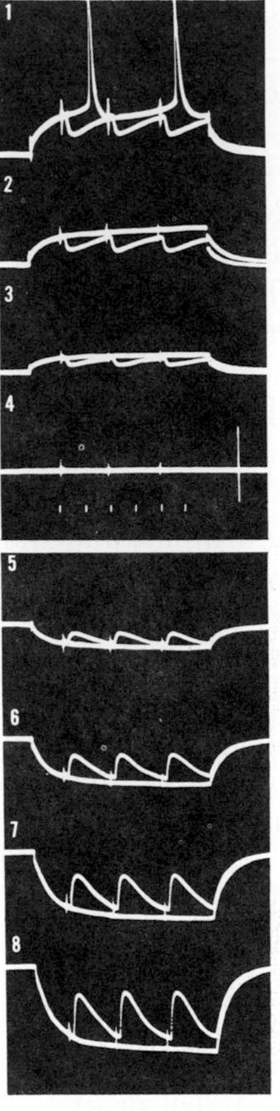

Figure 20–17. Inhibitory postsynaptic potentials recorded with an intracellular microelectrode from a stretch receptor neuron of a crayfish (*Astacus*). **Left**, a diagram of part of the preparation: two receptor neurons innervated by branches of one common inhibitory axon. The inhibitory axon is stimulated through a pair of electrodes applied near the "lower" nerve cell. The action potentials travel along the inhibitory axon and reach the inhibitory synapses on the other nerve cell, where the inhibitory postsynaptic potentials (i.p.s.p.'s) are being recorded at the site indicated by the arrow. (Since the original publication of this figure it has been found that inhibitory synapses are also located close to the recording site.)

Right, a series of records (numbered *1* through *8*) showing three i.p.s.p.'s each (each is preceded by a small vertical deflection, the stimulus artifact). Before the inhibitory axon was stimulated, the membrane potential of the sensory cell was artificially depolarized or hyperpolarized to different degrees, except in the case of record *4*. Note that the i.p.s.p.'s are hyperpolarizing during depolarization, and increasingly depolarizing during hyperpolarization of the membrane. The resting membrane potential happens to be equal to the reversal potential of the i.p.s.p.'s. (Left: after Kuffler, S. W., and C. Eyzaguirre: Synaptic inhibition in an isolated nerve cell. J. Gen. Physiol. *39*:155–184, 1955. Right: after Hagiwara, S., K. Kusano, and S. Saito: Membrane changes in crayfish stretch receptor neuron during synaptic inhibition and under action of gamma-aminobutyric acid. J. Neurophysiol. *23*:505–515, 1960.)

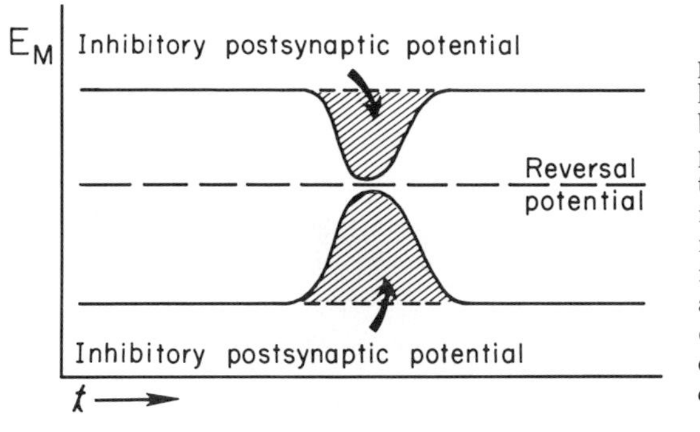

Figure 20–18. Conceptual diagram of postsynaptic membrane responses to inhibitory synaptic action. When the membrane potential is larger than the reversal potential, the inhibitory postsynaptic potential (i.p.s.p.) is depolarizing; when it is smaller than the reversal potential, the i.p.s.p. is polarizing. No potential change is recorded when the membrane potential and reversal potential are the same. (The effect of the inhibitory transmitter, however, is that of inhibition in each of these cases.)

The membrane potential level of the postsynaptic cell at which the postsynaptic potential reverses its sign is called the "*reversal potential*." Note that the term "potential" has several meanings. In this case it means just that—electric potential—but in the case of "postsynaptic potential" the term implies a potential change. The proper terminology would be "postsynaptic potential change." The difference in meaning is illustrated in Figure 20–18.

Postsynaptic potentials of both types have no refractory period so that presynaptic impulses can have postsynaptic actions at any time. Excitatory p.s.p.'s can sum to a certain extent, so that a second e.p.s.p. can summate with an ongoing e.p.s.p., thereby increasing the membrane depolarization. This is shown in Figure 20–19. Inhibitory p.s.p.'s, on the other hand, cannot sum—or, if so, only to a limited degree. A second i.p.s.p. arising while a previously elicited i.p.s.p. is still in progress can only prolong but not increase the potential change. This is known as the "ceiling effect" (Kuffler and Eyzaguirre, 1955)

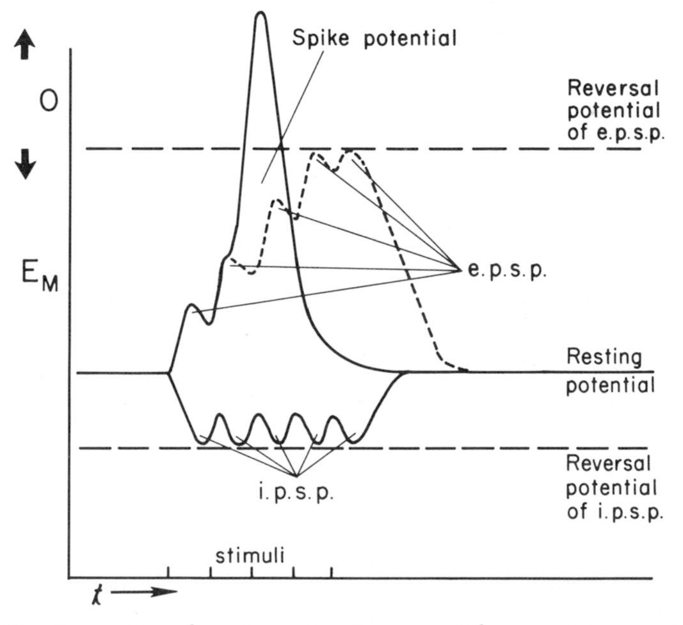

Figure 20–19. Summation of excitatory junction potentials or excitatory postsynaptic potentials (e.p.s.p.'s) and of inhibitory postsynaptic potentials (i.p.s.p.'s) can proceed only until the level of the reversal potential is reached ("ceiling effect").

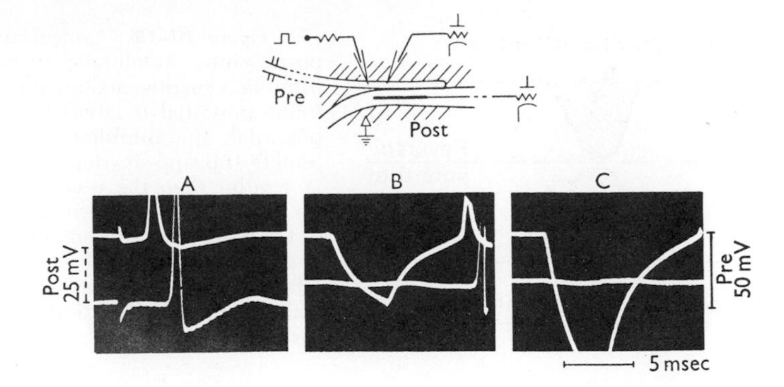

Figure 20–20. Diagram of experimental set-up and records obtained from the giant synapse (see Fig. 20–9) of the squid (Cephalopoda), *Loligo pealii*. Two microelectrodes are inserted into the presynaptic neuron, one for applying current (to change the membrane potential), the other for recording potential changes. Another recording electrode is inside the postsynaptic neuron. The upper curve of each record was obtained from the presynaptic ending, the lower curve from the postsynaptic neuron. **A**, spike potentials during normal synaptic transmission. **B** and **C**, demonstration of the absence of direct electric connection between the pre- and postsynaptic axons by hyperpolarizing the presynaptic membrane. A spike potential at the end of hyperpolarization is an off response. (From Hagiwara, S., and I. Tasaki: A study on the mechanism of impulse transmission across the giant synapse of the squid. J. Physiol. *143*:114–137, 1958.)

and is illustrated in Figure 20–19. Summation is limited because the postsynaptic potential changes are based on certain types of permeability changes leading to equilibrium potential or mixed equilibrium potentials (reversal potentials). Once these are reached, no further potential change is possible.

Facilitation of e.p.s.p.'s (see p. 503) is well known from several kinds of muscle fibers (see Chap. 24). The explanation is two-fold: (1) increasing mobilization of the chemical transmission processes and (2) increasing permeability change with each arriving presynaptic impulse due to residual changes in the subsynaptic membrane. Whenever the e.p.s.p. is not maximal this means that the permeability to Na^+ is not maximal. Facilitation, therefore, may be due to

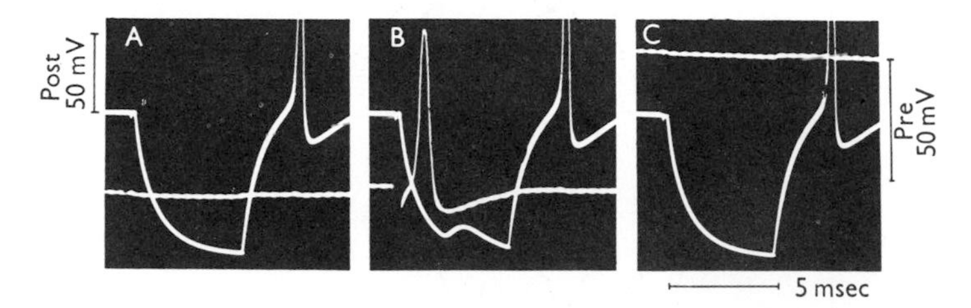

Figure 20–21. Effect of hyperpolarization of the postsynaptic axon upon the membrane potential of the presynaptic axon. The potential recorded across the presynaptic membrane is shown by the lower curve in **A** and **B**, and by the upper curve in **C**. Records shown in **A** demonstrate that even a marked change in potential of the postsynaptic membrane has no effect on the presynaptic membrane. In **B** a stimulating shock was delivered to the presynaptic axon to show that the recording electrodes were in place. Note the delayed, small depolarization that appears superimposed on the hyperpolarizing pulse. It is the result of chemical synaptic transmission. Record **C** was taken immediately after the disappearance of the resting potential of the presynaptic axon on gradual withdrawal of the recording electrode. (From Hagiwara, S., and I. Tasaki: A study of the mechanism of impulse transmission across the giant synapse of the squid. J. Physiol. *143*:114–137, 1958.)

increasing sodium activation, meaning increasing Na^+ permeability. With each increment in permeability the Na^+ battery becomes more dominant, thereby shifting the membrane potential closer and closer to the Na^+ equilibrium potential. (For the biophysical background see Chapter 16.)

The fact that both e.p.s.p. and i.p.s.p. show reversal potentials is the basis of one of the most potent arguments against electrical synaptic transmission. More direct evidence is obtained experimentally: by placing electrodes beneath both pre- and postsynaptic membranes one can observe directly that currents flowing through the presynaptic membrane do not affect the subsynaptic membrane, and vice versa. Experimental examples of the set-up and the records obtained are shown in Figures 20–9, 20–20, and 20–21.

The permeability change responsible for the e.p.s.p.'s and i.p.s.p.'s is assumed to be caused by a biochemical process, as mentioned. Strangely enough, we still do not know the precise nature of this process in the case of those synapses where the electrophysiological analyses of transmission have been most detailed: the synapses between sensory and inhibitory neurons and motoneurons in the spinal cord of mammals (Fig. 20–22), the synapses between motoneurons (and inhibitory neurons) and arthropod muscle fibers (see Chaps. 22 and 24), the synapses between second and third order giant nerve fibers

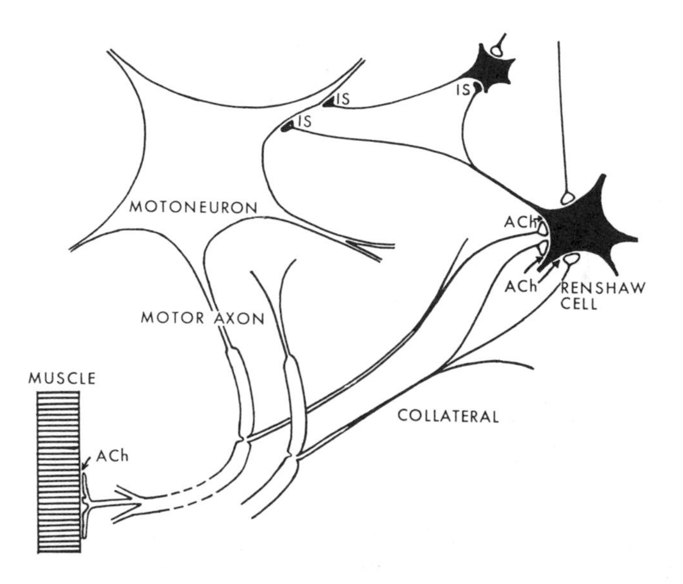

Figure 20–22. Schematic drawing to illustrate the relation between mammalian spinal motoneurons and certain inhibitory interneurons. The cholinergic motoneurons send collaterals to the Renshaw cell where they make synaptic contact. They activate the Renshaw cell by releasing acetylcholine (ACh) as transmitter substance. The Renshaw cell in turn releases "inhibitory" transmitter at its synapses (IS) with the motoneuron and with another, inhibitory interneuron. The motoneuron releases ACh at all its terminals (Dale's principle), the Renshaw cell releases "inhibitory" transmitter at all its terminals. Both types of neuron thus conform to Dale's principle. The pathway; motoneuron—Renshaw cell—motoneuron, constitutes a feedback loop (negative feedback). (From Eccles, J. C.: Spinal neurones: synaptic connexions in relation to chemical transmitters and pharmacological responses. Proceedings of the First International Pharmacological Meeting, 8:157–182, Pergamon Press, Oxford, 1962.)

of squid (Figures 20–8 and 20–9), and the synapses between inhibitory neurons and sensory receptor neurons of crustacean stretch receptor organs (Fig. 20–17).

For vertebrate motor end-plates, and synapses between many pre- and postganglionic autonomic neurons and between postganglionic parasympathetic neurons (postganglionic vagus fibers) and cardiac muscle of mammals and amphibians, biochemical information about the chemical mechanism of synaptic transmission is rather detailed: briefly, this consists in a release of a transmitter substance, *acetylcholine*, and the reaction of acetylcholine with receptor molecules present in the subsynaptic membrane. It is this reaction that effects the permeability change. The union between acetylcholine and the receptor is assumed to be brief, permitting the transmitter to diffuse away from the synapse within a short time. Calculations have shown that this diffusion, even when the transmitter substance is not destroyed enzymatically, follows a similar time course to that of the decay of the postsynaptic potential (Eccles and Jaeger, 1958). In the case of acetylcholine, the removal of the transmitter is greatly speeded up by the action of a hydrolyzing enzyme, *acetylcholinesterase*. The enzyme is predominantly present within the synaptic cleft (see Fig. 20–23).

The same schema of events is assumed to operate in all other types of synapses, perhaps excluding some of the electrically transmitting ones (however, see below). Other transmitter agents are believed to take the place of acetylcholine. Of these, one has been identified with certainty: noradrenaline is the transmitter substance of most postganglionic sympathetic neurons in vertebrates. There is suggestive evidence that *5-hydroxytryptamine* is the transmitter substance of certain vertebrate and invertebrate neurons. A number of amino acids are also implied as transmitters, notable *γ-aminobutyric acid, glutamic acid,* and *aspartic acid.* The chemical structure of compounds suspected of transmitter function is shown in Figure 20–24.

Acetylcholine is the most widely distributed transmitter substance. It has been detected in the nervous system of all coelomate phyla that have been studied in this regard. Neurons containing and releasing acetylcholine are

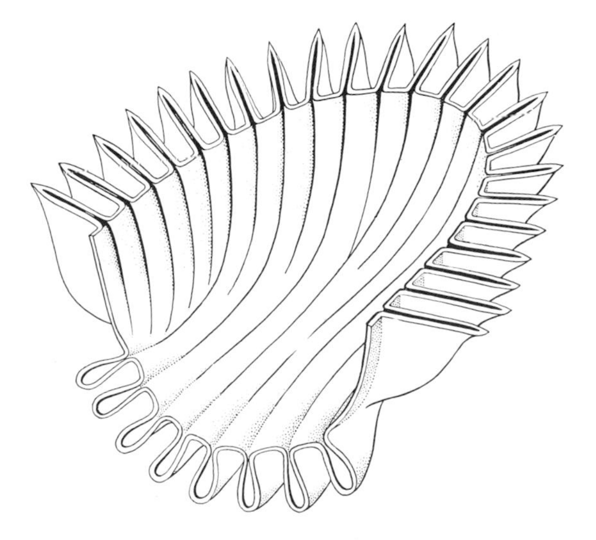

Figure 20–23. Three-dimensional presentation of the arrangement of the postsynaptic membrane, showing one extremity of a "synaptic gutter" (see Fig. 20–12) of a motor end-plate of lizard muscle. The deep folds contain cholinesterase. (From Couteaux, R.: Morphological and cytological observations on the post-synaptic membrane at motor endplates and ganglionic synapses. Exp. Cell Res., Suppl. 5:294–322, 1958.)

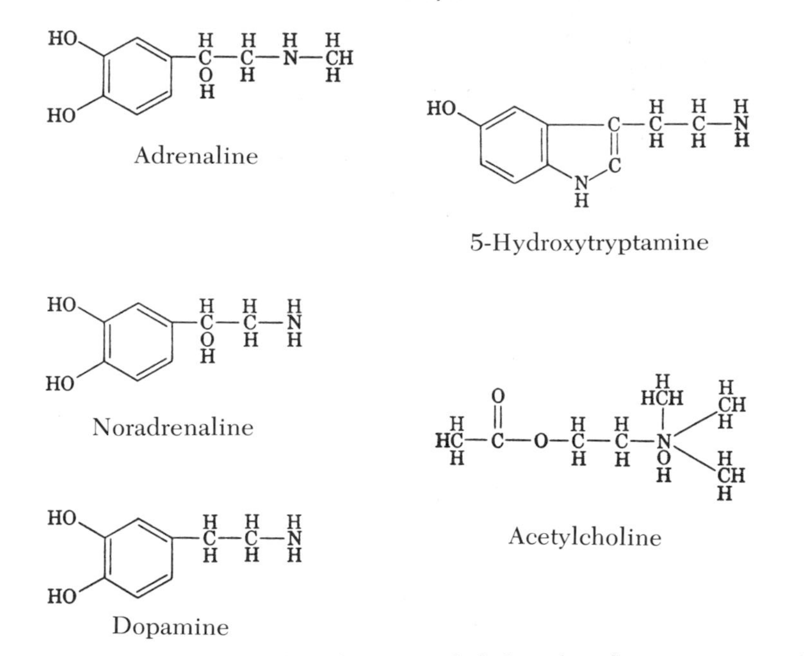

Figure 20–24. Structural formulae of compounds believed to function as transmitter substances.

called *cholinergic* (Dale, 1933). Cells that respond to applied acetylcholine in a manner similar to that of the response to activation of their cholinergic innervation are called *cholinoceptive*.

Noradrenaline (and its methylated form, adrenaline) occur in certain neurons of vertebrates (postganglionic sympathetic neurons, neurons in the basal ganglia) and in the nervous system of insects and annelids. The compound(s) is absent in crustaceans, molluscs, echinoderms, and many other phyla. Neurons containing and releasing noradrenaline are called *noradrenergic* (a modification of the original term "adrenergic" which was coined by Dale, 1933, at a time when adrenaline was believed to be the transmitter substance). Cells that respond to released or applied noradrenaline are referred to as *noradrenoceptive*. The terms used in the preceding two paragraphs are explained in Figure 20–25.

5-Hydroxytryptamine occurs in nerve tissue of the basal ganglia of the mammalian brain, in the ganglia of molluscs, annelids, sipunculids and Xiphosura, and in the pericardial organs (nerve endings) of Crustacea. The terms "tryptaminergic" and "tryptaminoceptive" have been suggested, but are, perhaps, awkward as they do not properly identify the transmitter substance.

γ-aminobutyric acid occurs in certain regions of the mammalian brain and spinal cord. The suggestion that it is a transmitter stems from experiments in which it was applied to crustacean synapses. It was found that it imitated rather well the action of inhibitory neurons. The matter is not settled yet because the compound has only dubious actions in the mammalian central nervous system, and its function in the crustacean nervous system is debated.

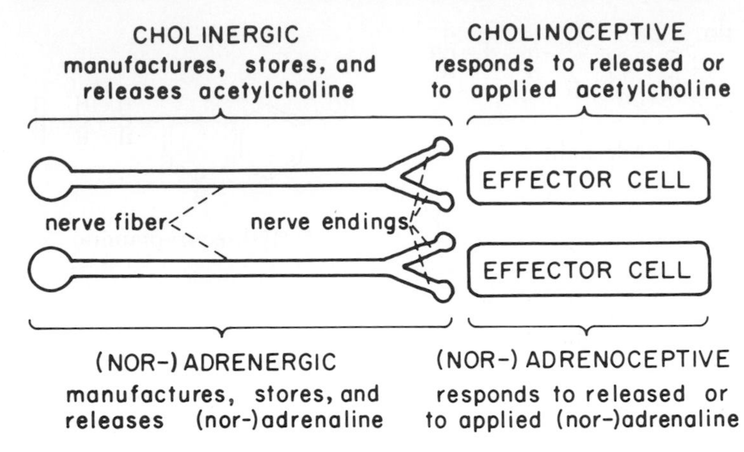

Figure 20–25. Representation of the terminology applied to synapses where acetylcholine and adrenaline (noradrenaline) are involved as transmitter substances.

Glutamic acid has been suggested as a transmitter substance of crustacean motoneurons. It does stimulate crustacean muscles to contract and occurs in their motoneurons in conspicuous quantities (Robbins, 1958; van Harreveld, 1959; van Harreveld and Mendelson, 1959). *Aspartic acid*, also a prominent constituent of crustacean nerve tissue (Lewis, 1952), has both inhibitory and excitatory actions on muscle and stretch receptor cells. Its role is still obscure.

Acetylcholine remains the unchallenged champion of the transmitter substances, and its biochemistry and functional role remain the model for the concept of chemical synaptic transmission.

Acetylcholine and the other proposed transmitter agents occur in nerve cells in conspicuous quantities. This is not immediately obvious when one looks at the acetylcholine contents of whole parts of nerve tissue, but only when it is realized that this compound is the exclusive property of the cholinergic neurons within this tissue. The true acetylcholine concentration of the cholinergic neurons is obtained by multiplying the acetylcholine concentration of the whole tissue sample studied by the reciprocal of the fraction of cholinergic neurons. If the sample contains 10 μg of acetylcholine per gram of tissue and the cholinergic neurons amount to 1/20 of the weight of the tissue, the cholinergic neurons contain 20×10 μg/gm.

Even when this calculation is not made – and the cases in which this can be calculated are rare – the acetylcholine concentrations are often impressive. Ganglia of crustaceans, insects, and molluscs contain several hundred micrograms of acetylcholine per gram of nerve tissue. Similarly, high values have been reported for certain vertebrate nerve tissues. The acetylcholine content of cholinergic neurons may thus be of the dimension of 1 mg/gm wet weight or 3 to 4 mg/gm dry weight. Considering that the proteins account for at least 75 per cent of the dry weight of a nerve cell, the transmitter substance accounts for a substantial portion of the remaining cell substance.

Transmitters occur throughout the neuron and are apparently not restricted to the terminals. It is widely assumed that transmitter substances are stored and accumulated in nerve endings. If this is so, the transmitter concentrations in the endings (terminals) must be even greater than in the rest of the neuron.

The concentrations of γ-aminobutyric acid, noradrenaline, 5-hydroxytryptamine, and particularly aspartic and glutamic acids in nerve tissue are comparable to, if not greater than, those of acetylcholine. A diagram showing the known chemical types of neurons in the mammalian nervous system is shown in Figure 20–26.

We may safely assume that the concentration of transmitter substance within the terminals of a neuron is at least as high as in the remainder of the neuron. Thus, there must be a steep concentration gradient across the terminal membrane and this must certainly favor the release of the compound. This event takes place during the arrival of a presynaptic nerve impulse. Transmitter release may be accomplished by a large general increase in membrane perme-

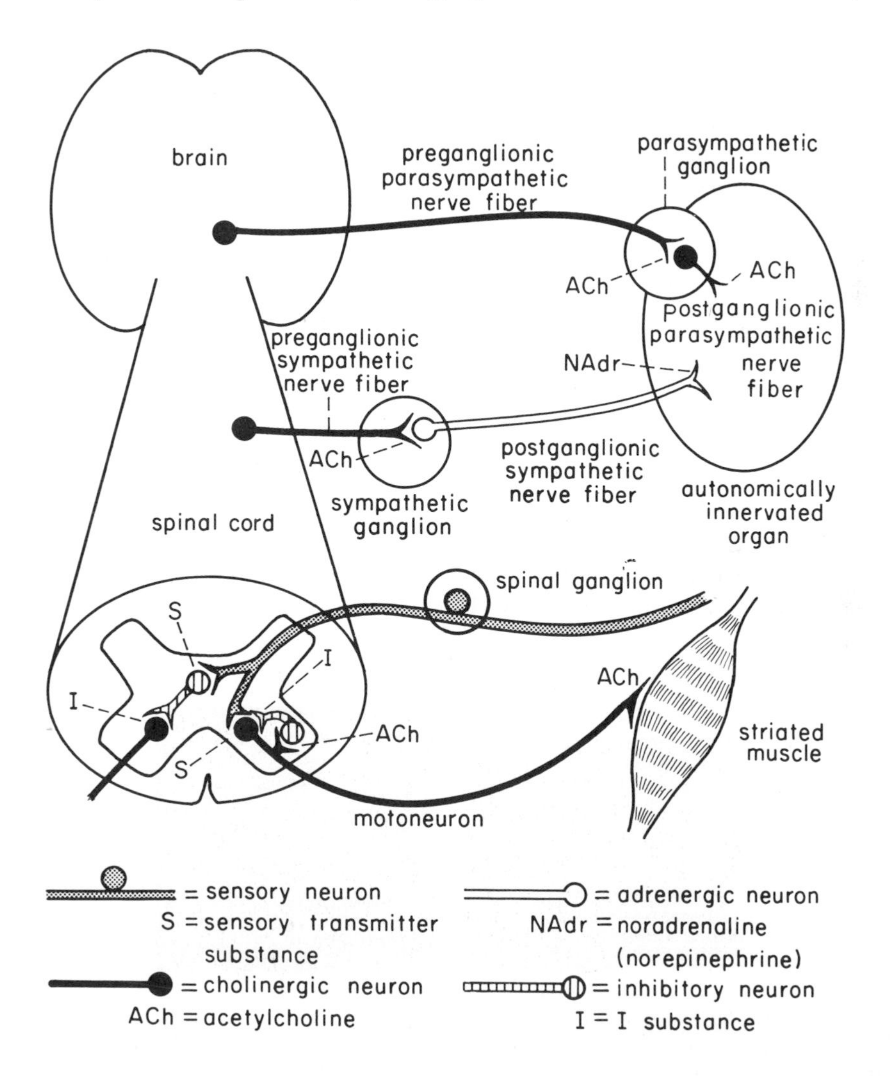

Figure 20–26. The neurochemical pattern of the vertebrate nervous system. The single neurons shown represent entire populations of similar neurons.

ability. It should be noted that the dimensions of all molecules that have been suggested as transmitters are similar to those of a hydrated sodium ion.

Synaptic Vesicles and Miniature Potentials

Electronmicroscope studies of synaptic structures of many animal types have demonstrated a peculiar system of "vesicles" that appear to be characteristic of presynaptic terminals (Figs. 20–2, 20–3, 20–4, and 20–14). These vesicles were first seen in the neuropile of the earthworm (De Robertis and Bennett, 1955) and have since been found in almost all kinds of synapses investigated with the electron microscope (for a summary of the literature see De Robertis, 1964). They are usually represented as spherical bodies surrounded by a simple membrane. They range from 0.01 to 0.05 μ in diameter.

Prior to the discovery of the vesicles, Fatt and Katz (1952) described "miniature potentials" recorded with microelectrodes placed in the vicinity of the motor end-plates of frog striated muscle fibers. These records showed continuous fluctuations of the membrane potential of the muscle fibers, transient depolarizations of discrete magnitudes, but considerably smaller than normal end-plate potentials. Drugs that inhibit cholinesterase were found to drastically increase the size and duration of each of these fluctuations (Fig. 20–27), whereas curare, a drug that prevents the action of acetylcholine on subsynaptic membranes of muscle, abolished them. The *miniature potentials*, as the fluctuations were called, were not caused by impulses in the motor fibers supplying the muscle. They occurred spontaneously. They were interpreted as being due to a spontaneous release of discrete packets or quanta of acetylcholine. Larger potentials were thought to be caused by the simultaneous release of two or more such packets.

The discovery of the vesicles by electron microscopy offered a simple explanation of this apparent quantal release of acetylcholine; one could assume that the quanta of acetylcholine were contained within the vesicles and whenever one or more vesicles popped through the terminal membrane they released their contained quantum of acetylcholine.

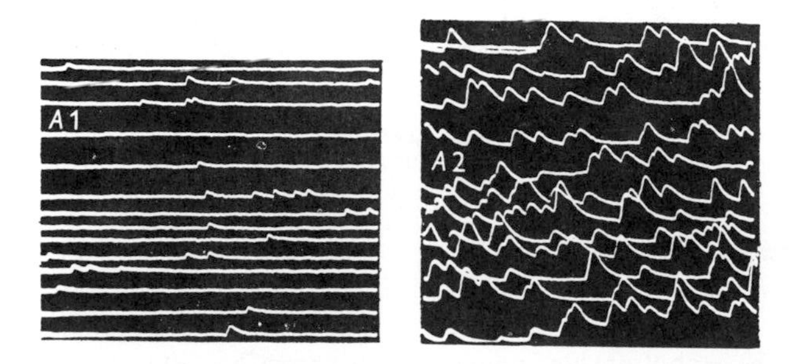

Figure 20–27. Miniature potentials recorded with an intracellular electrode from an end-plate region of the toe-extensor muscle of the frog. **A 1**, spontaneous frequency. **A 2**, miniature potentials after application of prostigmine (an anticholinesterase agent). Note that the potentials become larger and more prolonged. The increase in frequency seen here is not typical. (From Fatt, P., and B. Katz: Spontaneous subthreshold activity at motor nerve endings. J. Physiol. *117*:109–128, 1952.)

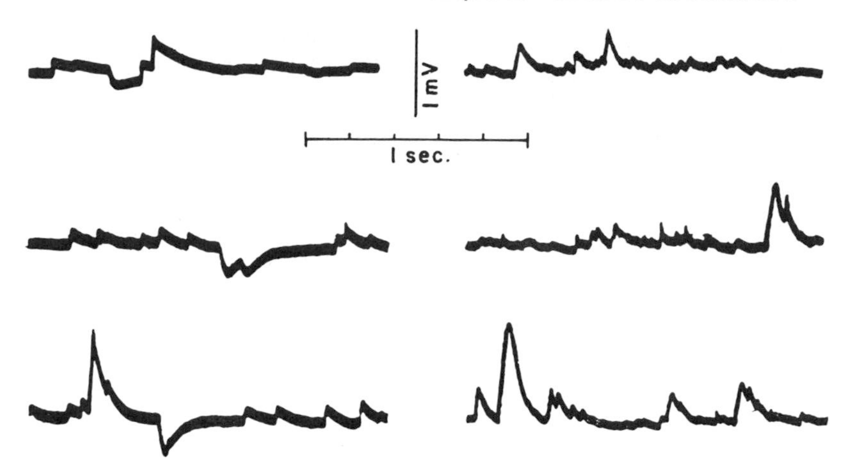

Figure 20–28. Depolarizing and hyperpolarizing miniature potentials recorded from skeletal muscle fibers of the lobster (*Homarus*). The traces on the left were obtained from untreated fibers, those on the right from muscle fibers treated with *picrotoxin*, a drug that prevents the action of the inhibitory transmitter substance: note that the hyperpolarizing potentials disappear. (From Grundfest, H.: General physiology and pharmacology of junctional transmission. *In* Biophysics of Physiological and Pharmacological Actions. A. M. Shanes, ed. Amer. Assn. Adv. Sci., Washington, D.C., 1961.)

The quantal release of acetylcholine by motor nerve terminals is rather well supported by direct physiological and pharmacological evidence. This is, in fact, one of the strongest supports of the concept of chemical synaptic transmission.

Recently miniature potentials have been recorded from crustacean muscle (see Fig. 20–28). It is most significant that in this case there are both depolarizing and hyperpolarizing potentials, which conforms strikingly to the presence of motor and inhibitory innervation. It can be concluded that spontaneous quantal transmitter release from nerve terminals is a widespread phenomenon.

General Features of Chemical Synaptic Transmission

It is likely that the number of different transmitter substances is limited. This is indicated by the almost universal occurrence of acetylcholine in nerve cells of almost all animal phyla, by the presence of acetylcholine in neurons of widely differing function within the same organism, and by the fact that so few transmitter substances have been discovered in a period of search lasting several decades. In addition, not many compounds may qualify as transmitters capable of producing specific, rapid, and transient permeability changes in subsynaptic membranes.

Functionally similar neurons usually produce and release the same transmitter substance. In vertebrates, for example, the motoneurons, pre- and postganglionic parasympathetic neurons and postganglionic sympathetic neurons are cholinergic, the postganglionic sympathetic neurons noradrenergic (Fig. 20–26). The sensory neurons of vertebrates are all noncholinergic and contain possibly all the same transmitter substance, tentatively called "sensory transmitter." In arthropods the sensory neurons are probably all cholinergic (Florey

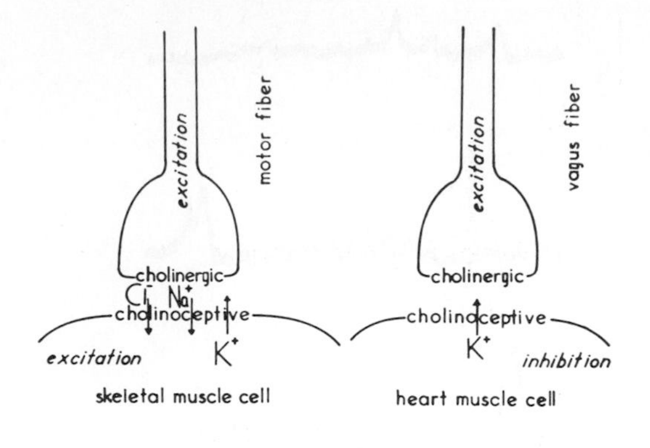

Figure 20–29. Conceptual diagram of the action of acetylcholine as an excitatory as well as an inhibitory transmitter substance: in the case of vertebrate skeletal muscle, acetylcholine released from terminals of excited motoneurons increases the permeability of the subsynaptic membrane to chloride, sodium, and potassium ions, causing excitation. Acetylcholine released from excited vagus fibers inhibits the heart muscle cell by causing the subsynaptic membrane to become more permeable to potassium ion. The arrows show the predominant ion movement during transmitter action. (From Florey, E.: Recent studies on synaptic transmitters. Amer. Zoologist 2:45–54, 1962.)

and Biederman, 1960). In lamellibranchs the cardio-inhibitory neurons are cholinergic and the cardio-accelerator neurons most likely "tryptaminergic."

One and the same neuron can synthesize only one transmitter and releases this transmitter at all its endings. This principle was first suggested by Dale (1933) and is now known as *Dale's principle* (so named by Eccles, 1957). Indeed, it has been found that mammalian spinal motoneurons release acetylcholine not only at their neuromuscular synapses but also at their collaterals which make synaptic contact with spinal interneurons (Renshaw cells). This is shown in Figure 22–22.

Whether a transmitter substance qualifies as an excitatory or an inhibitory transmitter is not so much a function of the transmitter as of the responsiveness of the subsynaptic membrane. Acetylcholine, for instance, is an excitatory transmitter at motor end-plates, but an inhibitory transmitter at the junction between postganglionic vagus fibers and heart muscle in vertebrates (Fig. 20–29). In

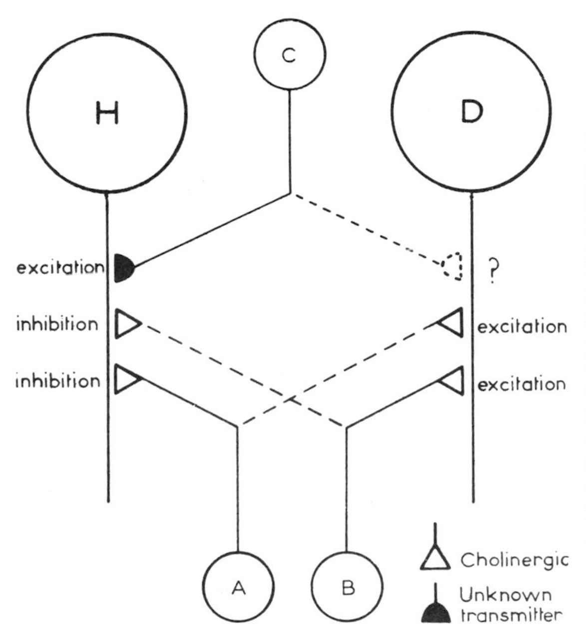

Figure 20–30. Diagram illustrating the nature of the synaptic contacts on H and D cells in the central nervous system (abdominal ganglion) of the opisthobranch (Gastropoda) *Aplysia depilans.* Dashed lines indicate probable connections, solid lines represent definitely established connections. Cells are labeled *A, B, C* for convenience. The letter H was chosen because acetylcholine causes *h*yperpolarization and inhibition of that cell. D symbolizes the *d*epolarization caused by acetylcholine on the other cell. (From Tauc, L., and H. M. Gerschenfeld: Cholinergic transmission mechanisms for both excitation and inhibition in molluscan central synapses. Nature *192*:366–367, 1961.)

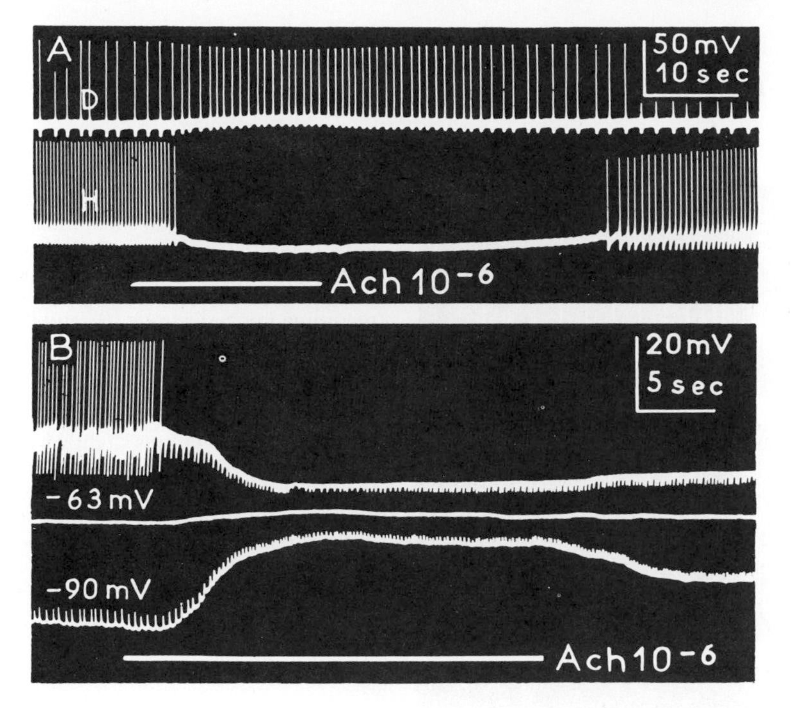

Figure 20–31. **A**, simultaneous intracellular recordings from two contiguous and spontaneously firing D and H cells (see Fig. 20–30) perfused with acetylcholine (*ACh*), 10^{-6} gm/ml, during the time indicated by the horizontal white line. **B**, action of ACh on a H cell which fires spontaneously and shows inhibitory postsynaptic potentials (i.p.s.p.'s), resulting from activity of a spontaneously active inhibitory neuron (like cell A in Fig. 20–30). Three superimposed records are shown. The upper one was taken under normal conditions; the average membrane potential is 40 mV. ACh causes hyperpolarization, cessation of spike discharge, and diminution of i.p.s.p.'s. The middle record was taken when the membrane potential was artificially raised to 63 mV. ACh now has no apparent effect, and the i.p.s.p.'s are no longer noticeable. The lower record was taken when the cell was artificially hyperpolarized to −93 mV. Under these circumstances the i.p.s.p.'s are larger. ACh causes depolarization and diminution of i.p.s.p.'s. The records demonstrate that the reversal potential of the i.p.s.p.'s is near −63 mV and that ACh shifts the membrane potential toward this value—evidence for the identity of the natural inhibitory transmitter with acetylcholine. (From Tauc, L., and H. M. Gerschenfeld: A cholinergic mechanism of inhibitory synaptic transmission in a molluscan nervous system. J. Neurophysiol. 25:236–262, 1962.)

Aplysia ganglia it has recently been shown that acetylcholine acts as both an inhibitory and an excitatory transmitter (Figs. 20–30, 20–31, and 20–32). Other transmitters, likewise, may cause excitation in some and inhibition in other synapses. Noradrenaline, which excites the mammalian heart, inhibits synapses in the brain of the same animals.

INTEGRATION

Synapses in which one presynaptic impulse (action potential) can bring about one postsynaptic action potential are rare. Among them are the electrically transmitting synapses, synapses within the vertebrate autonomic ganglia, synapses of certain sensory fibers with motoneurons in the spinal cord

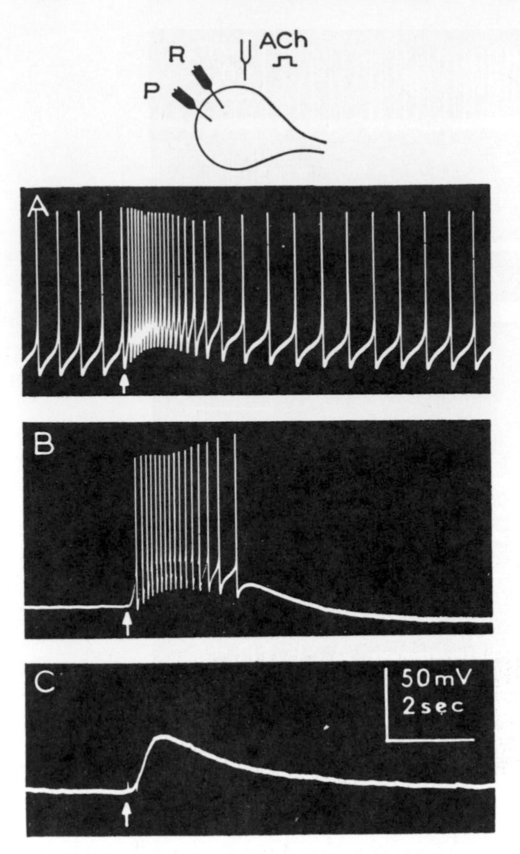

Figure 20–32. Effects of brief (200 msec) electrophoretic application of acetylcholine (at arrows) on somatic membrane potential of a D cell of a ganglion of the opisthobranch (Gastropoda) *Aplysia depilans*. Above the records is a diagram of the set-up, showing the recording microelectrode (*R*), and the polarizing microelectrode (*P*) inserted in the cell body, and the acetylcholine-filled micropipet (*ACh*) applied to the outside of the cell. In **A**, the cell shows rhythmic activity, accelerated by ACh action. In **B**, the cell was slightly hyperpolarized to avoid spontaneous firing; ACh depolarizes transiently and induces spikes. In **C**, the cell was hyperpolarized further; the depolarizing wave produced by ACh action does not reach the firing level. (From Tauc, L., and H. M. Gerschenfeld: A cholinergic mechanism of inhibitory synaptic transmission in a molluscan nervous system. J. Neurophysiol. *25*:236–262, 1962.)

of vertebrates, and synapses between certain kinds of motoneurons and twitch muscles (see Chaps. 22 and 24). Most synapses differ from this simple schema of events. For one thing, most postsynaptic cells (except certain types of muscle cells) receive presynaptic endings from several neurons, and in most synapses a full-blown action potential is generated only when several presynaptic nerve impulses arrive simultaneously or nearly simultaneously at the synapses with the postsynaptic cell. Further complications are introduced when inhibitory synapses are present.

The interaction of simultaneous and successive postsynaptic responses to simultaneously and successively arriving presynaptic nerve impulses is called *integration*. Integration consists of two primary events: *summation* and *facilitation*.

Summation

All local potentials, whether depolarizing or hyperpolarizing, that add on to, or subtract from, an ongoing local potential participate in summation. Summation, in fact, can be defined as the addition or subtraction of local postsynaptic responses to or from an ongoing local postsynaptic potential. Two kinds of summation are found: *spatial summation*, in which the local potentials are the result of presynaptic action potentials arriving over two or more presynaptic neurons, and *temporal summation*, in which presynaptic potentials arriving over one and the same presynaptic neuron appear in such close succession that the postsynaptic response to the first presynaptic impulse is still in progress when the second one arrives, etc. The difference between spatial and temporal summation is illustrated in the diagrams of Figure 20–33. Note that temporal summation requires a postsynaptic local response that is longer in duration than the presynaptic impulse with its refractory periods. Temporal summation does not exclude spatial summation; both may occur within the same postsynaptic cell.

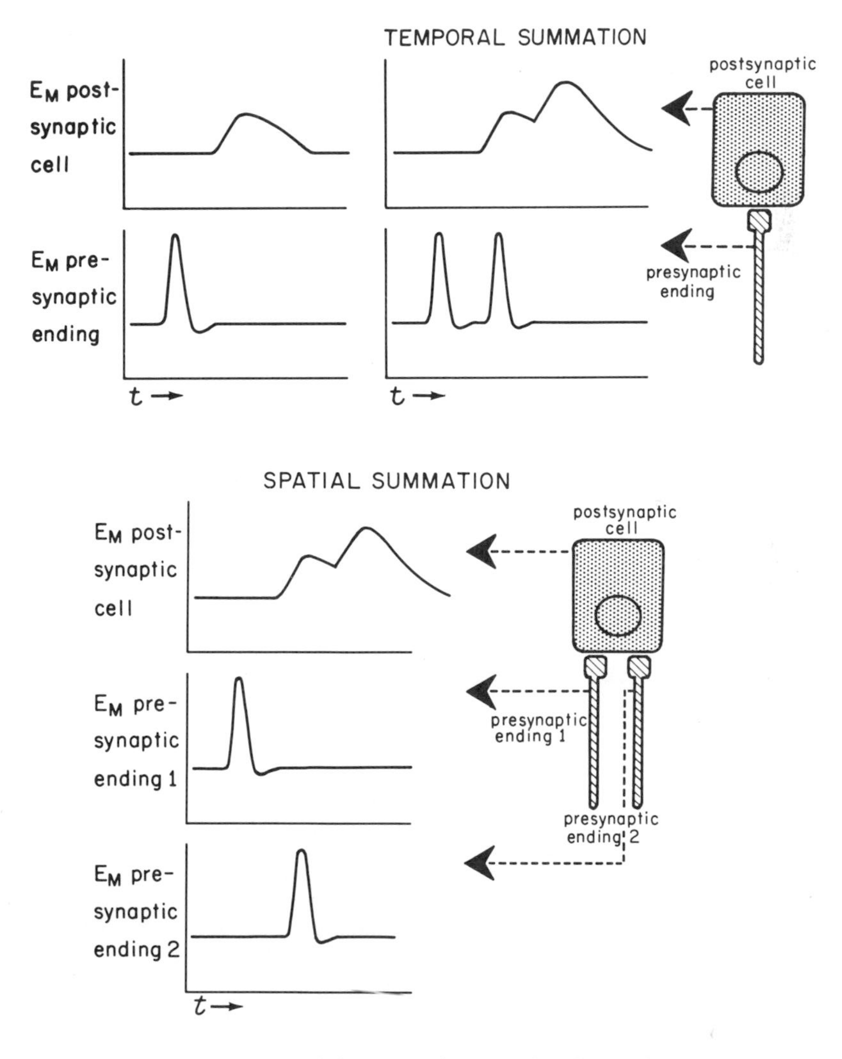

Figure 20–33. Conceptual diagrams of temporal and spatial summation.

Summation fails if a full-blown postsynaptic action potential is in progress. In this case local potential changes fall within the refractory period.

Excitatory postsynaptic potentials tend toward the Na equilibrium potential, inhibitory postsynaptic potentials tend toward the K and/or Cl equilibrium potentials. Since the resting potential is usually close to the latter, summation of inhibitory postsynaptic potentials is most prominent when the membrane is being depolarized, e.g., by excitatory postsynaptic potentials.

Interacting excitatory and inhibitory postsynaptic potentials should give a resultant membrane potential that can be approximately calculated according to the "constant field equation" of Goldman (p. 386). In actual fact the situation is far too complex to be amenable to simple calculation. For one thing, the different subsynaptic membrane patches are separated in space, and the postsynaptic responses are nonconducted, spreading only electrotonically. At

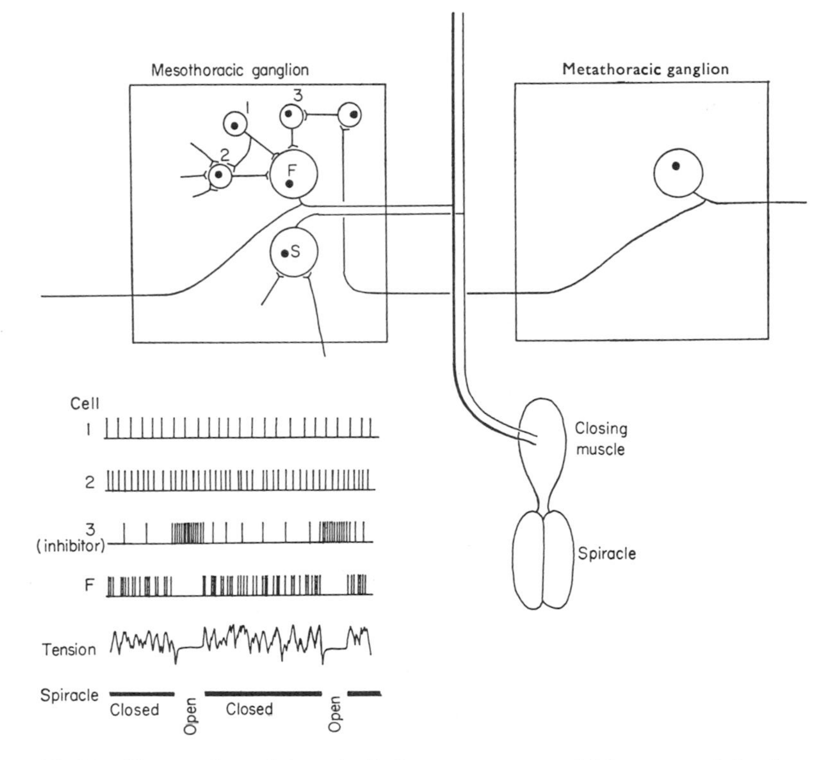

Figure 20-34. Neuronal model and discharge patterns which can explain the randomly spaced impulses in the "fast" motor neuron (*F*) that controls the spiracle muscle (closing muscle of the second spiracle of the locust (Orthoptera), *Schistocerca gregaria*). The model also explains the periodic cessation of the firing of F. Whenever this happens, the muscle relaxes and the spiracle opens. The timing of opening and closing is interpreted as determined by a rhythmically active inhibitory cell (*3*). Cell *1* is a simple, spontaneously active cell that excites F. It also synapses with a relay type cell (*2*), which in turn excites F. Cell 2 also receives excitation from other cells in the ganglion (only their endings are shown), some of them firing randomly. These impulses, insofar as they pass through 2, combine with those from cell 1 to excite F to discharge in a pattern that gives rise to the irregular fluctuations of tension of the muscle. For the metathoracic ganglion, only the F cell is shown. It sends a branch to an (unlabeled) inhibitory neuron that, when activated, suppresses the rhythmic activity of 3. In reality the synapses would be between cell processes within the neuropile. (From Hoyle, G.: The neuromuscular mechanism of an insect spiracular muscle. J. Insect Physiol. 3:378–394, 1959.)

the point where interactions occur, both kinds of responses are attenuated in accordance with the time and space constants of the different membrane regions. Also there are the complications introduced by the fact that the different presynaptic events are not necessarily synchronous so that one may be decaying while the other is still growing.

The level of the resulting membrane potential parallels the level of excitability of the postsynaptic cell, and if the membrane potential, in the process of summation, reaches the firing threshold, a regenerative, all-or-none impulse results. Complex patterns of impulse discharges in certain postsynaptic cells and the pre- and postsynaptic events that—by summation—cause them, are illustrated in Figure 20–34.

Facilitation

Facilitation consists in the increase of subsequent postsynaptic responses, caused by one or more previous synaptic transmissions. The opposite, *de-facilitation*, consists in the diminution of postsynaptic responses due to previous synaptic transmission. We speak of facilitation whenever one postsynaptic response is larger than the previous one, and of de-facilitation whenever a postsynaptic response is smaller than the previous one—provided both are caused by similar presynaptic action.

Autofacilitation is the increase in successive responses to activity in one and the same presynaptic neuron. *Heterofacilitation* is the increase of the postsynaptic response to the action of one presynaptic neuron by previous action(s) of another presynaptic neuron. The situation is explained in the diagrams of Figure 20–35.

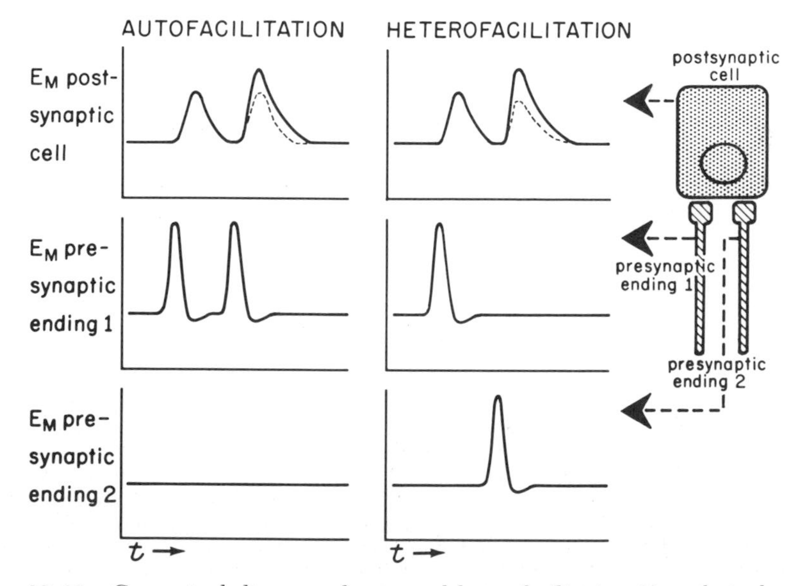

Figure 20–35. Conceptual diagram of auto- and heterofacilitation. Note that when two presynaptic fibers are active, the postsynaptic responses to activity in each need not be identical. The responses indicated in stipple represent the response to the second impulse as it would occur in the absence of facilitation.

Effects of Transmitter Level

Repetitive "bombardment" of a postsynaptic cell with presynaptic nerve impulses usually results in a shift in the membrane potential: the membrane potential does not return to its resting level in between postsynaptic responses but stays at a level that is nearer the peaks of the postsynaptic potentials. With few exceptions, synaptic transmission is achieved by the release of transmitter substance; thus the general shift in membrane potential during repetitive bombardment by nerve impulses is likely to be due to accumulating transmitter substance. If the presynaptic endings always release the same amount of transmitter substance with each arriving nerve impulse, the level of transmitter substance can then be assumed to build up to a level that represents a steady state between the decay (by enzymatic inactivation and by diffusion) of already present transmitter substance and the arrival of additional quantities of it.

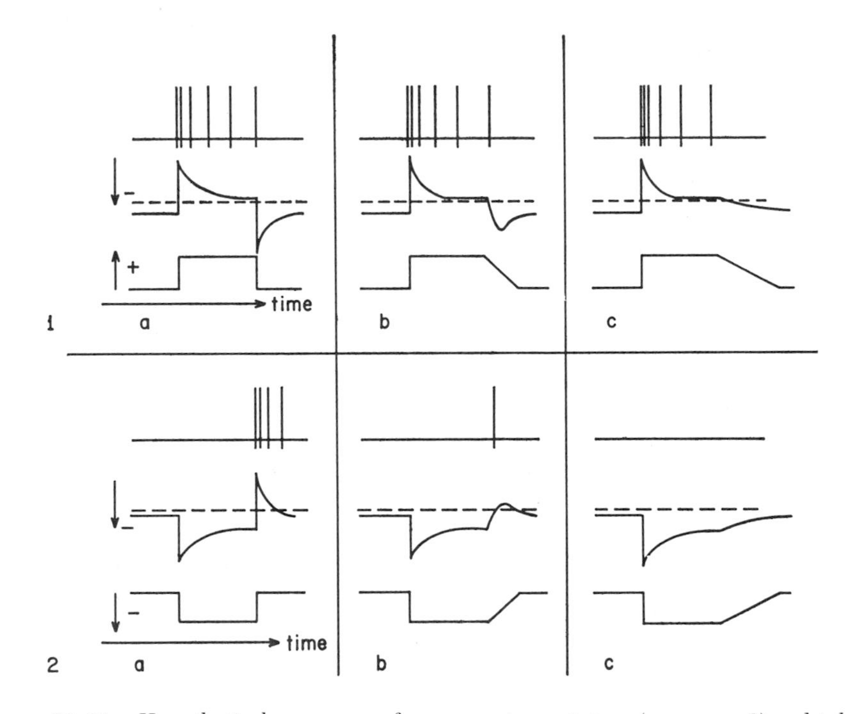

Figure 20–36. Hypothetical responses of a neuron to excitatory (sequence **1**) and inhibitory (sequence **2**) transmitter and to the active or passive removal of the transmitter. The first line in each diagram represents the nerve action potentials, the second line the changes in membrane potential, and the third line represents appearance and disappearance of the time course of appearance and disappearance of transmitter. The arrows point in the direction of increasing membrane potential and increasing amount of transmitter, respectively. *a*, *b*, and *c* represent increasing time courses of disappearance of transmitter. Rebound excitation (**2**) and rebound inhibition (**1**) diminish with increasing time course. It is assumed that the transmitters are released by presynaptic stimulation. The amounts represented in the diagram are taken as the average concentrations maintained between the individual releases of transmitter quanta, assuming a decay time greater than the interval between presynaptic impulses. (From Florey, E.: Excitation, inhibition and the concept of the stimulus. *In* Nervous Inhibition. E. Florey, ed. Pergamon Press, Oxford, 1961.)

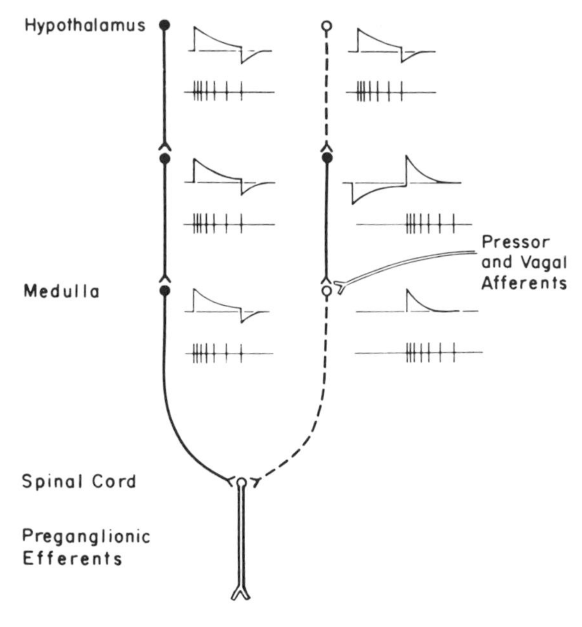

Figure 20–37. Hypothetical mechanism of postexcitatory inhibition (PEI) of sympathetic discharge. Solid lines: excitatory neurons. Broken lines: inhibitory neurons. Peripheral neurons are contoured. To the right of each central neuron the change in membrane potential (above) and the resulting discharge (below) is shown during and after the application of hypothalamic stimulation. The left chain represents the excitatory pathway. The first (inhibitory) neuron in the right chain is activated during hypothalamic stimulation and inhibits the second (excitatory) neuron. The latter rebounds after the end of stimulation, activating in turn the third (inhibitory) neuron, which inhibits preganglionic efferents during the PEI. The lower inhibitory neuron of the right chain also receives excitatory afferents from pressoreceptors and from the vagus. Subliminal changes in excitability of this neuron account for the influence of vagal and pressor afferents on the intensity of the PEI. (From Scherrer, H.: Postexcitatory inhibition of sympathetic discharge. Exp. Neurol. 7:343–354, 1963.)

In nerve cells it has been observed that they do accommodate to such a steady level of transmitter substance just as a receptor nerve cell does to the action of a maintained stimulus (see Chaps. 18 and 25). When the synaptic bombardment suddenly ceases, the membrane potential suddenly swings in the opposite direction from that in which it was previously displaced by the transmitter substance: thus, depending on whether the nerve cell had responded with hyperpolarizing (inhibitory) or with depolarizing (excitatory) postsynaptic potentials, it now shows momentary depolarization (excitation) or momentary hyperpolarization (inhibition). The concept is explained in Figure 20–36. Such postexcitatory inhibition or postinhibitory excitation are probably of great importance for the normal operation of central nervous systems. Figure 20–37 shows a diagram to explain the significance of such phenomena in the sympathetic pathways of the mammalian central nervous system.

Collision and Summation in Branched Nerve Cells

Branched nerve cells are known from ganglia of invertebrate animals. They may receive synaptic contacts on several branches (see Fig. 20–38) and consequently are subject to activation from different sites: action potentials generated in one branch may travel not only toward an effector organ but also toward the soma so that they may reach a branching point and travel on over the other branch. Whether they can actually "invade" another branch depends largely on the relative diameters of the branches: impulses can usually travel from a larger diameter to a smaller one, but not in the reverse direction since

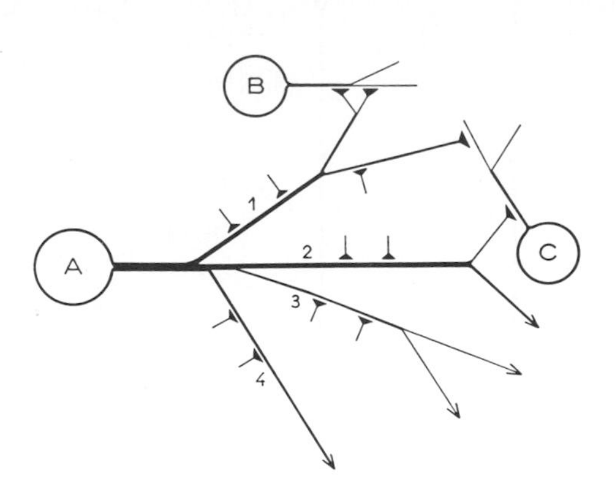

Figure 20–38. Schematic representation of a central neuron (A) with its ramifying axonal processes and various synapses, as observed in *Aplysia* (Gastropoda). Note that all synapses are on axonal branches. The membrane regions around the subsynaptic areas serve as generator regions in which the synaptic "input" may induce an "all-or-nothing" response which would propagate toward the effectors which the particular axonal branch innervates. Centripetal propagation would also occur, but other branches, particularly if they are of larger diameter, would not be invaded unless their generator regions were activated through synaptic endings in their vicinity. The simultaneous responses of a few branches could induce general invasion of the spike potential of the whole neuron. A conducted action potential in a large branch may be able to invade the other, smaller branches. (From Tauc, L., and G. M. Hughes: Modes of initiation and propagation of spikes in the branching axons of molluscan central neurons. J. Gen. Physiol. *46*: 533–549, 1963.)

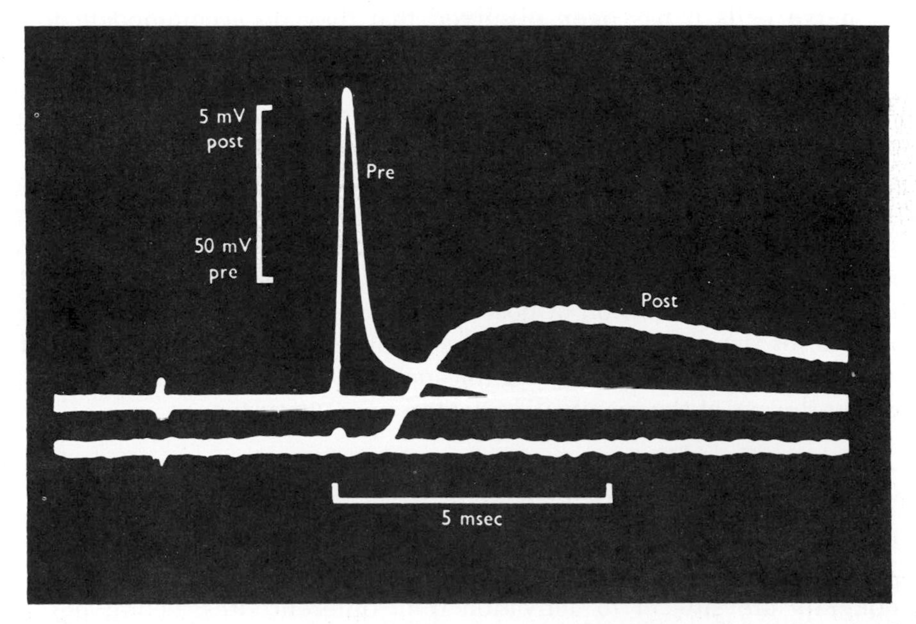

Figure 20–39. Electrical membrane responses recorded with intracellular electrodes from a presynaptic giant axon (crayfish nerve cord) and postsynaptic small motor axon (lower channel). The giant axon was stimulated at the time shown by the small vertical deflection on the upper channel. Note that there is no potential change in the postsynaptic membrane while the presynaptic spike is in progress. This is typical for chemically transmitting synapses. (From Furshpan, E. J., and D. D. Potter: Transmission at the giant motor synapses of the crayfish. J. Physiol. *145*:289–325, 1959.)

the density of the action current is not sufficient to fully activate the larger membrane area of a branch of larger diameter. Electrotonic spread from subthreshold excitation (depolarization) of a thick branch can make it possible for an impulse coming along a thin branch to traverse the branching point and move on over the thick branch. Summation is here of critical significance.

If two nerve impulses travel toward each other over the same stretch of nerve fiber (or nerve branch) they will collide and cancel each other since the membrane just behind them is in the refractory state and inexcitable.

Nerve cells in a central nervous system should not be considered as simple units capable of only one "all-or-none" response, and constructions of nerve fiber circuits in which the individual units are treated as simple links in a chain must fall far short of the almost infinite complexity of the actual performance of the individual neurons.

Conclusion

Electrical and chemical synaptic transmission show the following differences: electrical transmission leads always to a spike discharge in the postsynaptic cell; the potential change begins during the rising phase of the spike recorded from the presynaptic terminal. Chemical transmission often leads to local responses which may be inhibitory or excitatory. The postsynaptic response appears at the earliest during the falling phase of the presynaptic spike (see Fig. 20–39).

REFERENCES

Dale, H. (1933) Nomenclature of fibres in the autonomic system and their effects. J. Physiol. *80*:10–15.

De Robertis, E. (1964) Histophysiology of synapses and neurosecretion. Pergamon Press, Oxford.

De Robertis, E., and H. S. Bennett (1955) Some features of the submicroscopic morphology of synapses in frog and earthworm. J. Biophys. Biochem. Cytol. *1*:47–58.

De Robertis, E., and C. M. Franchi (1956) Electron microscope observations on synaptic vesicles in synapses of the retinal rods and cones. J. Biophys. Biochem. Cytol. *2*:307–318.

Eccles, J. C. (1957a) The generation of impulses by nerve cells. Austral. J. Sci. *19*:161–168.

Eccles, J. C. (1957b) Physiology of Nerve Cells. Johns Hopkins Press, Baltimore.

Eccles, J. C. (1964) The Physiology of Synapses. Springer-Verlag, Berlin.

Eccles, J. C., and J. C. Jaeger (1958) The relationship between the mode of operation of the junctional region at synapses and motor end-organs. Proc. Roy. Soc. B, *148*:38–56.

Fatt, P. (1950) The electromotive action of ACh at the motor end-plate. J. Physiol. *111*:408–422.

Fatt, P., and B. Katz (1952) Spontaneous subthreshold activity at motor nerve endings. J. Physiol. *117*:109–128.

Florey, E. (1961) Comparative physiology: transmitter substances. Ann. Rev. Physiol. *23*:501–528.

Florey, E. (1962) Comparative neurochemistry: inorganic ions, amino acids and possible transmitter substances of invertebrates. *In* Neurochemistry, 2nd Ed. (K. A. C. Elliott, I. H. Page, and J. H. Quastel, eds.) Charles C Thomas, Springfield, Ill.

Florey, E. (1965) Comparative pharmacology: Neurotropic and myotropic compounds. Ann. Rev. Pharmacol. *5*:357–382.

Florey, E., and M. A. Biederman (1960) Studies on the distribution of factor I and acetylcholine in crustacean peripheral nerve. J. Gen. Physiol. *43*:509–522.

Foster, M., and C. S. Sherrington (1897) A Textbook of Physiology. Part III: The Central Nervous System. Macmillan & Co., London.

Kirschner, L. (1959) The interaction between Na outflux and the Na transport system in the frog skin. J. Cell. Comp. Physiol. *53*:85–92.

Kuffler, S. W., and C. Eyzaguirre (1955) Synaptic inhibition in an isolated nerve cell. J. Gen. Physiol. *39*:155–184.

Lewis, P. R. (1952) The free amino-acids of invertebrate nerve. Biochem. J. *52*:330–338.

McLennan, H. (1963) Synaptic Transmission. W. B. Saunders Co., Philadelphia.

Robbins, J. (1958) The effects of amino acids on the crustacean neuromuscular system. Anat. Rec. *132*:492–493.

Sherrington, C. S. (1906) The Integrative Action of the Nervous System. Charles Scribner's Sons, New York.

Tauc, L., and H. M. Gerschenfeld (1962) A cholinergic mechanism of inhibitory synaptic transmission in a molluscan nervous system. J. Neurophysiol. *25*:236–262.

van Harreveld, A. (1959) Compounds in brain extracts causing spreading depression of cerebral cortical activity and contraction of crustacean muscle. J. Neurochem. *3*:300–315.

van Harreveld, A., and M. Mendelson (1959) Glutamate-induced contraction in crustacean muscle. J. Cell. Comp. Physiol. *54*:85–94.

21 NEUROSECRETION

In addition to their role in generating and conducting nerve impulses and in activating subsynaptic membranes, nerve cells also produce and secrete hormones. Only a few of these hormones have been identified as to precise function and chemical structure, but it is likely that many more will be recognized in the future.

Whereas in most species of animals, hormone production is restricted to certain specialized nerve cells, there are some species in which every nerve cell seems to have this capacity. Neurons that show morphological evidence for secretory activity are called *neurosecretory cells*; hormone secretion by nerve cells is called *neurosecretion*. The morphological signs of secretory activity are quite conspicuous (see Fig. 21–1): with appropriate staining (e.g., paraldehyde fuchsin, chrome hematoxylin; the latter is known as Gomori stain), and sometimes even without it, granular material and aggregates of colloidal granules and droplets can be seen not only in the cytoplasm of the neuronal soma, but also in cell processes (axons). The granular material, as seen with the light microscope, is composed of small elementary granules of 1000 to 3000 Å diameter. Electron microscopy reveals that they are bounded by a distinct membrane.

By no means does all such granular material contain hormone. It is likely that most, if not all, of the stainable material of the granules and droplets is physiologically inert, consisting of protein, lipid, and carbohydrate (lipoprotein, glycoprotein, glycolipoprotein). It has been assumed that the stainable colloidal material actually consists of carrier molecules to which the actual, much smaller hormone molecules are bound.

In a number of cases (neurosecretory cells in amphibians, teleosts, and molluscs) the granules contain pigment (melanin) and resemble the granules found in melanophores (chromatophores, see Chap. 15). Some authors consider this as evidence that such granules are physiologically inert and do not represent a stage in the production and secretion of hormones. Remember, however, that pigments, particularly melanin, may represent the product of transformation

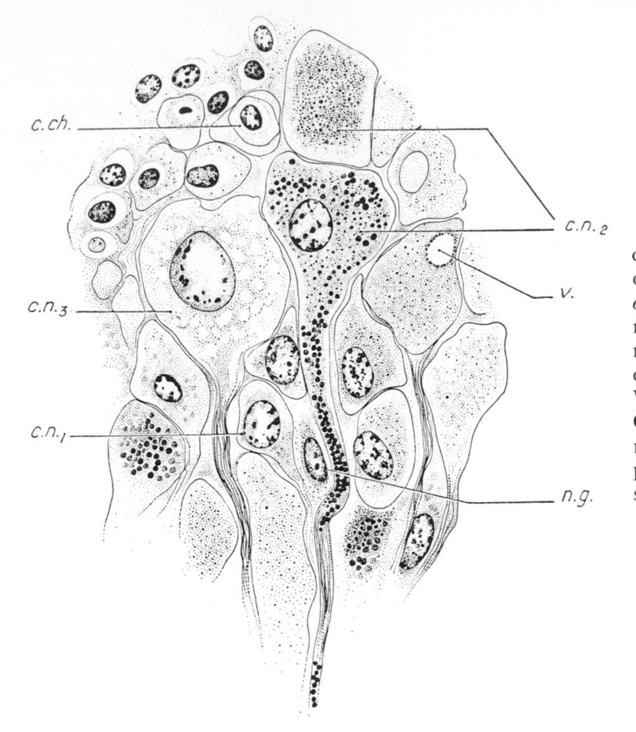

Figure 21–1. Neurosecretory cells of the *pars intercerebralis* of the orthopteran *Cuniculina annamensis*. *c.ch.*, chromatic cells; *c.n.*$_1$, young neurosecretory cell; *c.n.*$_2$, active neurosecretory cells; *c.n.*$_3$, aged neurosecretory cell; *n.g.*, nucleus of glia cell; *V.*, vacuole. (From Dupont-Raabe, M.: Quelques données relatives aux phénomènes de neurosecretion chez les phasmides. Ann. Sc. Nat., Zool. 11e serie, 293–303, 1956.)

(by polymerization) of physiologically active compounds. In the case of melanin, the precursors can be adrenaline or 5-hydroxytryptamine (see Chap. 14), and tyrosine, itself the precursor of the hormone thyroxine. There may well be other molecules related to tyrosine that also possess hormone activity and can be polymerized to melanin. Thus the presence of pigment in "neurosecretory" granules is not incompatible with the presence of hormone in the same granules.

It is particularly suggestive of hormone secretion if the morphological (cytological) signs of secretion of neurosecretory cells show seasonal or periodic variation, that is, alternating accumulation and depletion correlated with certain physiological states (e.g., dehydration, regeneration, reproduction, molting). Such correlations between accumulation or depletion of secretory granules in neurosecretory cells have been observed in many species of annelids, decapod crustaceans, insects, myriapods, spiders, and lamellibranch and gastropod molluscs. Correlations with regeneration of nerve tissue have, among others, been demonstrated for annelids (*Lumbricus, Eisenia*; Hubl, 1956). Morphological evidence for the existence of neurosecretory cells has, in fact, been obtained from almost all phyla of the Animal Kingdom. Specific functions of neurosecretory hormones are known only for some annelids, crustaceans, insects, and vertebrates.

The typical neurosecretory cells do not make synaptic contacts with other nerve cells or effector organs; their axon terminals are located near a blood vessel or blood sinus. A collection of such "secretory" terminals, because of its close association with a vascular bed or a blood sinus, is called a *neuro-*

hemal organ (Carlisle and Knowles, 1953). Neurosecretory neurons do, however, receive synaptic contacts from other nerve cells. Several cases are known (see p. 526) in which activation of certain nerves or nervous pathways causes release of neurosecretory products (hormones). It is thought that this is accomplished by synaptic activation of neurosecretory cells by presynaptic, "normal" neurons. Nothing is known about the mode of activation; this may be quite similar to the activation of contractile elements in muscle fibers where, again, synaptic activation of a cell causes intracellular events that are—somehow—associated with, and perhaps caused by, membrane responses of the (postsynaptic) cell. There is further evidence that nerve cells not only activate, but also suppress (inhibit) the release of secretory material from neurosecretory cells. Thus it is assumed that neurosecretory cells are true effector cells, receiving excitatory as well as inhibitory innervation. Like other effector cells (muscle cells, gland cells, pigment cells), they are last in a series of connecting links.

Several types of neurosecretory cells have been shown to be capable of generating, and conducting along their axons, action potentials (Bennett and Fox, 1962; Kandel, 1962; Kinosita, Yagi, and Yasuda, 1962; Morita, Ishibashi, and Yamashita, 1961; Yagi and Bern, 1963; Yagi, Bern, and Hagadorn, 1963). Much current research is concerned with the question whether these nerve impulses effect release of neurosecretory products and whether, in fact, they are a prerequisite for such release.

Although there is evidence that neurosecretory cells release colloidal granular material or microscopically visible droplets, the specific function of neurosecretory cells is seen in their release (or secretion) of specific hormones. To distinguish these from hormones released from regular gland cells of endocrine organs, such hormones are called *neurohormones*, sometimes *neurohumors*. The term "neurohormone" should not be applied to transmitter substances, and a neurohormone should certainly not be called a transmitter substance. Neurohemal organs may be some distance away from the cell bodies of the secretory cells; they are, of course, connected with them through their axons. Neurosecretory products can be released not only from axon terminals, but also from the axons themselves and from the cell body directly.

The study of neurosecretion, pioneered by Ernst and Berta Scharrer, and by Bargman, has intensified during the past decade and the literature has grown to vast dimensions. It is impossible to do full justice to this exciting field of physiology in a chapter designed for an introductory text. Only a highly simplified extract is presented here. For further reading, refer to the references listed at the end of this chapter.

ANNELIDS

Several types of neurosecretory cells have been described for various species of polychaete and oligochaete annelids (Scharrer, 1937; Durchon, 1960; Clark, 1959; Hubl, 1956, etc.). In the nereids, the morphological signs of secretory activity of certain nerve cell groups (c and d cells) is associated with the transformation of the formerly asexual, or atokous, worm into a sexually active, reproductive form, the heteronereid. The latter condition is referred

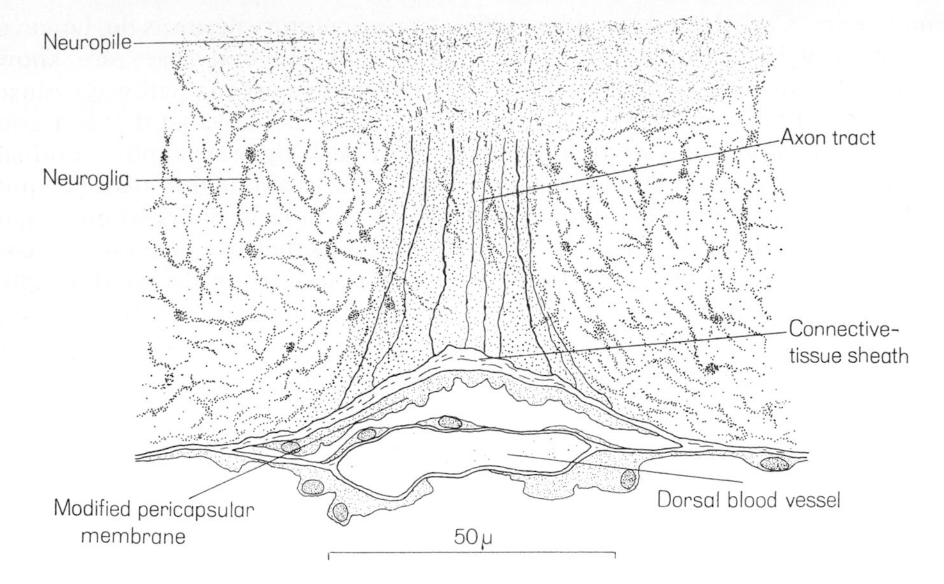

Figure 21–2. Neurohemal organ at the base of the brain of an annelid. *Nephtys Californiensis.* (From Clark, R. B.: The neurosecretory system of the supra-oesophageal ganglion of *Nephtys* (Annelida; Polychaeta). Zool. Jahrb., Allg. Zool. Physiol. Tiere 68:395–424, 1959.)

to as epitoky. Other cell groups, active during the atokous state, produce a "juvenile hormone" that inhibits gamete maturation and epitoky. The secretory products are released into and from a blood sinus at the base of the brain (Fig. 21–2). The situation in nephtids (Clark, 1959) is similar. In the Lumbricidae there is also a correlation between sexual activity and release of secretory products from certain neurosecretory cells (Hubl, 1956; Herlant-Meewis, 1956). In addition, neurosecretory cells of other types associated with initiation of regeneration are activated (Hubl, 1956).

CRUSTACEANS

In the decapod crustaceans, groups of neurosecretory cells occur in the optic ganglia, in various parts of the "brain," and in the ventral ganglia (see Figs. 21–3 and 21–4). From several of these cell groups, axons connect with a storage-and-release organ in the eyestalks, the so-called *sinus gland.* This is largely composed of the nerve terminals swollen with neurosecretory products. These are released into the blood stream. The sinus gland is thus a proper neurohemal organ. Prominent groups of neurosecretory cell bodies situated at the surface of the optic ganglia are referred to as *X-organs.* Thus both X-organs and sinus gland lie within the eyestalks (Fig. 21–5). This has facilitated experimentation: it is relatively easy to remove the eyestalks and thus to study the effects of removal of the neurosecretory organs; and it is also possible to extract eyestalk or even sinus glands, and to inject the material into whole animals or to apply it to tissues. From experiments of this type it was learned that the

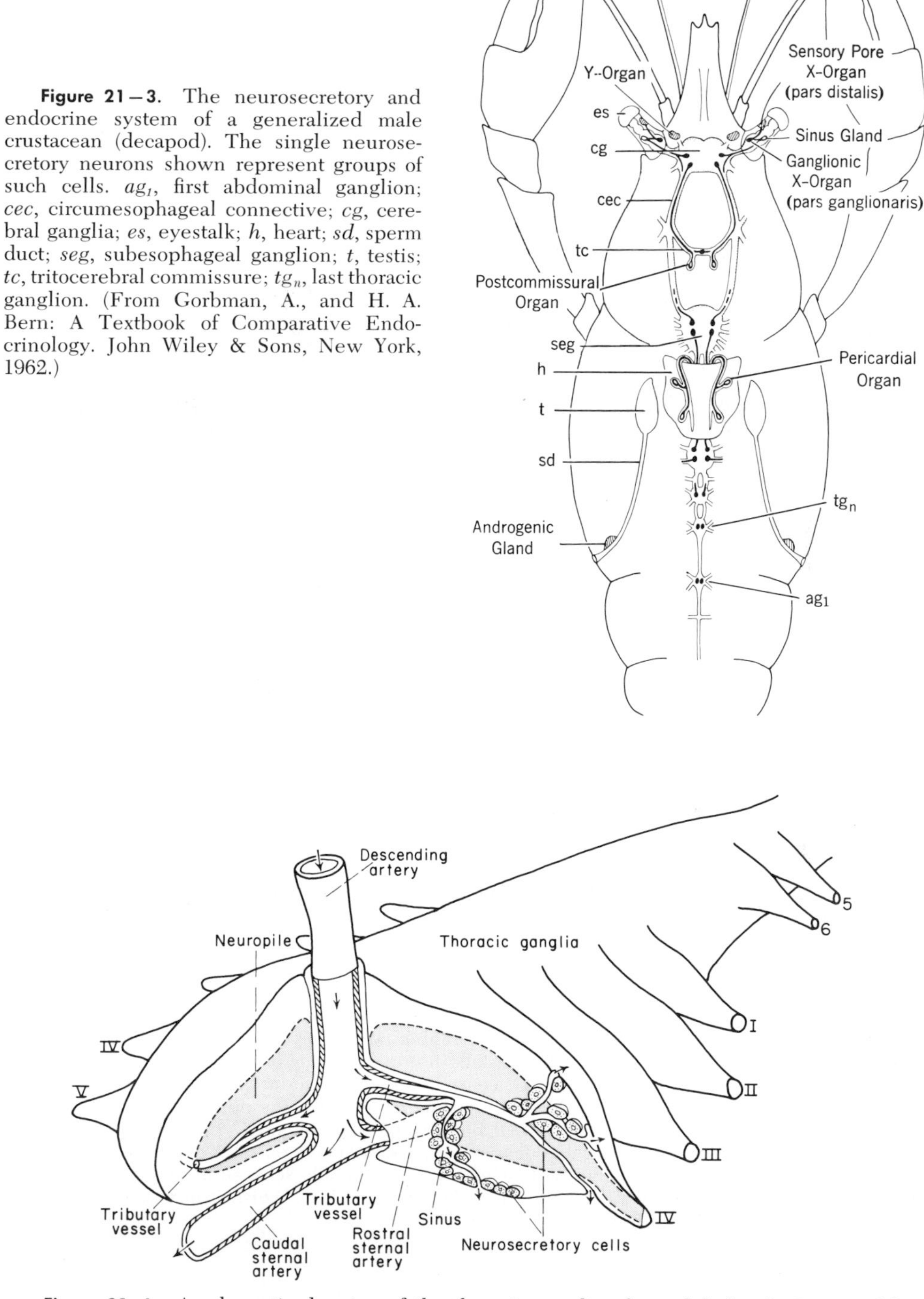

Figure 21–3. The neurosecretory and endocrine system of a generalized male crustacean (decapod). The single neurosecretory neurons shown represent groups of such cells. ag_1, first abdominal ganglion; *cec*, circumesophageal connective; *cg*, cerebral ganglia; *es*, eyestalk; *h*, heart; *sd*, sperm duct; *seg*, subesophageal ganglion; *t*, testis; *tc*, tritocerebral commissure; tg_n, last thoracic ganglion. (From Gorbman, A., and H. A. Bern: A Textbook of Comparative Endocrinology. John Wiley & Sons, New York, 1962.)

Figure 21–4. A schematic drawing of the thoracic ganglia of an adult female *Pinnixa faba*; drawn from a composite of serial sections. *5* and *6*, small nerves serving the second and third thoracic somites; *I–V*, larger nerves innervating the last five thoracic somites. The arrows show the general pattern of circulation in the ganglia. (Courtesy Dr. J. A. Pearce.)

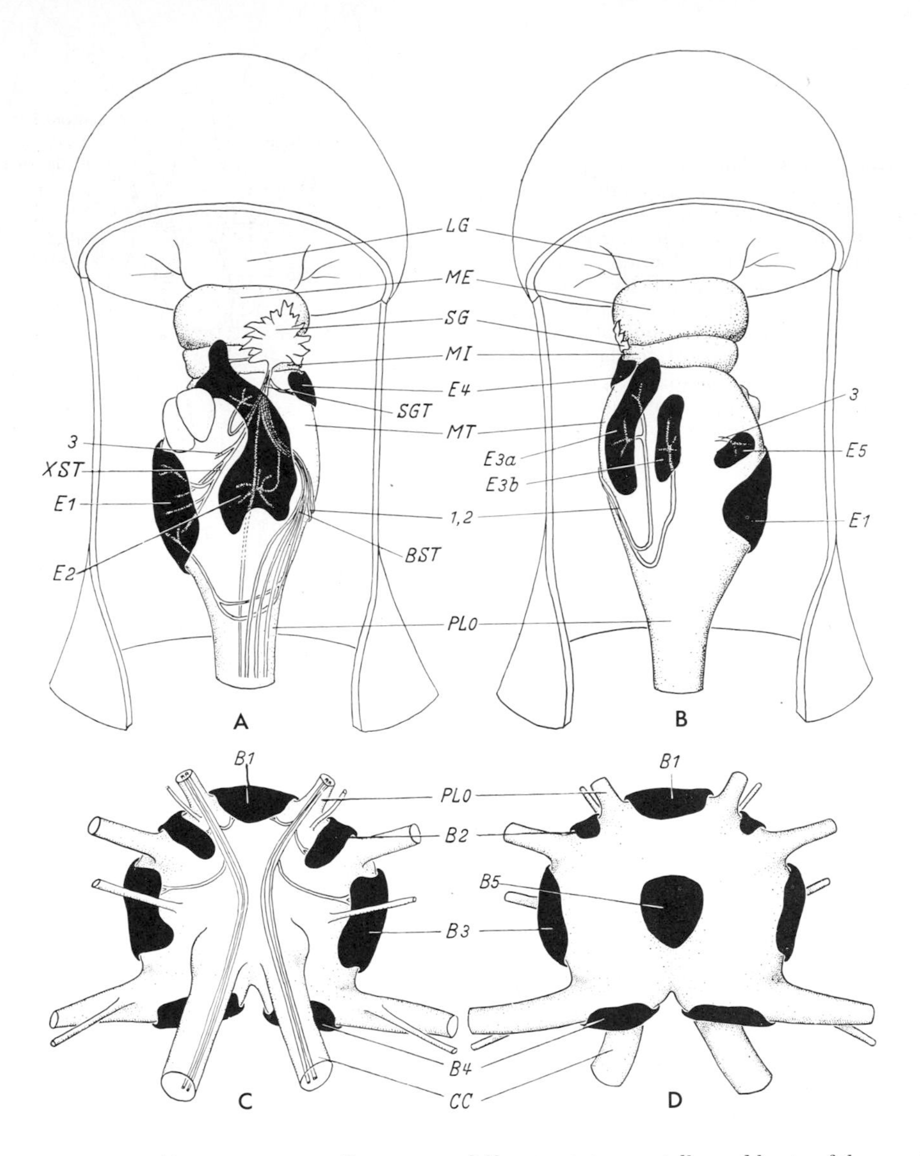

Figure 21-5. Neurosecretory cell groups and fiber tracts in eyestalks and brain of the crayfish *Orconectes virilis*. **A**, dorsal view of right eyestalk in normal seeing position. **B**, ventral view of the same eyestalk. **C**, posterior (dorsal) view. **D**, ventral view of the brain. The black areas *E 1* through *E 5* and *B 1* through *B 5* indicate regions of neurosecretory cells; the double lines indicate tracts of axons from these neurosecretory cells. *BST*, brain-sinus gland tract; *CC*, circumesophageal (tritocerebral) connective; *LG*, lamina ganglionaris; *ME*, medulla externa; *MI*, medulla interna; *MT*, medulla terminalis; *PLO*, optic lobe peduncle; *SG*, sinus gland; *SGT*, sinus gland tract; *XST*, X-organ–sinus gland tract. (From Bliss, D. E., J. B. Durand, and J. H. Welsh: Neurosecretory systems in decapod Crustacea. Z. Zellforsch. *39*:520–536, 1954.)

X-organ–sinus gland complex produces hormones that control pigment movement in chromatophores. Because of the ease of observation, numerous reports have appeared in the research literature that are concerned with the *chromatophorotropic* effects of "eyestalk extracts," and from the varied responses of different chromatophores, the existence of numerous *chromatophorotropic hormones* has been deduced. For detailed accounts, refer to the reviews and monographs of Carlisle and Knowles, 1959; Kleinholz, 1961; Welsh, 1961; and Fingerman, 1963; see also Chapter 15.

Precisely how many chromatophorotropins are released from the sinus gland is unknown. Extracts show a variety of chromatophorotropic activities depending on the extraction procedure and subsequent history of the extracts. Different types of chromatophores of the same animal show different behavior in response to the application of the same sample of extract. On the whole, however, "eyestalk extracts" of any decapod crustacean cause a lightening (due to pigment concentration in dark chromatophores) in shrimps and prawns, and a darkening (due to pigment expansion in dark chromatophores) in crabs. Edman, Faenge, and Östlund (1958) purified the red pigment-concentrating hormone (active on red chromatophores of *Palaemon*) of *Pandalus* by a factor of 100,000. Chemical tests indicate that this is a polypeptide.

In 1927, Koller showed that the sand shrimp *Crangon vulgaris* controls, independently, four different color types of pigment cells by hormones. In 1928, he was the first to demonstrate the hormonal control of the chromatophores. At the same time as Perkins (1928), he discovered the significance of the eyestalks in hormone production. The ability of *Crangon* and other shrimps—for instance, *Hippolyte varians* studied by Keeble and Gamble (1900)—to assume many different shades and patterns of color, suggest a multiplicity of hormones. As shown by Koller, the astounding ability of *Crangon* to imitate the background coloration is determined by the predominant wavelength of reflected light falling into the eyes, and not by the intensity of illumination. This suggested a delicate control of hormone release by the nervous system initiated by patterns of excitation of retinal photoreceptors. This is indeed one of the good examples of nervous control of the neurosecretory cells and of their activity.

Hormones from the sinus gland and "eyestalk" have also been implied in the control of crustacean carbohydrate metabolism and water regulation. There is good evidence that such hormones control molting; removal of the eyestalks in most decapod crustaceans shortens the intermolt period and leads to premature molting. The decapods have been found by Gabe (1953; see also Echalier, 1959) to possess either in the antennal or maxillar segment bilaterally situated endocrine glands, the so-called *Y-organs*. These appear to be under the control of some "eyestalk hormone" which inhibits its hormone secretion (or production). The hormone of the Y-organs initiates molting. Hormonal factors extractable from the X-organ–sinus gland complex inhibit the development of the gonads (ovaries as well as testes), according to Carlisle (1953) and Demeusy (1953, 1960). It is not yet certain whether they act directly on the gonads or whether they influence the gonads only indirectly by inhibiting the release of a gonad-stimulating hormone from the Y-organs or from the *androgenic gland*, a recently discovered endocrine organ situated near the genital

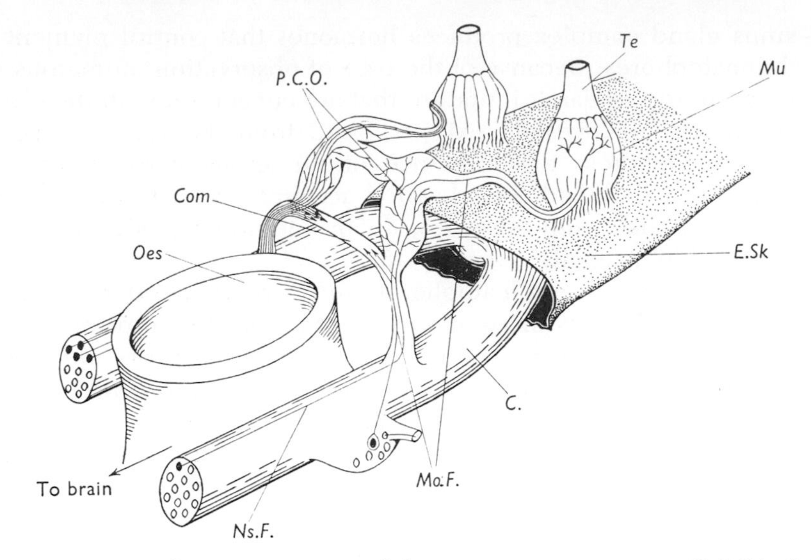

Figure 21–6. Semidiagrammatic view of the postcommissure organs (*P.C.O.*) of the prawn *Leander serratus*. Each circumesophageal connective (*C.*) contains four neurosecretory fibers (*Ns.F.*), of which only one is shown in the left C., and two motor fibers (*Mo.F.*)—only one is shown—that pass through the P.C.O. and innervate the muscle *Mu* (its tendon is marked *Te*). The subesophageal ganglion is mostly hidden by the endophragmal skeleton (*E.Sk*). The neurosecretory fibers which also send branches through the commissure (*Com*) just behind the esophagus (*Oes*) have their cell bodies in the brain (tritocerebrum). The products of neurosecretion are thought to pass from the bulbous nerve endings in the P.C.O. directly into the blood stream. (From Carlisle, D. B., and F. Knowles: Endocrine Control in Crustaceans. Cambridge University Press, London, 1959.)

pore. The latter occurs only in the males and is responsible for male sexual characteristics and testicular development.

A second neurosecretory "complex" of higher crustaceans is represented by the *postcommissure organs* (Fig. 21–6). Nerve cells, probably situated in the tritocerebral commissure, send out processes that ramify in a swelling associated with the postcommissure nerves. The swelling, disk or ribbon shaped, is filled with secretory granules obviously derived from secretory nerve endings. It is suspended in a blood sinus. Postcommissure organs have, so far, been found in shrimps and prawns (Knowles, 1953) and in crabs (Matsumoto, 1958) as well as in stomatopods (Carlisle and Knowles, 1959). Potent chromatophorotropic hormone can be extracted from postcommissural organs (Brown, 1946).

The *pericardial organs* represent a third type of neurosecretory-neurohemal organ of crustaceans. They have been discovered in the stomatopod *Squilla* by Alexandrowicz (1952), who later described similar organs in other crustacean groups, notably decapods, but also amphipods and possibly isopods and mysids (for a review of later papers, see Maynard, 1961, and Bern and Hagadorn, 1965). These ribbon-like structures contain neurosecretory nerve cells, but also receive axonal terminals of neurosecretory cells situated in the ventral ganglia. The organs are stretched out within the pericardium just across the openings of the gill veins that deliver blood into the pericardium (Fig. 21–7). Extracts prepared from pericardial organs cause pronounced increase in frequency and amplitude of the heartbeat (Alexandrowicz and Carlisle, 1953). This is assumed

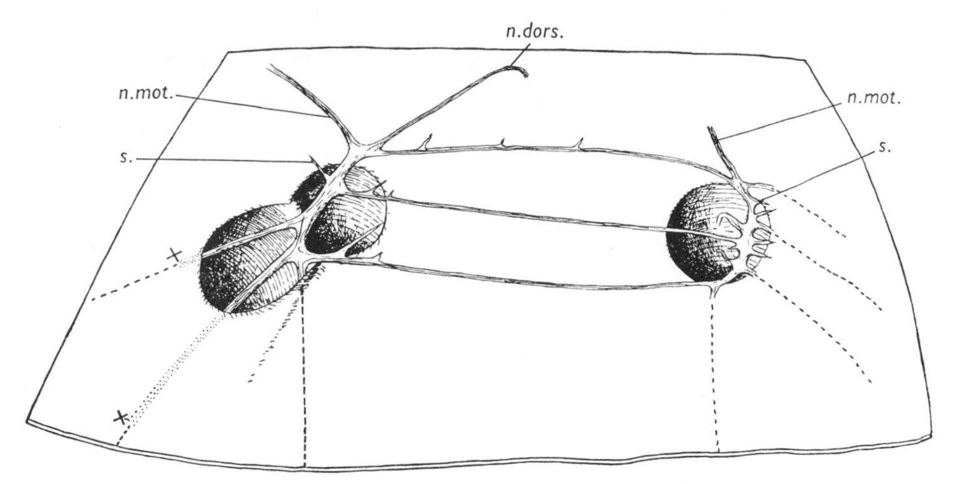

Figure 21–7. Semidiagrammatic view of the pericardial organs (right side) of the crab *Maia squinado*. Part of the lateral wall of the pericardium is shown with the three openings of the branchiocardiac veins. The nerves running from the central nervous system into the pericardial organs are drawn in dotted lines. At the points marked X the two anterior nerves pass into the lumen of the vein. *n.dors.*, dorsal nerve of the heart; *n.mot.*, nerves running to muscles; *s.*, strands suspending the trunks. (From Alexandrowicz, J. S.: Nervous organs in the pericardial cavity of the decapod *Crustacea*. J. Mar. Biol. Assn. U.K. *31*:563–580, 1953.)

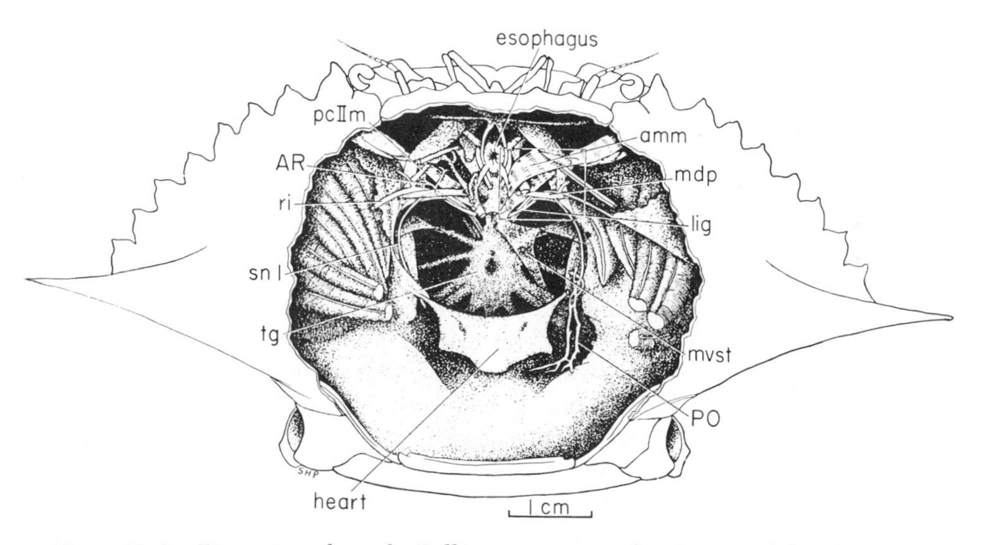

Figure 21–8. Dissection of a crab, *Callinectes ornatus*, showing two of the important neurohemal organs: pericardial organs and anterior ramifications. Digestive gland, stomach, and bladder removed. *amm*, musculus abductor maior mandibulae; *AR*, anterior ramifications; *lig*, ligament; *mdp*, musculus dorsoventralis posterior; *mvst*, musculi ventrales superficiales thoracis; *pcllm*, musculus proximalis coxopoditis II maxillae; *PO*, pericardial organ; *ri*, recurrent integumentary nerve; *sn 1*, first segmental nerve; *tg*, thoracic ganglia. The region bounded by a rectangle to the right of the esophagus is enlarged in Figure 21–9. Several overlying muscles and ligaments have been removed on the left half of the dissection. (From Maynard, D. M.: Thoracic neurosecretory structures in Brachyura. I. Gross anatomy. Biol. Bull. *121*:316–329, 1961.)

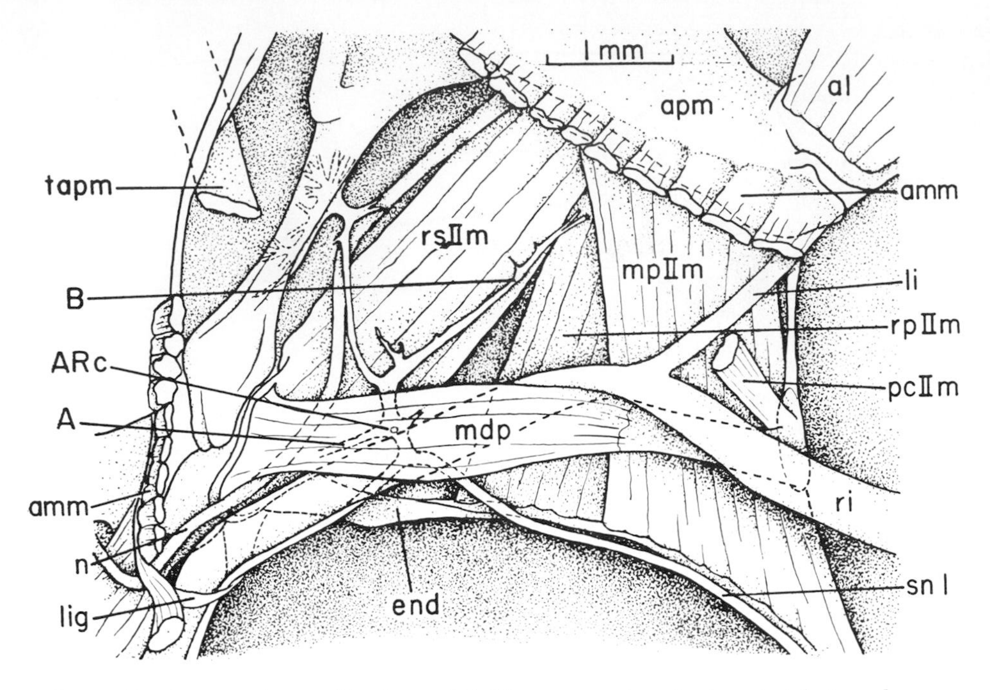

Figure 21–9. Anterior ramifications of *Callinectes ornatus*; fresh material. Dorsal exposure with digestive system removed. *A*, medial, posterior branch of anterior ramifications; *al*, musculus adductor lateralis mandibulae; *amm*, musculus abductor maior mandibulae, only cut segments at origin and insertion remain; the belly has been removed to expose underlying structures. *apm*, apophysis of mandible; *ARc*, location of neuron cell body in anterior ramifications; *B*, anterior, lateral branch of anterior ramifications; *end*, endopleurite of last head segment; *li*, lateral integumentary nerve; *lig*, ligament; *mdp*, musculus dorsoventralis posterior; *mpIIm*, musculus promotor II maxillae; *n*, anterior dorsolateral nerve of Echalier (1959); *pcIIm*, musculus proximalis coxopoditis II maxillae; *ri*, recurrent integumentary nerve; *rpIIm*, musculus respiratorius primus II maxillae; *rsIIm*, musculus respiratorius secundus II maxillae; *sn 1*, first segmental nerve; *tapm*, stump of tendon of musculus adductor posterior mandibulae. Note how one anterior branch of anterior ramifications spreads over the anterior nerve and continues beneath the head apodeme. (From Maynard, D. M.: Thoracic neurosecretory structures in Brachyura. I. Gross anatomy. Biol. Bull. *121*:316–329, 1961.)

to be due to a cardio-regulator hormone produced by the neurosecretory cells (and axons). Thus it is assumed that the pericardial organs play an important role in controlling heart rate by (nerve controlled?) release of a cardio-accelerator hormone. The hormone may consist of two active fractions: 5-hydroxytryptamine and a polypeptide (Maynard and Welsh, 1959). Maynard (1961) has shown that in brachyuran crustaceans, the pericardial organs have an extension reaching over the thoracic respiratory muscles. These are called *anterior ramifications* (Figs. 21–8 and 21–9). They are formed of the same neurons that contribute their endings to the pericardial organs. They are therefore assumed to release the same neurohormones.

INSECTS

The complex anatomical variants of the neurosecretory systems of insects can be sketched into a simple pattern: neurosecretory cells in the protocerebrum send axons to the *corpora cardiaca* (usually a paired structure just posterior of the supra-esophageal ganglia; where it is unpaired one refers to the *corpus cardiacum*). The corpora cardiaca act as neurohemal organs but may also contain nerve cells. Their processes as well as axons from the supra-esophageal ganglia pass on to another glandular organ, also usually paired, the *corpora allata*.

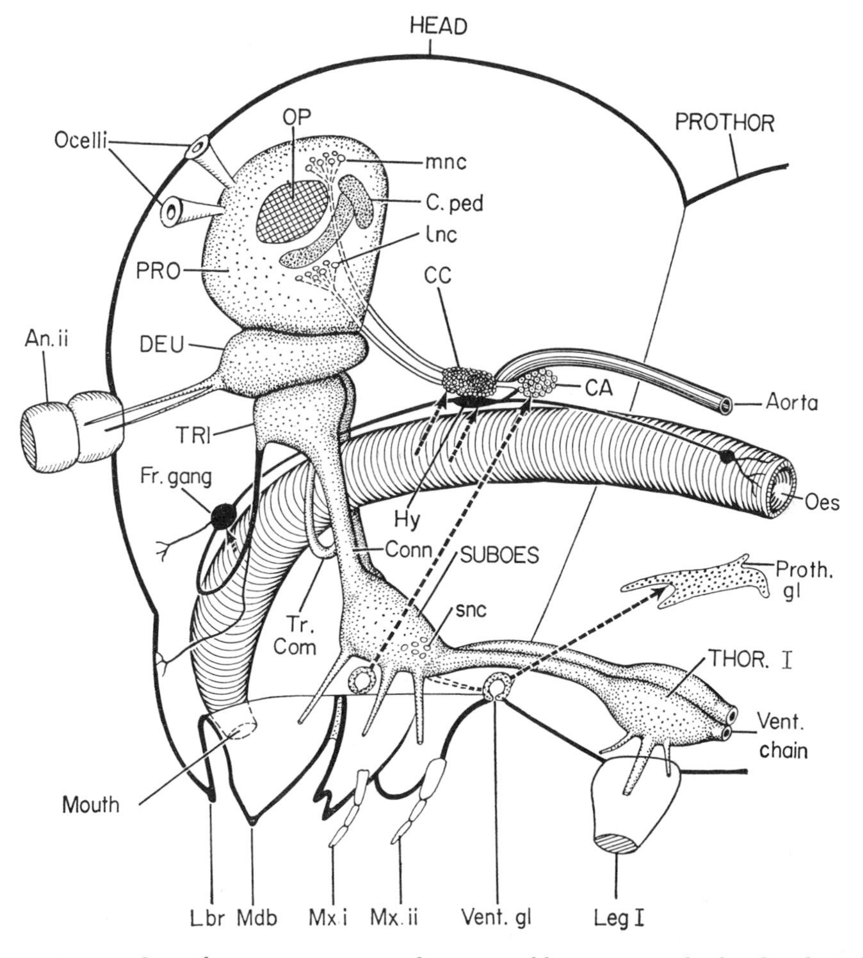

Figure 21–10. Central nervous system and sources of hormones in the head and prothorax of a hemimetabolous insect. The stomatogastric nervous system arises from the stomodeal ectoderm, and has paired nerves from the tritocerebrum *(TRI)*, a median frontal ganglion *(Fr.gang)*, a branch from the labrum (*Lbr*), and a recurrent nerve to the hypocerebral ganglion (*Hy*) and the paired ganglia on the gut near *Oes* (esophagus). Hormones are produced by median (*mnc*) and lateral (*lnc*) neurosecretory cells in the protocerebrum (*PRO*), and subesophageal neurosecretory cells (*snc*); perhaps also by cells in the paired corpora pedunculata (*C.ped*). These hormones pass in two paired nerves to the *corpora cardiaca* (*CC*) which arise from stomodeal ectoderm (dashed arrows). Hormones are also secreted by two paired glands, the *corpora allata* (*CA*), which arise as ectodermal invaginations near the first maxillae (*Mx i*) and move above the esophagus where they receive axons from the corpora cardiaca. The ventral glands (*Vent.gl*) persist in primitive insects; in others they form the prothoracic glands *(Proth. gl)*. Both function as *ecdysial glands; An ii,* antenna with nerves; *Conn,* circumesophageal connectives; *DEU,* deuterocerebrum; *Mdb,* mandible; *Mx ii,* second maxillae; *OP,* optic lobes; *SUBOES,* subesophageal ganglion; *Thor I,* first thoracic ganglion; *Tr.Com,* tritocerebral commissure; *Vent.chain,* ventral nerve cord; *PROTHOR,* prothorax. (Based on two diagrams by Weber, 1949. From Jenkin, P. M.: Animal Hormones, A Comparative Survey. Part I. Kinetic and Metabolic Hormones. Pergamon Press, New York, 1962.)

The latter may also receive nerves from the subesophageal ganglion. Although the corpora allata (or the corpus allatum, where the structure is unpaired) are non-neural epithelial glands; they are implied in the transformation and subsequent release of neurosecretory hormone. The anatomical situation is explained in Figure 21–10.

The hormone (or hormones) released by the corpora cardiaca activates an endocrine gland that is now called the *ecdysial gland.* In different insect groups this gland has a different anatomical position and structure; thus it has been known under a variety of names, such as *prothoracic gland, pericardial gland, ventral gland,* and *ring gland* (Weismann rings). Some of these are pictured in Figures 21–11 and 21–12.

The activated ecdysial glands release a hormone, *ecdyson,* which causes molting with simultaneous differentiation (metamorphosis). The hormone has been isolated and chemically analyzed by Butenandt and Karlson, 1954. The action of ecdyson is antagonized and modified by the hormone secreted by the corpora allata, known as *juvenile hormone* or *neotenin* (Wigglesworth, 1954), which favors larval characteristics and tends to delay molting. Removal of the corpora allata from an insect larva can induce molting (or shortens the intermolt period) and (premature) metamorphosis, leading to a small, metamorphosed insect. Implantation of additional corpora allata, on the other hand, delays molting, allowing for a longer growth period, and when the next molt takes place metamorphosis is suppressed and the animal emerges again as larva (supernumerary molt). Thus giant larvae (and finally giant imagines) are produced by this pro-

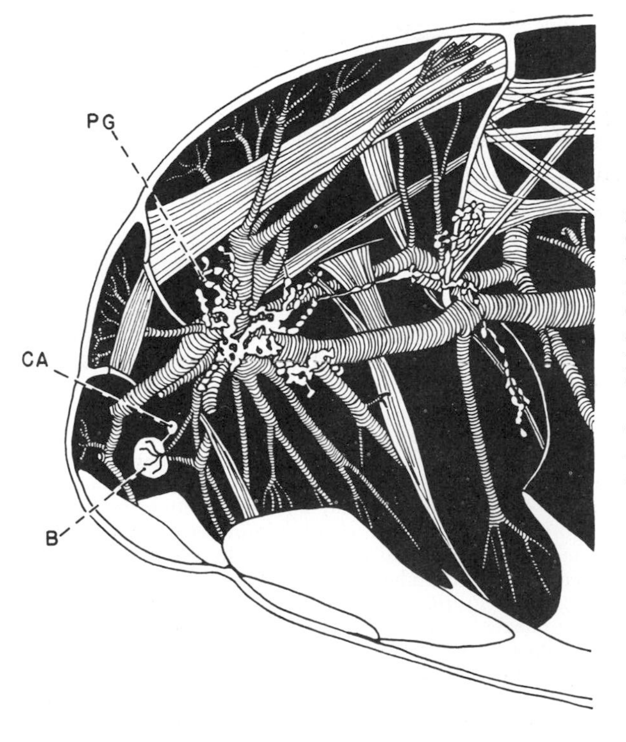

Figure 21–11. The prothoracic gland (ecdysial gland) in the right half of the thorax of a diapausing pupa of the silkworm, *Cecropia.* Fat body and numerous other tissues have been cleared away. *B,* brain; *CA,* corpus allatum and corpus cardiacum; *PG,* prothoracic gland. (From Williams, C. M.: Physiology of insect diapause. III. The prothoracic glands in the Cecropia silkworm, with special reference to their significance in embryonic and postembryonic development. Biol. Bull. *94*:60–65, 1948.)

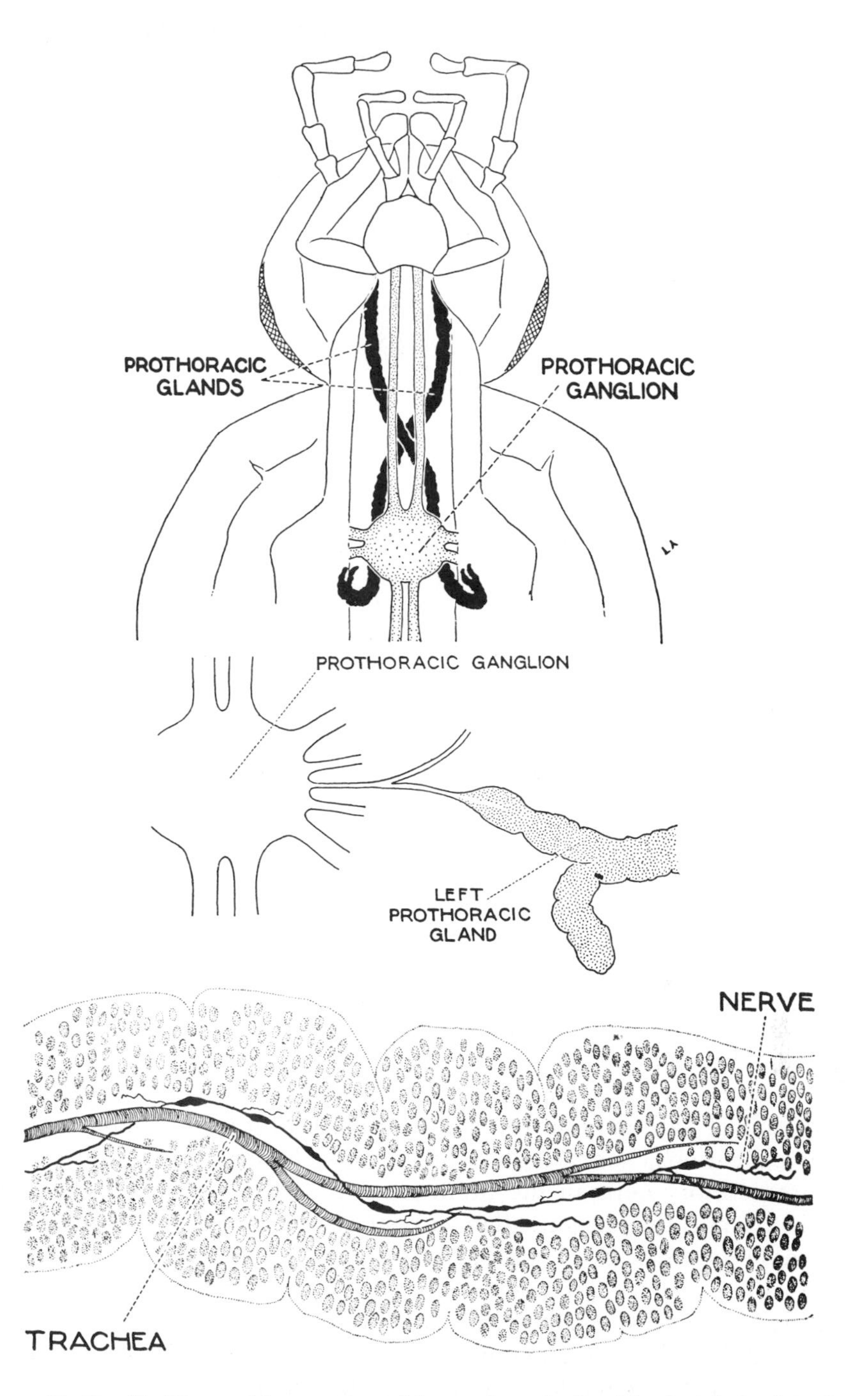

Figure 21–12. Position and innervation of the prothoracic gland (ecdysial gland) in the roach *Leucophaea maderae.* The gland is shown in a nymph (ventral aspect of anterior thorax with head tilted back); and with increasing magnification. The ecdysial glands are thus controlled by hormone(s) from the corpora cardiaca (see Fig. 21–10) and by nerves from the prothoracic ganglion. (From Scharrer, B.: The prothoracic glands of *Leucophaea maderae* (Orthoptera). Biol. Bull. 95:186–198, 1948.)

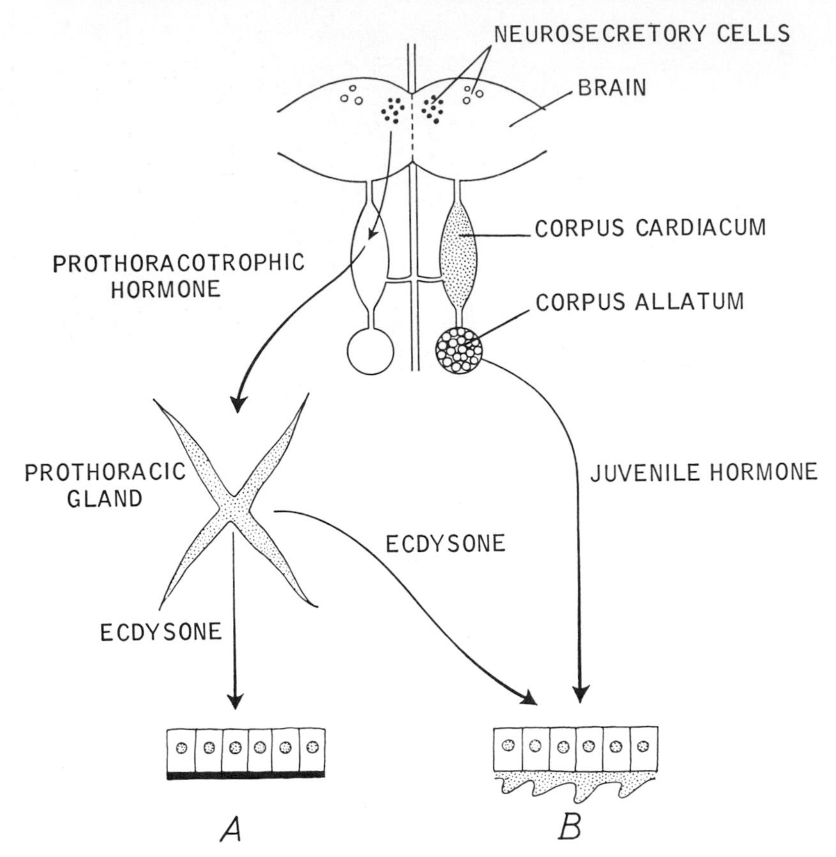

Figure 21–13. Diagrammatic representation of the neurosecretory and endocrine induction of larval molts (**A**) and of metamorphosis (**B**) in an insect. (From Turner, C. D.: General Endocrinology, 3rd Ed. W. B. Saunders Co., Philadelphia, 1960.)

cedure. The interaction of the neurosecretory structures and endocrine glands is represented in Figure 21–13. The classic studies are those of Wigglesworth on the bug *Rhodnius*, of Scharrer on the cockroach *Leucophaea*, of Pflugfelder on the stick insect *Dixippus* (now *Carausius*), of Piepho on the wax moth *Galleria*, and of Williams on the saturnid moth *Platysamia* (for a summary of these investigations, see Wigglesworth, 1954; Scharrer and Scharrer, 1963).

Neurosecretory cells in the brain as well as the corpora cardiaca, the ecdysial glands, and the corpora allata appear also to be involved in the development and function of the reproductive organs. At present it is not possible to fit the varied and numerous experimental results into a simple picture. Only the best documented and rather elaborate neuroendocrine mechanism of *Leucophaea*, as studied by Engelmann, is shown here (Figs. 21–14 and 21–15) as an example for the complex interactions between nervous, neurosecretory, and endocrine pathways in the control of reproductive processes.

The corpora cardiaca are also involved in the control of the heart: they have been shown to secrete an orthodiphenol (Cameron, 1953) that appears to stimulate the heart indirectly: it causes the pericardial cells to release a heart-accelerating substance of as yet unknown chemical structure (Davey, 1961).

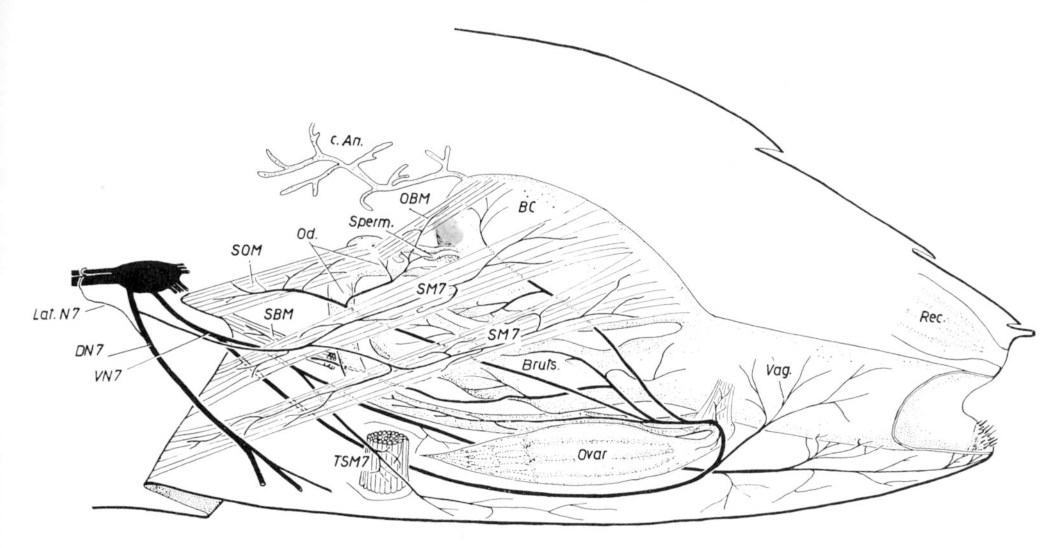

Figure 21–14. Innervation of female genital apparatus in the cockroach *Leucophaea maderae* by branches of the ventral nerve (*VN7*) of the ganglion of the seventh segment. *BC*, bursa copulatrix, *Bruts.*, brood pouch; *c.An.*, cranial accessory gland; *DN7*, dorsal nerve of seventh segment; *LatN7*, lateral nerve of seventh segment; *OBM*, bursa-oviduct muscle; *Od*, oviduct; *Ovar*, ovary; *Rec.*, receptaculum seminis; *SBM*, sternite-brood pouch muscle; *SM7*, sternal muscle of seventh segment; *SOM*, sternite-oviduct muscle; *Sperm.*, spermatheca; *TSM7*, tergosternal muscle of seventh segment; *Vag.*, vagina. The role of this nerve supply in the neuro-endocrine control of reproduction is shown in Figure 21–15. (From Engelmann, F.: Die Innervation der Genital- und Postgenitalsegmente bei Weibchen der Schabe *Leucophaea maderae*. Zool. Jb. Anat. *81*:1–16, 1963.)

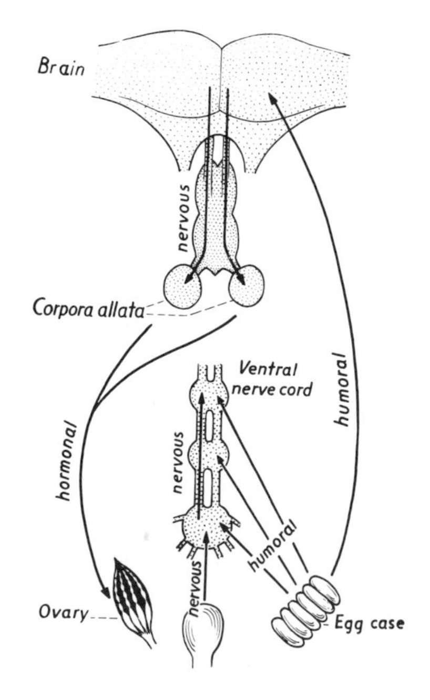

Figure 21–15. Diagrammatic representation of the nervous and humoral (hormonal) control of the reproductive system in the roach *Leucophaea*. The corpora allata secrete a hormone that induces yolk deposition and egg maturation. Mechanical stimulation of the bursa copulatrix activates neurons in the nerve cord which in turn activate inhibitory neurons of the brain that innervate the corpora allata. The activated inhibitory neurons inhibit the release of gonadotropic hormone. Similar nerve elements in the nerve cord respond to humoral factors released from the brood pouch when this holds an egg case. (Courtesy of F. Engelmann.)

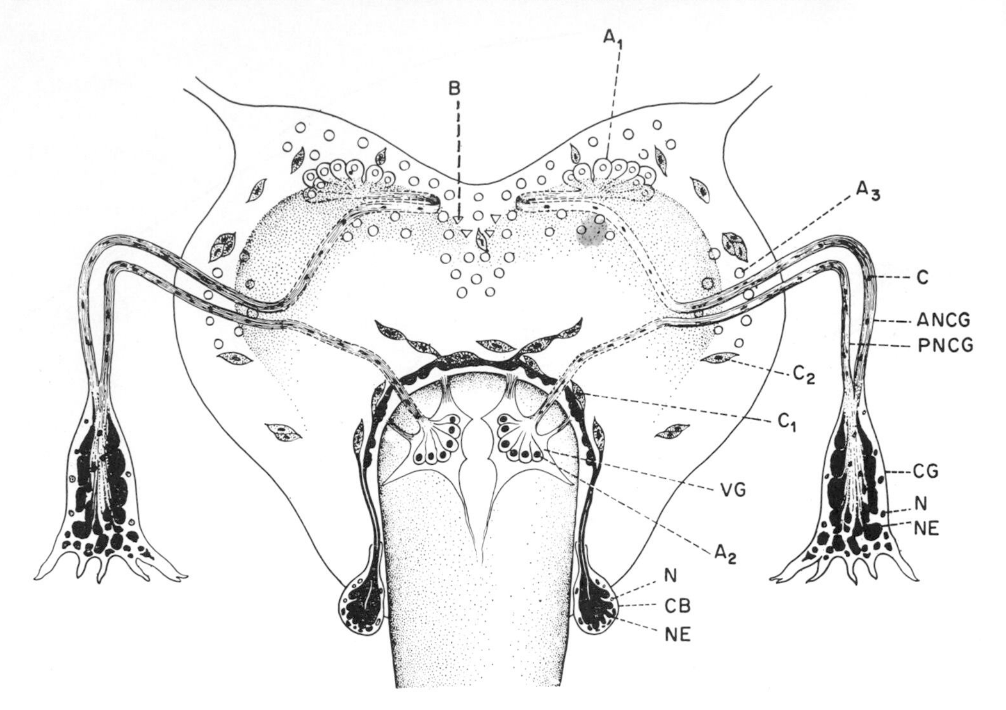

Figure 21–16. Neurosecretory system of a millipede, *Jonespeltis splendidus.* The neurosecretory cell types are indicated by letters (A_1, A_2, A_3, B, C_1, and C_2). Signs of secretory activity are shown by A cells in December and January, B cells at the end of the rainy season and beginning of summer, C cells during the rainy season and during the summer. Whereas the axons of some of the neurosecretory cells appear to end in the general area of the neuropile, the A_1 and A_2 cells send their axons toward the cerebral glands (*CG*) by way of the anterior and posterior nerves of the CG (*ANCG, PNCG*). The CG consists of swollen nerve endings and may well be the neurohemal organ. The same may be true for the "connective body," *CB*, which contains the swollen nerve terminals (*NE*) of C_1 cells. *C*, colloid; *N*, nucleus; *VG*, visceral ganglion. (From Prabhu, V. K. K.: Neurosecretory system of *Jonespeltis splendidus* Verhoeff [Myriapoda; Diplopoda]. *In* Neurosecretion. H. Heller and R. B. Clark, eds. Academic Press, New York, 1962.)

OTHER INVERTEBRATE GROUPS

Neurosecretory complexes occur in the Myriapoda (see Fig. 21–16) and in the mollusca (various ganglia), but although some of the neurosecretory cells show seasonal changes in the production (and presumably release) of secretory material, nothing is known about the possible role of the secretory products.

VERTEBRATES

The *hypothalamus* of the vertebrate brain contains neurosecretory neurons. Associated with them are two neurohemal organs: the *median eminence* of the tuber cinereum and the *posterior lobe* of the pituitary gland (both structures constitute the *neurohypophysis*). Blood vessels of the median eminence carry secretory products (as yet unidentified hormones of known function) to the *anterior lobe* of the pituitary gland (the adenohypophysis) where they initiate production and secretion of hormones by the gland cells. The anatomical situation is explained in Figure 21–17. The secretory products transported along neurosecretory axons into the posterior lobe (neurohypophysis) are largely known: they are octapeptides, originally named *oxytocin*, *vasopressin*, and *antidiuretic* hormone (ADH). The latter two are often considered identical (see, however, p. 527). The adenohypophysis secretes *somatotropin* (STH; see p. 265), *gonadotropins*, *prolactin* (in mammals), *adrenocorticotropic hormone* (ACTH; see p. 266), and *thyroid-stimulating hormone* (TSH). The thy-

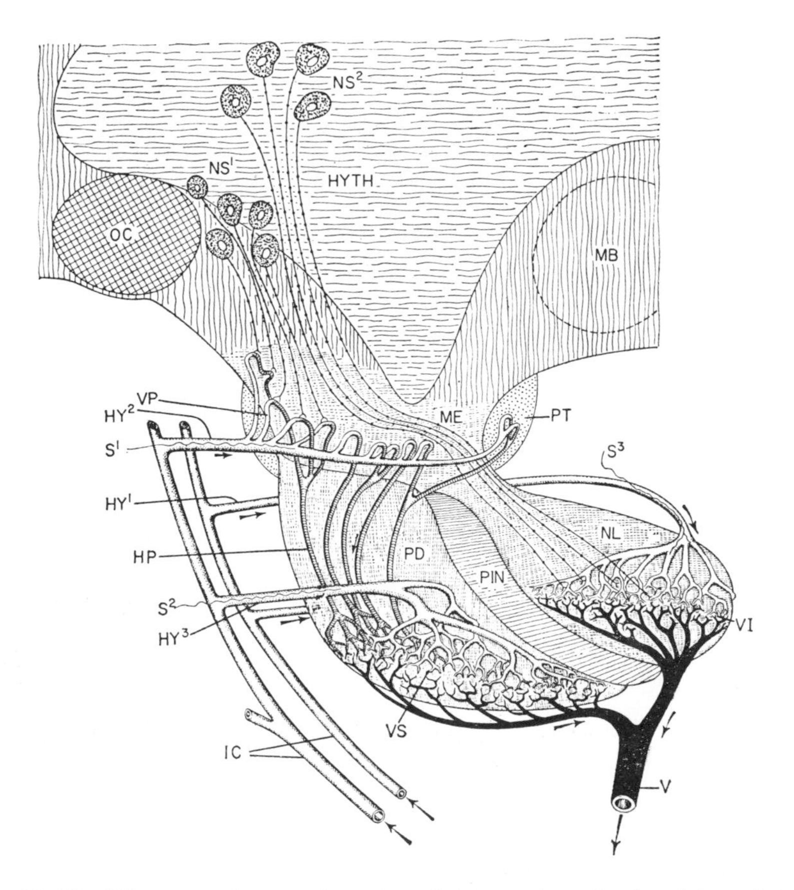

Figure 21–17. Diagrammatic sagittal section of the pituitary gland and hypothalamus of a rabbit, *Oryctolagus*, with the circulation superimposed and simplified. The neurosecretory cells (NS^1 and NS^2) have been disproportionately magnified to show their axons connecting with the primary plexus of veins (*VP*) in the median eminence (*ME*) and (*VI*) in the neural lobe (*NL*). The only other nerves are sympathetic vasomotor fibres (S^1, S^2, and S^3). Blood comes from the internal carotids (*IC*) by hypophyseal arteries; the upper right (HY^1) takes an independent supply to the neural lobe (*NL*), which is drained by the main vein (*V*). The pars intermedia (*PIN*) has practically no circulation. The upper left hypophyseal artery (HY^2) supplies the primary venous plexus in the pars tuberalis (*PT*), from which loops penetrate deeply into the median eminence and can receive neurosecretions. These vessels join again to give the hypophyseal portal system (*HP*) which breaks up into the secondary venous plexus (*VS*) in the pars distalis (*PD*) of the adenohypophysis. This part also receives blood directly from the lower hypophyseal arteries (HY^3). *HYTH*, hypothalamus; *MB*, mammilary body; *OC*, optic chiasma. (From Jenkin, P. M.: Animal Hormones, A Comparative Survey. Part I, Kinetic and Metabolic Hormones. Pergamon Press, New York, 1962.)

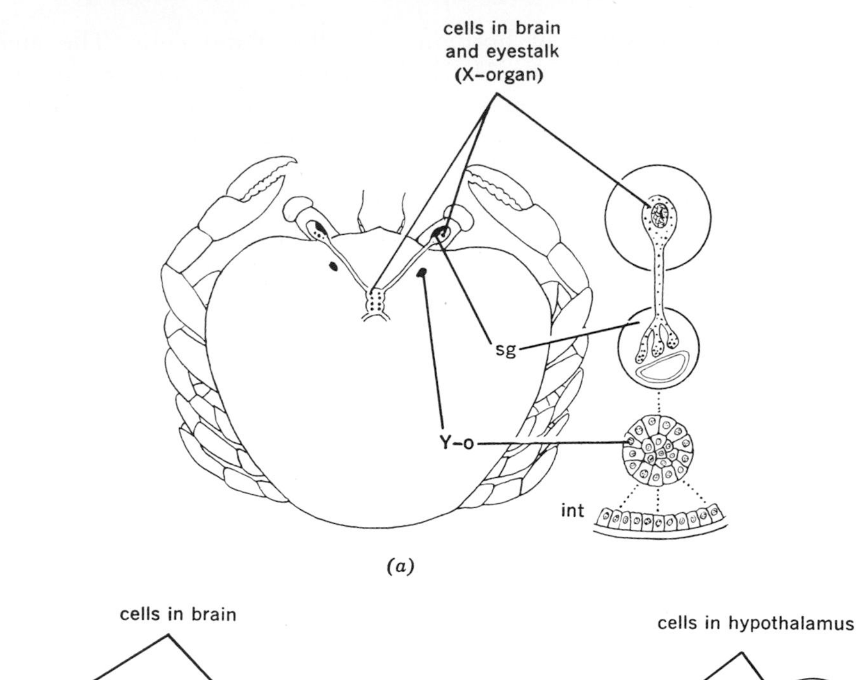

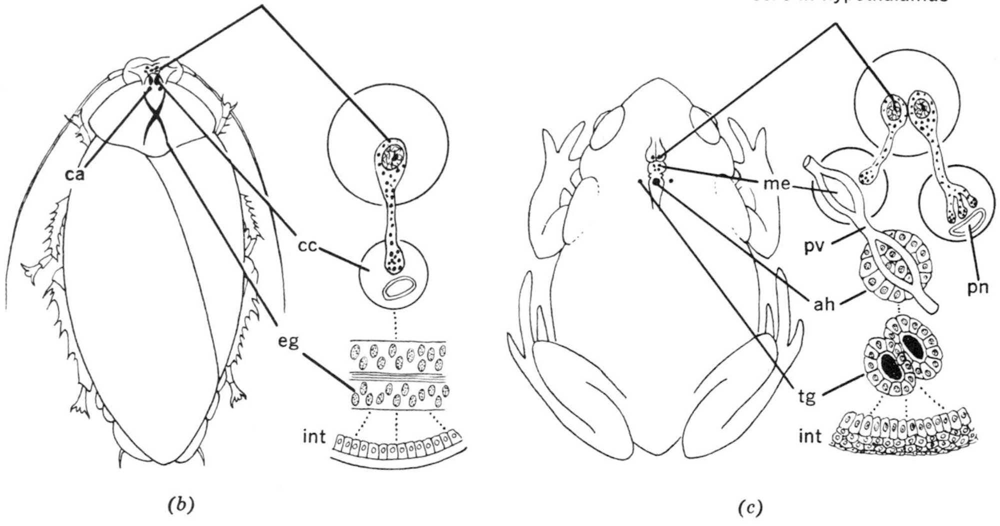

Figure 21–18. Diagrams illustrating the neuro-endocrine control of molting in the crustacean (**a**), the insect (**b**), and the amphibian vertebrate (**c**). In all instances the neurosecretory cells appear to be activated by afferent nervous impulses arising in response to environmental stimuli. *In the crustacean,* the X-organ's molt-controlling hormones are released from the sinus gland (*sg*)—a neurohemal organ in the eyestalk—and presumably act through the Y-organ (*Y-o*). The latter secretes an ecdyson-like "molting hormone" which acts on the integument (*int*) to initiate molting. *In the insect,* the brain's ecdysiotropic hormone is released from the corpus cardiacum (*cc*)—a neurohemal organ posterior to the brain—and stimulates the ecdysial gland (*eg*) to release ecdyson. The interaction of ecdyson and neotenin from the corpus allatum (*ca*) regulates molting. *In the amphibian,* the hypothalamic neurosecretory cells (of the preoptic nucleus) presumably secrete a thyrotropin-stimulating factor which is released into the hypophyseal portal vessels (*pv*) in the median eminence (*me*)—a neurohemal area in the floor of the diencephalon. The thyrotropin secreted by the stimulated adenohypophysis (*ah*) in turn stimulates the thyroid gland (*tg*) to secrete its hormones which initiate molting. *pn,* pars nervosa. (Modified slightly from E. Scharrer, in A. Gorbman [Ed.], Comparative Endocrinology, John Wiley & Sons, 1959.)

roid gland, in turn, produces thyroid hormones, notably *thyroxine*. In the Amphibia this thyroxine initiates molting.

It is most interesting that decapod crustaceans, insects, and vertebrates have quite similar arrangements with regard to the relation between nervous, neurosecretory, and endocrine regulations of such diverse phenomena as reproduction (gonad development, gamete maturation, secondary sex characteristics, etc.), and molting. The latter are illustrated in Figure 21–18, which emphasizes the analogies. The chemical structures of neurosecretory hormones released from the posterior lobe (pars distalis) of the pituitary have been identified, largely through the efforts of DuVigneaud and his colleagues. The hormones vasopressin and oxytocin were found to be octapeptides; in fact, four closely related octapeptides were found (and additional ones were synthesized): oxytocin, lysine vasopressin, arginine vasopressin, and arginine vasotocin. The structures are shown in Figure 21–19. As may be suspected from the similarity of structures, these hormones have similar actions: they all affect blood pressure (birds, mammals), decrease urine flow, and, in amphibians, cause increased influx of water through the skin and the urinary bladder. These latter effects are due to an increase in the permeability (distal tubule of kidney nephrons, skin, bladder) to water, and not to active water transport. The effect disappears if the fluids on both sides of the separating epithelium are isotonic.

The octapeptides effectively reduce the loss of water associated with production of hypotonic urine: both in the mammalian and amphibian kidney, the distal tubule serves in active reabsorption of sodium (see Chaps. 5 and 27), but it is normally impermeable to water. The same is true for the amphibian bladder (Fig. 21–20). This removal of solute makes the urine hypotonic. The octapeptides, however, increase permeability to water and thus increase the tonicity of the urine. Since production of hypotonic urine is called *diuresis*, the hormones that antagonize this are also known as *antidiuretic hormone*, or ADH.

Although antidiuretic effects are caused by all four of the known octapeptides, the responses differ widely among the different vertebrate species. In bullfrogs, for instance, arginine vasotocin is about 300 times more effective as oxytocin in stimulating water movement across the bladder. Blood pressure

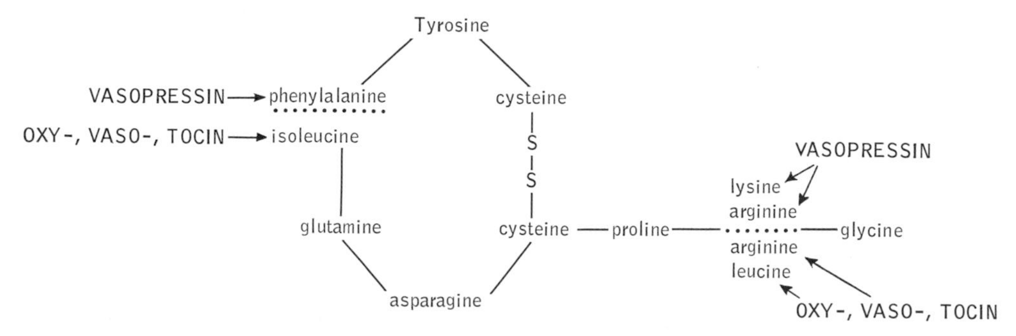

Figure 21–19. General structure of the four naturally occurring neurohypophyseal octapeptides. Only two of the amino acids are variable: the phenylalanine of vasopressin is replaced by isoleucine in the case of oxytocin and vasotocin; the lysine of lysine vasopressin is replaced by arginine in arginine vasopressin; the leucine of oxytocin is replaced by arginine in arginine vasotonin.

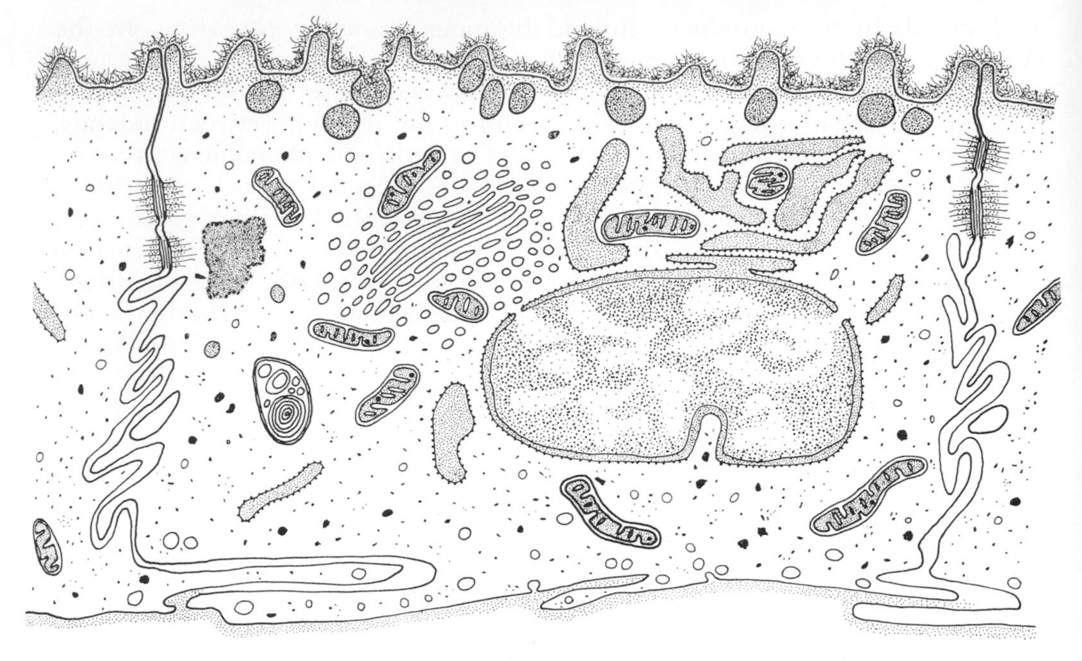

Figure 21–20. Fine structure of the epithelial cells of the urinary bladder of the toad *Bufo marinus* (magnification about 20,000 ×). The wall of the bladder (this is analogous to the collecting tubules of mammalian kidneys) consists of a layer of connective tissue (the *lamina propria*) that encloses blood vessels and smooth muscle fibers. It is covered by an epithelium consisting of a single layer of cells (1 to 10 microns thick) which continuously cover the inside surface of the bladder. One such cell is shown here. The serosal side of the epithelial cells (toward the lamina propria) is permeable to water: the mucosal side (toward the lumen of the bladder) is not unless it is activated by hormones from the neurohypophysis (oxytocin, vasopressin). These hormones allow a rapid transfer of water from the bladder to the tissue fluid and blood (in 6 seconds an amount equal to the total cell water moves then across each cell), and stimulate Na^+ transport in the same direction. In this diagram the serosal surface is up. The thin channels between adjacent cells are blocked near the serosal surface by dense membranous structures known as desmosomes. (From Peachey, L. D., and H. Rasmussen: Structure of the toad's urinary bladder as related to its physiology. J. Biophys. Biochem. Cytol. *10*:529–553, 1961.)

effects are likewise caused by all of these known neurosecretory hormones. But, again, the potencies, and even the actions, differ among different vertebrate groups: birds (hens) show a fall in blood pressure whereas the mammals (dog, rat, rabbit) show an increase. In the rabbit and hen oxytocin is the most effective pressor agent; in the rat it is arginine vasopressin (Munsick, Sawyer, and Van Dyke, 1960).

In mammals, oxytocin has a powerful stimulatory action on smooth muscle of the nonpregnant uterus and on the musculo-epithelial cells of the mammary glands. Also in mammals, oxytocin and vasopressin affect the adenohypophysis: oxytocin causes the release of *prolactin* (a hormone that stimulates milk production), whereas vasopressin stimulates the release of *ACTH* (adrenocorticotropic hormone) from the anterior lobe. The direct and indirect effects of oxytocin and vasopressin are illustrated in Figure 21–21.

In fishes there occurs, in addition to the hypothalamic-pituitary neurosecretory system, a second, caudal neurosecretory system, the *urohypophysis*, discovered by Enami in 1959. It consists of neurosecretory cell bodies situated

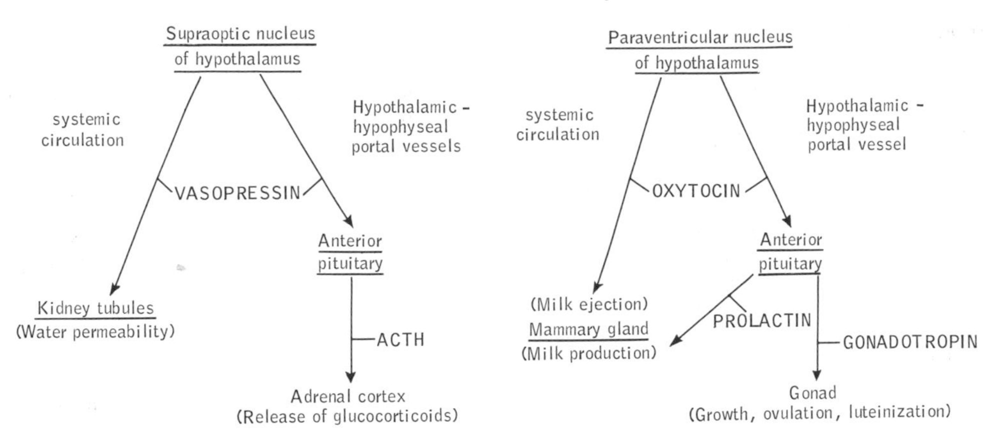

Figure 21–21. Primary and secondary actions of "oxytocin" and "vasopressin" in mammals. The term "gonadotropin" includes probably more than one hormone. The same is true for vasopressin and oxytocin (see the text).

in the caudal region of the spinal cord, and swollen endings of their axons occupying a ventral swelling of the terminal portion of the cord (Fig. 21–22). In different groups of fishes, the anatomical situation varies; in some the secretory nerve cells do not send axons into a special "storage and release organ."

The function of the caudal neurosecretory system has not been discovered, but it is suspected that the released neurohormones serve in osmoregulation (Yagi and Bern, 1963).

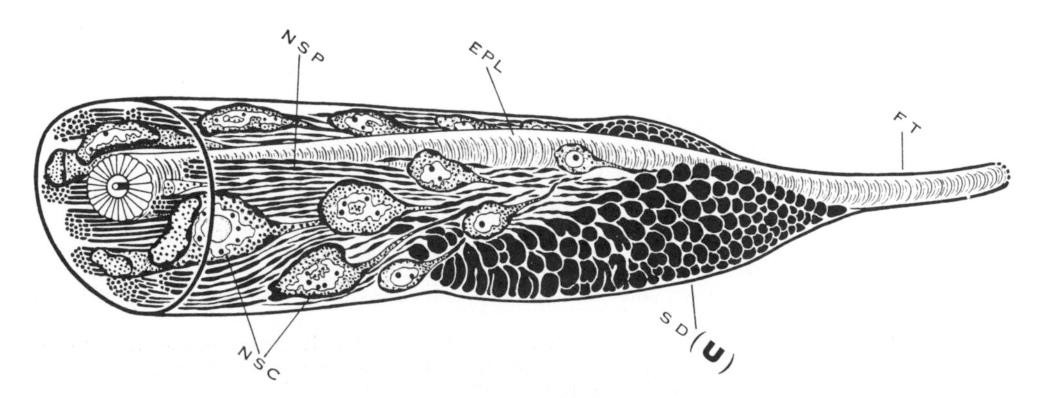

Figure 21–22. Pattern of arrangement of the caudal neurosecretory system (*urohypophysis*) of the eel. *EPL*, ependymal layer; *FT*, filum terminale; *NSC*, neurosecretory cells; *NSP*, neurosecretory pathway; *SD(U)*, storage-depot organ, or urohypophysis. (From Enami, M.: The morphology and functional significance of the caudal neurosecretory system of fishes. *In* Symposium on Comparative Endocrinology. A. Gorbman, ed. John Wiley & Sons, New York, 1959.)

REFERENCES

Alexandrowicz, J. S. (1952) Notes on the nervous system in the Stomatopoda. I. The system of median connectives. Pubbl. Staz. Zool. Napoli *23*:201–214.

Alexandrowicz, J. S., and D. B. Carlisle (1953) Some experiments on the function of the pericardial organs in Crustacea. J. Mar. Biol. Assn. U.K. *32*:175–192.

Bennett, M. V. L., and S. Fox (1962) Electrophysiology of caudal neurosecretory cells in the skate and fluke. Gen. Comp. Endocr. *2*:77–96.

Bern, H. A., and I. R. Hagadorn (1965) Neurosecretion. *In* Structure and Function in the Nervous Systems of Invertebrates, Vol. I, pp. 356–432. (T. H. Bullock and G. A. Horridge, authors.) W. H. Freemen & Co., San Francisco.

Bern, H. A., and N. Takasuki (1962) The caudal neurosecretory system of fishes. Gen. Comp. Endocr. *2*:96–110.

Brown, F. A. (1946) Endocrine activity of the tritocerebral commissure of *Crago* (Crustacea). Anat. Rec. *94*:405.

Butenandt, A., and P. Karlson (1954) Ueber die Isolierung eines Metamorphose-Hormons der Insekten in kristallisierter Form. Ztschr. Naturfschg. *9b*:389-391.

Cameron, M. L. (1953) Secretion of an *o*-diphenol in the corpus cardiacum of insects. Nature *172*:349–350.

Carlisle, D. B. (1953) Studies on Lysmata seticaudata Risso (Crustacea, Decapoda). V. The ovarian inhibiting hormone and the hormonal inhibition of sex-reversal. Pubbl. Staz. Zool. Napoli *24*:435–447.

Carlisle, D. B., and F. G. W. Knowles (1953) Neurohaemal organs in crustaceans. Nature *172*: 404–405.

Carlisle, D. B., and Sir Frances Knowles, B. (1959) Endocrine Control in Crustaceans. Cambridge University Press, London.

Clark, R. B. (1959) The neurosecretory system of the supra-esophageal ganglion of *Nephtys* (Annelida; Polychaeta). Zool. Jahrb., Allg. Zool. Physiol. Tiere *68*:395–424.

Davey, K. G. (1961) The mode of action of the heart accelerating factor from the corpus cardiacum of insects. Gen. Comp. Endocr. *1*:24–29.

Demeusy, N. (1953) Effects de l'ablation des pédonculés oculaires sur le développement de l'appareil génital mâle de Carcinus maenas Pennant. C. R. Acad. Sci. *236*:974–975.

Demeusy, N. (1960) Différentiation des voies génitales mâles du crabe Carcinus maenas Linnée. Role des pédonculés oculaires. Cahiers Biol. mar. (Sta. Biol. Roscoff) *1*:259–277.

Durchon, M. (1960) L'endocrinologie chez les annélides polychètes. Bull. Soc. Zool. Fr. *85*:275–301.

DuVigneaud, V. (1954–1955) Hormones of the posterior pituitary gland: oxytocin and vasopressin. Harvey Lect. *50*:1–26.

Echalier, G. (1959) L'organe Y et le déterminisme de la croissance et de la mue chez Carcinus maenas (L.), crustacé décapode. Ann. Sci. Nat. (Zool.) *1*:1–60.

Edman, P., R. Faenge, and E. Östlund (1958) Isolation of the red pigment concentrating hormone of the crustacean eyestalk. *In* Second International Symposium on Neurosecretion. (W. Bargman et al., eds.) Springer-Verlag, Berlin.

Enami, M. (1959) The morphology and functional significance of the caudal neurosecretory system of fishes. *In* Comparative Endocrinology. (A. Gorbman, ed.) John Wiley & Sons, New York.

Engelmann, F. (1964) Inhibition of egg maturation in a pregnant viviparous cockroach. Nature *202*:724–725.

Fingerman, M. (1963) The Control of Chromatophores. The Macmillan Co., New York.

Gabe, M. (1953) Sur l'existence, chez quelques crustacés malacostracés, d'un organe comparable à la glande de la mue des insectes. C. R. Acad. Sci. *237*:1111–1113.

Gorbman, A., and H. A. Bern (1962) A Textbook of Comparative Endocrinology. John Wiley & Sons, New York.

Heller, H., and R. B. Clark, eds. (1962) Neurosecretion. Academic Press, New York.

Herlant-Meewis, H. (1956) Reproduction et neurosécrétion chez *Eisenia foetida* Sav. Ann. Soc. Zool. Beld. *87*:151–183; Croissance et neurosécrétion chez Eisenia foetida Sav. Ann. Sci. Nat. (Zool.) *18*:185–198.

Hubl, H. (1956) Ueber die Beziehungen der Neurosekretion zum Regenerationsgeschehen bei Lumbriciden nebst Beschreibung eines neuartigen neurosekretorischen Zelltyps im Unterschlundganglion. Arch. Entwickl.-Mech. Org. *149*:73–87.

Jenkin, P. M. (1962) Animal Hormones, A Comparative Survey. The Pergamon Press, New York.

Kandel, E. R. (1962) Spike and synaptic potentials in hypothalamic neuroendocrine cells. Fed. Proc. *21*:361.

Keeble, F., and F. W. Gamble (1900) The colour physiology of *Hippolyte varians*. Proc. Roy. Soc. B, *65*:461.

Kinosita, H., K. Yagi, and M. Yasuda (1962) Electrophysiological studies on the caudal neurosecretory system in fish. Dob. Zasshi *71*:371.

Kleinholz, L. H. (1961) Pigmentary effectors. *In* The Physiology of Crustacea, Vol. II, pp. 133–170. (T. H. Waterman, ed.) Academic Press, New York.
Knowles, F. G. W. (1953) Endocrine activity in the crustacean nervous system. Proc. Roy. Soc. B, *141*:248–267.
Koller, G. (1925) Ueber den Farbwechsel bei *Crangon vulgaris*. Verh. dtsch. Zool. Ges. *30*:128–132.
Koller, G. (1928) Versuche über die inkretorischen Vorgänge beim Garneelenfarbwechsel. Z. vergl. Physiol. *8*:601–612.
Matsumoto, K. (1958) Morphological studies on the neurosecretion in crabs. Biol. J. Okayama Univ. *4*:103–176.
Maynard, D. M. (1961) Thoracic neurosecretory structures in Brachyura. I. Gross anatomy. Biol. Bull. *121*:316–329.
Maynard, D. M., and J. H. Welsh: Neurohormones of the pericardial organs of brachyuran Crustacea. J. Physiol. *149*:215–227.
Morita, H., T. Ishibashi, and S. Yamashita (1961) Synaptic transmission in neurosecretory cells. Nature *191*:183.
Munsick, R. A., W. H. Sawyer, and H. B. Van Dyke (1960) The antidiuretic potency of arginine and lysine vasopressins in the pig with observations on porcine renal function. Endocrinology *63*:688.
Nalbandov, A. V., ed. (1963) Advances in Neuroendocrinology. University of Illinois Press, Urbana.
Perkins, E. B. (1928) Colour changes in crustaceans, especially in *Palaemonetes*. J. Exp. Zool. *50*:71 – 105.
Schachter, M., ed. (1960) Polypeptides which affect smooth muscles and blood vessels. Pergamon Press, New York.
Scharrer, B. (1937) Ueber sekretorisch taetige Nervenzellen bei wirbellosen Tieren. Naturwissenschaften *25*:131–138.
Scharrer, B. (1964) Photo-neuroendocrine systems: general concepts. Ann. N.Y. Acad. Sci. *117*:13–22.
Scharrer, E., and B. Scharrer (1963) Neuroendocrinology. Columbia University Press, New York.
Takewaki, K., ed. (1962) Progress in Comparative Endocrinology. Academic Press, New York.
Turner, C. D. (1966) General Endocrinology, 4th Ed. W. B. Saunders Co., Philadelphia.
Welsh, J. H. (1961) Neurohumors and Neurosecretion. *In* The Physiology of Crustacea, Vol. II, pp. 281–312. (T. H. Waterman, ed.) Academic Press, New York.
Wigglesworth, V. B. (1954) The Physiology of Insect Metamorphosis. Cambridge University Press, London.
Yagi, K., and H. A. Bern (1963) Electrophysiologic indications of the osmoregulatory role of the teleost urophysis. Science *142*:491–493.
Yagi, K., H. A. Bern, and I. R. Hagadorn (1963) Action potentials of neurosecretory neurons in the leech *Theromyzon rude*. Gen. Comp. Endocr. *3*:490–495.

22 THE STRUCTURE AND FUNCTION OF MUSCLE

Muscle cells, a universal characteristic of animal organisms, contain special organelles called *myofibrils* or *myofilaments*, which are composed of strands of protein molecules known under the general chemical names *myosin* and *actin*. Several kinds of myosin and actin are known and are mentioned in Chapter 23. Typically, a muscle cell is elongated, and the myofibrils are oriented parallel to the long axis.

The other cell organelles are the same as those known from any other type of cell. The mitochondria and endoplasmic reticulum, however, are conspicuously organized and important for the specific action of muscle cells (see Figs. 22–1 and 22–9).

The physiological significance of muscle cells lies in their ability to rapidly and reversibly change shape and to exert on other cells, or on the environment, a mechanical force. The reversible changes by means of which muscle cells do work on other structures are usually under the control of the nervous system. Mechanical work performed by muscle cells is commonly initiated by synaptic activation, but in certain muscles (e.g., mammalian intestinal smooth muscle), electric excitations and subsequent contractions may arise independently of motor nerve action. Hormones may modulate the performance of muscle cells.

Muscle cells are of great importance for the functioning of many organ systems. Their most prominent achievements, however, are seen where they are organized into muscles. The variety of shapes of muscles is at least as great as that of the types of muscle cells. Muscle forms range from flat sheets to long, thin strands, from hollow tubes to solid cylinders, from a loose meshwork (Fig. 10–3) to a radial array (Fig. 15–2).

Muscle cells are employed in the most widely different functions, whether they operate singly or within muscles. They are responsible for the movements

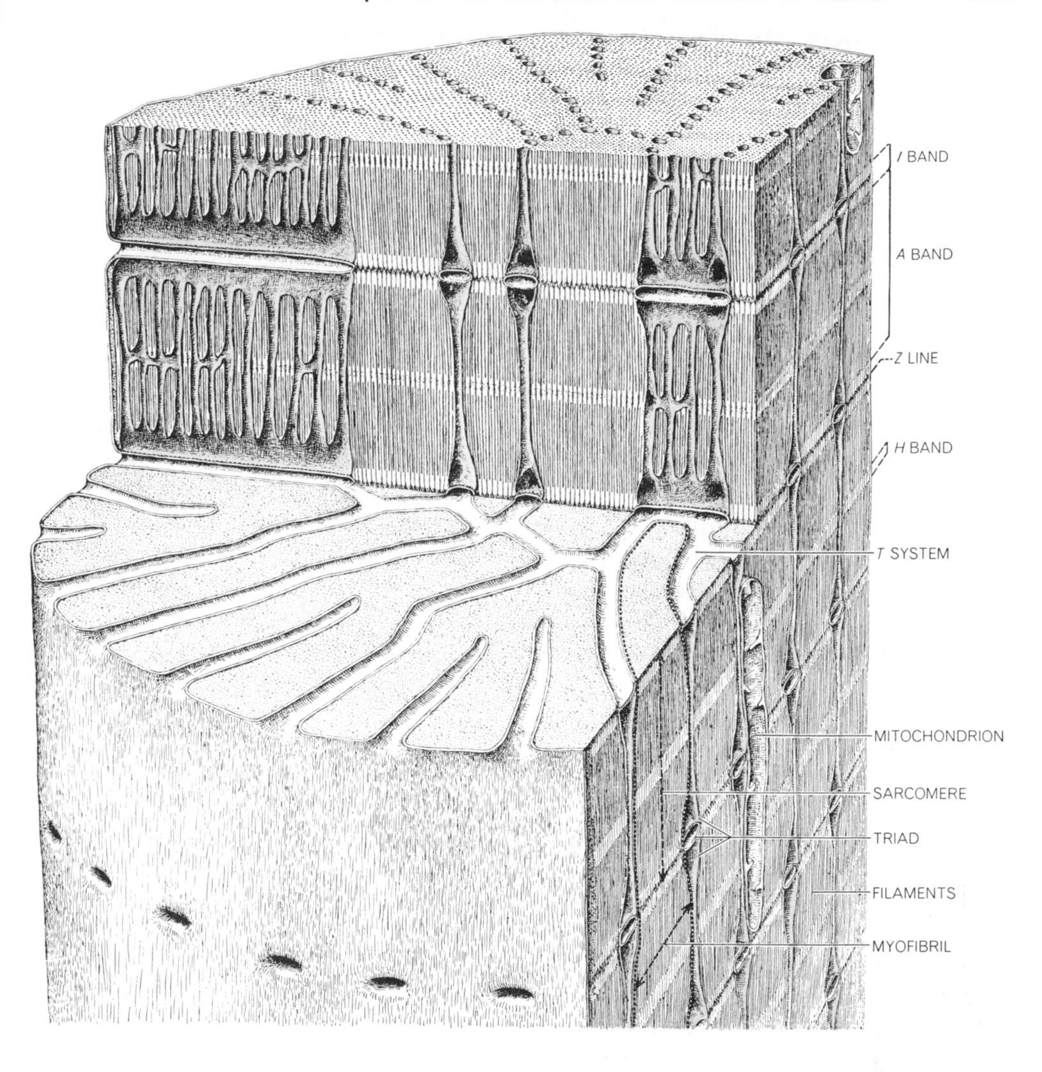

Figure 22–1. Three-dimensional presentation of part of a striated muscle fiber, showing transverse extensions of the plasma membrane into the interior of the muscle fiber (*T system*) and a connecting tubular network of endoplasmic reticulum. Note that the tubules of the endoplasmic reticulum are not continuous with the T system, and that they are separated from extracellular space by the plasma membrane. (From Porter, K. R., and C. Franzini-Armstrong: The sarcoplasmic reticulum. Sci. Amer. *212*:73–81, 1965.)

and postures of animals, and by their state of activity determine the shape of the organism: whether a "worm" is thick and short or long and thin depends to a large degree on the conditions of the muscles that constitute the body wall. Shape and expression of the human body are largely the result of position and functional state of skeletal muscles.

Muscle cells are the essential elements of hearts; they control the diameter of blood vessels—and thereby the peripheral vascular resistance to blood flow. Muscle cells are responsible for acquisition of food, they operate the mouth parts, permit swallowing, and propel the ingested food material through the digestive system. Muscle cells cause the expulsion of secretory products from glands and reservoirs; they control excretion by closing or opening the sphincters and valves. Others are involved in the birth process of viviparous animals. Muscle cells control the turgor of many kinds of soft-bodied animals. For example, earthworms or caterpillars, which normally are round and turgid, become flaccid and soft when anesthetized.

Muscles play a prominent role in the functioning of many sense organs. They move and direct eyes and ears, and, in general, bring sense organs into proper position. Often they form intrinsic parts of the sense organs themselves. For example, the retina in the frontal eyes of certain spiders is moved back and forth within the focal plane of the lens and in this way it is made to scan the visual field. In certain copepods, muscle cells are employed to rapidly move the one and only visual receptor cell through the image created by the lens of the eye. In our own eye, muscle cells change the shape of the lens, thereby permitting accommodation. The same is true for the eyes of many molluscs.

From mammals, amphibians, and crustaceans we know of receptor organs that monitor the state of muscle tension: the stretch-receptor organs. These consist of thin muscle strands which receive sensory innervation (Figs. 22–2, 22–3, and 22–4). Stretch-receptor organs are either incorporated in a muscle (vertebrates) or run parallel with certain muscles (crustaceans).

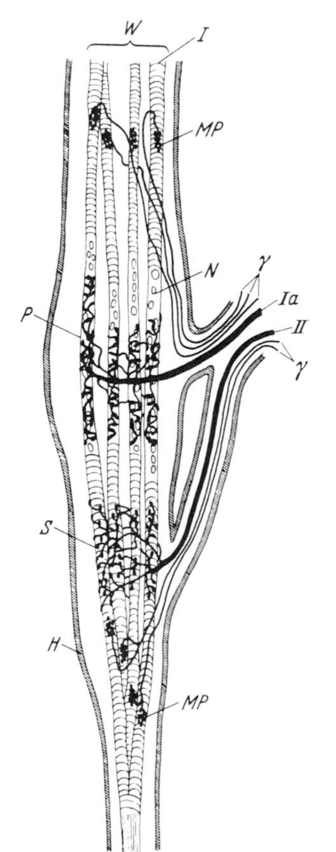

Figure 22–2. Semidiagrammatic representation of a vertebrate muscle spindle. A fibrous sheath (*H*) surrounds a bundle of muscle fibers, known as *intrafusal muscle fibers* (*I*) or *bundle of Weismann* (*W*). Their middle portion is noncontractile: the myofibrils are replaced by a collection of nuclei; this portion is known as a *nuclear bag (N)*. It is enveloped by ring and spiral endings of sensory fibers, known as primary sensory neurons, or group Ia neurons (*Ia*). The endings are called *annulospiral endings* (*P*). A second sensory neuron (or groups of sensory neurons), known as group II neurons (*II*), innervate with branched endings (*S*) parts of the contractile portion of the intrafusal muscle fibers. The latter are also innervated by thin motor fibers (usually three to five), known as *gamma-efferents* (γ), or simply *γ-fibers*, which form motor endplates (*MP*). (From Burkhardt, D.: Die Sinnesorgane des Skeletmuskels and die nervöse Steuerung der Muskeltätigkeit. Ergebn. Biol. *20*:27–66, 1958.)

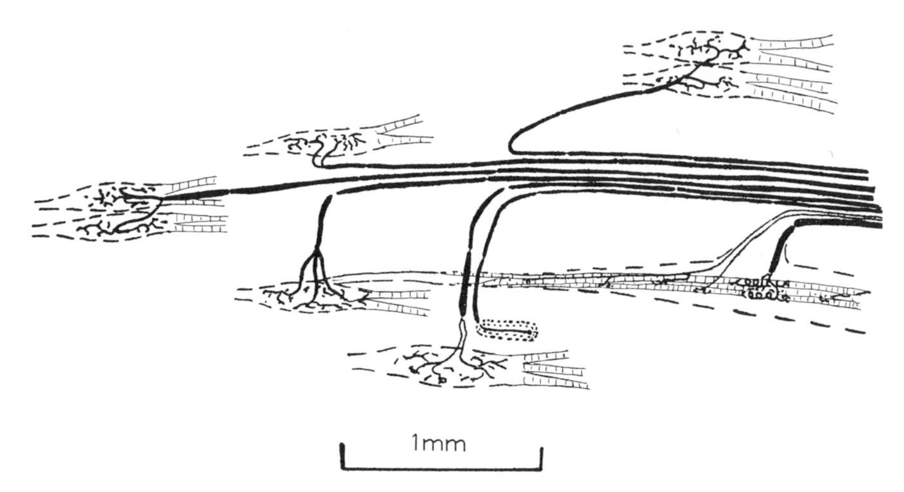

Figure 22-3. Drawing of a small piece of the distal tendon of the cat's sartorius muscle from a teased gold chloride preparation. There are five encapsulated tendon organs; two of these are double and the two parts share a nerve fiber, otherwise they each have a separate large nerve fiber. Half a simple muscle spindle is shown on the right; its muscle fibers pass beyond the capsule and finally end as tendinous threads attached to one side of a tendon organ; the nerves to the primary ending of the spindle and to this tendon organ are quite separate. Shown close to the lowest tendon organ is a small sensory corpuscle, again with a distinct nerve fiber. (From Cooper, S.: Muscle spindles and other muscle receptors. *In* The Structure and Function of Muscle, Vol. 1. G. H. Bourne, ed. Academic Press, New York, 1960.)

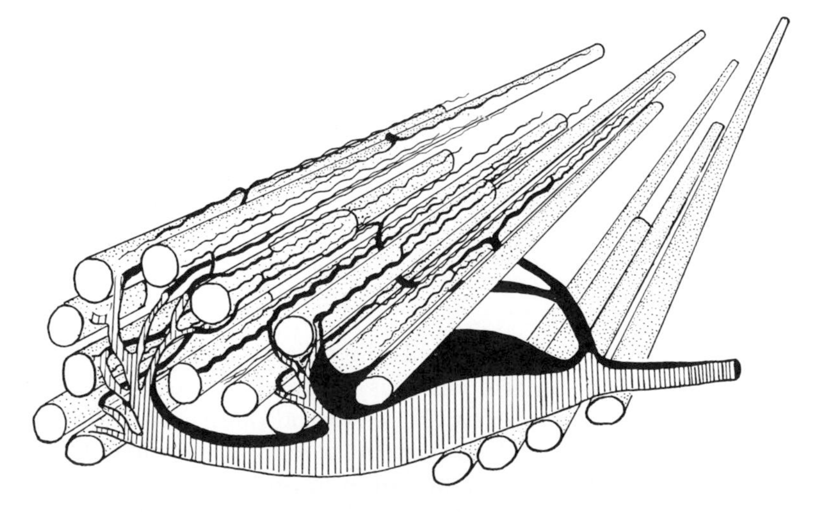

Figure 22-4. Schematic drawing to show the relationship of the sensory neuron of a crayfish stretch-receptor organ to its muscle fibers. (A diagram of a complete stretch receptor organ is shown in Fig. 25-9.) As the muscle fibers are stretched, the elastic dendrites of the receptor neuron are extended and depolarized. For a discussion of impulse generation in receptor neurons, see Chapter 19. (From Florey, E., and E. Florey: Microanatomy of the abdominal stretch receptors of the crayfish (*Astacus fluviatilis* L.). J. Gen. Physiol. 39:69–85, 1955.)

The rapid color change exhibited by cephalopod molluscs is caused by contraction and relaxation of the radially arranged muscle cells which surround each chromatophore (Fig. 15–2). In this way muscle cells control the adaptive coloration of the octopus or the flaming color-play of mating squid.

Muscle cells are employed in the positioning of hairs, particularly in mammals. In this way they can serve effectively in temperature regulation. Often muscle cells are used even more directly for heat production: shivering, which occurs not only in the human but also in bees, represents such an action.

Perhaps the most peculiar use of muscle cells is found in the electric organs of fish: here the structure of muscle cells is modified to form the equivalent of electric elements, the electroplates or electroplaques. Nerve impulses, in this case, cause an electric discharge rather than a mechanical action. Some fish can thus produce an electromotive force of several hundred volts and currents of several amperes (see pp. 595–603).

The organelles characteristic of muscle cells are also present in certain cell appendages. Cilia and flagella are examples. Their structure and chemical composition is identical with that of myofilaments. Ciliated or flagellated cells thus are closely related to muscle cells. They differ, however, in one important aspect: the movement of their cilia or flagella is not initiated by the nervous system. However, they are usually innervated; the nerve cells in this case modulate the action of the myofibrillar structures—either accelerate or inhibit it.

Muscle is investigated from different approaches. Apart from anatomical, histological, and cytological studies, the chemical constitution of muscle and the biochemical processes involved in muscular action are the concern of many scientists. Others study the mechanical performance and the electric events that precede and accompany the mechanical actions of muscle. At present many data can be correlated, and we have a fairly complete picture of the functioning of several types of muscle. But many mysteries still await a solution. The biophysical and physiological studies as well as the cytological ones have reached the molecular, if not the submolecular, level of the phenomena of muscle action. Through this convergence of the different approaches, our understanding of muscle physiology has increased rapidly.

STRUCTURAL ASPECTS

Organization of Muscle

The physiological unit of a muscle is the *muscle fiber*. Often this is derived from the fusion of several muscle cells, as is the case with vertebrate striated muscle. Muscle fibers, therefore, can have several nuclei. Even in some of the best studied groups of animals, however, the nuclei of muscle cells have never been described (decapod Crustacea are an example).

In many kinds of muscle the fibers appear branched. This has been described for vertebrate heart muscle, holothurian longitudinal muscle, and many striated muscles of insects. Many of the muscles containing branched fibers have been considered a *syncytium*. Vertebrate heart muscle, for instance, behaves physiologically like a single muscle cell. However, this muscle is

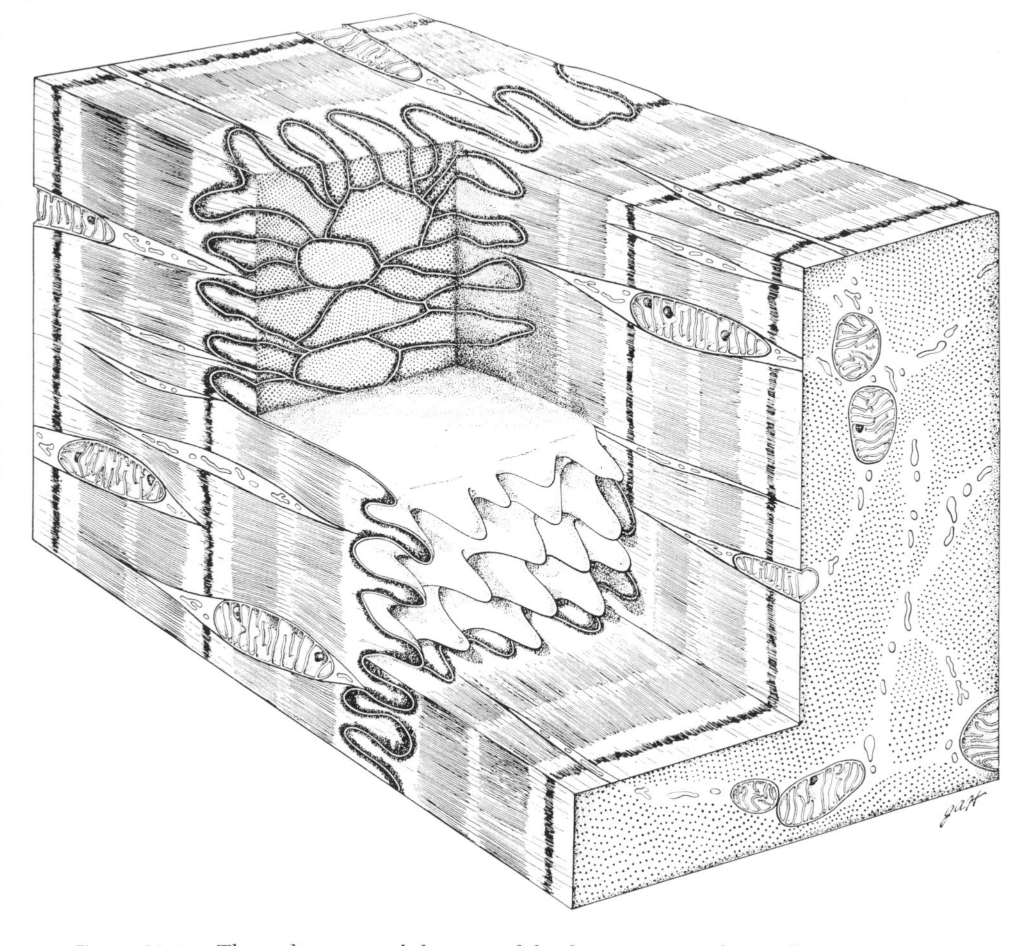

Figure 22–5. Three-dimensional diagram of the fine structure of a small segment of the junctional region between two cardiac muscle cells, showing an intercalated disc. The disc consists of highly interdigitated plasma membranes of two closely apposed muscle cells. The dense material resembling the substance of a Z band is concentrated in the cytoplasm adjacent to the cell membranes. Myofilaments of the I band insert into this dense material. The discs transect fibers in a stepwise manner. The disc in the upper portion of the diagram is shown in cross and longitudinal sections, whereas in the lower portion of the diagram, the cell surface of one fiber is shown in three dimensions. Mitochondria containing small, dense granules and a few tubular and vesicular elements of endoplasmic reticulum appear in the sarcoplasm between the myofibrils. (After Poche and Lindner, 1955, from Marshall, J. M.: The heart. *In* Medical Physiology, 11th Ed. P. Bard, ed. The C. V. Mosby Co., St. Louis, 1961.)

composed of discrete fibers, each completely surrounded by a membrane. The "joints" between the individual cells are known as *intercalated discs* (Fig. 22–5). Branched muscle fibers also occur in the decapod Crustacea.

The size of muscle fibers bears no direct and necessary relationship to that of the muscle which they constitute. In some cases a muscle consists of many small, short fibers, whereas in others the fibers have a large or small diameter but run the whole length of the muscle. Examples of the former type are the proboscis retractor muscles of sipunculid worms; examples of the latter are the insect flight muscles and the byssus retractor muscles of the mussel *Mytilus* (see Chap. 24).

Muscle fibers, bundles of muscle fibers, and muscles are covered by collagen fibrils and connective tissue. Near the opposite ends of a muscle these coverings converge to form tendons by means of which muscles are attached to skeletal elements. Hollow muscles, such as those of the gastrointestinal tracts and those of the body wall of coelenterates, "worms," tunicates, and other forms without defined skeletons, have no common tendon; nonetheless the muscle fibers are attached to epidermis, endothelium, septa, and cuticle by connective tissue.

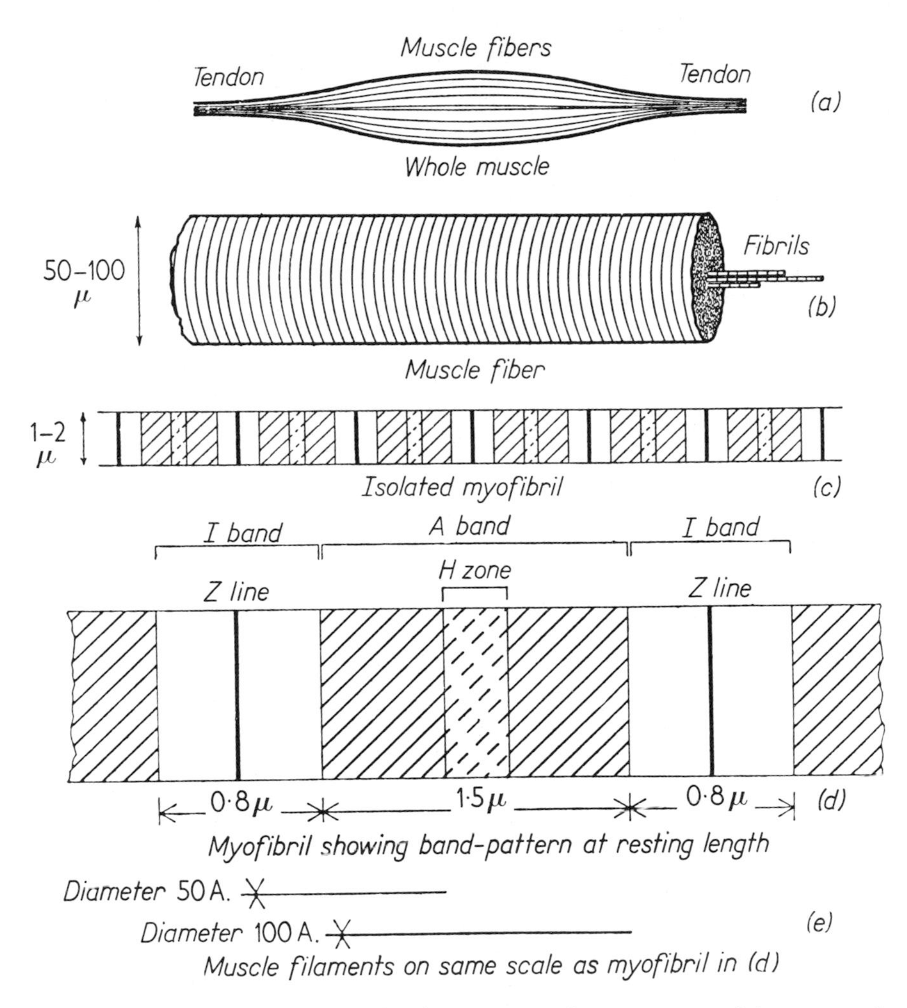

Figure 22–6. Diagram illustrating the dimensions and arrangement of the contractile components in amphibian striated skeletal muscle. The whole muscle (**a**) is made up of muscle fibers (**b**), each of which contains cross-striated myofibrils (**c**), (**d**). These fibrils are composed of longitudinal arrays of protein filaments (**e**), as shown in Figure 22–7. The diagram in (**d**) shows the appearance of a myofibril if observed in polarized light through the light microscope. The cross-hatching does not represent myofilaments but indicates areas that appear dark. The repeating units consisting of 1/2 I band, A band, and 1/2 I band occupying the space between two Z lines are called *sarcomeres*. (From Huxley, H. E., and J. Hanson: The molecular basis of contraction in cross-striated muscles. *In* The Structure and Function of Muscle. G. H. Bourne, ed. Academic Press, New York, 1960.)

Muscle fibers are covered by a membrane, the *sarcolemma* (Bowman, 1840), which, according to modern electron microscopy, consists of a typical plasma membrane with trilaminate structure, and of an outer covering that can be described as a basement membrane. The connective tissue strands are not part of it. The cytoplasm of muscle fibers is known as *sarcoplasm* (Rollett, 1891). Embedded in it are the *myofibrils* and *myofilaments*, thread-like structures composed of "contractile" proteins (Figs. 22–6 and 22–7). They are accompanied by numerous mitochondria, often referred to as *sarcosomes* (Figs. 22–8 and 22–9). In cross section, some types of muscle fiber appear to be filled with myofibrils, whereas others show fibrils (or filaments) only in the periphery. Patterns of the distribution of myofibrils within muscle fibers are shown in Figure 22–10. The myofibrils themselves are often composed of *myofilaments*, each of which represents a strand of protein, and of other protein whose structural organization is unknown. This is explained in Figures 22–6 and 22–7.

In some types of muscle fiber the filaments are not organized into fibrils, although they resemble in diameter and general structure the filaments of which myofibrils and other fiber types are composed. In some cases the filaments are as thick as whole fibrils of other muscle fiber types.

Myofilaments and myofibrils are collectively called the *contractile elements*, or, by some, the *contractile machinery* of muscle fibers.

The sarcoplasm contains a system of internal membranes known as the *sarcoplasmic reticulum* (Bennett and Porter, 1953) or as *sarcotubules* (Sjöstrand and Andersson-Cedergren, 1957). These membrane systems show a definite organization related to that of the myofibrils, as shown in Figures 22–1, 22–9, and 22–11.

The diversity of structural organization of muscle fibers is immense and no adequate nomenclature has been devised to accommodate all the different types, or even to name them. The old categories of "smooth" and "striated" muscle have become too narrow. If retained, the term "smooth muscle" should be reserved for the visceral musculature of vertebrates and a restricted number of invertebrate muscles. The term "striated muscle" can be used to denote all muscles whose fibers contain fibrils that show a periodic structure of repetitive parallel arrays of myofilaments. This latter category includes such functionally diverse muscles as the skeletal muscles of the frog, the tail muscles of ascidian larvae, the muscles of the crayfish gut, the muscle bundles of coelenterates, and the muscles that operate the spines of sea urchins. This term is obviously inadequate as a common denominator of physiological function.

Before describing the major cytological types of muscle fibers it should be emphasized that cytologically similar muscles may show widely different physiological behavior, and that muscles composed of obviously different types of fibers may exhibit close functional similarity.

Striated Muscle. Although differing widely in functional behavior, many vertebrate and invertebrate muscle fibers can be collectively called "striated muscle fibers" because they contain bundles of myofibrils of conspicuously similar ultrastructure: a periodic pattern of parallel arrays of myofilaments (Fig. 22–6). The periods of neighboring fibrils are aligned in register, and

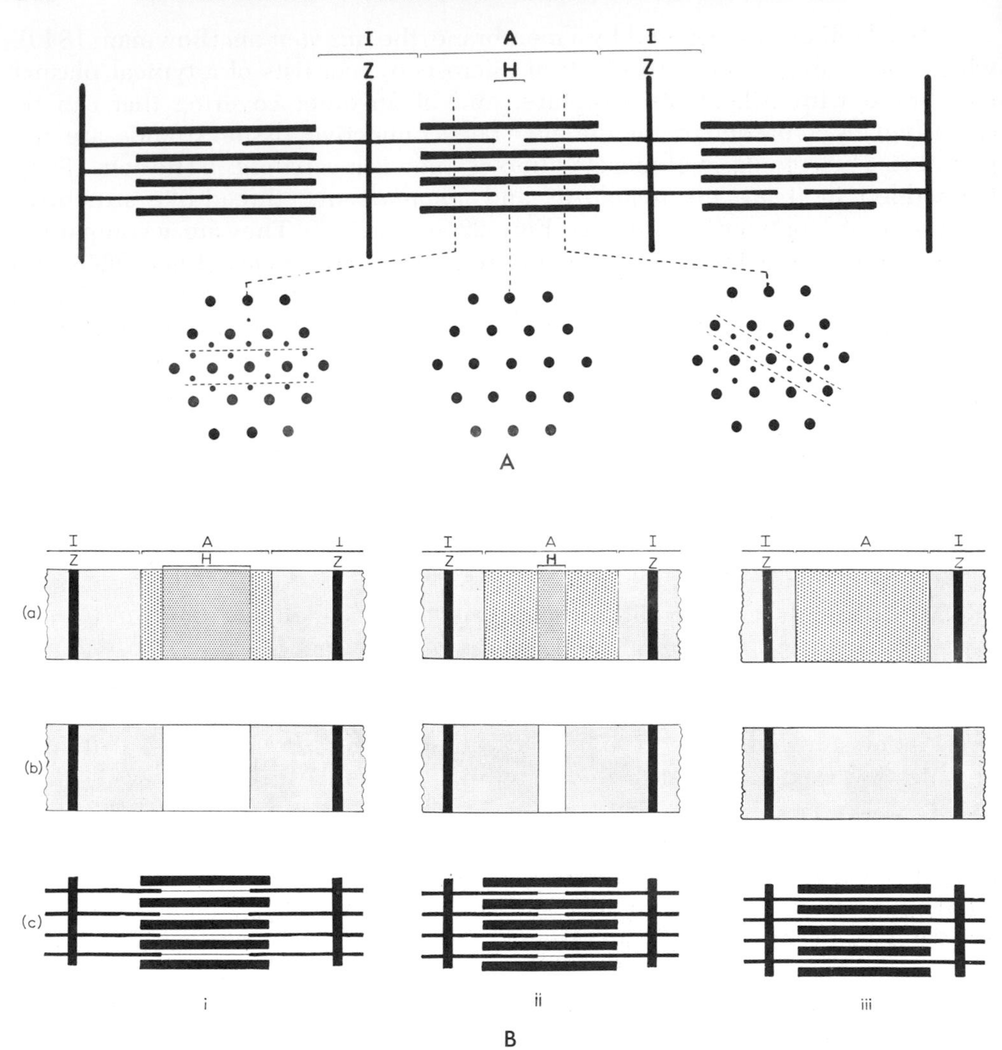

Figure 22–7. A, diagram illustrating the arrangement of actin and myosin filaments in a myofibril of striated muscle. Only a fragment of the cross-sectional area of the myofibril is represented. At the top are three sarcomeres drawn as they would appear in longitudinal section. Below are transverse sections taken through the H zone (center) and through the other parts of the A band (*right* and *left*) where the arrays of thick and thin filaments interdigitate. If a longitudinal section were cut in the plane which is indicated by dotted lines in the left-hand transverse section, it would show (apparently) one thin filament between each two thick ones. If it were cut in the other plane (dotted lines in the right-hand transverse section) it would show *two* thin filaments between each two thick ones.

B, diagram illustrating the structural changes associated with contraction (*iii*) and extension (*i*) from resting length (*ii*). The top row shows the band patterns of intact myofibrils (see Fig. 22–6). The next row (*b*) shows the band patterns after myosin has been removed by chemical extraction; the remaining I bands are composed of actin. In the intact myofibrils the bands are composed of actin filaments (I band) and myosin filaments (A band), as shown in the abstract diagrams of (*c*). Note that during contraction or extension the width of the A band does not change, whereas that of the I band and H zone is altered (*a*). The explanation is that the thin actin filaments and the thick myosin filaments slide past each other but do not change their length.

(From Huxley, H. E., and J. Hanson: The molecular basis of contraction in cross-striated muscles. *In* The Structure and Function of Muscle. G. H. Bourne, ed. Academic Press, New York, 1960.)

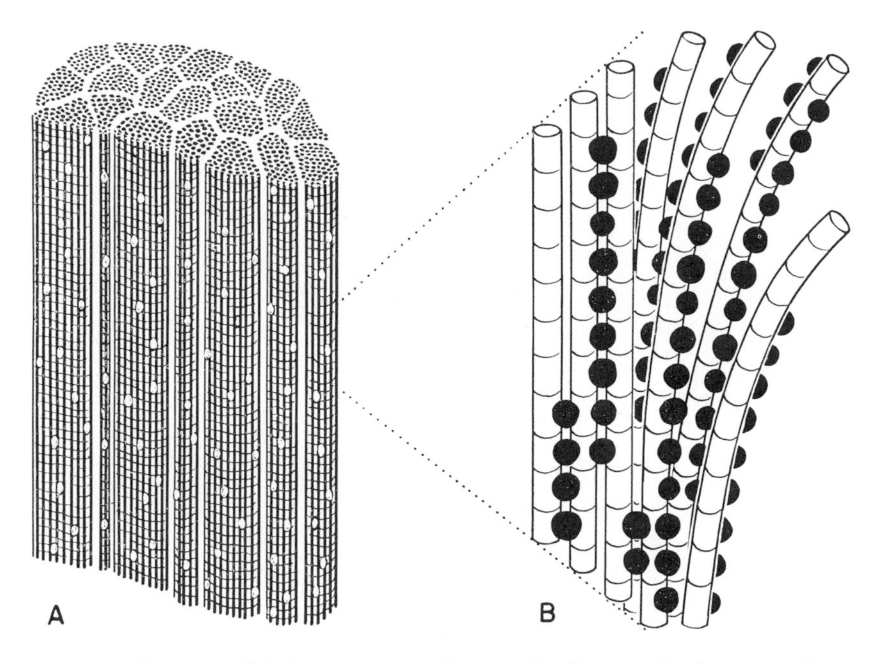

Figure 22–8. Diagram of the organization of insect fibrillar muscle (flight muscle), showing the relationship between sarcomeres and the sarcosomes (mitochondria) of myofibrils. **A**, a small segment of a muscle mass containing 20 fibers. **B**, part of a single fiber much enlarged to show its subdivision into fibrils and sarcosomes. The paper from which this illustration is taken presented the first direct evidence for the identity of flight muscle sarcosomes with mitochondria. (From Watanabe, M. I., and C. M. Williams: Mitochondria in the flight muscles of insects. I. Chemical composition and enzymatic content. J. Gen. Physiol. *34*:675–689, 1951.)

this alignment often holds true for the fibrils in neighboring fibers so that portions of a muscle appear uniformly striated.

Within the last few years the ultrastructure of vertebrate striated myofibrils has been elucidated, largely by the brilliant studies of Huxley and Hanson. The diagrams of Figures 22–6 and 22–7 are taken from their publications. Remember, however, that these diagrams represent electron microscope images and do not permit visualization of all components present. It is likely that the functional model derived from such images is incomplete.

The myofibrils of striated muscle fibers of a variety of species show more or less the same structural pattern.

The filaments of fibrils cannot be resolved by the light microscope, but their parallel orientation and spacing gives the fibrils a banded appearance. They exhibit an alternation of dark and light bands crossed by thin, dark lines. If linearly polarized light is used on unstained fibrils and if they are viewed through a polarizing filter oriented perpendicular to the orientation of the polarized light from the light source, the bands that appear dark in ordinary light shine brilliantly while the intervening bands remain dark. The former are anisotropic, the latter are singly refracting, or isotropic. The anisotropic bands are referred to as *A bands*, the isotropic as *I bands*. A dark line across the I bands is known as the Z membrane (from the German "Zwischenscheibe"),

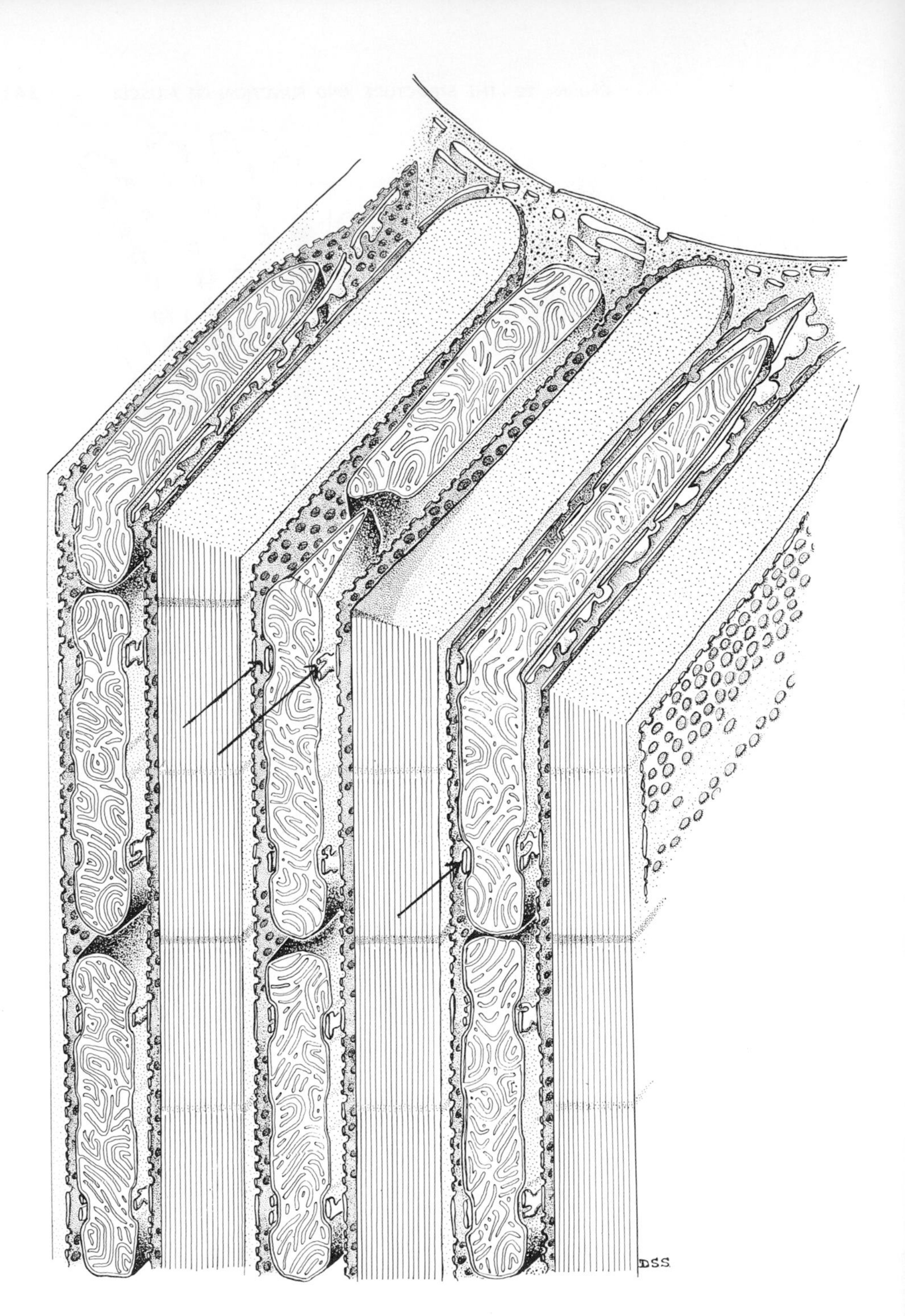

Figure 22–9. Diagram of the fine structure of a muscle fiber of the flight muscle of a dragonfly (*Aeschna*). The myofibrils are flat; their myofilaments are indicated, but no attempt has been made to represent the details of their organization. The Z bands and M bands are indicated in heavy and light stipple, respectively. Note the curtain-shaped endoplasmic reticulum that surrounds the myofibrils, and the large mitochondria. Near the Z band of the myofibrils the mitochondria have notches or grooves in which run tubular extensions of the plasma membrane of the muscle fiber. These are believed to carry excitation transmitted by motor nerve fibers to the interior of the muscle fiber and to serve in what is known as "excitation-contraction coupling." A few of these tubules are indicated by arrows. (From Smith, D. S.: The organization of the flight muscle in a dragonfly, Aeshna sp. [Odonata]. J. Biophys. Biochem. Cytol. *11*:119–146, 1961.)

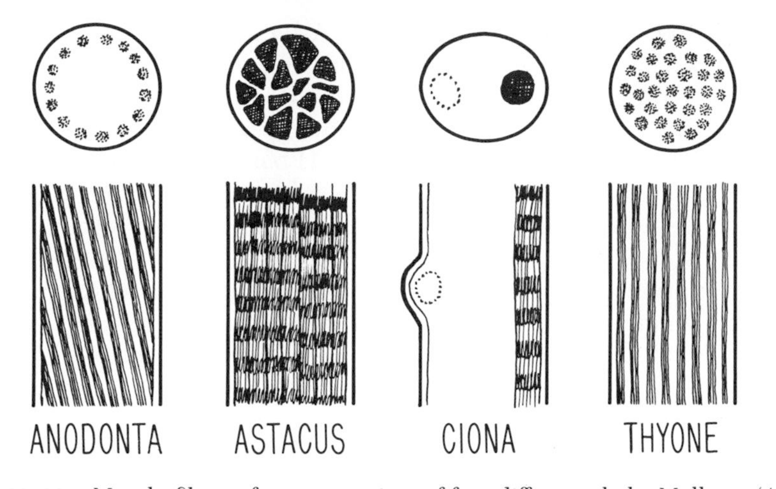

Figure 22–10. Muscle fibers of representatives of four different phyla: Mollusca (*Anodonta*), Arthropoda (*Astacus*), Tunicata (*Ciona*), and Echinodermata (*Thyone*) to show the distribution of myofibrils within the muscle fibers. The *Anodonta* muscle fiber is an example of helical smooth muscle. The muscle fibers of *Astacus* and *Ciona* are striated. Those of *Thyone* belong to the category of smooth muscle. All fibers are shown in cross section and in side view.

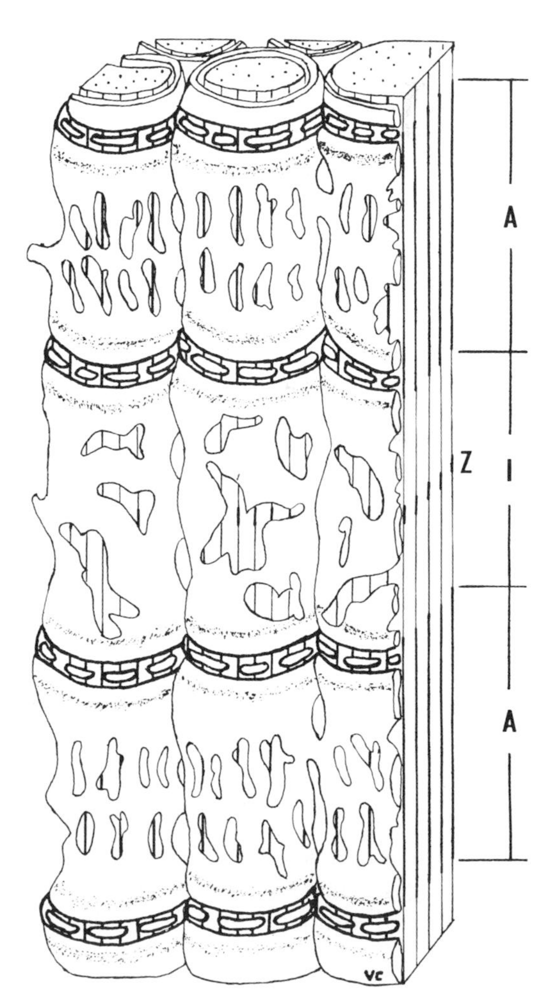

Figure 22–11. Three-dimensional diagram to show the morphology of the endoplasmic reticulum to myofibrils, as observed in the extrinsic eye muscles of the killifish, *Fundulus heteroclitus*. No attempt is made to present the myofilaments in their proper organization. The reticulum forms sleeves around the fibrils. At the junctions between A and I bands its membranes are thickened. Between these specialized "rings" of the reticular sleeves is a system of fine tubules (not shown) representing invaginations of the plasma membrane. The ring-like cysternae of the reticulum together with these tubules form a characteristic, repetitive structure referred to as a *triad*. The tubular system is believed to transfer excitation from the surface membrane of muscle fibers to the contractile elements. (From Reger, J. F.: The fine structure of neuromuscular junctions and the sarcoplasmic reticulum of extrinsic eye muscles of *Fundulus heteroclitus*. J. Biophys. Biochem. Cytol. *10*(Suppl.):111–121, 1961.)

and the dark line across the center of the A band is named the M membrane (from the German "Mittelmembran"). The region around the M membrane takes up less stain than the rest of the A band when subjected to some histological techniques, and it is less dense optically and as seen with the electron microscope. This region is referred to as the H band or H zone (from the original name "Hensen's line"). The situation is explained in Figure 22–6. Note that the pattern is periodic. The periods from Z membrane to Z membrane are called *sarcomeres.*

The electron microscope reveals two sets of filaments which are of more or less constant diameter and length, and which are arranged serially with areas of overlap (Fig. 22–7). Thicker filaments extend throughout the A bands, thinner ones constitute the I bands and extend into the A bands. Stretched and contracted muscle fibrils differ in the extent to which the I filaments reach into the A band. In maximally contracted muscles the thick filaments of neighboring sarcomeres may touch each other or may even overlap, and the I filaments are surrounded entirely by the thick A filaments so that I bands are no longer visible. The filaments, then, must be assumed to slide past each other during muscle contraction.

To appreciate the technical achievement that has permitted this analysis of the ultrastructure of striated muscle fibrils, one must realize that muscle fibers had to be sectioned into slices no thicker than 10 mμ. If human hair were sliced into longitudinal sections that thin, there would be no less than 10,000 slices. A myofibril of 1 μ diameter would contain about 5000 filaments in each cross section of an A band. There are millions of filaments present in the fibrils of each striated muscle fiber.

In rabbit psoas muscle the diameter of a thin filament is about 5 mμ, that of a thick one about 10 mμ. Similar diameters have been observed in muscles of other vertebrates and of insects. Filaments of larger diameter were described for certain crab muscles (Farrant and Mercer, 1952). The general name of the protein molecules of the thin filaments is *actin*, that of the thick filaments *myosin*. These names are much older than the discovery of the myofilaments. Both names must be considered collective names. Several kinds of actin and of myosin have been described (in the older literature one finds also a number of *myogens*), and biochemical and biophysical literature on chemical isolation, structure, and physicochemical properties of these muscle proteins is extensive. At this time it is impossible to restate current knowledge and argument in simple terms. This is a field of rapid progress in which findings must be re-evaluated continuously. Proteins isolated from muscle by one technique may turn out to be artifacts resulting from a particular chemical treatment of muscle. Different interpretations are possible, depending on the specific techniques relied on.

Visceral Smooth Muscle. Vertebrate visceral muscles (stomach, gut, bladder, ureter, uterus), the retractor muscles of the extrovert of sipunculids, and pharynx and penis retractor muscles of gastropods (*Helix*) are examples of muscles composed of rather small muscle fibers with usually only one nucleus. They do contain longitudinally arranged parallel filaments, but these do not form regular arrays so that no optical pattern of a periodic nature is visible.

Helical Smooth Muscle. The muscle fibers of these muscles contain helically wound myofibrils which do not exhibit a periodic structure although they appear to be composed of longitudinally aligned filaments. Such muscle fibers are characteristic of cephalopods (exceptions: heart, radial muscles in the arms of female decapods, and muscles in the eye of *Sepia*; these are composed of striated muscle fibers), and the somatic muscles of most annelids. The same type of fiber occurs in portions of the adductor muscles of several lamellibranchs, in the "fin" muscles of certain pteropods, and in the heart muscle of a number of molluscan species.

Paramyosin Muscle. The so-called tonic muscles of molluscs (see Chapter 24, p. 590) contain, in addition to actin and myosin filaments, rather large ribbons of a protein known as *paramyosin*, or as tropomyosin B (Bailey, 1957; Kominz et al., 1957). The diameters of these filaments or ribbons range from 15 to about 150 mμ. When the muscles are fixed in the contracted condition the ribbons show an axial periodicity of 15 mμ. The same periodicity is seen in crystals of isolated paramyosin (tropomyosin); this may mean that the protein crystallizes during tonic contraction. Because of their peculiar behavior, which appears to be associated with the presence of paramyosin, such muscles are referred to as paramyosin muscles. Their function will be discussed in Chapter 24.

Muscle Innervation

Probably all muscles are directly controlled by the nervous system. In many cases, muscle contractions do not occur unless they are initiated by nerve impulses. Nerve fibers that initiate muscle contraction are known as *motor fibers*. Nerve fibers that prevent the contraction of muscle fibers are called *inhibitory fibers*. Nerve fibers that regulate the excitability of spontaneously contracting muscles (e.g., vertebrate heart muscle) are known as *regulatory fibers*.

The supply of a muscle with endings of motor, inhibitory, regulatory, and sensory fibers is called its *innervation*. The point of synaptic contact between efferent nerve fibers and muscle fibers is referred to as a *neuromuscular junction*, or *myoneural junction*. The total supply of efferent nerve fibers to a muscle is known as its *efferent nerve supply*, or simply "efferent supply." The total supply of sensory fibers, by analogy, is called the *afferent nerve supply*, or afferent supply.

Often it is found that several muscle fibers of a muscle—or even fibers of different muscles—are innervated by branches of one and the same motor fiber. The motor fiber, together with all the muscle fibers it innervates, is known as a *motor unit*. This term applies only to a limited number of muscles and is used largely in connection with vertebrate skeletal muscles.

Many cases are known in which muscle fibers receive innervation from two or more efferent axons. Here one speaks of *polyneuronal innervation* (Hoyle, 1957).

Some types of muscle fibers receive only one nerve fiber terminal, but others have several junctions with nerve endings. If a muscle fiber is innervated by several branches of one or more axons, one speaks of *multiterminal innervation* (Hoyle, 1957). The terminology is summarized in Figure 22–12.

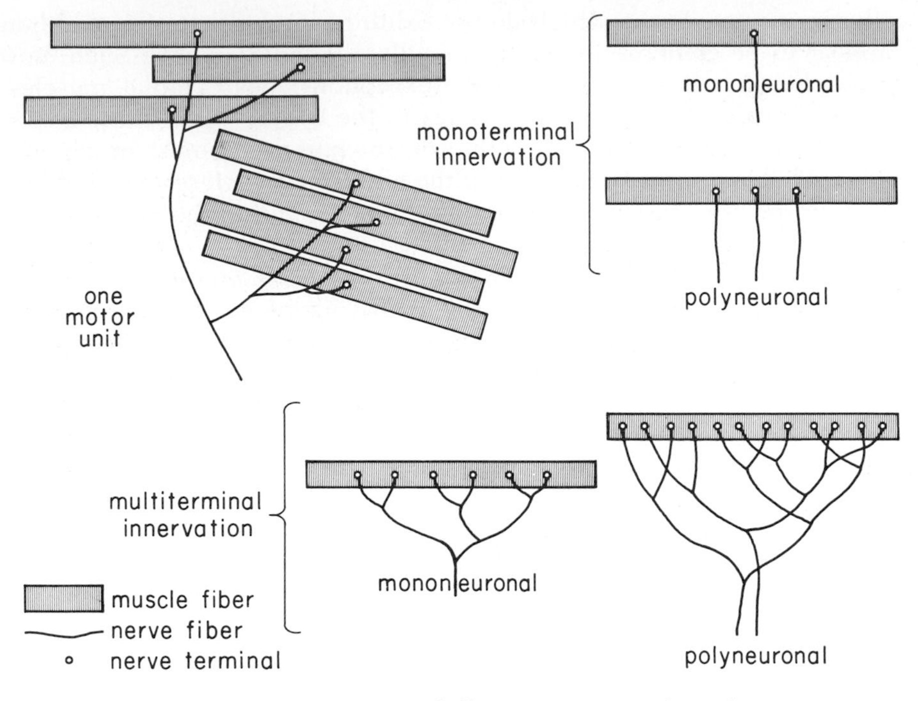

Figure 22–12. Patterns of efferent innervation of muscle.

FUNCTIONAL ASPECTS

Mechanical Behavior

The general physiological behavior of striated, smooth, and helical smooth muscle is similar. In fact, a muscle belonging to one group may behave more like a muscle belonging to another category than to one that shows the same principle of construction. The extrovert retractor muscles of sipunculids, for instance, give fast twitch contractions like frog gastrocnemius muscle, yet in structure they resemble the muscle fibers of the frog bladder, which are capable only of slow but sustained contractions. The striated rectus abdominis muscle of the frog, on the other hand, behaves more like a longitudinal muscle of a leech which is composed of helical smooth muscle fibers.

A muscle type that is functionally unique is the paramyosin or "holding" muscle. Therefore, it is treated separately in Chapter 24; the general statements given here, however, apply to any kind of muscle.

Muscles can be considered as machines that convert chemical energy into mechanical energy and mechanical work. The conversion is triggered by arriving nerve impulses or depolarizing events in the muscle fiber membrane. The primary moving parts of a muscle are the contractile elements: the myofibrils and myofilaments. When they are activated their molecular configuration and arrangement changes so that the overall length of their aggregate structure diminishes. This change represents a chemical reaction. The mechanical energy is derived from specific exothermic, energy-yielding chemical reactions. The mechanical force of the changing contractile elements is transmitted through the sarcoplasm (and sarcolemma) to the connective tissue and tendinous connections—and finally to the environment, the *load*.

Obviously, part of the work of the contractile elements is spent on deforming, pulling, and stretching the noncontractile parts of the muscle. Only a portion of the total work done by the contracting myofibrils (or filaments, as the case may be) is done on the load. The contractile elements act against the viscosity of sarcoplasm and its constituents, and against the elasticity of sarcoplasm, sarcolemma, and muscle connective tissue (including that of the tendons). Various models have been designed to describe the situation. A simplified version is represented by the diagram shown in Figure 22–13, which shows the contractile elements as a bar and the load as a weight attached to one end of the muscle (fiber). The series elastic elements are indicated as springs. The horizontal bars on the springs symbolize vanes which dampen the movements of the springs as they are moved through viscous fluid.

The overall shortening of the aggregate of contractile elements of a muscle is called *contraction*. This is a reversible process that "consumes" chemical energy derived from the metabolism of carbohydrate and lipids. The importance of lipid metabolism for the energy production in muscular contraction has only recently come to light (Bing, 1955; Beatty et al., 1959; Neptune, Sudduth, and Foreman, 1959; Neptune and Foreman, 1959; George and Naik, 1958; George and Jyoti, 1958).

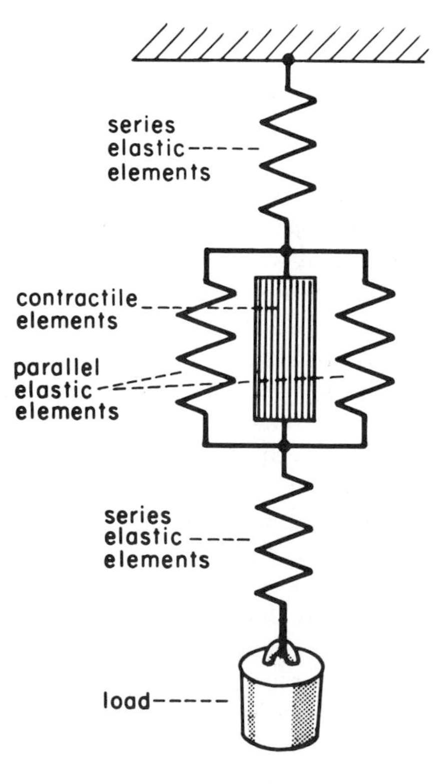

Figure 22–13. Diagram of a mechanical model of a muscle fiber to explain the relationship of the elastic and the contractile components.

The contraction process, as mentioned, is reversible, usually initiated by nerve impulses. After reaching its maximum, it reverses spontaneously and the contractile elements resume their original configuration. The return from the contracted to the original "resting" state is known as *relaxation*.

The terms "contraction" and "relaxation" may easily lead to the misconception that only the contraction is an active, energy-consuming and energy-liberating process, whereas relaxation is a passive return to the original conditions after the active phase is over. This, however, is not so.

As long as the contractile elements are shortened—and they are until nearly the end of relaxation—they are in an *active state*. The active state can be defined as *the load that a muscle can just bear without lengthening* (see Hill, 1950), or as *the tension exerted when the contractile elements neither lengthen nor shorten*, or as *the tension of the contractile elements if this could be measured directly without the series elastic elements intervening* (see Mommaerts, Brady, and Abbott, 1961). Contraction and relaxation simply reflect the increase and decrease of this active state.

This active state develops within a few milliseconds after the stimulus (junction potential or action potential), and is accompanied by a sudden increase in the heat production of the muscle. This increased heat production is referred to as *activation heat* and is independent of the load; it also occurs under strictly isometric conditions (see below). If the muscle is allowed to shorten, this shortening is accompanied by a slowly rising further increase in heat production, referred to as *shortening heat*. Activation heat accompanies the shortening of the contractile elements themselves; shortening heat accompanies the development of the force acting on the load while and after the series elastic elements are stretched (see below). The increased heat production decays rapidly with the decay of the active state; the heat produced is mainly the result of chemical events—only a small fraction is due to mechanical processes (friction, etc.). Activation heat begins during the latent period—and so does the shortening of the contractile elements themselves. Heat represents an inevitable loss of energy, but not the total energy production: the latter is equal to heat plus mechanical work. During ideal isometric conditions (see below), no mechanical work is performed beyond the initial stretching of the series elastic elements; thus nearly all the liberated energy appears as heat.

As mentioned, the contractile elements must first overcome the viscous elastic resistance of sarcoplasm, sarcolemma, and muscle connective tissue before they can act on the load to which the muscle is attached. For this reason, the active state of the contractile elements is not immediately reflected in the overall length changes of the whole muscle, or in its ability (observed for a sequence of moments) to do work on the load (e.g., to lift a weight). There is a considerable delay before the shortening of the contractile elements finally results in a shortening of the muscle fiber or the whole muscle. In fact, the active state may be declining before the muscle fiber or muscle begins to shorten, so that when the muscle shortening is maximal the contractile elements are already relaxing (Fig. 22–14). Therefore, *if the active state is brief, the whole muscle does not shorten maximally or develop maximal force,* even when the contractile elements themselves shorten maximally.

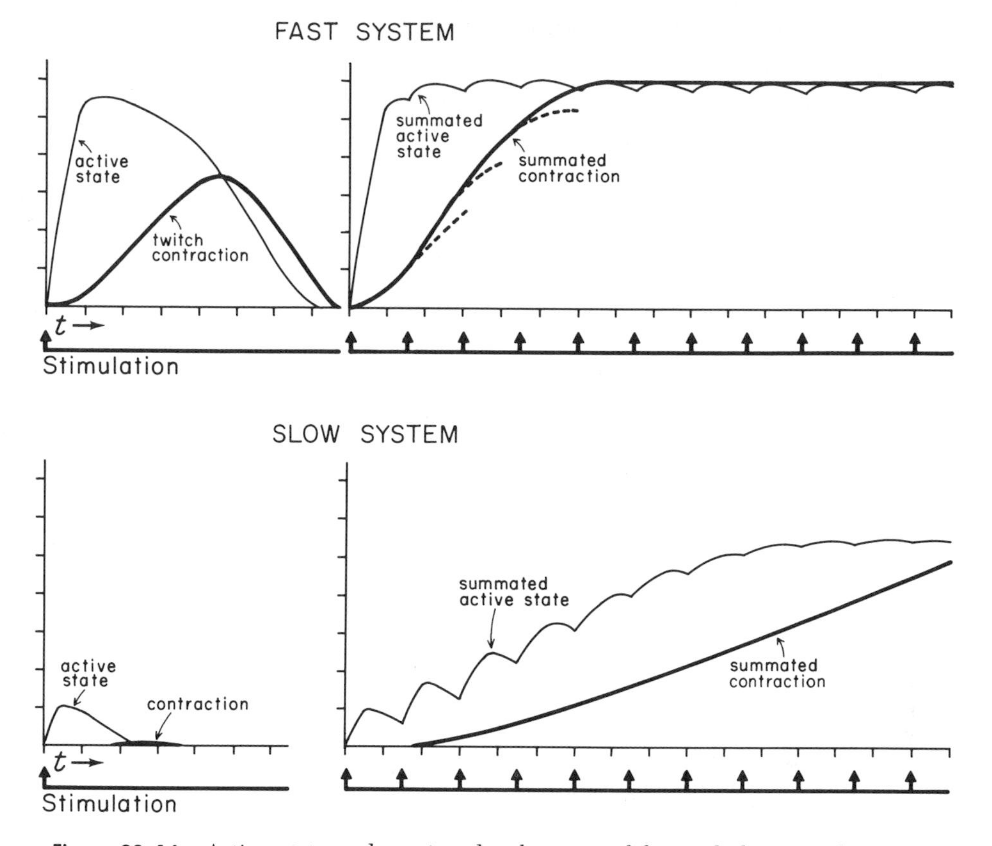

Figure 22–14. Active state and tension development of fast and slow muscle contraction. In both cases the active state can be evoked repeatedly, but in the fast system a single nerve impulse leads to nearly maximal development of active state, whereas in the slow system the active state develops only partially. Between these extreme cases are all kinds of intermediates. A typical example of the fast system is the frog gastrocnemius muscle. A typical example of the slow system is the opener muscle of the crayfish claw.

We may also compare the velocity with which the contractile elements shorten with the velocity with which the muscle (fiber) shortens. Again delays are introduced by the viscous elastic elements, and the active state of the contractile elements develops much faster than the overall shortening of the muscle (fiber). Therefore, *the maximum of the shortening of the muscle (fiber) is reached after the maximum of the active state.* This situation is illustrated in Figure 22–14.

The shortening of muscles or muscle fibers is not a measure of the energy liberated in the contraction process, although it is related to it. Shortening is optimal, of course, when the load is minimal. An arrangement (whether natural or experimental) that permits optimal shortening of muscle fibers is called *isotonic*, and a muscle under these conditions is said to undergo *isotonic contraction.*

The force with which a muscle pulls on its load is called the muscle *tension.* Again, we must distinguish this from the tension developed by the contractile elements during the active state: the force of the contractile elements is partially expended in deforming the viscous elastic elements of the muscle. Therefore,

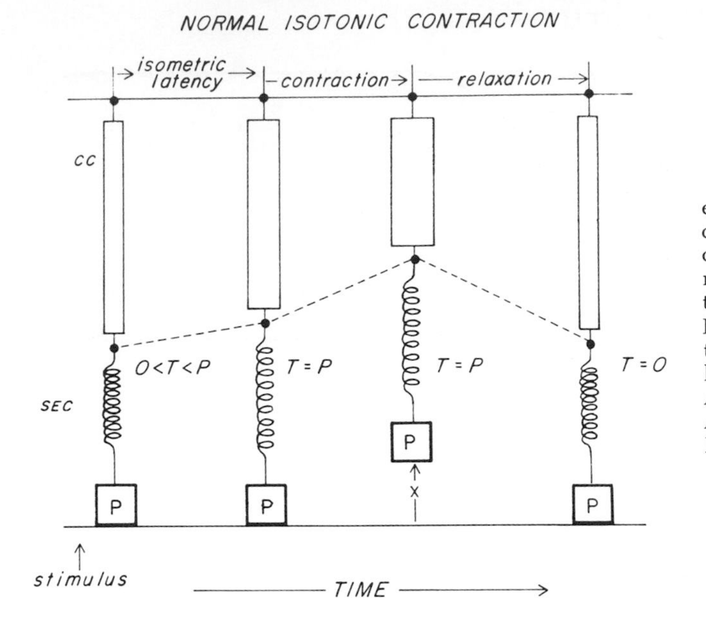

Figure 22–15. Mechanical equivalent diagram of muscle contraction. *CC*, contractile components; *P*, load; *SEC*, series elastic components; *T*, tension. (From Sandow, A.: Energetics of muscular contraction. *In* Biophysics of Physiological and Pharmacological Actions. A. M. Shanes, ed. Amer. Assn. Adv. Sci., Washington, D.C., 1961.)

the velocity of tension development is less than that of the development of the active state.

A muscle can develop tension even if it is prevented from shortening. In this case the contractile elements in the active state shorten and stretch the series elastic elements which, in turn, exert a force on the device that prevents the muscle from shortening. This is known as *isometric contraction.* The tension developed under these circumstances is called the *isometric tension.* Isotonic and isometric contraction are explained in Figures 22–15 and 22–16.

A truly isometric tension cannot be measured, since any measuring device registers tension by the calibrated movement of a tension-resisting part (spring). An apparatus for the recording of muscle tension, therefore, permits a small amount of shortening so that the force of the muscle tension can be utilized to pull on a spring, deform a crystal (mechano-electric transducer of the kind

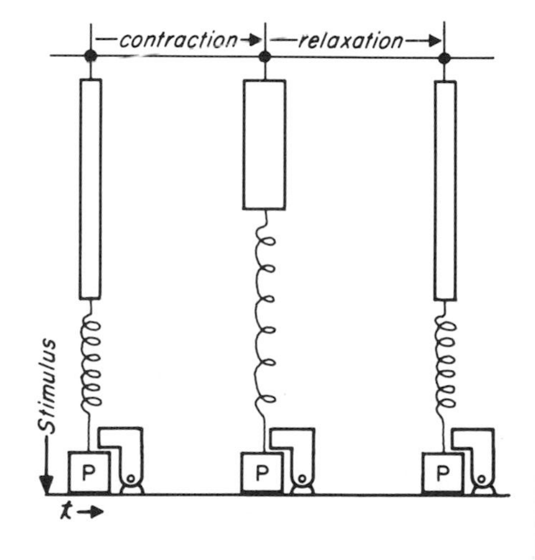

Figure 22–16. Mechanical equivalent diagram of isometric contraction. Symbols as in Figure 22–15. Note that tension is applied to the load even though the muscle as a whole does not shorten. (Simplified diagram after Sandow, A.: Energetics of muscular contraction. *In* Biophysics of Physiological and Pharmacological Actions. A. M. Shanes, ed. American Association for the Advancement of Science, Washington, D.C., 1961, pp. 413–451.)

used in phonograph cartridges), or alter a resistance network (another type of mechano-electric transducer).

Unstimulated muscles behave much like elastic bodies; they resist compression or stretching and the mechanical resistance (passive tension) increases exponentially with linearly increasing external force. This is the reason why we can speak of "elastic elements."

If a muscle is passively stretched, the elastic elements which are in series with the contractile elements are stretched also. Under these circumstances, the contractile elements can transmit their force more directly to the load. The more a muscle (fiber) is prestretched, the larger is the recorded isometric twitch tension after stimulation. Of course, as the passive (applied) tension exceeds the tension developed by the contractile elements, the "active" tension (tension recorded after muscle activation minus passive tension) diminishes again. The situation is explained in the diagram of Figure 22–17. Actual examples of *length-tension diagrams* are shown in Figure 22–18.

Prestretching of a muscle has another consequence: the velocity of the recorded contraction increases. The reason for this is that less time is lost in stretching the series elastic elements, since they are already stretched by the tension applied to the muscle from the outside. However, this situation is complex, because if the muscle has to contract against a load that is more than minimal, *the velocity of shortening decreases with increasing load*—this occurs in spite of the fact that the tension increases with increasing load. If the external force (load) acting on a muscle is plotted against the velocity of shortening, a

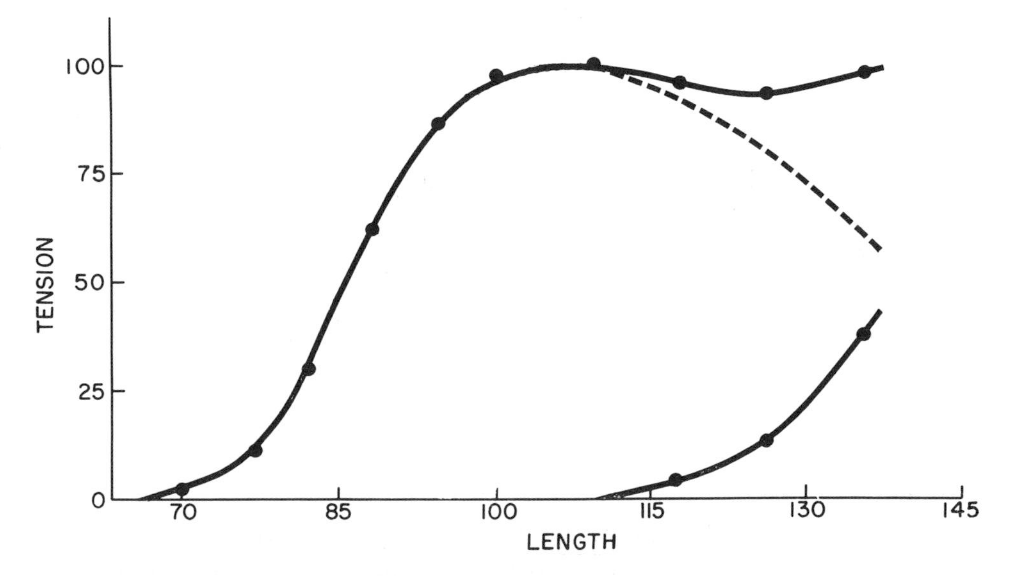

Figure 22–17. Imaginary length-tension diagram. 100 represents the resting length and maximal tension. The curve at the lower right represents the effect of passive stretch on tension (passive tension). When this is subtracted from the upper curve (representing the recorded tension, that is, the maximal tension obtained during tetanic stimulation), the curve shown by a dashed line is obtained. This, together with the first part of the upper, solid curve, represents the active tension. (After Zierler, K. L.: Mechanism of muscle contraction and its energetics. *In* Medical Physiology, 11th Ed. P. Bard, ed. The C. V. Mosby Co., St. Louis, 1961.)

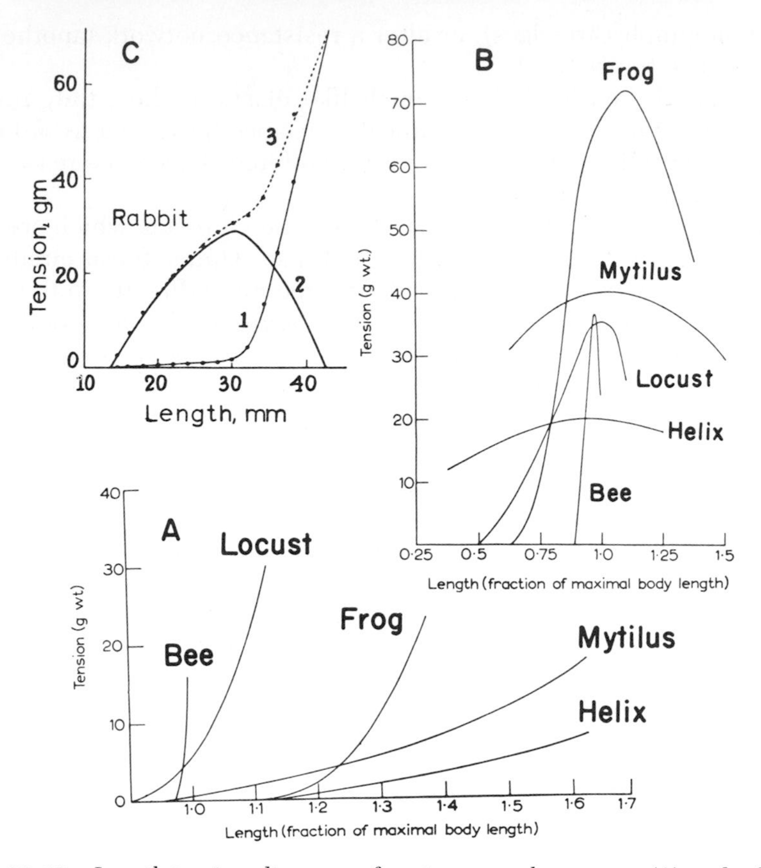

Figure 22–18. Length-tension diagrams of various muscles at rest (**A**) and while active, showing total tension minus passive (resting) tension (**B**). The muscles represented are: flight muscle of bumblebee (*Bombus*), flight muscle of locust (*Schistocerca*), sartorius muscle of frog (*Rana*), anterior byssus retractor muscle of *Mytilus*, and pharynx retractor muscle of *Helix*. **C**, length-tension diagram of rabbit uterus muscle: (*1*), passive tension, (*2*), active tension, and (*3*), total (passive + active) tension of activated muscle. (Modified from Csapo, A. *In* The Structure and Function of Muscle, Vol. 1. G. Bourne, ed. Academic Press, New York, 1960.)

force-velocity curve is obtained, as shown in Figure 22–19. However, the decrease in velocity is not linear and becomes less with increasing load. This behavior is connected with a most important property of muscle: *the rate of energy liberation during contraction increases with increasing load.* This phenomenon is known as the *Fenn effect* (Fenn, 1923).

Electric Behavior

The electric properties of muscle fibers are similar to those of nerve cells. Like the neuronal membrane, the sarcolemma separates extra- and intracellular aqueous media of different ionic composition. Accumulation of K^+ and extrusion of Na^+ are characteristics of all muscle fibers that have been studied in this regard. The capacitance of muscle fiber membranes, like that of nerve cells, is extraordinarily high. Representative values for muscle membrane characteristics, including ion distribution, are shown in Table 22–1.

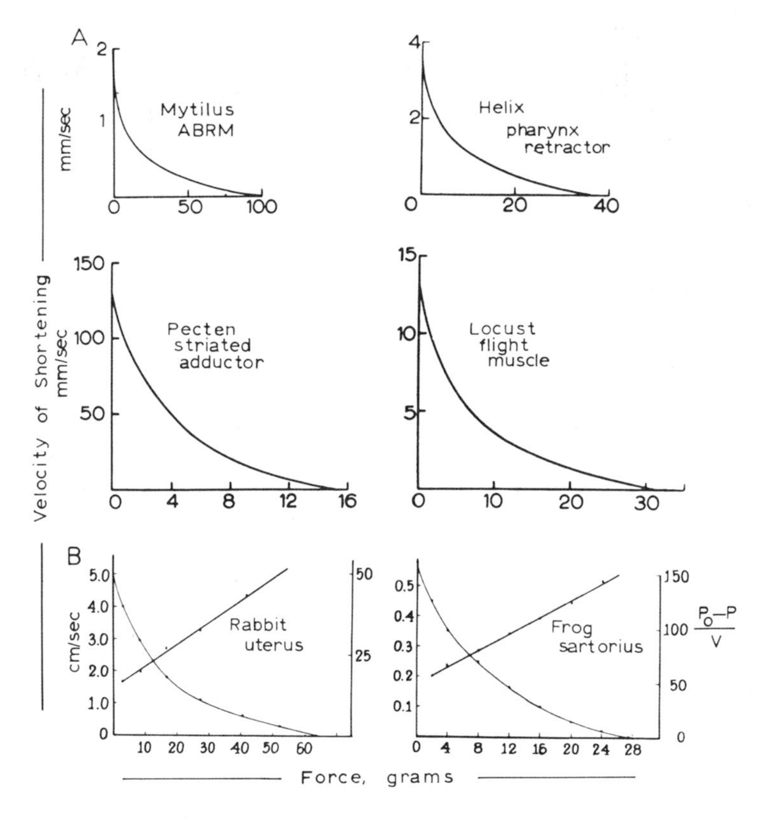

Figure 22–19. Force-velocity curves of different muscles, as indicated. The second curve (straight line) in **B** represents a "load-shortening-velocity curve" in which the ratio P_0 – P/V is plotted against the weight of the load. P_0 is the maximum tension the muscle can develop, *P* is the load, and *V* is the measured velocity of shortening. *ABRM*, anterior byssus retractor muscle. (From Csapo, A. *In* The Structure and Function of Muscle, Vol. 1. G. Bourne, ed. Academic Press, New York, 1960.)

Table 22–1. **Ion Distribution and Electric Constants of Frog Gastrocnemius Muscle**

	mM/l		
Extracellular K^+	2.5	Equilibrium potential for K^+	−101 mV
Na^+	120	for Na^+	+64 mV
Cl^-	120	for Cl^-	−88 mV
Intracellular K^+	140	Resting membrane potential	−94 mV
Na^+	9.2	Membrane capacitance	5–8 $\mu F/cm^2$
Cl^-	3.6	Membrane resistance	1180–2080 ohm cm^2
Organic anion	152	Length constant	0.55–0.8 mm
		Time constant	10.3 msec

Data from Horowicz, P.: Influence of ions on the membrane potential of muscle fibers. *In* Biophysics of Physiological and Pharmacological Actions. (A. M. Shanes, ed.) Amer. Assn. Advanc. Sci., Washington, D.C., 1961; and Katz, B: Electrical properties of the muscle fiber membrane. Proc. Roy. Soc. B, *135*:506–534, 1948.

Three types of activation of electric potential changes are known: (1) spontaneous or hormone-induced oscillations of the membrane potential; (2) chemical transmission of activity in presynaptic nerve terminals; (3) electric transmission from neighboring electrically active muscle cells. (Electric transmission proceeds much in the same way as in the giant synapses discussed on p. 485.)

Electric activity of the muscle fiber membrane consists of two phases: (1) graded, local responses, known as *postsynaptic potentials* (p.s.p.'s), or *junction potentials*, and (2) propagated all-or-nothing action potentials, or *spikes*. The distinction between the two types of action potential is explained in Chapter 16. The often used term "muscle action potential" may mean junction potential or spike potential.

In typical vertebrate skeletal muscle, in which the neuromuscular junction is known as the *motor end-plate* (Fig. 20–12), the junction potentials are called *end-plate potentials* (Fig. 22–20). They usually reach the firing level of the

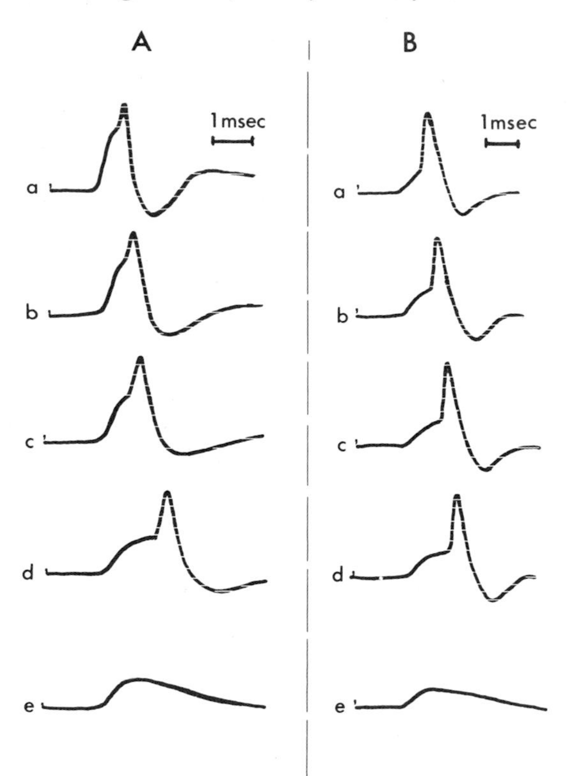

Figure 22–20. Electric potential changes recorded at (**A**), and a short distance away from (**B**), the motor end-plate of a single muscle fiber of the musculus adductor longus of the amphibian *Hyla aurea.* Curarine chloride was allowed to diffuse toward the end-plate. Note that when the electrode is directly at the junction, the normal end-plate potential is almost as large as the spike (dashed line). Only the *spike* is conducted, however, so that the end-plate potential appears smaller if the electrode is placed away from the end-plate while the spike height remains the same. Curarine lowers the end-plate potential and the spike is seen to arise later and later (*a–d*) until it drops out in an all-or-nothing manner. In (*e*) only the end-plate potential is left. These experiments provided conclusive proof that the end-plate potential initiates the muscle action potentials (spikes). (Redrawn from Kuffler, S. W.: Electric potential changes at an isolated nerve-muscle junction. J. Neurophysiol. 5:18–26, 1942.)

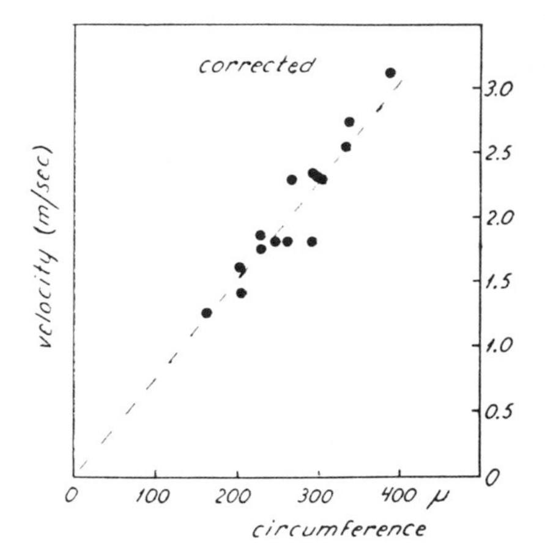

Figure 22–21. Relationship between conduction velocity of the action potential and the circumference of the fibers of the semitendinosus muscle of *Rana temporaria* (spring, 20° C, fiber in Ringer solution). Although it would be predicted on theoretical grounds that the conduction velocity is linearly related to the diameter (see Fig. 16–34) this is not the case: conduction velocity is linearly related to the circumference, indicating that the electrical properties of the membrane differ according to fiber size. (From Håkansson, C. H.: Conduction velocity and amplitude of the action potential as related to circumference in the isolated fiber of frog muscle. Acta Physiol. Scand. 37:14–34, 1956.)

excitable sarcolemma and lead to a full-blown, conducted action potential.

All depolarizing electric responses of muscle fibers are referred to as *excitation*. Hyperpolarizing responses are sometimes called "inhibition," but wrongly so unless the responses are shown to prevent or diminish the initiation or development of the active state of the contractile elements (see Excitation-Contraction Coupling, p. 560 and Chapter 24, p. 586).

In slow muscles, that is, in all muscles that contract slowly in response to repetitive synaptic activation, true spike potentials are usually absent and activation is entirely by junction potentials. These are not conducted. A whole muscle fiber contracts simultaneously because several terminals of the same motor fiber contact the muscle fiber at different points (multiterminal innervation).

Vertebrate skeletal muscle fibers give rise to conducted action potentials. The conduction velocity is proportional to the diameter or circumference of the muscle fiber, as shown in Figure 22–21. Conducted action potentials have also been observed in certain muscle fibers of crustaceans and insects (Fig. 22–22).

No refractory period is associated with nonconducted, local junction potentials. However, the electric excitability of the membrane does show refractoriness whenever conducted spike potentials occur. During the rising phase and plateau (if such exists), the membrane cannot be excited (*absolute refractory period*); during the falling phase of the action potential the membrane can be excited only by stimuli larger than those normally needed to excite (*relative refractory period*).

No refractory period is associated with the active state of the contractile elements. The active state can be evoked repeatedly.

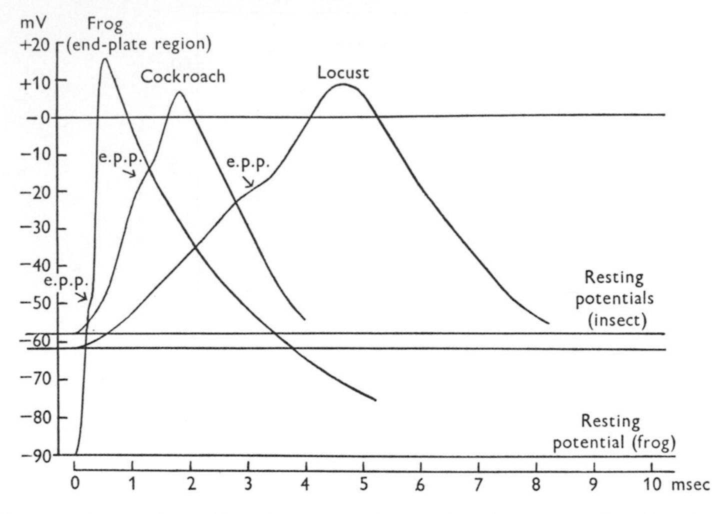

Figure 22–22. Comparison of resting potentials and action potentials of single muscle fibers of frog (*Rana pipiens*, musculus sartorius), cockroach (*Periplaneta americana*, extensor tibialis of metathoracic leg), and locust (*Locusta migratoria*, extensor tibialis of metathoracic leg). The records were obtained with intracellular microelectrodes, at 20° C (insects) and 23° C (frog). The transition from end-plate potential (*e.p.p.*) to spike potential is marked by arrows. (From Hoyle, G.: The effects of some common cations on neuromuscular transmission in insects. J. Physiol. *127*:90–103, 1955.)

Fast and Slow Muscles

The effect of repetitive stimulation of muscle fibers depends on two factors: the time course of the electric membrane response and the time course of the development of the active state (see Fig. 22–23). If stimuli fall within the refractory period of the previously induced action potential, they remain ineffective with regard to both membrane response and active state. If they follow at intervals longer than the refractory period of the membrane, they can again initiate an active state in the contractile elements.

An impulse that can activate the membrane while the active state induced by the previous pulse is still developing can accelerate, increase, or prolong this active state. Their effects, as it were, summate to give a larger or prolonged active state.

With some types of muscle fibers a single motor fiber impulse can initiate the full and maximal development of active state (Fig. 22–14). Therefore, a second impulse cannot increase its magnitude appreciably—however, it can increase the duration of this active state, which would otherwise have declined as soon as it reached its maximum. If the active state develops sufficiently after a single stimulus to produce a noticeable contraction, this is called a *twitch*, and a muscle composed of fibers that respond with twitches to single motor impulses is called a *twitch muscle*, or *"fast" muscle*. Such muscles are relatively rare in the Animal Kingdom. Several striated muscles of vertebrates, among them the well-studied gastrocnemius and sartorius muscles of frogs, the closer muscle of the crayfish (*Astacus, Cambarus, Procambarus*, etc.),

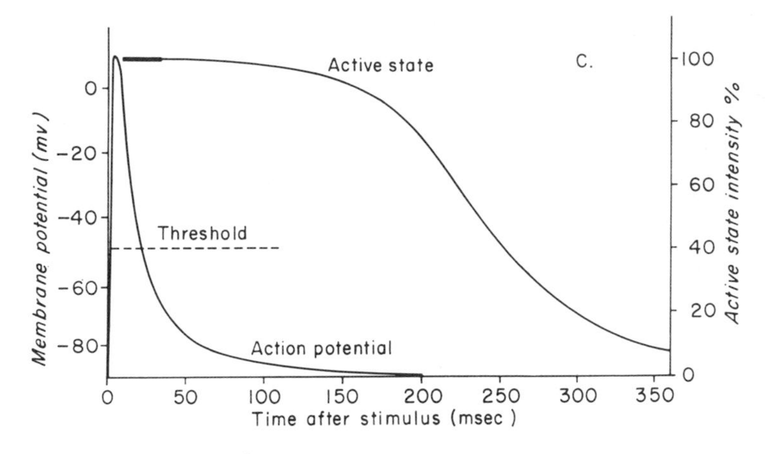

Figure 22–23. Time course of an action potential and of an active state of amphibian muscle fiber measured at 0° C. The rapid rise of the active state is not shown. The thick line represents the "plateau" of the active state, a maximal value that is maintained for some tens of milliseconds. It is assumed that tension does not develop until the action potential reaches a threshold value of −50 mV. (From Falk, G.: Electrical activity of skeletal muscle, its relation to the active state. *In* Biophysics of Physiological and Pharmacological Actions. A. M. Shanes, ed. Amer. Assn. Adv. Sci., Publication 69, Washington, D.C., 1961.)

and the pharynx retractor muscles of sipunculids (these are smooth muscles) belong to this category.

Twitch muscles are said to contract in an "all-or-none" manner, but this is not meant to be absolutely true, particularly if one refers to the actually recorded shortening or tension, which, as explained before, does not indicate the true magnitude or time course of the active state because of the intervening viscous-elastic elements. Successive twitches may well show a certain increase in magnitude, referred to as the *staircase phenomenon.* Although this may reflect a certain increment in the developing active states, it is most likely that the increase in recorded twitch height is due to a rearrangement of the noncontractile structures of the twitch muscle.

If twitch muscles are re-stimulated while the active state is near its maximum, the maximal active state can be maintained as long as this repetitive stimulation persists, provided, of course, that the refractory period of the membrane permits a high enough stimulation frequency (Fig. 22–14). The maintained state of contraction due to repetitive stimulation is called *tetanus.* The stimulation which is effective in producing tetanus is called *tetanic stimulation.* Some twitch muscles, like vertebrate heart muscles, cannot be tetanized because the refractory period of the membrane is nearly equal to the duration of the active state elicited by each stimulus. By the time a second stimulus becomes effective, the active state induced by the previous impulse has decayed.

Most muscles respond to each membrane activation with only a partial development of active state. They are called *"slow" muscles.* They contract maximally only if stimulated repetitively so that the active state grows by summation to its maximum value (Fig. 22–14). In such muscles the duration of the individual amounts of active state produced by each stimulus is relatively long compared to their magnitude, so that the increments in contraction

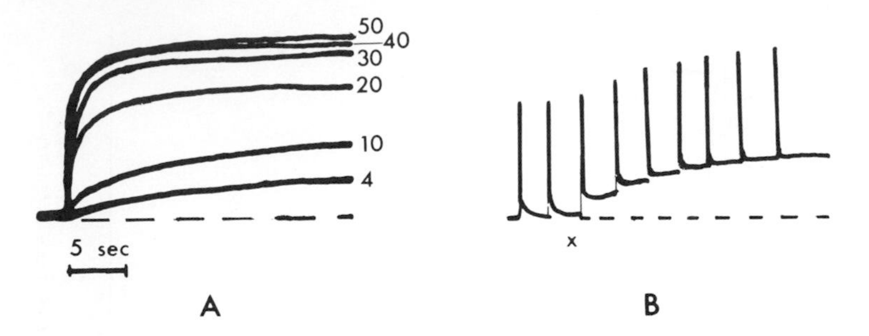

Figure 22–24. A, superimposed records of tension development in a "slow" striated muscle (*musculus ileofibularis* of the amphibian *Rana catesbeiana*). The so-called small-nerve fibers were stimulated with impulse frequencies of 4, 10, 20, 30, 40, and 50 pulses per second throughout the duration of each record. Relaxations are not shown. Note the slow development of tension, particularly during stimulation at low frequencies. **B**, summation of tension of slow and twitch muscle fibers of the *ileofibularis*. The so-called large-nerve fibers supplying the twitch fibers were stimulated once every second with a single pulse. Beginning at *x*, the small-nerve fibers were stimulated at a low frequency. Note that the twitch contractions retain their all-or-nothing character and are superimposed on the slow contraction. Note the speed of contraction *and* relaxation of the twitches. (Redrawn from Kuffler, S. W., and E. M. Vaughan Williams: Properties of the "slow" skeletal muscle fibres of the frog. J. Physiol. *121*:318–340, 1953.)

caused by successive stimuli may show a smooth transition. Of course, the maximal state of contraction is reached sooner the higher the repetition rate of the stimuli. This is illustrated by the kymograph records shown in Fig. 22–24.

Several striated muscles of amphibians and reptiles and most striated muscles of invertebrates are slow muscles. However, many muscle types are known that exhibit fast as well as slow contractions. Although in some cases such muscles are composed of slow and fast fibers, more often than not it is found that the same muscle fibers can respond with fast or with slow contractions. In these cases the type of response is determined by the innervation: the fibers are innervated by at least two motor axons; activation of one causes the fast response, whereas activation of the other causes the slow response. It is likely that the properties of the neuromuscular junctions are responsible for the different kinds of contraction.

Motor fibers that cause a slow contraction are known as *"slow" axons*; motor axons that cause fast contractions are called *"fast" axons*. The terminology may mislead one to think that the significant distinction is that the motor fibers themselves are fast or slow with regard to impulse conduction. It is true that slow motor fibers are usually thinner than fast ones and therefore the conduction velocities differ. However, the difference in conduction velocity is not responsible for the different actions on the muscle.

Summation, Facilitation, and Fatigue

Summation was defined as *the additive postsynaptic effect of two or more presynaptic events* (p. 500). In muscle there can be at least two types of postsynaptic effects: electric and mechanical. Therefore we observe two kinds of summation: (1) summation of synaptic effects on the electric behavior of the muscle fiber membrane, and (2) summation of synaptic effects on the contractile elements. In each case summation can logically take place only if the second synaptic event occurs while the process elicited by the first is still in progress. Since most electric membrane responses are relatively short in duration, electric effects can summate only within the brief time interval. The contractile response usually lasts much longer; thus the effects of synaptic actions may sum even if separated by a considerable amount of time.

In slow muscles a series of stimuli causes repetitive electric responses (junction potentials) and a contraction which continually increases with each junction potential. While the junction potentials appear at intervals too long to permit summation, the contraction produced by the repetitive stimulation is a summated response. Of course, if the stimuli follow each other closely, the electric responses may show summation too. Figure 22–25 explains the situation.

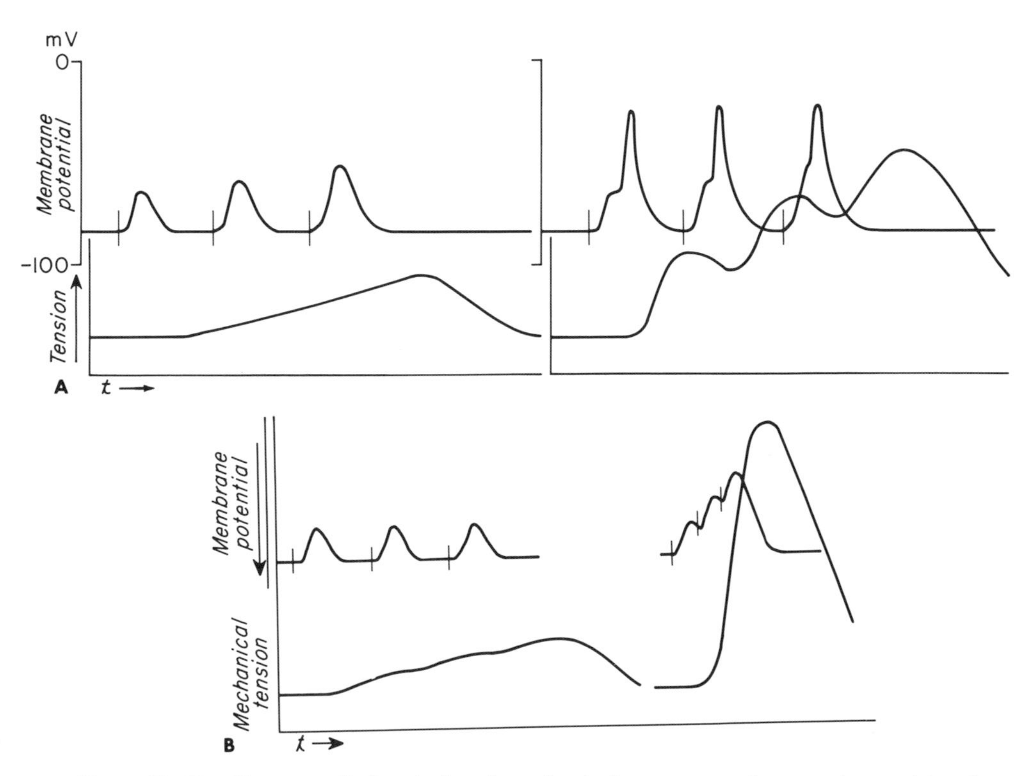

Figure 22–25. Patterns of electrical and mechanical responses of a muscle resulting from stimulation of its motor axons. The diagrams represent activities of a single fiber. The vertical lines in the potential records (upper curves) represent the stimulus artifact and indicate the times at which the motor axon is being electrically stimulated. **A** shows on the left three nonfacilitating junction potentials and a slow contraction that exhibits summation. On the right the stimuli are applied in rapid succession: the junction potentials summate and there results a large, summated contraction. **B** shows facilitating junction potentials and summated contraction (left) and facilitating junction potentials with spike potentials causing summated contraction with superimposed twitches (right). The latter type of response is characteristic of "fast" muscle fibers. Incomplete tetanus is shown here.

Whereas the term "summation" refers to one and the same postsynaptic response, the term "facilitation" is used to denote *the increasing size of subsequent postsynaptic responses to identical stimuli* applied to the presynaptic elements (see also p. 503). In muscle, the electric response is facilitated as well as the mechanical response. Facilitation probably cannot be explained as a single process. Several suggestions have been made: 1. The presynaptic terminals release more transmitter with each impulse if these follow each other sufficiently closely. 2. The released transmitter is not completely removed (or inactivated) by the time the next transmitter is released, thus more transmitter is active with each new impulse. 3. The presynaptic nerve impulse "activates" the subsynaptic membrane and this activation persists until the next impulse arrives; this activation may consist in the mobilization of certain chemical processes (activation of receptor proteins, de-inhibition of certain enzymes), or in structural changes affecting membrane permeability. 4. Facilitation of the mechanical (contractile) response may depend on a structural rearrangement of the contractile elements, but (5) may also be caused by activation of metabolic processes which deliver the energy for the active state.

Facilitation has a definite time course. It is largest when the presynaptic impulses follow each other most closely and does not occur when the impulses appear at too low a frequency. *The processes underlying facilitation are initiated by each presynaptic impulse and decay at a definite rate.* Facilitation does not go on indefinitely; the postsynaptic responses increase only up to a certain optimal value. If repetitive stimulation persists too long, the postsynaptic responses do, in fact, become smaller again and eventually may disappear altogether.

Reduction of the magnitude of subsequent postsynaptic responses is sometimes called "*defacilitation*," but more commonly "*fatigue*." Again, muscles can show two kinds of fatigue; fatigue of the electric membrane responses and fatigue of the mechanical (contractile) responses. The explanations for fatigue are: (1) reduction in transmitter output from presynaptic terminals because of exhaustion of stored transmitter; (2) postsynaptic membrane changes due to accumulated transmitter; (3) loss of K^+ ions from the postsynaptic cell and accumulation of this K^+ in the immediate extracellular space; (4) increase of Na^+ content of the postsynaptic cell; (5) exhaustion of metabolic reserves in the postsynaptic cell; and (6) intra- and extracellular accumulation of metabolic end products.

Time course of facilitation and fatigue of electric and of mechanical responses are usually not coupled. Examples are known where the electric responses are already fatiguing while the mechanical contractions of the same muscle are still increasing.

Excitation-Contraction Coupling

Of great concern to muscle physiologists is the question of how the electric events in the muscle fiber membrane affect the contractile elements. In some muscles the fiber diameter is 1 mm or even larger (insect flight muscle, skeletal muscle of decapod crustaceans). The innermost myofibrils are then 500 μ from the cell membrane. But even with thinner muscle fibers the problem exists: How are the membrane events communicated to the contractile elements? What is the mechanism of excitation transfer?

Vertebrate twitch fibers do not contract as a result of synaptic activation unless there is a full-blown, conducted action potential. The end-plate potential alone cannot induce contraction. On the other hand, slow muscles respond with contractions to graded, local junction potentials—but, although the degree of contraction is proportional to the frequency of junction potentials (see p. 557), it is not proportional to the height of the junction potentials. Furthermore, in partially fatigued crustacean muscles, stimulation of the fast motor axons may cause large junction potentials without eliciting contraction, whereas stimulation of the slow motor axons causes only small junction potentials and normal contraction—this is known as the "paradox" phenomenon of crustacean muscle (Wiersma and van Harreveld, 1938).

On the whole, the fact that the time courses of facilitation and fatigue (see pp. 558–560) of electric and mechanical events do not necessarily coincide indicates that there is no direct coupling of electric membrane events and contractile machinery. This is further brought out by experimental procedures which change the electric response without affecting the resulting contractions, or which affect the contractions without changing the electric membrane responses. Replacement of external Na^+ with tetrabutylammonium causes a dramatic increase of the junction potentials of crustacean muscles, but contraction fails (Fatt and Katz, 1952). Replacement of extracellular Cl^- by other inorganic anions causes an increase of twitch contraction of vertebrate striated skeletal muscle without appreciably altering the shape of the muscle action potential (Hill and Macpherson, 1954).

On the other hand, under physiological conditions the electric depolarization of the sarcolemma is a necessary condition for muscle contraction. Even muscles that contract spontaneously, that is, without synaptic activation (e.g., mammalian intestinal muscle), show electric activity prior to mechanical contraction (Fig. 22–26). Some experiments indicate that the duration of the muscle action potential is related to the duration of the resulting contraction. If the plateau of the action potential of vertebrate heart muscle fibers is prolonged to as much as 2 seconds by the use of intracellular microelectrodes, the twitch contraction of the muscle fibers also lasts 2 seconds (see Woodbury, 1964).

Indications concerning the mechanism of coupling of membrane excitation and contractile processes have come from combined optical and electrophysio-

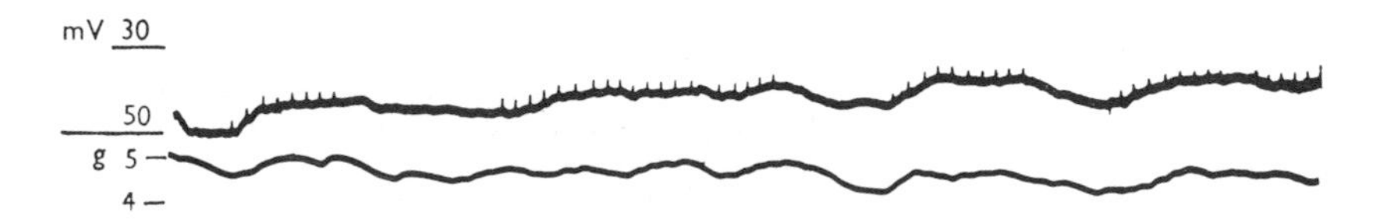

Figure 22–26. Parallelism of membrane potential and tension in a smooth muscle (teniae coli) of the guinea pig. Upper trace: membrane potential and bursts of spike discharges. Lower trace: tension. (From Bülbring, E.: Correlation between membrane potential and tension in smooth muscle. J. Physiol. *128*:200–221, 1955.)

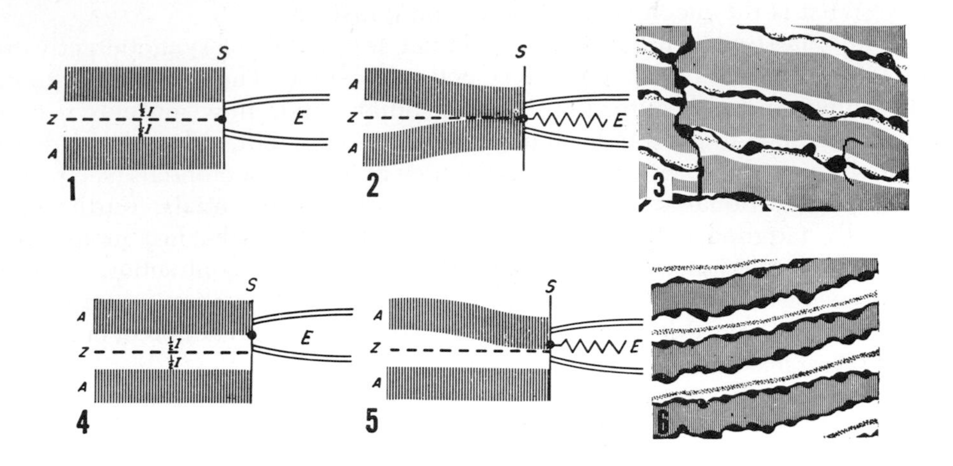

Figure 22–27. **1**, diagram of a portion of a muscle fiber of an adult frog as represented in the experiments of Huxley and Taylor (1958). The sarcolemma (*S*) is represented by a vertical line to the right of the representation of two A bands and the intervening I and Z bands. A sensitive spot is represented by a black dot at the projection of the Z band to the sarcolemma. Against this sensitive spot a stimulating pipet electrode is placed, with its contained electrolyte solution in contact with the outer surface of the sarcolemma. This represents the status when no stimulating current is flowing.

2, the same muscle fiber during the passage of a stimulating current through the electrolyte filling the pipet electrode and the sarcolemma at a sensitive spot as described by Huxley and Taylor (1958). The two adjacent half-sarcomeres are shown as responding to the stimulus by a localized contraction extending a few microns beyond the sarcolemma into the fiber. The widths of the A bands do not change, and the proximal borders of the A bands approach each other closely at the Z band. Sarcomeres above and below the ones represented are not caused to contract by the stimulus.

3, sarcoplasmatic reticulum of adult frog muscle as seen in the light microscope after metallic impregnation. The blackened strands of reticulum lie along the Z bands, at levels corresponding exactly to those found by Huxley and Taylor to be sensitive to localized stimulation (see **1** and **2**). Part of a "Nonius" unconformity is shown in the banding of the muscle. Along the "fault line" of the unconformity is a longitudinal strand which connects the transverse strands at the Z band levels. There is no evidence from Huxley's work of longitudinal conduction within the muscle fiber.

4, this corresponds to **1**, except that it represents muscle of the lizard *Lacerta*, rather than the frog. In lizard muscle, Huxley was able to elicit a localized contractile response only when the stimulating pipet electrode (*E*) was placed on certain sensitive spots on the sarcolemma (*S*) opposite the line of junction of A and I bands. The sensitive spot is indicated by a black dot on the sarcolemma. The electrolyte in the electrode is represented as being in contact with this spot. This figure represents the muscle when no stimulating current is flowing.

5, the lizard muscle of **4** while responding locally to a suitable stimulus applied through the electrode (*E*) to a sensitive spot on the sarcolemma (*S*). In this muscle, only the half-sarcomere opposite a sensitive spot responds to this type of stimulus. The localized contraction extends only a few microns onto the fiber from the stimulated spot on the sarcolemma, and is characterized by an approximation of the border of the A band of the responding half-sarcomere to the neighboring Z. Adjacent half-sarcomeres are not affected.

6, sarcoplasmatic reticulum of a muscle of the lizard *Lacerta*, as seen in the light microscope. In this muscle, the reticulum appears as a series of transverse networks, each located at the levels of A-I junctions, at positions corresponding exactly to the sensitive spots found by Huxley.

(From Bennett, H. S.: The structure of striated muscle as seen by the electron microscope. *In* The Structure and Function of Muscle, Vol. 1. G. H. Bourne, ed. Academic Press, New York, 1960.)

logical studies (Huxley and Taylor, 1958) and from studies on the movements of calcium ions.

Weak electric currents applied to extremely small areas of striated muscle fibers can produce local contractions, but only if the point of contact is opposite certain interior membranes of the muscle cell; the points where local contractions can be elicited are situated opposite the Z bands in frog muscle, and opposite the border between A and I bands in lizard and crab muscle fibers. It is precisely in these regions that transverse tubular membranes of the endoplasmic reticulum are situated. The evidence is suggestive, indeed, that these structures are responsible for the transfer of excitation from the membrane to the contractile myofibrils. Figure 22–27 describes the situation in diagrams. The discovery of the deep invaginations of the muscle fiber membrane (Fig. 22–1) now explains how electrical activity can spread locally into the "interior" of muscle fibers.

Another line of evidence implies Ca^{++} ions as an important link in excitation-contraction coupling. Not only does Ca^{++} injected into muscle fibers cause contraction, but it has also been found that the Ca^{++} influx increases by 30-fold over the resting value when a muscle (frog sartorius) is being stimulated (Bianchi, 1961). If the external K^+ concentration is increased (sartorius and rectus abdominis of frog) a long-lasting contraction (contracture) results and simultaneously large amounts of Ca^{++} enter the muscle fibers. No contraction takes place if Ca^{++} is omitted from the external medium. The duration of the contraction produced by increased external K^+ is proportional to the duration of the increased Ca^{++} influx (Shanes, 1961).

It has also been shown (guinea pig atrium) that the degree of contraction and the magnitude of Ca^{++} influx are linearly proportional (Winegrad, 1960).

It may well be, then, that membrane depolarization permits entry of Ca^{++}, and that this in turn causes activation of the contraction mechanism.

REFERENCES

Abbott, B. C., and J. M. Ritchie (1951) The onset of shortening in striated muscle. J. Physiol. *113*: 336–345.

Bailey, K. (1957) Invertebrate tropomyosin. Biochim. Biophys. Acta *24*:612–619.

Beatty, C. H., R. D. Peterson, R. M. Bocek, and E. S. West (1959) Acetoacetate and glucose uptake by diaphragm and skeletal muscle from control and diabetic rats. J. Biol. Chem. *234*:11–15.

Bennett, H. S. (1960) The structure of striated muscle as seen by the electron microscope. *In* The Structure and Function of Muscle, Vol. 1, pp. 137–181. (G. H. Bourne, ed.) Academic Press, New York.

Bennett, H. S., and K. R. Porter (1953) An electron microscope study of sectioned breast muscle of the domestic fowl. Amer. J. Anat. *93*:61–106.

Bianchi, C. P. (1961) Calcium movements in striated muscle during contraction and contracture. *In* Biophysics of Physiological and Pharmacological Actions, pp. 281–292. (A. M. Shanes, ed.) Amer. Assn. Advanc. Sci., Washington, D.C.

Bing, R. J. (1955) Myocardial metabolism. Circulation *12*:635–647.

Bowman, W. (1840) On the minute structure and movements of voluntary muscle. Phil. Trans. Roy. Soc. B, *130*:457–501.

Burnstock, G., M. R. Holman, and C. L. Prosser (1963) Electrophysiology of smooth muscle. Physiol. Rev. *43*:482–527.

Carlson, F. D., and A. Siger (1960) The mechanochemistry of muscular contraction. I. The isometric twitch. J. Gen. Physiol. *43*:33–60.

Farrant, J. L., and E. H. Mercer (1952) Studies on the structure of muscle. II. Arthropod muscles. Exp. Cell Res. *3*:553–563.

Fatt, P., and B. Katz (1952) The effect of sodium ions on neuromuscular transmission. J. Physiol. *118*:73–87.

Fenn, W. O. (1923) A quantitative comparison between the energy liberated and the work performed by the isolated sartorius muscle of the frog. J. Physiol. *58*:175–203.

Gasser, H. S., and A. V. Hill (1924) Dynamics of muscular contraction. Proc. Roy. Soc. B, *96*:398–437.

George, J. C., and D. Jyoti (1958) Structure and physiology of flight muscles in the bat. II. Relative reduction of fat and glycogen in pectoralis major muscle during sustained activity. J. Anim. Morphol. Physiol. *5*:57–60.

George, J. C., and R. M. Naik (1958) Relative distribution and chemical nature of the fuel store of the two types of fibers in the pectoralis major muscle of the pigeon. Nature *181*:709–711.

Hakansson, C. H. (1956) Conduction velocity and amplitude of the action potential as related to circumference in the isolated fibre of frog muscle. Acta Physiol. Scand. *37*:14–34.

Hanson, J., and J. Lowy (1960) Structure and function of the contractile apparatus in the muscles of invertebrate animals. *In* The Structure and Function of Muscle, Vol. 1, pp. 265–336. (G. H. Bourne, ed.) Academic Press, New York.

Hill, A. V. (1949) Heat of activation and heat of shortening in a muscle twitch. Proc. Roy. Soc. B, *136*:195–200.

Hill, A. V. (1950) Development of the active state of muscle during the latent period. Proc. Roy. Soc. B, *137*:320–329.

Hill, A. V. (1958) The priority of heat production in a muscle twitch. Proc. Roy. Soc. B, *148*:397–402.

Hill, A. V., and L. MacPherson (1954) The effect of nitrate, iodide and bromide on the duration of the active state in skeletal muscle. Proc. Roy. Soc. B, *143*:81–102.

Hodgkin, A. L., and P. Horowicz (1957) The differential action of hypertonic solutions on the twitch and action potential of a muscle fiber. J. Physiol. *136*:17P–18P.

Hoyle, G. (1957) Muscular Contraction. Cambridge University Press, London.

Huxley, A. F., and R. E. Taylor (1958) Logical activation of striated muscle fibers. J. Physiol. *144*: 426–441.

Jewell, B. R., and D. R. Wilkie (1958) An analysis of the mechanical components in frog's striated muscle. J. Physiol. *152*:30–47.

Kominz, D. R., F. Saad, J. A. Gladner, and K. Laki (1957) Mammalian tropomyosins. Arch. Biochem. Biophys. *70*:16–28.

Mommaerts, W. F. H. M., A. J. Brady, and B. C. Abbott (1961) Major problems in muscle physiology. Ann. Rev. Physiol. *23*:529–576.

Morales, M. F., J. Botts, J. J. Blum, and T. L. Hill (1955) Elementary processes in muscle action: an examination of current concepts. Physiol. Rev. *35*:475–505.

Neptune, E. M., and D. R. Foreman (1959) The endogenous glycogen of rat diaphragm and its theoretical capacity to support respiration. J. Biol. Chem. *234*:1942–1944.

Neptune, E. M., H. C. Suddith, and D. R. Foreman (1959) Labile fatty acids of rat diaphragm muscle and their possible role as the major endogenous substrate of maintenance of respiration. J. Biol. Chem. *234*:1659–1660.

Reichel, H. (1960) Muskelphysiologie. Springer-Verlag, Berlin.

Rollett, A. (1891) Ueber die Streifen N (Nebenscheiben), das Sarkoplasma und die Kontraktion der quergestreiften Muskelfasern. Arch. mikr. Anat. *37*:654–683.

Sandow, A. (1952) Fundamental mechanics of skeletal muscle contraction. Amer. J. Phys. Med. *31*:103–125.

Shanes, A. M. (1961) Correlation of calcium uptake and contractility in frog rectus abdominis muscle. *In* Biophysics of Physiological and Pharmacological Actions, pp. 309–316. (A. M. Shanes, ed.) Amer. Assn. Advanc. Sci., Washington, D.C.

Sjöstrand, F. S., and E. Andersson-Cedergren (1957) The ultrastructure of the skeletal muscle myofilaments of various states of shortening. J. Ultrastruct. Res. *1*:74–108.

Sjöstrand, F. S., and E. Andersson-Cedergren (1960) Intercalated discs of heart muscle. *In* The Structure and Function of Muscle, Vol. 1, pp. 421–445. (G. H. Bourne, ed.) Academic Press, New York.

Wiersma, C. A. G., and A. van Harreveld (1938) The influence of the frequency of stimulation on the slow and the fast contraction in crustacean muscle. Physiol. Zool. *11*:75–81.

Wilkie, D. R. (1956a) Measurement of the series elastic component at various times during a single muscle twitch. J. Physiol. *134*:527–530.

Wilkie, D. R. (1956b) The mechanical properties of muscle. Brit. Med. Bull. *12*:177–182.

Winegrad, S. (1960) The relationship of calcium uptake to contraction in guinea pig atria. Physiologist *3*:179.

Woodbury, J. W. (1964) Cellular electrophysiology of the heart. *In* Handbook of Physiology, Sec. 2, Vol. I, pp. 237–286. (J. Field, ed.) The Williams & Wilkins Co., Baltimore.

Zierler, K. L. (1961) Mechanism of muscle contraction and its energetics. *In* Medical Physiology, 11th Ed. (P. Bard, ed.) The C. V. Mosby Co., St. Louis.

23 THE CHEMISTRY AND MOLECULAR PHYSIOLOGY OF MUSCLE

IONS AND STRUCTURAL PROTEINS

1. The inorganic constituents of muscle fibers represent an aqueous solution of K^+-, Na^+-, Ca^{++}-, and Mg^{++}-chloride, -sulfate, -bicarbonate, and -phosphate. The internal K^+ concentration usually is much higher than that of extracellular body fluid, whereas the Na^+ concentration is lower. Still, there is usually more Na^+ present in the muscle fibers than in the nerve cells of the same animal. The Cl^- concentration within muscle fibers is usually much lower than outside, and the total of inorganic anions does not balance the cations present. Thus, with regard to the inorganic constituents of muscle, there is a so-called *anion deficit*. The number of cations is almost exactly balanced by the number of inorganic *and organic anions*. The latter category is represented by proteins and amino acids with an iso-electric point below the cell pH (see Chap. 4).

Ion concentrations are often given in terms of millimoles of ion per gram (or kilogram) of muscle. In order to be physiologically meaningful, ion concentrations should be given in millimoles per milliliter (or liter) of cell water.

2. The proteins that constitute the major portion of the sarcoplasm are not always known. Chief constituents of vertebrate sarcoplasm are dissolved albumins: *myogen A*, *myogen B* (Weber, 1934) and *myo-albumin* (Bate-Smith, 1937); and globulins: *globulin X* (Weber, 1934) and *myoglobin* (Millikan, 1939). The function of myoglobin as an oxygen carrier was discussed in Chapters 9 and 14.

3. Several proteins contribute to the contractile machinery of muscle fibers.

The most important are *L-myosin, actin, tropomyosin A, tropomyosin B,* and *paramyosin.* L-myosin is composed of two molecules of H-meromyosin and two molecules of L-meromyosin. Actin, now known as F-actin, is composed of several molecules of G-actin, each of which consists of two molecules of g-actin. F-actin and L-myosin form *actomyosin* (in the older literature this was also called myosin). Our knowledge of molecular weight, dimension, internal structure, and functional relationships of these proteins is largely due to the pioneering studies of H. H. Weber (Heidelberg, Germany), A. and A. G. Szent-Györgyi (Szeged, Hungary, and Woods Hole, Massachusetts, U.S.A.), T. C. Tsao (China), W. T. Astbury (England), and others. Much about their functional localization within the myofilaments has been learned by recent electron microscopy of H. E. Huxley, J. Hanson, J. Lowy, and C. L. Prosser. Summaries of these and related researches can be found in the textbooks and reviews by Szent-Györgyi, 1951; Weber and Portzehl, 1952; Mommaerts, 1950; Mommaerts, Brady, and Abbott, 1961; Prosser and Brown, 1961; Reichel, 1960; and Wilkie, 1966.

L-Myosin, F-actin, and actomyosin appear to be constituents of all muscle fibers throughout the Animal Kingdom. They are the chief contracting proteins; in fact, they may well be the only ones that actively participate in contraction. Tropomyosin A characteristically occurs in vertebrate striated muscle and in the muscles of molluscs and annelids, whereas tropomyosin B occurs predominantly in vertebrate visceral smooth muscle, but also in crustacean muscle and to a certain degree in molluscan muscle. Paramyosin appears to be structurally related to tropomyosin A; in some cases it may be identical with it. This protein was first identified in the holding muscles ("paramyosin muscles") of bivalve molluscs, but is now recognized as an important constituent of muscles of sipunculids and echinoderms, and even of vertebrate smooth muscle.

The myofilaments of the various types of muscle fiber consist of either L-myosin, F-actin, actomyosin, or tropo- (or para-) myosin. The thin filaments of vertebrate and arthropod striated muscle have been identified with F-actin, the thick (400 Å) filaments with L-myosin. The very thick filaments of molluscan holding muscles are composed of para- (or tropo-) myosin molecules. The structural localization of tropomyosin is not always known, but often (particularly where it has been identified with paramyosin) it is present in the form of separate, large filaments which are interspersed with actomyosin filaments.

The filaments must not be assumed to represent single protein molecules, rather they are strands of several such molecules.

THE ACTOMYOSIN SYSTEM

When actin and myosin combine to form actomyosin, the whole molecular complex shortens. The shortening is explained either as a movement of arrays of actin filaments toward and past the parallel arrays of myosin filaments with simultaneous actomyosin formation (*sliding filament theory* of Hanson and Huxley, 1955), or as contraction (by internal molecular folding) of actomyosin molecules or strands of such molecules. This shortening is part of the *active state* of the muscle fiber and is responsible for the mechanical work done by the muscle. In order for this shortening to occur chemical energy must be supplied to the actin-myosin system, which then, in turn, transforms this into mechanical energy and heat. The function of the para- (or tropo-) myosin filaments is still debated; they may hold the contracted actomyosin, preventing the reversal (relaxation) of this contraction and thus permit the maintenance of muscle contraction without continuous energy expenditure (see pp. 590–594).

The complete sequence of events that causes actomyosin contraction and paramyosin crystallization is not known, but several factors that affect their behavior are now recognized.

Actomyosin formation and shortening require the presence of nucleotide triphosphate (NTP), in particular adenosine triphosphate (ATP) and Ca^{++} ions. The chemical energy transformed into work is, perhaps directly, derived from the breakdown of ATP or possibly other *phosphagens* (see the following section as well as Chap. 7). Relaxation of vertebrate striated muscle is aided by an organic compound called "relaxing factor" (also "Marsh-Bendall factor") (March, 1951; Bendall, 1953), which is produced by microsomes and requires Mg^{++} ions if it is to be effective. Its action is inhibited by Ca^{++} ions. As mentioned in the section on excitation-contraction coupling, membrane activation is accompanied by entry of Ca^{++} into the muscle fiber. The action of Ca^{++} on actomyosin contraction may well explain, at least in part, excitation-contraction coupling.

Much of the research on the behavior of the contractile proteins of muscle has been carried out on so-called *muscle models*. These consist either of extracted and precipitated contractile proteins or of muscles from which the noncontractile proteins and other constituents have been removed by suitable extraction. The former models are usually referred to as actomyosin threads, the latter as glycerinated muscle (because glycerine is the chief extracting agent used to remove the noncontractile muscle constituents). Both types of models, prepared from mammalian striated muscle, contract in response to added ATP in the presence of Ca^{++}. The details of the experiments are, however, far too complex to be included in this rather elementary discussion. They are discussed in the reviews mentioned on the first page of this chapter.

It is unfortunate that the precise role of ATP in muscle contraction is still obscure. For a time it seemed obvious that myosin hydrolyzes the terminal phosphate bond of ATP, thereby gaining the energy for the combination with actin and for the concomitant shortening. For muscle models this is indeed the case. However, exact and detailed investigations of the chemical events during contraction of living muscle failed to demonstrate ATP hydrolysis during the initial contraction process.

MUSCLE METABOLISM

The chemical energy that is transformed into muscular work is ultimately derived from carbohydrate and lipid metabolism which is coupled to phosphorylation processes. These were described in detail in Chapter 7. Muscles are often found to store glycogen (Fig. 23–1) and can synthesize this compound

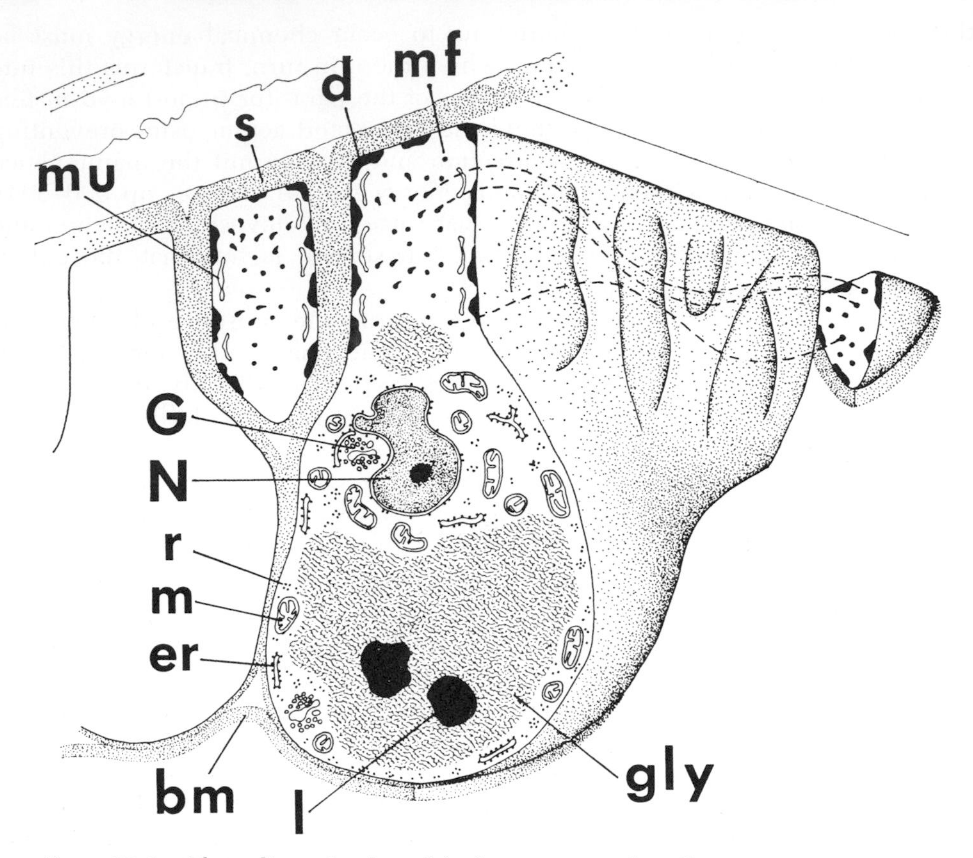

Figure 23–1. Three-dimensional model of somatic muscle cells, transversely sectioned, of a nematode, *Capillaria hepatica.* Note the large glycogen (*gly*) and lipid (*l*) reserves. The contractile elements (myofibrils) are packed near the integument of the body. *bm*, basement membrane; *d*, dense thickening; *er*, endoplasmic reticulum; *G*, Golgi zone; *gly*, glycogen; *l*, lipid; *m*, mitochondrion; *mf*, myofilament; *mu*, membrane unit; *N*, nucleus; *r*, ribosome; *s*, extracellular component of sarcolemma. (From Wright, K. A.: The fine structure of the somatic muscle cells of the nematode Capillaria hepatica [Barcroft, 1893]. Canad. J. Zool. *42*:483–490, 1964.)

from lactic acid. This synthesis requires oxygen. The energy needed to drive the reaction is provided by ATP that is synthesized with the energy released in the oxidation of hydrogen ions derived from the process known as the citric acid cycle, Krebs cycle, or tricarboxylic acid cycle. In other words, a part of the lactic acid formed in glycolysis is completely oxidized, and the energy derived from this oxidation is utilized in reconverting lactic acid into glycogen.

As long as the glycogen stores last, a muscle can do work even in the absence of oxygen. Lactic acid (or another end product) will then accumulate. As soon as oxygen becomes available to oxidize hydrogen ions, the acid is in part broken down into CO_2 and H_2 and in part is converted into glycogen. But because a considerable amount of the energy released in the oxidation process is lost as heat, and because the reversal of glycolysis is an endergonic reaction, the glycogen stores of a muscle must soon be replenished (nutrition) if it is to continue to do work. Oxidative metabolism increases the energy yield of glycogen.

The amount of glycogen used up by a muscle is directly proportional to the work output of this muscle. In a muscle whose glycogen stores are not replenished (isolated muscle in an experiment), the oxygen consumption is proportional to the work output. Thus 1 gram of glycogen, under aerobic conditions, yields an energy of 4 kilocalories (Cal), and 1 liter (N.T.P.) of oxygen yields 5 Cal if utilized in oxidative carbohydrate metabolism. About 80 per cent of this energy is liberated as heat (not only in the chemical reactions but also in the internal deformations of the contracting muscle), only 20 per cent as externally available mechanical energy. A muscle, under these conditions, is said to have an *efficiency* of 20 per cent. With a knowledge of these figures, one can calculate—or at least estimate—the carbohydrate and oxygen consumption of a muscle that does mechanical work. An example illustrates this: A 100 gm frog that jumps to a height of 10 cm does an amount of work equivalent to that of lifting 1 gm to a height of 10 meters, or 1 kg to a height of 1 cm. As explained in Chap. 12, it requires 1 cal to lift l kg to a height of 42.6 cm. Thus 1/42.6 cal is needed if the frog is to jump to a height of 10 cm. If the leg muscles are assumed to operate with an efficiency of 20 per cent, the frog actually expends 0.12 cal during the jump. This corresponds to 21 μg of glycogen and an oxygen consumption of about 15 μl (N.T.P.). How many flies does the frog have to eat in order to afford such a jump?

For every glucose unit completely oxidized, 6 molecules of water are produced, so that per mole glucose used, 108 ml of water is newly formed in the metabolizing tissue (1 liter of water equals 55.5 moles of water, 6 moles are 1/9.25 of 55.5 moles or of 1 liter). For every molecule (mole) of oxygen consumed there appears one molecule (mole or 19 ml) of water. The latter statement, of course, is true also if compounds other than glucose (glycogen) are metabolized. In the case of the 100 gm frog that jumps to a height of 10 cm, the gain in metabolically derived water is about 0.01 μl. It is unknown whether the water formed in muscle metabolism plays any functional role.

Muscle activity can be so intense that the oxygen supply is insufficient to oxidize the accumulating lactic acid or other end products of anaerobic glycolysis. Such muscles are then said to assume an oxygen debt. Their internal pH falls and the accumulating acid can eventually cause a contracture, known as *rigor*. When the activity ceases the oxygen supply once again becomes more than sufficient so that the accumulated lactic acid can be oxidized and—in part—reconverted into glycogen. The oxygen debt is thus repaid.

The important link between muscle metabolism and mechanical work seems to be molecules possessing three phosphate groups produced by this metabolism: the most common of these is *adenosine triphosphate*, known as ATP (Fig. 23–2). Other *nucleotide triphosphates* have, however, been observed, and often the more general term NPT is used to designate these key compounds (including ATP). It is characteristic of these NTP compounds that the hydrolysis of their terminal phosphate bond releases a considerable amount of energy—in the case of ATP this free energy change, ΔF, amounts to -4300 cal/mole (Podolsky and Morales, 1956). When it was discovered that myosin can achieve such a hydrolysis of ATP and that threads formed of isolated actomyosin contract when supplied with ATP, it was concluded that contraction utilizes the terminal phosphate bond energy of ATP.

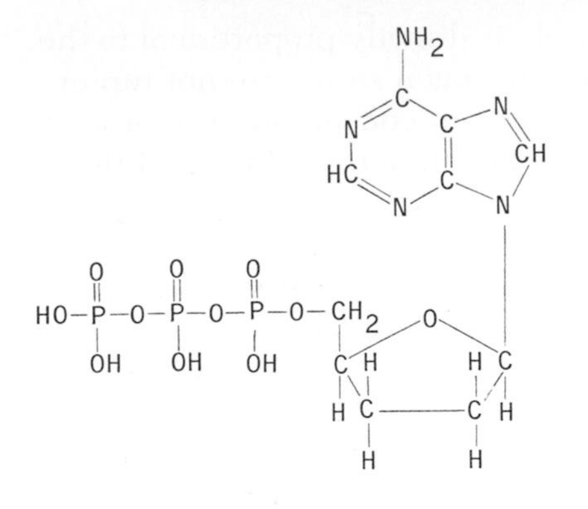

Figure 23–2. Structure of adenosine triphosphate.

Attempts to demonstrate the expected hydrolysis of ATP in living muscle fibers during single twitch contractions have failed consistently, although these results have not made the combination of ATP (or NTP) and myosin questionable. More recently it was found that this combination between contractile protein and ATP is by itself an energy-yielding reaction with a ΔF of –6600 cal/mole. The research of the next few years will undoubtedly resolve the question of whether muscles derive mechanical energy by utilizing the energy released upon binding of contractile protein and NTP, or by transforming the energy released upon hydrolysis of the terminal phosphate bond of NTP, catalyzed by myosin. Prominent research groups in this field are those of H. H. Weber in Germany, A. and A. G. Szent-Györgyi, W. F. H. M. Mommaerts, and M. F. Morales in the United States, and several others. For reviews of current and past literature, refer to the references at the end of this chapter.

At this stage of the discussion it is necessary to refer to the fine structure of muscle fibers. It must be understood that the oxidative metabolism (citric acid cycle, oxidative phosphorylation) is carried out by, and predominantly in, the sarcosomes (mitochondria).

Glycolysis and glycogenolysis are carried out within the sarcoplasm, and so is the resynthesis of glycogen from lactic acid. It is likely that glycogenolysis and glycogenesis occur in different "compartments" of the sarcoplasm (see Chap. 2).

The discovery of some new metabolic pathways suggests that glycogenesis does not proceed by way of a complete reversal of glycogenolysis and glycolysis but rather by such alternate pathways which, significantly, involve nucleotide triphosphates other than ATP. Oxaloacetate, for instance, may combine with NTP to give phosphoenolpyruvate and NDP (nucleotide diphosphate) plus CO_2 (Utter and Keech, 1960), and glucose-1-phosphate can combine with an NTP (nucleotide triphosphate) known as *uridine triphosphate* (Fig. 23–3), to give uridine diphosphoglucose yielding pyrophosphate, and uridine diphosphoglucose can then react with glycogen to add a glucose unit onto this molecule and yield uridine diphosphate (Stetten and Stetten, 1960). So far it is not known whether these synthetic pathways take place in cell compartments other than those in which the catabolic processes are going on. It is known, however, that there is definite competition for certain substrates between the glycolytic processes of sarcoplasm and the oxidative metabolism within sarcosomes

Figure 23–3. Structure of uridine triphosphate.

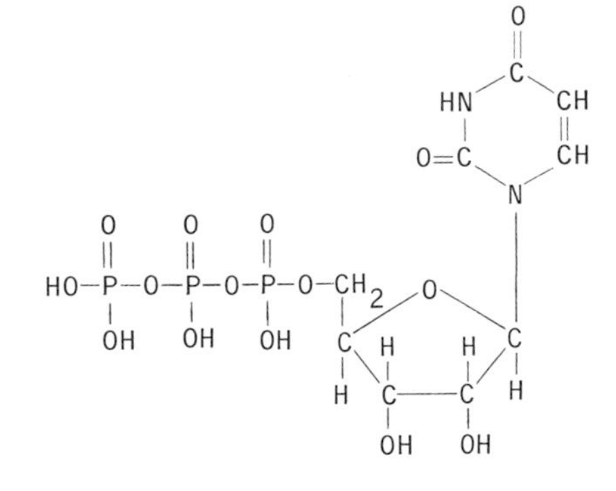

(mitochondria); the utilization of glucose is suppressed by intensified oxidative metabolism, probably because of competition for the limited amount of available phosphate. On the other hand, introduction of additional glucose can suppress oxidative metabolism. The former effect is known as the "Pasteur effect," the latter as the "Crabtree effect." Both are named after their discoverers.

Muscle fibers possess yet another group of functionally important compounds. These are collectively called *phosphagens*. Mommaerts has defined the term "phosphagen" as "a substance that is not a transitory intermediate on a major metabolic pathway, which can transfer a phosphate into a nucleotide diphosphate by an enzyme present in the tissue of its occurrence" (Mommaerts, Brady, and Abbott, 1961). Several phosphagens are known; all appear to be N-phosphorylated guanidine derivatives. In vertebrates the predominant phosphagen is *creatine phosphate* (Fig. 23–4); in most of the invertebrate phyla studied in this regard, *arginine phosphate* (Fig. 23–4) occurs instead of or in combination with creatine phosphate. The greatest variety of phosphagens occurs in the annelids (Fig. 23–5), in which creatine phosphate, *taurocyamine phosphate (Arenicola), glycocyamine phosphate (Nereis),* and *guanidyl-seryl phosphate (Lumbricus)* have been described (Thoai et al., 1953; Hobson and Rees, 1955; Thoai and Robin, 1954).

Phosphagens act, so to speak, as storage for "high energy phosphate bonds." Enzymes known as *phosphokinase* can transfer the phosphate group to NDP

Figure 23–4. Structure of two common phosphagens: Creatine phosphate (also known as phosphocreatine) and arginine phosphate (also known as phosphoarginine).

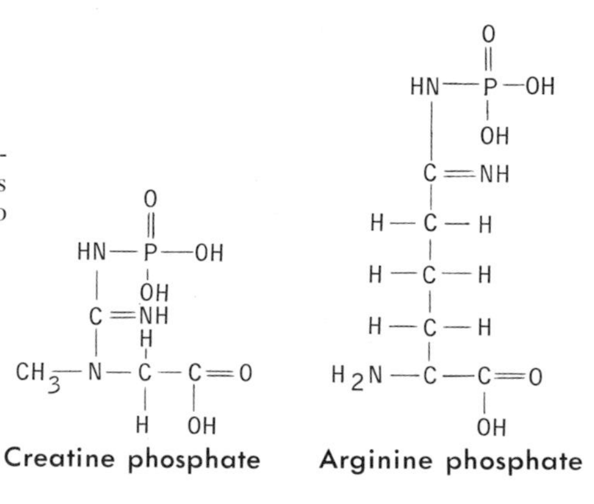

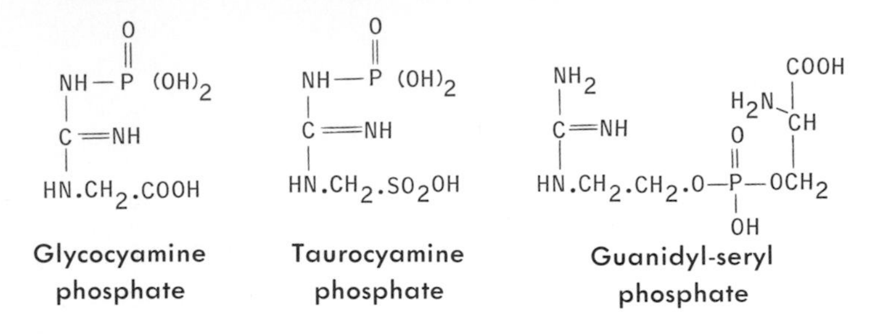

Figure 23–5. Structure of three annelid phosphagens.

(usually ADP) to form NTP (usually ATP). Phosphagens, therefore, can readily replenish the stores of NTP (ATP), a function that is of obvious significance during the increased energy expenditure of muscle contraction. Prolonged contractions (tetanus) are accompanied by a dephosphorylation of the phosphagen stores. When the muscle returns to the resting state the guanidine bases are rephosphorylated, ATP serving as intermediary.

The Regulation of Muscle Metabolism

When a muscle is stimulated, its oxygen consumption increases. In fact, the activation of energy-yielding metabolism always precedes muscular contraction – it is a condition for muscular work. The increased oxygen consumption is only a secondary effect resulting from an increase in oxidizable material – lactic acid among others. Many experimental studies have shown that it is the breakdown of glycogen (formation of 1-phospho-glucose) that is rate-limiting in glycolysis. Stimulation of muscle (or muscle fibers) leads to a great increase in glycogenolysis. Frog muscle at 20° C in nitrogen shows a thousand-fold increase during 10 seconds of tetanic stimulation (Cori, 1956).

In resting frog muscle most of the phosphorylase (the enzyme that phosphorylates and removes glucose units from glycogen) exists as an inactive proenzyme, *phosphorylase b*. In the presence of NTP and the enzyme *phosphorylase kinase*, the proenzyme is transformed into the active enzyme *phosphorylase a* (Cori and Green, 1943; Fischer and Krebs, 1955). Phosphorylase kinase itself, however, requires activation by Ca^{++} ions (Krebs, Graves, and Fischer, 1959). From these experiments emerges the following schema:

Stimulation of frog muscle causes a change in membrane permeability. This leads to an influx of Ca^{++} ions which activate phosphorylase kinase. This enzyme in turn catalyzes the transformation of the inactive phosphorylase b into the active phosphorylase a, which transfers its phosphate group to a terminal glucose unit of a glycogen molecule, thus causing glycogenolysis and the first step in glycolysis.

A similar situation is found with insect muscle (Saktor, 1959).

The role of inorganic ions in the regulation of muscle function cannot be overemphasized. Ca^{++} ions stimulate glycogenolysis as well as hydrolysis of ATP by myosin – they prevent relaxation of contracted myofibrils by inhibiting the action of the "relaxing factor." Mg^{++} ions appear to be necessary for both contraction and relaxation. The significance of intracellular K^+ and Na^+ in living muscle fibers is unknown, but there is a wealth of information concerning the effects of different concentrations of these ions on actomyosin threads (see p. 557). Minute changes in the ionic strength of K^+, for instance, cause actomyosin threads to liquefy and dissolve.

The action of inorganic anions, in particular Cl^-, is not known.

There is no question, however, that the changes in the internal ionic concentrations and activities as brought about by permeability changes of the muscle fiber membrane are the determining factors of muscle action.

REFERENCES

Bate-Smith, E. C. (1937) Native and denatured muscle proteins. Proc. Roy. Soc. B, *124*:136–150.

Bendall, J. R. (1953) Further observations on a factor (the "Marsh" factor) effecting relaxation of ATP-shortened muscle-fibre models, and the effect of Ca and Mg ions upon it. J. Physiol. *121*:232–254.

Cori, C. F. (1956) *In* Enzymes: Units of Biological Structure and Function, Chap. 7. (O. H. Gaebler, ed.) Academic Press, New York.

Cori, C. F., G. T. Cori, and A. A. Green (1943) Crystalline muscle phosphorylase. III. Kinetics. J. Biol. Chem. *151*:39–55.

Cori, G. T., and A. A. Green (1943) Crystalline muscle phosphorylase. II. Prosthetic group. J. Biol. Chem. *151*:31–38.

Dixon, K. C. (1937) The Pasteur effect and its mechanism. Biol. Rev. *12*:431–460.

Fischer, E. H., and E. G. Krebs (1955) Conversion of phosphorylase b to phosphorylase a in muscle extracts. J. Biol. Chem. *216*:121–132.

Green, A. A., and G. T. Cori (1943) Crystalline muscle phosphorylase. I. Preparation, properties, and molecular weight. J. Biol. Chem. *151*:21–29.

Hanson, J., and H. E. Huxley (1955) The structural basis of contraction in striated muscle. Symp. Soc. Exp. Biol. *9*:228–264.

Hobson, G. E., and K. R. Rees (1955) The annelid phosphagens. Biochem. J. *61*:549–552.

Huxley, H. E. (1957) The double array of filaments in cross-striated muscle. J. Biophys. Biochem. Cytol. *3*:631–648.

Huxley, H. E., and J. Hanson (1960) The molecular basis of contraction in cross-striated muscle. *In* The Structure and Function of Muscle, Vol. 1, pp. 183–227. (G. H. Bourne, ed.) Academic Press, New York.

Krebs, E. G., D. J. Graves, and E. H. Fischer (1959) Factors affecting the activity of muscle phosphorylase b kinase. J. Biol. Chem. *234*:2867–2873.

Marsh, B. B. (1951) A factor modifying muscle fiber synaeresis. Nature *167*:1065–1066.

Millikan, G. A. (1939) Muscle hemoglobin. Physiol. Rev. *19*:503–523.

Mommaerts, W. F. H. M. (1950) Muscular contraction, a topic in molecular physiology. Interscience Publishers, New York, 191 pp.

Mommaerts, W. F. H. M., A. J. Brady, and B. C. Abbott (1961) Major problems in muscle physiology. Ann. Rev. Physiol. *23*:529–576.

Podolsky, R. J., and M. F. Morales (1956) The enthalpy change of adenosine triphosphate hydrolysis. J. Biol. Chem. *218*:945–959.

Prosser, C. L., and F. A. Brown, Jr. (1961) Comparative Animal Physiology, 2nd Ed. W. B. Saunders Co., Philadelphia.

Reichel, H. (1960) Muskelphysiologie. Springer-Verlag, Berlin.

Saktor, B. (1959) A biochemical basis of flight muscle activity. Proc. 4th Int. Congr. Biochem., Vienna *12*:138–150.

Slater, E. C. (1960) Biochemistry of sarcosomes. *In* The Structure and Function of Muscle, Vol. 2, pp. 105–140. (G. H. Bourne, ed.) Academic Press, New York.

Stetten, D., Jr., and M. R. Stetten (1960) Glycogen metabolism. Physiol. Rev. *40*:505–537.

Szent-Györgyi, A. G. (1951) Chemistry of Muscular Contraction, 2nd Ed. Academic Press, New York.

Thoai, N. V., and Y. Robin (1954) Métabolisme des dérives guanidyles. IV. Sur une nouvelle guanidine monosubstituée biologique: L'ester guanidoéthylséryl-phosphorique (Lombricine) et le phosphagene correspondant. Biochim. biophys. Acta *14*:76–79.

Thoai, N. V., J. Roche, Y. Robin, and N. V. Thiem. (1953) Sur deux nouveaux phosphagenes: la phosphotaurocyamine et la phosphoglycocyamine. C. R. Soc. Biol. *147*:1241–1243.

Utter, M. F., and D. B. Keech (1960) Pyruvate carboxylase. Fed. Proc. *19*:36.

Weber, H. H. (1934) Die Muskeleiweisskörper und der Feinbau des Skeletmuskels. Ergebn. Physiol. *36*:109–150.

Weber, H. H., and H. Portzehl (1952) Muscle contraction and fibrous muscle proteins. Advanc. Protein Chem. *7*:161–252.

Wilkie, D. R. (1966) Muscle. Ann. Rev. Physiol. *23*:529–576.

24 EXTERNAL CONTROL OF MUSCULAR ACTION

EXCITATION BY STRETCHING

Muscle fibers are always elongated structures which are directly, or indirectly, attached at both ends to a substratum (connective tissue, skeletal elements, etc.). Unless both areas of attachment are moving simultaneously and in the same direction, any displacement of one or the other end of a muscle fiber produces a mechanical deformation. If the two points of attachment are moved closer together, the externally applied tension is diminished or even abolished and the muscle fiber shortens in accordance with its elastic properties. If the attachments are being separated, the external tension increases and the muscle fiber is being stretched.

Such induced length changes have profound effects on muscle excitability. As a general rule, *passive shortening of muscle* (reduction of externally applied tension) *decreases, stretching of muscle increases the excitability of its muscle fibers.*

The action of externally applied tension is four-fold: it affects (1) the muscle fiber membrane, (2) the elastic components of muscle, (3) the contractile elements directly, and (4) the nerve endings. The effects on the membrane lead to changes in membrane potential, to changes in membrane permeability, and to a redistribution of ions across the membrane. The latter changes induce alteration of the metabolic activity.

If muscle fibers are stretched, the membrane potential usually decreases. Several smooth muscles show active electric and mechanical responses to this induced depolarization. Examples are mesenteric muscles of dogfish and several mammalian visceral muscles (Bülbring, 1955; Burnstock and Prosser,

1960b). The electric activation by stretch has not been studied extensively, but we may assume this to be a widespread phenomenon.

When the elastic elements of muscle are stretched, the efficiency of the muscle increases so that it does more work when stimulated to contract. This is, perhaps, most pronounced in the muscles of hollow organs, such as heart muscles, the muscles of pulsating blood vessels, intestinal muscle, and the muscles of the body wall. They contract more forcefully when they are distended. For the mammalian heart this has been described in Starling's "law of the heart": *"the energy of contraction is a function of the length of the muscle fiber"* (Starling, 1915).

Stretching of a muscle fiber causes myofilaments to slide past each other and to change their relative positions. However, the effect of this on the performance of stretched muscle is difficult to assess.

For neuromuscular junctions of the frog it has been shown that stretch applied to muscle fibers increases the rate of spontaneous release of transmitter (acetylcholine). Such an effect might be an important mechanism in the control of synaptic excitability of muscle.

It is difficult to exclude the action of nerve fibers in any stretch-induced excitation of muscle. In the case of the spindle muscle around which the intestine of *Goldfingia* (a sipunculid) is coiled, no nerve supply is present and excitation appears to be entirely by applied stretch (Prosser, et al., 1959). Many molluscan hearts cease to contract rhythmically when they are not distended. Stretching seems to be a prerequisite for rhythmic excitation arising in pacemaker regions of the heart muscle. (See last section of this chapter.)

EXCITATION BY EPHAPTIC TRANSMISSION

With most muscles, activation occurs only in response to synaptic transmission of excitation from motor nerve fibers. However, several muscles are known where excitation of one muscle fiber can be transmitted to neighboring fibers by ephaptic, presumably electric, transmission.

Smooth muscle fibers in the intestine of the mouse, for instance, have specialized regions of contact where the fiber membranes approach each other closely. These regions offer a relatively low resistance to the passage of membrane current. Whereas the average membrane resistance of such a muscle cell is 70 megohms, the resistance between two cells is only 17 megohms. Progression of a wave of contraction (*peristalsis*) over larger areas of intestine is thus made possible by the electric transfer of excitation from one cell to the next (Prosser, 1962). It is reasonable to assume that the situation occurs in intestinal smooth muscle of other mammals.

Vertebrate cardiac muscle is another example of the transmission of excitation from one muscle fiber to the next. These fibers are joined end to end by highly folded membrane complexes (intercalated discs) as shown in Figure 22–5. These membrane areas offer a rather low resistance to electric current. While the resistance of the rest of the fiber membrane is estimated to be 500 ohm·cm^2, that of the membrane of the intercalated discs is about 1 ohm·cm^2 (Woodbury and Crill, 1961). The increase in membrane area due to the folding enhances further the passage of current from one cell to the other. Excitation, once initiated, can thus spread over the whole heart muscle without the need for nervous coordination.

Nothing is known about the transmission of excitation through the heart muscles and pulsating muscles of other phyla.

EXCITATION BY LIGHT

The iris muscle (sphincter pupillae) of a number of amphibians and teleost fishes contracts in response to illumination so that the pupil of the eye becomes constricted. This response depends on the presence of photosensitive pigment in the iris muscle. In the eel it has been shown that the action spectrum (see p. 638) of the contractile response of the iris is the same as the action spectrum of eel rhodopsin (Seliger, 1962). Since the sphincter pupillae develops from retinal pigment epithelium, it is likely that the pigment of both retinal cells and sphincter muscle are identical.

Similar induction of muscular excitation by light has been observed with cardiac muscle cells of the snail *Helix* (Arvanitaki and Chalazonitis, 1947).

It is uncertain whether the light-induced contractions are mediated by membrane activation (action or junction potentials, depolarization) or whether the activated pigments transfer their increased energy directly to the contractile elements. The mechanism of energy transfer has been discussed by Arvanitaki and Chalazonitis (1961).

It would be interesting to know whether other pigmented muscles (containing rhodopsins or hemoglobins) also respond to light. Changes in muscle excitability in response to illumination could be most important for plankton organisms.

(For further literature on photic activation of muscle, see Young, 1931, 1933a, 1933b; d'Arsonval, 1891.)

SYNAPTIC ACTIVATION AND INHIBITION

Fast and Slow Responses

Although excitability and mechanical performance of a muscle are modified by the mechanical forces and electric fields acting on it, the normal and usual mode of activation is by way of nerve impulses arriving over its motor innervation. Muscles that respond with maximal or near maximal contractions to single nerve impulses are rare even among vertebrates. Good examples are the gastrocnemius muscle of frogs (jumping muscle), the metathoracic extensor tibiae of locusts (jumping muscle), and the mantle muscle of squid (jet propulsion muscle). Most vertebrate skeletal muscles and some muscles of other animals belonging to different phyla do respond with submaximal contraction to single motor nerve impulses. The membrane of the fibers of all these muscles responds to a single nerve impulse with an all-or-nothing spike potential and this is followed by a definite contraction, the twitch. The duration of the contraction is long compared to that of the initiated muscle action potential. A sequence of action potentials can therefore give rise to a summated contraction (tetanus) of a magnitude greater than that of a single twitch.

Depending on the relative duration of twitch contractions, one speaks of *fast* and *slow twitch muscles*—but this terminology is applied only to vertebrate skeletal muscles that are composed of singly innervated muscle fibers. The term "twitch muscle" is impractical when applied to the other muscles capable of twitch contractions, because practically all of them are capable of *graded contractions* in response to graded junction potentials elicited by excitation of motor nerve endings.

Muscle fibers innervated by endings from only one motor axon are the exception. Most muscles, including the jumping muscle of the locust hindleg and the squid mantle muscle, receive a multiple innervation: their muscle fibers have a *polyneuronal innervation* (Fig. 22–12). The mode of electric excitation as well as the mode of contraction is not so much a function of the muscle fiber itself as of the kind of synaptic activation. The twitch contractions of multiply innervated muscles are termed *fast contractions*. The other mode of contraction is *slow contraction*. This is not elicited by single motor nerve impulses but requires a series of impulses—at least two. The motor nerve impulses elicit only small junction potentials which show marked facilitation. The first sign of contraction is noticed after the second or even later impulses. Contraction proceeds by stepwise increments (*summation*) which may become larger with each successive synaptic activation (*facilitation*). As a rule, the motor fibers responsible for "slow" contraction innervate their muscle fibers with many branches (*multiterminal innervation*) (Fig. 22–12).

Certain cases are known in which muscle fibers are innervated only by a "slow" motor axon and can contract only slowly. To these belong the muscle fibers of the nictitating membrane of the cat's eye, the fibers of the mammalian iris muscle, the extrafusal fibers of vertebrate skeletal muscle, certain muscle fibers of amphibians, notably the ileofibularis, semitendinosus, and gastrocnemius muscles of frogs, all muscle fibers of the frog rectus abdominis, and the abductor muscle of the dactylopodite of the legs of decapod Crustacea.

By far the most common type of motor supply is that of a double innervation consisting of fast and slow motor axons (vertebrate striated muscles are an exception). Not all muscle fibers of a muscle supplied with these two kinds of motor axon are innervated by both; some receive only the endings from the fast motor axon(s). The extent to which slow motor fibers innervate a muscle appears to be related to the extent to which the muscle is involved in the control of posture. Since the fast responses are generally involved in flight or aggressive behavior, the total activation of a particular muscle by its fast motor system is almost a logical necessity.

For many muscles that have been studied physiologically, the complete picture of both the electric and the mechanical activation is not known, owing to the difficulty of placing intracellular electrodes into extremely small fibers—or simply to lack of attention given by the experimenter to the electric or the mechanical signs of muscle action. In these cases the terms "fast" and "slow" do not necessarily imply presence or absence of all-or-nothing spikes, or presence or absence of mechanical responses to single stimuli.

Extracellular recording may, however, be sufficient in many cases: it can be assumed that all-or-nothing action potentials do not summate (because of the refractory period), whereas graded junction potentials do. These characteristics *can* be observed with extracellular electrodes. They have been used successfully in the analysis of the double innervation of the proboscis retractor muscles of *Golfingia* (Prosser and Sperelakis, 1959). Stimulation of their nerve supply gives rise to nonfacilitating and nonsummating muscle action potentials which are associated with twitch contractions, and to smaller and slower potentials associated with slow contractions, that facilitate and summate.

The existence of true fast and slow systems can be inferred for circular muscles in the bell of jellyfish (*medusae*) (Bullock, 1943; Horridge, 1956), for the longitudinal muscles of the body wall of annelids that possess giant motor fibers (Wilson, 1960), and for the mantle muscle of squid (Wilson, 1960). All can respond with strong, rapid contractions to single nerve impulses (through-conducting system, giant motor axons) and with graded slow contractions to series of impulses (arriving over another set of motor fibers). A dual innervation has also been suggested for the adductor muscles of lamellibranchs (Pumphrey, 1938; Ramsay, 1940; Röchling, 1922), and for muscles of the sphincter and body wall of certain sea anemones (literature in Hoyle, 1957a).

Two types of contraction are observed in the pharynx retractor muscles of sea cucumbers (*Cucumaria*); the slow responses to nerve stimulation are probably due to the activity of internuncial neurons present in the motor nerve complex of the muscle (Pople and Ewer, 1954).

Although the dual motor innervation represents the most common pattern, the fibers of some muscles are supplied with three or even more motor axons. They are then capable of three or more modes of contraction. Obviously the terms "fast" and "slow" are insufficient to describe such a situation, unless one speaks of fast, slow, and slower responses. The best documented cases of such multiple motor innervations are those of certain crustacean and insect muscles. The flexor muscle of the carpopodite of crayfish (*Procambarus*) and rock lobster (*Panulirus*) receives four motor axons (Figs. 24–1 and 24–2). Only 4 per cent of its muscle fibers receive branches from all four axons (1, 2, 3, and 4), 29 per cent receive branches from three axons (1, 2, 3 or 1, 3, 4 or 2, 3, 4 or 1, 2, 4), 26 per cent from two (1, 2 or 2, 3 or 3, 4 or 1, 3 or 1, 4 or 2, 4), and 38 per cent of the muscle fibers are innervated by branches of only one motor axon (1 or 2, 3 or 4) (Furshpan, 1955).

Upon stimulation none of the four motor axons gives rise to all-or-nothing spike potentials, nor do single impulses elicit a twitch contraction (van Harreveld and Wiersma, 1939). For this reason none of the responses can be classified as "fast," yet one of the four axons gives rise to a rapid contraction after two impulses, whereas the other requires several stimuli per second in order to achieve a contraction. In fact, four different types of junction potential and contraction are elicited by the four different axons (Figs. 24–3 and 24–4); the fastest of these responses is almost comparable to a true "fast" response as observed, for instance, in the adductor muscle of the dactylopodite of the same leg.

The transition between "fast" and "slow" responses in arthropod muscles may be delicate indeed: (1) if the electric responses from individual muscle

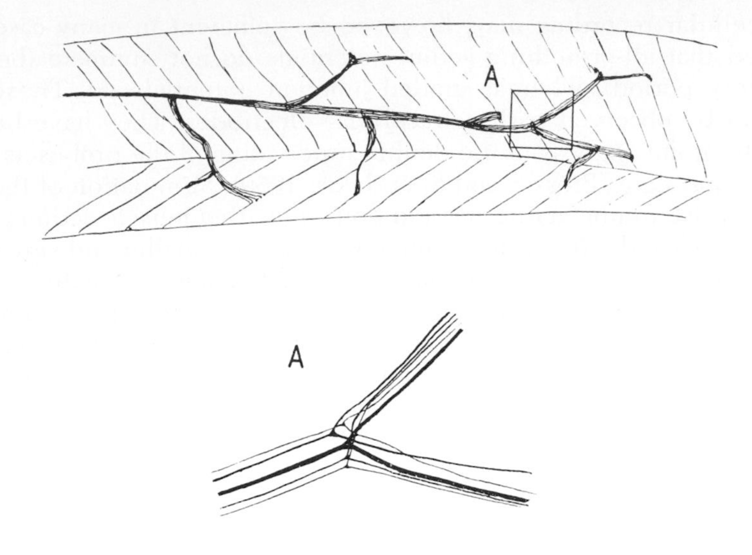

Figure 24–1. Sketch of the ramifications of the five axons (one inhibitory, four motor) innervating the flexor muscle of the carpopodite of the lobster *Panulirus*. **A** shows a quintuplotomic branching enlarged. All muscle fibers are supplied by the branches of these five axons. (From van Harreveld, A., and C. A. G. Wiersma: The function of the quintuple innervation of a crustacean muscle. J. Exp. Biol. *16*:121–133, 1939.)

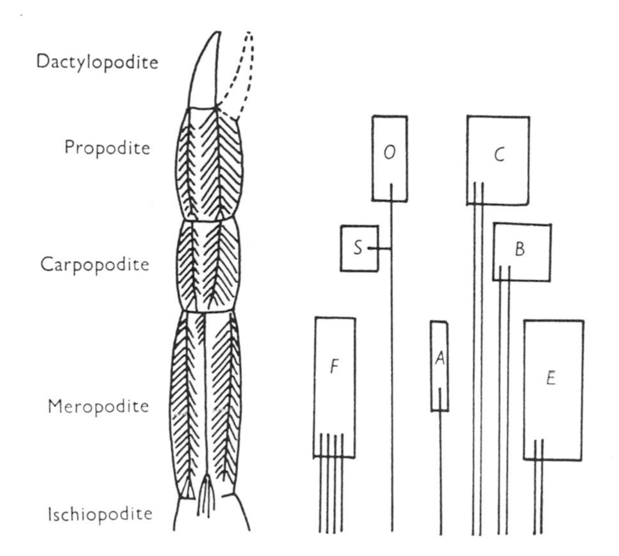

Figure 24–2. Schema of the motor nerve fibers innervating the seven muscles in the thoracic legs of the decapod Crustacea (Reptantia). **Left**, a semischematic drawing of the muscles as they are situated in the podites. **Right**, rectangles represent these muscles as follows: *A*, accessory flexor (of carpopodite); *B*, bender, flexor of propodite; *C*, closer, adductor of dactylopodite; *E*, extensor (of carpopodite); *F*, main flexor (of carpopodite); *O*, opener, abductor of dactylopodite; *S*, stretcher, extensor of propodite. Each line represents a single motor axon. (From Hoyle, G., and C. A. G. Wiersma: Excitation at neuromuscular junctions in Crustacea. J. Physiol. *143*:403–425, 1958.)

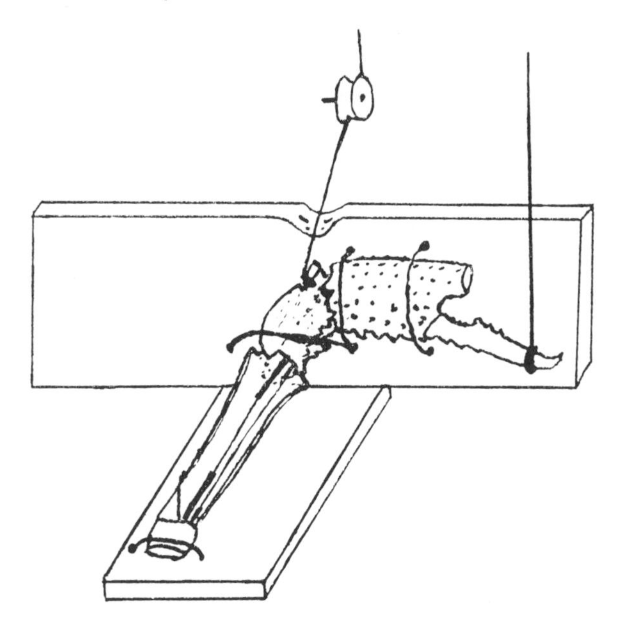

Figure 24–3. Example of how a crayfish cheliped is mounted for stimulation of its motor (inhibitory) axons and for simultaneous recording of the resulting muscle contractions. The nerve has been exposed in the meropodite and all but two axons have been cut. In this case threads have been attached to the tendon of the extensor muscle in the carpopodite and to the dactylopodite (the tip of the propodite has been cut off). The threads connect with writing levers. Pairs of platinum wires (not shown) are used to stimulate the nerve fibers. (From van Harrevald, A., and C. A. G. Wiersma: The triple innervation of crayfish muscle and its function in contraction and inhibition. J. Exp. Biol. *14*:448–461, 1937.)

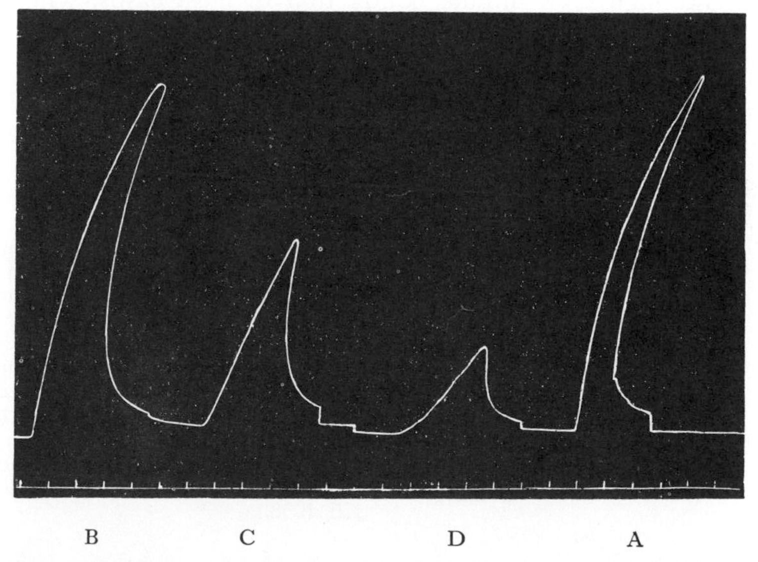

Figure 24–4. The four modes of contraction of the flexor muscle of the lobster (*Panulirus*), elicited by stimulation of each of the four motor fibers at a frequency of 30 per second. **A** shows the fastest, **D** the slowest contraction. The time marks on the kymograph record (bottom line) indicate 1 minute intervals. (For the position of the muscle, see Fig. 24–9.) (From van Harreveld, A., and C. A. G. Wiersma: The function of the quintuple innervation of a crustacean muscle. J. Exp. Biol. *16*:121–133, 1939.)

fibers (extensor tibiae, locust) supplied by branches of the same fast motor axon are recorded, it may be seen that nerve impulses elicit large spike potentials in some of the muscle fibers, but facilitating junction potentials in others (Hoyle, 1957b). (2) If stimuli to the fastest of the four motor axons of the carpopodite flexor muscle of *Panulirus* are applied in close succession, the junction potentials may summate and give rise to a spike potential (Furshpan, 1955). (3) The true "fast" response of many insect and crustacean muscles fatigues rapidly and becomes more and more like a slow response: several nerve impulses are required to start and maintain a contraction.

From this and other evidence, in part referred to in this chapter, the following picture of motor nerve control of muscle emerges: (1) Different muscle fibers of a muscle may be controlled by different motor axons or by different combinations of motor axons. (2) The different muscle fibers supplied by branches from the same motor axon may respond differently to one and the same nerve impulse originating in that axon. (3) One and the same muscle fiber may respond differently to impulses arriving over one and the same motor axon, depending on its functional history.

The electric responses of muscle fibers of decapod Crustacea are, probably, the most widely investigated. From these we know that spike responses, if they occur at all, are rather variable. Often the junction potential gives rise only to an abortive spike (Fig. 24–5). Hoyle and Wiersma (1958a), who have done much of the work referred to here, state that "the existence of spikes is not characteristic of fast systems. Large spikes are not observable in the majority of muscles in response to either slow or fast excitation. Local abortive spikes are, however, not uncommon at high frequencies of both fast and slow stimulation. Only in rare instances are the spikes fully regenerative and all-or-nothing. Although j.p.'s initiate contraction in most cases, when 'spiking'

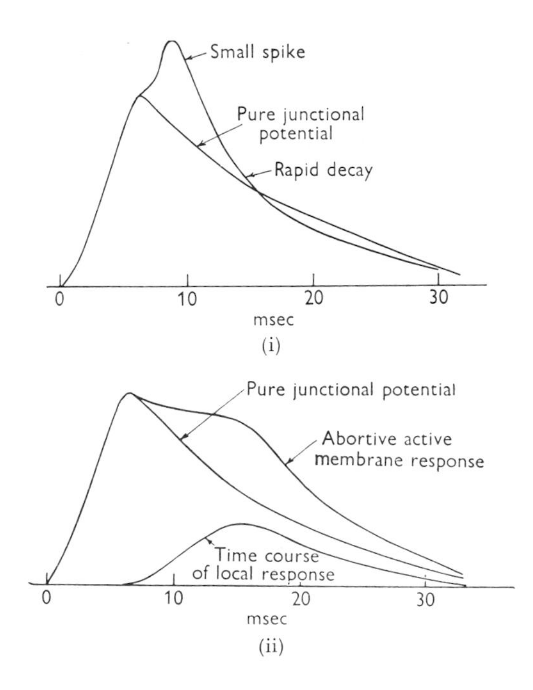

Figure 24–5. Drawings of observed potentials to illustrate two different types of departure of the response from the "pure" junction potential (j.p.) from the closer of *Panulirus*, fast response. **i**, comparison of "pure" j.p. and a j.p. giving rise to a small spike. **ii**, comparison of a j.p. giving rise to an abortive secondary response, and the time course of the latter alone, when the j.p. is subtracted. (From Hoyle, G., and C. A. G. Wiersma: Excitation at neuromuscular junctions in Crustacea. J. Physiol. *143*:403–425, 1958.)

occurs a visible additional degree of quick contraction ensues in the muscle fiber and small humps appear on the total-tension record. Muscles which give spikes to single shocks are by many times the faster, and in these cases the spikes do serve as a distinguishing feature."

This statement illustrates again the difficulty of the terminology: the true fast responses (all-or-nothing spike potential and twitch contraction) are indeed restricted to a few muscles; best known of these is the closer muscle of the chelipeds (adductor of the dactylopodite) of crayfish. In other crustacean muscles the term "fast" response refers to the faster of two or more types of responses. Since double innervation is a most common pattern also in non-crustacean animals, the distinction between fast and slow response is simply relative—but within an absolute framework of reference such fast responses may not be truly fast responses.

Considering the extreme fatiguability of true "fast" synapses and the fact that the blood circulation of muscles subjected to experimentation is always interrupted, one wonders whether true spike responses are not more common than is apparent from the experiments conducted so far.

Interaction of Fast and Slow Responses

As a general rule, simultaneous stimulation of all motor axons supplying a muscle fiber gives a summated electric as well as mechanical response. If, in the case of a doubly innervated crustacean muscle fiber, both fast and slow, responses consist of junction potentials, the summated junction potentials may give rise to a spike potential. Such summation of junction potentials elicited by different motor axons is called *hetero-summation* (Furshpan, 1955).

The electric responses of true fast responses show no facilitation (they are already maximal), whereas those of slow responses do. In the case of those fast responses where no all-or-nothing spike potential occurs, facilitation is only brief. In all slow systems, however, facilitation of electric responses is prominent. Examples are shown in Figure 24–6.

Even in fast systems there is usually pronounced facilitation of the mechanical responses. If the facilitation decays rapidly, it becomes noticeable only after high-frequency stimulation. An example is shown in Figure 24–7. Facilitation in response to stimulation of one and the same motor axon is termed *autofacilitation*.

In crustacean muscles where this has been investigated, there appears to be no influence of a previous sequence of electric responses to stimulation of one motor axon on the facilitation process of the *electric* responses to stimulation of another motor axon. In other words, the height of a junction potential is not affected if junction potentials had been elicited by *another* motor fiber, but is definitely affected if there had been previous responses to stimulation of the *same* motor axon (Wiersma and van Harreveld, 1938; van Harreveld and Wiersma, 1939). The effect of spike potentials elicited by fast motor axons on junction potentials caused by slow motor axons innervating the same muscle fiber has not been studied.

Although there appears to be no mutual interaction between junction responses elicited by different motor axons (unless they arrive in time to sum-

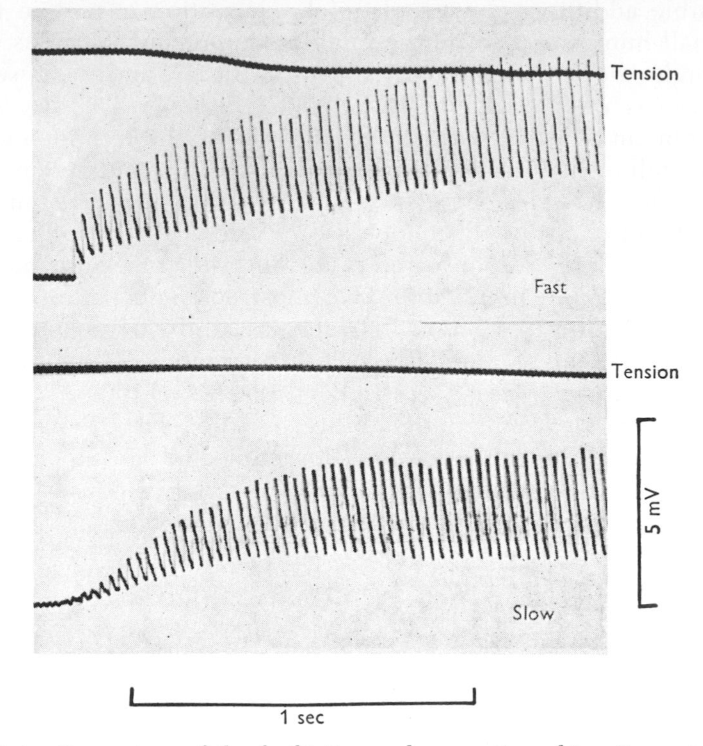

Figure 24–6. Comparison of the facilitation and summation of junction potentials elicited by stimulation of the "fast" and "slow" motor axons supplying the closer muscle of a leg of the lobster *Panulirus*. In the particular muscle fiber both fast and slow junction potentials reached the same height after full facilitation. The greater degree of maintained depolarization during the "fast" response is atypical, however. The upper trace of each recording indicates muscle tension as downward deflection. Note that the tension develops more rapidly during the fast response and that even the first junction potential is large. The first junction potential of the "slow" response is almost invisible and there is considerable facilitation until the maximal electrical response is obtained. (From Hoyle, G., and C. A. G. Wiersma: Excitation at neuromuscular junctions in Crustacea. J. Physiol. *143*:403–425, 1958.)

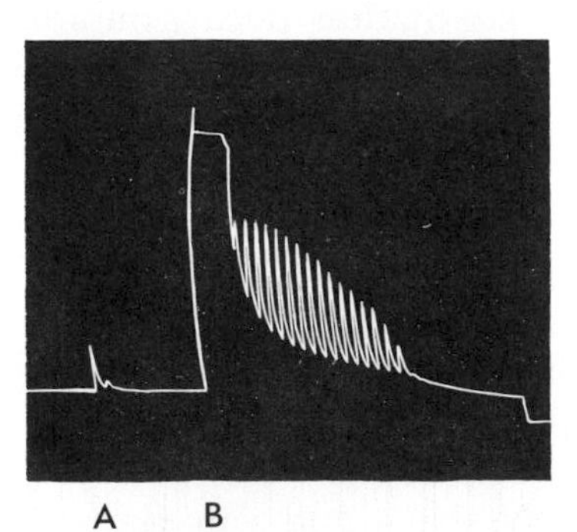

Figure 24–7. Kymograph records of contractions of the closer muscle of the cheliped of the crayfish *Cambarus clarkii*. Beginning at *A*, the fast motor axon was stimulated with 10 single pulses (1 per second). Only the first two result in a contraction. At *B* the frequency was suddenly increased to 40/sec for 3 sec. The kymograph was stopped during that time. One second later the stimulation was resumed at a frequency of 1/sec. Large twitches resulted which gradually declined. This phenomenon is called *autofacilitation*. (From Wiersma, C. A. G., and A. van Harreveld: The interaction of the slow and fast contractions of crustacean muscle. Physiol. Zool. *12*:43–49, 1939.)

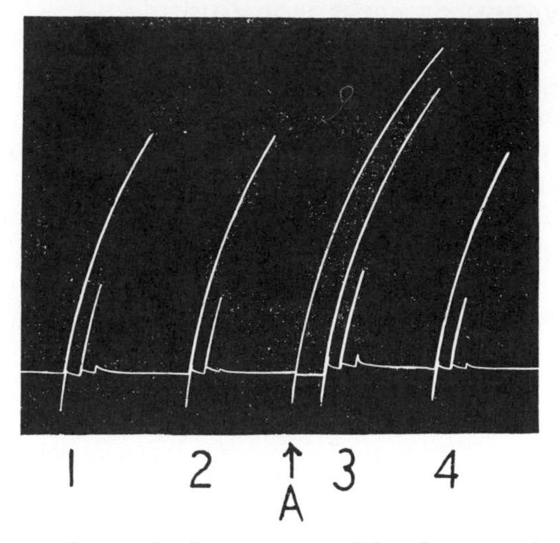

Figure 24–8. Kymograph records of contractions of the closer muscle of the cheliped of the crayfish (*Cambarus clarkii*), showing *heterofacilitation* of the fast contraction. Four series of five stimuli applied to the fast fiber at intervals of 1 minute are shown. Only the first three stimuli of each series give a visible effect. The third series is preceded by a faradic stimulation of the slow fiber for 30 seconds. This contraction is recorded at *A* (drum stopped). All three visible contractions elicited by the next stimulation series are obviously facilitated. This heterofacilitation has almost completely disappeared in the fourth series of stimuli. (From Wiersma, C. A. G., and A. van Harreveld: The interaction of the slow and fast contractions of crustacean muscle. Physiol. Zool. *12*:43–49, 1939.)

mate), there is definite interaction with regard to the mechanical response. A series of impulses arriving over one motor axon facilitates the mechanical response to stimulation of the other motor axon(s) innervating the same muscle (fiber). This has been shown for the adductor muscle of the dactylopodite and for the flexor of the carpopodite of crayfish (Wiersma and van Harreveld, 1938; van Harreveld and Wiersma, 1939), Figure 24–8.

The experiments on crustacean muscle led Wiersma and van Harreveld to propose the following schema of events*:

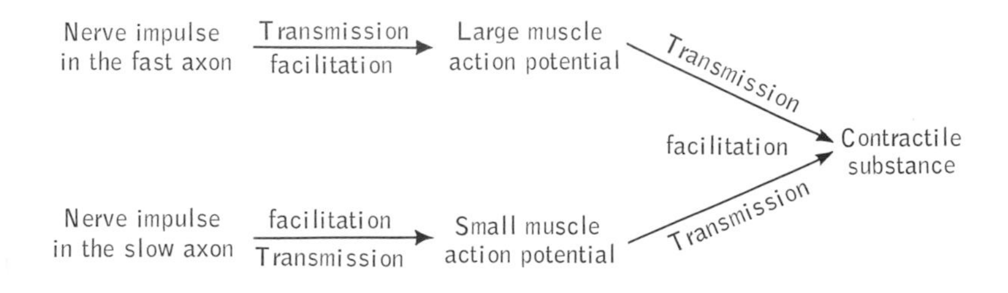

The importance of this schema lies in the recognition of the two-fold transmission of excitation: (1) from nerve impulse to muscle membrane, (2) from membrane response to muscle contraction. The second of these, in modern physiological language, is known as *excitation-contraction coupling*.

*Modified from Wiersma, C. A. G., and A. van Harreveld: Physiol. Zool. *11*:75–81, 1938.

INHIBITORY INNERVATION OF ARTHROPOD MUSCLE

As far as is known, all skeletal muscles of decapod Crustacea receive, in addition to their motor innervation, endings of one, or in some cases two, axons, the action of which prevents or reduces muscle contraction. Axons of this type are known as *inhibitory axons*.

The pattern of the total efferent innervation of leg muscles of different groups of Crustacea is shown in Figure 24–9. Several muscles may receive branches from the same inhibitory axon—in rock lobsters one inhibitory axon supplies six muscles of the same leg, in crabs, five. Wiersma (1941) has called

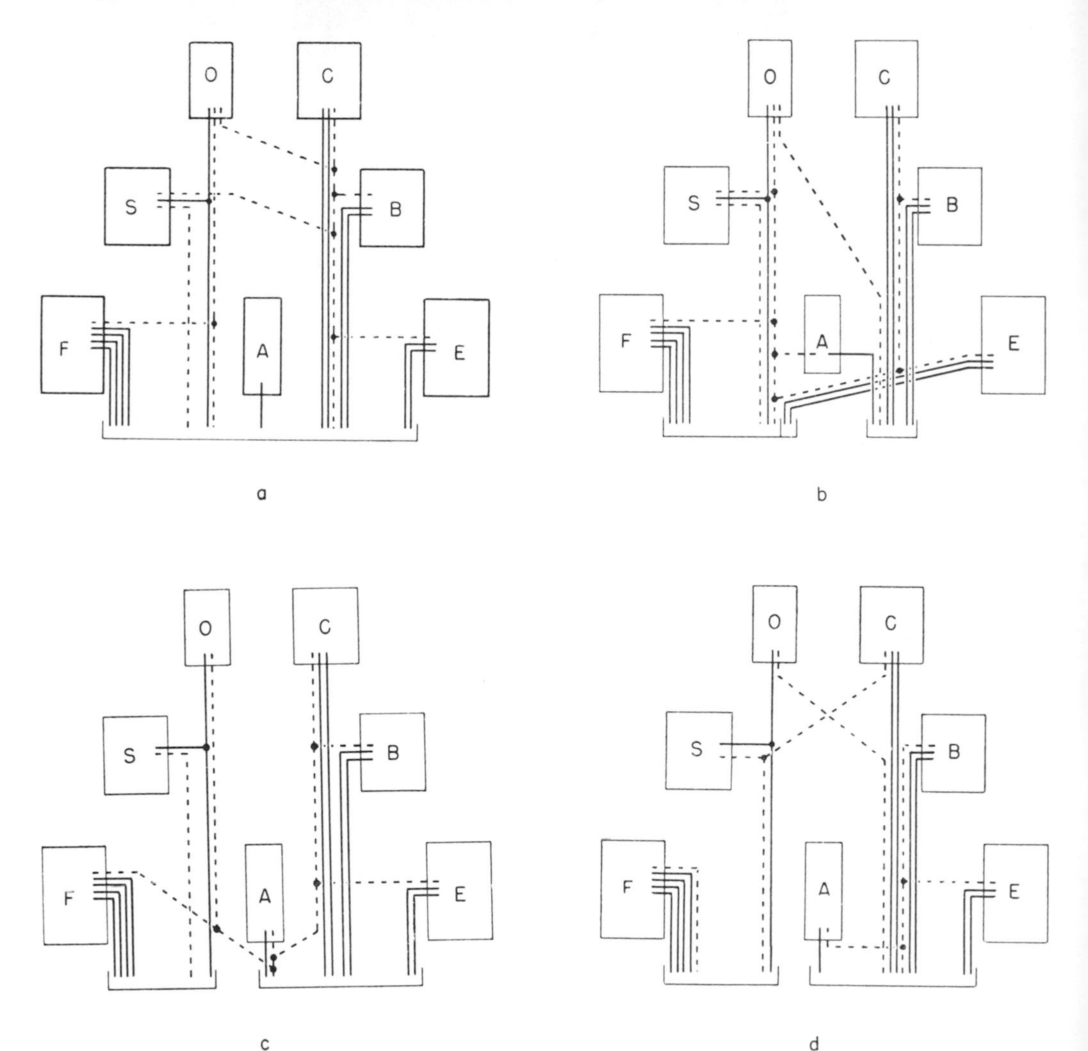

Figure 24–9. Innervation schemas for the distal muscles in the thoracic limbs of the four Decapoda Reptantia tribes. **a**, Brachyura; **b**, Anomura; **c**, Palinura; **d**, Astacura. In the Anomura the common inhibitor is variable in position and may occur in the large nerve bundle. *A*, accessory flexor; *B*, bender; *C*, closer; *E*, extensor; *F*, main flexor; *O*, opener; *S*, stretcher. Solid lines represent single motor axons; broken lines, inhibitory axons; square brackets, distribution of axons between nerve bundles, the largest bundle being on the right. (From Wiersma, C. A. G., and S. H. Ripley: Innervation patterns of crustacean limbs. Physiol. Comp. Oecol. 2:391–405, 1952.)

this the *common inhibitor*, in contrast to the *true inhibitors*, which inhibit only one or two muscles. Double inhibitory innervation is known only for muscles of two tribes of decapods, Brachyura and Anomura. Wiersma and Ripley (1952) suggest that perhaps all inhibitory axons supplying the leg muscles of Astacura are branches of the same common inhibitory axon with the exception of the inhibitory axon that supplies the opener muscle.

Impulses arriving over the inhibitory axons give rise to small, usually hyperpolarizing junction potentials. If the muscle membrane potential is artificially raised or is high (as is the case of *Procambarus* caught in spring), the inhibitory junction potentials are depolarizing (Fatt and Katz, 1953; Hoyle and Wiersma, 1958b). No electric response is observable if the membrane potential of the muscle fiber is at the reversal potential level (see Fig. 20–18).

But even if they cause no electric response or a depolarizing one, inhibitory axons prevent slow and faster mechanical muscle responses when properly stimulated (Fig. 24–10). However, the true fast responses of the closer muscle

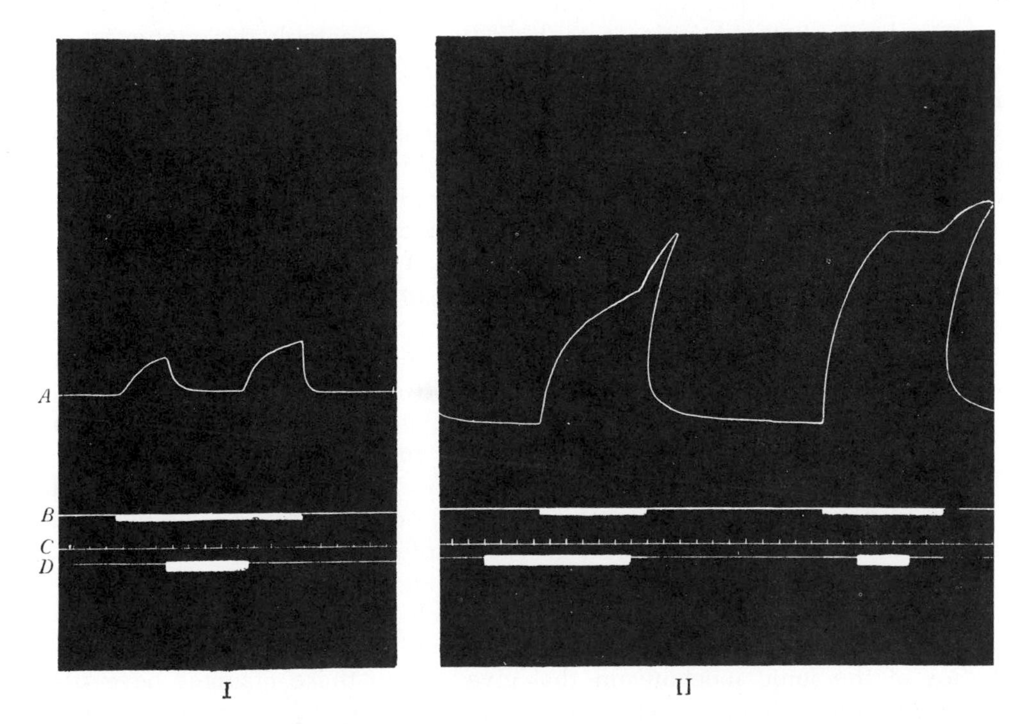

Figure 24–10. Kymograph records of the contractions of the flexor muscle of the propodite in the cheliped of a crayfish (*Procambarus clarkii*), showing mechanical inhibition of slow and fast contraction produced by repetitive stimulation of the appropriate inhibitory axon (see Fig. 24–9). *A*, isotonic mechanical record of contraction; *B* indicates stimulation of the slow (curve **I**) or fast (curve **II**) motor axon; *C*, time in seconds; *D* indicates stimulation of the inhibitory axon. Curve **I** shows complete inhibition of the contraction; in curve **II** it can be seen that the same frequency of stimulation in the inhibitory axon results only in incomplete inhibition. Note that in the first curve of **II** stimulation of the inhibitory fiber commences before that of the motor axon. Notice the difference in speed of the slow and fast contractions, especially that of the uninhibited onset of the fast one (both contractions are elicited by the same frequency of stimulation. (From van Harreveld, A., and C. A. G. Wiersma: The triple innervation of crayfish muscle and its function in contraction and inhibition. J. Exp. Biol. *14*:448–461, 1937.)

of *Procambarus* and of *Carcinus* (perhaps the only true fast responses known from the Crustacea), cannot be inhibited. There is convincing evidence that inhibition is due to a direct action on excitation-contraction coupling. The effect of an inhibitory impulse can be long-lasting; to prevent a contraction caused by a certain frequency of motor nerve impulses, it is often sufficient for the impulses from the inhibitory axon to arrive at a frequency about half that of the motor impulses.

The ratio of the frequency of inhibitory nerve impulses to the frequency of motor impulses that are just blocked has been named the *Rc ratio* (Marmont and Wiersma, 1938; Wiersma and Ellis, 1942). It was found to be remarkably constant over wide frequency ranges. Rc values for the different nerve-muscle systems of the walking legs of the rock lobster, *Panulirus*, are shown in Figure 24–11. The constancy of the Rc ratio indicates clearly that the action of each inhibitory impulse outlasts the inhibitory junction potential.

In most crustacean muscles the excitatory junction potentials are not significantly affected by simultaneously or previously arriving inhibitory impulses (note also that the inhibitory junction potentials are usually small compared to excitatory junction potentials). In some, notably the opener muscle of *Procambarus* and the closer muscle of *Cancer*, the excitatory junction potential is definitely reduced—provided the inhibitory impulse arrives just ahead of or during the excitatory junction potential. This depression of the excitatory junction potential takes place even in muscle fibers where the inhibitory junction potentials are depolarizing. An example is shown in Figure 24–12.

Muscle inhibition involving only contraction has been termed *simple inhibition*. When, in addition, the amplitude of excitatory junction potentials is reduced, this is referred to as *supplemented inhibition* (Marmont and Wiersma, 1938). Another nomenclature calls the effect of inhibitory impulses on excitatory junction potentials *alpha-inhibition* and the effect on the contractile processes *beta-inhibition* (Kuffler and Katz, 1946).

The effect of inhibitory impulses on excitatory junction potentials is obviously only incidental and probably not of functional importance. This is shown by the fact that the resulting inhibition is about the same whether the inhibitory impulses arrive just before, during, or in the interval between, the arriving motor impulses—in most cases complete inhibition results even if only half as many inhibitory pulses arrive as motor impulses.

Inhibitory junction potentials have much in common with excitatory junction potentials in that they show summation and facilitation. Detailed studies of the ionic mechanisms that give rise to these changes have been published—the general conclusion is that inhibitory junction potentials are associated with an increase in Cl^- conductance. However, according to Fatt (1961), "this conductance change has no apparent role in the function of the muscle fiber, and is thought of as an accidental property of the membrane."

The mode of action of the inhibitory axons thus remains obscure, although there is no doubt as to the final effect: the reduction or abolition of induced muscle contractions. From the pictures of recorded contractions (Figure 24–10), it is evident that the facilitation process which affects subsequent activations of the contractile elements of the muscle continues during inhibition although mechanical activation is prevented. The inhibitory action must therefore take

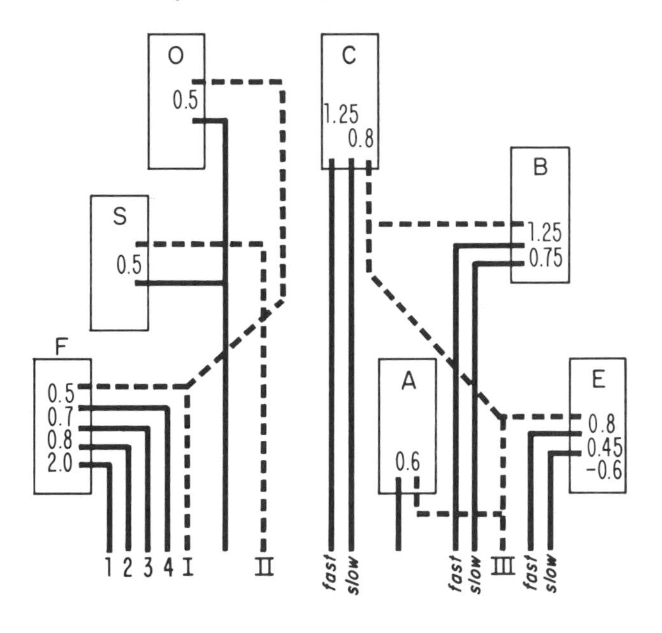

Figure 24–11. Rc values for the inhibitory systems of leg muscles of the lobster *Panulirus interruptus*. The values are shown between the particular motor axon and the appropriate inhibitory axon. Nomenclature as in Figure 24–9. (After data and figures from Wiersma, C. A. G., and C. H. Ellis: A comparative study of peripheral inhibition in decapod crustaceans. J. Exp. Biol. *18*:223–236, 1942; and Wiersma, C. A. G., and S. H. Ripley: Innervation patterns of crustacean limbs. Physiol. Comp. ['s-Grav.] *2*:391–405, 1952.)

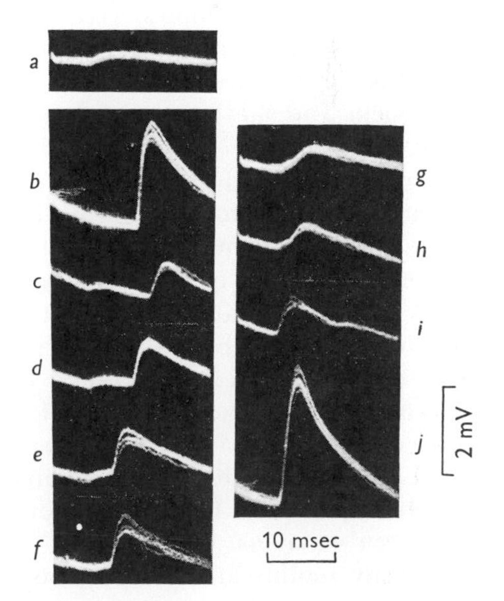

Figure 24–12. Demonstration of the effect of inhibitory postsynaptic potentials: even if they are depolarizing, they depress the amplitude of (depolarizing) excitatory postsynaptic potentials. Supplemented (α) inhibition in a muscle fiber of *Cambarus* opener which showed depolarizing inhibitory potentials. *a*, inhibitory potential alone; *b*, excitatory junction potential alone; *c–h*, progressively closer timing of inhibitory and excitatory potentials; *i*, late arrival of inhibitory potential—note summation of depolarizations; *j*, excitatory potential alone at end of inhibition. This is larger than in *b* through the facilitatory process taking place notwithstanding the inhibitory stimulation. (From Hoyle, G., and C. A. G. Wiersma: Inhibition at neuromuscular junctions in Crustacea. J. Physiol. *143*:426–440, 1958.)

place at a step between this facilitation and the activation response. The schema of events is represented below:

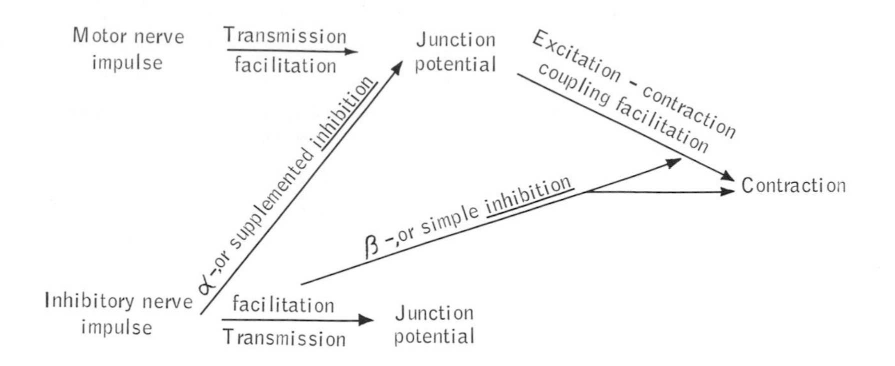

It is most significant that the action of inhibitory axons causes faster relaxation than normally occurs. This implies not only "uncoupling" but also interruption of the active state of the muscle fiber.

Readers interested in pursuing this topic further are advised to be aware that the physiological behavior of different crustacean muscles is strikingly diverse.

PARAMYOSIN MUSCLES AND THE CATCH MECHANISM

In 1912 von Uexküll described experiments on the adductor muscle of a scallop, *Pecten maximus*, carried out at the famous Stazione Zoologica in Naples, Italy. In these experiments he discovered a property that has since been found in many other molluscan muscles as well: the ability to maintain tension for prolonged periods of time in the absence of motor nerve impulses. The study was carried out as follows: von Uexküll inserted a block of wood between the gaping shells of a "relaxed" *Pecten* and tapped the animal, thereby stimulating it to close its shells. As soon as the shells pressed against the wood he dislodged the block. The shells remained gaping and effectively resisted his attempts to close or open them. His observations that the muscle "set" upon contraction led him to formulate the concept of a ratchet or catch mechanism which would, on the one hand, provide for a gliding internal rearrangement of the constituents of the contracting muscle, and on the other hand, permit catching these elements in their rearranged configuration and for holding them in this state.

Von Uexküll also noted that prompt relaxation followed stimulation of certain afferent pathways to the visceral ganglion and that relaxation of a contracted muscle can be prevented by cutting the visceral nerve that supplies, among others, the adductor muscle. From these early experiments it appeared that contraction and relaxation were produced by separate sets of nerve fibers.

Later investigators noted similar "holding" ability in the adductor muscles of other species of Pecten, but none showed the phenomenon as pronounced as *Pecten maximus*.

Many molluscan muscles consist of two types of muscle fibers, or of two separate bundles of muscle fibers, one responding with fast contractions of short duration, the other with slower but long-lasting contractions. The former are often called phasic, the latter tonic muscle fibers or muscle portions. In the case of *Pecten* the adductor muscle consists of two portions: a more transparent phasic, and a more whitish-opaque muscle which is responsible for the prolonged tonic contractions mentioned above. The relaxation of the phasic muscle portion does not seem to require the action of "relaxing" nerves and it is sufficiently fast to permit the rapid sequence of muscle contractions that cause the animal to swim. In the snail, *Helix*, the retractor muscles of the tentacles consist of a pigmented phasic and a nonpigmented tonic bundle (TenCate and Verleur, 1952). The former permits quick retraction of the delicate and vulnerable tentacles, while the latter permits prolonged retraction.

The byssus retractor muscles of *Mytilus* must stay in a shortened condition for days and months (Fig. 24–13). Relaxation occurs only when the animal is about to change its position. No ordinary muscle could sustain contraction for such extended periods of time, since tetanic contraction is bound to lead to neuromuscular fatigue, probably even before the metabolic reserves are exhausted. Many physiologists have studied this muscle, and although their interpretation of the mechanisms involved differ, they agree that the muscle can be maintained in the contracted state as long as it is occasionally (every few seconds, perhaps minutes) activated by a volley of nerve impulses.

The literature on the anterior byssus retractor muscle (ABRM) fills several hundred pages. It begins with the important discovery by Winton (1937) that repetitive stimulation of the ABRM causes contraction with immediate relaxation (phasic contraction) whereas stimulation with a long pulse of direct current causes contraction with extremely slow relaxation (tonic contraction). During tonic contraction the viscosity of the muscle is enormously increased. Twarog (1954) discovered that the tonic contraction can be initiated by acetylcholine and that only phasic responses can be obtained from the muscle after this has

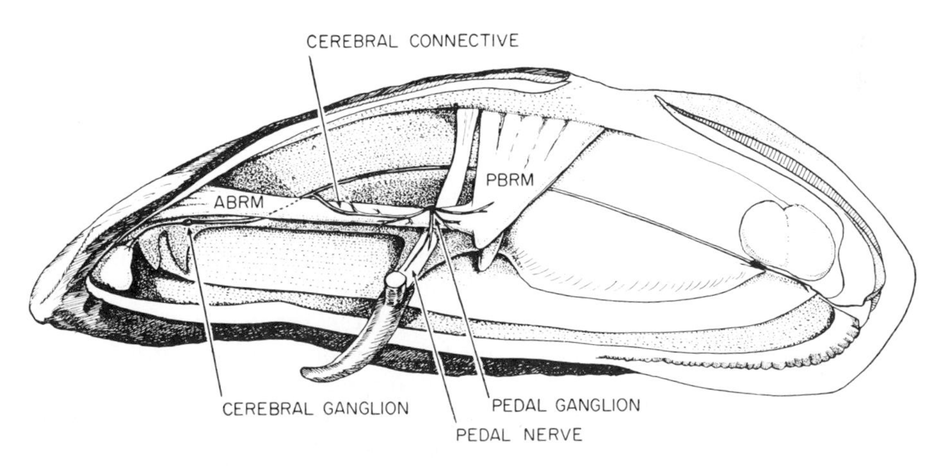

Figure 24–13. Inside view of right half of *Mytilus* to show the position and innervation of the anterior byssus retractor muscle (*ABRM*) and its innervation. *PBRM*, posterior byssus retractor muscle. (From Hoyle, G.: Muscle and neuromuscular physiology. *In* Physiology of Mollusca, Vol. 1. K. M. Wilbur and C. M. Yonge, eds. Academic Press, New York, 1964.)

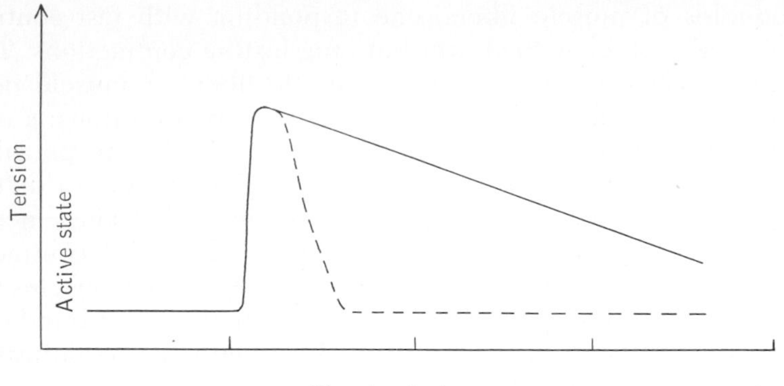

Figure 24–14. Duration of active state and of contraction in the anterior byssus retractor muscle of *Mytilus*. Solid line: contraction; dashed line, active state. (Constructed from data by Johnson, W. H., and B. M. Twarog: The basis for prolonged contractions in molluscan muscles. J. Gen. Physiol. *43*:941–960, 1960.)

been treated with 5-hydroxytryptamine. She considers these two substances to be the transmitter substances of the motor fibers and relaxing nerve fibers respectively. Hoyle and Lowy (1956) attributed the maintained contraction to continued activation of the muscle, either by spontaneously arising action potentials or by the action of intrinsic ganglion cells. However, later investigations failed to show ganglion cells in the ABRM and revealed that there is no definite correlation between the electrical activity that can be recorded from the muscle and the tension which the muscle maintains during tonic contraction. Perhaps the best published illustration of the fundamental responses of the ABRM is that given by Hoyle and Lowy (1956) and reproduced in Figure 24–15.

Johnson and Twarog (1960) have, in fact, demonstrated that tonic contraction can be induced and maintained (after d.c. stimulation) even after all electrical (spontaneous?) activity has been abolished by tetracaine, an anesthetic. They have also shown that the active state of the ABRM, defined as the ability to redevelop tension after a quick tension release, disappears long before the decay of tension (see Fig. 24–14).

In 1957, Bailey discovered that the ABRM contain large amounts of tropomyosin A in the form of rather conspicuous filaments that are many times thicker than those of actin and myosin. The filaments have been known as paramyosin filaments and they characteristically occur only in the slow, or holding, muscles (for instance, only in the slow-acting portion of the adductor muscle of *Pecten*). Many experiments were designed to elucidate the mechanism of these paramyosin filaments. They have led to the formulation of an intriguing concept: while contraction is caused by acto-myosin interaction, the muscle is held in the contracted state by the paramyosin filaments due to a change of state (crystallization) of the paramyosin (see Philpott, Kahlbrock, and Szent-Györgyi, 1960; Ruegg, 1962; and Ruegg, Straub, and Twarog, 1962); relaxation is brought about by the action of relaxing neurons that release 5-hydroxytryptamine. This compound is assumed to disengage the paramyosin system.

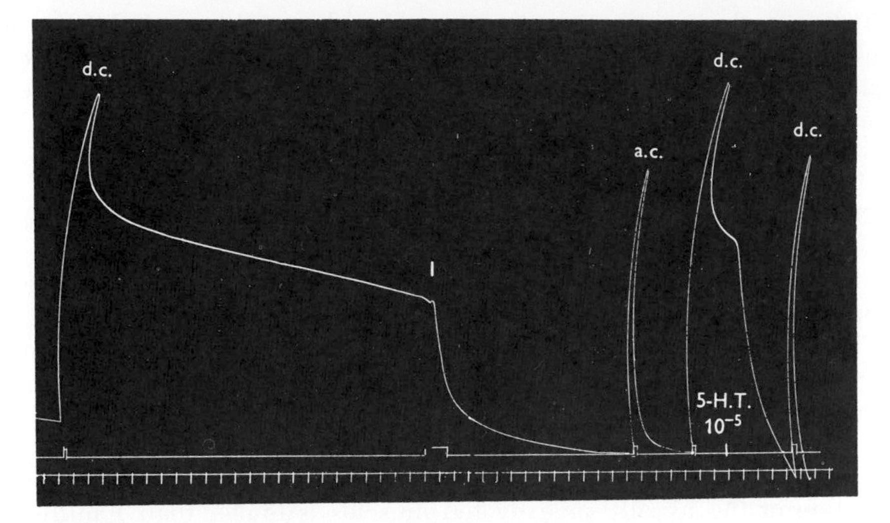

Figure 24–15. Isometric recording of contractions of the anterior byssus retractor muscle of the lamellibranch *Mytilus californianus*. Upper curve: tension. Middle curve: event marker indicating duration of electrical stimulation or time of addition of drugs. Lower curve: time marks every minute. The record shows: prolonged contraction in response to a pulse of direct current (*d.c.*); relaxation due to stimulation of inhibitory nerve (at 1); short-lasting contraction (phasic response) caused by brief stimulation with alternating current (*a.c.*) (50 pulses/sec); tonic contraction induced by d.c. stimulation, relaxation after addition of 5-hydroxytryptamine (*5-H.T.*), final concentration 10^{-5} gm/ml; after treatment with 5-H.T. the muscle responds to d.c. stimulation with a phasic contraction, as it is no longer capable of a sustained, tonic response. (From Hoyle, G., and J. Lowy: The paradox of Mytilus muscle. A new interpretation. J. Exp. Biol. *33*:295–310, 1956.)

The various responses of the ABRM can be explained as follows (this has already been stated by Jewell, 1959): stimulation of the excitatory neurons (e.g., d.c. stimulation) only gives rise to tonic contraction whereas stimulation of both the excitatory and the relaxing neurons (a.c. stimulation) causes a phasic contraction. But as early as 1959, Cambridge, Holgate, and Sharp pointed out that d.c. stimulation most likely affects the muscle directly and my own recent experiments indicate that the chromatophore muscles of squid, which do not contain paramyosin filaments, also respond to d.c. stimulation with a prolonged contraction. These chromatophore muscles go into tonic contraction in response to acetylcholine and are relaxed by 5-hydroxytryptamine (Florey, 1966). It becomes more and more likely that the "catch mechanism" of molluscan holding muscles is not dependent on the paramyosin filaments. On the basis of extensive experimentation with *Mytilus* ABRM's, Lowy and Millman (1963) have proposed an alternative hypothesis that explains the catch mechanism in the following way: whereas active state is represented by the formation of linkages between actin and myosin filaments, the decay of tension is governed by the rate of linkage breakage. This rate depends on the amount of a relaxing substance, probably 5-hydroxytryptamine, within the muscle. The most convincing evidence in support of this "link hypothesis" is the finding that the amount of shortening and the velocity of shortening are identical in phasic and tonic contraction. If the increased stiffness of the ABRM during tonic contraction were due to crystallization of tropomyosin (paramyosin), one would expect the shortening to proceed more slowly and less extensively.

There can be no question, however, that the molluscan holding muscles represent a rather unique type of muscle which is capable of maintaining (passive) tension for prolonged periods of time without requiring frequent activation and concomitant elevated metabolism.

INSECT FLIGHT MUSCLES AND TYMBAL MUSCLES

Anyone modestly acquainted with physics who has experienced the alarming sound of an approaching mosquito is aware that the wing-beat frequency of insects can reach several hundred per second. If each downstroke of the wing is caused by a muscle contraction, we would have to assume an extraordinary performance of the wing muscles—a cycle of shortening and relaxation within 1 to 2 milliseconds. Action potentials alone are known to last longer than that, and the delay between muscle action potential and onset of contraction of the usually investigated muscles is longer than 1 millisecond.

A few physiologists have designed ingenious experiments and have obtained results that explain how these fast-acting wing muscles operate. These muscles act against the elastic exoskeleton which, in turn, moves the wings. The exoskeleton, therefore, resembles a spring. The muscle contraction is isometric, because the load increases as the muscle shortens.

In insects with lower wing-beat frequencies, such as large beetles and moths, the flight muscles can give twitch contractions to single motor nerve impulses and reach contraction frequencies sufficient to account for the frequency of wing beats. It is interesting, however, that this is so only under isometric conditions and at temperatures somewhat higher than ambient. Such insects are known to raise their body temperature during the initial phase of preparation for flight (Krogh and Zeuthen, 1941).

In flies (Diptera), in which high wing-beat frequencies are the rule, the wings are inserted at a junction between two major skeletal elements, the (lateral) pleurum and the (dorsal) scutum, and the major wing muscles attach to the apophysis of the pleurum. When these muscles develop tension they eventually cause the base of the wing to snap over the edge of the pleurum while the pleurum suddenly advances toward the edge of the scutum. As this happens the muscle is suddenly released and tension falls to zero. In the absence of a restraining force the elastic pleurum returns toward its original position, forcing the base of the wing again inward over its edge. As it does so the pleurum stretches the muscle—and if this is still in the active state it develops tension anew and the cycle begins once again.

The mechanical resistance of the pleurum is aided by the pull of certain antagonistic muscles. The whole process is actually much more complex than is described here. In essence, however, the principle of function of the wing muscles is: one nerve impulse causes an active state which permits repeated redevelopment of tension: relaxation—or tension release—is caused by a sudden mechanical "give" of the skeletal element in which the muscle is inserted (details of this click mechanism are described in Boettiger and Furshpan, 1952, 1954; Boettiger, 1955, 1957; and Pringle, 1957).

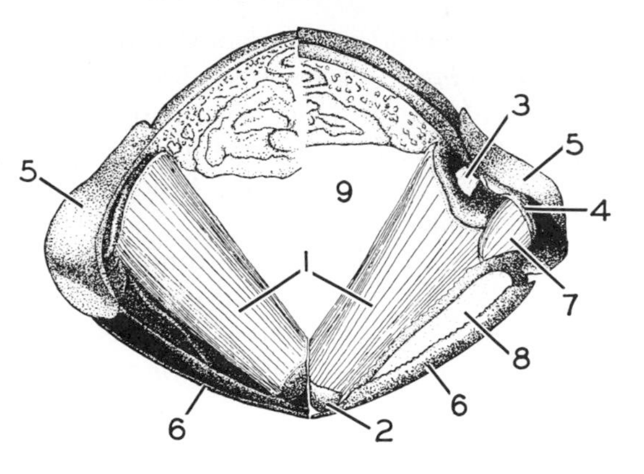

Figure 24–16. Tymbal muscle and its accessories, of the cicada (Orthoptera) *Graptopsaltria nigrofuscata.* Left half: posterior view. Right half: anterior view. *1*, tymbal muscle; *2*, chitinous process; *3*, apodeme; *4*, tymba; *5*, tymbal cover; *6*, operculum; *7*, tensor muscle; *8*, tympanum; *9*, resonance chamber. (From Ikeda, K.: Studies on the origin and the pattern of the miniature electrical oscillation in the insect muscle. Japan. J. Physiol. 9:484–497, 1959.)

Similar to these fast flight muscles are the muscles of the sound-producing organ, the *tymba,* of cicadas (Fig. 24–16). The organ consists of a stiff, curved membrane over a resonance chamber in which the tymbal muscle is situated. The main part of the muscle attaches to the center of the tymbal membrane; the other portion (not present in all species) attaches to the edge of this membrane. A motor-nerve impulse causes a muscle action potential in the main muscle. This leads to tension development. The muscle contracts isometrically against the membrane until the membrane buckles inward. At this moment the muscle is allowed to shorten, and tension falls instantly. This sudden reduction of muscle tension permits the membrane to buckle outward again; thereby the muscle is stretched once more. Tension redevelops and again the membrane buckles inward. Thus one muscle action potential is responsible for an active state which permits a series of membrane movements. The sound frequency emitted by the organ is therefore several times higher than the frequency of motor nerve impulses or muscle action potentials (Pringle, 1954). The other part of the muscle contracts tetanically to series of motor nerve impulses. It is employed in the "tuning" of the tymbal membrane.

There is great variation of the general schema, as outlined here, from species to species. In some forms, in fact, the ratio of action potential to sound pulses is 1:1. Organs of these species emit only low-frequency sound.

For an illuminating review and discussion of the topic of insect flight—and of tymbal muscles—see Pringle (1957).

ELECTRIC ORGANS

An extraordinary modification of muscle function is found in the so-called electric organs of fish. Such organs have been discovered in representatives of many families of marine elasmobranchs and fresh-water teleosts. Of these the mediterranean electric ray, *Torpedo*, and the South American electric eel, *Electrophorus*, are the most famous, largely because they have been known for centuries. There is also one family of marine teleosts with representatives that possess electric organs, namely, the *Uranoscopidae*, with *Astroscopus* ("stargazer") occurring on the Atlantic coast of America.

The electric organs consist of modified muscle fibers, the *electroplates* or *electroplaques*, so-named after their platelike structure. In the elasmobranch fishes they are derived from branchial or skeletal muscle, in the teleost star-gazers they represent modified ocular muscles. The electroplaques do not contract and are devoid of a functional contractile apparatus. They are stacked up in columns.

The electroplaques are innervated by cholinergic "motor" fibers. Characteristically only one side of each plate is innervated, and all innervated sides of a column face the same way. As a rule the orientation of the plates of all columns is identical, but in *Gymnotus carapo* one of the four columns on each side of the animal shows rostral innervation, whereas the other three are caudally innervated. A similar situation occurs in *Narcine brasiliensis*. Figure 24–17 shows several species of electric fish and their electric discharges.

The electroplates may be smooth on both sides (Torpedinidae), or one side is highly digitated or provided with one or more stalks (Rajidae, electric skates), whereas the other side is more or less smooth. The *Raja* electroplaques are innervated on their smooth side; in the others the stalks are innervated. In other types of electric organs (those of *Electrophorus*, for instance) both faces

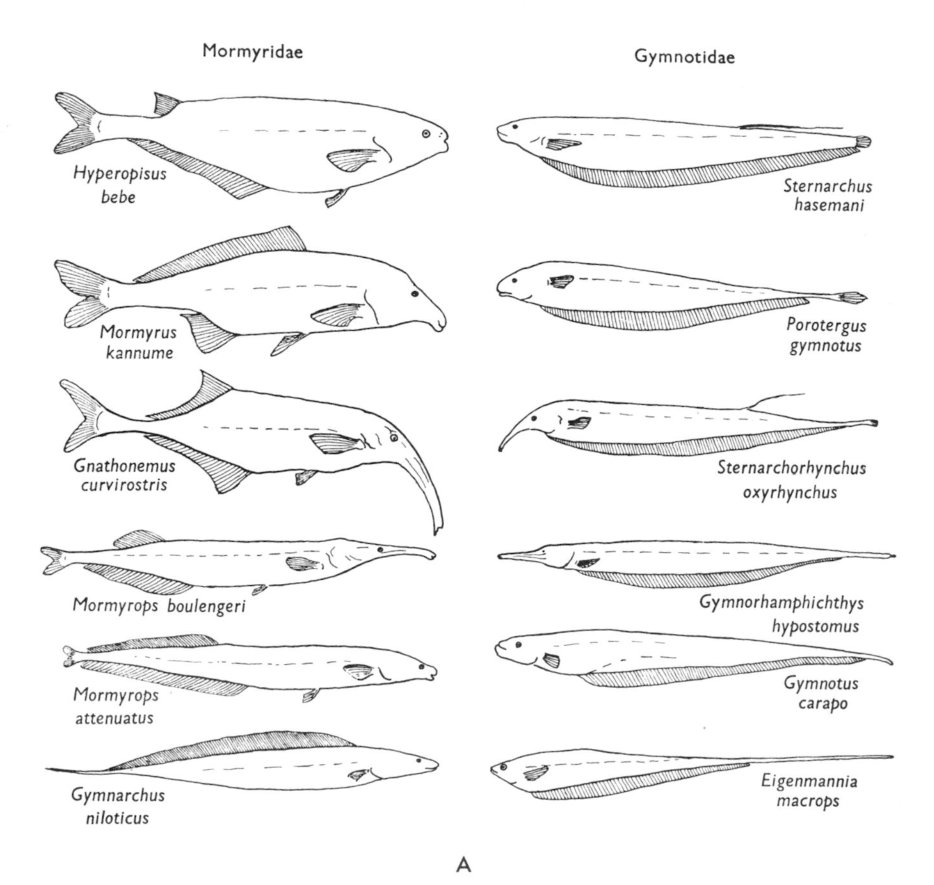

Figure 24–17. *See opposite page for legend.*

are irregular, but the noninnervated side of each plate is the more irregular one and is provided with numerous papillae. Examples of electric organs and electroplaques are shown in Figure 24–18.

The innervating nerve fibers usually branch profusely and make numerous synaptic contacts with the electroplaque. The innervated portions of the electroplaques show an extraordinarily high acetylcholinesterase activity. Even if the enzyme activity is determined in extracts of the whole electroplaques, it is higher than that of any other organ of vertebrate or invertebrate origin.

The columns of electroplaques function like voltaic piles.* They are synchronously activated by nerve impulses. In the marine forms and in the electric eel only the innervated face of each electroplaque responds by a depolarization, whereas the other side maintains its resting potential. In many of the fresh-water forms the noninnervated side participates in the response; it may reach its peak earlier than that of the innervated side, but as a rule the response of the innervated side precedes that of the noninnervated side (gymnotids, mormyrids) giving rise to a diphasic current flow. The experimental arrangement and examples of electric responses recorded from diverse electroplaques of *Electrophorus* with microelectrodes are shown in Figures 24–19 and 24–20.

Since, in many of the cases (see above) one side of the electroplaques depolarizes while the other retains its resting potential (although in certain organs it may later follow with an active response), each plate becomes elec-

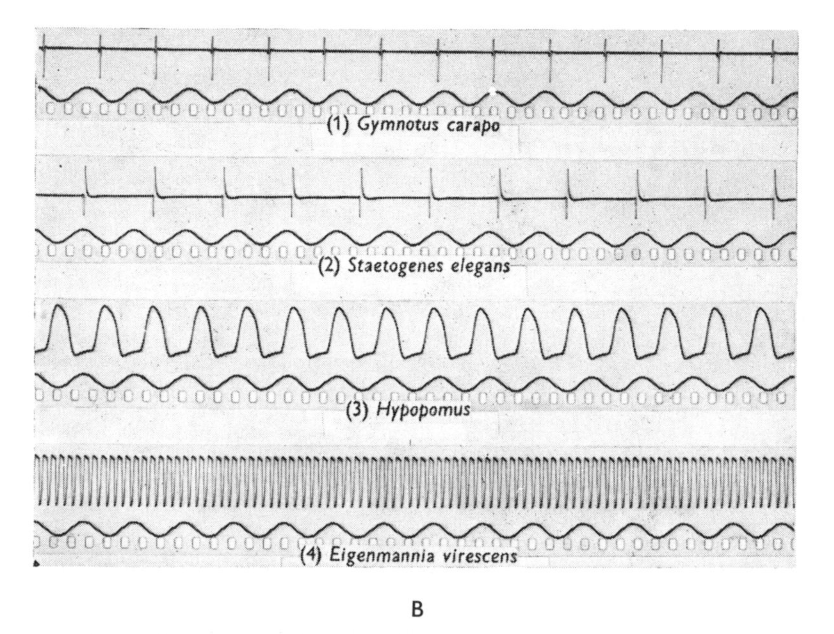

B

Figure 24–17. A, Examples of electric fishes of two families (Mormyridae and Gymnotidae). They inhabit fresh water and continuously send out low-voltage electric pulses, samples of which are shown in **B.** The upper line of each recording represents the wave form of the pulses as they appear on the screen of an oscilloscope; the lower trace represents a 50 cycle sine wave as a time marker. If fed into a loudspeaker, the pulses of the lower two examples are audible as a steady tone. (From Lissmann, H. W.: On the function and evolution of electric organs in fish. J. Exp. Biol. 35: 156–191, 1958.)

*Volta called his "pile" an artificial electric organ.

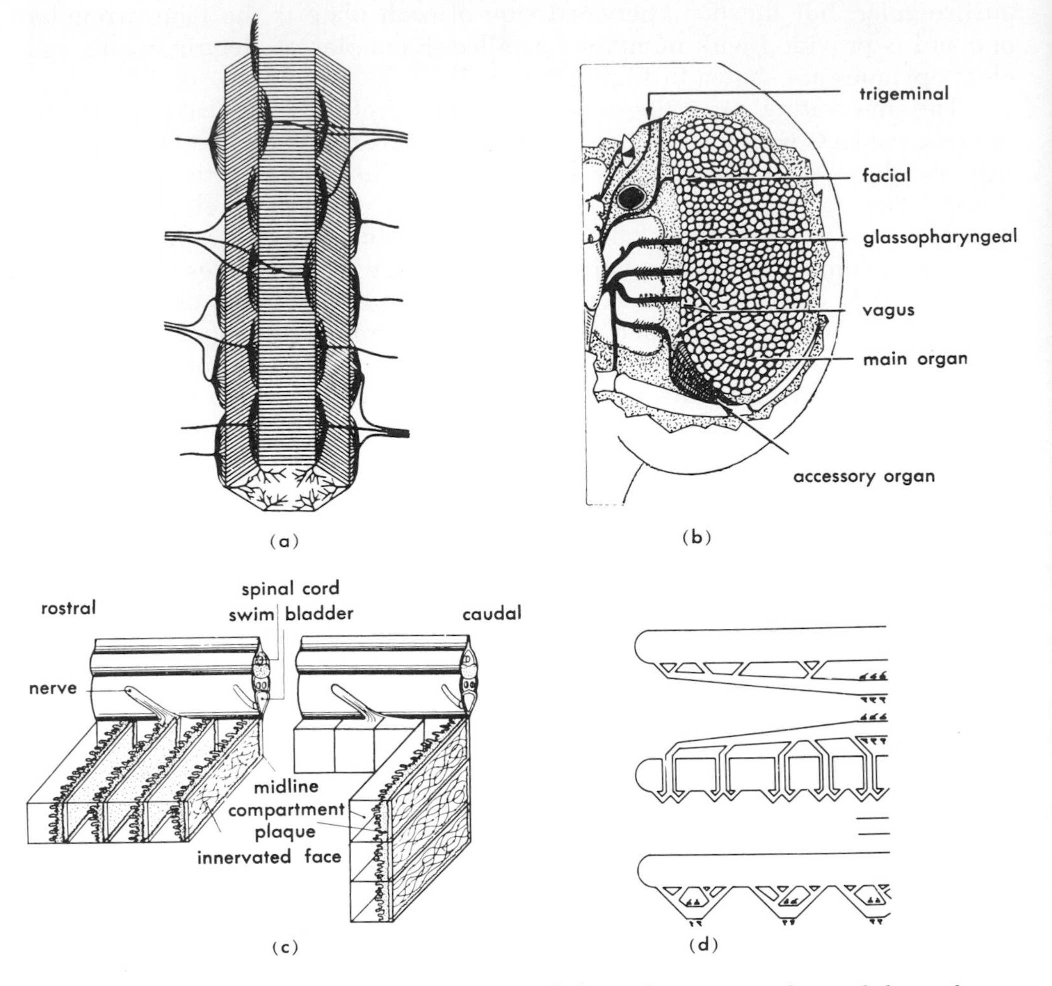

Figure 24–18. Examples of electric organs and electroplaques. **a**, a column of electroplaques as found in *Torpedo* and *Astroscopus*. **b**, dorsal view of the main electric organ (shown in cross section) and the accessory organ and their innervation by cranial nerves, as present in *Torpedo* and *Narcine* (in *Torpedo* the accessory organ is absent). **c**, series and parallel arrays of electroplaques in the electric eel (*Electrophorus*). **d**, the electroplaques of mormyrid fishes and of *Malapterurus* are innervated on one or more stalks which arise on the caudal surface, and in some species penetrate the electroplaque body. In *Malapterurus* there is only a single stalk which arises from the center of the caudal face of the electroplaque. (From Grundfest, H.: Electric Organ (Biology). McGraw-Hill Encyclopedia of Science and Technology 4:427–433, 1960.)

trically polarized so that the innervated face of each electroplaque becomes temporarily negative with respect to the noninnervated face. This particular relationship (reversed only in the electric organs of *Malapterurus*), is called *Pacini's rule* (Garten, 1910–1914). Each column of electroplaques thus becomes a series of electric elements consisting of alternating positive and negative "plates" (Fig. 24–21). The potential difference of each activated electroplaque is usually several tens of millivolts, and in some cases more than 100 mV (150 mV in *Electrophorus*, Keynes and Martins-Ferreira, 1953), because of a large overshoot of the action potential.

The *voltage* developed by the whole column depends on the number of elements *in series*. The *current* is proportional to the number of elements *in parallel* and to the surface area of each element (electroplaque). In the elasmobranchs the columns are short, but many are in parallel. Consequently the voltage produced during one discharge is relatively small (up to a few tens of volts, see Table 24–1), whereas the current amounts to several amperes. In *Electrophorus* there are several thousand plates per column. Consequently the electric discharge of each column can reach several hundred volts, although the current is relatively weak because of the small number of parallel columns (Table 24–1). Even so, the current is unusually strong, considering that it

Table 24–1. Discharge of Electric Organs and Response Patterns of Their Constituting Electroplaques

Species	*Discharge*			*Response*			
						Duration, msec	
	Amplitude, volts	*Form*	*Frequency*	*Amplitude, mV*	*Type**	*Postsynaptic potential*	*Spike*
Torpedo nobiliana	60	Monophasic	Repetitive on excitation	Max. 80	1	5	None
Narcine brasiliensis							
Main organ	30	Monophasic	Repetitive on excitation	Max. 80	1	5	None
Accessory organ	0.5	Monophasic	Repetitive on excitation	Max. 80	1	5	None
Raia clavata	4	Monophasic	Repetitive on excitation	Max. 80	1	25	None
Astroscopus y-graecum	7	Monophasic	Repetitive on excitation	Max. 80	1	5	None
Electrophorus electricus	700	Monophasic	Repetitive on excitation	Min. 100	2	2+	2+
Eigenmannia virescens	1	Monophasic positive direct current	250/sec	Min. 100	2	1	2
Sternopygus elegans	1	Monophasic positive direct current	50/sec	Min. 100	2	2	10
Gymnotus carapo	1	Triphasic	50/sec	Min. 100	3	1.5	1
Sternarchus albifrons	1	Diphasic	750/sec	Min. 100	3		
Gnathonemus compressirostris	10	Diphasic	Variable	Min. 100	4		0.2
Mormyrus rume	12	Diphasic	Variable	Min. 100	4		5
Gymnarchus niloticus	Low	Monophasic	300/sec	?	?		
Malapterurus electricus	300	Monophasic	Repetitive on excitation	Min. 100	4		2

*Response types: *1*, electrically inexcitable electroplaques which produce only a postsynaptic potential and only on the innervated surface; *2*, responses are both postsynaptic potentials and spikes, produced only at the innervated surface; *3*, opposite, uninnervated surface also is electrically excitable, producing a spike, whereas the innervated surface develops both a postsynaptic potential and a spike; *4*, the synaptic junction is at a distance from the major surfaces of the electroplaque on one or several stalks produced by the caudal surface, and both major surfaces produce spikes. Grundfest, H.: Electric Organ (Biology). McGraw-Hill Encyclopedia of Science and Technology, *4*:427–433, 1960.

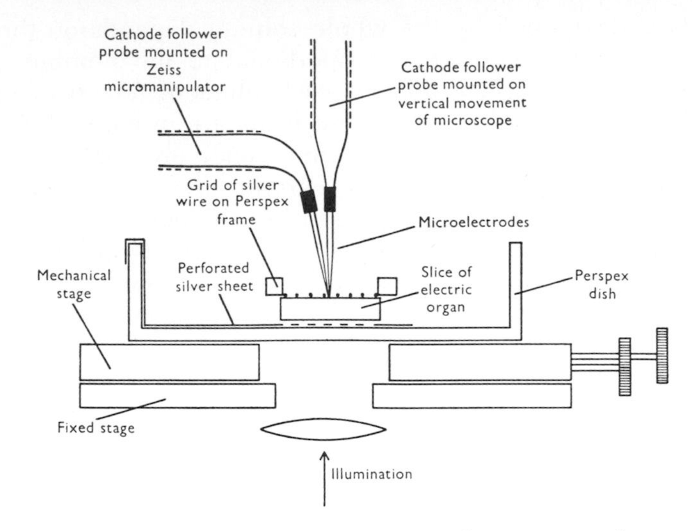

Figure 24–19. Simplified diagram of the experimental arrangement for stimulation and recording of membrane potentials from electroplaques (electric eel, *Electrophorus*). Electrical stimuli (square waves) are applied through the perforated silver sheet and the grid of silver wire. (From Keynes, R. D., and H. Martins-Ferreira: Membrane potentials in the electroplates of the electric eel. J. Physiol. *119*:315–351, 1953.)

represents nothing but a series of action currents. The reason for this is the rather low resistance of the membranes of the electroplaques. In *Electrophorus*, for instance, the innervated electroplaque membrane has a resistance of about 5 ohm·cm^2, the noninnervated membrane one of about 0.2 ohm·cm^2(Keynes and Martins-Ferreira, 1953). These values are about 1/100 to 1/1000 of those generally found for muscle fiber membranes.

Not all electric fishes produce such spectacular voltages and currents as do the electric eel, the rays, and the skates. Most fresh-water forms produce rather small voltages and currents (see Table 24–1). The animals capable of strong electric discharges seem to employ them in self-defense and—as far as one can judge from scarce records of direct observation—to stun or kill prey. The other "low-voltage fish" employ the pulses of electric current for a sensory process of electro-locating. The latter produce patterned current pulses. Examples are shown in Figure 24–17.

The electric currents must, of course, flow through the skin of the electric fish. Patterns of such current flow are shown in Figure 24–17. The currents of marine electric fish have to be much stronger than those of fresh-water electric fish because the electric resistance of sea water is so low that the amount of current that would pass through a living organism (prey) is small by proportion. The rather high resistance of fresh water, on the other hand, offers a most suitable environment, particularly for electric guidance systems, for it allows a distinction of object resistances higher as well as lower than that of the aquatic medium.

The electroplaques of the marine electric fishes (including Rajidae, Torpedinae, and *Astroscopus*) are electrically inexcitable: they respond only to indirect stimulation via their nerve supply but not to direct electric stimulation. Their membrane responses can be characterized as local, postsynaptic potentials

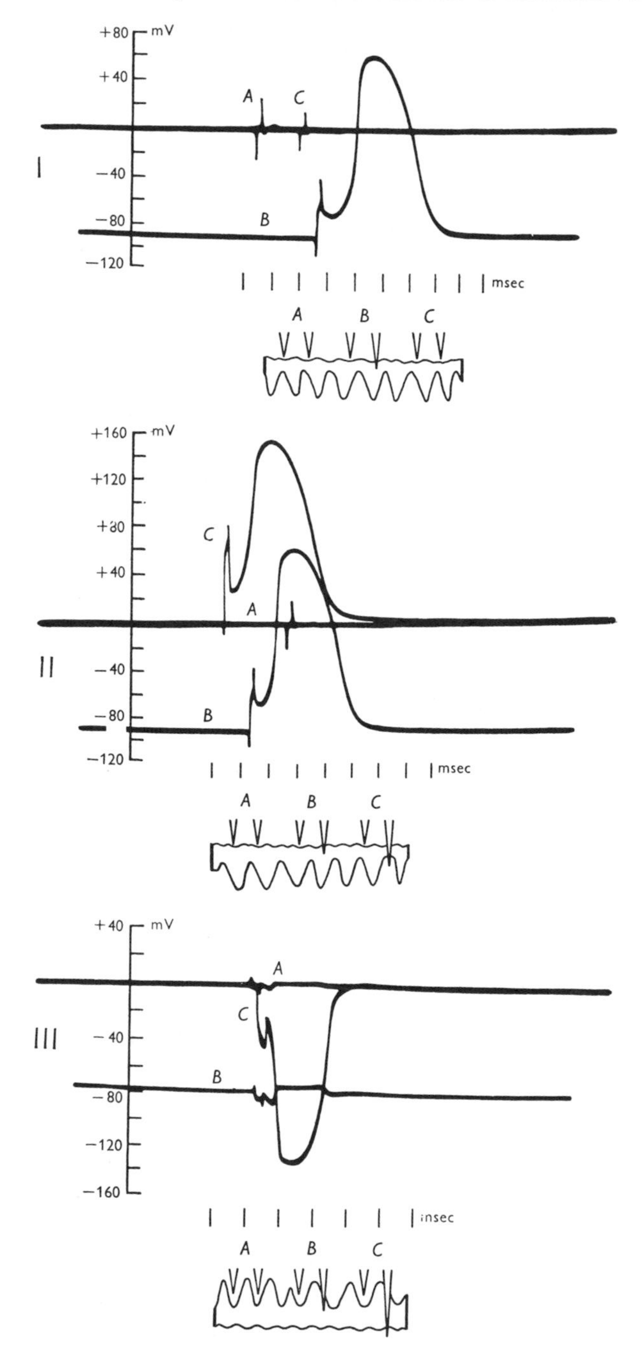

Figure 24–20. Membrane potentials recorded from single electroplaques of the electric eel, *Electrophorus*. The inserts show the positions of the microelectrode tips. (The experimental arrangement is that shown in Figure 24–19.) In **I** and **II** the innervated side points upward; in **III** it points downward. Note that resting potentials (about –80 mV) are recorded only with electrodes in position *B*, and that spikes occur only at the innervated membrane. (From Keynes, R. D., and H. Martins-Ferreira: Membrane potentials in the electroplates of the electric eel. J. Physiol. *119*:315–351, 1953.)

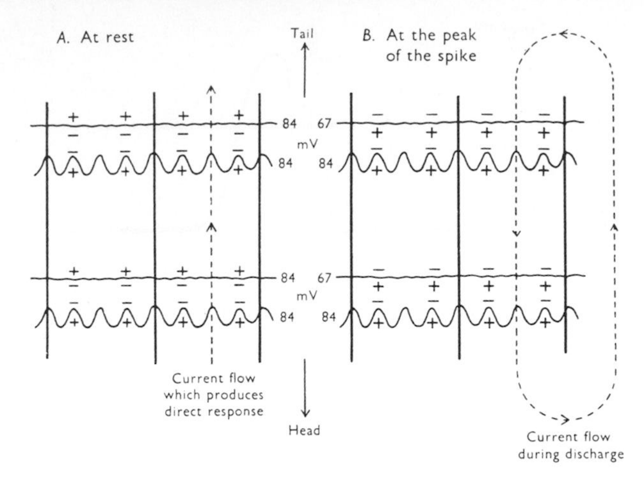

Figure 24–21. Diagram illustrating the additive discharge of the electroplaques of an electric organ (*Electrophorus*). At rest (**A**) there is no net potential across the electroplaques, but at the peak of the spike potential (**B**) all the potentials are in series, and the head of the eel becomes positive with respect to its tail. (From Keynes, R. D., and H. Martins-Ferreira: Membrane potentials in the electroplates of the electric eel. J. Physiol. *119*:315–351, 1953.)

(homologous to end-plate potentials), even though they may reach the extraordinary height of nearly 100 mV (the full extent of the resting potential).

The electroplaques of fresh-water electric fishes respond to indirect as well as to direct stimulation. Indirect stimulation results in a dual response: first to appear, after a certain latent period, is a postsynaptic potential, and then an all-or-nothing, conducting spike potential. In the electric eel, *Electrophorus*, both responses are restricted to the innervated side of each electroplaque, but in the "low-voltage fish" (Gymnotidae, Gymnarchidae, Malapteruridae, and Mormyridae) the noninnervated portion of the electroplaques responds with a spike potential and can be directly excited electrically.

Because of their relatively large size, and particularly because of the extent of the synaptic regions, electroplaques have yielded invaluable information for the understanding of impulse transmission and spike generation. A clear-cut separation of the properties of membrane portions responsible for the postsynaptic, local responses and of the properties of the spike-generating membrane regions has been obtained and has led to the concept of *electrically excitable* and *electrically inexcitable membrane* areas. This has been formulated extensively and repeatedly by Grundfest and his school (Columbia University, New York), who are also responsible for most of the recent experimental work on electroplaque physiology. The concept can be summarized as follows:

The subsynaptic membrane and, to varying degrees, surrounding membrane areas are electrically inexcitable. At best, only extremely strong currents produce a response, but if so this occurs after a considerable delay, indicating that an intermediate process precedes the response to the applied current pulse (Fig. 24–20). This type of membrane, however, responds to indirect stimulation of its presynaptic nerve supply, and it responds also to the application of the transmitter substance (acetylcholine) that is normally released by the presynaptic endings. The response is always local and represents a typical graded response capable of summation (see Chap. 16). This response is not accompanied or followed by a refractory period. It never overshoots zero membrane potential. Its duration can be extended by successive indirect stimuli, provided they arrive while a previous response is still in progress.

An electrically excitable membrane responds to direct electric stimulation or to the current flow induced by subsynaptic, local membrane responses with an overshooting, all-or-nothing spike potential. This is of fixed duration and is accompanied by refractory periods. Application of prolonged current pulses leads not to an extension of spike duration but to repetitive discharge. The spike response is conducted over the entire electrically excitable membrane. It cannot be directly elicited by the application of transmitter substance (acetylcholine).

Extrapolating to other synapses, it has been stated that as a rule subsynaptic membranes of chemically transmitting synapses are electrically inexcitable. From the behavior of the electroplaques and other subsynaptic membranes, electrically inexcitable membranes, the so-called "electrically inexcitable responses" have been characterized: they show variable magnitude and electric sign, depending on the state of polarization of the membrane (see the discussion on reversal potentials in Chapter 20, p. 489), whereas spike potentials ("electrically excitable responses"), if they occur, are always of the same electric sign and reach the same peak, regardless of the initial value of the membrane potential. It is this generalization of the concept, however, that is still under debate. Even among electroplaques, there are cases where the same general membrane area (e.g., the innervated side of eel electroplaques) shows both local and conducted responses. Only the assumption of a mosaic of electrically excitable and inexcitable membrane patches can salvage the concept here. It is even more difficult in the case of excitatory synaptic areas of normal muscle or nerve cells to assess its validity directly, because select application of electric stimuli to subsynaptic membrane areas is technically impossible.

SPONTANEOUSLY ACTIVE MUSCLE

Perhaps throughout the animal kingdom, certainly within a large number of phyla, there occur certain types of muscle that have the property of self-excitation. These muscles are said to be spontaneously active or to show spontaneous activity. The term "activity" refers to both electrical and mechanical signs of muscle action. Spontaneously active muscles develop action potentials and contract without requiring activation by motoneurons. Muscles that exhibit this property may belong to different histological classes of muscle. The striated muscle of the vertebrate heart is a typical example, and so are the visceral smooth muscles of the mammalian gut or the esophagus of the polychaete *Arenicola*.

In Chapter 10 (Circulation) reference was made to the hearts of many animals that exhibit a myogenic heartbeat. Such heart muscles are indeed spontaneously active and much of the terminology of the general physiology of spontaneously active muscle is derived from the physiology of heart muscle.

It is an outstanding characteristic of spontaneously active muscle that the activity is rhythmical. Electrical and mechanical activity recur at more or less regular intervals and the activity cycles of many or all cells of the muscle are somehow synchronized. Although all muscle fibers of such a muscle have the ability to generate action potentials and to contract, certain groups of muscle fibers dominate and "dictate" their rhythm to the others. These "leading" muscle fibers are known as *pacemaker fibers*, and the portions of a muscle in which these occur are called *pacemaker regions*. It is generally believed that the pacemaker cells (or fibers) are those muscle cells that have the fastest rhythm. It has indeed been observed with many types of spontaneously active muscle, that removal of a pacemaker region is usually followed by the establishment of a new pacemaker region, and that the rhythm of the new pacemaker is slower than that of the previous one.

It is reasonable to suppose that the rhythm is dictated by periodic chemical changes that proceed in a cyclical manner causing a gradual increase in a certain substance until a critical concentration is reached. This concentration triggers a secondary reaction which in turn removes the substance (either by discharging it from the cell or by metabolizing it). If all muscle fibers of a spontaneously active muscle have the ability to become pacemakers, it can be assumed that they all show this same cyclical pattern of chemical change. The cycles are obviously correlated with electrical activity; not only does the chemical process determine the periodicity of the electrical events, but the electrical phenomena, in turn, affect the chemical processes. This is evident from the fact that artificial stimulation leading to an action potential critically alters the time pattern of the subsequent spontaneous excitation.

From what has been stated here it is not difficult to understand (at least in principle) how even a single pacemaker cell can dictate its own rhythm to the entire population of cells (or fibers) of a muscle; the pacemaker cell develops an action potential before any of the other cells of the muscle. This action potential propagates not only over the entire membrane of this pacemaker cell, but across the cell boundaries as well. As far as is known, all spontaneously active muscles behave electrically as a syncytium, that is, all their cells (or fibers) are electrically connected by low resistance membrane contacts. The action potential causes the activation of the contractile machinery. The chemical events associated with action potential and contraction reverse the chemical "buildup" that has occurred in the nonpacemaker cells, thereby resetting their chemical cycle. And again, before this cycle is completed, there occurs another activation from the pacemaker cell, and another cycle begins.

The electrical activity (as recorded with an intracellular electrode) of a pacemaker cell differs from that of the nonpacemaker cells (Figs. 24–22 and 24–23). Characteristically the action potential of pacemaker cells is preceded by a slowly developing depolarization, variously called *generator depolarization*, *generator potential*, or *pacemaker potential*. In some visceral smooth muscles, notably those of the mammalian intestine (taenia coli), longer-lasting waves of depolarization produce sequences of action potentials (see Fig. 22–26).

In nonpacemaker cells or fibers the action potentials are not preceded by generator depolarization and resemble the so-called simple conducted action potentials of other nerve activated muscle, or nerve fibers. There is one dif-

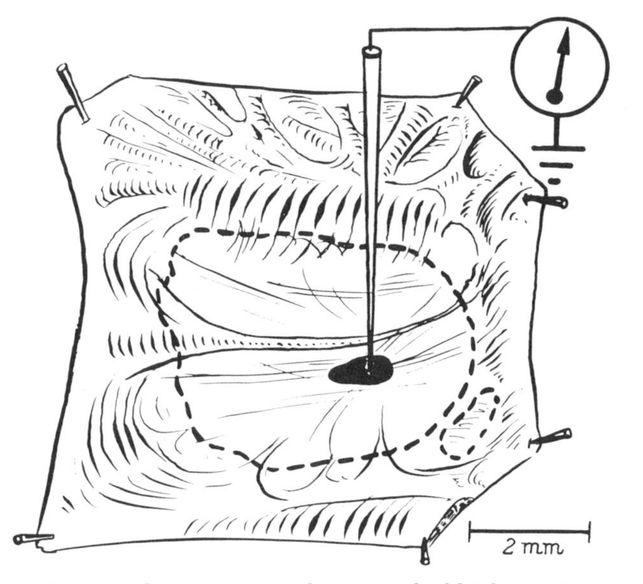

Figure 24–22. Diagram of a preparation of an opened rabbit heart. A microelectrode is shown inserted into a cell of the sino-atrial node (black area). The dotted line marks the junction between sinus and atrial myocardium. (From Trautwein, W., and K. Uchizono: Electron microscopic and electrophysiologic study of the pacemaker in the sino-atrial node of the rabbit heart. Z. Zellforsch. *61*:96–109, 1963.)

ference however: even the conducted action potentials of spontaneously active muscle are preceded by slight or brief depolarizations that are the immediate result of the electrical activity of neighboring cells or fibers. Thus it is often found that the rising phase, and sometimes even the falling phase, of the conducted action potential shows "humps" or "notches." All this is due to the electrical connections between cells.

Spiking is usually associated with contraction. It is interesting that many types of cardiac muscle (myogenic type) and of spontaneously active smooth

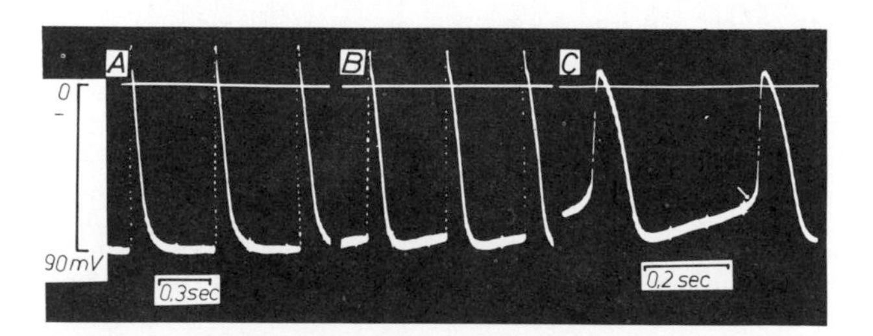

Figure 24–23. The course of the membrane potential during the cardiac cycle recorded from muscle fibers within the preparation shown in Figure 24–22. *A*, microelectrode in a myocardial fiber of the atrium. During the intervals between action potentials the membrane potential remains steady. *B*, microelectrode in a latent pacemaker cell. *C*, microelectrode in a pacemaker cell of the node itself. Note the increasing depolarization ("pacemaker potential") that precedes the action potential. (From Trautwein, W., and K. Uchizono: Electron microscopic and electrophysiologic study of the pacemaker in the sino-atrial node of the rabbit heart. Z. Zellforsch. *61*:96–109, 1963.)

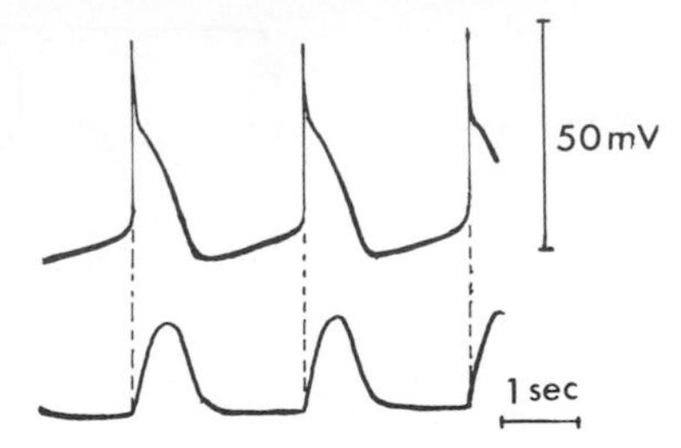

Figure 24–24. Electrical and mechanical activity of heart muscle of a mollusc, *Dolabella*. Note that the action potentials (top record) are preceded by a slowly developing generator potential and that the muscle contraction does not begin until the moment the spike occurs. Note also the long duration of the action potential. (Redrawn from Nomura, H.: Potassium contracture and its modification by cations in the heart muscle of the marine mollusc, *Dolabella auricula*. Japan. J. Physiol. *15*:253–269, 1965.)

muscle (mammalian uterus) show greatly prolonged ("plateau" type) action potentials (Figs. 24–23, 24–24, and 16–30).

Spontaneously active muscles are not independent of the nervous system. They receive a regulatory innervation that controls the general excitability of their cells. The common pattern is that of a dual innervation by "excitatory" and "inhibitory" nerve fibers. Nerve impulses in these regulatory neurons do not cause junction potentials that lead to spike potentials and contraction, but by the process of synaptic transmission they accomplish an alteration in the rhythm of the pacemakers and an increase or decrease in the strength of the contractions. Examples have already been discussed in Chapter 10 in connection with the nervous control of the heart beat.

For more advanced treatment of spontaneously active muscle refer to Burnstock, Holman, and Prosser (1963) and Brooks, Hoffman, Suckling, and Orias (1955).

REFERENCES

d'Arsonval, A. (1891) La fibre musculaire est directement excitable par la lumière. C. R. Soc. Biol. *43*:318–320.

Arvanitaki, A., and N. Chalazonitis (1947). Réactions bioélectriques à la photoactivation des cytochromes. Arch. Sci. Physiol. *1*:382–405.

Arvanitaki, A., and N. Chalazonitis (1961) Excitatory and inhibitory processes initiated by light and infra-red radiations in single identifiable nerve cells (giant ganglion cells of Aplysia). *In* Nervous Inhibition, pp. 194–231. (E. Florey, ed.) Pergamon Press, London.

Bailey, K. (1957) Invertebrate tropomyosin. Biochim. Biophys. Acta *24*:612–619.

Bennett, M. V. L. (1961) Modes of operation of electric organs. Ann. N. Y. Acad. Sci. *94*:458–509.

Boettiger, E. G. (1957a) *In* Physiological Triggers, pp. 103–116. (T. H. Bullock, ed.) American Physiological Society, Washington, D.C.

Boettiger, E. G. (1957b) The machinery of insect flight. *In* Recent Advances in Invertebrate Physiology (a symposium), pp. 117–142. (B. T. Scheer, ed.) University of Oregon Press, Eugene.

Boettiger, E. G., and E. Furshpan (1952a) The mechanics of flight movements in Diptera. Biol. Bull. *102*:200–211.

Boettiger, E. G., and E. Furshpan (1952b) The recording flight movements in insects. Science *116*:60–61.

Boettiger, E. G., and E. Furshpan (1954a) Mechanical properties of insect flight muscle. J. Cell. Comp. Physiol. *44*:340.

Boettiger, E. G., and E. Furshpan (1954b) The response of fibrillar flight muscle to rapid release and stretch. Biol. Bull. *107*:305.

Brooks, C. M., B. F. Hoffman, E. E. Suckling, and O. Orias (1955) Excitability of the Heart. New York. Grune and Stratton, Inc.
Bülbring, E. (1955) Correlation between membrane potential, spike discharge and tension in smooth muscle. J. Physiol. *128*:200–221.
Bullock, T. H. (1943) Neuromuscular facilitation in Scyphomedusae. J. Cell. Comp. Physiol. *22*:251–272.
Burnstock, G., and C. L. Prosser (1960a) Conduction in smooth muscles: comparative electrical properties. Amer. J. Physiol. *199*:553–559.
Burnstock, G., and C. L. Prosser (1960b) Responses of smooth muscles to quick stretch; relation of stretch to conduction. Amer. J. Physiol. *198*:921–925.
Burnstock, G., M. E. Holman, and C. L. Prosser (1963) Electrophysiology of smooth muscle. Physiol. Rev. *43*:482–527.
Fatt, P. (1961) The change in membrane permeability during the inhibitory process. *In* Nervous Inhibition, pp. 87–91. (E. Florey, ed.) Pergamon Press, London.
Fatt, P., and B. Katz (1953) The effect of inhibitory nerve impulses on a crustacean muscle fibre. J. Physiol. *121*:374–389.
Florey, E. (1966) Nervous control and spontaneous activity of the chromatophores of a cephalopod, Loligo opalescens. Comp. Biochem. Physiol. *17*: in press.
Furshpan, E. J. (1955) Studies on certain sensory and motor systems of decapod crustaceans. Ph.D. Thesis. California Institute of Technology, Pasadena.
Garten, S. (1910–1914) Die Produktion von Elektrizität. *In* Handbuch der vergleichenden Physiologie, Vol. 3, pp. 105–224. (H. Winterstein, ed.)
Grundfest, H. (1957) The mechanisms of discharge of the electric organs in relation to general and comparative physiology. Progr. Biophys. *7*:1–85.
Grundfest, H., and M. V. L. Bennett: Studies on the morphology and electrophysiology of electric organs. I. Electrophysiology of marine fishes. *In* Bioelectrogenesis, pp. 57–101. (C. Chagas and A. Paes de Carvalho, eds.) Elsevier, Amsterdam.
van Harreveld, A., and C. A. G. Wiersma (1939) The function of the quintuple innervation of a crustacean muscle. J. Exp. Biol. *16*:121–133.
Horridge, G. A. (1956) The nerves and muscle of Medusae. V. Double innervation in Scyphozoa. J. Exp. Biol. *33*:366–383.
Hoyle, G. (1957a) Comparative Physiology of the Nervous Control of Muscular Contractions. Cambridge University Press, London, 146 pp.
Hoyle, G. (1957b) Recent Advances in Invertebrate Physiology. University of Oregon Press, Eugene.
Hoyle, G., and J. Lowy (1956) The paradox of Mytilus muscle. A new interpretation. J. Exp. Biol. *33*:295–310.
Hoyle, G., and C. A. G. Wiersma (1958a) Excitation at neuromuscular junctions in Crustacea. J. Physiol. *143*:403–425.
Hoyle, G., and C. A. G. Wiersma (1958b) Inhibition at neuromuscular junctions in Crustacea. J. Physiol. *143*:426–440.
Jewell, B. R. (1959) The nature of the phasic and the tonic responses of the anterior byssal retractor muscle of Mytilus. J. Physiol. *149*:154–177.
Johnson, W. H., and B. M. Twarog (1960) The basis for prolonged contractions in molluscan muscles. J. Gen. Physiol. *43*:941–960.
Krogh, A., and E. Zeuthen (1941) The mechanism of flight preparation in some insects. J. Exp. Biol. *18*:1–10.
Kuffler, S. W., and B. Katz (1946) Inhibition at the nerve muscle junction in Crustacea. J. Neurophysiol. *9*:337–346.
Keynes, R. D., and H. Martins-Ferreira (1953) Membrane potentials in the electroplates of the electric eel. J. Physiol. *119*:315–351.
Lowy, J. and B. M. Millman (1963) The contractile mechanism of the anterior byssus retractor muscle of Mytilus edulis. Phil. Trans. B. *246*:105–148.
Marmont, G., and C. A. G. Wiersma (1938) On the mechanism of inhibition and excitation of crayfish muscle. J. Physiol. *93*:173–193.
Nachmansohn, D., C. W. Coates, M. A. Rothenberg, and M. V. Brown (1946) On the energy source of the action potential in the electric organ of *Electrophorus electricus*. J. Biol. Chem. *165*:223–231.
Parnas, J. (1910) Energetik glatter Muskeln. Pflügers Arch. ges. Physiol. *134*:441–495.
Pavlov, J. (1885) Wie die Muschel ihre Schale öffnet. Versuche und Fragen zur Allgemeinen Muskel- und Nerven-physiologie. Pflügers Arch. ges. Physiol. *37*:6–31.

Pople, W., and D. W. Ewer (1954) Studies on the myoneural physiology of Echinodermata. I. The pharyngeal retractor muscle of *Cucumaria*. J. Exp. Biol. *31*:114–126.

Pringle, J. W. S. (1954) A physiological analysis of cicada song. J. Exp. Biol. *31*:525–560.

Pringle, J. W. S. (1957) Insect Flight. Cambridge Monographs in Experimental Biology. Cambridge University Press, London, 132 pp.

Prosser, C. L. (1962) Conduction in nonstriated muscles. Physiol. Rev., Suppl. 5, *42*:193–206.

Prosser, C. L., and C. E. Melton (1954) Nervous conduction in smooth muscle of Phascolosoma proboscis retractors. J. Cell. Comp. Physiol. *44*:255–275.

Prosser, C. L., C. L. Ralph and W. W. Steinberger (1959) Responses to stretch and the effect of pull on propagation in non-striated muscles of Golfingia (= Phascolosoma) and Mustelus. J. Cell. Comp. Physiol. *54*:135–146.

Prosser, C. L., and N. Sperelakis (1959) Electrical evidence for dual innervation of muscle fibers in the sipunculid Golfingia (Phascolosoma). J. Cell. Comp. Physiol. *54*:129–133.

Pumphrey, R. J. (1938) The double innervation of muscles in the clam (*Mya arenaria*). J. Exp. Biol. *15*:500–505.

Ramsay, J. A. (1940) A nerve-muscle preparation from the snail. J. Exp. Biol. *17*:96–115.

Röchling, E. (1922) Der Kolumellarmuskel von *Helix pom.* und seine Beziehung zur Schale. Z. wiss. Zool. *119*:285–325.

Ruegg, J. C. (1962) Actomyosin inactivation by thiourea and the nature of viscous tone in a molluscan smooth muscle. Proc. Roy. Soc. B, *158*:177–195.

Ruegg, J. C., R. W. Straub, and B. M. Twarog (1963) Inhibition of contraction in a molluscan smooth muscle by thiourea, an inhibitor of the actomyosin contractile mechanism. Proc. Roy. Soc. B, *158*:156–176.

Seliger, H. H. (1962) Direct action of light in naturally pigmented muscle fibers. J. Gen. Physiol. *46*:333–342.

Starling, E. H. (1915) The Linacre Lecture on the Law of the Heart, given at Cambridge, 1915. Longmans, Green and Co., London, 1918, 28 pp.

TenCate, J., and J. D. Verleur (1952) Recherches sur la fonction du m. rétracteur du tantacule majeur d'*Helix pomatia* (L.) Physiol. comp. (s'-Grav.) *2*:346–349.

Twarog, B. M. (1954) Responses of a molluscan smooth muscle to acetylcholine and 5-hydroxytryptamine. J. Cell. Comp. Physiol. *44*:141–163.

von Uexküll, J. (1912) Studien über den Tonus. 6: Die Pilgermuschel. Z. Biol. München *58*:305–322.

Wiersma, C. A. G. (1941) The inhibitory nerve supply of the leg muscles of different decapod crustaceans. J. Comp. Neurol. *74*:63–79.

Wiersma, C. A. G., and C. H. Ellis (1942) A comparative study of peripheral inhibition in decapod crustaceans. J. Exp. Biol. *18*:223–236.

Wiersma, C. A. G., and G. Marmont (1938) On the motor and inhibitory innervation of the legs of brachyuran decapods. Physiol. Zool. *11*:312–316.

Wiersma, C. A. G., and S. H. Ripley (1952) Innervation patterns of crustacean limbs. Physiol. comp. Oecol. *2*:391–405.

Wiersma, C. A. G., and A. van Harreveld (1938) The influence of the frequency of stimulation on the slow and the fast contractions in crustacean muscle. Physiol. Zool. *11*:75–81.

Wilson, D. M. (1959) Long term facilitation in a swimming sea anemone. J. Exp. Biol. *36*:526–532.

Wilson, D. M. (1960) Nervous control of movement in annelids. J. Exp. Biol. *37*:46–56.

Wilson, D. M. (1961) The central nervous control of flight in a locust. J. Exp. Biol. *38*:471–490.

Woodbury, J. W., and W. E. Crill (1961) On the problem of impulse conduction in the atrium. *In* Nervous Inhibition, pp. 124–135. (E. Florey, ed.) Pergamon Press, London.

Young, J. Z. (1931) The pupillary mechanism of the teleostean fish *Uranoscopus scaber*. Proc. Roy. Soc. B, *107*:464–485.

Young, J. Z. (1933a) Comparative studies on the physiology of the iris. I. Selachians. Proc. Roy. Soc. B, *112*:228–241.

Young, J. Z. (1933b) Comparative studies on the physiology of the iris. II. *Uranoscopus* and *Lophius*. Proc. Roy. Soc. B, *112*:242–249.

25 THE SENSE ORGANS AND SENSORY PHYSIOLOGY

Sense organs have offered the greatest challenge to the human mind. Their recognition poses problems that have puzzled philosophers and scientists for literally thousands of years. How is it that we see, hear, and smell? What, in fact, *do* we see or feel? Is it really the "outside world" or is it simply a change in the properties of our sense organs? And if the latter is true, then how can we *know* what the outside world is like? Worse still, if I see, does that prove that somebody else can see also? Can I ever know what someone else sees? After all, I can only see his eyes and hear with my ears what he tells me that he sees; in fact, as I see this "somebody," I cannot even be sure that what I see is not just a change in the state of excitation of the sensory cells of my own eyes.

Such reasoning, inevitably, leads to the question: if there is no proof that the outside world exists, do the sense organs exist outside of my mind, or are they not, like everything else, images of my mind? The philosophical position that only I exist and that everything within the reach of my experience and reasoning exists only within my own mind is called *solipsism.* Immanuel Kant, the great rationalist of the eighteenth century, has shown with immaculate reasoning that there is no logical way to disprove this position and that the only way out is to rely on common sense.

The belief that the outside world is just about as we see (hear, feel, smell, etc.) it, is called *naïve realism.* It is the task of sensory physiology to examine the extent and the limitations of the performance of sense organs. Obviously, the physiologist is here in a most tricky position: How is he to test the relationship between the outside world and the sensation produced by the sense organs, when he can recognize the outside world only through his own sense organs?

At this point of the argument, it is of utmost importance to realize the nature of the method of physiology: to establish the space-time pattern of physical and chemical events within organisms and their relation to the physical and chemical aspects of their environment. The philosophical position of the physiologist is really rather simple (because of the self-imposed restrictions of his method): he is not concerned with sensation as conscious experience, but considers sensation as a constellation of physicochemical events that are mediated by sense organs and caused by physical and chemical actions of the outside world, the latter being described in purely physical and chemical terms. The experimental animals don't *see* colored lights, don't *hear* sounds, don't *feel* the warmth of another body—they *respond* to different wavelengths of "light," to the frequency of changes of mechanical pressure, or to temperature changes.

The responses consist of (1) physicochemical changes in receptor cells, (2) changes in the discharge pattern of sensory nerve cells, (3) activation of nerve cells within the central nervous system, (4) activation of efferent neurons, and (5) changes in the physicochemical properties of the innervated effector organs (e.g., muscle contraction, glandular secretion, etc.).

Although sensory physiology is generally considered to be concerned with all five of these aspects of response, this chapter is concerned only with the first two, perhaps three. The rest is nowadays the domain of animal psychology and is appropriately treated in psychological literature. Good introductory books are those of Carthy (1958) and Hebb (1966). Important, in this regard, is also von Buddenbrock (1952) and the Symposium of the Society for Experimental Biology (1950).

RECEPTORS, SENSE ORGANS, AND SENSES

The physiology of receptor neurons and receptors was discussed in Chapter 19, pp. 461–473. A receptor cell is a cell strategically situated to be affected by certain changes in the environment of an organ or organism in such a way that it, in turn, affects the excitability of neurons in the central nervous system. *Primary receptor cells* are receptor neurons proper: their cell bodies are directly affected by the environmental change and this determines their discharge pattern with which they act on other (central) nerve cells. *Secondary receptor cells* (sensory cells), are not nerve cells but modified epithelial cells. They are innervated by endings of sensory neurons. They are affected by environmental changes, and by their response determine the discharge pattern of the innervating sensory neuron. Compare, for example, the receptor cells of the insect ear (Fig. 25–1) with those of the mammalian ear (Fig. 19–1).

Sense organs are distinct anatomical units, usually composed of several tissues, which contain one or more sensory cells and provide for their *adequate stimulation*. The term "adequate stimulation" means preferential or exclusive stimulation by the one particular modality (pressure, temperature, light, chemical property) that most commonly activates the sense organ or its receptors during the normal life of the animal. The term "sense organ" is rather loose. The skin of the human body, which contains many receptors and free sensory nerve

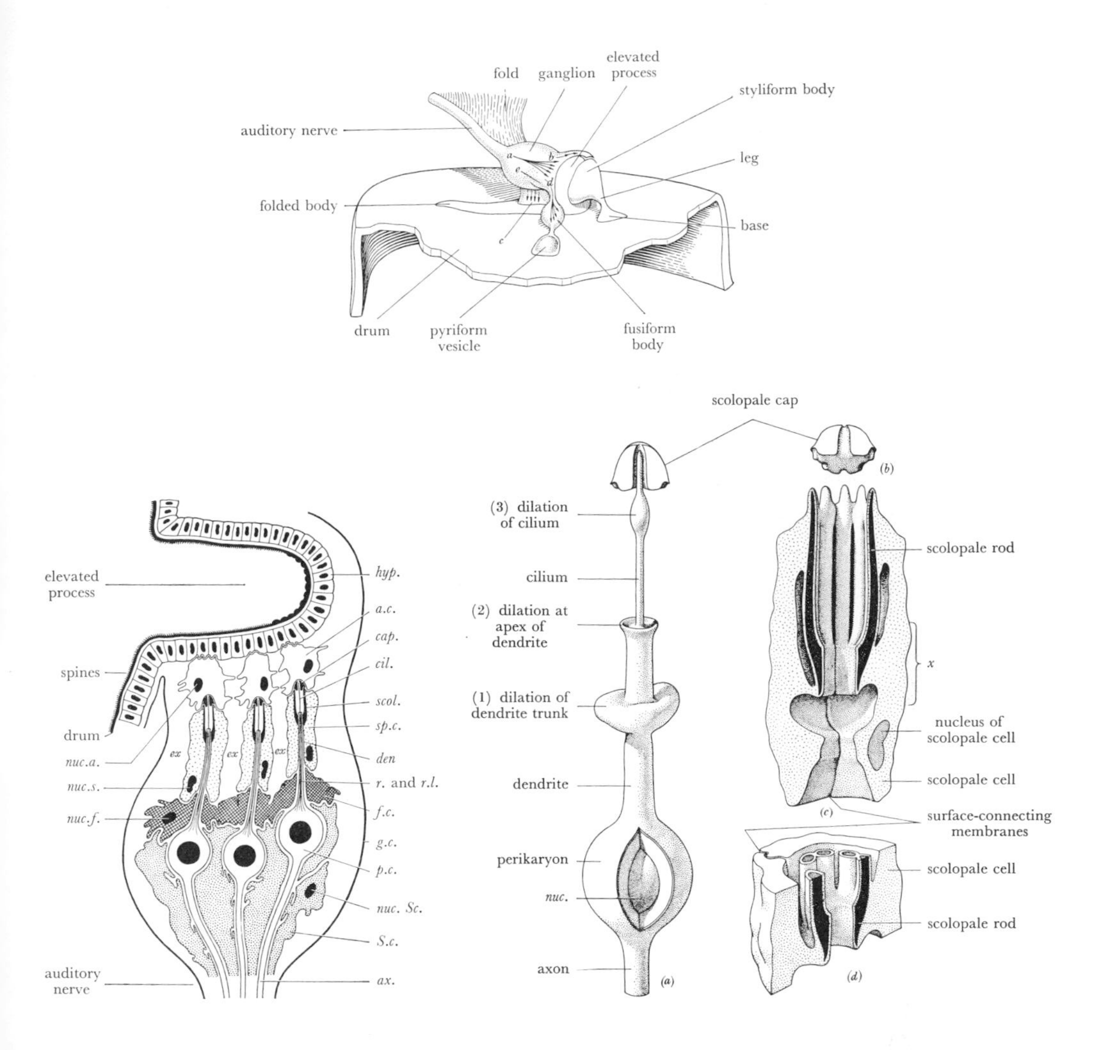

Figure 25–1. Fine structure of the insect ear as revealed by electron microscopy of the ear of the locust (*Locusta migratoria*). The eardrum, or tympanic membrane, is located laterally on the first abdominal segment. The auditory ganglion is attached to its inner surface. It contains 60 to 80 sensory neurons. Their perikaryon (*p.c.*) and axon (*ax.*) are surrounded by Schwann cells (*S.c.*); one Schwann cell enfolds several sensory neurons. The proximal part of the dendrite is enclosed by a fibrous sheath cell (*f.c.*); the distal part of the dendrite (*den*) is surrounded by another type of satellite cell, the scolopale cell (*sp.c.*). A cilium (*cil.*) extends from the dendrite into a scolopale cap (*cap.*). This in turn is in contact with an attachment cell (*a.c.*) that connects with the hypodermal cells (*hyp.*) of the elevated process of the tympanic membrane. The root (*r.*) and rootlets (*r.l.*) of the cilium can be seen inside the dendrites. Note the extracellular fluid space (*ex*) between the scolopale cells. The nature of the mechanical deformation of the sensory neurons during vibration of the tympanic membrane is still unknown, but there is no doubt that these ears permit the female locusts to hear the "songs" of the courting males. *g.c.*, capsule of ganglion; *nuc.a.*, nucleus of attachment cell; *nuc.s.*, nucleus of scolopale cell; *nuc.f.*, nucleus of fibrous sheath-cell; *nuc.Sc.*, nucleus of Schwann cell; *scol.*, scolopale. (From Gray, E. G.: The fine structure of the insect ear. Phil. Trans. Roy. Soc. B, *243*:75–94, 1961.)

Figure 25–2. A male moth, *Hyalophora cecropia.* Each large antenna bears more than 50,000 sensillae. They are supplied by more than 130,000 sensory nerve cells. Many of them serve in olfaction. (From Schneider, D.: Untersuchungen zum Bau und zur Funktion der Riechorgane von Schmetterlingen und Käfern. Ber. Phys. Med. Ges. Würzburg, N.F., *70*:158–168, 1963.)

endings, can be considered a sense organ (temperature and pressure) and so can the antennae of a moth (Fig. 25–2), which are organs exclusively concerned with sensory function (chemical and mechanical). On the other hand, the antennae are covered with structures which, again, are called sense organs (sensillae). The term "sense organ" is best suited for such compact structures as eyes or statocysts. An alternate term to "sense organ" is *"receptor organ."*

The term "sense" is often employed to denote the ability to detect a particular modality: a *light sense* is present when an animal has structures that enable it to respond to light of an intensity normally encountered in the day to day functions of the animal, whereas a *chemical sense* is the ability to detect, and respond to, certain chemicals present in concentrations that can be expected in the organism's normal environment.

CLASSIFICATION OF RECEPTORS AND OF SENSE (RECEPTOR) ORGANS

Receptors or sensory cells that respond to changes in the external environment of the organism are called *extero-receptors*, or *exteroceptors*. They are situated at or near the external surface of the animal. Receptors or sensory cells that respond to changes within an organism are known as *proprio-receptors*, or *proprioceptors*.

Regardless of whether they are exteroceptors or proprioceptors, receptors that respond to mechanical deformation are called *mechanoreceptors*, those that respond to chemicals are *chemoreceptors* (Figs. 25–3 to 25–6), those that respond to temperature changes are *temperature receptors* or thermoreceptors,

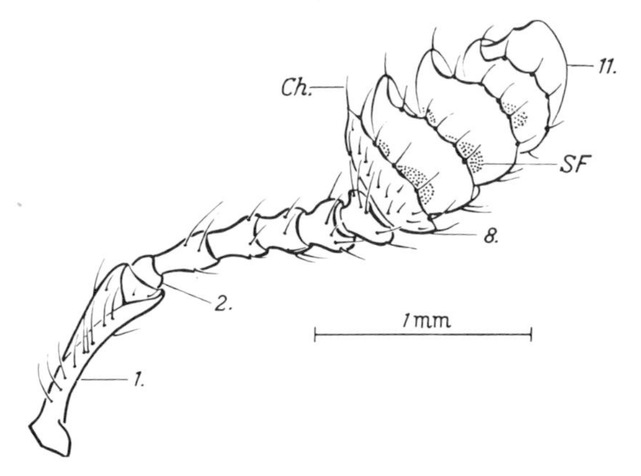

Figure 25-3. Antenna of an adult *Necrophorus* (Coleoptera), a carion beetle. *1*, scapus; *2*, pedicellus; *8*, eighth antennal segment; *11*, eleventh (last) antennal segment; *Ch.*, sensillum chaeticum; *SF*, field of sensillae which respond to olfactory stimulation. Two types of these are shown in Figure 25-4. (From Boeckh, J.: Elektrophysiologische Untersuchungen an einzelnen Geruchsrezeptoren auf den Antennen des Totengraebers [Necrophorus, Coleoptera]. Z. vergl. Physiol. *46*:212-248, 1962.)

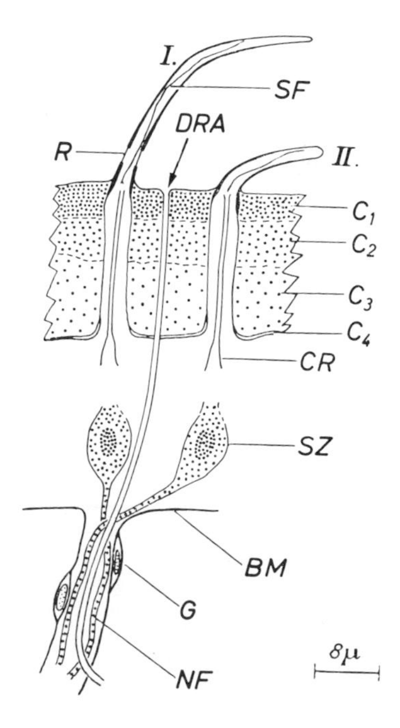

Figure 25-4. Sensillae of types I and II from a "field" of one segment of an antenna of the carion beetle, *Necrophorus*. *BM*, basal membrane; C_1-C_4, layers of the cuticle; *CR*, cuticular sheath surrounding the distal processes of sensory cells (*SZ*); *DR*, duct of a gland; *G*, connective tissue cell; *NF*, nerve fiber; *R*, ring-like constriction; *SF*, fiber, most likely sensory nerve ending; *SZ*, sensory cell body. (From Boeckh, J.: Elektrophysiologische Untersuchungen an einzelnen Geruchsrezeptoren auf den Antennen des Totengraebers [Necrophorus, Coleoptera]. Z. vergl. Physiol. *46*:212-248, 1962.)

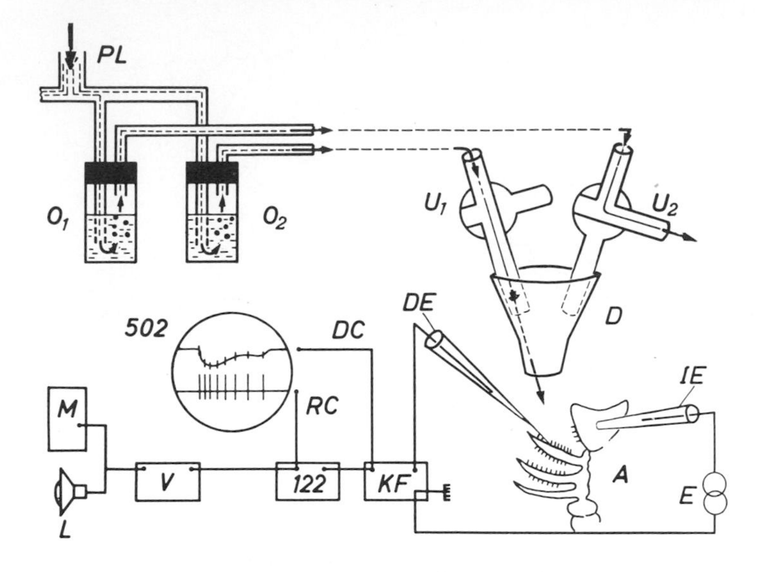

Figure 25–5. Diagrammatic representation of the arrangement for olfactory stimulation of, and recording from, olfactory receptors of the carion beetle, *Necrophorus* (see Figs. 25–3 and 25–4). *A*, antenna; *D*, jet; *DC*, d.c. channel (records generator potential); *DE*, different (recording) electrode; *E*, generator for calibrating voltage; *IE*, indifferent (reference) electrode; *KF*, cathode follower; *L*, loudspeaker; *M*, tape recorder; O_1 and O_2, vessels containing odorous solutions; *PL*, compressed air; *RC*, a.c. channel (records action potentials); U_1 and U_2, stopcocks; *V*, power amplifier; *122*, a.c. amplifier (Tektronix, model 122); *502*, screen of cathode ray oscilloscope (Tektronix, model 502). (From Boeckh, J.: Elektrophysiologische Untersuchungen an einzelnen Geruchsrezeptoren auf den Antennen des Totengraebers [Necrophorus, Coleoptera]. Z. vergl. Physiol. *46*:212–248, 1962.)

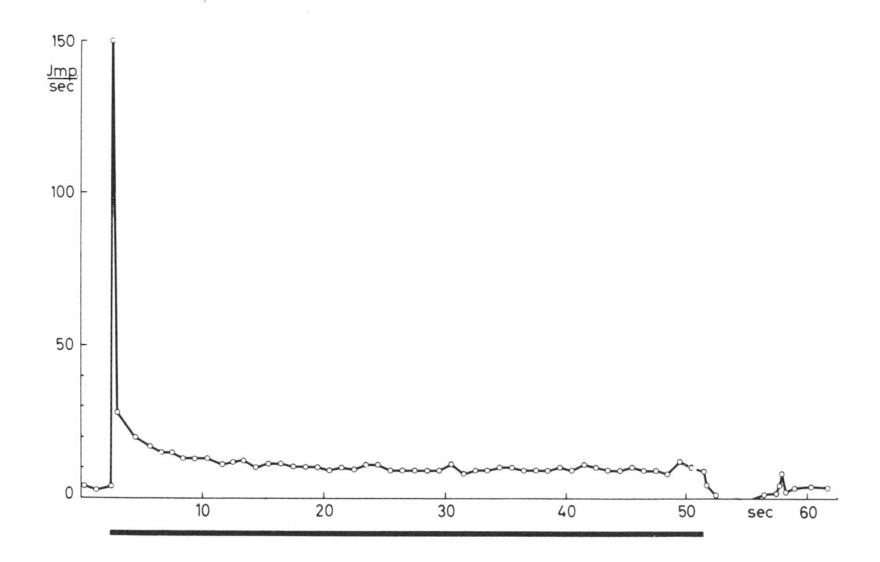

Figure 25–6. Response (frequency of nerve impulses) of a receptor neuron of a sensillum of the antenna of a carion beetle (*Necrophorus*), as obtained in an experimental set-up as pictured in Figure 25–5. The duration of the stimulus (application of a stream of air with the odor of rotting meat) is indicated by the heavy black line below the abscissa. (From Schneider, D.: Untersuchungen zum Bau und zur Funktion der Riechorgane von Schmetterlingen und Käfern. Ber. Phys. Med. Ges. Würzburg, N.F., *70*:158–168, 1961.)

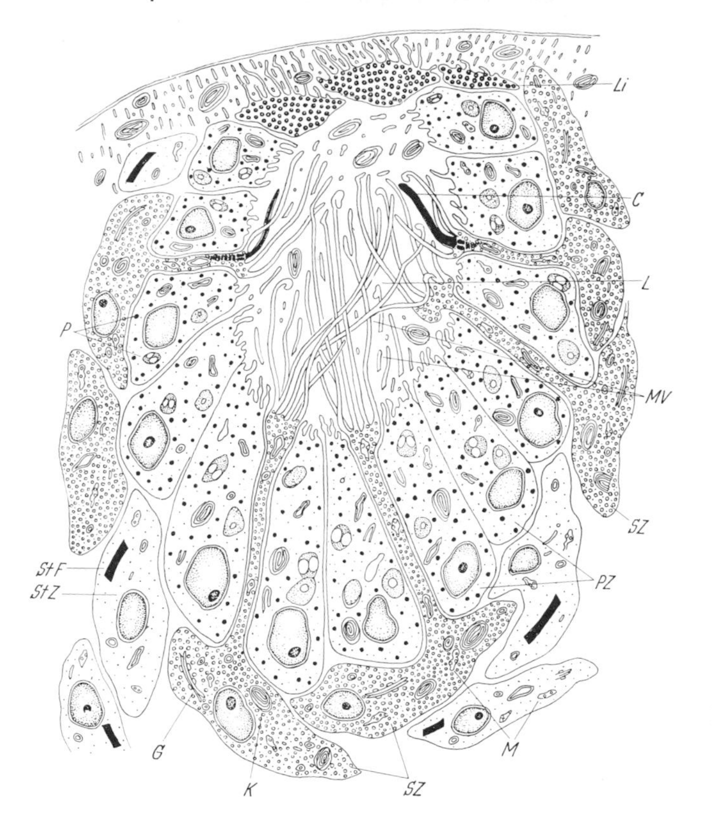

Figure 25–7. Diagrammatic representation of an eye spot of the asteroid *Asterias rubens* (starfish), as seen with the electron microscope. *C*, cilium; *G*, Golgi apparatus; *K*, concentrically laminated body; *L*, lumen; *Li*, lens; *M*, mitochondria; *MV*, microvilli; *P*, pigment granules; *PZ*, pigment cells; *StF*, supporting fibers; *StZ*, supporting cells; *SZ*, sensory (visual) cells. (From Vaupel-von Harnack, M.: Ueber den Feinbau des Nervensystems des Seesternes [Asterias rubens]. Z. Zellforsch. *60*:432–451, 1963.)

and those that respond to light are *photoreceptors* (Figs. 25–7 and 25–8). In addition, we recognize *electroreceptors* (responding to changes in the external electric field), and *osmoreceptors* (responding to changes in external "osmotic concentration").

Sense organs containing chemoreceptors and equipped to permit absorption from the atmosphere of certain diffusible chemicals by these chemoreceptors are known as *olfactory* organs. Their receptors are the *olfactory receptors*. If the latter are situated in large numbers within an epithelium, one speaks of an olfactory epithelium. Sense organs or receptors that respond to dissolved chemicals are known as taste organs or *gustatory* (taste) *receptors*. Alternative names are *distance chemoreceptors* for olfactory receptors, and *contact chemoreceptors* for taste receptors. The physiological term for smelling is *olfaction*, that for tasting is gustation (the latter is rarely employed).

Sense organs containing mechanoreceptors are of numerous varieties: Stretch-receptor organs occur in the musculature of vertebrates (Fig. 22–2) and many invertebrates (Fig. 25–9). They consist of modified muscle fibers and associated sensory neurons. *Chordotonal organs* (Fig. 25–10) are also

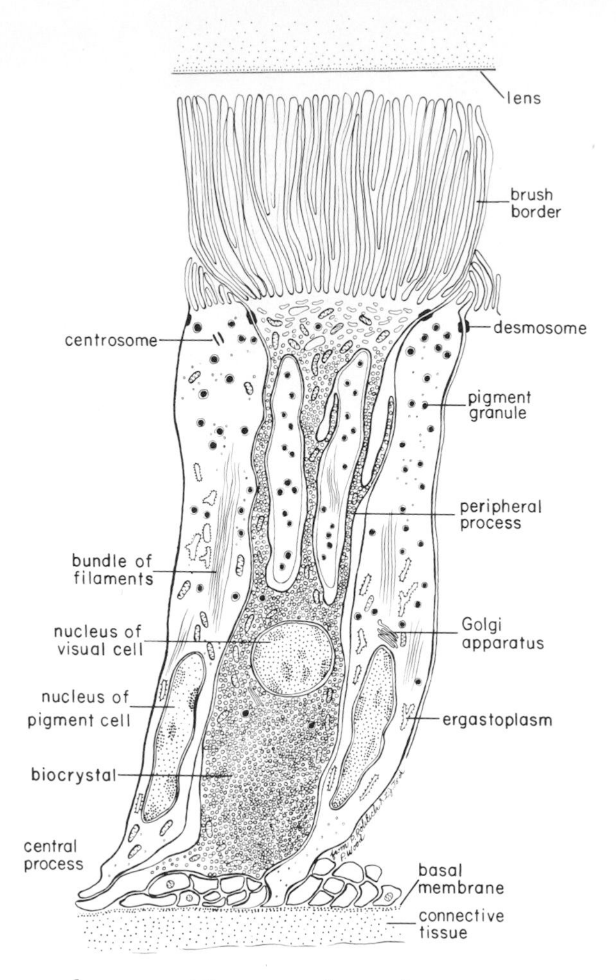

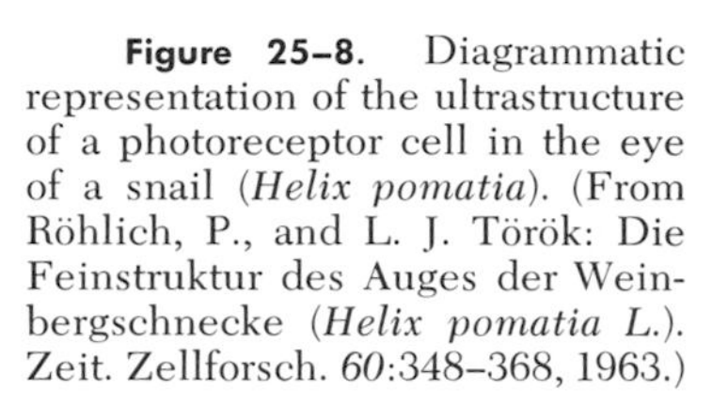

Figure 25–8. Diagrammatic representation of the ultrastructure of a photoreceptor cell in the eye of a snail (*Helix pomatia*). (From Röhlich, P., and L. J. Török: Die Feinstruktur des Auges der Weinbergschnecke (*Helix pomatia L.*). Zeit. Zellforsch. *60*:348–368, 1963.)

mechanosensitive proprioceptive organs, consisting of one or more mechanoreceptors attached to a tendon or to a ligament of connective tissue. They are characteristically found in arthropods. *Sensory hairs* are sense organs consisting of a hollow or solid rod (usually the product of secretion of hair cells), to the base of which are attached the endings of one or more sensory neurons. In many, if not all, cases, the attachment is asymmetrical, so that bending of the hair in one direction results in stretching, in the other, in shortening (or compression) of the nerve processes (see Fig. 25–11).

These sensory hairs are not to be confused with the *hair cells* which are secondary sensory cells occurring in vertebrate sense organs of the acusticolateralis complex: on their "external" surface are hairs attached to a gelatinous rod, velum, or "mass." Movement of this gelatinous body causes bending or shearing of the hairs and leads to the production of a generator potential (see p. 465) in the sensory cell which, in turn, alters the state of the excitability or the discharge pattern of the sensory neuron that innervates the hair cell. Such hair cells occur in the organ of Corti and the ampullae, sacculus, and utriculus of the inner ear as well as in the lateral line organs (Figs. 25–12 to 25–18).

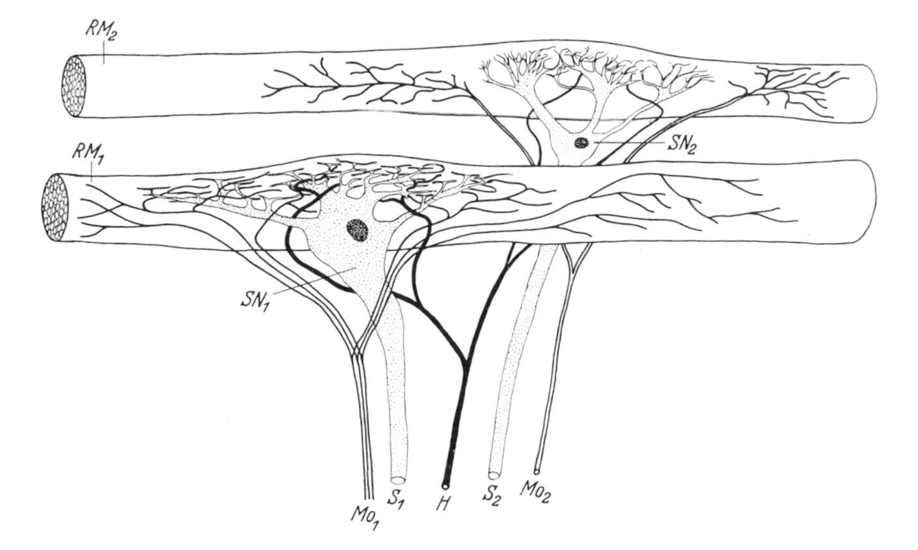

Figure 25–9. Semi-schematic representation of a stretch-receptor organ of a crayfish (*Astacus fluviatilis*), based on figures of Florey and Florey, 1955. RM_1 and RM_2 are two muscle strands; RM_1 can be classified as a slow muscle, RM_2 as a fast muscle. SN_1 and SN_2 are the two sensory receptor neurons; SN_1 is a tonic receptor, SN_2 is a phasic receptor. The corresponding axons are labeled S_1 and S_2. The motor innervation of RM_1 and RM_2 is labeled Mo_1 and Mo_2. *H* is the inhibitory fiber. The action of this neuron is shown in Figure 20–17. (From Burkhardt, D.: Die sinnesorgane des Skeletmuskels und die nervöse Steuerung der Muskeltätigkeit. Ergebn. Biol. *20*:27–66, 1958.)

Statocysts are compact, mechanosensitive sense organs consisting of a hollow, fluid-filled sphere which contains a mass of solid material (the statolith) usually held together by a gelatinous substance (Figs. 25–19 and 25–20). This mass rests on "hairs" protruding into the statocyst lumen from the statocyst wall. Since the mass has a higher specific gravity than the fluid, it tends to rest on those hairs that are between it and the center of gravity of the earth. Any rotation of the animal's body causes the statolith to change its position, thereby applying a shearing force to the statocyst hairs. In arthropods the hairs are chitinous structures, each innervated in its hollow base by a sensory nerve fiber (Fig. 25–18). In all other phyla, the hairs are processes of secondary sensory cells, or of primary sensory cells, or of ciliated epithelial cells interspersed between primary sensory cells.

The statocysts of fish (the sacculus) and of lobsters serve also in hearing: particularly at low frequency sound waves, the sensory nerve fibers show action potentials. Sense organs for hearing (sound waves from about 30 to 40,000 cycles) occur throughout vertebrates and in many insects (Fig. 25–21). In the Diptera and Coleoptera they are located in the antennae and are known as the organ of Johnston (Fig. 25–22). In some Orthoptera the organs are situated in the tibia of the front legs and are known as tympanal organs. Similar organs occur in the thorax or abdomen of other insect groups (see Fig. 25–1). Tympanal organs are formed of an enlargement of a trachea which gives rise to one or

(Text continued on page 621.)

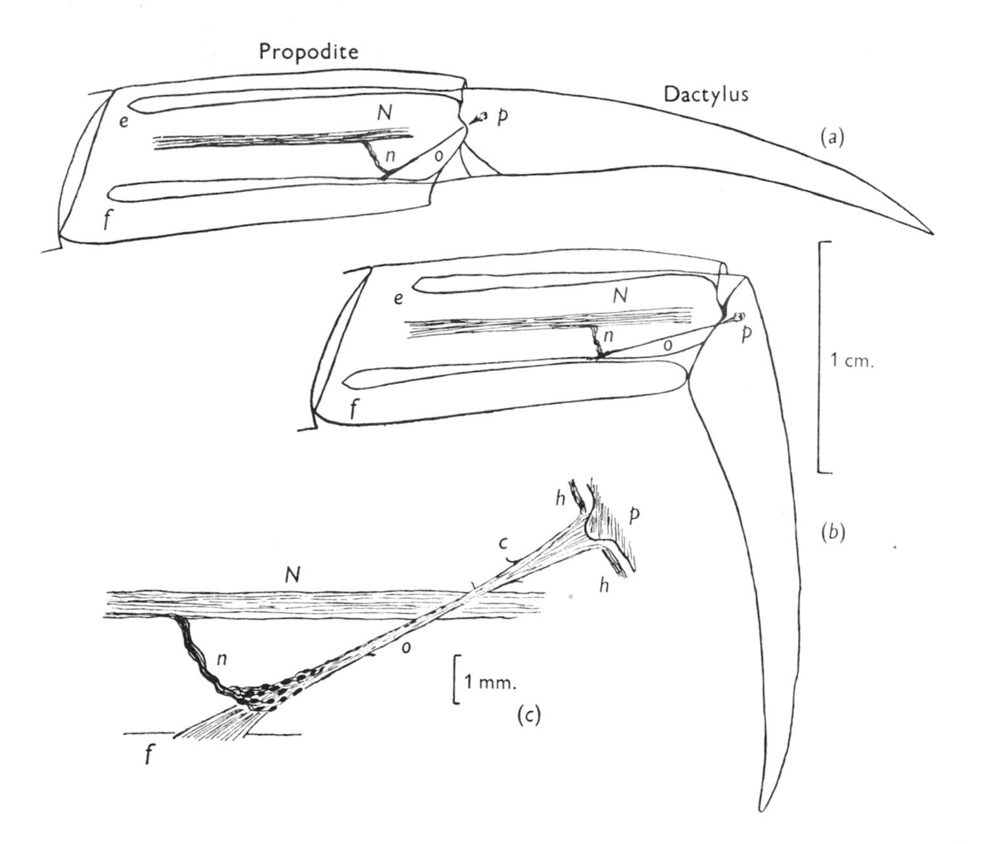

Figure 25–10. Semidiagrammatic sketches of a myochordotonal organ: the propodite-dactylus organ of *Carcinus maenas*, a crab. The organ itself consists of a bunch of receptor nerve cells embedded in a strand of connective tissue which runs across the joint between the propodite and dactylopodite. *C*, small connective tissue attachment; *e*, apodeme of extensor muscle; *f*, apodeme of flexor muscle; *h*, hypodermis; *n*, nerve bundle to organ; *N*, main nerve bundle; *o*, elastic organ; *P*, attachment to small protuberance on the dactyl. (From Burke, W.: An organ for proprioception and vibration sense in *Carcinus maenas*. J. Exp. Biol. *31*:127–138, 1954.)

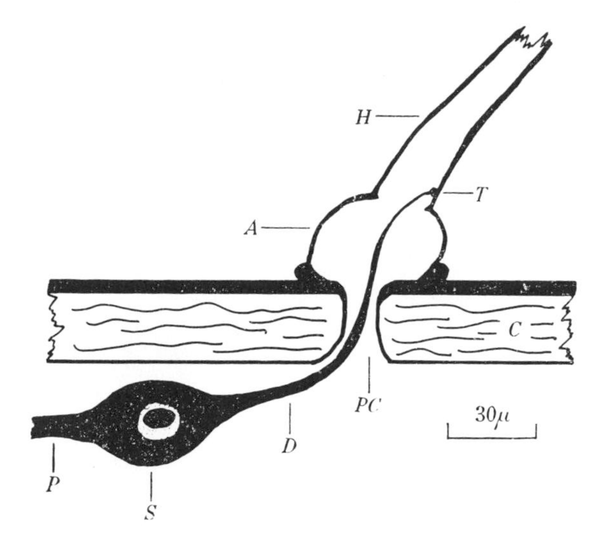

Figure 25–11. *Homarus*: relationship between the statocyst hair and its single sensory neuron. The cell body (*S*) of the sensory neuron lies in the hypodermis surrounding the statocyst and sends a distal process (*D*) through a pore canal (*PC*) in the cyst wall (*C*) to enter the hair base and terminate in the region where hair shaft (*H*) joins the dilated basal ampulla (*A*). A proximal process (*P*) runs to the brain in the statocyst nerve. The precise location and nature of the nerve terminal junction (*T*) with the hair is not yet clear and this picture represents an approximation from the best available evidence. The drawing is to scale except that the distal nerve process may sometimes be as long as 500 μ. (From Cohen, M. J.: The response patterns of single receptors in the crustacean statocyst. Proc. Roy. Soc. B, *152*:30–49, 1960.)

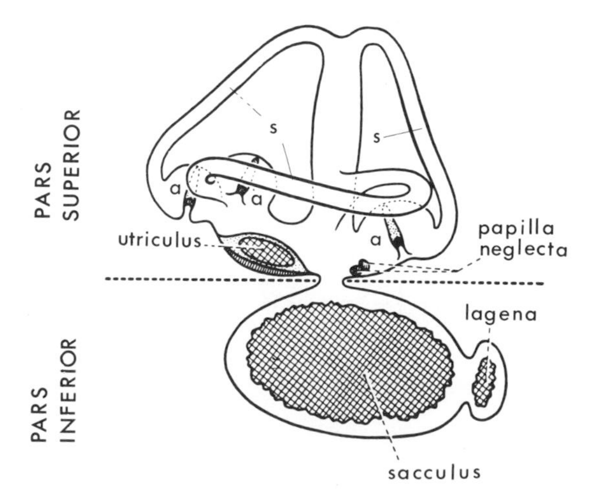

Figure 25–12. General diagram of the labyrinth of fish. The connection between the pars superior and the pars inferior is lacking in many teleosts. The elasmobranch labyrinth has a connection to the outside world, the *ductus endolymphaticus*. *a*, ampulla; *s*, semicircular canal. (After Dijkgraaf, S.: Bau und Funktionen der Seitenorgane und des Ohrlabyrinths bei Fischen. Experientia 8:205–216, 1952.)

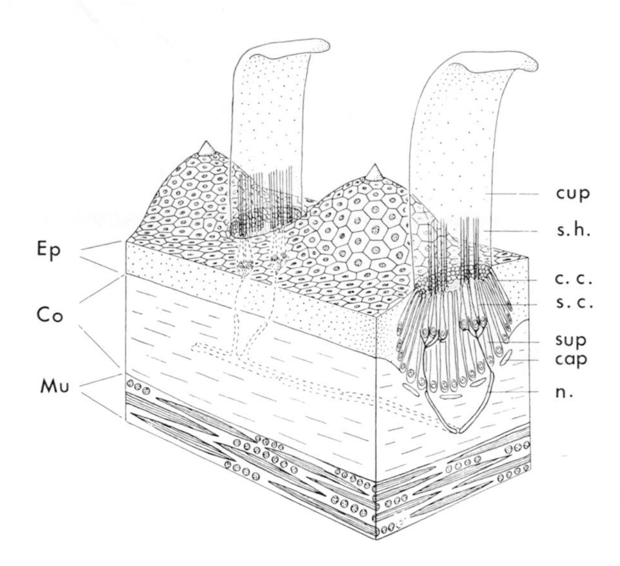

Figure 25–13. Section of the skin of the amphibian *Xenopus*, with two lateral line organs. *cap*, capillary; *c.c.*, cupula cells; *Co*, corium; *cup*, cupula; *Ep*, epidermis; *Mu*, muscularis; *n.*, nerve fiber; *s.c.*, sensory cell; *s.h.*, sensory hairs; *sup*, supporting cells. (After Goerner, P.: Beitrag zum Bau und zur Arbeitsweise des Seitenorgans von Xenopus laevis. Zool. Anz., Suppl. 25:193–198, 1962.)

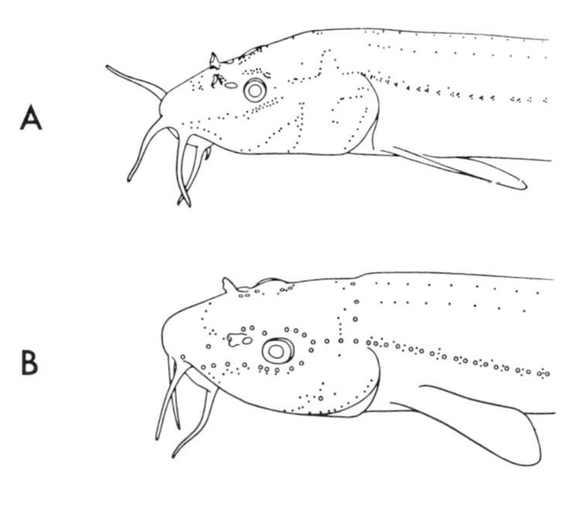

Figure 25–14. Lateral line organs of two closely related fresh-water fishes: *Misgurnus fossilis* (A) and *Nemachilus barbatulus* (B). · free sensory hillock; (see Fig. 25–16); o, canal pore. (From Dijkgraaf, S.: Bau und Funktionen der Seitenorgane und des Ohrlabyrinths bei Fischen. Experientia 8:205–216, 1952.)

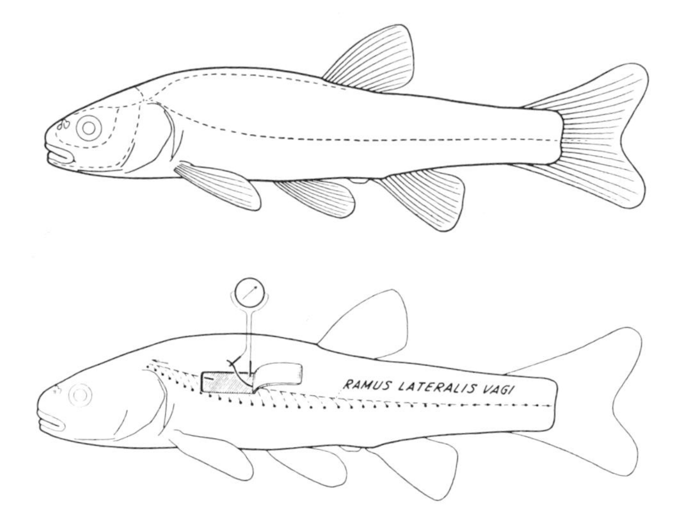

Figure 25–15. General diagram of position of lateral lines and of the set-up used for recording of action potentials from the lateral line nerve. The symbol of a potentiometer stands for the complex recording equipment (including amplifier, oscilloscope, and camera). (From Dijkgraaf, S.: Bau und Funktionen der Seitenorgane und des Ohrlabyrinths bei Fischen. Experientia 8:205–216, 1952.)

two tympanic membranes. In amphibians, reptiles, birds, and mammals, a specialized part of the inner ear, the cochlea, serves as sense organ for hearing (Figs. 25–18 and 25–21).

Vibrations transmitted to the legs excite receptors in the so-called *subgenual organs* of lipidopteran, dipteran, hymenopteran, and orthopteran insects (Fig. 25–23). These are situated in the tibia and consist of nerve cells stretched out between exoskeleton and trachea.

Analogous organs are the *lyriform* organs in the legs of spiders (Fig. 25–24), whose sensory neurons respond with nerve impulses to minute vibrations of the chitinous exoskeleton.

Receptors that respond to sound waves are generally known as *phonoreceptors*, and response to sound is called *phonoreception*. To question whether a sense organ or receptor permits an animal to hear or whether it simply allows

(Text continued on page 628.)

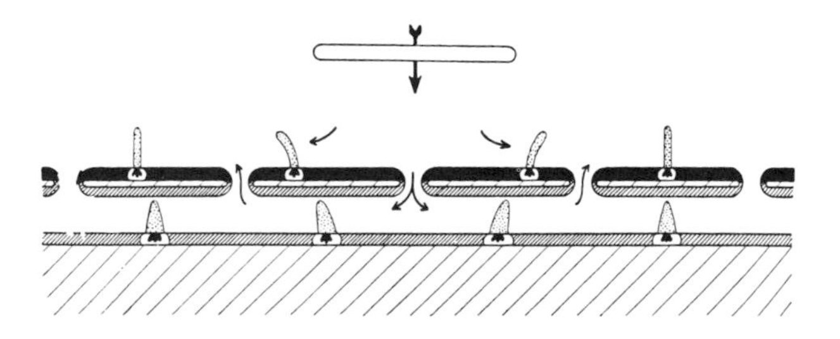

Figure 25–16. Movements of the cupulae of lateral line organs due to water current and water pressure caused by an approaching object (a small disc). The diagram shows free sensory hillocks, canal organs, and canal pores. The direction of fluid movement is indicated by arrows. (From Dijkgraaf, S.: Bau und Funktionen der Seitenorgane und des Ohrlabyrinths bei Fischen. Experientia 8:205–216, 1952.)

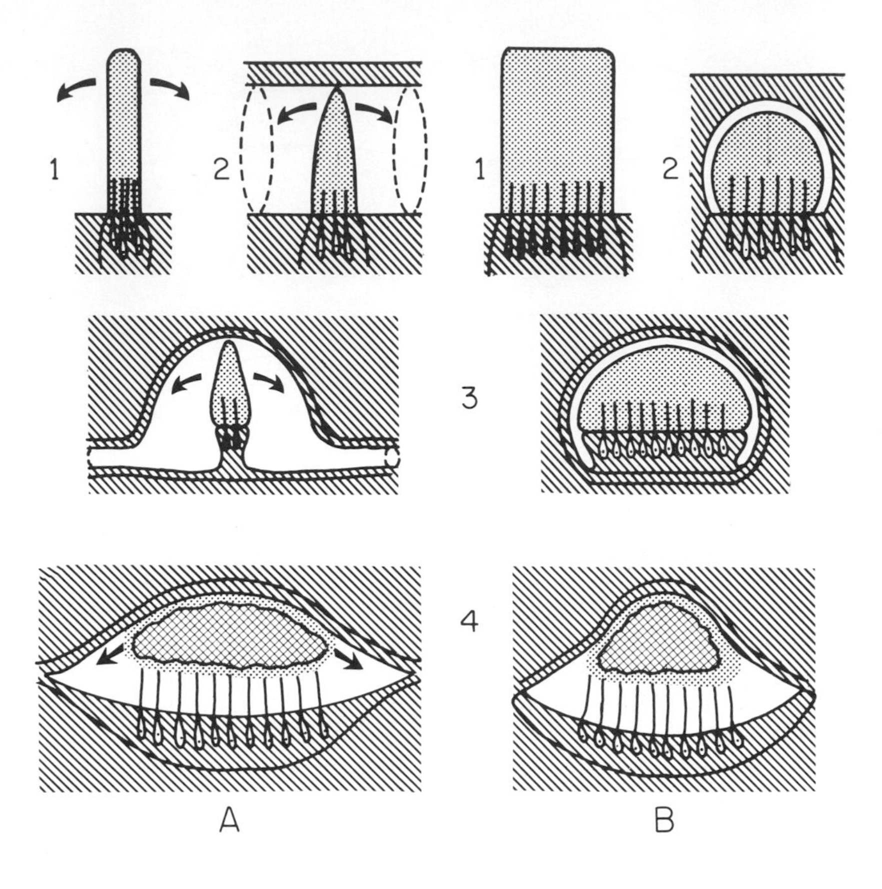

Figure 25-17. Diagrammatic representation of the structural features of the acoustico-lateralis system of vertebrates **A**, lateral view; **B**, front view. *1*, free-standing cupula of a neuromast organ (some fishes, amphibia, see Fig. 25-13). *2*, canal organ of lateral line (fish). *3*, crista ampullaris of semicircular canal (vertebrates; see Figs. 25-12 and 25-21). *4*, otolith organ (teleost fish). Sensory cells are shown in white with a dot marking the nucleus. Their hair processes are shown entering or contacting the gelatinous mass (indicated in stipple) of the cupulae or the otolith; the latter is shown by cross-hatching. Arrows indicate the possible movements of cupulae and otolith. (**A** after Dijkgraaf, S.: Bau und Funktionen der Seitenorgane und des Ohrlabyrinths bei Fischen. Experientia 8:205-216, 1952.)

Figure 25-18. **A**: Cross section of the cochlear canal of the human inner ear. **B** shows the organ of Corti enlarged. The outer and inner hair cells are secondary sensory cells that are innervated by the sensory fibers of the acoustic nerve. They are activated by the shearing force exerted by the tectorial membrane when it and the basilar membrane are set in motion by pressure waves transmitted through the fluid that fills the inner ear (endolymph and perilymph) when sound waves make the tympanic membrane vibrate. (From Rasmussen, A. T.: Outline of Neuro-anatomy, 3rd Ed. W. C. Brown Co., Dubuque, Iowa, 1943.)

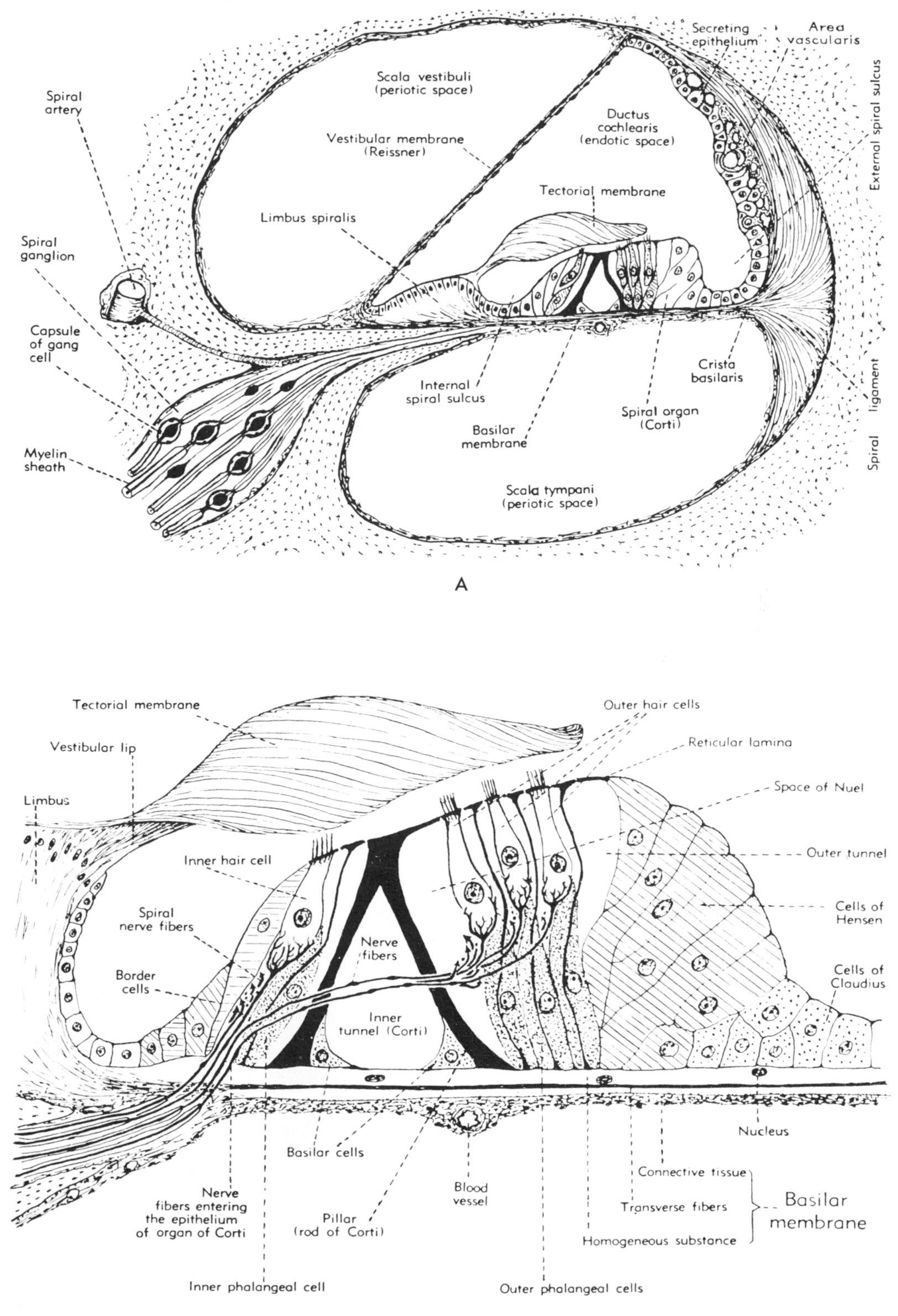

Figure 25–18. *See opposite page for legend.*

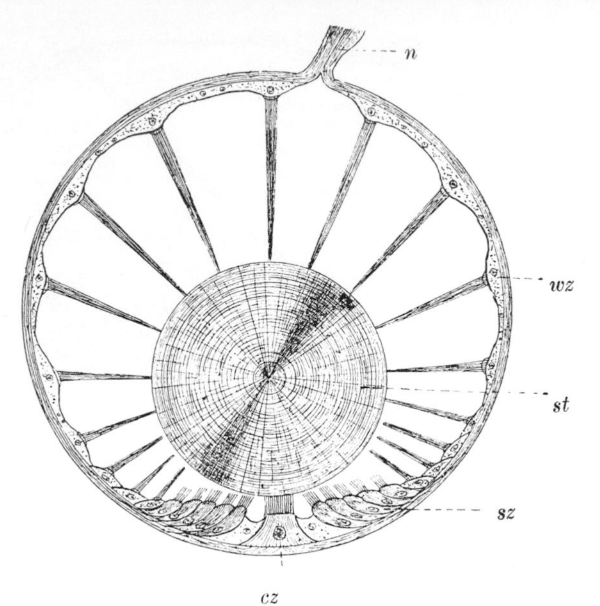

Figure 25–19. Statocyst of a mollusc, *Pterotrachea* (Heteropoda). The long cilia of the ciliated cells (*wz*) beat rhythmically, lifting the statolith (*st*) and allowing it to fall on the hairs of the sensory cells (*sz*). One of the latter is of particular size; it is called the central cell (*cz*). Depending on the position of the animal, different groups of sensory cells can be activated. The generated nerve impulses travel along the statocyst nerve (*n*) to the central ganglia. (From Stempell, W., and A. Koch: Elemente der Tierphysiolgie. G. Fischer Verlag, Jena, 1923.)

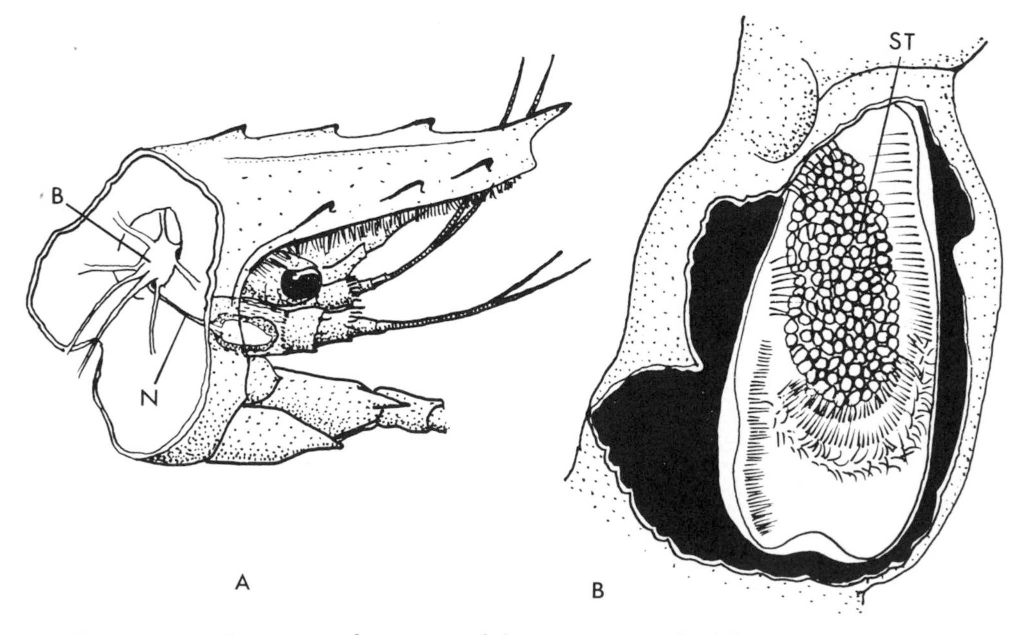

Figure 25–20. Location and structure of the statocysts in the lobster *Homarus americanus*. **A**, the dissected head region with the statocyst exposed in the basal segment of the right antennule. **B**, the statocyst with its dorsal wall removed to reveal the statolith mass (ST) and the rows of sensory hairs. Each sensory hair is innervated at its base by a sensory nerve fiber. *B*, brain; *N*, statocyst nerve (runs together with the antennular nerve). (Redrawn from Cohen, M. J.: The function of receptors in the statocyst of the lobster *Homarus americanus*. J. Physiol. *130*:9–34, 1955.)

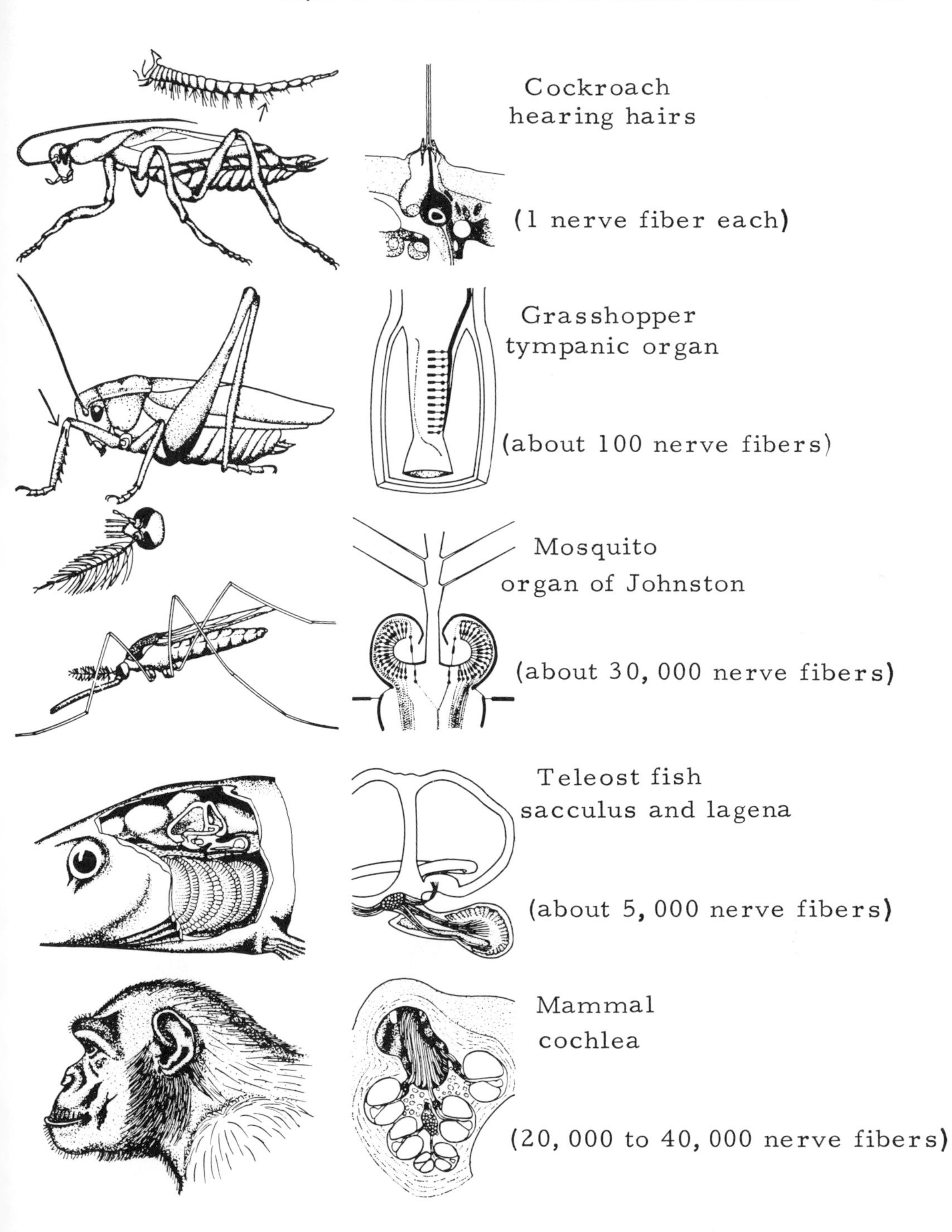

Figure 25-21. The ears (organs of hearing) of insects and vertebrates. (From Schwartzkopff, J.: Die Uebertragung akustischer Information durch nerventätigkeit nach dem Salvenprinzip. *In* Aufnahme und Verarbeitung von Nachrichten durch Organismen. S. Hirzel Verlag, Stuttgart, 1961.)

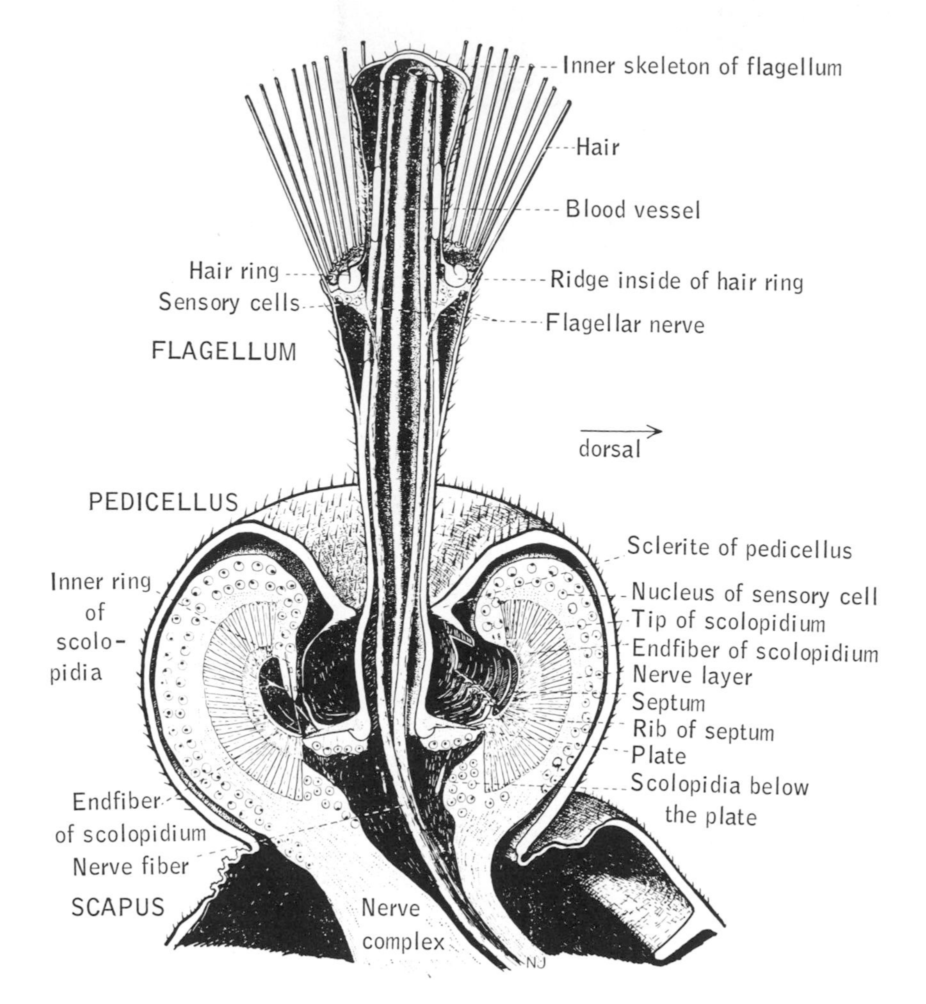

Figure 25–22. Structure of the hearing organ of a mosquito (*Anopheles*), the organ of Johnston. It is situated in the pedicellus of the antennae. The flagellum with its hairs vibrates in response to sound waves and transmits its movements through the "plate" to the sensory cells, the so-called scolopidia that are arranged in the form of an inner and an outer ring within the pedicellus. (From Risler, H.: Das Gehörorgan der Männchen von *Anopheles stephensi* Liston (Culicidae). Zool. Jahrb. Abt. Anat. Ontog. 73:165–186, 1953.)

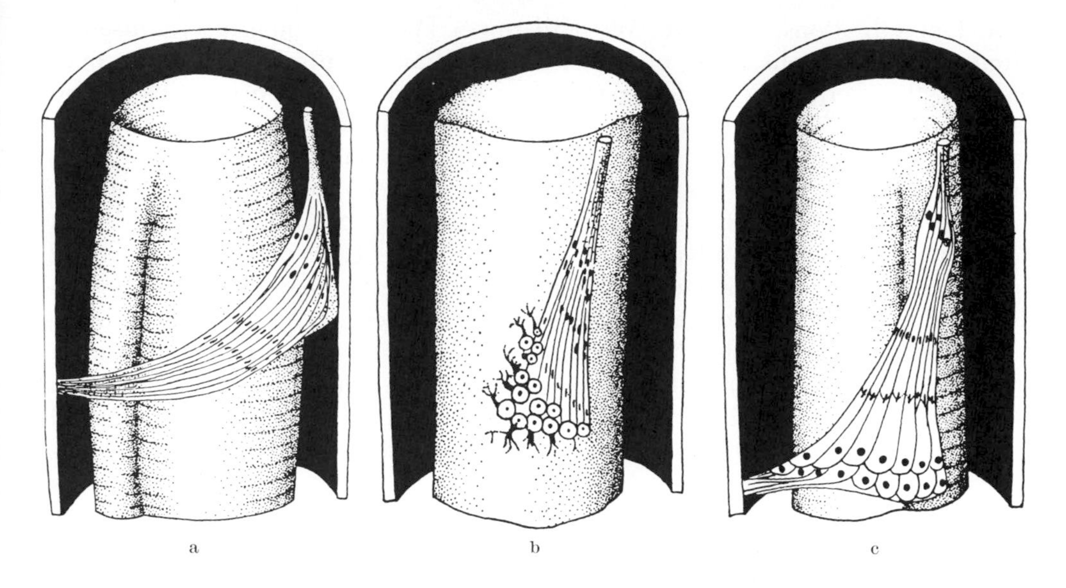

Figure 25–23. Schematic diagram of the structure of subgenual organs of insects: **a**, Orthoptera; **b**, Lepidoptera, and **c**, Hymenoptera. Part of the exoskeleton of the tibia is removed to show the large trachea and the sensory neurons that are stretched over it. The neurons respond with excitation to vibrations of frequencies from about 100 to about 10,000. (From Autrum, H., and W. Schneider: Vergleichende Untersuchungen über den Erschütterungssinn der Insekten. Z. vergl. Physiol. *31*:77–88, 1948.)

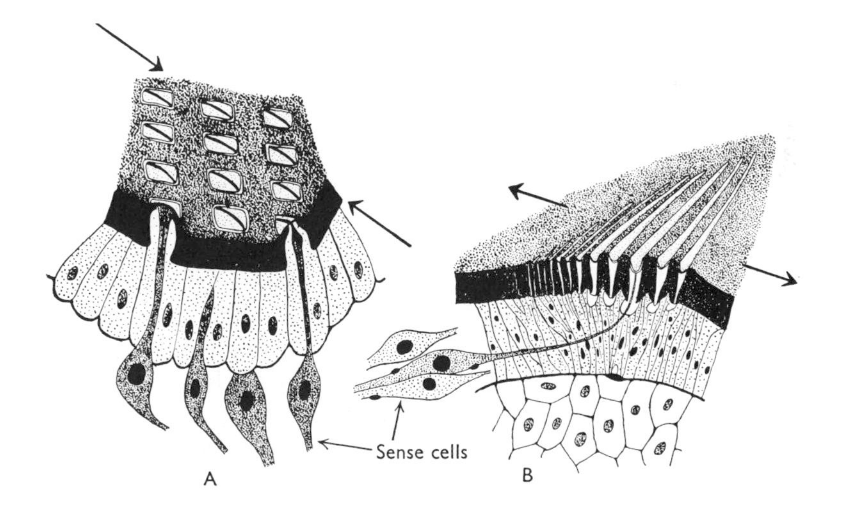

Figure 25–24. Diagrammatic drawings of: **A**, a campaniform sensillum (basal plate sensillum of the haltere of a dipteran insect), **B**, a lyriform organ (slit sensillum) of a spider. The arrows show the directions of the mechanical strain that causes excitation of the sensory cells. (From Pringle, J. W. S.: The function of the lyriform organs of arachnids. J. Exp. Biol. *32*:270–278, 1955.)

it to feel vibrations, is futile. We will never know the quality of sensation elicited by excitations going on in a sense organ of an animal. All we can ever learn is the frequency of nerve impulses elicited in the nerve cells or the sense organs. When a physiologist speaks of hearing, he means a response to sound waves, that is, to rapid mechanical oscillations of a gaseous, liquid, or solid body.

Photoreceptors are primary or secondary sensory cells which respond with a generator potential (and action potentials in the case of primary sensory cells) to illumination by a narrow or wide range of electromagnetic waves within the band width of wavelengths of 200 to 800 millimicrons. Aggregates of photoreceptors are usually called "eyespots," but when associated with a transparent lens, they are part of a *retina* and the whole organ-containing lens and retina is referred to as an *eye*. The term "eye" thus has a clear-cut physiological meaning, in contrast to the term "ear," which denotes a number of functionally different structures.

Light-sensitive sensory cells occur in the skin or epithelium of the body wall of a number of animals (amphibians, annelids, and others). Where whole areas of the body are thus equipped with photoreceptors without provision of a special optic apparatus outside of the sensory cells, one speaks of a *diffuse light sense* ("Hautlichtsinn" in the German literature).

Pigmented ganglion cells in the central nervous system of the gastropod *Aplysia*, and certain nerve cells in the sixth abdominal ganglion of various species of crayfish (decapod Crustacea) are excited by illumination. The light-sensitive neurons, obviously, have photoreceptor properties even though they are not sensory cells.

RECEPTOR PROPERTIES

The receptor cells of sense organs not only transduce or transform one form of the input energy (light, heat, pressure, chemical energy) into another form (electrochemical energy) of output energy, but they also serve as amplifiers: receptors are unusually sensitive cells. Their responses may involve free energy changes several orders of magnitude higher than those needed to elicit the response. As in an electronic amplifier, the output energy is not supplied by the input but by the amplifier and its power source which, in this case, is the cellular metabolism.

The hair cells in the mammalian cochlea and the sensory cells of the lyriform organs of spiders (to mention only two examples) respond with generator potentials to vibrations, the amplitude of which is lower than the diameter of a hydrogen atom. Certain photoreceptors and olfactory receptors are reported to respond to the impact of a single photon and molecule, respectively, with generator potential and action potential.

Energy Relations

Before continuing this discussion, it is, perhaps, worthwhile to recollect the terminology related to energy: any object that exerts a continuously acting *force* on another object through a distance in the direction of that force does *work*. Force then is expressed in terms of grams (gm), distance in centimeters (cm), and work in gram-centimeters (g-cm). The work done on an object is equal to the energy transferred to it. The absolute unit of force is the *dyne*, defined as that force which imparts to a free mass of 1 gm an acceleration of 1 cm/sec/sec, or 1 cm/sec^2. The absolute unit of work is the *erg*, defined as the force of 1 dyne exerted over a distance of 1 cm. 10^7 ergs is equal to 1 *joule*. Energy can be expressed in the same units (erg and joule). The time rate of doing work is called *power* and is defined as work (or energy) per time. The unit of power is the *watt* and is defined as 1 joule/sec. Energy can also be expressed as power times time, and the unit of energy then becomes 1 *watt-sec*.

The minimum energy necessary to excite a receptor cell can be described in two ways: we can either determine the smallest amount of continuously acting energy and express it in watts, or we can determine the minimum energy required to excite the receptor in the shortest possible time. In the latter case, we express the energy in terms of watt-seconds.

In a most stimulating paper, H. Autrum (1948) gave some estimates, derived from his own work and that of others, of the minimal energies required to stimulate certain sense organs so that their response elicits behavioral responses of the whole organism. The figures are listed in Table 25–1. Note that the values given are those effective on the whole sense organ and not those characteristic of single receptor cells. The latter are even smaller, up to a factor of 100 in the case of the rods in the human eye. To give an idea of the dimension of 5.10^{-17} watt, Autrum explains that at the rate of 5.10^{-17} watt/sec, it would take 10 billion years to accumulate enough electric current to light up a 15 watt light bulb for 1 second.

The energy expenditure of a single nerve impulse in a sensory nerve fiber is of the order of magnitude of 10^{-11} watt-sec. A receptor with a threshold energy requirement of 10^{-17} watt thus acts as an amplifier of considerable gain.

Not all receptors are that sensitive, however. It is known, for instance, that the minimum energy required to elicit a response in touch receptors in the human skin is 4.10^{-8} watt, and for stimulation of receptors at the base of a hair, 2.10^{-10} watt. A cutaneous cold receptor has a threshold of -10^{-7} watt (all data from Autrum, 1948). In these cases, the energy of a single nerve impulse is smaller than that of the input energy. In such cases, the receptor does not act as an amplifier.

Table 25–1

	Minimal Power Needed Under Optimal Conditions (Watt)
Ear of man	8.10^{-18}–4.10^{-17}
Tympanal organ of grasshopper	5.10^{-17}
Subgenual organ of cockroach	6.10^{-17}
Eye of man	6.10^{-17}

It should be clear that the energy-input is not directly utilized to produce a receptor potential or generator potential or action potential. The energy for the latter processes stems from the receptor or sensory cell itself. The best evidence for this is the case of the cold receptors: these respond with excitation to a negative energy input; in other words, they are excited by a loss of energy. The input energy (positive or negative) merely serves as a trigger (or better still: to pull the trigger).

The significant feature of any receptor function, whether it is that of a secondary or a primary receptor, is the production of nerve impulses or the change in discharge pattern of the sensory neuron. Details of the processes involved in the generation of nerve impulses in receptor neurons were discussed in Chapter 19, p. 465.

Spontaneous Activity

Remember that many sensory neurons are spontaneously active; that is, they fire (produce action potentials) at regular intervals, even without stimulation. This is characteristic of many mechanoreceptors, such as the slowly adapting stretch receptor neurons of decapod Crustacea (see p. 470), the statocyst receptor neurons of lobster (Cohen, 1955), the receptors in the semicircular canals of the inner ear of vertebrates (Löwenstein and Sand, 1940, and others), and lateral line neurons of fishes (Sand, 1937; Dijkgraaf, 1952, 1963). It has also been found to be characteristic of certain molluscan photoreceptors (Kennedy, 1960), photoreceptor neurons in the compound eyes of *Limulus* (Fuortes, 1959), and in chemoreceptors, such as those found in the carotis sinus of mammals (von Euler, Liljestrand, and Zotterman, 1939).

This so-called spontaneous activity is, of course, not without cause. It is understandable if one recalls that every neuron is under the influence of all modalities of the environment from which it cannot escape: this environment of every neuron has chemical, mechanical, electrical, and thermal properties. These, by interacting with the properties of the neuron itself, determine its state of excitability. What the so-called adequate stimuli do is nothing else but alter the excitability of the neuron. Spontaneously active neurons are even under normal conditions, in a state of excitation; in other words, their physicochemical properties are such that the prevailing condition of their immediate environment (temperature, ionic composition, etc.) keeps their excitability at such a high level that they "fire" repetitively. The spontaneity is, therefore, only apparent.

In view of the multiple sensitivity of sensory neurons (see also p. 472), the concept of the *adequate stimulus* assumes a special significance. Now we can define this term precisely: the adequate stimulus of a sensory cell is the addition or removal of a quantity of that form of energy which per unit power causes the largest change in excitability of the sensory neuron involved.

Regardless of whether they add or remove energy from a receptor, stimuli are classified as excitatory if they cause a depolarizing receptor-potential or generator potential and if they aid in the production of action potentials in the sensory axon. Stimuli are classified as inhibitory if they cause a hyperpolarizing response that diminishes the excitability of the receptor cells.

The significance of so-called spontaneously active sensory neurons lies in their ability to reflect in their discharge pattern both the action of excitatory as well as of inhibitory stimuli. Normally "silent" sensory neurons can indicate only excitatory stimuli, since the only message they can transmit is "excitation," signaled by nerve impulses. The functional difference between these two kinds of sensory neurons is illustrated in the diagrams of Figure 25–25.

Both normally silent and normally active sensory neurons show the phenomenon of *adaptation*: while the stimulus persists unaltered, the frequency of the neuron returns to a value near the original, normal condition. Examples are shown in Figures 25–26 to 25–29. The mechanism underlying adaptation was discussed in Chapter 19, (p. 465).

It must by now be clear to the reader that sensory neurons monitor environmental changes in the form of a *frequency code*. This code was first described in a classic paper by Adrian and Zotterman published in 1926 in the Journal of Physiology. The sheer elegance of reasoning expressed in this paper is the more impressive when one realizes the limitations posed by the earliest electrophysiological recording devices. Figure 25–30 is taken from this publication. It is still one of the best demonstrations of the behavior of a single sensory neuron, showing the typical pattern of frequency response.

Figure 25–31 shows in a series of examples the possible varieties of types of frequency responses to excitatory as well as inhibitory stimuli. If their meaning is not immediately clear, refer to Chapter 19, p. 465 for further explanations. Suffice it here to say that the same kind of stimulus, e.g., increase in light intensity, increases the excitability of some receptors and decreases that of others.

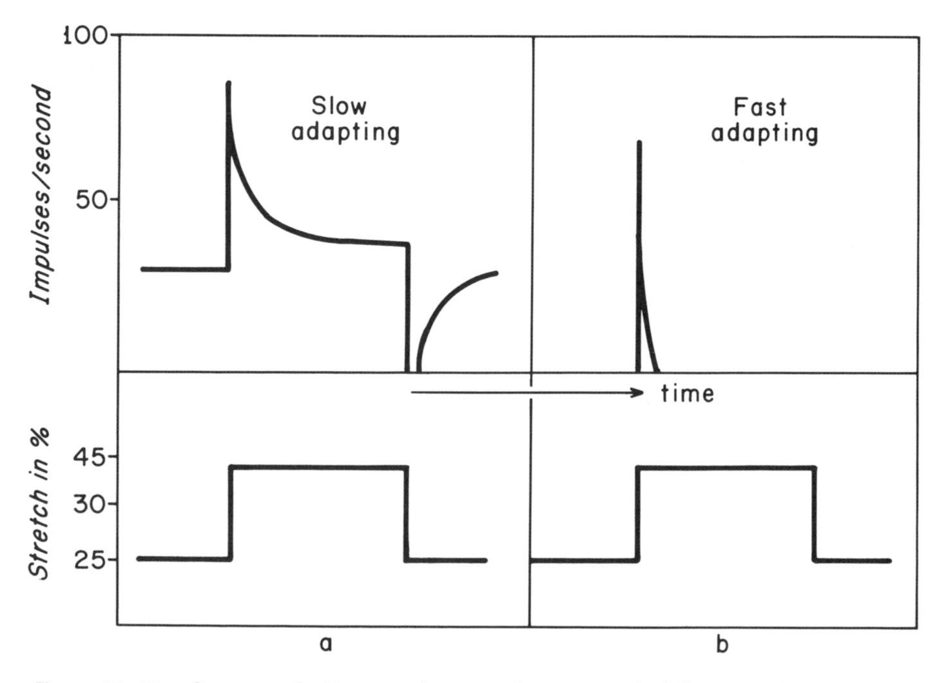

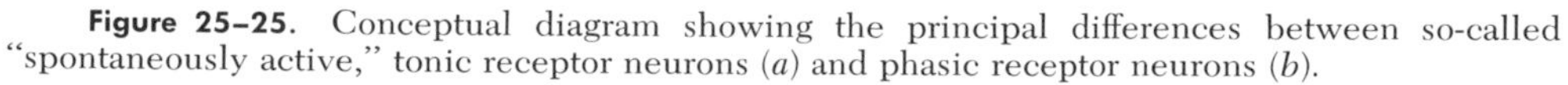
Figure 25–25. Conceptual diagram showing the principal differences between so-called "spontaneously active," tonic receptor neurons (*a*) and phasic receptor neurons (*b*).

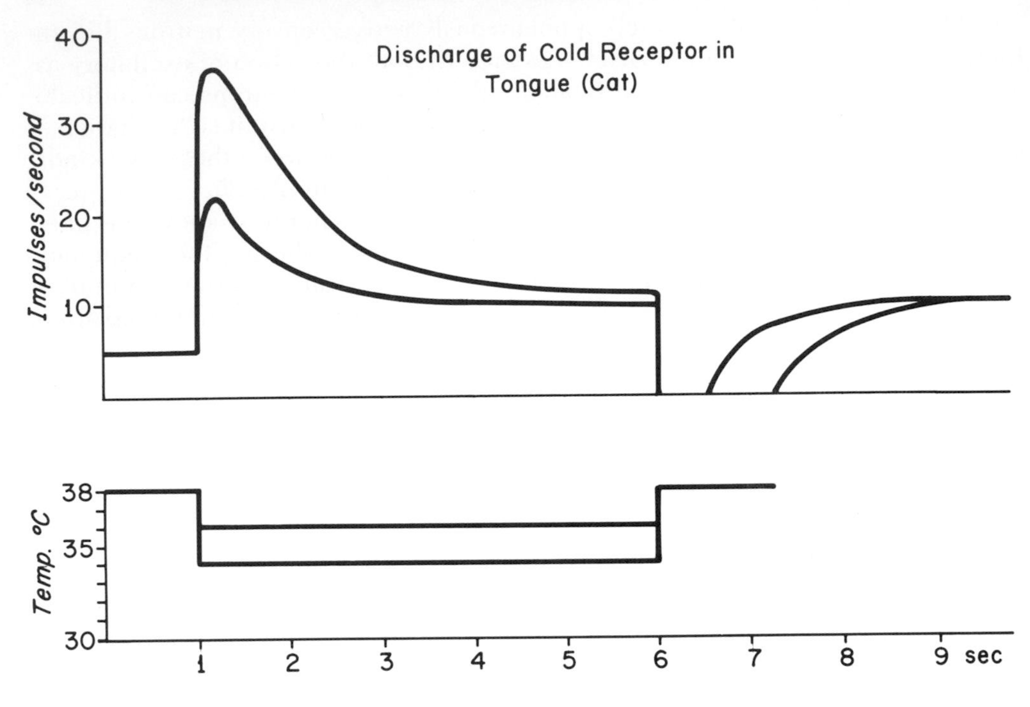

Figure 25–26. Adaptation in a cold receptor neuron. (After Hensel, H., and Y. Zotterman: Quantitative Beziehungen zwischen der Entladung einzelner Kältefasern und der Temperatur. Acta Physiol. Scand. 23:291–319, 1951.)

When, after adaptation has been allowed to take place, the original conditions are restored, the former type of receptor shows momentary inhibition (this type is called an *"on" receptor*); the other shows momentary excitation and is referred to as an *"off" receptor*.

The frequency pattern of a sensory neuron is a reflection of the changes in generator potential. For a variety of sensory neurons, it has been shown that the impulse frequency is directly proportional to the magnitude of the generator potential (see Fig. 19–7). The generator potential, however, is not directly proportional to the magnitude of the stimulus. It is often found that the generator potential (or receptor potential in the case of secondary receptor cells) increases linearly with logarithmically increasing strength of the stimulus.

These findings have supplied the objective basis for an important observation: the *sensation* of stimulus intensity shows a linear increment when the actual stimulus increases logarithmically. This has been known as the *law of Weber-Fechner*, which, near the end of the last century, revolutionized psychology because it demonstrated in a most convincing manner that psychic experience is subject to laws that can be given a mathematical expression like a law of physics. Under the impression of this relationship, Fechner founded a new branch of psychology which he called *psychophysics*. With the new understanding of the physiological basis of sensation, this field has meanwhile matured into *physiological psychology*.

Sensations can be explored only in human beings capable of adequate verbal expression. They are not the object of physiology. Sensory responses, however, are definitely the domain of physiology, and these can be explored in all animals that can be subjected to adequate experimentation. As stated, the Weber-Fechner law finds its counterpart in the characteristic relationship between stimulus strength and magnitude of resulting physiological response. The physiological significance of this relationship lies in the fact that receptors show a relative decrease in sensitivity with increasing stimulus strength. At lowest stimulus intensities minute changes in stimulus strength affect the response, but the larger the stimulus, the greater has to be the difference between it and another stimulus in order to give rise to a difference in the sensory response.

It is interesting, and significant, that temperature receptors do not follow the relationship mentioned; the same is true for certain mechanoreceptors. All these types of receptors show a more or less parallel increase of response with increasing stimulus strength.

It is important to point out that, in any case, the relationship holds true only within a limited range of stimulus strengths. Even so, the known cases—largely photoreceptors, pressure receptors, and phonoreceptors—have an amazing range (the minimal and maximal light intensity perceived by the human eye differ by a factor of 30,000) and it can be easily understood that this range is made possible by the fact that a logarithmic increase in stimulus strength is required to achieve a linear increase in the response.

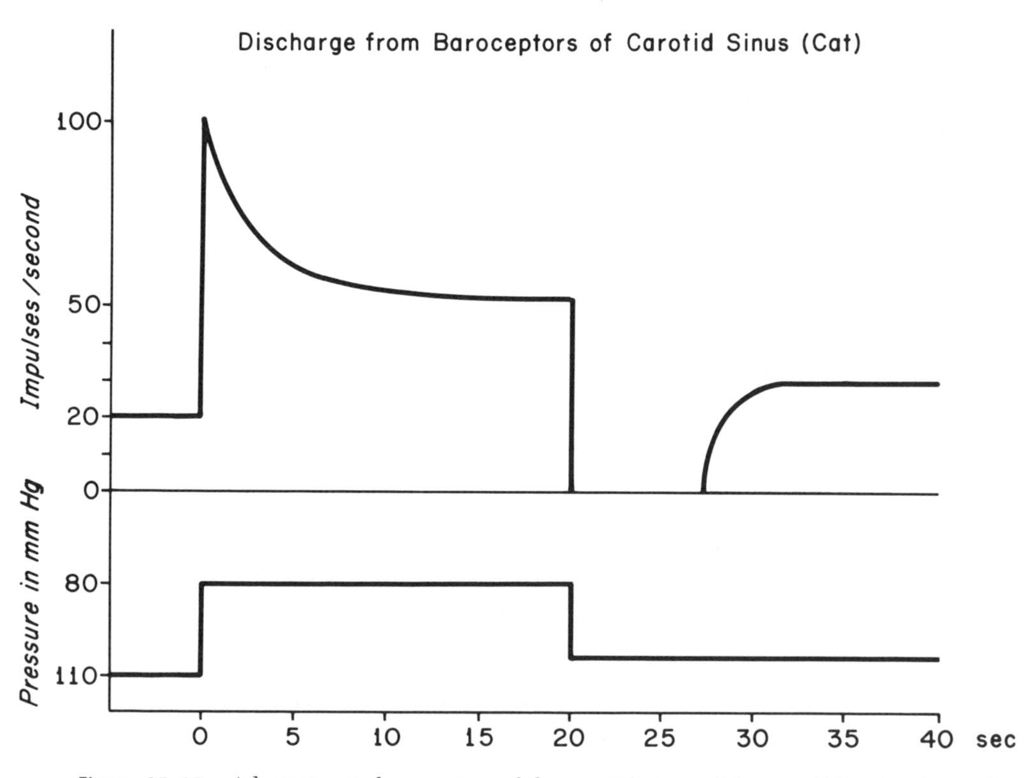

Figure 25–27. Adaptation in baroceptors of the carotid sinus of the cat. (After Landgren, S.: On the excitation mechanism of the carotid baroceptors. Acta Physiol. Scand. *26*:1–34, 1952.)

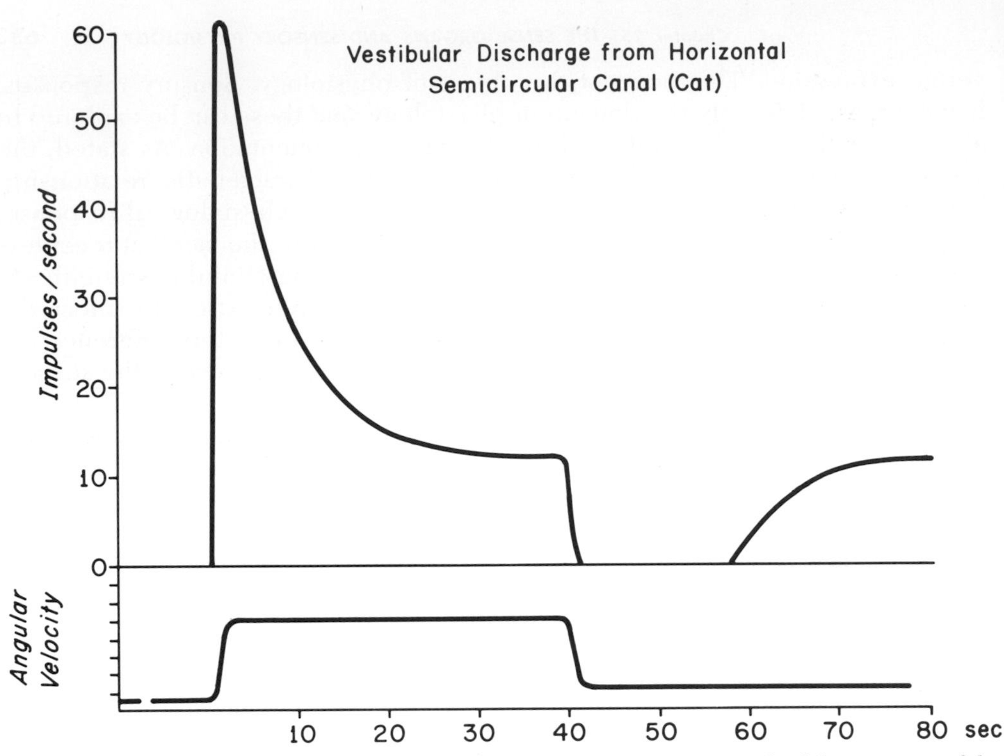

Figure 25–28. Adaptation in receptors of horizontal semicircular canals of the inner ear of the cat. (After Adrian, E. D.: Discharges from vestibular receptors in the cat. J. Physiol. *101*:389–407, 1943.)

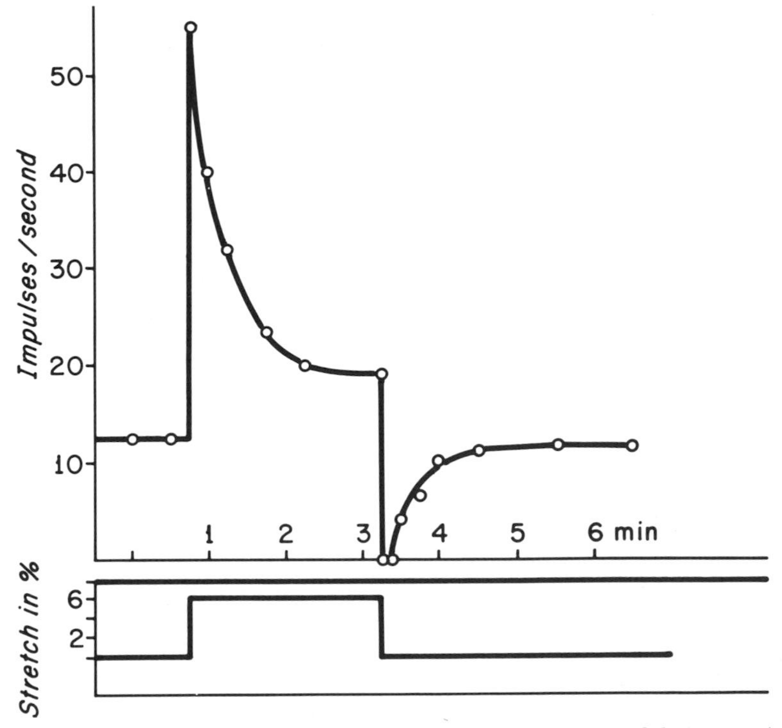

Figure 25–29. Adaptation in a stretch receptor neuron of a crayfish (*Astacus*). The circles represent the actually measured frequencies.

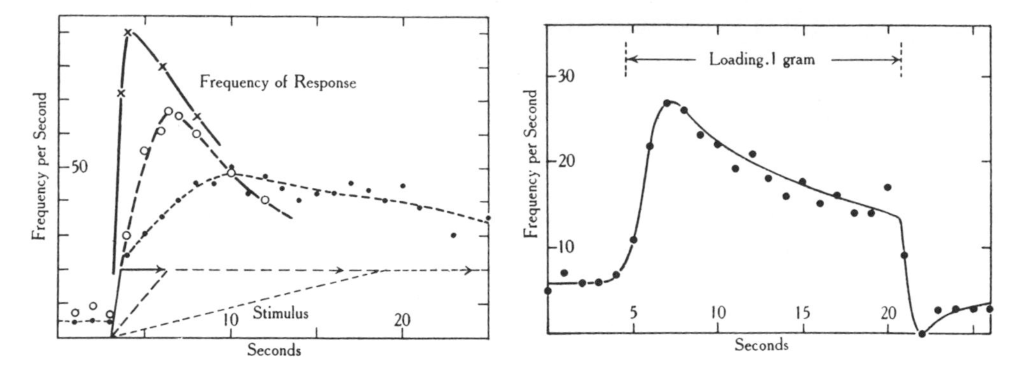

Figure 25–30. The graphs of Adrian and Zotterman which present the first analysis of the electrical responses of a receptor neuron (muscle receptor of frog skeletal muscle): The graph on the left shows how the magnitude of the initial increase in frequency depends on the rise time of the stimulus (even though the final stimulus amplitude is the same). The graph on the right shows a typical adaptation curve. The stimulus consisted of the pull of a weight (load) on the muscle. (From Adrian, E. D., and Y. Zotterman: The impulses produced by sensory nerve endings. Part II. The response of a single end-organ. J. Physiol. *61*:151–171, 1926.)

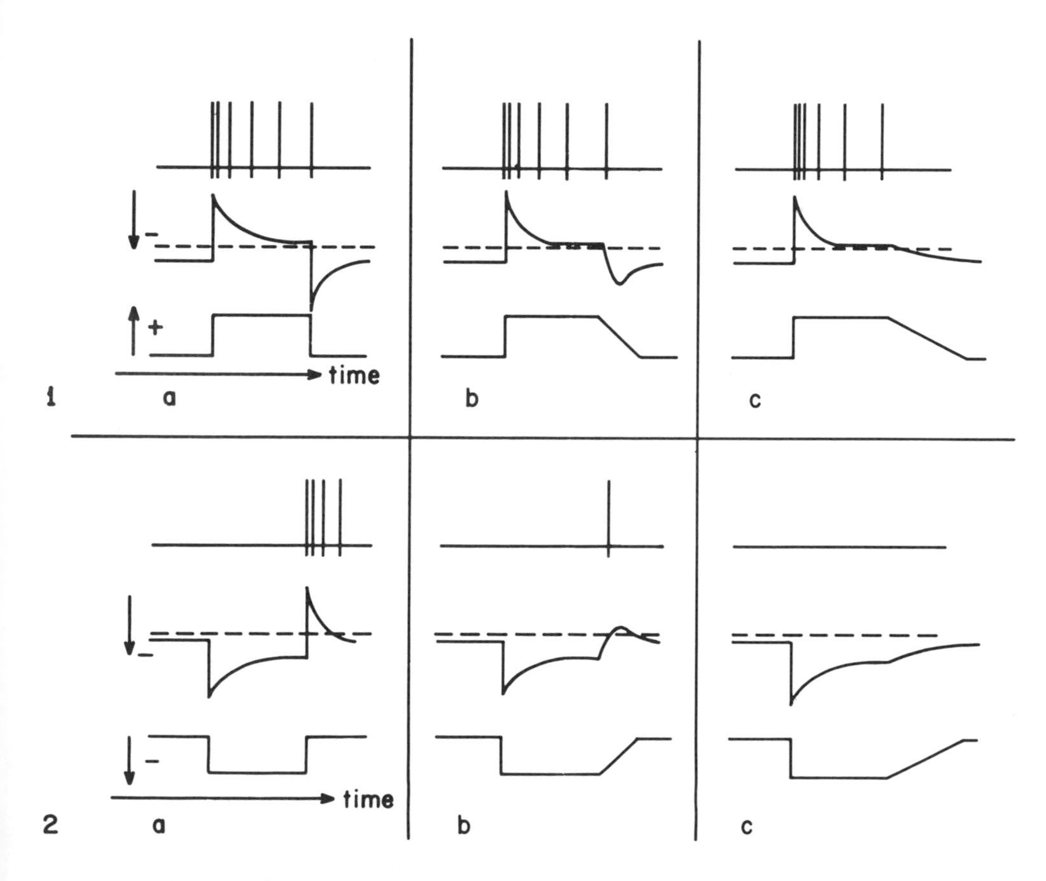

Figure 25–31. Changes in membrane potential and impulse frequency resulting from excitatory and inhibitory stimuli. In **1** the excitatory stimulus comes first; in **2** the inhibitory stimulus comes first. In *a*, *b*, and *c* the opposite stimulus has different slopes. In each of the six diagrams, nerve impulses are shown above, the middle is the membrane potential and firing threshold, and below is the stimulus (change in environmental conditions).

FUNCTIONAL PROPERTIES OF SENSE ORGANS

Range Fractionation

The receptors of a sense organ are often found to respond only to a certain fraction of the total range of sensitivity of the whole sense organ. The vertebrate eye that is equipped with rods and cones has two types of receptors, each with a different range of sensitivities. In addition, the cones are not all equal but some respond predominantly to one wavelength, whereas others have a different optimum wavelength to which they respond maximally. A comparable situation has been found in the eyes of insects; see Figure 14–7.

Among mechanoreceptor organs are several that show the principle of range fractionation in a striking manner. In the joint between propodite and dactylopodite, crabs (e.g., *Carcinus maenas*) have a proprioceptor organ, "PD-organ") shown in Figure 25–10 (Burke, 1954). Using a special technique, Wiersma and Boettiger (1959) moved with controlled angular velocities and positioned the dactylopodite of amputated legs, and recorded the action potentials from sensory fibers belonging to the PD-organ. It was found that there are two classes of sensory neurons present: (1) fibers that respond only to extension of the dactyl and (2) fibers that respond only to flexion. Each class has two major subdivisions: (a) neurons that respond only during actual movement—these were called *movement receptors*, and (b) neurons that do respond to changes in position and show a maximum frequency at a particular extreme position. These were named *position receptors*. These show little adaptation and can monitor position over long periods of time.

The movement receptors were found to be of many different kinds; some respond maximally to slow movements such as 1 degree of arc per second), others begin to respond only at higher angular velocities, and some reach their maximum firing rate only at speeds of 100 degrees/second. Each movement receptor by itself is a poor indicator of velocity, since the range is in most cases limited. Together, however, these receptors cover the total range of movements. The firing of each sensory neuron thus carries a specific message.

In a way, the range fractionation exhibited by such a PD-organ is comparable in significance to the respective position of photoreceptors within the retina of an eye: in the latter case, excitation of a given photoreceptor signifies the location in space of a light spot within the total image projected onto the retina. Retinal photoreceptors, of course, also exhibit another kind of range fractionation: different receptors have different spectral sensitivities (see Chap. 14, p. 332); that is, they respond optimally to different ranges of the visual spectrum.

We learn here a most important lesson: in addition to the frequency code by which a given receptor carries information concerning the intensity of a stimulus, a receptor by virtue of its position in space or by the position of its limited range of responsiveness within the total range of all the receptors of the sense organ, signals the position or the quality of the stimulus. The mere fact that receptor number X of a given retina fires, means that there is a spot of light in area X, and if receptor Y of the PD-organ fires, it means that the dactylopodite is being flexed at a rate of, say, 41 to 65 degrees/sec. The intensity of the light spot is indicated by the frequency with which X fires, the actual velocity (e.g., 45 degrees/sec.) is given by the frequency with which Y fires. If there is a code, there must be a decoding station where the code is being read. It must be assumed that the central nervous system reads the code and not only identifies the meaning of the frequency with which a given receptor fires, but recognizes the meaning of the fact that this and not another receptor is firing. In other words, the central nervous system must recognize each receptor.

Range fractionation has another, most important significance: it helps to avoid ambiguity of the frequency code. Although many types of mechanoreceptors show a direct relationship between intensity of stimulus and magnitude of response, there are others where the response curve is bell shaped: this is the case with the mechanoreceptors in various statolith organs (see Figure 25–32). Rotation of the animal gives rise to first increasing then decreasing frequency of nerve impulses in a given receptor cell. If a receptor fires at any frequency, this frequency therefore has a double meaning. If, however, there is another receptor that has a different range, the combined messages of both receptors can have only one meaning. This is explained in Figure 25–33.

The same applies to photoreceptors with regard to their sensitivity to various wavelengths of light. If the magnitude of the generator potential (or that of the corresponding impulse frequency) is plotted against the wavelength (the light of each wavelength consisting of equal energy content), a bell-shaped curve results. A given receptor response thus indicates two different wave-

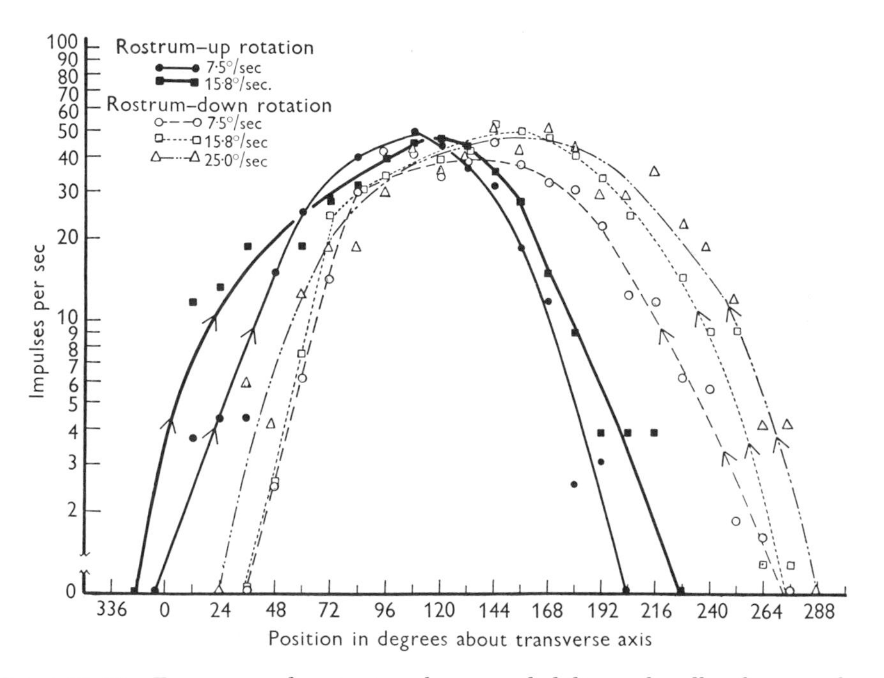

Figure 25–32. Frequency of nerve impulses recorded from a bundle of axons of position receptors in the statocyst of a lobster, *Homarus*, while the cephalothorax is being rotated about the transverse axis at constant velocities. Each point on the different curves represents the average frequency over a 12 degree of arc interval. Curves obtained with single receptor axons are similar. Note that for each curve there are two positions that give identical frequencies of nerve impulses. (From Cohen, M. J.: The function of receptors in the statocyst of the lobster *Homarus americanus*. J. Physiol. *130*:9–34, 1955.)

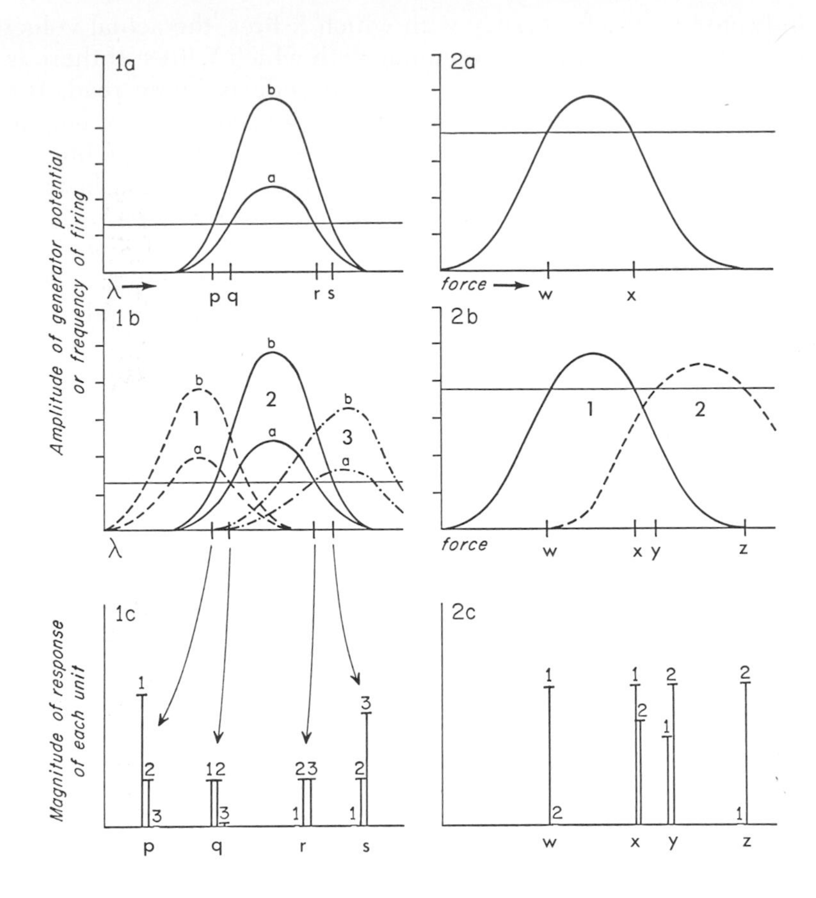

Figure 25–33. Diagrams to explain the ambiguity of information provided by single receptor neurons and how this ambiguity is resolved when the same mode of stimulation activates two or more receptors that have different action spectrums (response characteristics). Diagrams *1a* to *1c* represent photoreceptors, *2a* to *2c*, mechanoreceptors. In *a* and *b* of each set the magnitude of the response (in arbitrary units) is plotted against wavelength (λ) and force, respectively; *1c* and *2c* represent the simultaneous magnitudes of the receptors represented in *1b* and *2b* at wavelengths and forces indicated by the vertical lines on the x-axis of *1b* and *2b*.

1a, when a photoreceptor is stimulated by lights of equal energy content but of different wavelength an action spectrum is obtained; that is, for each wavelength there is a characteristic magnitude of response (e.g., frequency of nerve impulses). For the two intensities employed, two curves, *a* and *b*, are obtained. It can be seen that if the receptor exhibits a given generator potential (shown by the horizontal line) or frequency of firing, the response indicates four possible wavelengths: if only the response is known, it is impossible to tell whether the response is caused by wavelength *p* at intensity *b*, *q* at intensity *a*, *r* at intensity *a* or *s* at intensity *b*.

1b, the information becomes unambiguous with regard to wavelength and intensity if two more receptors (*2* and *3*) are added. - - - -, action spectra of receptor *2* at light of energy content *a*, and *b*; - · - · - ·, action spectra of receptor *3* at light of energy contents *a* and *b*.

1c, columns *1*, *2*, and *3* represent the relative magnitudes of the responses of the three receptors when they are stimulated by lights of wavelength *p*, *q*, *r*, and *s* at intensities of *b*, *a*, *a*, and *b*, respectively. The symmetries in the diagrams are coincidental.

2a, a given response of a mechanoreceptor corresponds to two intensities of stimulation.

2b, addition of a second receptor with different response characteristics resolves the ambiguity.

2c, relative magnitude of the responses of the two receptors when stimulated at intensities *w*, *x*, *y*, and *z*.

lengths. Again, if there are two receptors with a different range (spectral sensitivity), the frequencies of both together give unambiguous information about the wavelength of the stimulating light. How complicated the coding of visual information actually must be can be appreciated when one considers that frequency is also employed to code intensity (regardless of the wavelength).

Range fractionation must not necessarily take place at the level of the receptors themselves. It can take place at the level of the first and second synapses on the way to the receiving or de-coding center.

Redundancy (or Multiplication) of Channels

In many sense organs, the receptor cells have such an enormous sensitivity that they may easily be activated by random fluctuations of the properties of the environment. A good example for this are the photoreceptors (e.g., rods in the vertebrate retina) that are excited by single light quanta. We also recall here the receptor cells in the vertebrate cochlea or those in the lyriform organs of spiders which all respond to vibrations of an amplitude that is less than the diameter of a hydrogen atom.

Such sensitive receptors may even be brought into activity by events within themselves. Information provided by a single channel of extreme sensitivity is therefore of dubious value, since it is never certain that excitation actually reflects a *significant* event in the environment and that it is not the result of some random fluctuation.

If two or more receptors are excited simultaneously, it is less likely that the cause for this is random fluctuation. Multiplication of sensory channels thus provides a mechanism that overcomes the uncertainties introduced by extreme sensitivity. Of course, in order for this scheme to work, it is necessary that the redundant channels converge upon the same "receiving station." In the vertebrate retina, several rods make synaptic contact with one and the same ganglion cell (see Fig. 25–34).

This ganglion cell is responsible for passing the information received from the rod cells on to the later stations within the central nervous system which are engaged in analyzing the sensory data. We find in this system a striking application of the principle of summation: excitation coming from a single rod cannot excite the ganglion cell sufficiently so that it responds with a conducted action potential. Only if the excitations from several rods are received simultaneously is the ganglion cell brought into full action.

The principle of redundancy explains why the statocysts of decapod Crustacea contain such a large number of sensory hairs and associated sensory neurons, a finding that is so surprising in view of the fact that arthropods are so "conservative" with the number of neurons they employ for various purposes. One might indeed ask why these animals do not have just one or at most a few sensory hairs attached to the statoliths. The answer (first proposed by Cohen, 1955) is that multiplication of sensory channels permits a much greater sensitivity.

In certain cases, redundancy may have yet another significance: chemoreceptors are known to respond to a few, sometimes even to a single molecule of a substance for which they are specialized. The reaction acts as a trigger that

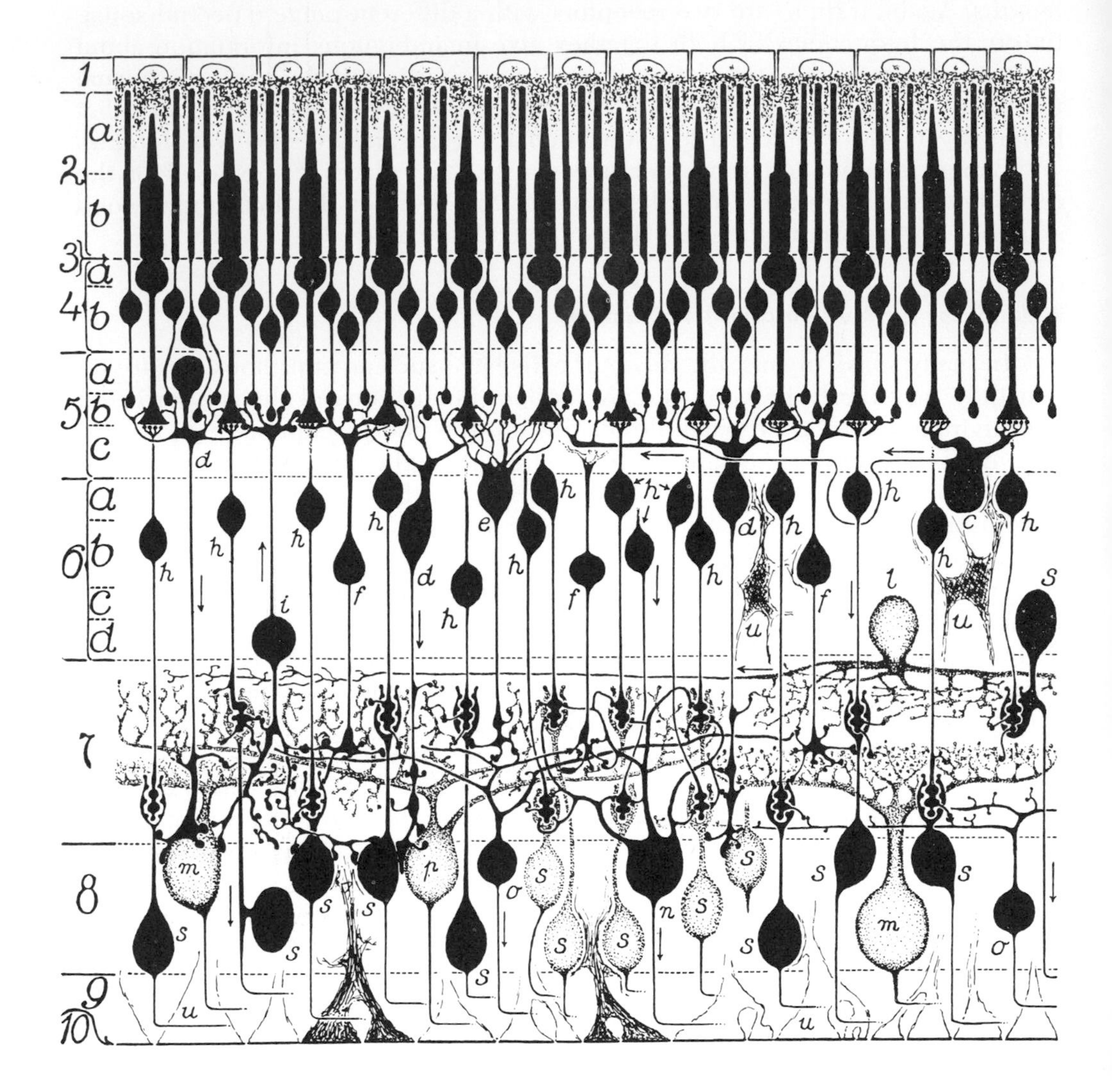

Figure 25–34. Schematic presentation of neuron varieties of primate retina and their synaptic relationships, with the essential features preserved, based on the Golgi method of staining. Layers and zones, indicated along the left margin. In the upper part of the diagram are photoreceptors, both rods (*a*) and cones (*b*), the bacillary parts sticking into the pigment layer, the inner fibers of the rods terminating with round spherules, and those of the cones, with conical pedicles, which form zone 5-*b* of the outer plexiform layer. Here the synaptical contacts are made with upper or dendritic expansions of horizontal cells (*c*), along which the impulses spread in adjoining parts of the retina, and with the bipolars of centripetal varieties (*d, e, f, h*), along which they pass to the inner plexiform layer, where synaptical contacts are established with the ganglion cells (*m, n, o, p, s*). From the ganglions arise nerve fibers which, as the optic nerve, enter the brain. Other types of neurons, called "centrifugal bipolars" (*i*), may condition photoreceptors under the influence of the ganglion cells, hence in a direction opposite to that of the centripetal bipolars (*d, e, f, h*). There may be still other neuron varieties whose connections are lateral, spreading in the inner plexiform layer (*l*). This indicates that the primate retina is a complex organ whose function is not only to react to physical light as an external stimulus but also to sort the generated impulses in many ways before they are further transmitted to the brain. (From Polyak, S.: The Vertebrate Visual System. H. Klüver, ed. University of Chicago Press, Chicago, 1957.)

sets up excitation in the receptor. Because of the specificity of the chemical reaction between the substance and the receptor, the resulting excitation cannot be regarded as the result of a random or chance event. The enormous number of olfactory receptors and the expansion of the receptive area (folded nasal mucosa and olfactory epithelia of mammals, highly branched antennae of male moths) increases the chances of a "hit." Multiplication of sensory channels serves here to increase the sensitivity of the sense organ as a whole. Sensitivity in this case depends on the ability to detect a substance whose molecules are widely separated in space. Male moths are reported to detect the odor of a female of the same species over distances of several miles. Experiments of Schneider (1954 and later—see Schneider, 1963) have shown that a concentration of the odorous substance as low as 10^{-16} gm/cm^3 excites the receptors.

Inhibitory Interactions

In the eyes of mammals and of *Limulus* the multiplicity of sensory channels has another feature: inhibitory interaction. In *Limulus* this takes the form of so-called *lateral inhibition*: the photoreceptor neurons (known as the excentric cells) are connected by collateral branches which establish inhibitory synapses. Thus the activity in one receptor inhibits the activity in a neighboring receptor. This is illustrated in Figure 25–35. Lateral inhibition leads to an exaggeration

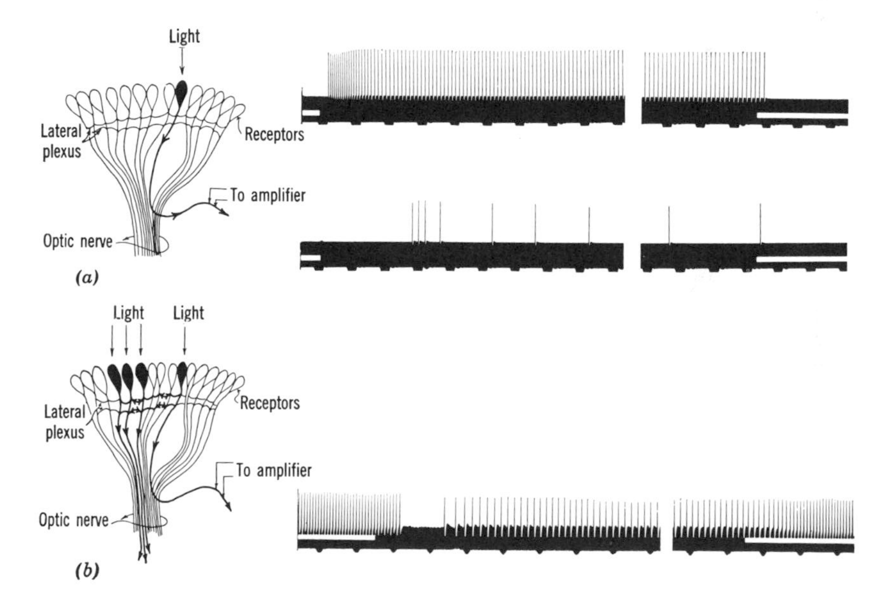

Figure 25–35. Oscillograms of action potentials in a single optic nerve fiber of the xiphosuran *Limulus*. The experimental arrangements are indicated in the diagrams at the left. a, response to prolonged steady illumination. For the upper record the intensity of the stimulating light was 10,000 times that used for the lower record. The signal of exposure to light blacks out the white line above the 1/5-sec time marks. Each record is interrupted for approximately 7 seconds. **b**, inhibition of the activity of a steadily illuminated ommatidium in the eye of *Limulus*, produced by illumination of other ommatidia near it. The oscillographic record is of the discharge of impulses in the optic nerve fiber arising from one steadily illuminated ommatidium. The blackening of the white line above the 1/5-sec time marks signals the illumination of the neighboring ommatidia. (From Ratliff, F.: Inhibitory interaction and the detection and enhancement of contours. *In* Sensory Communication. W. Rosenblith, ed. Massachusetts Institute of Technology Press, Cambridge, Mass., 1961.)

of image contrast. A similar inhibitory interaction is found in the mammalian retina, but there the inhibition takes place at the level of the ganglion cells with which the sensory neurons establish inhibitory contacts. The consequence (exaggeration of contrasts) is the same. (See Hartline, Ratliff, and Miller, 1961, and Kuffler, 1953, listed in Chapter 19.)

Sense Organs That Modulate Central Excitability

The primary function of the sense organs discussed so far is to transfer information concerning the external or "internal" environment to the central nervous system. It has come to light, however, that there are some types of sense organs whose primary function seems to be to change the general excitability of certain nerve centers.

So far, only two such organs are known: the muscle spindles of vertebrates and the myochordotonal organs of certain crabs. In both cases, the sense organ consists of an association of muscle fibers and sensory neurons, the latter responding with an increased frequency of nerve impulses to increases in muscle tension. What makes these organs so remarkable is that the muscle elements receive a specific motor innervation which is independent of the motor innervation of muscle elements whose function is to cause the animal or one of its appendages to move. In other words, the motor innervation of the sense organs is concerned with the production of electric discharges (action potentials) in the sensory units of the sense organ. By way of this motor innervation, the central nervous system can modulate the sensory input that reaches it from these sense organs. The sensory input itself, in turn, modifies the excitability of the regular motor neurons that supply the movement muscles.

Vertebrate Muscle Spindles. The skeletal muscles, particularly those of the limbs, contain numerous muscle fibers that are modified into sense organs. Their structure is shown in Figure 22–2. The middle portion of the organ, known as the muscle spindle, is innervated by branches of sensory neurons. The proximal and distal portions are innervated by endings of motor neurons, known as the γ-efferent fibers. When the latter are activated, that is, when they send potentials to the spindle muscle, the proximal distal portions of the muscle contract, thereby stretching the middle region which is noncontractile. Stretching of this middle region activates the sensory neurons. The central ends of the sensory neurons make synaptic contact with motor neurons that innervate the nonsensory muscle fibers of the same muscle.

There is good evidence that initiation of limb movement is preceded by activation of the γ-efferent motor fibers, and that it is indirectly elicited by reflex activation of the motor neurons proper. This is explained in the diagrams of Figure 25–36.

Translated into our own experience, this would mean that whenever we want to move a finger or a leg, we cannot activate the appropriate muscles directly: we cause them to contract by activating the γ-efferent system of nerve fibers and thereby produce a "stretch reflex."

Research on this γ-efferent control of muscle contraction was pioneered by Ragnar Granit and his collaborators in Stockholm.

Crustacean Myochordotonal Organs. The so-called accessory flexor muscle

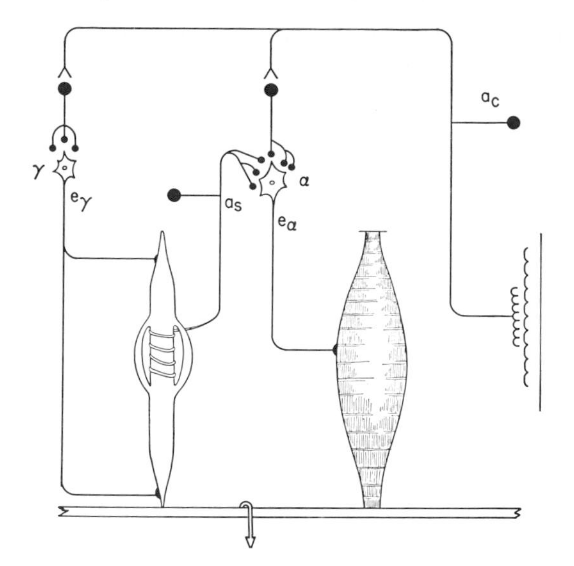

Figure 25–36. Diagram to illustrate the role of muscle spindles in the reflex control of motor activity (muscle contraction) in mammals. Higher centers of the central nervous system cause activation of γ-efferent neurons ($e\gamma$). These innervate the intrafusal muscle fibers that are part of the muscle spindles (see Fig. 22–2). Note that the middle portion of the intrafusal muscle fibers are not contractile; thus the middle portion is being stretched by the contracting parts. Stretching acts as a stimulus on the sensory nerve endings of the afferent neurons (a_s) which excite the regular motoneurons ($e\alpha$) which in turn activate the regular (*extrafusal*) muscle fibers of the muscle. The latter process is responsible for the tension developed by the whole muscle. The γ-efferent system, also known as the *fusimotor system*, thus constitutes the efferent limb of a "peripheral loop" of a reflex arch and is engaged in a delicate control of the motoneurons (α-neurons) and thus of muscle tension. a_c, cutaneous afferent neuron. (From Patton, H.: Reflex regulation of movement and posture. *In* Medical Physiology and Biophysics, 18th Ed. T. C. Ruch and J. F. Fulton, eds. W. B. Saunders Co., Philadelphia, 1960.)

in the meropodite of walking legs of the edible crab *Cancer magister* consists of a long tendon which stretches, threadlike, between a proximal and a distal head of muscle fibers. Both groups of muscle fibers are innervated by branches of the same two motor neurons. Near the proximal muscle head, an elastic strand inserts in the tendon and spans the distance to the joint between the meropodite and the ischiopodite. Attached to this elastic strand is a cluster of sensory cells, the axons of which form a nerve that joins the leg nerve. They end in the central nervous system. When the joint between meropodite and carpopodite is flexed, or when the muscle fibers of the accessory flexor are activated, a pull is exerted on the sensory cells and they respond with series of nerve impulses that travel toward the central nervous system. The accessory flexor muscle has negligible power. Its main function appears to be the stimulation of the sensory cells which, together with the elastic strand, are known as myochordotonal organs.

The myochordotonal organs are not involved in the reflex control of the leg in which they are situated. The use of a leg is not impaired in any way after removal of its myochordotonal organ. When several of the organs are removed, however, the animal becomes listless, exhibits general loss of muscle tone, and becomes rather unresponsive to disturbance in the environment. It appears clear that the sensory nerve impulses from the myochordotonal organs are needed to maintain the excitability of the central nervous system. They appear to provide a mechanism by which the central nervous system can control the level of its excitability.

Structure and function of the myochordotonal organs has been analyzed by Cohen and his coworkers in Eugene, Oregon. They have shown that the posture of the animal, that is, the general position of its legs, must also profoundly influence the discharge from the sensory cells of myochordotonal organs and thus modulate behavior.

It is likely that this kind of sense organ which responds to the output from the animal's own central nervous system is much more common than is suggested by the present limited knowledge about such organs.

REFERENCES

Adrian, E. D. (1928) The Basis of Sensation. The Action of Sense Organs. Christophers, London.

Adrian, E. D., and Y. Zotterman (1926) The impulses produced by sensory nerve endings. Part II. The response of a single end-organ. J. Physiol. *61*:151–171.

Autrum, H. (1948) Ueber Energie- und Zeitgrenzen der Sinnesempfindungen. Naturwissenschaften *35*:361–369.

Autrum, H. (1961) Physiologie des Sehens. Fortschr. Zool. *13*:257–302.

Autrum, H., and W. Schneider (1948) Vergleichende Untersuchungen über den Erschütterungssinn der Insekten. Z. vergl. Physiol. *31*:77–88.

von Buddenbrock, W. (1952) Vergleichende Physiologie, B. I: Sinnesphysiologie. Birkhäuser Verlag, Basel.

Bullock, T. H. (1959) Initiation of nerve impulses in receptor and central neurons. Rev. Mod. Physics *31*:504–514.

Burke, W. (1954) An organ for proprioception and vibration sense in *Carcinus maenas*. J. Exp. Biol. *31*:127–138.

Burkhardt, D. (1958) Die Sinnesorgane des Skeletmuskels und die nervöse Steuerung der Muskeltätigkeit. Ergebn. Biol. *20*:27–66.

Burkhardt, D. (1961) Allgemeine Sinnesphysiologie und Elektrophysiologie der Receptoren. Fortschr. Zool. *13*:146–189.

Carthy, J. D. (1958) An Introduction to the Behaviour of Invertebrates. The Macmillan Co., New York.

Cohen, M. J. (1955) The function of receptors in the statocyst of the lobster *Homarus americanus*. J. Physiol. *130*:9–34.

Cohen, M. J. (1960a) The crustacean myochordotonal organ as a proprioceptive system. J. Comp. Biochem. Physiol. *8*:223–243.

Cohen, M. J. (1960b) The response patterns of single receptors in the crustacean statocyst. Proc. Roy. Soc. B, *152*:30–49.

Cohen, M. J. (1964) The peripheral organization of sensory systems. *In* Neural Theory and Modeling. (R. F. Reiss, ed.) Stanford University Press, Stanford.

Dijkgraaf, S. (1952) Bau und Funktionen der Seitenorgane und des Ohrlabyrinths bei Fischen. Experientia *8*:205–216.

Dijkgraaf, S. (1963) The functioning and significance of the lateral-line organs. Biol. Rev. *38*:51–105.

Dotterweich, H. (1931–1932) Bau und Funktion der Lorenzini'schen Ampullen. Zool. Jahrb., Allg. Zool. Physiol. Tiere *50*:347–418.

Eldred, E., R. Granit, and P. A. Merton (1953) Supraspinal control of muscle spindles and its significance. J. Physiol. *122*:498–523.

von Euler, U. S., G. Liljestrand, and Y. Zotterman (1939) The excitation mechanism of the chemoreceptors of the carotid body. Skand. Arch. Physiol. *83*:132–151.

Florey, E. (1957) Chemical transmission and adaptation. J. Gen. Physiol. *40*:533–545.

Fuortes, M. G. F. (1959) Initiation of impulses in visual cells of Limulus. J. Physiol. *148*:14–28.

Granit, R. (1955) Receptors and Sensory Perception. Yale University Press, New Haven. (Paperback edition, 1962.)

Hebb, D. O. (1966) A Textbook of Psychology. W. B. Saunders Co., Philadelphia.

Hensel, H. (1952) Physiologie der Thermoreception. Ergebn. Physiol. *47*:165–368.

Hensel, H., and Y. Zotterman (1951a) Quantitative Beziehungen zwischen der Entladung einzelner Kältefasern und der Temperatur. Acta Physiol. Scand. 23:291–319.

Hensel, H., and Y. Zotterman (1951b) The response of mechanoreceptors to thermal stimulation. J. Physiol. *115*:16–24.

Katz, B. (1950) Depolarization of sensory terminals and the initiation of impulses in the muscle spindles. J. Physiol. *111*:261–282.

Kennedy, D. (1960) Neural photoreception in a lamellibranch mollusk. J. Gen. Physiol. *44*:277–299.

Kuffler, S. W., C. C. Hunt, and J. P. Quilliam (1951) Function of medullated small-nerve fibers in mammalian ventral roots; efferent muscle spindle innervation. J. Neurophysiol. *14*:29–54.

Leskell, L. (1945) The action potential and excitatory effects of small ventral root fibers to skeletal muscle. Acta Physiol. Scand., Suppl. 31, *10*:1–84.

Lindauer, M. (1963) Allgemeine Sinnesphysiologie, Orientierung im Raum. Fortschr. Zool. *16*:57–140.

Löwenstein, O., and T. D. M. Roberts (1950) The equilibrium functions of the otolith organs of the thornback ray (Raja clavata). J. Physiol. *110*:392–415.

Löwenstein, O., and A. Sand (1940) The individual and integrated activity of the semicircular canals of the elasmobranch labyrinth. J. Physiol. *99*:89–101.

Sand, A. (1937) The mechanism of the lateral sense organs of fishes. Proc. Roy. Soc. B, *123*:472–495.

Sand, A. (1938) The function of the ampullae of Lorenzini, with some observations on the effect of temperature on sensory rhythms. Proc. Roy. Soc. B, *125*:524–553.

Schneider, D. (1963) Electrophysiological investigation of insect olfaction. Proc. First Internat. Symp. on Olfaction and Taste. Pergamon Press, Oxford, pp. 85–103.

Schwartzkopff, J. (1962a) Die akustische Lokalisation bei Tieren. Ergebn. Biol. *25*:135–176.

Schwartzkopff, J. (1962b) Vergleichende Physiologie des Gehoers und der Lautaeusserungen. Fortschr. Zool. *15*:213–336.

Symposium of the Society for Experimental Biology (1950) Physiological Mechanisms in Animal Behaviour. Academic Press, New York.

Wiersma, C. A. G., and E. Boettiger (1959) Unidirectional proprioceptive movement fibres from a sense organ of *Carcinus maenas*. J. Exp. Biol. *36*:102–112.

26 NEUROCHEMISTRY AND NEUROPHARMACOLOGY

This chapter is concerned with those aspects of neurochemistry and neuropharmacology that elucidate synaptic transmission. In particular, it is concerned with the metabolism of transmitter substances and the mode of action of drugs that interfere with synaptic transmission. It is assumed that the reader is familiar with the topics discussed in Chapter 20 (Synaptic Transmission).

Neurochemistry is concerned with the chemical constitution of the nervous system, the metabolism of nerve cells, and the changes in chemical constitution and metabolic activity during and following activity.

Neuropharmacology is concerned with the interaction of drugs with chemical processes underlying the function of nerve cells. This includes those processes that are evoked in effector cells by synaptic transmission.

Neurochemistry and neuropharmacology are inseparable. Not only have drugs become most important tools in the study of neurochemistry, but neuropharmacology is to be considered an extension of neurochemistry. The reason for this is that compounds that are commonly known as *drugs* are now more and more recognized as structural modifications of naturally occurring molecules. Their action on nerve processes can be interpreted as a modification of the normally occurring molecular events. This provides for an extraordinary extension of experimental analysis and theoretical explanation.

It is unfortunate that the neurochemical and neuropharmacological knowledge is almost exclusively derived from studies on vertebrate animals. An elementary explanation for this is that those investigators that are well trained in chemistry and biochemistry are seldom experienced in animal morphology. Although they know how to obtain brains from rats, mice, or cats—or even sciatic nerves—they prefer to homogenize invertebrate animals whole. However, beginnings have been made, and a number of sophisticated neurochemical and neuropharmacological investigations on invertebrate organisms have been carried out and published.

ACETYLCHOLINE AND CHOLINERGIC SYNAPTIC TRANSMISSION

It was not until Otto Loewi in Austria performed his classic experiments on frog and toad hearts that there was convincing evidence for the "chemical transmission" of the action of nerve impulses. For his first, classic paper, Loewi used 14 frogs and four toads. He removed the heart together with a stretch of the left vagus nerve, inserted a cannula filled with Ringer's solution into the ventricle, and suspended the organ from it. The nerve was hung over a stimulating electrode. After the blood had been washed out of the heart, Loewi allowed the saline-filled heart to beat for a certain time (about 15 minutes), and then removed the saline and saved it in a test tube. After the cannula and heart were again filled with saline, the vagus nerve was stimulated repetitively for 15 minutes (the frequency of stimulation is not indicated in the publication), and then the saline was withdrawn and saved. Addition of the first saline sample to the heart (after this was allowed to recover from the vagal inhibition), resulted in no noticeable change in amplitude and frequency, but when he replaced this with the saline collected after 15 minutes of vagal stimulation, Loewi found a marked reduction in amplitude and frequency (see Fig. 26–1).

During springtime the vagus nerve of toads causes acceleration of the heartbeat, owing to the presence and functional predominance of sympathetic nerve fibers. Loewi proved (apparently in a single experiment) that the saline in the cannula contained a heart-accelerating substance after 25 minutes of stimulation of the vagus nerve.

With this four page article, Loewi opened up a vast field of research and laid the foundation for a theory of the "humoral transmission" of nerve action.

In its original formulation and implications, the theory today applies only to exceptional situations, such as that found in vertebrate organs inner-

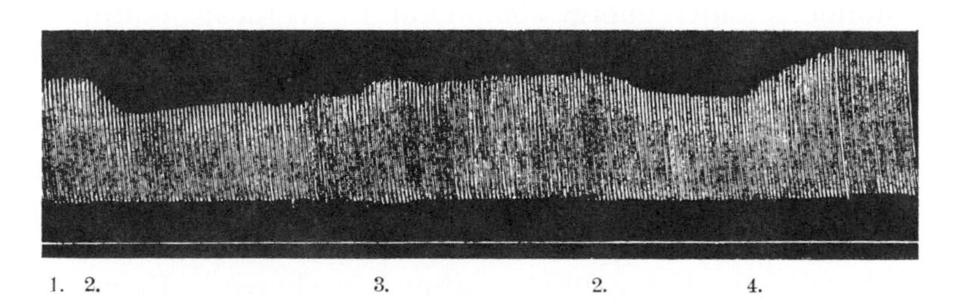

Figure 26–1. Original illustration from the classic paper by Otto Loewi which for the first time proved chemical synaptic transmission. The record shows the amplitude of heartbeats of an isolated frog heart during (*1*) normal perfusion with Ringer's solution, (*2*) perfusion with fluid obtained during a 15 minute period of vagus stimulation, (*3*) perfusion with fluid obtained during a 15 minute period without stimulation, and (*4*) same as (*2*), but with atropine added to the fluid during the stimulation period. "Fluid" here means Ringer's solution that has been in contact with the heart during the specified time. (From Loewi, O.: Über humorale Übertragbarkeit der Herznervenwirkung. I. Mitteilung. Pflügers Arch. ges. Physiol. *189*:239–242, 1921.)

Table 26–1. Acetylcholine Content of Nerve Tissues (in μg/gm Wet Weight)

Vertebrate	Dog	ventral spinal roots	23 – 48
		dorsal spinal roots	0 – 0.25
		brain	1.5 – 3.8
Chordata	Ciona	ganglion	20 –120
Arthropoda	Limulus	ganglia	7.5 – 13.2
	Carausius	ganglia	100 –200
	Calliphora	brain	500
	Homarus	ganglia	90
Mollusca	Octopus	ganglia (brain)	350

For more extensive and precise data see Hebb and Krnjevic (1962) and Florey (1963).

vated by the autonomic nervous system. In its modern form, the object of the theory is better called chemical synaptic transmission.

The agent released by parasympathetic (vagus) nerve endings has been identified with *acetylcholine*, and this ester has been detected in the nervous system of numerous animal species throughout the Animal Kingdom.

The acetylcholine content of some nerve tissues is listed in Table 26–1. Note that the amounts (per unit weight) are often remarkably high. It is likely that the acetylcholine found in a given nerve tissue is predominantly present in those nerve cells that are cholinergic, that is, in those that release acetylcholine at synapses. The concentration of acetylcholine in a given part of the nervous system can thus be taken as an index of the relative number of cholinergic neurons. Where cholinergic neurons are absent (vertebrate sensory nerves, crustacean efferent nerve bundles) the acetylcholine content is negligible.

It has been well established that acetylcholine occurs throughout the (cholinergic) neuron and not only in the nerve terminals. When a cholinergic nerve is cut, acetylcholine accumulates just proximal to the cut while it disappears from the distal part of the transected nerve; this indicates that acetylcholine or its synthesizing enzyme (see below) are transported by the centrifugal flow of axoplasm from the cell soma toward the nerve terminals.

Acetylcholine is a high energy compound. Its synthesis requires adenosine triphosphate (ATP) as an energy source and proceeds in two steps: (1) the formation of acetyl coenzyme A ("active acetate") and (2) the acetylation of choline by transfer to choline of the acetyl group from coenzyme A. The enzyme responsible for the latter reaction is known as *choline acetylase* (Nachmansohn and Machado, 1943). If sufficient ATP is available, the synthesis of acetylcholine can proceed under anaerobic conditions. In living tissue within the organism this is unlikely to occur. The synthetic pathway is shown in Figure 26–2.

Synthesized acetylcholine occurs in two forms: *free acetylcholine* and *bound acetylcholine* (Mann, Tennenbaum, and Quastel, 1939; Corteggiani, 1938; Schallek, 1945). Acetylcholine can be released from the bound form by agents that denature proteins (heat, certain organic solvents, alcohol, chloroform and ether, acid, etc.) or by hypotonic solutions, indicating that bound acetylcholine is enclosed within vesicles (perhaps mitochondria or other sub-

ATP + acetate → adenyl acetate + pyrophosphate

adenyl acetate + coenzyme A → acetyl coenzyme A + AMP

citrate ·
· · · · · → acetyl coenzyme A
pyruvate ·

acetyl coenzyme A + choline ——*choline acetylase*——→ acetylcholine + coenzyme A

Figure 26–2. Pathways of acetylcholine synthesis. Citrate and pyruvate can serve as donors of acetyl groups in a pathway not shown here. They can also contribute indirectly, like glucose or mannose, by giving rise to the production of adenosine triphosphate (*ATP*) during oxidative phosphorylation, the produced ATP being utilized in the formation of acetyl coenzyme A, as shown in the two top lines. *AMP*, adenosine monophosphate.

cellular particles). Acetylcholine can also be released from its bound form by the lecithinase of cobra venom (Gautrelet, Corteggiani, and Carayon-Gentil, 1941) and by potassium ions (Brown and Feldberg, 1936; Schallek, 1945). Added potassium ions increase the rate of acetylcholine synthesis (Mann et al., 1939), and it has been assumed that this is due to the loss of bound acetylcholine, perhaps because this frees the binding sites.

It looks very much as if the action of potassium on bound acetylcholine is a cation exchange: not only does added potassium free acetylcholine, but added acetylcholine frees potassium (Dulière and Loewi, 1939; Schallek, 1945).

In normal tissue, acetylcholine synthesis depends on aerobic conditions and utilizes glucose or mannose (Mann et al., 1939). In homogenates, glucose inhibits synthesis because it is being phosphorylated and thus uses up the available ATP. Glycolysis, in homogenates, proceeds only to the triosephosphate stage, because diphosphopyridine nucleotide (DPN) is being destroyed by a DPN-ase. If DPN is preserved by adding *nicotinamide*, which inhibits DPN-ase, glucose is metabolized to pyruvate and further (citric acid cycle), and yields ATP; under these circumstances acetylcholine synthesis is enhanced (Harpur and Quastel, 1949; Mann and Quastel, 1941).

From experiments on vertebrate cholinergic nerves comes the strong suggestion that choline acetylase is formed in the cell soma and that it is carried inside the nerve cell processes (axon) toward the nerve terminals. Acetylcholine synthesis occurs in all regions of a cholinergic neuron (Hebb and Waites, 1956; Hodgkin, 1951).

Acetylcholine is destroyed (hydrolyzed) by esterases, particularly those known as *cholinesterases*. These can be grouped into two classes: *acetylcholinesterases* and *nonspecific* (or *pseudo-*) *cholinesterases*. The former characteristically occur in nerve tissue and in effector organs innervated by cholinergic neurons, the latter occur predominantly in non-nervous tissue. Acetylcholinesterases hydrolyze acetylcholine at a greater rate than other cholinesters; acetylcholinesterases are inhibited by high substrate concentrations. Nonspecific cholinesterases hydrolyze other choline esters as well as acetylcholine, some at a greater rate (for instance, butyryl choline). They

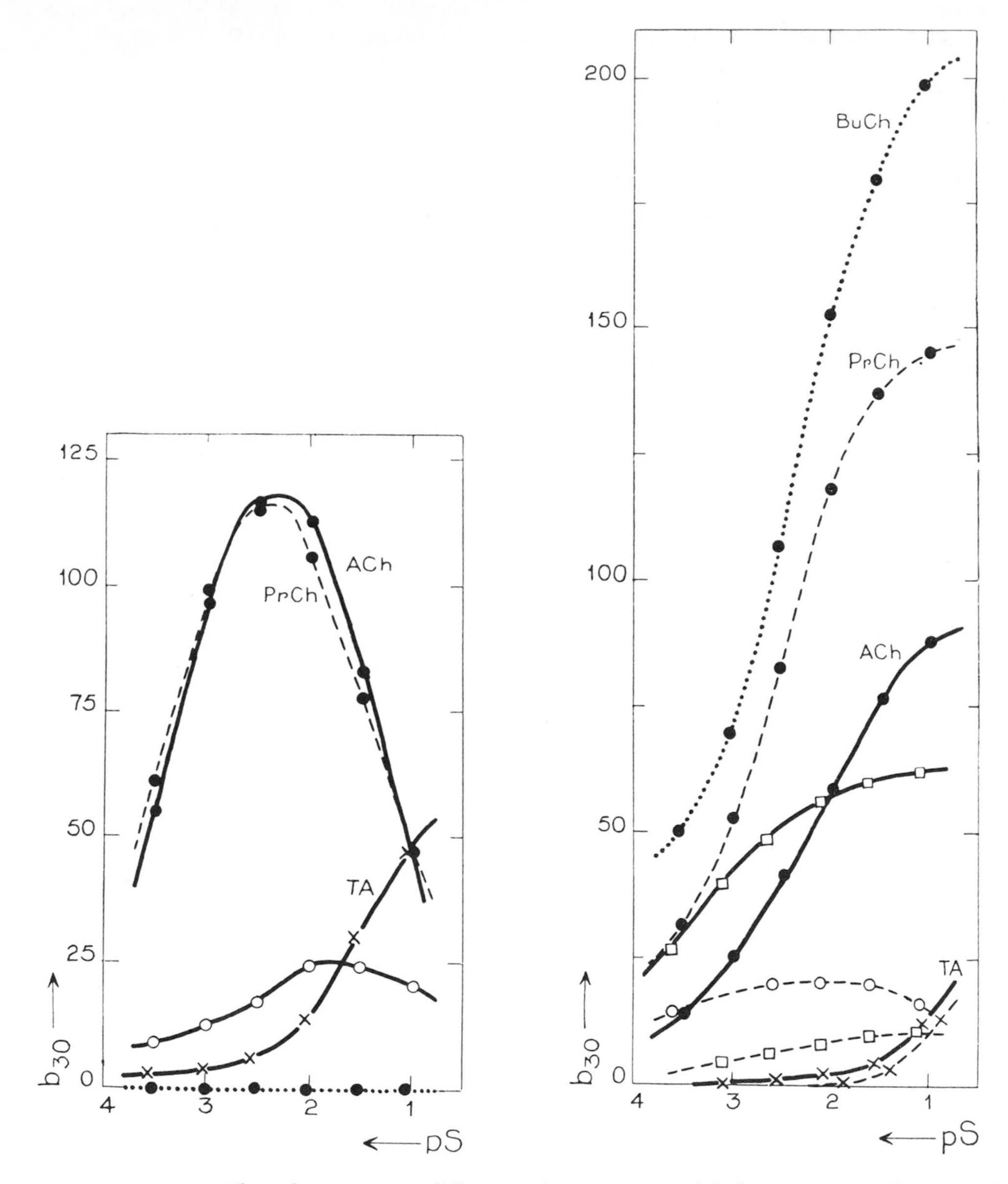

Figure 26–3. The characteristic difference between acetylcholinesterase (ACh-esterase) and cholinesterase: Ach-esterase hydrolyses acetylcholine faster than any other cholinester and in inhibited by high concentrations of acetylcholine; cholinesterase hydrolyzes other choline esters faster than acetylcholine and is not inhibited by high substrate concentrations. Ordinate: enzyme activity. Abscissa: negative logarithm of substrate concentration (*pS*). ○———○, acetylcholine (*ACh*); ○ · · · · · ○, butyrylcholine (*BuCh*); ○ - - - - - ○, propionylcholine (*PrCh*); ○———○, DL-acetyl-β-methylcholine; x———x, triacetin *(TA)*, (From Augustinsson, K. B., and D. Nachmansohn: Distinction between acetylcholine-esterase and other choline ester-splitting enzymes. Science *110*:98–99, 1949.)

are not inhibited by high substrate concentrations. The differences in the activities of the two enzyme types in relation to substrate concentration are illustrated in Figure 26–3.

Since the literature on cholinesterases is extensive, refer to reviews that provide guidance to research literature, such as those of Quastel (1962), Hebb, and Krnjević (1962), and Nachmansohn (1962). These should also be consulted about other aspects of neurochemistry, physiology, and pharmacology related to acetylcholine.

Acetylcholinesterase is one of the most active enzymes known. It hydrolyzes one acetylcholine molecule in just 40 microseconds (Lawler, 1961), or up to 1,500,000 molecules per minute. The enzyme is inhibited by drugs known as *anticholinesterases*, such as eserine (physostigmine), Prostigmin, diisopropylfluorophosphate (DFP), tetraethyl pyrophosphate (TEPP), parathion, and other phosphate esters (Fig. 26–4). The inhibition with eserine and Prostigmin is readily reversible, that is, the drugs can be quickly washed off a physiological preparation and the cholinesterase activity is thereby restored. The organophosphorus compounds, on the other hand, give long-lasting, often irreversible inhibition.

Cholinesterase occurs in a wide variety of tissues, and its occurrence is not necessarily correlated with cholinergic synapses. Mammalian red blood cells, for instance, but also blood cells and coelomocytes of a number of invertebrates (Florey and Loe, unpublished), contain considerable amounts of acetylcholinesterase; the same is true for gills of fish and crustaceans (Fleming, Scheffel, and Linton, 1962; Koch, 1954), for kidney tubules (Kamemoto, Keister, and Spald-

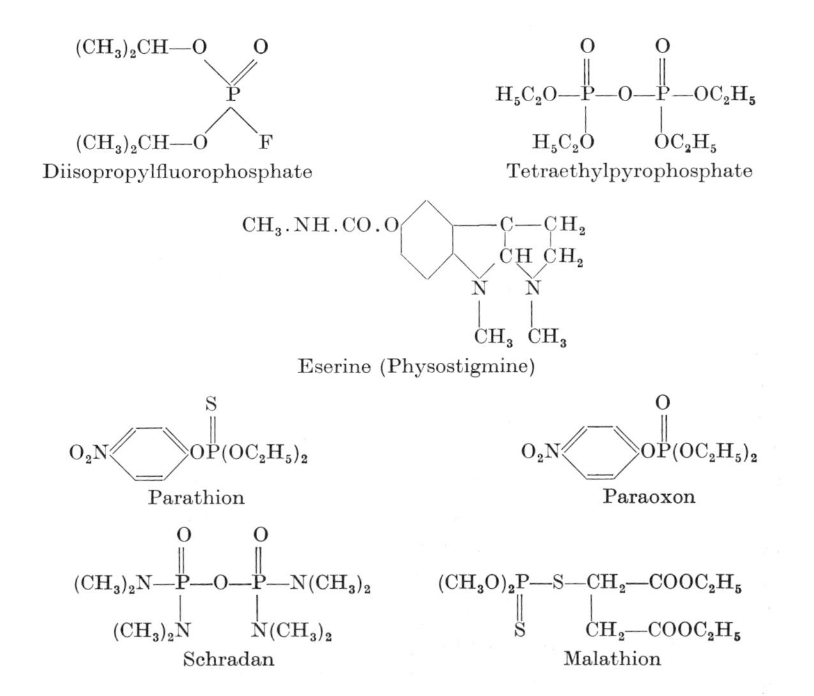

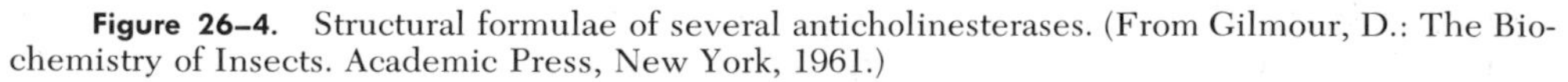

Figure 26–4. Structural formulae of several anticholinesterases. (From Gilmour, D.: The Biochemistry of Insects. Academic Press, New York, 1961.)

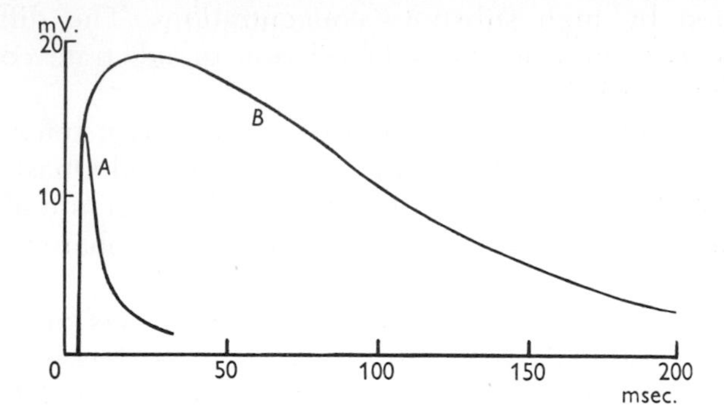

Figure 26–5. Superimposed tracings of motor end-plate potentials recorded with a microelectrode from frog skeletal muscle. *A* before, *B* after application of prostigmine (an anticholinesterase agent). Note the increase in amplitude and duration. When cholinesterase located at the synapse is inhibited by prostigmine, the acetylcholine released from the motor nerve terminals is not hydrolyzed; thus more of it is available for action on the subsynaptic membrane, and for a longer period of time. (From Fatt, P., and B. Katz: An analysis of the endplate potential recorded with an intracellular electrode. J. Physiol. *115*:320–370, 1951.)

ing, 1962), and for frog skin (Kirschner, 1953; Koblick, 1959). It has been assumed that cholinesterases are involved in active ion transport (especially of Na^+), because inhibition of the enzyme leads to abnormal distributions of Na^+ ions across gills, tubules, and frog skin—and even in amphibian muscle (Van der Kloot, 1958).

Acetylcholinesterase occurs in cholinergic synapses and appears to be a functional part of them. When this enzyme is inhibited, postsynaptic potentials in response to nerve impulses arriving over a cholinergic nerve fiber (e.g., motoneuron) are larger and prolonged (see Fig. 26–5), indicating that in normal synaptic transmission the action of released acetylcholine is reduced, both in intensity and in time, by cholinesterase activity. It is quite uncertain, however, that this inactivation of transmitter substance is the sole or even the chief function of the cholinesterase located in synapses.

Acetylcholinesterase occurs also at synapses where the presynaptic neurons are noncholinergic (crayfish heart ganglion, Florey, 1963), and it occurs in sensory neurons and terminals where, as far as we know, acetylcholine has no functional role. The cholinesterase in the locations mentioned may well function in controlling ion exchange or ion transport.

The action of synaptically released acetylcholine is believed to be restricted to the postsynaptic cell membrane, in particular to the subsynaptic membrane. It consists in changing the ion permeability of the membrane and involves the formation of a chemical complex between acetylcholine and a receptor substance that forms an integral part of the subsynaptic membrane. The receptor substance, most likely a protein, can be assumed to behave very much like an enzyme as far as the union between receptor substance (enzyme) and acetylcholine (substrate) is concerned. The receptor substance must possess a specific structure or configuration to permit the union with the acetylcholine molecule. It can also associate with other compounds that contain a configuration similar to that of acetylcholine. Such agents either imitate the action of acetylcholine (examples are nicotine, muscarine, and pilocarpine, as well as several cholinesters), or prevent it (curare, tubocurarine, atropine, scopolamine, banthine [β-diethylamino-ethylxanthene-9-carboxylate methobromide], and many others) by combining with the receptor substance.

Whereas acetylcholine and its imitating analogues give rise to the characteristic action when they combine with the receptor substance, the *blocking agents* mentioned above do not—they simply prevent acetylcholine molecules from combining with the receptor substance. This effect is reminiscent of enzyme inhibition, in particular of competitive inhibition (see Chap. 7). According to experiments with radioactive curare, there are about 8,000,000 receptor molecules present in the subsynaptic membrane of a vertebrate motor end-plate. With each motor nerve impulse there are about 1,000,000 molecules of acetylcholine released at each end-plate (Waser, 1960; Krnjevic and Mitchell, 1961).

With vertebrate skeletal muscle it has indeed been demonstrated that acetylcholine acts only on the outside of the cell membrane and only at or near the end-plates (see Figs. 26–6 and 26–7).

At motor end-plates of vertebrate striated muscle, the release of acetylcholine is prevented by botulinus toxin (Brooks, 1956; Thesleff, 1960). When this happens the muscle fiber membrane becomes hypersensitive to applied acetylcholine. This occurs also when the motor nerves are allowed to degenerate.

Prolonged application of acetylcholine to subsynaptic membranes makes these insensitive to acetylcholine and to synaptic (cholinergic) transmission; the phenomenon is known as *desensitization* (Thesleff, 1960). It occurs also when the subsynaptic membrane is repetitively activated by synaptically released acetylcholine.

No drug is known that specifically inhibits choline acetylase, but some agents are known to prevent acetylcholine synthesis. Most prominent is hemicholinium; it prevents entry of choline into membrane-enclosed compartments in which acetylcholine is synthesized (Birks and MacIntosh, 1961). Activation of synthesis (choline transport) requires Na^+ ions. Entry of sodium ions during nerve impulses can thus control the rate at which acetylcholine is synthesized (Birks, 1963).

A diagram representing some factors that affect synthesis and release of acetylcholine is shown in Figure 26–8.

Acetylcholine-sensitive (cholinoceptive) membranes are by no means equal in their responsiveness to acetylcholine and cholinergic drugs. Vertebrate cholinoceptive membranes can be grouped into those in which the action of acetylcholine is imitated by nicotine ("nicotinic action of acetylcholine"), and those in which muscarine can replace acetylcholine ("muscarinic action of acetylcholine"). Skeletal muscle belongs to the former type, visceral smooth muscle and heart muscle to the latter type. The "nicotinic" action can be blocked by curare or tubocurarine, the "muscarinic" action by atropine. A most interesting case is that of the frog lymph heart. Its muscle cells receive a dual cholinergic innervation by motoneurons and parasympathetic neurons. The subsynaptic membranes of the motor end-plates are of the nicotinic type, those with the parasympathetic terminals of the muscarinic type. This is illustrated in Figure 26–9.

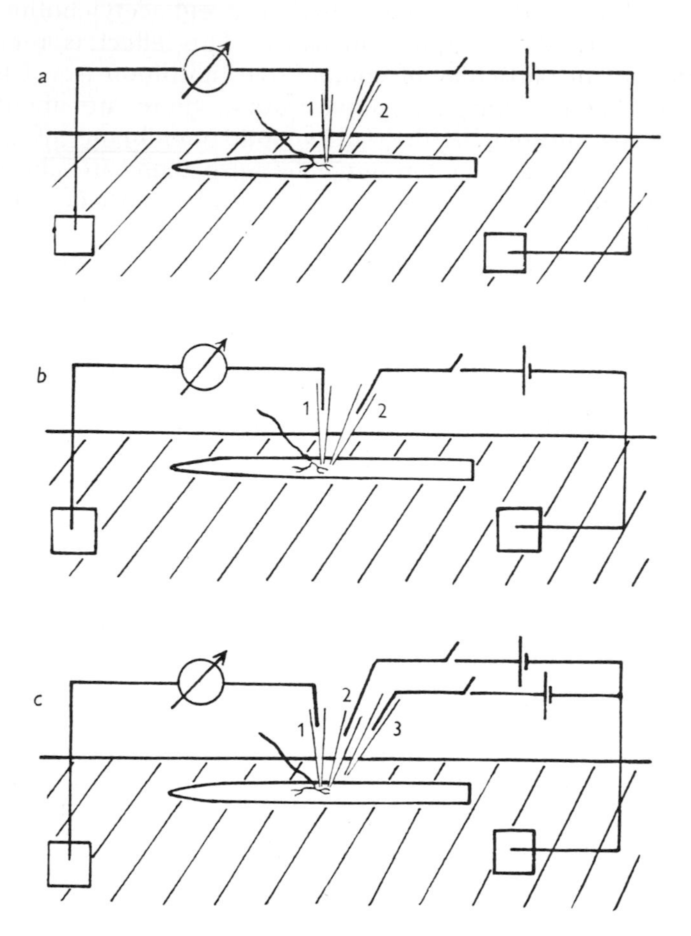

Figure 26–6. Diagram showing methods of applying acetylcholine to a motor end-plate (sartorius muscle of frog). A superficial muscle fiber with its nerve supply is represented in each case. Pipet *1* is the intracellular recording electrode, filled with 3 M KCl. Pipets *2* and *3* are filled with ACh chloride and are connected to a d.c. source. In **a**, ACh is discharged into the bath, external to the end-plate membrane. In **b**, ACh is discharged into the interior of the muscle fiber. In **c**, the two methods of application are combined. The recordings obtained are shown in Figure 26–7. (From Del Castillo, J., and B. Katz: On the localization of acetylcholine receptors. J. Physiol. *128*:157–181, 1955.)

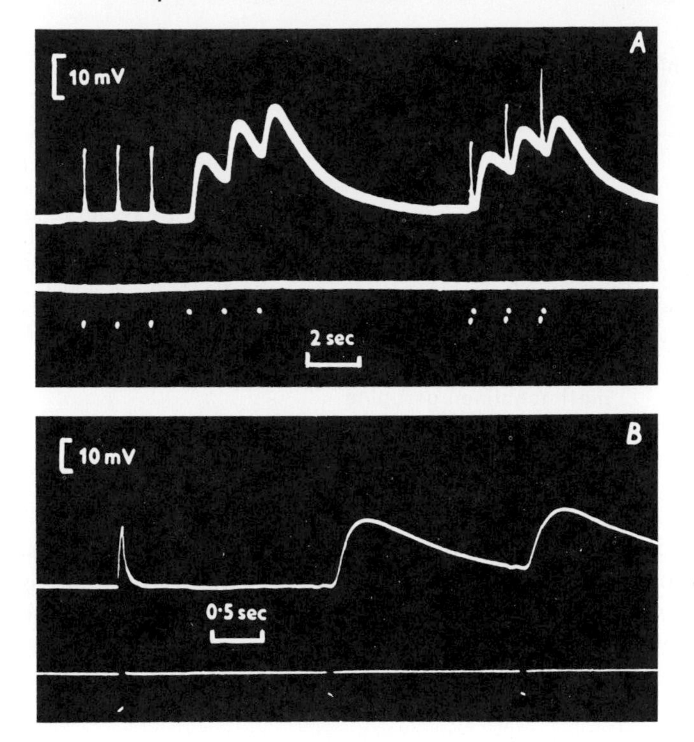

Figure 26–7. Recordings obtained with the intracellular electrode from an end-plate region of a muscle fiber of the musculus sartorius of a frog. The experimental set-up is shown in Figure 26–6. The upper channel of each recording shows the membrane potential; the lower channel monitors the electric pulses applied to the acetylcholine-containing pipets (pipets *2* and *3* of Figure 26–6). **A**, slow time base. The first three pulses were applied to the internal pipet, the next three pulses to the external pipet; finally there were three combined applications through both pipets. **B**, on a faster time base, showing first an intracellular, then two extracellular applications of ACh. The intracellular pipet produces only a catelectrotonic potential change; the external pipet produces an end-plate potential like the "ACh potential." The experiment proves that acetylcholine receptors are located only on the external surface of the subsynaptic membrane. (From Del Castillo, J., and B. Katz: On the localization of acetylcholine receptors. J. Physiol. *128*:157–181, 1955.)

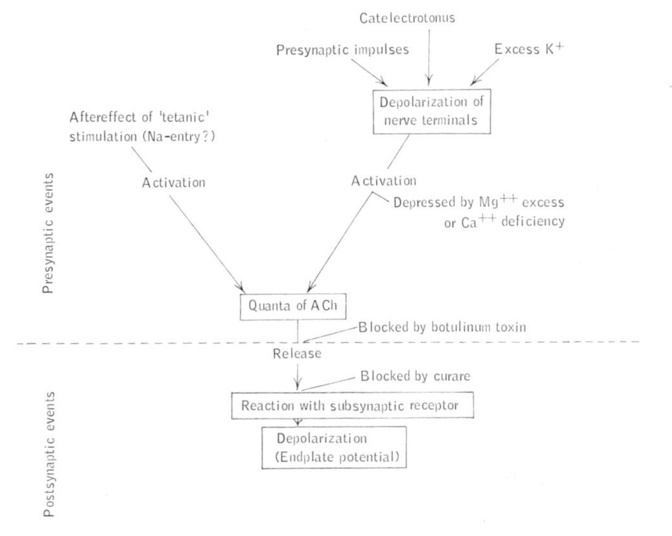

Figure 26–8. Diagram of the concept of quantal release of acetylcholine (*ACh*) and of the factors affecting it or interacting with it. (Adapted from Eccles, J. C.: The Physiology of Nerve Cells. Johns Hopkins Press, Baltimore, 1957.)

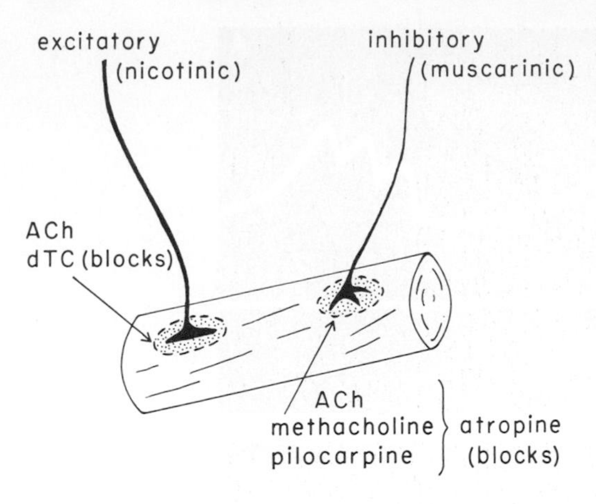

Figure 26–9. Diagrammatic representation of the dual cholinergic innervation of a muscle fiber of a frog lymph heart. The muscle is excited by motor fibers and inhibited by parasympathetic fibers. The former action is blocked by d-tubocurarine (*dTC*), the latter by atropine. (From Day, J. B., R. H. Rech, and J. S. Robb: Pharmacological and microelectrode studies on the frog lymph heart. J. Cell. Comp. Physiol. 62:33–41, 1963.)

The classification cannot be extended to cholinergic synapses or cholinoceptive membranes of other animal phyla, even though many cases are known from invertebrates where either nicotine or muscarine have acetylcholine-like actions. The pharmacology of such membranes is usually different from the typical vertebrate pattern.

ADRENERGIC MECHANISMS

This discussion is limited to data obtained from vertebrate animals. At present there is little evidence that adrenergic compounds play the role of transmitter substance, or even of hormones, in any invertebrate group. *Adrenaline* and *noradrenaline* have been detected in annelids (*Arenicola, Lumbricus*) and in insects (*Tenebrio, Vanessa, Musca, Apis, Forficula*) (Östlund, 1954), and *dopamine* (3-hydroxytyramine), the precursor of noradrenaline, has been found in the insects just mentioned, and, more recently, in molluscan ganglia (Sweeney, 1963). No experiments have been designed, however, to examine whether or not one or the other of these compounds is released from nerve cells, nor is it certain that they are predominantly contained in nerve cells rather than in cells associated with the nerve cells—or even other types of body cells. On the other hand, in many studies the actions of a number of catccholamines and indolamines on invertebrates have been observed (see p. 222).

The chief metabolic sequence of production of adrenergic transmitters is *dopa* (3,4-dihydroxyphenylalanine), *dopamine* (3-hydroxytyramine or 3,4-dihydroxyphenylethylamine), *noradrenaline*, *adrenaline*, as shown in Figure 26–10. Dopa is probably derived from tyrosine. Dopamine is formed by decarboxylation of dopa, a reaction that is catalyzed by the enzyme *dopa decarboxylase*. The transformation of dopamine to noradrenaline is due to an enzyme, *dopamine hydroxylase* (Kirshner, 1960). Adrenaline is formed by N-methylation of noradrenaline; the methyl group is usually derived from adenosylmethionine.

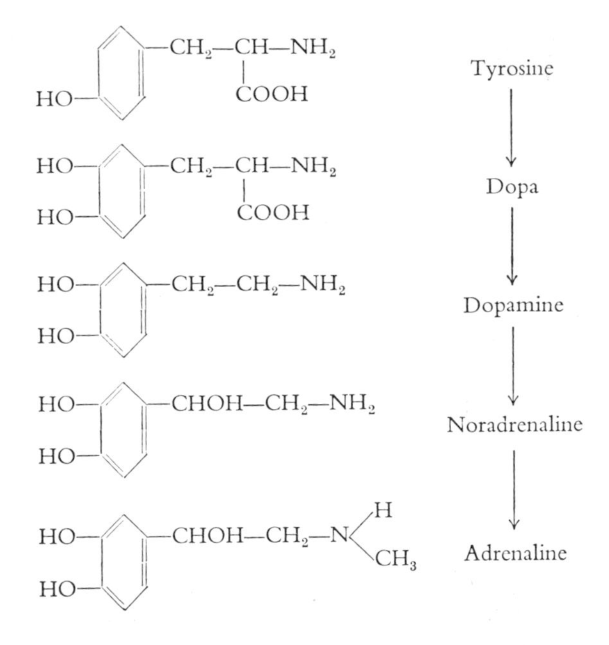

Figure 26–10. Main pathway of biosynthesis of catecholamines. (From Schümann, H. J.: Formation of adrenergic transmitters. *In* Adrenergic Mechanisms. Ciba Foundation Symposium. Little, Brown and Co., Boston, 1960.)

An alternative route has recently been suggested but must await clarification: *tyramine–octopamine*–noradrenaline (adrenaline). Octopamine was discovered in the salivary glands of *Octopus*, but occurs also in mammals (Erspamer, 1952b; Kakimoto and Armstrong, 1960). The relationship of all the compounds mentioned here is shown in Figure 26–11.

It appears that some parts of nervous tissue can carry the process only as far as to the formation of dopamine. Others (e.g., mammalian postganglionic sympathetic neurons) can form noradrenaline but cannot methylate this compound to adrenaline. Certain tissues, however, including vertebrate adrenal medulla and amphibian sympathetic neurons, can produce adrenaline from noradrenaline.

Dopamine, noradrenaline, and adrenaline have pharmacological actions. Although there is, as yet, no conclusive proof for this, it is likely that there are nerve cells (mammalian central nervous system) that synaptically release dopamine as transmitter. The mammalian sympathetic neurons release noradrenaline as transmitter, and the amphibian sympathetic neurons appear to release adrenaline. The actions of noradrenaline-releasing neurons can be imitated only by noradrenaline, not by adrenaline; those of adrenaline-releasing neurons can be imitated by adrenaline applied to the organ or cell innervated by adrenaline-releasing neurons.

According to Dale (1935), neurons that release adrenaline are named adrenergic. Extending this nomenclature, one calls noradrenaline-releasing neurons noradrenergic. When transmission by dopamine is established there will be "dopaminergic" neurons.

Catecholamines, the group of compounds to which adrenaline and noradrenaline belong, occur not only in nerve cells, but also in certain types of cells which, because of characteristic histochemical reactions, are called *chromaffin cells* (Kohn, 1903); they are darkened by potassium bichromate.

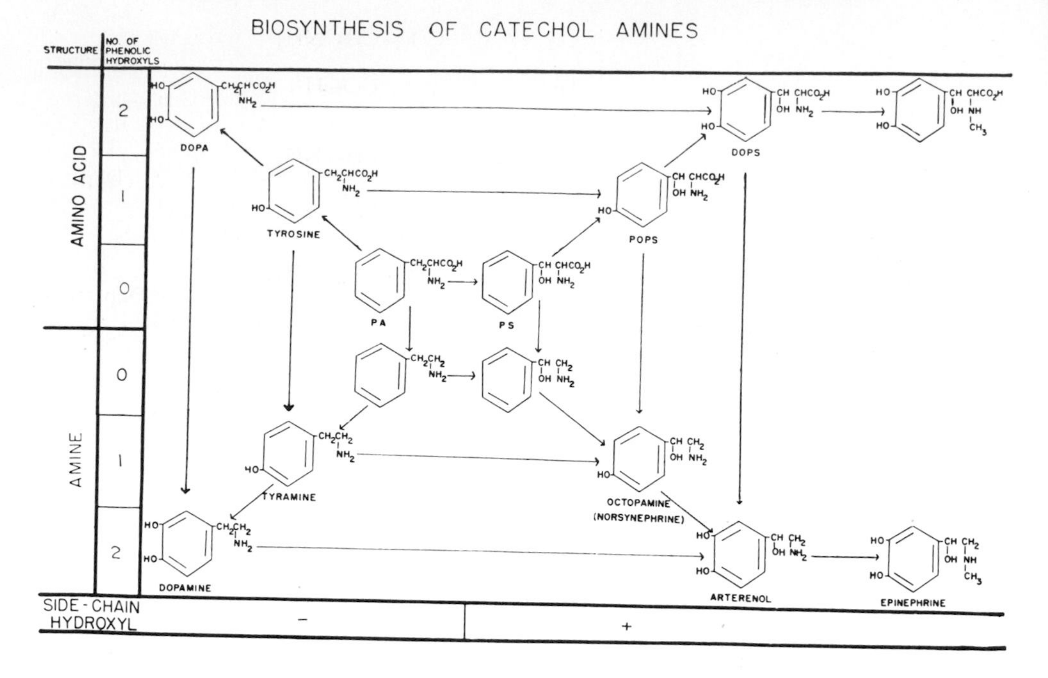

Figure 26–11. Interrelations and pathways of formation of catecholamines. (From Sourkes, T. L.: Biochemistry of the catecholamines. *In* Neurochemistry, 2nd Ed. K. A. C. Elliott, I. H. Page, and J. H. Quastel, ed. Charles C Thomas, Springfield, Ill., 1962.)

This compound oxidizes catecholamines and the product forms, by condensation, polymeres of melanin-like structures (see melanin, p. 335). To the group of chromaffin cells belong, of course, the adrenergic and noradrenergic neurons. The group, however, includes also the cells of the adrenal medulla and cells situated in the wall of the digestive tract, in the wall of certain blood vessels, and in the heart of vertebrate animals. These cells are derived embryologically from neural crest tissue. As shown later, even chromaffin cells that are clearly not nerve cells retain some of the original neural properties: upon suitable stimulation, they release the contained noradrenaline or adrenaline.

Chromaffin cells can take up catecholamines that are present in body fluids or extracellular fluid. Catecholamines released by nerve cells may be taken up by other, non-nervous chromaffin cells. Dopamine is often the chief storage form of catecholamines: together with ATP and protein, it forms storage granules (Fig. 26–12) (Blaschko and Welch, 1953). Dopamine may represent up to 95 per cent of the total catecholamine content of a cell (Schümann, 1960), although in sympathetic neurons it represents not more than 50 per cent and in adrenal medulla only 2 per cent (the rest being largely adrenaline) (Schümann, 1956). Noradrenaline (and adrenaline) is synthesized within the storage granules (Kirshner, 1959).

Within the cytoplasm dopa is formed from tyrosine or tyramine and dopa is decarboxylated to dopamine (Schümann, 1958).

Adrenaline and noradrenaline can be metabolized to physiologically inert compounds. This, among others, is the mechanism by which synaptically

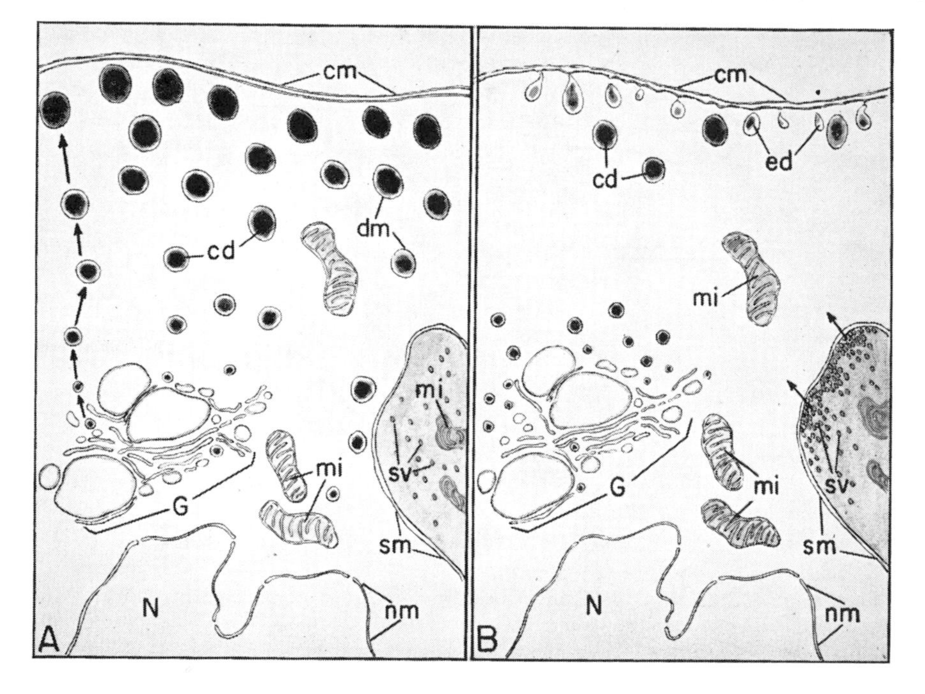

Figure 26–12. Diagrammatic representation of the formation of catecholamine droplets (*A*) and release of catecholamine (*B*) by chromaffin cells in the adrenal medulla of the hamster. The cell is activated by release of acetylcholine from synaptic vesicles (*sv*) of preganglionic sympathetic nerve endings. The catecholamine droplets (*cd*) originate in the Golgi apparatus (*G*); they are surrounded by a membrane (*dm*). The action of acetylcholine on the subsynaptic membrane appears to cause an increase in the rate of formation of catecholamine droplets and to cause the discharge of catecholamine (noradrenaline, adrenaline) across the cell membrane (*cm*). *mi*, mitochondria; *N*, nucleus; *nm*, nuclear membrane; *sm*, surface membrane. (From De Robertis, E. D. P., and D. D. Sabatini: Submicroscopic analysis of the secretory process in the adrenal medulla. Fed. Proc. *19*:70, 1960.)

released catecholamines are inactivated. In the older literature (up to the 1950's) it was assumed that the chief route of metabolism was via oxidation by amino oxidase. However, it is clear now that there is a much more predominant pathway: it begins with *O-methylation*, catalyzed by *O-methyltranferase* (Axelrod, et al., 1958 and 1959). Noradrenaline is O-methylated to *normetanephrine*, adrenaline to *metanephrine*. The further pattern of metabolism is shown in Figure 26–13. However, oxidative metabolism of catecholamines is by no means excluded, and may turn out to be an important mechanism in less investigated animal species. It is important to understand that the most recently suggested pathway of catecholamine metabolism involving O-methylation is deduced from studies in which catecholamines are administered to animals and the excreted metabolites are isolated from urine.

The physiologically important metabolism that takes place immediately after release from nerve cells or from chromaffin cells may be quite different. From this point of view, it is worthwhile to mention the other metabolic pathways that have been described: oxidative deamination, oxidation to adrenochrome, and dehydrogenation to the keto form of adrenaline (or noradrenaline)—*adrenalone* (or the analogous noradrenalone) (Imaizumi and Kawamoto, 1952).

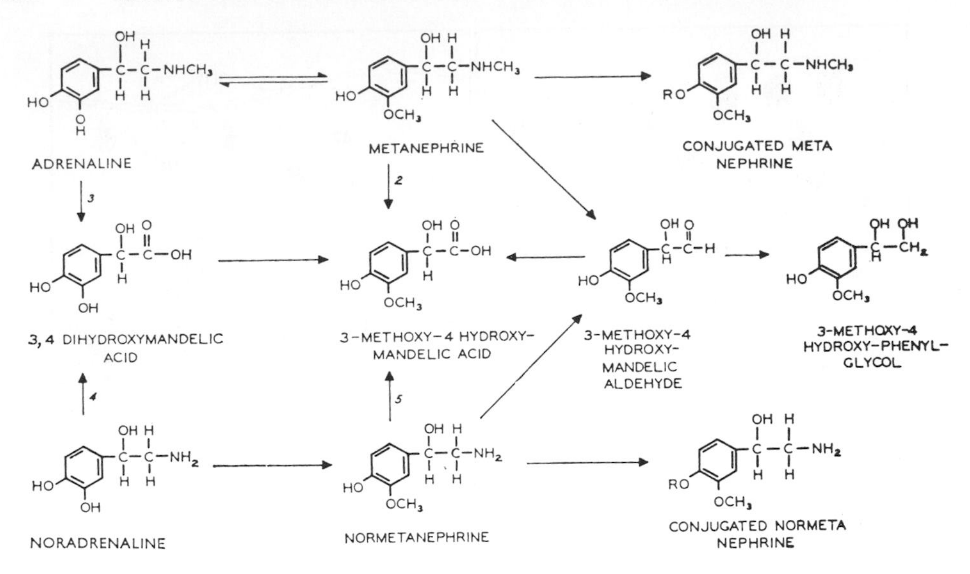

Figure 26–13. Routes of metabolism of adrenaline and noradrenaline. (From Axelrod, J.: The fate of adrenaline and noradrenaline. *In* Adrenergic Mechanisms. Ciba Foundation Symposium. Little, Brown and Co., Boston, 1960.)

One or the other of these mechanisms may be predominant in certain synapses, or in certain mammalian or nonmammalian species.

The Action of Catecholamines

According to the classic hypothesis of chemical transmission, the released transmitter substance achieves its postsynaptic effect by reacting with a specific receptor substance present in the subsynaptic membrane. This reaction, in turn, is supposed to cause a permeability change that gives rise to a new membrane (equilibrium) potential. The current knowledge of the mechanism of action of catecholamines demonstrates that the hypothesis is insufficient. It has puzzled investigators for many decades that adrenaline, and noradrenaline, have stimulating actions on some organs (heart muscles, nictitating membrane) and inhibitory actions on others (intestinal smooth muscle, vascular smooth muscle). One explanation was that there are two types of receptor substances: E-receptors, giving rise to excitation, and I-receptors, giving rise to inhibition. It has now become clear that smooth muscle inhibition may not be due to a reaction between adrenaline (or noradrenaline) and receptor substance in the membrane, but to an action within the postsynaptic cell.

Intestinal smooth muscle membranes normally have an unstable membrane potential; they are inclined to discharge "spontaneously," giving rise to a fluctuating muscle tone. Adrenaline and noradrenaline increase and stabilize the membrane potential (Bülbring, 1954; Burnstock, 1958). The effect resembles that of the sympathetic component of the innervation of the muscle. It is brought about as follows: the catecholamine causes the transformation of ATP to *cyclic adenosine-3′,5′-phosphate* (Fig. 26–14). This compound activates phosphorylase

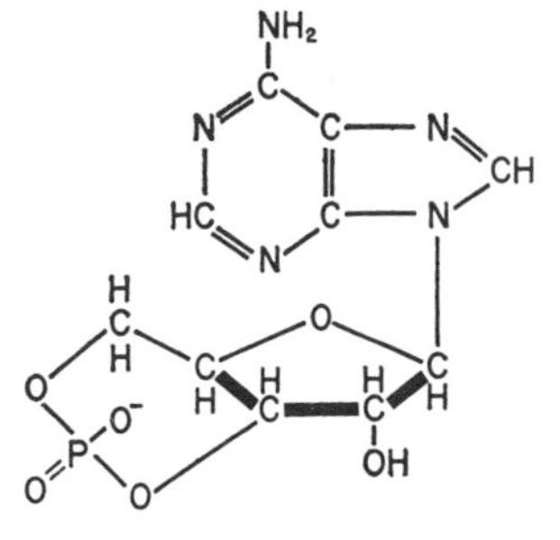

Figure 26–14. Chemical structure of adenosine-3′,5′-phosphate. (From Sutherland, E. W., and T. W. Rall: The relation of adenosine-3′,5′-phosphate to the action of catechol amines. *In* Adrenergic Mechanisms. Ciba Foundation Symposium. Little, Brown and Co., Boston, 1960.)

(phosphorylase b to phosphorylase a, see p. 572). The quantity of the active form of phosphorylase is the rate-limiting factor of glycolysis (this was discussed in Chapter 23, p. 572). The stimulation of glycolysis provides extra energy for Na extrusion. Thus three effects of catecholamine can be observed: increased glycolysis, increased Na extrusion, and increased membrane potential (Axelsson, Bueding, and Bülbring, 1959). The result is relaxation of the smooth muscle.

The relaxing effect of catecholamines is prevented by agents that interfere with glycolysis (Na-fluoride, Na-azide, iodo-acetate) (Lundholm and Mohme-Lundholm, 1957).

The accelerating action of catecholamines on the vertebrate heart may also be mediated by metabolic actions of these compounds: The accelerating action parallels the phosphorylase activation. Further evidence is provided by the fact that a slowing of the heart results when cyclization of ATP to the phosphorylase-activating adenosine-3,5-phosphate is prevented (by acetylcholine) (Murad, Rall, and Sutherland, 1960).

Pharmacology of Adrenergic Systems

From vertebrate pharmacology, we know of a number of compounds that interfere with certain steps in the production or action of catecholamines. The enzyme dopa-decarboxylase is inhibited by *alpha-methyldopa* (Sourkes, 1954). The enzyme O-methyltransferase is inhibited by *pyrogallol* (Axelrod and Laroche, 1959; Bacq et al., 1959) and *catechol* (Bacq et al., 1959).

Dibenamine blocks adrenergic (and noradrenergic) transmission by combining with the receptor substance in the subsynaptic membrane (Nickerson and Nomaguchi, 1948). The so-called *ergot* alkaloids (ergotamine, ergotoxin) act in a similar manner (Dale, 1906).

The release of catecholamines is prevented by *xylocholine* (choline-2, 6-xylyl-ether bromide) (Bain and Fielden, 1957). This is illustrated in Figures 26–15 and 26–16.

At least in heart muscle, the ATP cyclizing action of catecholamines is inhibited by acetylcholine which, apparently, acts here intracellularly.

Amino oxidase is inhibited by iproniazid (Zeller et al., 1952).

The transfer of catecholamines into tissue stores (chromaffin cells), as well as the release of catecholamines from storage sites (including nerve endings), is prevented by *cocaine* (Fleckenstein and Stöckle, 1955; MacMillan, 1959). Similar observations have been made with regard to the action of methyl-

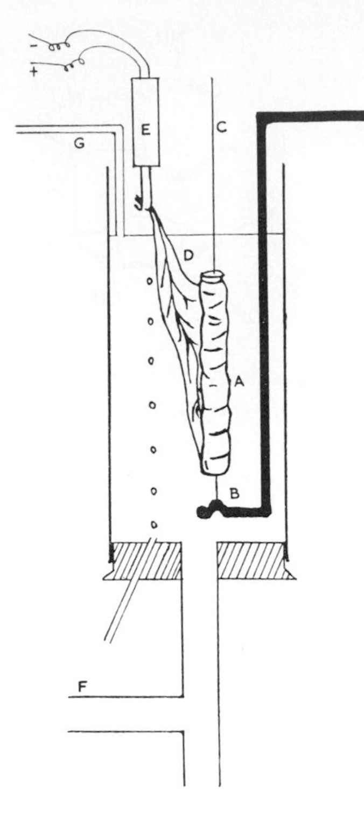

Figure 26–15. Diagram of a set-up for the indirect electric stimulation of an isolated piece of gut, and for application of drugs. *A*, rabbit intestine attached below to a glass supporting rod *(B)* and above by a thread *(C)* to a writing lever which marks the contractions of the intestine on the drum of a kymograph. The mesentery *(D)* containing the adrenergic nerves to the gut, is laid across nonpolarizable electrodes *(E)*. During wash-out the saline solution enters the bath through the tube *F*, and fluid is sucked out through the tube *G*, so that the level in the bath remains constant and disturbance of the gut by the changing of the fluid is minimal. (From Bain, W. A.: Interference with the release of transmitter in response to nerve stimulation. *In* Adrenergic Mechanisms. Ciba Foundation Symposium. Little, Brown and Co., Boston, 1960.)

phenidate and pipradrol (Farrant, 1960). *Cocaine* causes the adrenoceptive tissues to become hypersensitive to catecholamines.

Tyramine and *reserpine* cause complete release and depletion of catecholamine from storage sites (Burn, 1960; Bertler, Carlsson, and Rosengren, 1956; Burn and Rand, 1957, 1958, and 1959a,b).

INTERACTION OF CHOLINERGIC AND ADRENERGIC MECHANISMS

As in the preceding section, this discussion is concerned chiefly with results obtained from vertebrate animals.

The autonomically innervated organs often show complex responses to applied adrenergic and cholinergic substances. In fact, at first sight, the results of pharmacological investigations on such organs as the guinea pig ileum, the vas deferens of the possum, or the rat bladder—to name but a few of the physiological preparations used—appear to contradict everything that is generally claimed as the main and normal role of a number of drugs: acetylcholine is found to act like adrenaline, cholinesterase inhibitors do not potentiate its action, adrenergic blocking agents prevent the action of acetylcholine, and atropine is ineffective in blocking acetylcholine.

The complications have frustrated some investigators to the point where they became willing to disclaim the merits of analytical pharmacology altogether. However, such pessimism is not yet warranted. In recent years, several

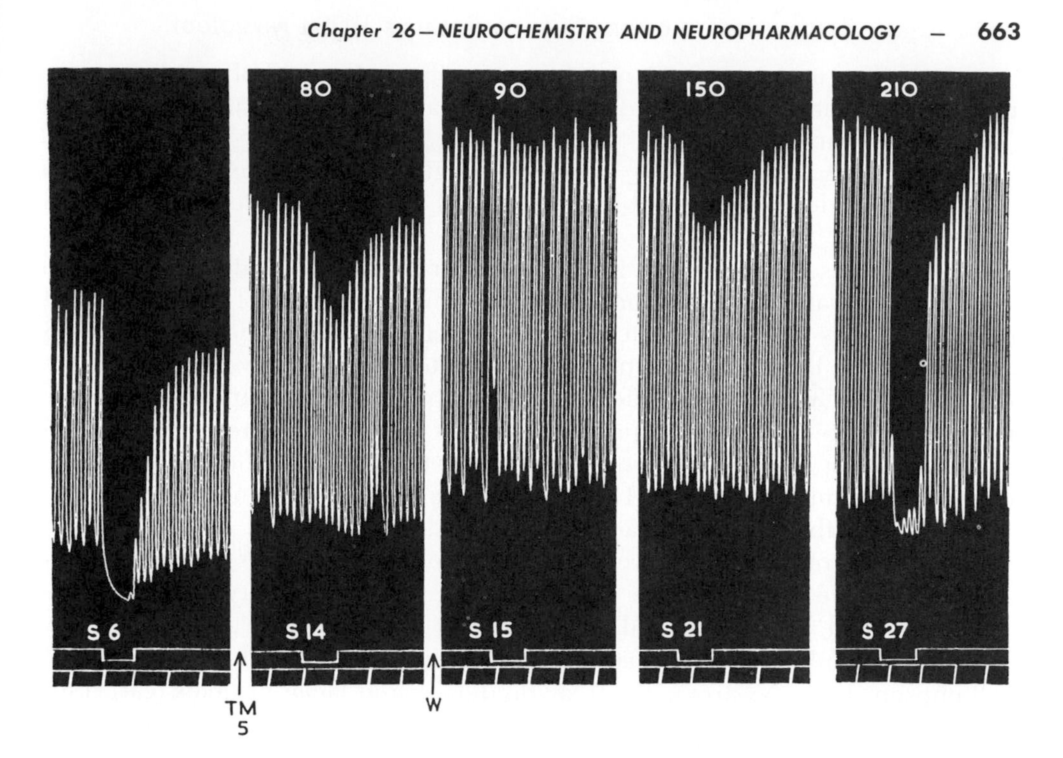

Figure 26–16. Segments of kymograph records obtained with a preparation as shown in Figure 26–15. The figures after *S* are the numbers of consecutive periods of stimulation (50 pulses per second for 30 seconds). Addition of 0.5 mg of choline-2,6-xylyl-ether bromide (xylocholine), indicated by the letters *TM 5*, slowly abolishes the effect of nerve stimulation. This is not due to blocking of released transmitter (noradrenaline), but to interference with the last stage in the synthesis of transmitter so that the transmitter stores become exhausted. The block is incomplete after 80 minutes but becomes complete just after change of fluid (at *W*). Recovery takes place within 2 hours without further washing. Downward deflection of the lower curve indicates stimulation; the time marks on the lowest curve represent 30 second intervals. The time in minutes after application of xylocholine is indicated by the figure at the top of each segment. (From Bain, W. A.: Interference with the release of transmitter in response to nerve stimulation. *In* Adrenergic Mechanisms. Ciba Foundation Symposium. Little, Brown and Co., Boston, 1960.)

facts have been reported, which, together, permit a perfectly logical explanation of the apparently abnormal pharmacological behavior:

1. Acetylcholine occurs not only in the parasympathetic neurons, but also in a small number of nerve fibers of postganglionic sympathetic nerves. Stimulation of sympathetic nerves may cause not only the release of adrenaline—or noradrenaline—but also acetylcholine. (Dale and Feldberg, 1934; Bülbring and Burn, 1935; Burn and Rand, 1960b).

2. Acetylcholine released from autonomic nerve endings has two kinds of action: it reacts with receptor substance on the postsynaptic membrane of the effector cells (e.g., smooth muscle) and it acts on the stores of catecholamines, causing release of adrenaline or noradrenaline (Burn and Rand, 1959b; Brandon and Rand, 1961). The stores are represented by chromaffin cells or by adrenergic (noradrenergic) nerve endings. In fact, it is likely that the cholinergic fibers within postganglionic sympathetic nerves do not make direct contact with the effector organ but end on nerve terminals of the regular

adrenergic (or noradrenergic) neurons. Activity in these cholinergic neurons therefore activates the (nor-) adrenergic sympathetic nerve endings to release (nor-) adrenaline.

It becomes obvious, then, why adrenergic blocking agents prevent the action of acetylcholine: they block the (nor-) adrenaline released by acetylcholine.

Several cases are known in which adrenergic agents affect cholinergic systems: adrenaline, for instance, increases the frequency of miniature end-plate potentials on amphibian skeletal muscle (Krnjević and Miledi, 1958) and increases the end-plate potentials (Hutter and Trautwein, 1956). The mechanism by which these effects are achieved is, as yet, unknown. On the motor end-plate, the adrenergic agents cause an increased release of acetylcholine, but, in addition, the sensitivity to acetylcholine of the postganglionic membrane seems to increase. In autonomic ganglia, adrenaline and noradrenaline enhance the stimulating action of applied acetylcholine.

A number of cholinoceptive structures also respond to adrenaline and noradrenaline. The actions of the two types of compounds, acetylcholine on the one hand, and adrenaline and noradrenaline on the other, are similar. The nictitating membrane of the cat contracts in response to both kinds of agents (Thompson, 1958; Nystrom, 1962), as do denervated facial muscles (cat) (Luco and Sanchez, 1956; Sanchez and Luco, 1956) and the spleen (Fotino and Stoculesco, 1957). Cholinergic and adrenergic blocking agents block the responses; it can be assumed that there are "bivalent" receptor substances which can react with both cholinergic and adrenergic agents. It appears that the nictitating membrane is innervated by both cholinergic and adrenergic neurons.

I NEURONS

The mammalian central nervous system and that of decapod Crustacea contains neurons of a neurochemical type distinctly different from that of cholinergic or (nor-) adrenergic neurons: from them can be extracted an agent called Factor I (Elliott and Florey, 1956; Florey, 1954) which, when applied to the appropriate synapses, imitates the action of the neurons from which it is extracted (Florey and McLennan, 1955a,b; Florey, 1957). The neurons, as far as is known, belong to the functional group of inhibitory neurons, that is, they cause inhibition in postsynaptic cells by stabilizing their membrane at the K^+ or Cl^- equilibrium potential level.

The chemical identity of Factor I is not clear. From the inhibitory neurons—and apparently exclusively from them—can be extracted *gamma-aminobutyric acid* (GABA) (Florey, 1960; Kravitz, Potter, and van Gelder, 1962). This amino acid also occurs in muscle in significant quantities. It has rather pronounced pharmacological actions in the group Astacura of the decapod Crustacea: in these animals, in fact, it duplicates precisely the actions of the natural (still hypothetical) transmitter substance (Kuffler and Edwards, 1958; Grundfest, Reuben, and Rickles, Jr., 1958, 1959). In other decapods—the Brachiura (crabs), for instance—this is, however, not the case (Florey and Hoyle, 1961; Aljure,

Gainer, and Grundfest, 1962), nor is there any conclusive evidence that GABA acts like the transmitter of inhibitory neurons in the mammalian central nervous system (Curtis, Phillis, and Watkins, 1959; McLennan, 1961). The unique distribution of GABA in the nervous system, however, makes this compound a distinct characteristic of inhibitory neurons, and there is every indication that this compound is intimately involved in the synaptic action of these neurons, even if it is not identical with the actual transmitter.

GABA is formed by *decarboxylation* from glutamic acid (Roberts and Fraenkel, 1951). The reaction is catalyzed by the enzyme *glutamic decarboxylase* (GAD) and requires pyridoxal phosphate (vitamin B_6) as coenzyme (Roberts, 1962).

GABA is metabolized as follows: Its amino group is transferred to α-ketoglutaric acid (Roberts, 1962). This transamination is catalyzed by the enzyme γ-aminobutyric acid-α-ketoglutaric acid-transaminase (GABA-T), and like GAD requires pyridoxal phosphate. GABA thus becomes succinic semialdehyde and α-ketoglutaric acid becomes glutamic acid. Succinic semialdehyde is oxidized to succinic acid (Albers and Salvador, 1958). This reaction is catalyzed by a dehydrogenase enzyme with DPN as coenzyme. Succinic acid is then further metabolized via the tricarboxylic acid cycle (see pp. 147–151). The metabolic sequence is shown in Figure 26–17.

It appears, at least from studies on mammalian brain, that the distribution of GAD is similar to that of GABA. GABA-T, on the other hand, has a much more general distribution (Lowe, Robins, and Eyerman, 1958; Salvador and Albers, 1959; Albers and Brady, 1959).

The quantities of GABA present in nerve tissues are often high. It is highest when the tissue consists entirely of I neurons. Inhibitory neurons of decapod Crustacea contain several milligrams of GABA per gram wet weight. Unless GABA is enclosed in special compartments, it must play an important role in cell metabolism.

The function of GAD (as well as of other decarboxylase enzymes) is inhibited by hydrazides, such as *thiosemicarbazide* (Killam and Bain, 1957). This drug effectively lowers the amount of GABA present in mammalian brain tissue. GABA-T is inhibited by *hydroxylamine* (NH_2OH) (Baxter and Roberts, 1959). The latter drug, therefore, causes an increase of the concentration of GABA in brain tissue. It has not yet been established whether these drugs have similar actions in the crustacean nervous system.

The inhibitory actions of GABA (as well as of inhibitory neurons) in astacuran crustaceans are blocked by *picrotoxin* (Elliott and Florey, 1956; Van der Kloot and Robbins, 1959). No drug has yet been found that specifically blocks the physiological actions of GABA in other animals—vertebrate or invertebrate (Kuno, 1961; Curtis, Phillis, and Watkins, 1959).

The natural transmitter of I neurons in all Crustacea is blocked by picrotoxin, and that in all vertebrates studied is blocked by *strychnine* (Eccles, 1957). The fact that the two groups of animals require two different blocking agents does not necessarily indicate that the I transmitters are different. However, it means that the inhibitory subsynaptic membranes have different properties. The situation is similar to that found in relation to the action of acetylcholine on the heart of vertebrates and of lamellibranch molluscs:

$$\underset{\text{L-Glutamic acid}}{HOOCCH_2CH_2(NH_2)COOH} \xrightarrow[\textit{pyridoxal phosphate}]{\textit{glutamic decarboxylase}} \underset{\gamma\text{-Aminobutyric acid}}{HOOCCH_2CH_2CH_2NH_2} + CO_2$$

$$\underset{\gamma\text{-Aminobutyric acid}}{HOOCCH_2CH_2CH_2NH_2} + \underset{\alpha\text{-Ketoglutaric acid}}{HOOCCH_2CH_2C\text{-}COOH} \xrightarrow[\textit{pyridoxal phosphate}]{\textit{GABA-T}} \underset{\text{Succinic semialdehyde}}{HOOCCH_2CH_2CHO} + \underset{\text{L-Glutamic acid}}{HOOCCH_2CH_2CH(NH_2)COOH}$$

$$\underset{\text{Succinic semialdehyde}}{HOOCCH_2CH_2CHO} + DPN^+ + H_2O \xrightarrow{\textit{dehydrogenase}} \underset{\text{Succinic acid}}{HOOCCH_2CH_2COOH} + DPNH + H^+$$

Figure 26–17. Metabolic relations of γ-aminobutyric acid. GABA-T = γ-aminobutyric acid-α-ketoglutaric acid—transaminase.

atropine blocks this in the first group but is ineffective in the second where another drug, mytolon, has this action. The transmitter (acetylcholine) is the same in both cases.

5-HYDROXYTRYPTAMINE

The compound *5-hydroxytryptamine* (5-HT) occurs in nerve tissues of vertebrates, molluscs, arthropods, and, perhaps, other phyla (Welsh and Moorhead, 1960). Its occurrence is, however, not restricted to nerve tissue. Quantities of this compound, much larger than any found in nerve tissue, have been extracted from metastatic carcinoids of the human intestine (Lembeck, 1954), blood platelets of oxen (Zucker, Friedman, and Rapport, 1954), the posterior salivary glands of *Octopus* (Erspamer and Boretti, 1951), the hypobranchial gland of *Murex* (Erspamer, 1954), the venom of *Vespa* (Jaques and Schachter, 1954), the skin of the toad *Bombinator* (Erspamer, 1954), and in coelentric tissue of the sea anemone *Caliactis* (Mathias, Ross, and Schachter, 1957).

5-HT has profound physiological actions. Like adrenaline, it stimulates mammalian visceral smooth muscle (Erspamer, 1952a). There are indications that 5-HT has inhibitory actions in vertebrate brain (Marrazzi and Hart, 1955), but it has not yet been conclusively shown that these inhibitions are not caused indirectly by the excitation of inhibitory neurons. Such a situation is known from the action of *dopamine* on spinal reflexes in the cat (see p. 657): this compound inhibits spinal monosynaptic reflexes not by directly inhibiting motoneurons, but by activating inhibitory interneurons which, in turn, inhibit the motor cells (McLennan, 1962).

In lamellibranch molluscs, 5-HT stimulates the heart (Welsh, 1957), and there is good evidence that this compound is, in fact, the transmitter substance of the cardio-accelerator neurons. In the central nervous system of *Aplysia*, 5-HT excites some, and inhibits other, nerve cells (Gerschenfeld and Tauc, 1961).

The actions of extracted 5-HT had been known years before the active agent of the extracts was identified. Before this chemical identification the (then) unknown compound was called *enteramine* (Erspamer and Asero, 1952) and *serotonin* (Rapport, Green, and Page, 1948). The latter name is still in use.

5-HT is produced from 5-hydroxytryptophan (an oxidation product of tryptophan) by the enzyme *5-hydroxytryptophan decarboxylase* (Udenfriend, Weissbach, and Bogdanski, 1957b), which requires metallic ions and pyridoxal phosphate (vitamin B_6) as coenzyme (Buzard and Nytch, 1957). 5-HT is metabolized by oxidation to 5-hydroxyindole-acetaldehyde under the influence of the enzyme monoamine oxidase (Blaschko, 1952). This compound is then oxidized to 5-hydroxyindole acetic acid. The reaction is catalyzed by the enzyme *aldehyde dehydrogenase* (Page and McIsaac, 1962). A second pathway involves acetylation of 5-HT to acetyl-5-hydroxytryptamine; a third pathway involves methylation to 5-methoxytryptamine and oxidation (oxidative deamination) to 5-methoxyindole acetic acid. The pathways are illustrated in Figure 26–18.

The pharmacology related to 5-HT, its production and its metabolism, is

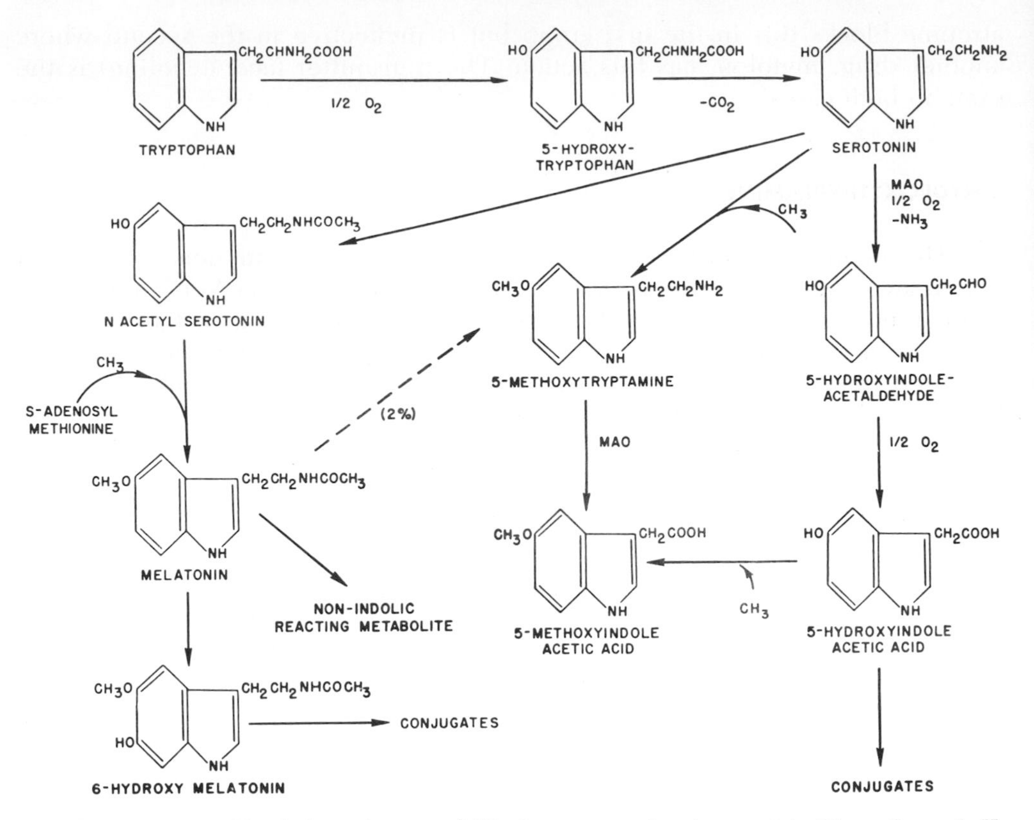

Figure 26–18. Metabolic relations of 5-hydroxytryptamine (serotonin). (From Page, I. H., and W. M. McIsaac: Serotonin. *In* Neurochemistry, 2nd Ed. K. A. Elliott, I. H. Page, and J. H. Quastel, eds. Charles C Thomas, Springfield, Ill., 1962.)

almost exclusively known from studies on vertebrate tissues. Lysergic acid diethylamide (LSD) was found to mimic (cat brain) or to block (visceral smooth muscle) the action of 5-HT (Bradley and Hance, 1956; Gaddum, 1954). *Reserpine* and *chlorpromazine* release 5-HT from the stores in nerve cells (Spector, Shore, and Brodie, 1959). *Iproniazid* and *nialamide*, by inhibiting monoamine oxidase, cause an increase in the amounts of 5-HT present in nerve tissue and potentiate the action of applied 5-HT (Gluckman, Hart, and Marrazzi, 1957). *Alpha-methyl-dopa* (Sourkes, 1954) inhibits the 5-hydroxytryptophan decarboxylase and causes a fall in 5-HT content of nerve tissue. Methysergide(1-methyl-D-lysergic acid-butanolamine) and *10-methoxyharmalan* are potent blocking agents: they prevent the action of applied 5-HT (Loveland, 1963).

Inhibition (or muscle relaxation as seen in *Mytilus* byssus retractor muscles, see p. 592) may well be due to an intracellular action of 5-HT, similar to that described in a previous section for adrenaline (pp. 660–661). In liver flukes, 5-HT causes formation of cyclic 3,5-adenosine monophosphate from ATP and thereby stimulates activation of phosphorylase (see pp. 572 and 661) which, in turn, leads to increased glycolysis (Mansour, 1959). It is interesting that adrenaline does not have this action in liver flukes (in contrast to the situation in vertebrates).

Since the drugs chlorpromazine, LSD, and reserpin (as well as several structurally related agents) have potent actions on human mental activity, 5-HT has been implied as a key substance for those processes in the central nervous system that underlie mental activity (the term "mentation" is used instead in many pharmacological papers). Abnormalities in 5-HT metabolism have been blamed for mental disease, especially schizophrenia.

REFERENCES

Albers, R. W., and R. O. Brady (1959) The distribution of glutamic decarboxylase in the nervous system of the Rhesus monkey. J. Biol. Chem. *234*:926–928.

Albers, R. W., and R. A. Salvador (1958) Succinic semialdehyde oxidation by a soluble dehydrogenase from brain. Science *128*:359–360.

Alure, E., H. Gainer, and H. Grundfest (1962) Differentiation of synaptic and GABA inhibitory action in crab neuromuscular junctions. Biol. Bull. *123*:479.

Axelrod, J. (1960) The fate of adrenaline and noradrenaline. *In* Adrenergic Mechanisms, pp. 28–39. Ciba Foundation Symposium, Little, Brown and Co., Boston.

Axelrod, J., J. K. Inscoe, S. Senoh, and B. Witkop (1958) O-Methylation, the principal pathway for the metabolism of epinephrine and norepinephrine in the rat. Biochim. biophys. Acta *27*: 210–211.

Axelrod, J., and M. J. Laroche (1959) Inhibitor of O-methylation of epinephrine and norepinephrine *in vitro* and *in vivo*. Science *130*:800.

Axelsson, J., E. Bueding, and E. Bülbring (1959) The action of adrenalin on phosphorylase activity and membrane potential of smooth muscle. J. Physiol. *148*:62P–63P.

Bacq, Z. M. (1936a) Recherches sur la physiologie et la pharmacologie du système nerveux autonome. XX. Sensibilisation à l'adrénaline et à l'excitation des nerfs. Arch. Int. Physiol. *42*: 340–366.

Bacq, Z. M. (1936b) Recherches sur la physiologie et la pharmacologie du système nerveux autonome. XXII. Nouvelles observations sur la sensibilisation à l'adrénaline par les antioxygenes. Arch. Int. Physiol. *44*:15–23.

Bacq, Z. M., L. Gosselin, A. Dresse, and J. Renson (1959) Inhibition of O-methyl-transferase by catechol and sensitization to epinephrine. Science *130*:453–454.

Bain, W. A., and R. Fielden (1957) In vitro formation of noradrenaline from dopamine by human tissue. Lancet *2*:472–473.

Baxter, C. F., and E. Roberts (1959) Elevation of γ-aminobutyric acid in rat brain with hydroxylamine. Proc. Soc. Exp. Biol. Med. *101*:811–815.

Bertler, A., A. Carlsson, and E. Rosengren (1956) Release by reserpine of catechol amines from rabbits' hearts. Naturwissenschaften *43*:521.

Birks, R. I. (1963) The role of sodium ions in the metabolism of acetylcholine. Canad. J. Biochem. *41*:2573–2597.

Birks, R. I., and C. F. MacIntosh (1961) Acetylcholine metabolism of a sympathetic ganglion. Canad. J. Biochem. *39*:787–827.

Blaschko, H. (1952) Enzymic oxidation of 5-hydroxytryptamine in mammalian and cephalopod tissue. Biochem. J. *52*:x.

Blaschko, H., and A. D. Welch (1953) Localization of adrenaline in cytoplasmic particles of the bovine adrenal medulla. Arch. Exp. Path. Pharmak. *219*:17–22.

Born, G. V. R., and E. Bülbring (1956) The movement of potassium between smooth muscle and the surrounding fluid. J. Physiol. *131*:690–703.

Bradley, P. B., and A. J. Hance (1956) The effects of introventricular injections of D-lysergic acid diethylamide (LSD 25) and 5-hydroxytryptamine (serotonin) on the electrical activity of the brain of the conscious cat. J. Physiol. *132*:50P–51P.

Brandon, K. W., and M. J. Rand (1961) Acetylcholine and the sympathetic innervation of the spleen. J. Physiol. *157*:18–32.

Brooks, V. B. (1956) An intracellular study of the action of repetitive nerve volleys and of botulinum toxin on miniature end-plate potentials. J. Physiol. *134*:264–277.

Brown, G. L., and W. Feldberg (1936) The action of potassium on the superior cervical ganglion of the cat. J. Physiol. *86*:290–305.

Bülbring, E. (1954) Membrane potentials of smooth muscle fibers of the Taenia coli of the guinea-pig. J. Physiol. *125*:302–315.

Bülbring, E., and J. H. Burn (1935) The sympathetic dilator fibres in the muscles of the cat and dog. J. Physiol. 83:483–501.

Burn, J. H. (1961) Tyramine and other amines as noradrenaline-releasing substances. *In* Adrenergic Mechanisms, Ciba Foundation Symposium, pp. 326–336. Little, Brown and Co., Boston.

Burn, J. H., and M. J. Rand (1957) Reserpine and noradrenaline in artery walls. Lancet *2*:1097.

Burn, J. H., and M. J. Rand (1958) Noradrenaline in artery walls and its dispersal by reserpine. Brit. Med. J. *1*:903–908.

Burn, J. H., and M. J. Rand (1959a) Sympathetic postganglionic mechanism. Nature *184*:163–165.

Burn, J. H., and M. J. Rand (1959b) The cause of the supersensitivity of smooth muscle to noradrenaline after sympathetic degeneration. J. Physiol. *147*:135–143.

Burn, J. H., and M. J. Rand (1960a) Sympathetic postganglionic cholinergic fibres. Brit. J. Pharmacol. *15*:56–66.

Burn, J. H., and M. J. Rand (1960b) The effect of precursors of noradrenaline on the response to tyramine and sympathetic stimulation. Brit. J. Pharmacol. *15*:47–55.

Burnstock, G. (1958) The action of adrenaline on excitability and membrane potential in the guinea-pig and the effect of DPN on this action and on the action of acetylcholine. J. Physiol. *143*: 183–194.

Buzard, J. A., and P. D. Nytch (1957) Some characteristics of rat kidney 5-hydroxy-tryptophan decarboxylase. J. Biol. Chem. *227*:225–230.

Corteggiani, E. (1938) Contribution à l'étude de l'acetylcholine libre et disimilée sous forme d'un complexe dans le cerveau. Doullens, Paris.

Curtis, D. R., J. W. Phillis, and J. C. Watkins (1959) The depression of spinal neurones by γ-amino-N-butyric acid and beta-alanine. J. Physiol. *146*:185–203.

Dale, H. H. (1906) On some physiological actions of ergot. J. Physiol. *34*:163–206.

Dale, H. H., and W. Feldberg (1934) The chemical transmission of secretory impulses to the sweat glands of the cat. J. Physiol. *82*:121–128.

Dulière, W., and O. Loewi (1939) Liberation of potassium by acetylcholine in the central nervous system. Nature *144*:244.

Eccles, J. C. (1957) The Physiology of Nerve Cells, pp. 193–198. Johns Hopkins Press, Baltimore.

Elliott, K. A. C., and E. Florey (1956) Factor I—Inhibitory factor from brain. Assay. Conditions in brain. Stimulating and antagonizing substances. J. Neurochem. *1*:181–191.

Erspamer, V. (1952a) Enteramina e 5-metessitriptamina. Tossicita. Azione sulla diuresi, sulla pressione del sangue e su alcuni organi a muscolatura liscia. Ricerca Scient. *22*:694–702.

Erspamer, V. (1952b) Identification of octopamine as 1-p-hydroxyphenylethanolamine. Nature *169*:375–376.

Erspamer, V. (1954) Il sistema cellulare enterocromaffine e L'Enteramina (5-idrossitriptamina). Rendiconti Scientifici Farmitalia *1*:1–193.

Erspamer, V., and B. Asero (1952) Identification of the enteramine, the specific hormone of the enterochromaffin cell system, as 5-hydroxytryptamine. Nature *169*:800–801.

Erspamer, V., and G. Boretti (1951) Identification and characterization, by paper chromatography, of enteramine, octopamine, tyramine, histamine and allied substances in extracts of posterior salivary glands of Octopoda and in other tissue extracts of vertebrates and invertebrates. Arch. Int. Pharmacodyn. *88*:296–332.

Farrant, J. (1960) Discussion remark after paper presented by P. A. Nasmyth on "Some observations on the effects of tyramine." *In* Adrenergic Mechanisms, pp. 348–349. Ciba Foundation Symposium, Little, Brown and Co., Boston.

Fleckenstein, A., and D. Stöckle (1955) Zum Mechanismus der Wirkungs-Verstärkung und Wirkungs-Abschwächung sympathomimetischer Amine durch Cocain und andere Pharmaka. Arch. Exp. Path. Pharmak. *224*:401–415.

Fleming, W. R., K. G. Scheffel, and J. R. Linton (1962) Comp. Biochem. Physiol. *6*:205–213.

Florey, E. (1954) An inhibitory and an excitatory factor of mammalian central nervous system, and their action on a single sensory neuron. Arch. Int. Physiol. *62*:33–53.

Florey, E. (1957) Further evidence for the transmitter-function of Factor I. Naturwissenschaften *44*:424–425.

Florey, E. (1960) Evidence for Factor I containing neurons in mammalian central nervous system. *In* Inhibitions of the Nervous System and γ-Aminobutyric Acid, pp. 202–206. Pergamon Press, Oxford.

Florey, E. (1963) Acetylcholine in invertebrate nervous systems. Canad. J. Biochem. *41*:2619–2626.

Florey, E., and G. Hoyle (1961) Neuromuscular synaptic activity in the crab (*Cancer magister*). *In* Nervous Inhibition, pp. 105–110. (E. Florey, ed.) Pergamon Press, Oxford.

Florey, E., and H. McLennan (1955a) Effects of an inhibitory factor (Factor I) from brain on central synaptic transmission. J. Physiol. *130*:446–455.

Florey, E., and H. McLennan (1955b) The release of an inhibitory substance from mammalian brain and its action on peripheral synaptic transmission. J. Physiol. *129*:384–392.
Fotino, S., and Stoculesco, P. (1957) J. Physiol. *48*:1011–1034.
Gaddum, J. H. (1954) *In* Ciba Foundation Symposium on Hypertension, Humoral and Neurogenic Factors, pp. 75–77. Little, Brown and Co., Boston.
Gautrelet, J., E. Corteggiani, and A. Carayon-Gentil (1941) Mise en évidence de lécithides dans le complexe acétylcholinique cérébral par action du venin de Cobra et des sels biliaires. C. R. Soc. Biol. *135*:832–835.
Gerschenfeld, H., and L. Tauc (1961) Pharmacological specificities of neurones in an elementary central nervous system. Nature *189*:924–925.
Gluckman, M. I., E. R. Hart, and A. S. Marrazzi (1957) Cerebral synaptic inhibition by serotonin and iproniazid. Science *126*:448–449.
Grundfest, H., J. P. Reuben, and W. H. Rickles, Jr. (1958) Electrophysiology and pharmacology of lobster muscle fibers. Biol. Bull. *115*:332.
Harpur, R. P., and J. H. Quastel (1949) Relation between acetylcholine synthesis and metabolism of carbohydrates and D-glucosamine in the central nervous system. Nature *164*:779–782.
Hebb, C. O., and K. Krnjević (1962) The physiological significance of acetylcholine. *In* Neurochemistry, 2nd ed., pp. 452–521. (K. A. C. Elliott, I. H. Page and J. H. Quastel, eds.) Charles C Thomas, Springfield, Ill.
Hebb, C. O., and G. M. H. Waites (1956) Choline acetylase in antero- and retrograde degeneration of a cholinergic nerve. J. Physiol. *132*:667–671.
Hodgkin, A. L. (1951) The ionic basis of electrical activity in nerve and muscle. Biol. Rev. *26*:339–409.
Hillarp, N.-Å. (1959) The construction and functional organization of the autonomic innervation apparatus. Acta Physiol. Scand., Suppl. 157, *46*:1–38.
Hukovic, S. (1959) Isolated rabbit atria with sympathetic nerve supply. Brit. J. Pharmacol. *14*:372–376.
Hutter, O. F., and W. Trautwein (1956) Vagal and sympathetic effects on the pacemaker fibers in the sinus venosus of the heart. J. Gen. Physiol. *39*:715–733.
Imaizumi, R., and K. Kawamoto (1952) Adrenaline dehydrogenase in blood. Med. J. Osaka Univ. *3*:269–278.
Imaizumi, R., K. Kawamoto, T. Kita, and H. Sato (1952) Adrenaline dehydrogenase in blood. Med. J. Osaka Univ. *3*:279–283.
Jaques, R., and M. Schachter (1954) The presence of histamine, 5-hydroxytryptamine and a potent, slow contracting substance in wasp venom. Brit. J. Pharmacol. *9*:53–58.
Kakimoto, Y., and M. D. Armstrong (1960) Identification of octopamine in animals treated with monoamine oxidase inhibitors. Fed. Proc. *19*:295.
Kamemoto, F. I., S. M. Keister, and A. E. Spalding (1962) Cholinesterase activities and sodium movements in the crayfish kidney. Comp. Biochem. Physiol. *7*:363–370.
Killam, K. F., and J. A. Bain (1957) Convulsant hydrazides. I: *In vitro* and *in vivo* inhibition of vitamin B_6 enzymes by convulsant hydrazides. J. Pharmacol. Exp. Therap. *119*:255–262.
Kirschner, L. B. (1953) Effect of cholinesterase inhibitors and atropine on active transport across frog skin. Nature *172*:348.
Kirshner, N. (1959) Biosynthesis of adrenaline and noradrenaline. Pharmacol. Rev. *11*:350–357.
Kirshner, N. (1960) Formation of adrenaline and noradrenaline. *In* Adrenergic Mechanisms, pp. 17–24. Ciba Foundation Symposium. Little, Brown and Co., Boston.
Koblick, D. C. (1959) An enzymatic ion exchange model for active sodium transport. J. Gen. Physiol. *42*:890–900.
Koch, H. J. (1954) Cholinesterase and active transport of sodium chloride through isolated gills of the crab *Eriocheir sinensis* (M. Edw.). *In* Recent Developments in Cell Physiology, pp. 15–31. 7th Symposium of the Colston Research Society. Academic Press, New York.
Kohn, A. (1898) Prag. med. Wschr. *23*:197.
Kohn, A. (1903) Die Paraganglien. Arch. mikr. Anat. *62*:263–365.
Kravitz, E. A., D. D. Potter, and N. M. van Gelder (1962) Gamma-aminobutyric acid distribution in the lobster nervous system: CNS, peripheral nerves and isolated motor and inhibitory axons. Biochem. biophys. Res. Commun. *7*:231–236.
Krnjević, K., and R. Miledi (1958) Some effects produced by adrenaline upon neuromuscular propagation in rats. J. Physiol. *141*:291–304.
Krnjević, K., and J. F. Mitchell (1961) The release of acetylcholine in the isolated rat diaphragm. J. Physiol. *155*:246–262.
Kuffler, S. W., and C. Edwards (1958) Mechanism of gamma aminobutyric acid (GABA) action and its relation to synaptic inhibition. J. Neurophysiol. *21*:589–610.
Kuno, M. (1961) Site of action of systemic gamma-aminobutyric acid in the spinal cord. Japan. J. Physiol. *11*:304–318.

Lawler, C. (1961) Turnover time of acetylcholinesterase. J. Biol. Chem. *236*:2296–2301.

Lembeck, F. (1954) Über den Nachweis von 5-Oxytryptamin (Enteramin, Serotonin) in Carcinoid-metastasen. Arch. Exp. Path. Pharmak. *221*:50–66.

Loewi, O. (1921) Über humorale Übertragbarkeit der Herznervenwirkung. Pflügers Arch. ges. Physiol. *189*:239–242.

Loveland, R. E. (1963) 5-Hydroxytryptamine, the probable mediator of excitation in the heart of Mercenaria (Venus) mercenaria. Comp. Biochem. Physiol. *9*:95–104.

Lowe, I. P., E. Robins, and G. S. Eyerman (1958) The fluorometric measurement of glutamic decarboxylase and its distribution in brain. J. Neurochem. *3*:8–18.

Luco, J. V., and P. Sanchez (1956) Spontaneous activity and contractile responses to adrenaline of denervated auricular muscles. Acta Physiol. Lat.-Amer. *6*:171–172.

Lundholm, L., and E. Mohme-Lundholm (1957) The effect of adrenaline on the glycogen metabolism of smooth muscle. Acta Physiol. Scand. *38*:237–254.

MacIntosh, F. C. (1963) Synthesis and storage of acetylcholine in nervous tissue. Canad. J. Biochem. *41*:2552–2571.

MacMillan, W. H. (1959) A hypothesis concerning the effect of cocaine on the action of sympathomimetic amines. Brit. J. Pharmacol. *14*:385–391.

Mann, P. J. G., and J. H. Quastel (1941) Nicotinamid, cozymase and tissue metabolism. Biochem. J. *35*:502–517.

Mann, P. J. G., M. Tennenbaum, and J. H. Quastel (1939) Acetylcholine metabolism in the central nervous system. Biochem. J. *33*:822–835; 1506–1518.

Mansour, T. E. (1959) The effect of serotonin and related compounds on the carbohydrate metabolism of the liver fluke, *Fasciola hepatica*. J. Pharmacol. Exp. Therap. *126*:212–216.

Marrazzi, A. S., and E. R. Hart (1955) Relationship of hallucinogens to adrenergic cerebral neurohumors. Science *121*:365–367.

Mathias, A. P., D. M. Ross, and M. Schachter (1957) Identification and distribution of 5-hydroxytryptamine in a sea anemone. Nature *180*:658–659.

McIsaac, W. M., P. A. Khairallah and I. H. Page (1961) 10-Methoxyharmalan, a potent serotonin antagonist which affects conditioned behavior. Science *134*:674–675.

McLennan, H. (1961) Inhibitory transmitters—A review. *In* Nervous Inhibition, pp. 350–368. (E. Florey, ed.) Pergamon Press, Oxford.

McLennan, H. (1962) On the action of 3-hydroxytyramine and dichloroisopropyl-noradrenaline on spinal reflexes. Experientia *18*:278–279.

Murad, F., T. W. Rall, and E. W. Sutherland (1960) Formation of adenosine-3′, 5′-phosphate (3,5-AMP) by particulate preparations of ventricular muscle. Fed. Proc. *19*:296.

Nachmansohn, D. (1962) Chemical and molecular basis of nerve activity. *In* Neurochemistry, 2nd ed., pp. 522–557. (K. A. C. Elliott, I. H. Page and J. H. Quastel, eds.) Charles C Thomas, Springfield, Ill.

Nachmansohn, D., and A. L. Machado (1943) The formation of acetylcholine. A new enzyme: "choline acetylase." J. Neurophysiol. *6*:397–403.

Nickerson, M., and G. M. Nomaguchi (1948) Locus of the adrenergic blocking action of dibenamine. J. Pharmacol. Exp. Therap. *93*:40–51.

Nystrom, R. A. (1962) Nervous control of the cat nictitating membrane. Amer. J. Physiol. *202*:849–855.

Östlund, E. (1954) The distribution of catechol amines in lower animals and their effect on the heart. Acta Physiol. Scand. Suppl. 112, *31*.

Page, I. H., and W. M. McIsaac (1962) XXV. Serotonin. *In* Neurochemistry, 2nd Ed., pp. 620–635. (K. A. C. Elliott, I. H. Page, and J. H. Quastel, eds.) Charles C Thomas, Springfield, Ill.

Quastel, J. H. (1962) Acetylcholine distribution and synthesis in the central nervous system. *In* Neurochemistry, 2nd ed., pp. 431–451. (K. A. C. Elliott, I. H. Page and J. H. Quastel, eds.) Charles C Thomas, Springfield, Ill.

Rapport, M. M., A. A. Green, and I. H. Page (1948) Serum vasoconstrictor (serotonin). IV. Isolation and characterization. J. Biol. Chem. *176*:1243–1251.

Roberts, E. (1962) γ-Aminobutyric acid. *In* Neurochemistry, 2nd Ed., pp. 636–656. (K. A. C. Elliott, I. H. Page, and J. H. Quastel, eds.) Charles C Thomas, Springfield, Ill.

Roberts, E., and S. Fraenkel (1951) Further studies of glutamic acid decarboxylase in brain. J. Biol. Chem. *190*:505–512.

Salvador, R. A., and R. W. Albers (1959) The distribution of glutamic-γ-aminobutyric transaminase in the nervous system of the Rhesus monkey. J. Biol. Chem. *234*:922–925.

Sanchez, P., and J. V. Luco (1956) Study of curare-acetylcholine antagonism in normal and denervated auricular muscles. Acta Neurol. Lat.-Amer. *2*:189–193.

Schallek, W. (1945) Action of potassium on bound acetylcholine in lobster nerve cord. J. Cell. Comp. Physiol. *26*:15–24.

Schümann, H. J. (1955) Nachweis von Oxtyramin (Dopamin) in sympathischen Nerven und Ganglien. Arch. Exp. Path. Pharmak. *227*:566–573.

Schümann, H. J. (1958) Über die Verteilung von Noradrenalin und Hydroxytyramin in sympathischen Nerven (Milznerven). Arch. Exp. Path. Pharmak. *234*:17–25.

Schümann, H. J. (1960) Formation of adrenergic transmitters. *In* Adrenergic Mechanisms, pp. 6–16. Ciba Foundation Symposium. Little, Brown and Co., Boston.

Sourkes, T. L. (1954) Inhibition of dihydroxyphenylalanine decarboxylase by derivatives of phylalanine. Arch. Biochem. *51*:444–456.

Sourkes, T. L. (1962) Biochemistry of the catecholamines. *In* Neurochemistry, 2nd Ed., pp. 590–619. (K. A. C. Elliott, I. H. Page, and J. H. Quastel, eds.) Charles C Thomas, Springfield, Ill.

Spector, S., P. A. Shore, and B. B. Brodie (1959) Biochemical and pharmacological effects of the monoamine oxidase inhibitors, iproniazid, 1-phenyl-2-hydrazinopropane (JB 516) and 1-phenyl-3-hydrazinobutane (JB 835). J. Pharm. Exp. Therap. *128*:15–21.

Sutherland, E. W., and T. W. Rall (1960) The relation of adenosine-3′,5′-phosphate to the action of catechol amines. *In* Adrenergic Mechanisms, pp. 295–304. Ciba Foundation Symposium. Little, Brown and Co., Boston.

Sweeney, D. (1963) Dopamine: Its occurrence in molluscan ganglia. Science *139*:1051.

Thesleff, S. (1960) Supersensitivity of skeletal muscle produced by botulinum toxin. J. Physiol. *151*:598–607.

Thompson, J. W. (1958) Studies on the responses of the isolated nictitating membrane of the cat. J. Physiol. *141*:46–72.

Udenfriend, S., H. Weissbach, and D. F. Bogdanski (1957a) Biochemical findings relating to the action of serotonin. Ann. N.Y. Acad. Sci. *66*:602–608.

Udenfriend, S., H. Weissbach, and D. F. Bogdanski (1957b) Increase in tissue serotonin following administration of its precursor 5-hydroxytryptophan. J. Biol. Chem. *224*:803–811.

Van der Kloot, W. G. (1958) The effect of enzyme inhibitors on the resting potential and on ion distribution of the sartorius muscle of the frog. J. Gen. Physiol. *41*:890–900.

Van der Kloot, W. G., and J. Robbins (1959) The effects of γ-aminobutyric acid and picrotoxin on the junctional potential and the contraction of crayfish muscle. Experientia *15*:35–36.

Waser, P. G. (1960) The cholinergic receptor. J. Pharm. Pharmacol. *12*:577–594.

Welsh, J. H. (1957) Serotonin as a possible neurohumoral agent: evidence obtained in lower animals. Ann. N.Y. Acad. Sci. *66*:618–630.

Welsh, J. H., and M. Moorhead (1960) Quantitative distribution of 5-hydroxytryptamine in the invertebrates, especially in their nervous systems. J. Neurochem. *6*:146–149.

Zeller, E. A., J. Barsky, J. R. Fouts, W. F. Kirchheimer, and L. S. Van Orden (1952) Influence of isonicotinic acid hydrazide (INH) and 1-isonitinyl-2-isopropyl hydrazide (IIH) on bacterial and mammalian enzymes. Experientia *8*:349–350.

Zucker, M. B., B. K. Friedman and M. M. Rapport (1954) Identification and quantitative determination of serotonin (5-hydroxytryptamine) in blood platelets. Proc. Soc. Exp. Biol. Med. *85*:282–285.

27 ACTIVE TRANSPORT ACROSS CELL MEMBRANES AND CELLULAR MEMBRANES

Previous chapters mentioned and discussed certain substances or ions that are carried across the plasma membrane of certain body cells against concentration or electrochemical gradients. Examples are the outward transport of sodium ions across the membrane of nerve and muscle cells, the transfer of glucose from the lumen of vertebrate kidney tubules across the tubular cells into the tissue fluids, and the absorption of certain inorganic ions into the body fluids across the gill membranes of fresh-water crustaceans.

In this chapter this widespread phenomenon of *active transport* is examined briefly, and the mechanisms that have been proposed to account for it are outlined. The topic of active transport is more typical for the nature of general physiology than any other topic discussed in this book—in fact it is the most abstract subject matter of physiology, since it ranges across all boundaries of the diverse organ functions and cell functions, and although it sheds light on all of them, it is treated as a fundamental process for which the diverse cell and organ functions merely yield examples.

Active transport can be defined as *movement across cell membranes of molecules and ions by forces additional to those of thermal agitation.* It cannot be accounted for by the laws of diffusion and it achieves a distribution of the particular molecules or ions which is not an equilibrium distribution. Active transport requires the expenditure of metabolic energy. The phenomenon, wherever it occurs, shows the following characteristics:

1. Active transport is highly specific. Of the numerous constituent molec-

ular and ionic species of a given extracellular or intracellular fluid, only certain species are selected and transported against an electric potential or a concentration gradient.

2. The rate of transport is proportional to the concentration of the substance on one side of the membrane but only up to a certain concentration; no further increase, but sometimes a decrease, occurs when the concentration reaches higher values. The rate of transport is largely independent of the concentration gradient across the membrane.

3. Active transport is strongly diminished or abolished when metabolic inhibitors (such as azide, dinotrophenol, or fluoride) are applied to the cell.

4. Active transport of a given species of molecule or ion is inhibited by the presence of certain chemically related species of molecules or ions, even though the latter are not themselves being transported. The kinetics of this inhibition are similar to those of competitive enzyme inhibition (see Chap. 6).

5. Noncompetitive inhibition of active transport by enzyme poisons and specific inhibitors is also quite common.

6. The temperature coefficient of active transport is usually rather high, with a Q_{10} of 2 to 3 (with a rise, say, from 20 to 30° C, the rate is doubled or even tripled), quite in contrast to ordinary diffusion, in which the rate change is proportional to the absolute temperature and consequently changes much less with a change in temperature.

7. Active transport of ions (or ionized molecules) is the cause of an electric potential difference across the membrane.

The commonly accepted view is that the mechanisms for active transport reside in or close to the cell membrane and that the particular molecule or ion is transferred by specific carrier molecules. It is a correlate with active transport that the cell membrane has a low permeability for the molecular or ionic species to be transported; in fact, high permeability and active transport are incompatible. This is understandable when one considers that active transport requires the expenditure of metabolic energy, and that its effects (namely the accumulation of the substance transported, on one side of the membrane) can become significant only if the rate of active transport is greater than the rate of diffusion through the membrane in the opposite direction (see Fig. 27–1). In order to maintain a high concentration difference, a steady state must be maintained at which the passive outflow of the particular substance just equals the active inflow. Thus the rate of energy expenditure for active transport must be directly proportional to the "leakiness" of the membrane. If the permeability to a given substance is as high, for instance, as that of most cell membranes to urea, namely, of the dimension of 10^{-15}cm^2/sec, it would require about 1000 cal/gm tissue/hr to maintain a gradient of 20:1 between the intra- and extracellular media. This value corresponds to an oxygen consumption of 200 ml/gm/hr, which is far in excess of even the most active tissue respiration known (that of active insects is about 100 ml/gm/hr). Obviously, such active transport is not feasible in this case.

Many cases have been reported in which the oxygen consumption rises with the rate of active transport; in fact, the number of molecules (or ions) actively transported could be directly related to the number of extra oxygen molecules consumed. For active Na transport, for instance, as it occurs in frog

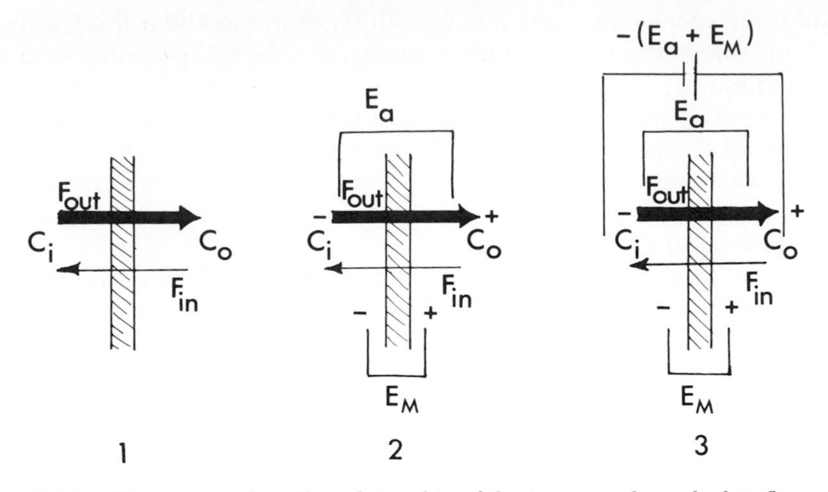

Figure 27–1. Diagrams to show the relationship of the terms used to calculate flux ratios and work involved in passive and active transport. **1**, the situation in which a nonelectrolyte is passively transported in the absence of a membrane potential. **2**, the case in which a membrane potential exists (due to causes other than the active transport under consideration), and active transport of a cation out of the "cell" produces an electric potential, E_a. The direction of E_M as indicated by the symbols + and – is arbitrarily chosen. **3**, same situation as described in **2**, except that a "short-circuit current" is applied to set the membrane potential to zero.

skin (see below), it was experimentally found that for every 3.4 Na ions carried, one molecule of oxygen is consumed (Linderholm, 1952); in frog muscle cells, four Na ions (Conway, 1960), and in mammalian kidney tubules 29 Na ions (Thaysen, Lassen, and Munck, 1961) are transported for every extra oxygen molecule consumed (extra-oxygen consumption means consumption above the resting level).

To appreciate the significance of the relation between extra oxygen consumed and active transport, it is necessary to understand the energy requirements of active transport. In the most simple case the flux ratio, that is, the proportion of flux in one direction to that in the opposite direction, in the absence of active transport is equal to the ratio of the concentrations on either side of the membrane across which the fluxes occur, so that

$$\frac{F_{in}}{F_{out}} = \frac{C_o}{C_i} \tag{1}$$

where F_{in} is the inward flux, F_{out} is the outward flux, and C_o and C_i are the outside and inside molar concentrations, respectively. If the substance involved is a species of ion, the relation holds only as long as there is no electric potential difference across the membrane. If such a potential difference exists, the relation becomes

$$\frac{F_{in}}{F_{out}} = \frac{C_o}{C_i} \cdot \exp\left(\frac{z \cdot F \cdot E_m}{R \cdot T}\right) \tag{2}$$

where z is the valency of the ion, F is the Faraday (96,500 coulombs), E_m is the membrane potential, R is the universal gas constant (numerical value 8.3), and T is the absolute temperature in degrees Kelvin.

When *active* transport occurs, the measured fluxes do not follow these equations (this is, in fact, one of the tests employed to detect active transport). If the transported substance is ionized, an electric potential will be generated by the active transport; we may call it the *active transport potential* and assign to it the symbol E_a. If there is no other potential difference, the flux ratio is

$$\frac{F_{in}}{F_{out}} = \frac{C_o}{C_i} \cdot \exp\left(\frac{z \cdot F \cdot E_a}{R \cdot T}\right) \tag{3}$$

In the presence of a membrane potential due to causes other than the active transport of the particular ionic substance under consideration, the relation becomes

$$\frac{F_{in}}{F_{out}} = \frac{C_o}{C_i} \cdot \exp\left(\frac{z \cdot F \cdot E_a + z \cdot F \cdot E_m}{R \cdot T}\right) \tag{4}$$

Equation (4) can be rewritten

$$R \cdot T \cdot \ln \frac{F_{in}}{F_{out}} = R \cdot T \cdot \ln \frac{C_o}{C_i} + z \cdot F \cdot E_a + z \cdot F \cdot E_m \tag{5}$$

Now, the term $z \cdot F \cdot E_a$ represents the work necessary to transport a given mole fraction across the membrane, and is equal to the electric potential energy difference thus achieved. It is equal to the work done by the active transport system, and we can state that

$$W = z \cdot F \cdot E_a \tag{6}$$

Thus we can calculate W by modifying Equation 5 to

$$W = R \cdot T \cdot \ln \frac{F_{in}}{F_{out}} + R \cdot T \cdot \ln \frac{C_i}{C_o} - z \cdot F \cdot E_m \text{ joules} \tag{7}$$

If a nonionized substance is actively transported, or if an ion is actively transported but the potential difference across the (cellular or cell-) membrane is artificially abolished (short-circuit technique, see p. 682), the work performed is given by the much simpler equation

$$W = R \cdot T \cdot \ln \frac{F_{in}}{F_{out}} \text{ joules} \tag{8}$$

Since 1 joule is equal to 0.239 cal, this work can be calculated in calories by multiplying W by 0.239.

This makes it now possible to calculate the power developed by active transport. Power is the time rate of doing work, and can be expressed in cal/sec, cal/min, or cal/hr. Thus an active transport system that maintains a certain concentration difference by uphill transport in the face of a certain membrane potential (total potential difference minus E_a) develops a power of $W \cdot 0.239$ cal/unit time. It derives its energy from cellular metabolism and can therefore be directly related to oxygen consumption, since it is known that 1 mole of oxygen yields 101,000 to 112,000 cal, depending on whether fat, protein, or carbohydrate is metabolized (see Chap. 12, p. 270). Thus, active transport at a steady rate performs work per unit time that is equivalent to the energy released by a certain amount of oxygen consumed during the same unit of time. The actual rate of oxygen consumption is higher than that calculated from the computed active transport, since a certain amount of energy is lost in the transformation of energy.

The ratio of 100 · (0.239 W/unit time)/(moles of oxygen consumed/unit time) · (caloric value of oxygen) is called the *energetic efficiency*. In order to compute the energetic efficiency of a given active transport system, one must first clearly separate and exclude that proportion of the total oxygen consumption that is not directly related to the particular transport process.

There is another way in which oxygen consumption may be linked with active ion transport; a theory, known as the *redox-pump theory* (Lund, 1947; Conway, 1953) explains this as follows: a chain of iron-containing electron transport molecules (cytochromes) removes the electrons from pairs of hydrogen atoms, generating two H^+ and two electrons which are passed along the chain (see Fig. 7–4) and transferred to $\frac{1}{2}$ to O_2, giving rise to an oxygen ion, O^{--}. In order for an ion to be transported, one or more of the electron transport molecules must serve as a carrier according to the reaction: (neutral carrier) + $\frac{1}{2}$ H_2 + $(ion)^+$ = $(carrier)^-$ $(ion)^+$ + H^+ or (neutral carrier) + e^- + $(ion)^+$ = $(carrier)^-$ $(ion)^+$. When the carrier passes its electrons on to the next electron transfer molecule, the ion may either move along with the electron to the next molecule which then assumes the property of ion carrier, or it may be released. For this schema to work, it is necessary that back diffusion of the ion be prevented and that the electron transport system be organized in such a way as to prevent a reversal of the process. This may be accomplished by a rotation of the next electron acceptor after the one that released the ion, or by preferential direction of diffusion of the complex $(carrier)^-$ $(ion)^+$.

It is easy to see that the maximum number of moles transported cannot be higher than four times the number of moles of oxygen consumed in the process: each molecule of O_2 accepts 2 × 2 electrons, corresponding to a production of 4 H^+ which are potentially available for exchange with a cation to be transported. In other words, 1 mole of O_2 can give rise to a maximal transport of 4 Faradays of charge (in the form of ion carried), that is, 4 × 96,500 coulombs. This number is the *coulombic equivalent of oxygen*. The ratio 100 (number of coulombs transported by the membrane/unit of time)/(coulombic equivalent of the oxygen consumed/unit of time) is called the *coulombic efficiency*, or *coulomb efficiency*, of the transport system. If the calculation demonstrates a coulombic efficiency greater than 100 per cent, the transport system in question cannot be operating as a "redox pump," but the redox theory may apply in cases in which the coulombic efficiency is 100 per cent or less.

Coulombic efficiency and energetic efficiency are not correlated, and whereas coulombic efficiencies can be higher than 100 per cent, the energetic efficiency must always be less than 100 per cent.

Active transport has often been considered to involve utilization of ATP (or similar high energy compounds). This, again, provides a link between oxygen consumption and active transport; and the relationship is amenable to calculation. It may be assumed that 1 mole of oxygen gives rise to 6 moles of ATP. The energy available through hydrolysis of the terminal phosphate bond is about 7000 cal/mole. One mole of oxygen thus yields 42,000 cal of energy available for active transport. This is 42 to 44 per cent of the caloric value of oxygen.

Before passing on to an outline of some of the transport systems that have been studied, it may be of help to illustrate the relationships discussed in the preceding paragraphs with a simple example: In the case in which active transport involves a nonionized compound, or in which it involves an ionized substance but the membrane potential is set at zero, Equation 8 applies and it can be stated as $W = 0.239\ R \cdot T \ln \frac{F_{in}}{F_{out}}$ cal. At 20° C, the term T becomes 293 and $R \cdot T = (8.3) \cdot (293) = 2432$. W thus is equal to $0.239 \times 2432 \ln \frac{F_{in}}{F_{out}}$, or 581.25 $\ln \frac{F_{in}}{F_{out}}$ cal. By multiplying by 2.3, the logarithm to the base of 10 is obtained and we can write

$$W = 2.3 \times 581.25 \log \frac{F_{in}}{F_{out}} = 1337 \log \frac{F_{in}}{F_{out}} \text{ cal}$$

If the flux ratio is 10:1, $W = 1337 \times 1 = 1337$ cal. If the flux ratio is 100:1, $W = 1337 \times 2 = 2674$ cal. A 10-fold difference in the flux ratio increases the energy requirement only by a factor of 2.

When ions are transported, it is often possible to measure the electric current produced. If this is the case, the measured or calculated current can be used to calculate the number of ions transported per unit time and the energy required to accomplish this in the following manner:

One equivalent of ion is equal to 1 Faraday, or 96,500 coulombs. A current of 1 ampere is equal to 1 coulomb/sec; thus a current of 1 microampere is equal to 10^{-6} coulomb/sec. The electric charge of one univalent ion is 1.6×10^{-19} coulomb. Now, since 1 Equivalent contains 6.023×10^{23} ions and carries a charge of 96,500 coulombs, 1 coulomb corresponds to $6.023 \times 10^{23}/96{,}500$, or 6.24×10^{18} ions. Thus a current of 1 ampere represents a net flux of 6.24×10^{18} ions/sec, or 3.744×10^{20} ions/min, or 2.244×10^{22} ions/hr. This is equal to $2.244 \times 10^{22}/6.023 \times 10^{23}$, or 0.0372 Equivalent, or 37.2 milliEquivalents/hr. Expressed the other way around: 1 microEquivalent of monovalent ion transported per hour represents a current of 26.8 microamperes. In order to be meaningful, the values obtained must be related to the membrane area. The most frequently used relation is microEquivalents/cm^2/hr.

This kind of calculation does not yield information about the energies involved, because neither the term "ampere" nor "equivalent" has the dimension of energy. The energies required for the transport can be known if the membrane potential, as well as the actively produced ionic current, are known: the product of volts × amperes equals the number of watts, and watt/unit time has the dimension of energy. One watt-hour is equal to 860 cal, or 3600

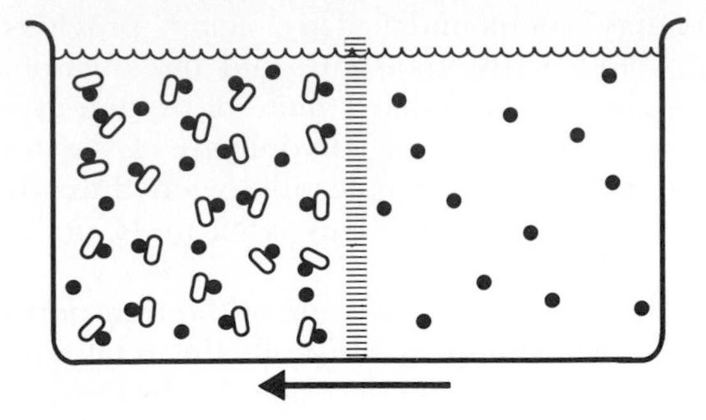

Figure 27–2. Passive transport that appears to be uphill transport (in the direction of the arrow). It is made possible because most of the solute entering the left compartment is bound to a large particle that cannot penetrate the membrane. The concentration of free solute is smaller in the left than in the right compartment.

joules, or 367.1 kilogram-meters (kg-m). The other way around: 1 cal is equal to 0.00116 watt-hour, to 0.427 kg-m, or to 4.186 joules, while 1 joule is equal to 1 watt-second or 0.000278 watt-hour and to 0.239 cal or 0.102 kg-m.

Before discussing specific examples, it is worthwhile to mention those processes that give the appearance of active transport without truly involving energy-consuming carrier processes. Passive uphill transport is possible whenever the substance transported combines, on the other side of the membrane, with another molecule (hydrogen bonds, van der Waal forces), forming a non-permeating, perhaps even nondiffusing, complex. The total concentration of the substance can then be much higher in the latter compartment, as long as the uncombined, free substance is present in a concentration lower than that on the other side of the membrane (Fig. 27–2).

Another process that can give the appearance of active transport is *facilitated diffusion.* It occurs when charged pores in membranes facilitate or accelerate the passage of oppositely charged ions so that diffusion through the membrane is faster than can be accounted for by the concentration gradient. Facilitated diffusion can also occur if the cell membrane contains a carrier with which the substance can form a membrane-soluble complex from which it can dissociate as soon as it reaches the aqueous medium on the other side of the membrane.

Facilitated diffusion leads to equilibria that are not different from those that would occur with normal diffusion; the only difference lies in the greater velocity with which equilibrium is achieved.

ACTIVE TRANSPORT SYSTEMS

The physiologist encounters active transport in a variety of cell and cellular structures. In studies on nerve and muscle function, he finds active sodium transport often coupled with potassium transport. When he investigates the digestive system he meets with active transport of certain nutrients across the epithelia of portions of the digestive tract or of digestive glands. He finds active ion transport when he concerns himself with osmoregulation and ionic regulation, particularly when he studies the so-called excretory organs (kidneys, nephridia) and gills. Active transport is also conspicuous in the elaboration of certain types of secretion, for instance, in the production of hydrochloric acid by the oxyntic cells of the vertebrate stomach. Reabsorption of "sugar" by kidney tubules represents active transport, and a similar process occurs most likely in all body cells that take up glucose from body fluids.

In fact, one and the same type of transport system can be found in a variety of different cell systems and can play—within the context of the whole organism—a number of different roles. Na transport is a good example: it occurs in the gills of fresh-water crustaceans and in the skin of amphibians, and serves in osmoregulation; it takes place in the kidney tubules of most animals and plays a fundamental role in osmoregulation and ionic regulation and in the acid-base balance of body fluids. Na transport across most cell membranes of the nervous system is a prerequisite for the high membrane potential, and thus provides the physicochemical basis for the generation of nerve impulses. For this reason it is practical to organize the following discussion according to the kinds of substances transported rather than according to the organ or cell systems in which active transport occurs.

Active transport occurs probably across all cell membranes, but certain transport systems of a few types of cells have been particularly well studied. Two types of transport are considered: transport across single cell membranes, and transport across cellular membranes. The latter phenomenon involves one-way transport across layers of cells (epithelium, epidermis) whereby the particles of a given substance are first carried into the cells, then, on their other side, out of the same cells. In most cases the first, or the second process is active, the other passive transport. Figure 27–3 illustrates the different possibilities.

Although many cases are considered as involving the transport of only one

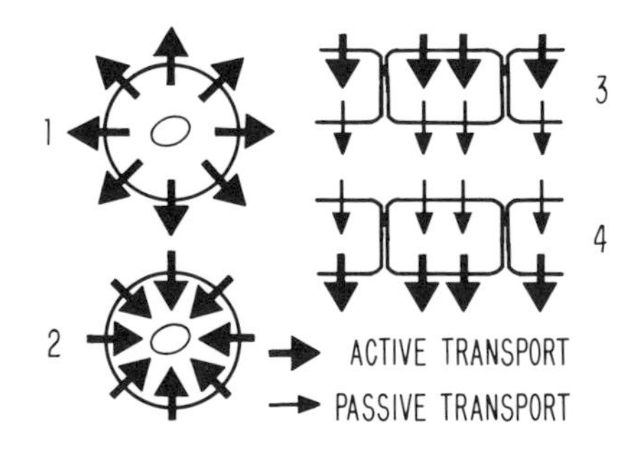

Figure 27–3. Patterns of active transport: although active transport of a given compound or ion species may occur across the entire cell membrane out of (**1**) or into (**2**) a cell, it may be restricted to only part of the membrane. This is particularly true for epithelial or endothelial cells forming cellular membranes (examples: gills, kidney tubules, frog skin), which can pass certain substances from one side of the membrane to the other. Active transport here occurs only at the "outer" (**3**) or the "inner" (**4**) cell membrane of the cells that constitute the cellular membrane. Note that the same cells may show both patterns (**3** and **4**), each representing a transport mechanism for a different substance.

substance, it is known that there are others in which the transport of one substance is coupled with that of another. Of the latter kind of coupled transport there are two kinds: (1) the two compounds are transported in the same direction or (2) the two substances are carried in opposite directions. It is interesting that in coupled transport the two substances carried may be of radically different chemical structure; for example, Na ions may be transported simultaneously with glucose molecules by the same carrier mechanism (see below). However, in other cases, the coupled transport involves similar substances, such as Na^+ and K^+ ions (see below).

Na Transport

Perhaps the most widely studied Na transport system is that in the amphibian skin. The Danish physiologist August Krogh (1937, 1938) discovered that frogs take up NaCl from dilute solutions (to 10^{-5} M) through their skin, and that the mechanism responsible for this uptake is specific for Na^+, since neither K^+ nor Ca^{++} could substitute for it, whereas Cl could be replaced by Br^- or HCO_3^-. Also in Denmark, Ussing (1947) demonstrated that the NaCl transport consists in an active transport to Na^+, and that the Cl^- follows passively because of the electric potential difference set up by the one-way Na^+ transport. This potential difference (inside—that is, corium side—positive; outside—that is, corneum side—negative) was described by DuBois-Reymond in 1857 and has been investigated repeatedly. The frog skin acts like an electric battery, being capable of producing electric currents of about 50 micro-amperes/cm^2 and an electromotive force of up to 100 mV. Ussing and Zerahn (1951) have shown that practically all the current is carried by Na^+ ions, and that, with equal sodium concentrations on both sides of the skin, the inward Na flux is about 10 times greater than the outward flux (*note*: this has been determined in experiments in which initially a known proportion of the sodium on one side of the skin was in the form of Na^{22} and on the other side in the form of Na^{24}). The distribution of the two forms of radioactive Na^+ at the end of a certain time gives a measure of the flux ratio.

Ussing and Zerahn used the apparatus explained in Figure 27–4 to demonstrate and measure the ionic currents across amphibian skin. The principle of operation is to monitor the potential difference across the skin and then to apply a counter-electromotive force through a second pair of electrodes and measure the electric current ("short-circuit current") just necessary to reduce the skin potential to zero. This current can then be taken to be equal (but in opposite direction) to the ionic current produced by the active transport system. Comparing the fluxes of radioactive Na^+ with the measured short-circuit current, it could be shown that the measured potential is entirely due to Na^+ transport.

As shown in Figure 4–18, the electric potential measured across the frog skin increases in two steps, as the recording microelectrode passes through the layer of large epithelial cells of the stratum germinativum. It was found that the "outer" membrane of these cells is selectively permeable to Na ions, whereas the "inner" cell membrane is permeable to K ions but almost impermeable to Na^+. Sodium transport through the skin was shown to be pro-

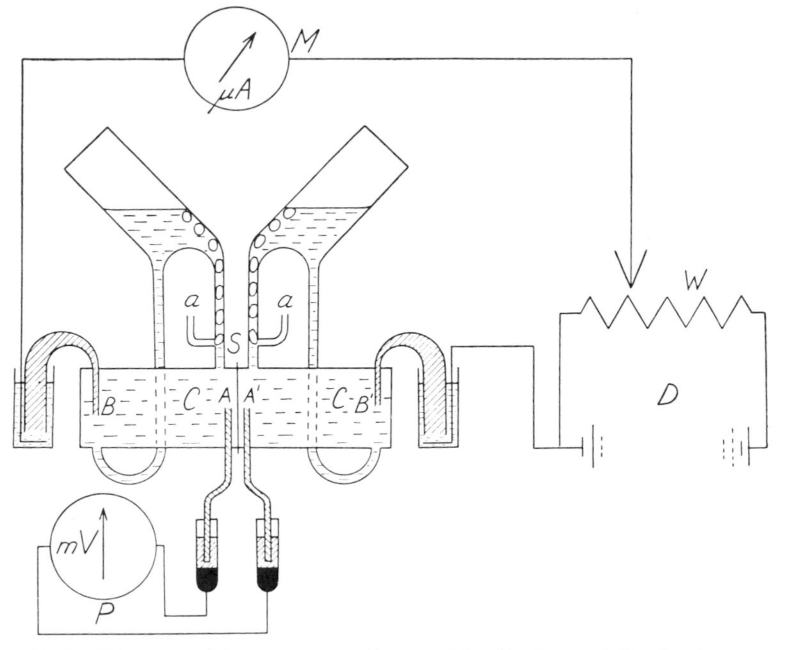

Figure 27–4. Diagram of the apparatus designed by Ussing and Zerahn to measure Na flux and short-circuit current. *C*, celluloid chamber, containing on each side of the frog skin (*S*) 40 ml of Ringer's solution. *a*, inlets for air; the air bubbles lift saline up into the top vessels and initiate circulation of the saline while, at the same time, accomplishing aeration. Agar-Ringer bridges (*A*) and (*A'*), connect the two saline compartments with calomel electrodes used to determine the membrane potential with the aid of a potentiometer (*P*). Current opposing the potential is applied through agar-Ringer bridges (*B*) and (*B'*); it is supplied by a battery (*D*). The current can be adjusted by a variable resistor; it is monitored with the aid of a microammeter (*M*). (From Ussing, H. H., and K. Zerahn: Active transport of sodium as the source of electric current in the short-circuited isolated frog skin. Acta Physiol. Scand. 23:110–127, 1951.)

portional to the K ion concentration of the inner side of the skin. It is therefore assumed that Na enters the outer cell membrane passively, simply following the electrochemical gradient. Once diffusion has brought a Na ion to the other, inner side of the cell, it is carried outward in exchange for a K ion, a process known as *exchange* diffusion. A model that describes the Na transport according to this hypothesis (Koefoed-Johnsen and Ussing, 1958) is shown in Figure 4–19.

It is interesting that part of the membrane of these skin cells behaves like an excited nerve cell membrane, while the other portion behaves like a resting nerve membrane. In the classic case of the squid giant axons (mantle nerves), as investigated by Hodgkin and Keynes (1954, 1955) and by Shaw (1955), active Na transport is coupled with active K transport. Evidence for this is, among other findings, that lack of external K^+ inhibits Na extrusion from the cells, whereas after artificial, but partial exchange of the intracellular K for Na, the cells extrude Na and accumulate K—both processes proceeding against concentration gradients. Similar linkage between Na and K transport has been reported for vertebrate striated muscle. Note, however, that the coupling is usually not such as to give a 1:1 ratio of the ions transported; usually more Na ions are extruded than K ions taken up. A coupled—or at least linked—

Na and K transport has also been found in studies on many kinds of vertebrate erythrocytes; again the Na transport system is more active than the K transport system. For discussions of this complex topic, refer to Maizels (1954) and Harris (1960).

Sodium and potassium are also actively transported in the vertebrate kidney tubules. Again, this appears to be coupled transport, localized at the cell membranes facing the tissue fluid and blood. This is shown in Figure 5–22. In the proximal tubules of *Necturus*, for instance, net flux of Na^+ (active reabsorption) amounts to $5.2 - 9.2 \times 10^{-3}$ microEquivalents/cm^2 sec (Giebisch et al., 1964) Sodium is actively transported across the gills of fresh-water fish and crustaceans. This involves ion exchange processes, H^+ and ammonium ions (NH_4^+) being exchanged for Na^+ ions (Shaw, 1960; Maetz and Garcia Romeu, 1964).

Chloride Transport

Chloride ions are actively transported in many instances. In frog skin, Cl^- usually moves passively, following the electric potential gradient set up by the active sodium transport. When the skin is treated with adrenaline, however, Cl^- is actively transported in the opposite direction (secretion of chloride by gland cells), so that the electric potential across the skin increases markedly (Koefoed-Johnsen, Ussing, and Zerahn, 1952).

In the small intestine of the rat, Cl^- as well as Na^+ are transported in the same direction from the lumen to the serosal side of the intestinal epithelium. Fresh-water fish, and fresh-water crustaceans can actively absorb Cl^- from the external medium through the gills. Amphibia can actively absorb Cl^- through the skin (Jørgensen, Levi, and Zerahn, 1954; Zadunaisky, Candia, and Chiarandini, 1963), but the ability is apparently lost when the skin is removed from the animals for *in vitro* studies.

Chloride absorption in the gills of goldfish has been shown to be due to active transport. The mechanism involves exchange of Cl^- for HCO_3^-, the bicarbonate ion being derived from carbonic acid (Garcia Romeu and Maetz, 1964). The H^+ that appears during the dissociation of carbonic acid combines with ammonium (derived from deamination of certain amino acids) to form ammonia which, in turn, is exchanged for Na^+. The situation is explained in Figure 27–5; it is practically identical with that occurring in the distal tubule of the kidney of alligators (Hernandez and Coulson, 1954). Active chloride transport has also been postulated for mammalian kidney tubules, but an exchange with bicarbonate ions has not been demonstrated as yet.

Much studied, and complicated, is the secretion of hydrochloric acid by the oxyntic cells of the vertebrate stomach. It involves active transport of both H^+ and Cl^- ions in the direction of the lumen of the stomach. The complications in the experimental analyses arise from the fact that there is, in addition, exchange diffusion that carries Cl^- back toward the serosal side of the gastric epithelium and passive transfer of H^+ and Cl^-, likewise in a direction opposite to that of the active transport. Active Cl^- transport here involves forced exchange with HCO_3^-. The hydrogen ions derive mostly from dissociating H_2CO_3. For

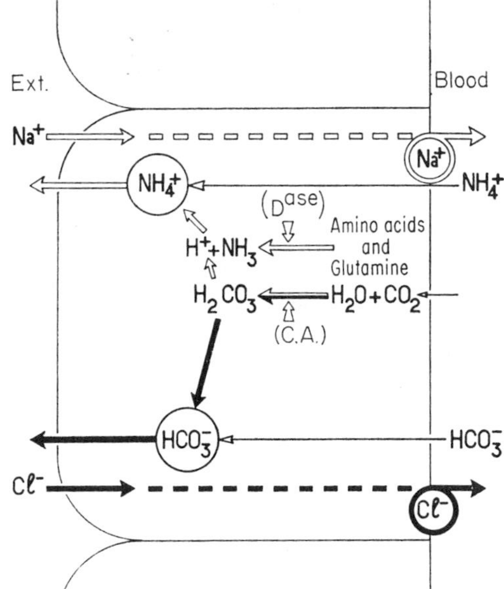

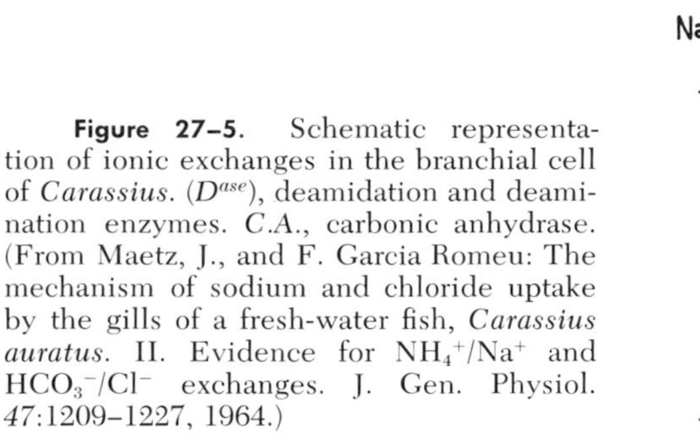

Figure 27–5. Schematic representation of ionic exchanges in the branchial cell of *Carassius*. (D^{ase}), deamidation and deamination enzymes. *C.A.*, carbonic anhydrase. (From Maetz, J., and F. Garcia Romeu: The mechanism of sodium and chloride uptake by the gills of a fresh-water fish, *Carassius auratus*. II. Evidence for NH_4^+/Na^+ and HCO_3^-/Cl^- exchanges. J. Gen. Physiol. *47*:1209–1227, 1964.)

an introduction to the complexities of the situation, refer to the reviews of Hogben (1955) and Wilbrandt (1960).

Sugar Transport

Sugar is actively transported in the vertebrate intestine (most likely invertebrate intestine as well), and active sugar transport has long been known to take place in the vertebrate kidney tubules. Not all sugars are transported with the same efficiency. Evidence is now accumulating that this sugar transport is coupled with Na transport, and that they are interdependent. Both substances are transported in the same direction. A recent hypothesis to explain the mechanisms involved is shown in Figure 27–6 (Schultz and Zalusky, 1964).

Sulfate Transport

Whereas marine invertebrates and fish excrete sulfate and it is known that in many of them the SO_4^{--} concentration maintained in the body fluids is lower than that of sea water, the mammals reabsorb sulfate ions in their kidney tubules. Both processes appear to involve active transport. The mammalian kidney has been more extensively studied in this regard. A mechanism proposed for this by Berglund (1960), involves the formation of "active sulfate" (adenosine-3′-phosphate-5′-phosphosulfate) by the combination of SO_4^{--} with 2 ATP, and transfer of the sulfate group to a carrier that diffuses through the (cellular) membrane and releases the sulfate at the "other side" of the membrane.

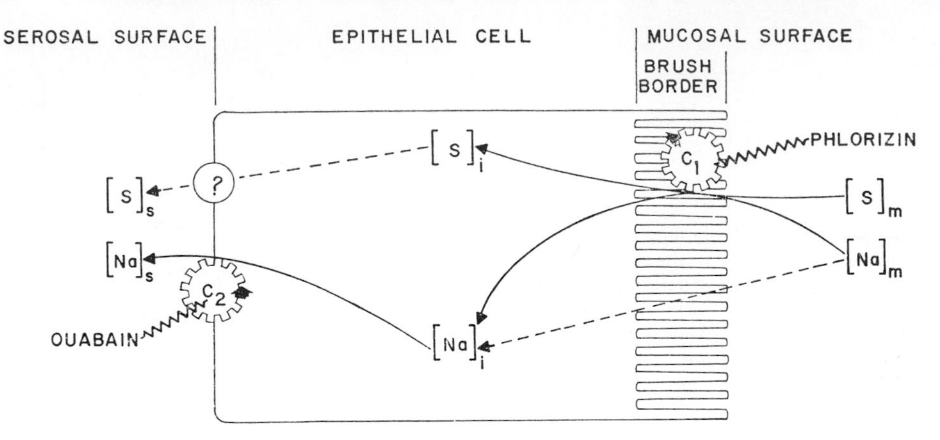

Figure 27–6. Model of the Na^+ and sugar transport mechanisms of epithelial cells in the distal ileum of the rabbit. The cogwheels represent the active transport mechanisms: C_1 resides in or near the membrane of the brush border and transports both sugar and Na^+ into the cell. The rate of transport is a function of both sugar and Na^+ concentrations. Phlorizin inhibits C_1. Sugar transport through the serosal surface of the cell may or may not be "active." The active Na^+ extrusion across the serosal membrane is accomplished by another active transport mechanism (C_2) whose rate of transport is a function of the intracellular Na^+ concentration. Mechanism C_2 can be inhibited by ouabain. (From Schultz, S. G., and R. Zalusky: Ion transport in isolated rabbit ileum. II. The interaction between active sodium and active sugar transport. J. Gen. Physiol. *47*:1043–1059, 1964.)

Phosphate Transport

Active transport of inorganic phosphate into eggs of sea urchins and marine annelids has been demonstrated (Abelson, 1947; Brooks and Chambers, 1954; Griffiths and Whiteley, 1964). This does not involve initial formation of high energy phosphate bonds or phosphorylation of sugars. Phosphate transport into erythrocytes, on the other hand, may involve formation of 1,3-diphosphoglyceraldehyde (Prankerd and Altman, 1954). The studies on sea urchin eggs show that phosphate is actively transported against enormous concentration gradients, perhaps as high as 1:1,000,000 (Whiteley, 1966). The transport commences immediately after fertilization of the eggs. Before that, the eggs are surrounded by completely impermeable membranes.

Amino Acids

Evidence for active transport of amino acids is accumulating. Particularly in the case of nerve and muscle cells of a variety of animal types, it is well established that large concentration gradients are maintained across the cell membrane (see Table 5–7). Transcellular transport of amino acids has been reported for intestinal and renal epithelia. The published experiments offer many examples of "competition," that is, of competitive inhibition of the transport of one amino acid by the simultaneous presence of another. The D-forms often prevent transport of the L-forms of the same amino acid. In the mammalian intestine L-methionine inhibits transport of L-tyrosine and of glycine; similarly, L-alanine inhibits transport of glycine, but interestingly L-glutamate and L-arginine do not. Studies of the interaction of amino acids with regard to transport provide valuable information about the number and specificity of the carriers present. Important reviews of the rather extensive literature on amino acid transport are those of Christensen (1962) and of Schoffeniels (1964).

THE ACTION OF HORMONES ON ACTIVE TRANSPORT

Several hormones are known to affect transfer of solute across cell membranes and across cellular membranes. The pituitary hormones of the oxytocin-vasopressin type (see Chap. 5) increase the permeability of the amphibian bladder (serosal side) and of vertebrate tubular epithelia to water and ions. Hormones of the adrenal gland, the steroid hormones (aldosterone, deoxycorticosterone), enhance reabsorption of Na by kidney tubules. The ovarian hormones, stilbestrol, estradiol, and other steroids are known to change membrane permeability and thus to alter net fluxes; they increase the uptake of certain amino acids in a number of cell types. The pancreatic hormone, *insulin*, has similar effects, but it is best known for accelerating glucose transport.

The hormone effects are extremely difficult to assess, particularly since all of them have a multiplicity of actions. They affect not only cell permeability as such, but also metabolism, and it is easy to see that one of these actions necessarily affects the other. Stimulation of ion transport by insulin, for instance, may result from stimulation of metabolism, etc. For a guide to the literature, refer to endocrinology textbooks, such as Turner (1960) and Gorbman and Bern (1962).

THE ACTION OF DRUGS ON ACTIVE TRANSPORT

Active transport is usually reduced or abolished in the presence of metabolic inhibitors. *Dinitrophenol* (DNP), which inhibits oxidative phosphorylation without impeding respiration, blocks ATP-dependent transport, whereas *fluoride* and *monoiodoacetate*, which prevent glycolysis, inhibit transport that depends on glycolysis (for example, cation transport in erythrocytes). *Phlorizin* prevents glucose (sugar) transport (vertebrate kidney tubules and octopus kidney, see Figure 13–16; intestinal epithelium), and in the intestine it also prevents Na transport (see Fig. 27–6); the latter effect may be dependent on the inhibition of glucose transport which is coupled with Na transport, as mentioned in the preceding section on sugar transport.

The Na transport system of many different types of cells is inhibited by the glycosides *ouabain, digitoxin,* and *g-strophantin*. These drugs have become important tools in the analysis of ion-transport systems.

Na transport through frog skin is inhibited by anticholinesterases, such as tetraethylpyrophosphate and eserine after an initial stimulation (Kirschner, 1953); a similar inhibition is found with frog muscle (Van der Kloot, 1956), crab gill (Koch, 1954), and erythrocytes (Holland and Klein, 1956). Na transport through crab gills and frog skin is enhanced by atropine and curare, and in crab gills also (but transiently) by nicotine (Kirschner, 1955b; Koch, 1954).

REFERENCES

Abelson, P. H. (1947) Permeability of eggs of *Arbacia punctulata* to radioactive phosphorus. Biol. Bull. *93*:203.

Andersen, B., and H. H. Ussing (1960) Active transport. *In* Comparative Biochemistry, Vol. 2, pp. 371–402. (M. Florkin and H. S. Mason, eds.) Academic Press, New York.

Berglund, F. (1960) Transport of inorganic sulfate by the renal tubules. Acta Physiol. Scand. *49*, Suppl. 172:1–37.

Berliner, R. W. (1959) Membrane transport. *In* Biophysical Science—A Study Program, pp. 342–348. (J. L. Oncley, ed.) John Wiley & Sons, New York.

Brooks, S. C., and E. L. Chambers (1954) The penetration of radioactive phosphate into marine eggs. Biol. Bull. *106*:279–296.

Brown, R., and J. F. Danielli, eds. (1954) Active Transport and Secretion. Cambridge University Press, London.

Christensen, H. N. (1962) Biological Transport. W. A. Benjamin, Inc., New York.

Conway, E. J. (1953) A redox pump for the biological performance of osmotic work, and its relation to the kinetics of free diffusion across membranes. Int. Rev. Cytol. *2*:419–445.

Conway, E. J. (1960) Critical energy barriers to active transport in muscle and the redox pump theory. *In* Regulation of the Inorganic Ion Content of Cells, pp. 2–14. (G. E. W. Wolstenholme and C. M. O'Connor, eds.) Little, Brown and Co., Boston.

Garcia Romeu, F., and J. Maetz (1964) The mechanism of sodium and chloride uptake by the gills of a fresh-water fish, *Carassius auratus*. I. Evidence for an independent uptake of sodium and chloride ions. J. Gen. Physiol. *47*:1195–1207.

Giebisch, G., R. M. Klose, G. Malnic, W. J. Sullivan, and E. E. Windhager (1964) Sodium movement across single prefused proximal tubules of rat kidneys. J. Gen. Physiol. *47*:1175–1194.

Gorbman, A., and H. A. Bern (1962) A Textbook of Comparative Endocrinology. John Wiley & Sons, New York.

Griffiths, W. M., and A. H. Whiteley (1964) A study of the mechanism of phosphate transport in sea urchin eggs by ion exchange analysis of rapidly labeled compounds. Biol. Bull. *126*:69–82.

Harris, E. J. (1960) Transport and Accumulation in Biological Systems, 2nd Ed. Academic Press, New York.

Hernandez, T., and R. A. Coulson (1954) The effect of carbonic anhydrase inhibition on the composition of urine and plasma of the alligator. Science *119*:291–292.

Hodgkin, A. L., and R. D. Keynes (1954) Movements of cations during recovery in nerve. Symp. Soc. Exp. Biol. *8*:423–437.

Hodgkin, A. L., and R. D. Keynes (1955) Active transport of cations in giant axons from *Sepia* and Loligo. J. Physiol. *128*:28–60.

Hogben, C. A. M. (1955) Biological aspects of active chloride transport. *In* Electrolytes in Biological Systems, pp. 176–204. (A. M. Shanes, ed.) American Physiological Society, Washington, D.C.

Holland, W. C., and R. L. Klein (1956) Effects of diazonium salts on erythrocyte fragility and cholinesterase activity. Amer. J. Physiol. *187*:501–504.

Jørgensen, C. B., H. Levi, and K. Zerahn (1954) On active uptake of sodium and chloride ions in anurans. Acta Physiol. Scand. *30*:178–190.

Kirschner, L. B. (1953) Effect of cholinesterase inhibitors and atropine on active sodium transport across frog skin. Nature *172*:348–349.

Kirschner, L. B. (1955a) On the mechanism of active sodium transport across the frog skin. J. Cell. Comp. Physiol. *45*:61–87.

Kirschner, L. B. (1955b) The effect of atropine and the curares on the active transport of sodium by the skin of *Rana esculenta*. J. Cell. Comp. Physiol. *45*:89–102.

Koch, H. J. (1954) Cholinesterase and active transport of sodium chloride through the isolated gills of the crab *Eriocheir sinensis* (M. Edw.) *In* Recent Developments in Cell Physiology, pp. 15–27. (J. A. Kitching, ed.) Butterworths Scientific Publications, London.

Koefoed-Johnsen, V., and H. H. Ussing (1958) The nature of the frog skin potential. Acta Physiol. Scand. *42*:298–308.

Koefoed-Johnsen, V., H. H. Ussing, and K. Zerahn (1952) The origin of the short-circuit current in the adrenaline stimulated frog skin. Acta Physiol. Scand. *27*:38–48.

Krogh, A. (1937) Osmotic regulation in the frog (*R. esculenta*) by active absorption of chloride ions. Skand. Arch. Physiol. *76*:60–74.

Krogh, A. (1938) The active absorption of ions in some freshwater animals. Z. vergl. Physiol. *25*:335–350.

Linderholm, H. (1953) The electrical potential across isolated frog skins and its dependence on the permeability of the skins to chloride ions. Acta Physiol. Scand. *28*:211–217.

Lund, E. J. (1947) Bioelectric Fields and Growth. University of Texas Press, Austin.
Maetz, J., and F. Garcia Romeu (1964) The mechanism of sodium and chloride uptake by the gills of a fresh-water fish, *Carassius auratus*. II. Evidence for NH_4^+/Na^+ and HCO_3^-/Cl^- exchanges. J. Gen. Physiol. *47*:1209–1227.
Maizels, M. (1954) Active cation transport in erythrocytes. *In* Active Transport and Secretion, pp. 202–227. (R. Brown and J. F. Danielli, eds.) Cambridge University Press, London.
Prankerd, T. A. J., and K. I. Altman (1954) A Study of the metabolism of phosphorus in mammalian red cells. Biochem. J. *58*:622–633.
Schoffeniels, E. (1964) Cellular aspects of active transport. *In* Comparative Biochemistry, Vol. 7, pp. 137–202. (M. Florkin and H. S. Mason, eds.) Academic Press, New York.
Schultz, S. G., and R. Zalusky (1964) Ion transport in isolated rabbit ileum. II. The interaction between active sodium and active sugar transport. J. Gen. Physiol. *47*:1043–1059.
Shanes, A. M., ed. (1955) Electrolytes in Biological Systems. American Physiological Society, Washington, D.C. (Waverly Press, Baltimore.)
Shaw, J. (1960) The absorption of chloride ions by the crayfish, *Astacus pallipes* Lereboullet. J. Exp. Biol. *37*:557–572.
Shaw, T. I. (1955) Squid giant axons, mantle nerves, reactive transport. J. Physiol. *128*:28–60.
Thaysen, J. H., N. A. Lassen, and O. Munck (1961) Sodium transport and oxygen consumption in the mammalian kidney. Nature *190*:919–921.
Tosteson, D. C. (1955) Sodium and potassium transport in red blood cells. *In* Electrolytes in Biological Systems, pp. 123–156. (A. M. Shanes, ed.) American Physiological Society, Washington, D.C.
Turner, C. D. (1966) General Endocrinology, 4th Ed. W. B. Saunders Co., Philadelphia.
Ussing, H. H. (1949) Active ion transport through the isolated frog skin in the light of tracer studies. Acta Physiol. Scand., *17*:1–21.
Ussing, H. H. (1957) General principles and theories of membrane transport. *In* Metabolic Aspects of Transport across Cell Membranes, pp. 39–56. (Q. R. Murphy, ed.) University of Wisconsin Press, Madison.
Ussing, H. H., and K. Zerahn (1951) Active transport of sodium as the source of electric current in the short-circuited isolated frog skin. Acta Physiol. Scand. *23*:110–127.
Van der Kloot, W. G. (1956) Cholinesterase and sodium transport by frog muscle. Nature *178*:366–367.
Whiteley, A. H. (1966) Personal communication.
Wilbrandt, W. (1960) Permeabilitaet und Stofftransporte. Fortschr. Zool. *12*:28–127.
Zadunaisky, J. A., O. A. Candia, and D. J. Chiarandini (1963) The origin of the short-circuited current in the isolated skin of the South American frog *Leptodactylus ocellatus*. J. Gen. Physiol. *47*:393–402.

Index

CLASS NO.

L. C. CARD NO. 64-17711

LIST PRICE 10.00

AUTHOR
Florey, E.

DATE ORDERED

TITLE
An introduction to general and comparative animal physiology.

ORDER NO.

PLACE N. Y.

PUBLISHER Saunders

YEAR 1966

DEALER Eastern

VOLS.

SERIES

EDITION

NO. OF COPIES

RECOMMENDED BY Pollack

FUND CHARGED

COST

DATE REC'D.

Out
C
R
On
Oe
Ci
Rd
P
D
Np
NR

in prep.

Vermont Coll.
2828 Gary Lib.
-c,e -R 2sa